NONVOLATILE SEMICONDUCTOR MEMORIES

TECHNOLOGIES, DESIGN, AND APPLICATIONS

NONVOLATILE
SEMICONDUCTOR
MEMORIES

TECHNOLOGIES, DESIGN, AND APPLICATIONS

Edited by
Chenming Hu
Professor of Electrical Engineering and Computer Sciences
University of California, Berkeley

A volume in the IEEE PRESS Selected Reprint Series,
prepared under the sponsorship of the IEEE Electron Devices Society.

IEEE
PRESS

The Institute of Electrical and Electronics Engineers, Inc., New York

ISBN 0-87942-269-6
IEEE Order Number : PC0263-4

Printed in the United States of America
10 9 8 7 6 5 4 3 2 1

Library of Congress Cataloging-in-Publication Data

Nonvolatile semiconductor memories : technologies, design, and
applications / edited by Chenming Hu.
    p.   cm. — (IEEE Press selected reprint series)
  Includes bibliographical references and index.
  ISBN 0-87942-269-6
  1. Semiconductor storage devices. I. Hu, Chenming.
TK7895.M4N63 1991
621.39′732—dc20   90-29044

Contents

Preface

THE NONVOLATILE semiconductor memory devices covered in this volume can all be programmed electrically. Some cannot be erased; others can be erased with ultraviolet light or by an electrical pulse. They are the foundation of an IC technology with a multibillion US dollar market with applications in nearly all fields of the electronics industry.

The selected papers cover a 20-year span from 1971 to 1991. In selecting the papers, I tried to include a few older papers to give an historical sense of the technologies. The main aim, however, was to provide an understanding of the underlying physics and principles so that readers can appreciate the large number of device structures, processing technologies, and circuit designs, whether presented in this volume or not. Another aim was to survey the states of the art and future trends in technology, design, and application.

Many people are attracted to the study of nonvolatile memory technology by the richness of the subject matter. They find interesting physics and opportunities for innovative device and circuit designs and applications, as well as the challenge of building reliability into the varied device structures that employ sundry physical mechanisms. This richness has not shown signs of diminishing; new concepts involving new materials, structures, principles, or applications are being introduced at a higher rate today than ever before. It was also one of my goals in editing this volume to convey that sense of excitement and freshness.

With tutorial introductions provided for the book as well as for each part, this book can be used both as an introductory treatise as well as an advanced reference book. It pulls together in one book various aspects of nonvolatile memory technology: the physics and design, manufacturing and applications, the practical and the novel, the limitations and the possibilities. This book should be useful to scientists, technologists, teachers, and students interested in the subject matter, as well as to engineers engaged in the use of programmable memory and logic devices, or in IC technology, manufacturing, design, or reliability. College training in engineering or science, or familiarity with IC technology is adequate preparation for reading this book.

Taking advantage of the reprint format, this book presents a wide range of nonvolatile semiconductor technologies in the words of authors who performed research and development firsthand. Fuses and antifuses for programmable read-only memory (PROM) and for programmable gate arrays are presented first. UV-erasable EPROMs, including one-time programmable (OTP) EPROMs, and EEPROMs using floating-gate and MNOS technologies are covered in two parts. Two separate parts are devoted to flash EEPROMs and nonvolatile RAMs of the floating-gate and ferroelectric types.

Additional parts provide an overview of the book and address the issue of thin dielectrics in relation to nonvolatile memory technologies. Thirteen memory-design papers make up another section. Reliability is also covered in its own section. The final part addresses new or emerging applications of the nonvolatile memory technologies in such fields as logic circuits, ASIC, wafer-scale integration, neural networks, smart cards, and magnetic disk replacement.

For those readers who wish to research the topic further, suggestions for locating additional references can be found on page 2 of the Introduction.

I would like to thank my many friends and colleagues in industry and academia who have helped me acquire my understanding of the subject matter of this book. My past experience as a consultant at National Semiconductor and SEEQ Technology is directly responsible for my long interest in nonvolatile memory technology. For that I thank Pierre Lamond, Tom Klein, George Perlegos, Phil Salsbury, and Ting Wong. Needless to say, I am indebted to each and every author of the papers reprinted in this book. I thank my wife and my sons, Raymond and Jason, who have indirectly but definitely contributed to the making of this book.

Finally, I thank you for reading this book and hope that you will find in it what you are looking for—and perhaps something more.

CHENMING HU
Berkeley, CA

A POCKET HISTORY OF FLOATING-GATE NONVOLATILE MEMORIES

THE FIRST nonvolatile semiconductor memory was introduced by Kahng and Sze in 1967 [1]. In this memory, a conventional p-channel MOSFET was modified to incorporate a metal floating gate. Electrons were transferred between the floating gate and the substrate by tunneling through 30-Å thin silicon dioxide. Storage of charge on the floating gate allowed the transistor threshold voltage to be electrically altered between a low and high value to represent logic 1's and 0's.

In 1970, Frohman-Bentchkowsky developed a floating polysilicon-gate transistor. Electrons were injected into the floating gate through normal thick gate oxide via hot-electron injection and removed from the floating gate by ultraviolet internal photoemission. His 1971 paper on a 2048-bit electrically programmable read-only memory (EPROM) is presented here as Paper 3.2. The n-channel version of this UV-erasable EPROM (UVEPROM) and its derivatives have steadily grown to become a major memory technology with a market size second only to that of DRAM. Paper 3.1 describes the operation of EPROMs. Please see the "Nonvolatile Memory Nomenclature" on the following pages for explanations of the acronyms and terms.

In the late 1970s, there were many efforts to develop electrically erasable EPROMs using electron tunneling through thin oxide or the more conductive interpoly oxide. Most of these laboratory devices combined tunneling-erase with EPROM's hot-electron programming method—a combination that would become popular some years later with flash EEPROMs. These efforts were abruptly abandoned when Intel, the dominant EPROM supplier, introduced the 2816, a 16-kb 10 000 WRITE/ERASE-cycle EEPROM using tunneling for WRITE and ERASE (Paper 4.2). Many other manufacturers immediately decided to develop this EEPROM technology. Only Xicor continued to develop a triple-poly EEPROM technology using tunneling through textured polyoxide.

The EEPROM cell, consisting of two transistors and a tunnel oxide, is two to three times the size of an EPROM cell, and tunnel-oxide breakdown limits the endurance reliability. Reliability can be improved with error correction circuitry, which further increases the die size. Today, at about 20% of the EPROM market, EEPROM is an important technology with a somewhat uncertain path for future growth. Papers 1.1, 4.1 and 4.2 describe the EEPROM in detail.

Around 1984, the combination of hot-electron programming and tunnel ERASE was rediscovered as the means for achieving a single-transistor EEPROM cell. Unlike the "full-featured" EEPROMs, the new genre of EEPROMs cannot be erased by bytes but must be erased by the entire chip or large sections of the chip (flash ERASE). In return for this limitation, cell size and endurance reliability are improved. The new memory is called flash EEPROM or flash EPROM. Being the newest floating-gate technology, many different flash EPROM cells, including some using tunneling for programming or three levels of polysilicon, are being pursued. Papers 1.1 and 5.1–5.3 describe flash memories in greater detail.

One-time-programmable (OTP) EPROM, also developed in the early 1980s, represents another tradeoff. OTPs are EPROMs without the UV transparent windows in the packages. OTP therefore cannot be erased and can be classified as a PROM. By giving up reprogrammability, OTP can use plastic or even surface-mount packages for cost savings, ease of automatic assembly into circuit boards, and greater board density. Paper 3.12 gives further information on OTP EPROMs.

OTHER NONVOLATILE SEMICONDUCTOR MEMORIES

An MNOS memory transistor has a gate dielectric consisting of about 30 Å of thermal SiO_2 and several hundred angstroms of deposited silicon nitride. The electric charge is stored in the nitride and charge injection and removal is effected through tunneling via the very thin oxide.

MNOS memories have been in continual development or production since 1967 [2], although mostly in the shadow of their floating-gate cousins. Before developing the floating polysilicon-gate transistor, Frohman-Bentchkowsky also investigated the MNOS memory transistor [3]. N-channel technology and an additional oxide between the nitride and the polysilicon gate (SONOS) were introduced in the early 1980s. Today, MNOS is a serious competitor in the EEPROM market, especially in Japan due to Hitachi's backing of the technology. MNOS technology excels in endurance reliability and radiation hardness but provides little margin in data retention due to the presence of the 30-Å oxide. Papers 4.7–4.9 describe this technology in detail.

The historic Kahng/Sze cell used floating-gate storage and thin-oxide tunneling. The MNOS cell uses nitride storage and thin-oxide tunneling. The EPROM cell uses floating-gate storage and hot-electron programming. The fourth combination—nitride storage and hot-electron programming—has been studied recently and is the subject of Paper 5.5.

Ferroelectric nonvolatile memory is an old idea that holds forward exciting new possibilities. Several studies on ferroelectric memories have been published since 1963 [4]. The original concept was to use a ferroelectric film, which can be permanently polarized by an electric voltage pulse, as (a portion of) the gate dielectric of a transistor. Ferroelectric memory has fast WRITE time ($\sim$ 10 ns) and good endurance.

One problem was that READ disturbance can occur because of a lack of distinct threshold voltage for polarization.

In 1987, a new concept of ferroelectric memory was reported. Basically, a ferroelectric film was used as the dielectric in the capacitor of a DRAM cell. Since the cell is refreshed every time it is read, READ disturbance is no longer a concern. If extreme endurance (10^{16} WRITE/READ cycles), good data retention, and manufacturability can be achieved, this could be the ideal memory—with small cell size, RAM-like functions, plus nonvolatility. Papers 6.5–6.8 report some of the recent studies.

TRADITIONAL AND NEW APPLICATIONS

EPROMs compete with mask-programmed ROMs for the same applications—mainly program code storage in computers or microcontrollers. For small-volume applications, the ROM's nonrecurring engineering cost is prohibitive. For high-volume orders, the ROM price has always been lower than EPROMs by a factor of two or more. Yet, EPROMs are often chosen over ROMs for ease of design change and inventory control. Erasing, however, is cumbersome. As a result, reprogrammability is often not utilized and OTPs may well take over a large portion of the EPROM market.

EEPROMs offered the first real possibility of electrically changing the nonvolatilely stored code without removing the memories from the circuit board. In the early 1980s, some industry analysts predicted that the EEPROM market would surpass that of the EPROM by 1990. As it turned out, costs associated with cell size, yield, and reliability testing have prevented EEPROMs from fulfilling that prediction.

Today, flash EPROM, at two to three times the cost of EPROM, appears to have a good chance of eclipsing EPROM in the future, as EPROM eclipsed ROM in the past, and in the process, bring electrical reprogrammability to the center stage of nonvolatile memories.

The combination of high density, low cost, and electrical reprogrammability makes flash EPROM a candidate for *data storage*—from "smart card" to replacement for magnetic disk storage. If the disk replacement market materializes, nonvolatile semiconductor memories would enter a new level of economic importance.

Even more astounding is the possibility of replacing SRAM and DRAM with nonvolatile memories. Ferroelectric memory can potentially match DRAM in WRITE and READ speed and beat DRAM in cell size, with nonvolatility thrown in as a bonus. Simply put, it is the ideal memory. Difficulties that might burst the bubble include compatibility with silicon technology, defect density, and reliability.

Less futuristic, but equally exciting, is the new trend in applying nonvolatile memory technologies to logic ICs. Programmable logic devices (PLDs) with thousands of gates are available. PLDs are to gate arrays what EPROMs are to ROMs. On the one hand, the PLD provides new applications for traditional nonvolatile memory technologies such as EPROM and EEPROM technologies. On the other hand, it stimulates the development of new, denser, higher conductance programmable devices such as amorphous silicon or dielectric-based antifuses.

Combining programmable elements and circuit blocks logically leads to some form of wafer-scale integration. The same combination may also be required to physically construct neural network computers. The push and pull between new technologies and new applications is bringing a new wave of commercial and scientific interests to nonvolatile memories.

SELECTION OF REPRINT PAPERS

I have tried to select the most informative reprints and to present a broad cross section of interesting ideas from a rich literature without regard to chronological order. Many relevant articles not selected because of space limitations are listed in the Reference sections of part introductions. Don't forget to use the reference list at the end of each reprint article as a means to search through earlier publications.

To look for additional publications, including those published after this reprint volume was compiled, try the *Technical Digest of the International Electron Devices Meeting* (IEDM), an IEEE publication available each December. Look through the section on nonvolatile memories for the latest advances in cell concept and technology. References to papers covering these same subjects are often found in the annual subject index in each December issue of the *IEEE Transactions on Electron Devices* and *Electron Device Letters* under the heading of memories, nonvolatile memories, or dielectrics. Articles on circuits are almost always published in the *IEEE International Solid State Circuits Conference* (ISSCC) *Digest of Technical Papers*, published every February, or the *IEEE Journal of Solid-State Circuits* (see the subject index in every December issue), especially the October special issues on logic and memory. Finally, reliability articles are almost always published in the *Proceedings of the International Reliability Physics Symposium*, published every March or April.

Happy reading!

REFERENCES

For a review of pre-1980 technology, please see, "Nonvolatile memories," by Y. Nishi and H. Lizuka in *Silicon Integrated Circuits, Part A*, edited by D. Kahng. New York: Academic Press, 1981.

[1] D. Kahng and S. M. Sze, "A floating gate and its application to memory devices," *Bell Syst. Tech. J.*, vol. 46, p. 1288, 1967.
[2] H. A. R. Wegener, A. J. Lincoln, H. C. Pao, M. R. O'Connel, and R. E. Oleksiok, "Metal-insulator-semiconductor transistor as a nonvolatile storage element," *Internat. Electron Devices Meet.* (Abstracts), 1967, p. 58.
[3] D. Frohman-Bentchkowsky, "The metal-nitride-oxide-silicon (MNOS) transistor—Characteristics and applications," *Proc. IEEE*, vol. 58, pp. 1207–1219, 1970.
[4] J. L. Moll and Y. Tarui, "A new solid state memory resistor," *IEEE Trans. Electron Devices*, vol. ED-10, p. 338, 1963.

Antifuse: A nonconductive element that may be made conductive by an electrical pulse; opposite of *Fuse*.

Array: Repetition of memory cell in a two-dimensional matrix; together with the peripheral circuitry making up the IC chip.

Array Efficiency: Ratio of array area to chip area.

Battery Back-Up (in the context of memory): Prevention of SRAM or DRAM memory loss when power-supply is off by providing batteries. See *Zero Power RAM*.

Bit: The basic unit of memory, storing a "1" or a "0." Abbreviation of binary digit.

Bit Lines: Electrical interconnect lines that carry the data into and out of the memory array; traditionally the up–down running lines in the array.

Block Erase: Bulk Erase; also possibly *Sector Erase*.

Bulk Erase: Erase of the entire chip simultaneously; *Chip Erase*. See also *Flash Erase*.

Byte: A group of bits, e.g. eight, that can usually be read simultaneously.

Cell: The physical semiconductor structure that stores one bit of data.

Charge Gain: Inadvertent gain of stored charge; may lead to error in stored data. Opposite of *Charge Loss* .

Charge Loss: Inadvertent loss of stored charge; may lead to loss of stored data. See *Charge Gain*.

Charge Pumping: A technique for generating higher voltages on-chip using a lower power supply voltage. This voltage is typically used for the *Write/Erase* operation.

Charge Retention: See *Data Retention*.

Chip: A piece of semiconductor containing a useful circuit or device.

Chip Erase: Bulk Erase

Clear: Setting data to "1" state.

Control Gate: The (top) EPROM or EEPROM gate that controls the memory transistor by capacitively coupling to the floating gate.

Cycling: Repeated writing and erasing. See *Endurance*.

Data Retention: Also *Charge Retention,* the ability to hold charge (retain memory content) through long-term high temperature storage. See *Charge Loss* and *Charge Gain*.

Density: Number of bits in a memory chip; often rounded, for example, to 1 kb for 1024 bits and 1 Mb for 1 048 576 bits.

Disturb: Inadvertent change of memory content during *Read* or *Write*.

Double Poly: Standard MOS technology for floating-gate memories; the first polysilicon layer providing for the floating gate and the second layer, the control gate.

DRAM: Dynamic Random Access Memory.

EAROM: Electrically Alterable Read-Only Memory. An earlier name for EEPROM.

ECC: Error-Code Correction; a technique for correcting errors to improve reliability (and yield) by correcting for the failures of a small number of randomly located bits.

EEPLD: Electrically Erasable PLD; EEPROM-based PLD.

EEPROM: Electrically Erasable/Programmable Read-Only Memory, especially those erasable byte by byte. See *Flash EEPROM*.

E^2PROM: EEPROM

Endurance: Write/Erase cycles a memory can endure before failure; 10 000 cycles is a common specification.

EPLD: Erasable PLD; EPROM-based PLD.

EPROM: Electrically Programmable Read-Only Memory. Usually refers exclusively to the UV erasable, hot-electron programming floating-gate memory, UVE-PROM.

Erase: The operation of removing electrons from the storage medium of a memory cell, for example, the floating gate.

ETOX™: EPROM-Tunnel Oxide; a flash EEPROM technology using hot-electron programming and tunnel-oxide erase. Intel trademark.

FAMOS™: Floating-Gate Avalanche MOS memory; Intel tradename; an apt name for the original p-channel EPROM, in which the programming electrons were generated by holes through avalanche (impact ionization); still used to describe n-channel EPROM, in which impact ionization is only an unavoidable side effect of high field and current.

Ferroelectrics: Materials capable of exhibiting permanent electric polarization, whose polarity may be switched by a pulse of electric field.

Five-Volt-Only: Requiring only a 5V external power supply; usually generating high voltage for programming and/or *Erase* with on-chip circuitry. See *Charge Pumping*.

Flash EEPROM: EEPROM that cannot be erased by bytes but can be erased by the entire chip or large sections thereof.

Flash EPROM: Same as *Flash EEPROM*.

Flash Erase: Bulk or *Chip Erase*, especially when referring to flash EEPROMs.

Floating Gate: A piece of polysilicon over the memory transistor channel insulated on all sides by dielectrics; a unique and essential feature of EPROM and flash EPROM and some EEPROM. See *Double Poly*.

FLOTOX™: Floating-gate Tunnel Oxide technology for making EEPROM. Intel trademark.

FN: Fowler–Nordheim.

Fowler–Nordheim Tunneling: Electron tunneling from the cathode into the conduction band of insulator before reaching the anode; mechanism of *Erase* and programming in EEPROM and *Erase* in flash EEPROM cells.

FPGA: Field Programmable Gate Array.

FPLA: Field Programmable Logic Array; a PLD with programmable AND and OR arrays. See *PAL*.

FPLD: Field Programmable Logic Devices; also *PLD*.

Fuse: A conductive element that may be rendered nonconductive by an electrical pulse; may also mean *Antifuse*.

FPLS: Field Programmable Logic Sequencer.

Fusible: Operable as a fuse.

Hot-Electron Injection: Injection of energetic electrons from the MOSFET channel over the energy barrier into the oxide (and the floating gate).

Inadvertent Write Protection: Circuitry to prevent inadvertent *Write* operation from occurring during power on/off or noise transitions.

LCA: Logic Cell Array; an array of logic blocks, each containing several logic gates and input/output cells, building blocks of FPGA.

Magnetic Memory: One of the oldest and still the densest and the dominant nonvolatile memory, seen today mainly in the form of hard disks and floppy disks. Magneto-optic memory will further enhance density.

Mask Programmable: Programmable only through using at least one photolithography step in the factory; device may be memory (ROM) or logic (gate array).

MNOS: Metal–Nitride–Oxide–Semiconductor nonvolatile memory; an MOS transistor with very thin (< 2 nm) oxide and thicker nitride under the metal (polysilicon) gate so that electrons/holes can tunnel into/out of the nitride. See *SONOS*.

Nonvolatile Memory: A memory in which data are retained without having power supplied to it.

NOVRAM: Same as *NVRAM*.

NRE: Non-Recurring Engineering Charges (for manufacturing ROMs).

NVRAM: Non-Volatile Random Access Memory, a nonvolatile memory with fast writing and infinite *Write* cycle capabilities. Only implementations so far are SRAM or DRAM backed up by EEPROM at loss of power. Also see *Shadow RAM*.

ONO: Oxide–Nitride–Oxide; a superb dielectric often used between two polysilicon layers.

OTP: One-Time-Programmable EPROM; EPROM in a plastic package without UV window for cost savings, therefore can be programmed once but not erased; a PROM made with EPROM technology.

Page: A large group of bits, usually many bytes, that can be programmed or erased simultaneously.

PAL: Programmable Array Logic; a PLD with fixed OR array and programmable AND array.

Peripheral: Or peripheral circuit; all on the memory IC except for the array.

PLD: Programmable Logic Devices. See *FPLD*.

Program: The operation of changing the data state of a memory cell; especially by injecting electrons into the storage medium, e.g., the floating gate.

PROM: Programmable Read-Only Memory, also known as field-programmable ROM. Electrically programmable ROM that cannot be erased or reprogrammed. See *Fuse, OTP, EPROM*.

Read Disturb: Change of stored data by repeated reading of the data.

Redundancy: A design technique to improve circuit yield by providing more rows or columns in cell array than necessary.

Retention: See *Data Retention*.

ROM: Read-Only Memory, whose content is stored or programmed at the IC fabrication plant.

Security: A feature that prevents unauthorized access to *Write*, or *Write* and *Read*.

Self-Aligned Gate: Standard EPROM and a flash EEPROM cell design where the floating gate is etched with the control gate as the etch mask. See *Split Gate*.

Sector Erase: Page Erase; Erase of a portion of the memory on a chip.

Shadow RAM: An NVRAM. The name emphasizes the pairing of one EEPROM cell to each SRAM cell, ready to store the SRAM content at loss of power.

SONOS: Semiconductor (poly-Si gate)-Oxide–Nitride–Oxide-Semiconductor memory; MNOS with an additional oxide between nitride and gate to improve charge retention.

Split Gate: An EPROM or flash EEPROM cell design where the floating gate and the control gate separately control two halves of the channel in series. Not a *Self-Aligned Gate*.

SRAM: Static Random Access Memory.

Textured Poly: An EEPROM technology making use of the high conductivity of oxide grown on polycrystalline silicon due to naturally occurring or edge roughness (asperities); often implemented in triple-poly technology.

Triple Poly: MOS technology using three layers of polysilicon; often used to implement textured-poly memory.

Tunnel Oxide: Oxide thin enough for electron tunneling to occur; used in EEPROM and flash EEPROM.

Volatile Memory: DRAM and SRAM. See *Battery Back-Up*.

Window: Threshold window; the difference between the threshold voltages in the programmed and erased states.

Word: A bit string considered as an entity.

Word Lines: Electrical interconnect lines running perpendicular to the bit lines serving the function of selecting the individual rows in a memory array.

Write: Program or *Erase*, the operation of changing the data state.

Zero Power RAM: A trade name for a low stand-by power SRAM and a long-life battery in one package to maintain memory storage at loss of external power. See *Battery Back-Up*.

A Memory to Remember

by Michael Bloom, Technology Communications Group, West Linn, OR

Designers dream of the ideal nonvolatile memory, which would offer low cost per bit, high density, fast random access, read/write and cycle times of equal duration, low power consumption, operation over a wide temperature range, a single low-voltage power supply, a high degree of radiation tolerance, and inherent nonvolatility. But the ideal memory cannot yet be made. Although nonvolatility is desired for many memory applications, it is often sacrificed in favor of other important characteristics. Minimizing the impact of this trade-off is a primary goal.

Current nonvolatile memory applications generally fall into several broad areas. The first group includes low-density memories for use in TV tuners, postage meters, and automotive applications. A second group includes various types of nonvolatile storage for microprogram control and remote alteration of these systems. A third group consists of rad-hard applications. And two promising areas in which significant applications await further technical progress include solid-state disks and electronic image storage, both of which require large amounts of high-density, cost-effective nonvolatile memory.

Many question whether recent progress in MNOS and exotic ferroelectric technology will seriously cut into the now-dominant technologies, or if progress in Flash memory will keep it one step ahead. Ferroelectric technology, which is approaching but still hasn't reached the "ideal" memory, could become the technology for solid-state disks. Or this important application may require little more than extensions of current flotox technologies. Also, since battery-backed applications are pseudo-nonvolatile, the limitations of the battery technology could be significant.

Elaborating on EPROMs

EPROM represents a well-known nonvolatile technology that is about to make new strides in performance and density (**Table 1**). An EPROM is programmed by removing it from the target system and exposing it to UV light for 20 minutes. Because the EPROM cell contains a single transistor, densities comparable to DRAM are achieved. To provide a UV window to the EPROM die, EPROMs are packaged in space-consuming and expensive ceramic packages. EPROMs at the leading edge of density are Intel's 27C240 (4-Mbit, 150-nsec), Waferscale's (Fremont, CA) WS27C040L (4-Mbit, 120-nsec) using its proprietary split-gate

technology, and Fujitsu's (San Jose, CA) MBM27C1028-15 (1-Mbit, 150-nsec). On the leading edge of performance is Microchip Technology's (Chandler, AZ) 27HC256 (256-Kbit, 35-nsec) EPROM. Taking advantage of BiCMOS speed and density, Fujitsu will soon be announcing 256-Kbit, 25-nsec BiCMOS EPROMs. For ECL designers, National Semiconductor's (Santa Clara, CA) NM10E149 (512-bit × 4) ECL-compatible BiCMOS UV-erasable EPROM provides a 5-nsec access time.

Advanced Micro Devices (Sunnyvale, CA) claims one of the fastest/densest EPROMs: the 1-Mbit, 55-nsec Am27C128. AMD stresses that these are truly commodity parts. Combining both density and performance, Intel and Toshiba (Tustin, CA) recently presented papers on 4-Mbit 90-nsec EPROMs using 1-μm lithography. Many of these dense parts are now provided in "×16" versions.

In applications where data density is limited, access time is not critical, and cost is a major consideration, serial access EPROMs offer an interesting option. Plus, it is more difficult to corrupt data in a serial device. Fujitsu's MBM8541 is such a device offering 256 bits of serial storage.

Raw speed and density can be pushed only so far. Clever application-specific memory architectures can push performance still further. By designing 27C203 EPROMs closely coupled to Intel's pipelined 8086/80386 architecture, an effective 35-nsec access time is achieved by interweaving two 70-nsec EPROMs within the pipeline. Application-specific EPROMs from Intel and Texas Instruments (Dallas, TX) take advantage of a microprocessor's burst mode to yield cache-like performance. Another architectural approach to squeezing the most out of an EPROM is to integrate some of the surrounding circuitry onto the EPROM. For example, the latches between a microcontroller and an EPROM can be combined onto the EPROM. Also, since tying the EPROM to the microcontroller sacrifices one of the ports, the EPROM can be built with a port expander like Intel's 87C75F so the port can be reconstructed on the memory.

A new approach combining the low cost of a masked ROM with the fast turnaround of an EPROM is dubbed ExpressROM by AMD and QTP by Microchip Technology. The resultant devices are plastic-packaged EPROMs that are programmed and tested to customers' specifications. Unlike ROMs, which can only be programmed economically in very large volumes, these devices can be programmed in small lots, making them suitable

Figure 1: Xicor's X28C010 1-Mbit monolithic EEPROM offers read access time of 200 nsec. Page size is 128 bytes.

for customers using as few as 5000 devices. But this technology is not for everyone. Many designers wait until the final stages of production to program their PROMs and EPROMs with the latest versions of the code. ExpressROM and QTP would not serve this need.

Featuring Full-featured EEPROMs

Full-featured EEPROMs can be electrically erased and reprogrammed in the target system without opening the cabinet. System code can even be altered over long distance by remote control. Telecomm field service engineers traveling through Europe have little trouble crossing borders, but experience difficulty transporting EPROM boards through Customs. Using EEPROMs, changes can now be downloaded via telephone across international boundaries.

Using two transistors per cell, one for access and one for storage, EEPROMs are architecturally similar to a DRAM except that the DRAM's capacitor is replaced by a floating gate device that stores charge. The charge in that gate is accessed and can be electrically removed by the access transistor. Since access transistors are used, it is possible to erase data row by row. While EEPROMs require a minimum of 12V to write, they are often supplied with an on-board charge pump, so that only a single 5V external supply is required; thus there are no true 5V EEPROMs.

On the leading edge of full-featured EEPROMs are Xicor's (Milpitas, CA) 1-Mbit, 200-nsec X28C010 (**Figure 1**) and Microchip Technology's 256-Kbit, 100-nsec 29CP256B. Samsung (San Jose, CA) offers a 32-Kbit × 8, 150-nsec CMOS 5V-only EEPROM with a choice of endurance of 10K or 100K cycles. The higher endurance is achieved using redundant circuitry; if there is a cell defect, data is automatically rerouted to

Feature	EPROM	NAND EEPROM	Full-Featured EEPROM	Flash EEPROM	Stepped-Gate Flash	MNOS (SNOS)	Ferroelectric	Battery-Backed DRAM	Battery-Backed SRAM
Density	4 Mbytes	4 Mbytes	1 Mbyte	1 Mbyte	1 Mbyte	64K	16K	16 Mbytes (Proj)	256K
Die Size (mm^2)	83.4	163	91.5	38	51	25	25	N/A	N/A
Cell Size (μm^2)	11.9	12.9	30.4	15.2	24.6	120	270	3.4	N/A
Elements/Cell	1	1.25	2	1	1.5	2	2	2	6
Lithography (μm)	1	0.5	1	1	1	2	1.5	0.5	1.2
Typ. Access Time (nsec)	90	1600	110	90	150	200	100	1000	45
Current Consumption									
Operating (mA)	20	20	66	8	N/A	30	5	5	120
Standby (μA)	10	10	100	4	N/A	10	10	.5	1
Write/Erase Voltage	12.5/-	22/17	16/16	12/12	21/21	15/15	5/5	1.5/1.5	5(3 hold)
Charge Pump	No	Yes	Yes	No	No	Yes	Not nec.	Not nec.	Not nec.
Write Speed (μsec/byte)	.5	4000	2000	10	.5	5000	.2	1	.045
Erase Speed (sec)	1200/mem	.01/4 Kbyte	.002/byte	.9/mem	5/mem	.005/mem	10^{-7}/byte	10^{-6}/bit	45x10^{-9} bit
Max Write/Erase Cycles	10^2 to 10^3	10^4 to 10^5	10^4 to 10^5	10^5	10^2 to 10^3	10^5	10^{10}	Infinity	Infinity
Min Erase Block Size	All bits	4 Kbytes	1 byte	All bits	128 bytes	32 bytes	1 byte	1 bit	1 bit
Radiation Tolerance (Rads)	10^5	10^5	10^5	N/A	N/A	10^6	10^7 to 10^8	0	Low
Retention (Years)	>10	>10	>10	>10	>10	>10	>10	5@2AH Battery	4@35mAH Battery
Manufacturer	**Intel**	**Toshiba**	**Mitsubishi**	**Intel**	**Seeq**	**Hitachi**	**Ramtron**	**Hitachi**	**Dallas Semi**
	1900 Prairie City Rd. Folsom, CA 95630 (916) 351-8080	2441 Michelle Dr. Tustin, CA 92680 (714) 730-5000	1050 E. Arques Dr. Sunnyvale, CA 94086 (408) 730-5900	1900 Prairie City Rd. Folsom, CA 95630 (916) 351-8080	1849 Fortune Dr. San Jose, CA 95131 (408) 432-7400	2210 O'Toole Ave. San Jose, CA 95131 (408) 435-8300	1873 Austin Buff Pkwy. Colorado Springs, CO 80918 (303) 594-4455	2210 O'Toole Ave San Jose, CA 95131 (408) 935-8300	4350 Beltwood Pkwy. S. Dallas, TX 75244 (214) 450-0400
	Circle 230	**Circle 231**	**Circle 232**	**Circle 233**	**Circle 234**	**Circle 235**	**Circle 236**	**Circle 237**	**Circle 238**

Table 1: Comparison of Important Features of Some Recent Nonvolatile Memories

Courtesy of Ramtron

another cell. Incidentally, there is no mechanism available in either EEPROMs or Flash memory to signal when the device is nearing the limits of its endurance.

Serial EEPROMs, like serial PROMs, are also used as peripheral devices to store user-programmable features for microcontrollers typically equipped with a serial interface. National Semiconductor's EEPROM offerings are concentrated in this area, with densities ranging from 256 bits up to 4 Kbits. Alan Ankerbrand, National's EEPROM marketing manager, notes that the low-density EEPROM market is far larger than that for high-density parts. Catalyst Semiconductor (Santa Clara, CA) and Microchip Technology have produced lower-power replacements for the National parts and have upgraded density to 4 Kbits. Both National and Catalyst claim 100,000-cycle endurance and Catalyst claims 100-year retention. Catalyst just introduced CAT35C804, a 4-Kbit secure access serial EEPROM that embeds a password-oriented user-access control mechanism in the silicon, preventing selected data viewing and/or alteration by unauthorized users.

Low-voltage EEPROMs are starting to find their way into portable battery-powered and phone-line-powered telecomm applications such as cellular phones, pagers, remote controls, smart credit cards, VCRs, cameras, and battery-operated games. For example, Catalyst, National, and Xicor have families of products that operate between 3V and 6V. Trade-offs for low-voltage operation consist of a drop in access speed, difficulty in establishing a reasonable threshold voltage level for the V_{CC} lockout feature (which prevents inadvertent writes), and the need to modify the on-chip charge pump to allow erases/writes. Exel Microelectronics (San Jose, CA) has announced what it claims is the first EEPROM to support low-power, 3V operation: the XL93CS46 (serial, 1024-bit).

Memory in a Flash

With limited endurance, Flash memories, like EEPROMs, are "read-mostly" devices. Flash is particularly beneficial in cost-sensitive applications (like PCs) where full-featured EEPROMs are too expensive. By using Flash, upgrades in the BIOS can be made remotely, even via modem. Similarly, in PAL programmers, the firmware is stored in an EPROM. Using a Flash, the PAL programmer can be upgraded remotely instead of having the EPROM changed in the field. Intel Flash devices appear in Tektronix' (Vancouver, WA) new 4.5-lb portable oscilloscope. And Flash technology is certain to be applied in ASIC environments, such as Flash macrocells in cell libraries.

The difference between a Flash EPROM and a Flash EEPROM has not been settled. Some manufacturers, like AMD, split Flash offerings into two categories according to their endurance: Flash EPROM and Flash EEPROM. Flash EPROMs are meant to replace existing EPROMs and are limited to perhaps 100 write/erase cycles. They have standard EPROM pinouts, including a write-enable pin, and are relatively low-cost. Flash

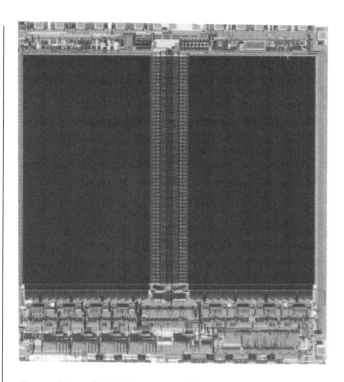

Figure 2: Intel's 28F010 is a 1-Mbit, 120-nsec Flash memory. The device erases in under 1 sec and programs in under 2 sec. It ships with an endurance of 100,000 cycles.

EEPROMs are meant to replace full-featured EEPROMs and can cycle many thousands of times. The distinction is somewhat artificial and tends to force users to view Flash devices as replacements for either EPROM or EEPROM, instead of as a solution quite distinct from both.

All Flash memory can be categorized by "generation." First-generation Flash memory uses dual power supplies (typically 5V/12V), and requires the use of an external sequencer and waveshaping circuits to implement the programming algorithm. Second-generation Flash memory uses an on-board charge pump

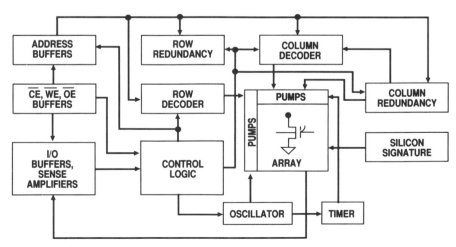

Figure 3: This 48F010 1-Mbit Flash memory (courtesy of Seeq Technology) is typical of second-generation Flash architectures. Note the charge pumps to allow 5V-only operation and analog circuits used to help implement the programming algorithms.

to achieve 5V-only operation, and contains an on-board sequencer and waveshaping circuits to make programming easier. Second-generation parts are not necessarily more advanced than first-generation parts; both have advantages and trade-offs.

The Flash EEPROM cell consists of one transistor per cell. The small cell and simple architecture permit dense high-performance nonvolatile memories to be built at prices that approach DRAM. For example, the costs of 1-Mbit memories are: EPROM, $3; DRAM, $5; Flash, $30; SRAM, $200; and EEPROM, $1000. To explain the relationship between DRAM pricing and Flash pricing, it is interesting to note that Intel's 28F010 (128-Kbit $\times$ 8) 1-Mbit Flash consumes 60,116 mil^2—smaller than today's dynamic RAMs which measure more than 70,000 mils^2. Only the difference in production volumes prevents Flash memory from reaching down to DRAM price levels.

Flash price/density advantages are offset by several disadvantages. One is that all bits must be erased before programming one bit. Further, all bits must be programmed before erasing. Since in many applications program and data are changed only incrementally, when data contained within the Flash is changed, it has to be offloaded to some other memory location. During this data transfer the data is volatile again. With Flash there is a trade-off between the ability to perform a section-only erase versus endurance. If sector erase is needed, endurance drops drastically.

Intel recently introduced a 1-Mbit, 120-nsec Flash memory, the 28F010 (**Figure 2**). Intel claims it has the only Flash memory currently shipping with an endurance of 100,000 cycles, being tested out to 1,000,000 cycles. The 28F010 erases in under 1 sec and programs in under 2 sec. A 2-Mbit part will be introduced early next year, and probably a 4-Mbit one by year's end. To achieve such endurance Intel has sacrificed the flexibility of sector erase.

AMD uses the same first-generation Flash architecture as Intel, but achieves somewhat improved performance at a lower density with its Am28F256-90 (32-Kbit $\times$ 8, 90-nsec) part. Higher-speed parts are being jointly developed by AMD and International CMOS Technology (San Jose, CA) with sampling to begin 4Q/89. As part of this agreement, AMD will acquire an option to purchase an equity interest in ICT. AMD doesn't expect manufacturers to ship 2- or 4-Mbit parts for at least another year.

Second-Generation Flash

Second-generation Flash memory differs from the first generation by the presence of on-board charge pumps to produce a 5V-only part, and analog circuitry such as an oscillator and control logic to implement the programming algorithm. Seeq Technology's 48F010 1-Mbit Flash (**Figure 3**) with sector erase of 1024 bytes is an example of such memory. Seeq uses a stepped-gate Flash that averages 1.5 transistors/cell, allowing the user to erase 128-byte blocks instead of all bits. National Semiconductor has announced that it is supporting Seeq Technology in the development and introduction of the 48F512 and 48F010 (512-Kbit and 1-Mbit) Flash devices. National will leave the development of the next-generation Flash devices to Seeq while it focuses on developing next-generation EPROMs. This is the first example of second-sourcing of Flash parts.

Atmel's (San Jose, CA) second-generation Flash memories, dubbed PEROMs (Programmable Erasable Read Only Memories), use a two-transistor cell that is more like an

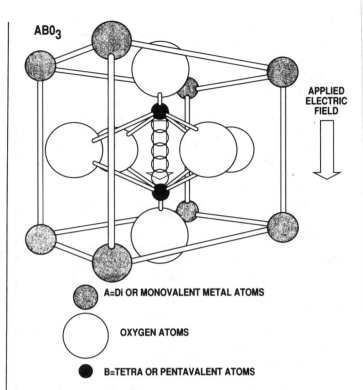

Figure 4: The innovative ferroelectronic process uses a thin film of ceramic PZT (lead-zirconate-titanate) sandwiched between two metal electrodes to form a "digital memory capacity" which is built above existing semiconductor circuitry. Nonvolatile operation results from the film's two stable polarization states. A simplified model of a ferroelectric PZT is shown here.

EEPROM than a first-generation Flash memory. Since the two-transistor PEROM cell is larger than a one-transistor Flash memory cell, the core area of the PEROM chip is about 50% larger. The larger area and 50% premium over standard EPROM devices is compensated for by the fact that the PEROM operates from a 5V supply (charge pump on-board chip). More importantly, there is an on-board sequencer.

The writing requirements of a first-generation Flash are very complex. The designer essentially has to duplicate the specialized sequencers and circuit controls normally found in an EPROM programmer in order to sequence the write voltages and control the write slew rate. It is a complicated algorithm that can consume valuable board real estate and add considerable cost.

Key to second-generation Flash is that it has the same system interface as SRAM. Atmel will ship 1-Mbit PEROMs this year and expects to ship 4-Mbit parts in 1990 and 16-Mbit parts in 1992. Texas Instruments also has a 5V-only Flash EEPROM (256-Kbit, 170-nsec) with an endurance to 1000 cycles.

With predicted die penalties of 30% to 100% over dual-voltage first-generation Flash, AMD's Steve Grossman, memory marketing manager, cautions that, "to a large degree people are going to Flash because it's a lot less expensive than EEPROMs. Until we figure out how to do it economically, and, trust me, Atmel and Waferscale haven't figured out how do it yet, just look at their published die sizes, it's not going to be a good deal for customers." Both 5V and 12V/5V parts will likely coexist in the market for the foreseeable future.

Ferroelectric Promise

The promise of ferroelectric memories—dubbed FRAMs by Ramtron Corp. (Colorado Springs, CO)—to provide the ultimate memory is still just that—a promise (**Figure 4**). If the promise is fulfilled, FRAM will provide low cost per bit, high density, fast random access, read/write and cycle times of equal duration, low power consumption, operation over a wide temperature range, a single low-voltage power supply, a high degree of radiation tolerance, and inherent nonvolatility.

At low density (such as the existing 4-Kbit parts), FRAMs compete with both EEPROMs and battery-backed SRAMs. Comparing it to EEPROM, FRAM has a much faster write cycle time (0.2 μsec/byte versus 2000 nsec/byte) and longer write endurance (10^{10} max write/erase cycles versus 10^4-10^5). In fact, the erase, write, and access times are essentially equal. This is important for uses that are not read-mostly, such as SRAM applications. EEPROM is a good read-mostly memory, but not a good read/write memory. Compared to SRAM, FRAMs have similar read/write cycle times, but FRAMs are nonvolatile without a battery. The typical approach to a nonvolatile SRAM is to purchase one with the battery enclosed, such as the Dallas Semiconductor or SGS-Thomson (Phoenix, AZ) parts, or to use the system-level lithium battery. In that case, SRAM nonvolatility endurance is a function of battery life—it might range from 6 months to 10 years. FRAM endurance is a function of the number of cycles, not the length of time. The FRAM device will be much more reliable than a battery-backed SRAM.

Ramtron is now building 4-Kbit FRAMs, and the 16-Kbit FM1408 will be sampling early next year. Ramtron will be using ITT's 1.5-μm fab facilities, although the process can be produced on almost any fab.

A very high-density process with cell size similar to DRAM is being developed, but with nonvolatility. These parts will compete with DRAMs and ferromagnetic disk memories. FRAM technology will have the same performance profile as DRAM. Ramtron sees no limitations to scaling and is actively working on memory designs scalable to 4 Mbits. High-density parts are predicted for 1991. FRAM cells may turn out to be more scalable than DRAM cells because the ferroelectric capacitors have a greater dielectric constant than CMOS SiO_2 capacitors. The most difficult part of the task may be integrating ferroelectric material into the CMOS process.

Will FRAM deliver on its promise? Fujitsu's Ravi Sethi, product line manager for programmable products, thinks it will be another five years before FRAM's manufacturability and data retention problems are overcome.

Nonvolatile and Battery-backed SRAM

One interesting nonvolatile architecture is the nonvolatile SRAM, a combination of EEPROM and SRAM. Each SRAM cell has a corresponding "shadow" EEPROM cell. NOVRAMs (nonvolatile RAMs) appear to the system as a normal SRAM, but when a STORE command is issued the data is transferred to the on-board shadow EEPROM. When used for critical data storage (when the supply voltage falls below some threshold level), data is transferred to nonvolatile storage. Fujitsu has the MBM 2212 (1-Kbit × 4, 200-nsec SRAM) and Xicor has a family of NOVRAMs ranging up to 512 bits × 8. Catalyst's NOVRAMs include a 256-bit serial part (CAT24C44). SNOS is finding its way into NOVRAM with Simtek's (Colorado Springs, CO) debut of the STK10C68A/STK11C68A (8-Kbit × 8, 34-nsec).

Battery-backed SRAM is the only technology that yields SRAM-like performance with equal read/write times. SGS-Thomson's new MK48Z08-55 combines a 55-nsec, 8-Kbit × 8 full-CMOS SRAM and a long-life lithium carbon monofluoride battery in a single plastic DIP. The densest battery-backed SRAM is Dallas Semiconductor's (Dallas, TX) DS1245 (1-Mbit, 70-nsec). It is a nonvolatile pin- and function-equivalent to any JEDEC standard 8-Kbit × 8 SRAM. It fits easily into many EPROM and EEPROM sockets, providing the nonvolatility of PROMs without any requirement for special write timing, or limitations on the number of writes that can be performed.

One of the most unusual battery-backed SRAMs is the EconoRAM from Dallas Semiconductor. The EconoRAM, the "lowest cost" battery-backed SRAM yet produced, is a 256-bit read/write memory in a 3-pin transistor package which sells for $0.25 in quantity. Address, data, and control lines are multiplexed on a single pin, which connects directly to a microcontroller, providing a low-cost processor interface. Because of EconoRAM's frugal use of energy, a pea-size battery retains data for 10 years and powers over a million read/writes.

The Choice: EEPROM or Flash

Flash memory technology has received extraordinary industry-wide attention. But in the rush to try the new technology, many designers are experiencing unexpected problems. To make an informed decision, a few myths must be dispelled. First is that very dense EEPROMs are not available. Xicor claims that its thick oxide technology, which eliminates the need for cell redundancy, is easily scalable for reduced feature size. Using 0.8-μm technology, Xicor is working on a 4-Mbit, full-featured EEPROM, so apparently leading-edge EEPROMs don't lag that far behind Flash memories, though admittedly the EEPROM dies are larger... which leads to another myth.

EEPROMs are inherently more expensive. Comparing the cost of Flash memory versus full-featured EEPROM is not a simple apple-to-apple comparison. In addition to the direct cost of the Flash, the following costs must be included (for dual-voltage Flash): V_{pp} source, V_{pp} regulator, V_{pp} switch, V_{pp} board space, algorithm development, cost of reliability based on mixing memory components, and support circuits. Further, EEPROM companies, cognizant of the need to reduce costs, are redesigning old parts using the latest fab lines. Xicor, for instance, is using its 1.2-μm technology to redesign the 256-Kbit part, and uses a 2-μm technology to redesign the old 3- to 4-μm technology, low-density parts. Xicor also expects to be the first EEPROM manufacturer to switch over from 4″ to 6″ wafers, further reducing costs. With 1-Kbit serial EEPROMs selling for less than $1, Krish Panu, Xicor's director of marketing, believes that every "household" will have 5 to 10 nonvolatile memories within the next decade. **ESD:**

9

Part 2
Fuse, Antifuse, and PROM Technologies

THE SCOPE of this reprint volume is limited to *electrically programmable* nonvolatile memories. Thus, mask programmable ROM is excluded, and PROM is the simplest nonvolatile memory covered in this volume. However, most review articles and conferences on nonvolatile semiconductor memories do not even include PROM, and the term nonvolatile memories is generally used to represent EPROM, EEPROM, and their derivatives only.

PROM technologies are included in this volume for two reasons. First, the physics and technologies of programmable elements, i.e., the fuses and antifuses, are alternatives to EPROM or EEPROM elements in many applications. Memory redundancy (Paper 10.6) is one such application. Potentially important new applications are programmable logic devices and wafer-scale integration, as discussed in Part 10. Therefore, the subject of this section is not so much the PROM memory per se as the fuses and antifuses. This intention is reflected in the part title.

PROMs have a much smaller market than EPROMs. The main deficiencies of PROMs relative to EPROMs are not the lack of reprogrammability or the resultant inability to guarantee programming performance through testing, although those are shortcomings. After all, OTPs also lack reprogrammability, yet are much more popular than PROMs. The real shortcoming is that PROM cells are much larger in area than EPROM cells. This means PROM is not competitive in price and density. The large cell areas result from the fact that the fuse element is large and is not merged with the select transistor. Furthermore, the fusing operation typically requires more current, e.g., 10 mA, than a minimum-size MOSFET can supply; therefore PROMs are traditionally fabricated with the less dense bipolar technology. Paper 2.7 reports an experimental high-density PROM technology. (The one-time-programmable EPROM described in Paper 3.12 is also a high-density PROM, and a hard one to beat.)

The PROM's advantage over EPROMs is superior speed. Fuses and antifuses, in their conductive states, typically have much lower resistances than an EPROM transistor in its conductive state. This fact plus the speed of bipolar circuitry tended to make PROM a faster memory than EPROM.

For programmable logic circuits, circuit speed and, therefore, the current-carrying capability of the programmable element, which determines the speed of charging and discharging the capacitive loads, are critically important. This makes low-resistance fuses and antifuses attractive. Fuses and antifuses may be less susceptible to READ-disturb and data-retention problems than EPROM or EEPROM elements. Finally, advanced CMOS transistors of reasonable size will be able to conduct sufficient current for fusing (programming).

An ideal fuse or antifuse would be very small in area, can be programmed with a relatively low voltage and current so that it is compatible with advanced CMOS technology, and is reliable. Both traditional fuses and some new antifuses are described in this part.

Paper 2.1 reviews several PROM cell designs mostly employing a fuse made of Nichrome (Ni–Cr), titanium–tungsten, or polysilicon. Paper 2.2 describes a state-of-the-art PROM. The polysilicon fuse is also a popular choice for MOS memory redundancy circuits. Paper 2.3 analyzes the mechanism of lateral polysilicon fuse programming, while Paper 2.4 studies vertical polysilicon antifuses. Vertical antifuses occupy smaller areas than lateral fuses. Papers 2.5 and 2.6 describe attempts to develop vertical amorphous silicon antifuses for bipolar and MOS PROMs, respectively. Although amorphous antifuses are still under development, their small size is very attractive for future logic applications. Paper 10.8 describes the use of amorphous silicon antifuses for intercircuit connections.

Silicon dioxide and other dielectrics can also be employed as antifuse materials and are described in Papers 2.7 and 2.8. Paper 2.8 addresses the use of antifuse in field-programmable gate arrays. Reference [9] in the introduction to Part 9 discusses the reliability of a dielectric antifuse. Finally, Paper 2.9 describes junction shorting as another antifuse programming mechanism.

Traditional fuse programming requires removal of significant amounts of materials by evaporation. In contrast, vertical antifuses use less violent mechanisms for programming and can be more compact in size. One can expect growing interest in using antifuses in the future.

Fuse/antifuse and EPROM/EEPROM will increasingly be considered as alternatives to each other. Fast CMOS or BICMOS EPROMs are encroaching on traditional bipolar PROM and PLD territories, while fuse/antifuse will challenge EPROM/EEPROM in CMOS programmable logic devices.

Finally, it should be mentioned that there are reversible, i.e., reprogrammable, fuse-antifuses. Reversible "memory switching" has been reported for vertical thin-film fuses made of many materials including amorphous chacalgenide [1], amorphous silicon, and CVD polycrystalline silicon [2]. These articles are not included in this reprint volume due to space limitations and the lack of recent research and development interest. There is little understanding of the reversible switching phenomenon. Nevertheless, these reversible fuses may become practical reprogrammable nonvolatile memories in the future.

REFERENCES

[1] S. R. Ovshinsky and H. Fritzsche, "Amorphous semiconductors for switching, memory, and imaging applications," *IEEE Trans. Electron Devices*, vol. ED-20, no. 2, pp. 91–105, Feb. 1973.
[2] H. Kroger, H. A. R. Wegener, and W. M. Shedd, "Memory switching in polycrystalline silicon films," *Thin Solid Films*, vol. 66, pp. 171–176, 1980.

Simple process propels bipolar PROMs to 16-K density and beyond

Double-level metalization and polysilicon fuses guarantee dense high-speed memories and cleanly burned links that don't grow back

by Robert K. Wallace and Arthur J. Learn, *Intel Corp., Santa Clara, Calif.*

☐ At present, high-speed bipolar programmable read-only memories are being manufactured with an assortment of memory cell designs and programming techniques. Cells made of npn or pnp transistor emitter followers, base-collector diodes, or Schottky diodes are programmed by blowing Nichrome, titanium-tungsten or polysilicon fuses or by shorting out reverse-biased junctions with aluminum.

Eventually, though, under the twin pressures of increasing PROM complexity and the need to optimize manufacturing, the simplest and densest technology will dominate. For this position, stacked-fuse bipolar technology is a likely candidate.

The base-emitter diode it uses for the memory cell (see Fig. 1) takes maximum advantage of the polysilicon fuse materials, which makes direct contact to the emitter region. Such a diode in an emitter-follower array has the added advantages of providing current gain, relatively good conductance per square micrometer, and self-isolation. A double, rather than single, level of metalization ensures high speed while guaranteeing each cell highly consistent fusing current. It also yields a clean and permanent break of the polysilicon fuse and aids in reducing cell size (see Table 1).

The technology is currently being used to produce 4-K and 16-K devices. The 4-K 3625A memory has a worst-case access time of 50 nanoseconds; the 16-K 3636, one of 65 ns. A scaled-down variation of the process recently yielded a typical access time of 25 ns at the 16-K level (see "A super-fast new PROM,").

The stacked-fuse cell is shown in Fig. 2. The word lines are of bottom-level metal, and the bit lines are of

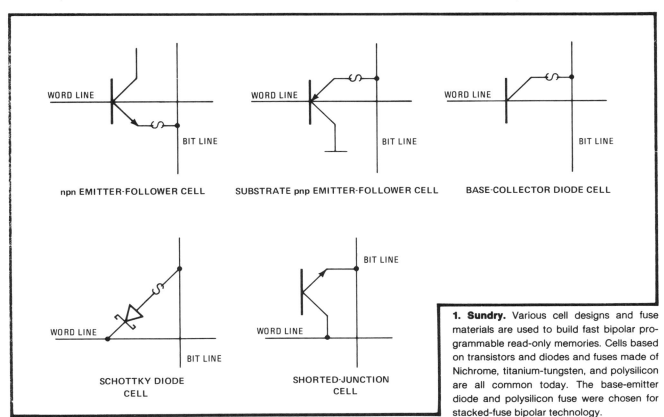

npn EMITTER-FOLLOWER CELL   SUBSTRATE pnp EMITTER-FOLLOWER CELL   BASE-COLLECTOR DIODE CELL

SCHOTTKY DIODE CELL   SHORTED-JUNCTION CELL

1. Sundry. Various cell designs and fuse materials are used to build fast bipolar programmable read-only memories. Cells based on transistors and diodes and fuses made of Nichrome, titanium-tungsten, and polysilicon are all common today. The base-emitter diode and polysilicon fuse were chosen for stacked-fuse bipolar technology.

Cell type	Fuse type	Cell area	4-K PROM die size
Emitter-follower	polysilicon	1.3 mils^2	119 mils/side
Emitter-follower	nichrome or titanium-tungsten	2.1 mils^2	150 mils/side
Schottky diode		1.8 mils^2	140 mils/side
Base-collector diode		1.8 mils^2	140 mils/side

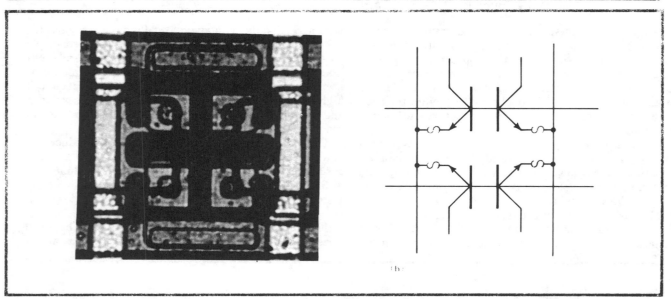

2. Layout. The photomicrograph on the left and the schematic on the right depict 4 bits in a stacked-fuse array. The word lines are of bottom-level metal, the bit lines of top-level. The 1.3-mil^2 cell is the smallest because some masking tolerances are eliminated.

top-level metal. There are two key cell features. First, the bit line (upper-level metal) makes direct contact to the bit-line side of the polysilicon fuse instead of using the traditional top-metal-to-bottom-metal contact.

Second, the other end of the fuse makes direct contact to the emitter of the emitter-follower circuit element. In so doing, the traditional masking alignment tolerances associated with making contacts to the silicon and between metal layers are eliminated. This results in a cell size of less than 1.3 square mils, 30% smaller than any other material and cell combination using the same design rules.

Moreover, each bit has its own bit- and word-line contact, virtually eliminating bit-to-bit nonuniformities. This design is superior to other two-level–metalization PROM cell designs where a contact is shared by 8 or even 16 cells in order to make a small cell viable.

Technology considerations

Impurity diffusion through polysilicon to form transistor emitter regions creates a structure similar to the so-called "washed" emitter (Fig. 3). No allowance is necessary for the emitter contact and the most compact geometry is thus achieved.

Additional benefits are realized through use of the polysilicon emitter. Since the polysilicon shields the epitaxial silicon from dissolution in the metal, no other precautions need be taken to avoid spiking (and hence, shorting) of the emitter-base junction. Also, a low donor concentration at the surface of the epitaxial silicon aids in minimizing collector-emitter shorts. Presumably because of this low surface concentration, the emitter push effect is absent, too. All such factors simplify processing, increase control, and raise yield.

A second level of metalization in lieu of diffused conductors ensures ample power delivery to the fuses even in the case of very large memory chips. This also minimizes the emitter-collector area, greatly reducing the probability of collector-emitter leakage or shorts. The result: higher yields.

Two-level metalization is conducive to higher density as well, further enhancing yield. With the two-level design, excellent fusing is achieved even at the most remote fuse locations, as indicated in the example of Fig. 4. The wide gap, free of fuse material, together with the absence of any regrowth phenomena for the polysilicon fuse, guarantees superior reliability.

Careful attention must be accorded the choice of materials and processing techniques if two-level metalization is to realize a high degree of manufacturability

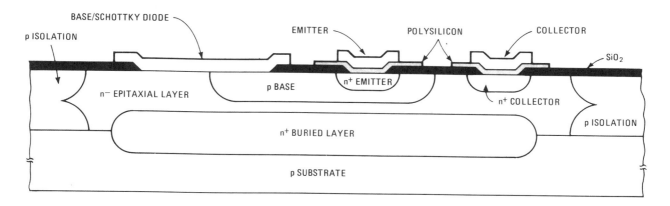

BASE/SCHOTTKY DIODE
p ISOLATION
EMITTER
POLYSILICON
COLLECTOR
SiO₂
n⁻ EPITAXIAL LAYER
p BASE
n⁺ EMITTER
n⁺ COLLECTOR
p ISOLATION
n⁺ BURIED LAYER
p SUBSTRATE

3. Section. Standard diffused-isolation Schottky bipolar technology is used for stacked-fuse memories because of its long history in manufacture. Impurities are diffused right through the thin polysilicon layers to increase alignment tolerances.

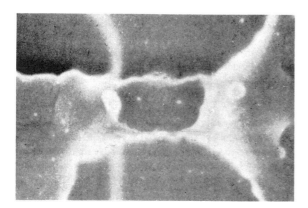
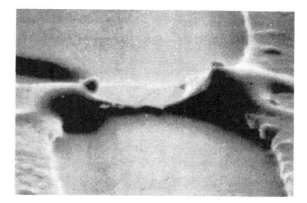

4. Blown. With stacked-fuse bipolar technology, consistent fusing current is guaranteed, even if the fuses are in remote locations. The top view (left) and side view (right) of a blown fuse show a wide gap free of fuse material. And polysilicon fuses exhibit no regrowth phenomena.

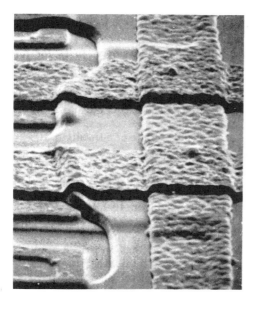

5. Two-level metal. Key to the density, speed, and consistent fusing current is stacked-fuse technology in the use of double-level metalization. The side view (left) shows the uniform coverage by the second level. At right is a metal-metal via.

15

A super-fast new PROM

Positive-resist photolithography and 3-micrometer design rules have recently been applied to polysilicon stacked-fuse technology. The result is a 2-K-by-8-bit memory, now in development, with a typical access time of only 25 nanoseconds (35 ns maximum). The device was described at the International Solid State Circuits Conference, held last month in San Francisco [*Electronics*, Feb. 14, 1980 p. 138].

The memory, shown below, is fabricated on a 140-square-mil die and consumes 600 milliwatts. It uses the same two-level metalization scheme and polysilicon fuses as the devices described in this article. In fact, it was brought out at the conference that the stacked-fuse process, which employs lateral fuses, may be used to build high-speed 64-K devices. This is a significant finding, because formerly it was thought that vertical fuses—which may pose more manufacturing and reliability problems—would be necessary for this high density.

-John G. Posa

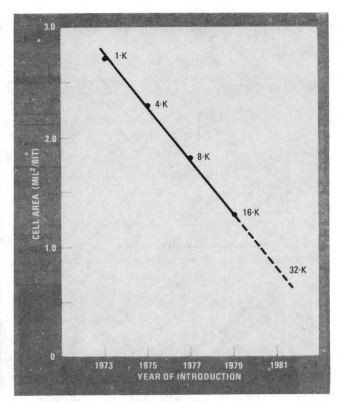

6. Learning curve. The stacked polysilicon fuse has successfully been applied to PROMs ranging in capacity from 1 to 16 K. Density has doubled about every two years and higher-density lithography and dry processing may even accelerate this trend.

and reliability. Aluminum-alloy metalization exhibits freedom from factors that degrade reliability, such as electromigration, and yield, such as surface reconstruction under heating. The latter is particularly important in promoting pinhole-free insulation between the two metal levels.

In the presence of surface reconstruction (hillock growth), difficulties will arise in achieving uniform and complete interlevel dielectric coverage or photoresist coverage (with concomitant dielectric etching at unwanted points). Plasma-enhanced deposition of the dielectric alleviates the coverage problem to some degree, however, and provides a topography more amenable to a second level of metalization. The technique promotes higher-integrity insulation between levels.

Plasma etching processes are also useful in providing a more gentle taper to the vias in the interlevel dielectric. This, in turn, enhances second-level metalization coverage and minimizes the resistance associated with vias. Examples of the two-level metalization structure and an enlarged view of a via are presented in Fig. 5.

Use of the two-level metalization and polysilicon stacked-fuse method on Intel's 3625A 4-K PROM has dramatically increased yield and decreased worst-case access time by 30% from 70 ns to 50 ns. Organized as 1,024 by 4 bits and housed in an 18-lead dual in-line package, the 3625A has a density of 1.3 mil^2 per bit and a die size of 14,000 mil^2.

The potential of polysilicon fuses for higher density has also been demonstrated on the Intel 3636, a high-speed 16-K PROM. No technology changes were necessary to go from the 4-K to the 16-K level. The 3636 has the same cell as the 3625A, but has a die size of 38,000 mil^2 and a worst-case access time of 65 ns from 0° to 75°C at a supply voltage of 5.0 volts ±10%.

The device is arranged as 2 K by 8 bits and is packaged in a 24-pin DIP to be compatible with existing 512-by-8- and 1,024-by-8-bit 4-K and 8-K PROMs. Despite the increased density, total power consumption remains unchanged from the older 4- and 8-K PROMs.

Future applications

The polysilicon cell has now been applied successfully to PROMs ranging in bit density from 1 to 16 K. Figure 6 shows the evolution of cell size from the 1-K to the 16-K level and beyond; memory density has doubled about every two years. Application of higher-density photolithography and dry etching techniques may even accelerate this trend. Polysilicon fuse technology promises to remain viable through the 64-K density level. □

A 35ns 128K Fusible Bipolar PROM

Phi Thai, S.C. Chang, Mann C. Yang

Advanced Micro Devices

Sunnyvale, CA

A 128K BIPOLAR PROM organized as 16K x 8b will be described. The IMDX III process, outlined in Table 1, utilizing slot isolation, as well as various circuit techniques, have been optimized to create a 35ns 128K PROM with a die size of 306 x 224 mil^2; Figure 2. The slot isolation process utilizes a shallow ion-implanted transistor isolated from adjacent devices by a vertical poly-filled slot whose size is less than $2\mu m$. The base and emitter elements of the transistor are walled by field oxide; Figure 3. The reduction in transistor size and slot isolation not only contribute to the density advantage necessary for the VLSI devices, but also lead to increased performance. This device also utilizes the same platinum silicide fuse that is common to many bipolar PROMs. The cell size is 13 x 14.5μm^2 which is less than 0.3mil^2 and smaller than the vertical fuse structure used in other bipolar technologies. Platinum silicide has been chosen to form the fuse for several reasons. It has been demonstrated to be an extremely reliable fuse material. The manufacturing process is easily controlled with regard to reliability factors and fusing currents. The fuses are quite easy to form without a substantial number of additional process steps. The array matrix has been organized as 256 rows x 512 columns, with additional test rows and columns to test the programming circuitry and ac performance.

Circuit techniques include a column current multiplex scheme; Figure 4. This circuitry allows a maximum current I_3 flowing through the selected column and standby currents I_1 and I_2 to sustain the deselected ones. This arrangement results in a 100 to 130mA power supply current saving without penalizing device performance. Thus, the 128K PROM's performance level of 35ns uses 1/8 the power-per-bit of bipolar 16K PROMs and 1/4 the power-per-bit of high performance 16K CMOS PROMs. Other circuit features include a temperature compensated sense amplifier and current sources that allow the access time of the device to be relatively flat over temperature; Figure 5.

The 128K PROM has been designed to follow a generic programming algorithm which minimizes the requirements on the programmer, yet allows the circuit to fuse the platinum silicide links quickly and reliably. Programming is accomplished by disabling the outputs with $\overline{CS}$ at logic high, raising output to 20V, then raising the $\overline{CS}$ to 15V. The programming time of the 128K PROM is approximately 60s including all verification checks. Each bit takes about $100\mu s$ to program using the normal algorithm. The true programming time for an individual bit is below $5\mu s$.

Figure 6 is a photograph of the chip.

Acknowledgments

The authors would like to thank J. Bourgoin, G. Brown and BPM's design engineers for their helpful suggestions, A. Hansen and the technology development group for wafer processing, and P. Seales's support group and mask design for producing the masks.

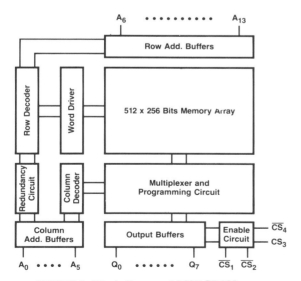

FIGURE 1—Block diagram of 128K PROM.

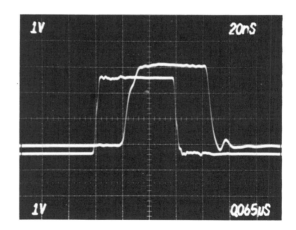

FIGURE 2—Typical address to output delay at V_{cc} = 5V.

Reprinted from the *IEEE ISSCC Dig. Tech. Pap.*, pp. 44–45, 299, 1986.

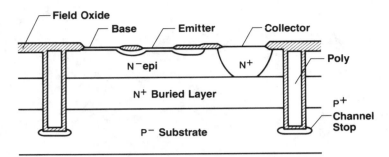

FIGURE 3—Cross section of transistor.

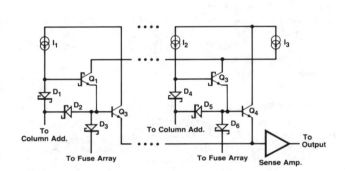

FIGURE 4—Column current multiplex circuit.

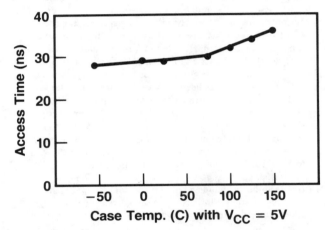

FIGURE 5—Temperature dependence of access time.

T_{AA}: 30ns

T_{AC}: 20ns

I_{CC}: 160mA

TECHNOLOGY: STEPPER TECHNOLOGY & DRY ETCH

MIN. FEATURE SIZE: 1.2 μ

Ist METAL PITCH: 5 μ

2nd METAL PITCH: 8 μ

CELL SIZE: 188.5 μ^2

DIE SIZE: 68544 mil^2

TABLE 1—Typical characteristics and design rule of the 128K PROM.

18

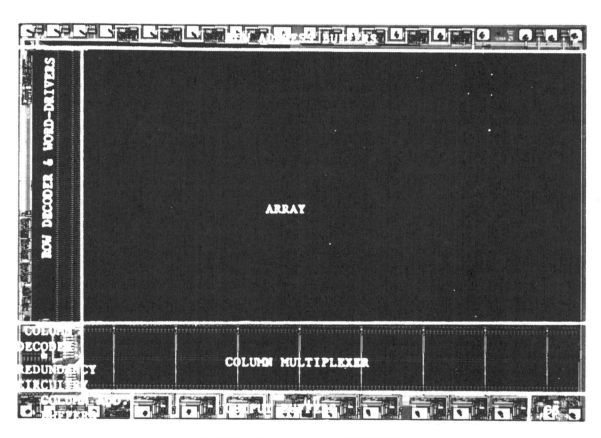

FIGURE 6—Photograph of the 128K PROM.

Programming Mechanism of Polysilicon Resistor Fuses

DAVID W. GREVE, MEMBER, IEEE

Abstract—The programming characteristics of polysilicon resistor fuses were investigated. It was found that an open circuit occurs only after the fuse makes a transition to a second-breakdown state in which the current flow is mainly through a molten filament. Filamentary current flow is stable since the resistivity of silicon decreases abruptly upon melting. A simple model was developed which explains the observed I-V characteristics.

Fuse opening occurs when the current in second breakdown exceeds a critical current I_{min} which depends strongly on the fuse thickness and the presence or absence of a passivation layer over the fuse. The gap forms at the positive end, suggesting that the silicon ions move by drift in the applied electric field.

NOMENCLATURE

a	Width of molten filament (cm).
c	Silicon heat capacity ($\simeq$2.2 J/cm$^3 \cdot$ °C).
d_{ox}	Oxide thickness under fuse (cm).
d_p	Polysilicon fuse thickness (cm).
g_{ox}	Oxide thermal conductivity ($\simeq$0.014 W/cm $\cdot$ °C).
I	Total fuse current (A).
I_t	Fuse current at P_{crit} (A).
J	Lateral heat flux (W).
l	Fuse length (cm).
p_i	Power density: i = 1,2 for unmelted and melted regions, respectively (W/cm).
P_i	Power dissipation: i = 1,2 for unmelted and melted regions, respectively (W).
P_{crit}	Critical power dissipation necessary to cause second breakdown (W).
r_{Si}	Silicon thermal resistivity ($\simeq$4.7 cm $\cdot$ °C/W at 1400°C).
R_s	Resistance between contacts and molten filament (Ω).
t_d	Delay time before second-breakdown transition (s).
T_{crit}	Critical temperature for second breakdown (°C).
T_m	Silicon melting temperature (°C).
V_t	Voltage across fuse at P_{crit} (V).
v	Voltage across molten filament exclusive of contact resistance (V).
w	Fuse width (cm).
x	Distance across fuse (cm).
σ_i	Electrical conductivity of polysilicon: i = 1,2 for unmelted and melted regions, respectively (1/$\Omega \cdot$ cm).

I. INTRODUCTION

RECENTLY, there has been increasing interest in the use of polysilicon for permanently programmable circuit elements. Applications include bipolar PROM's [1], [2] and

Manuscript received August 16, 1981; revised November 13, 1981.
The author is with Philips Research Laboratories Sunnyvale, Signetics Corporation, Sunnyvale, CA 94086.

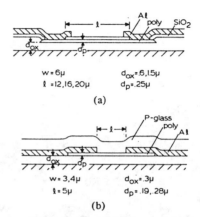

w = 6μ d_{ox} = .6,.15μ
l = 12,16,20μ d_p = .25μ

(a)

w = 3,4μ d_{ox} = .3μ
l = 5μ d_p = .19,.28μ

(b)

Fig. 1. Two types of polysilicon resistor fuses. (a) Type A oxide isolated fuse. (b) Type B etched fuse.

selection of redundant circuit blocks in MOS memories [3]–[8]. Both electrical and laser programming have been described in the literature, and it is not yet clear which approach is best.

In this paper we will discuss electrical programming of polysilicon fuses. It will be shown that formation of a state of second breakdown [9] is necessary for programming. This has important consequences for the design of programming circuits. Published data suggest that second breakdown also occurs during programming of polysilicon devices which include p-n junctions [8].

In Section II of this paper, we will describe the fuse structures and the programming circuit. Section III will present the evidence for second breakdown in polysilicon resistor fuses. In Section IV, we will calculate the fuse I-V characteristics and in Section V the programming behavior of the fuses will be described.

II. FUSE STRUCTURE AND PROGRAMMING CIRCUIT

Fig. 1(a) and (b) illustrates the two types of resistor fuses which were studied. The type A fuses were defined by selective oxidation as shown in Fig. 1(a); the polysilicon was doped by phosphorus diffusion to give $R_{\square} \simeq 60$ Ω. The fuses were covered with 4000 Å densified undoped SiO$_2$ and the metallization was aluminum. These fuses were comparatively large but several variations of fuse dimensions were available.

Etched fuses fabricated as in Fig. 1(b) (type B) were of practical dimensions. Several polysilicon thicknesses were used, with $R_{\square} \simeq 90$ Ω for a thickness of 0.28 μm. The fuses were covered with 2 μm of phosphorus-doped SiO$_2$. For both type A and B fuses, good ohmic contacts were obtained without alloying after aluminum deposition.

Reprinted from *IEEE Trans. Electron Devices*, vol. ED-29, no. 4, pp. 719–724, April 1982.

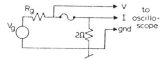

Fig. 2. Circuit for programming polysilicon fuses. The current and voltage transients are recorded simultaneously by the oscilloscope.

The programming circuit is shown in .Fig. 2. Current and voltage transients were recorded with a Nicolet Explorer III digital oscilloscope with 8-bit resolution and 50 ns/point sampling rate. A Hewlett-Packard 214A pulse generator was used for rectangular pulses and an HP3310B function generator for ramped measurements. The source resistance R_g was changed by placing an external resistor in series or parallel with the generator output; in this way an output resistance of 10–350 Ω could be obtained. Initial and final fuse resistances were measured using a curve tracer at a current of 1 mA. Programmed fuses were examined with a scanning-electron microscope (SEM).

III. EVIDENCE FOR SECOND BREAKDOWN

Study of single-crystal silicon films on sapphire has shown [10] that large dissipated power causes contraction of the current flow to a filament together with a drop in terminal voltage. This behavior is characteristic of second breakdown [9]. The transition to this state begins when the film temperature at some point exceeds a critical temperature T_{crit} at which the resistivity decreases strongly with increasing temperature. The lower resistivity causes a higher current density at that point; adjacent areas then have both a high current density and high resistivity. The increased power dissipation causes the hot spot to grow into a filament. The critical temperature can be as low as 300°C for lightly doped films or as high as the silicon melting point where the resistivity drops abruptly [10].

We first present the evidence for second breakdown in polysilicon fuses. Fig. 3(a)–(c) shows the measured current and voltage transients for a type A fuse. A rectangular pulse was used with a duration of 45 μs and an output resistance of 50 Ω. The transients for a small pulse are shown in Fig. 3(a), where the ratio V/I during the pulse is of the order of the initial fuse resistance. SEM photographs of these fuses show no visible change. Larger pulses cause a transition to a low-impedance or second-breakdown state as shown in Fig. 3(b). The transition occurs only when the power dissipated in the fuse exceeds a critical value P_{crit}. The SEM photograph of Fig. 4 shows gross physical changes in the fuse, but the second-breakdown state does not always cause an open circuit. A further increase in pulse amplitude is necessary to give an open circuit as shown in the transients of Fig. 3(c).

The critical temperature T_{crit} for these fuses can be estimated in two ways. First, we can calculate the temperature corresponding to a dissipated power P_{crit}. For a long fuse, the heat loss is mainly through the oxide under the fuse and the temperature is given approximately by $T_{crit} = P_{crit} d_{ox}/g_{ox} lw$, where g_{ox} is the oxide thermal conductivity ($\simeq 0.014$ W/cm $\cdot$ °C) [11]. Alternatively, the delay time t_d before second breakdown occurs can be measured as a function of the dissipated power. For large excess power, the temperature is

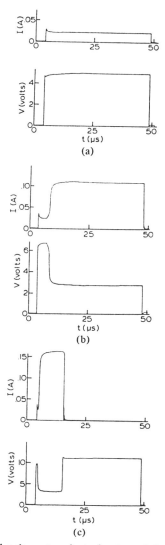

Fig. 3. Current and voltage transients for type A fuses with different pulse amplitudes. (a) Small pulse (final fuse resistance smaller than initial resistance). (b) Larger pulse showing second breakdown transition-fuse still continuous but with increased resistance. (c) Pulse large enough to open fuse. The fuse was 12 μm long with oxide thickness $d_{ox} = 1.5$ μm; the generator resistance was 50 Ω.

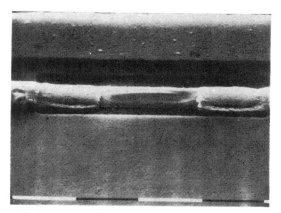

Fig. 4. SEM photograph with top oxide removed; typical of fuses with transients as in Fig. 3(b). The fuse was 16 μm long with $d_{ox} = 1.5$ μm and was programmed with the top oxide on. The resistance increased from 205 to 330 Ω during programming; the right-hand contact was positive.

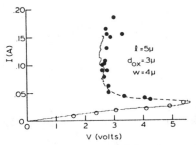

Fig. 5. Fuse *I-V* characteristic measured by two methods: voltage ramp (solid line) and rectangular pulses (o, •). The solid points represent fuses which showed the second-breakdown transition.

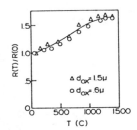

Fig. 6. Temperature dependence of polysilicon resistivity obtained from ramped measurements on two type *A* fuses of length 20 μm.

determined by the charging rate of the thermal capacitance; we expect $T_{crit} = t_d \overline{P}/cd_p wl$, where $\overline{P}$ is the average power dissipation during the delay time t_d and c is the silicon heat capacity ($\simeq 2.2$ J/cm$^3 \cdot$ °C) [12]. These two methods give the estimates 1400 and 2300°C, respectively, or approximately the silicon melting point. This is consistent with the observation of material transport only after second breakdown.

The behavior of the fuse can be represented by an *I-V* characteristic which was measured in two ways. Using the circuit of Fig. 2, a ramp was applied at a rate slow compared to the reciprocal of the thermal equilibration time ($\lesssim 0.5$ μs). The measured current was plotted directly as a function of voltage using the storage oscilloscope; the result is the solid line shown in Fig. 5. Alternatively, the final steady-state values of V and I were measured with a rectangular pulse. Nearly the entire curve was measured by changing the slope of the load line with different generator source resistances. Fig. 5 also shows data obtained this way (O, •) where the solid points indicate that the second breakdown transition occurred. The two methods agree quite well. It should be noted that this *I-V* characteristic is correct only for the first pulse, since melting during second breakdown will cause permanent changes in the fuse.

The temperature dependence of the polysilicon resistivity can be calculated from the *I-V* data of Fig. 5. For a long fuse, the temperature is uniform and is given by $T = IVT_m/P_{crit}$. The measured resistance is plotted as a function of temperature in Fig. 6. The resistance increases by about 50 percent up to the melting point; this is much less than expected from the temperature dependence of the single-crystal silicon mobility [13]. In the absence of other data, we will use the resistivity measured from the *I-V* characteristic below the melting point. We will assume that it drops by a factor of 30 upon melting as observed by Pontius *et al.* [10].

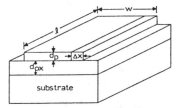

Fig. 7. Fuse geometry for calculation of the lateral temperature profile.

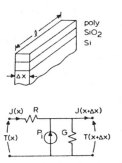

Fig. 8. DC thermal equivalent circuit of strip of fuse of length *l* and width Δx.

IV. THEORY OF THE *I-V* CHARACTERISTIC

We will now develop a simple model for calculation of the *I-V* characteristic of a resistor fuse in second breakdown. It was shown in the previous section that the temperature dependence of the resistivity of heavily doped polysilicon is small apart from a sharp decrease upon melting. We therefore assume that the fuse divides into two regions during programming: an unmelted part with resistivity given by V/I before second breakdown and a molten part with resistivity 30 times lower.

For purposes of a simple calculation, we first neglect end effects. Referring to Fig. 7, we consider a section of fuse of length l and width w. We assume that the molten region is in the center and that the temperature distribution is symmetric. For a given voltage v, solution of the heat-transport equations gives the width a of a molten region and, therefore, the terminal current.

We first derive the differential equation for the lateral temperature distribution. The dc thermal equivalent circuit for a strip of fuse of length l and width Δx is shown in Fig. 8. The thermal resistance for lateral heat flow is $R = r_{Si}\Delta x/d_p l$, where r_{Si} ($\simeq 4.7$ cm $\cdot$ °C/W) [12] is the high-temperature thermal resistivity of silicon, and $G = g_{ox}\Delta x l/d_{ox}$ is the thermal conductance of the oxide, with g_{ox} the oxide thermal conductivity. $P_i = \sigma_i v^2 \Delta x d_p/l$ is the power dissipated in the strip where v is the voltage drop along the length l and $\sigma_i = \sigma_1$ or σ_2 is the polysilicon electrical conductivity in the unmelted and melted states, respectively. (There is also a change in thermal conductivity on melting which is neglected compared to the much larger change in electrical conductivity [12].) For $\Delta x \to 0$, we obtain the equations

$$\frac{\partial T}{\partial x} = -J(x)\frac{r_{Si}}{d_p l}$$

$$\frac{\partial J}{\partial x} = -g_{ox}\frac{l}{d_{ox}}T(x) + \sigma_i v^2 \frac{d_p}{l}.$$

Combining, we have

$$\frac{\partial^2 T}{\partial x^2} = rgT(x) - rp_i \tag{1}$$

where $r = r_{\text{Si}}/ld_p$, $g = g_{\text{ox}} l/d_{\text{ox}}$, and $p_i = \sigma_i v^2 d_p/l$. Equation (1) has the general solution

$$T_i(x) = \frac{p_i}{g} + A_i e^{\sqrt{rg}\,x} + B_i e^{-\sqrt{rg}\,x}.$$

We choose the origin $x = 0$ at the center of the fuse; for a symmetric temperature distribution, the boundary conditions are then $\partial T/\partial x = 0$ at $x = 0$ and $x = w/2$, $\partial T/\partial x$ continuous at $x = a/2$, and $T(a/2)$ continuous and equal to the melting temperature of silicon T_m. These conditions are sufficient to determine the A_i and B_i together with the filament width a through

$$\frac{T_m - p_2/g}{T_m - p_1/g} = \frac{\tanh\left(\sqrt{rg}\,(a - w)/2\right)}{\tanh\left(\sqrt{rg}\,a/2\right)}. \tag{2}$$

The voltage threshold for second breakdown V_t is calculated by setting $a = 0$ to give

$$V_t^2 = \frac{g_{\text{ox}}}{d_p d_{\text{ox}}} \frac{l^2}{\sigma_1} T_m$$

or, since $V_t/I_t = l/\sigma_1 w d_p$, we verify

$$P_{\text{crit}} = I_t V_t = \frac{wlg_{\text{ox}}}{d_{\text{ox}}} T_m$$

as shown in Section III.

The I–V characteristic is most easily constructed by solving (2) for $v(a)$

$$v(a) = \left(\frac{l^2 g_{\text{ox}} T_m}{\sigma_1 d_p d_{\text{ox}}} \frac{1 - F(a)}{30 - F(a)}\right)^{1/2}$$

where

$$F(a) = \frac{\tanh\left(\sqrt{rg}\,(a - w)/2\right)}{\tanh\left(\sqrt{rg}\,a/2\right)}.$$

To calculate the terminal voltage and current we need to account for a small unmelted transition region at the filament ends. This contact region can be modeled by a resistor where the value is chosen to provide the best fit to the measured characteristic at high current. We use, therefore, the equivalent circuit of Fig. 9, where $R_1 = l/\sigma_1 d_p(w - a)$ represents the resistance of the unmelted portion; $R_2 = l/30\sigma_1 d_p a$ the melted part, and R_s the contact resistance. The only adjustable parameter is R_s; σ_1 is determined from I_t and V_t on the measured I–V characteristic and all the other parameters are dimensions or material constants.

Fig. 10 compares the predicted and measured I–V characteristics for type A and B fuses. For the larger type A fuse, the agreement in the second-breakdown region is excellent and the calculated V_t is within 20 percent of the measured value; this error can be attributed to the uncertainty in material parameters and dimensions. For the type B fuse, the agreement in the second-breakdown region is not quite as good since the contacts are much more important and a resistor does not model them accurately. This agreement between measured

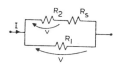

Fig. 9. Electrical equivalent circuit for calculation of the terminal voltage V and terminal current I. R_1 represents the resistance of the unmelted material, R_2 the resistance of the molten filament, and R_s the contact resistance due to the unmelted area just under the contacts.

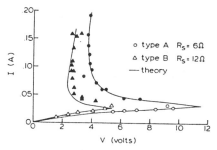

Fig. 10. Predicted (solid line) and measured (o, $\triangle$) I–V characteristics for type A and B fuses. Type A (o): $l = 20$ μm, $d_{\text{ox}} = 0.6$ μm, $d_p = 0.25$ μm; type B ($\triangle$): $l = 5$ μm, $d_{\text{ox}} = 0.3$ μm, $d_p = 0.28$ μm.

and calculated I–V characteristics, together with the SEM photographs, confirm the model we have proposed. We will use this model in the next section to estimate the current required for complete melting of the fuse.

V. Fuse Programming Behavior

In this section, we discuss the fuse microstructure after programming and the programming behavior. We first consider the type A fuses where changes in the contact region are dominated by changes in the body of the fuse. We will then discuss the type B fuses where intermetallic reactions at the contacts are most important.

Referring to the transients in Fig. 3(a), for low power ($P < P_{\text{crit}}$) there is no melting and no visible change in the fuse; the final resistance is however up to 30 percent less than the initial resistance. This change cannot be due to reactions at the contacts since the fractional change in resistance is greater for long fuses. This phenomenon is probably similar to solid-phase laser annealing [14] where temperatures near the melting point produce some increase in impurity activation.

Programming pulses large enough to produce second breakdown (Fig. 3(b)) result in visible changes, as previously shown in Fig. 4. Depressions appear at the end of the fuse near the contacts and a ridge is formed in the center of the fuse. We can understand the appearance in the following way: as the melt filament grows, the contraction of the silicon on melting [12] pulls material toward the fuse center. This forms depressions near the contacts; the depression near the positive end grows because positively charged silicon ions are swept along in the applied electric field. When the pulse ends, the molten silicon expands, forcing the oxide up and forming a ridge. The ridge, therefore, indicates the path of the filament. Fuses with this appearance have a resistance up to three times higher than initially. This is probably due to the decrease in the cross-sectional area at the depressions; another possibility is a higher resistivity for the resolidified material [10].

Larger pulses result in a complete open (transients and SEM

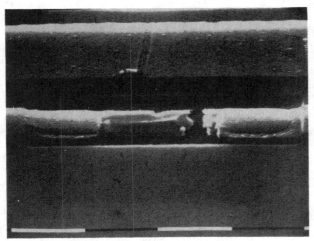

Fig. 11. SEM photograph of open type A fuse (same dimensions as fuse of Fig. 4). The right-hand contact was positive during programming.

Fig. 13. SEM photograph of type B fuse after programming at low current for 0.26 ms. The final fuse resistance was 7.5 Ω.

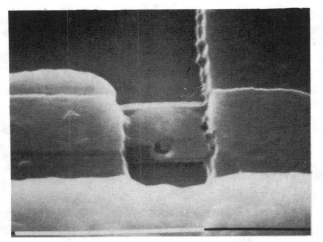

Fig. 12. SEM photograph of type B fuse after programming with 45-μs pulse (d_p = 0.28 μm). The fuse resistance decreased from 120 to 30 Ω.

TABLE I
SUMMARY OF OBSERVED FUSING CURRENTS AND CURRENT
NEEDED TO COMPLETELY MELT FUSE

FUSE TYPE	TOP OXIDE	$\ell(\mu)$	$w(\mu)$	$d_p(\mu)$	$d_{ox}(\mu)$	$I_{min}(A)$	$I_{melt}(A)$
A	yes	16	6	.25	1.5	.16	.13
A	no	16	6	.25	1.5	.13	.13
A	yes	16	6	.25	.6	.19	.20
B	yes	5	4	.28	.3	.19	.15
B	no	5	4	.28	.3	.072	.15
B	yes	5	4	.19	.3	.12	.15

photographs in Fig. 3(c) and Fig. 11, respectively). A gap forms near the positive contact where the largest depression was. For purposes of comparison, we define the minimum opening current I_{min} as the current required to produce an open in 45 μs. For an oxide thickness of 1.5 μm and fuse length 16 μm, we find I_{min} = 0.16 A with the top oxide on and I_{min} = 0.13 A with the top oxide removed.

We now consider the short (type B) fuses. A similar annealing phenomenon is observed for $P < P_{crit}$; higher power levels cause a decrease in fuse resistance, to as low as $\frac{1}{5}$ the initial value. The SEM photograph after programming (Fig. 12) shows that the fuse is no longer homogeneous. Energy dispersive X-ray analysis confirms the presence of aluminum in these fuses. As before, the gap forms near the positive contact when the current is high enough. The type B fuses show a larger difference (about a factor of 2) between I_{min} with and without top oxide.

A summary of the observed fusing currents is presented in Table I. Also shown is an estimate of the current needed for complete melting (obtained from the model of Section IV). The results show that I_{min} is of the order of or less than the current required for complete melting. Since opening can occur even when part of the fuse is still solid, the mechanism cannot be liquid instability as in the case of nichrome fuses [15]. This conclusion is further supported by the SEM photographs which show transport of molten silicon in the applied field.

We also note a large difference between I_{min} with and without the top oxide, particularly for the type B fuses. It is easily verified that this thickness of oxide has only a minor effect on the temperature distribution. The effect of the oxide must be purely mechanical in that it impedes the movement of the molten silicon. In both types of fuses, the oxide just on top of the fuse is heavily phosphorus doped and, therefore, has a low melting point [16]. A molten layer of oxide forms but the viscosity is apparently high enough to make movement of the silicon difficult. This effect is smaller in the type A fuses where the top oxide is thinner.

At present, I_{min} cannot be predicted from the fuse geometry. The results of Table I show, however, that the two most important factors are the polysilicon thickness and the presence or absence of a top oxide.

Since the currents in Table I are fairly high, it is worth asking if lower currents can be used with longer programming times. This does not appear to be feasible for fuses with aluminum contacts. Fig. 13 shows a fuse which was programmed at I = 0.075 A (approximately $I_{min}/2$ for this fuse geometry). Within 0.26 ms, the voltage dropped from 2.6 V (as expected for this current in second breakdown) to 0.93 V. The final resistance was 7.5 Ω and a spike with metallic appearance was visible with an optical microscope. As noted before, a small region of unmelted fuse material near the contacts has large power dissipation once the second-breakdown filament is formed. Eventually, an aluminum–silicon eutectic forms and migrates through the fuse. Thus currents much below I_{min} are likely to produce shorted fuses.

VI. CONCLUSION

We have shown that polysilicon fuses only open after a transition to a second-breakdown state. The transition occurs when part of the fuse reaches the silicon melting point, and is characterized by the formation of a highly conductive molten filament between the two contacts. Molten silicon is transported from the positive end of the fuse to the negative end due to drift of ions in the applied field. Open fuses can be guaranteed if the available current is high enough.

A simple model has been described which predicts the I-V characteristics of polysilicon fuses in second breakdown. Good agreement with experiment was demonstrated.

Our experiments have shown that it is necessary to remove the passivation layer over the fuse to obtain reasonable programming currents. This is an important shortcoming of polysilicon fuses since it has been demonstrated that contamination can enter through these openings resulting in reliability problems [17]. Good long-term reliability in MOS memories required guard rings around the fuses [17], which is practical only when a few fuses are used on each die. For this reason, bipolar PROM's with polysilicon fuses are packaged in hermetically sealed ceramic packages [1] at additional expense. In MOS memories, the potential increase in yield needs to be balanced against the additional area required for fuses.

ACKNOWLEDGMENT

The author would like to thank K. Hart for initiating the project and for many helpful discussions, and C. Neville and G. De Groot for fabricating the wafers. He would also like to thank E. van de Ven and M. Collet for comments concerning the manuscript.

REFERENCES

[1] R. C. Smith et al., "Reliability studies of polysilicon fusible PROMs," in 14th Annual Proc. Reliability Phys. (Las Vegas, NV, 1976), p. 193.
[2] R. K. Wallace, "A 35ns 16K PROM," in ISSCC Dig. Tech. Papers, p. 148, 1980.
[3] O. Minato et al., "HI–CMOS II 4K static RAM," in ISSCC Dig. Tech. Papers, p. 14, 1981.
[4] K. Kokkonen et al., "Redundancy techniques for fast static RAMs," in ISSCC Dig. Tech. Papers, p. 80, 1981.
[5] S. Eaton et al., "A 100 ns 64K dynamic RAM using redundancy techniques," in ISSCC Dig. Tech. Papers, p. 84, 1981.
[6] J. Bindels et al., "Cost-effective yield improvement in fault-tolerant VLSI memory," in ISSCC Dig. Tech. Papers, p. 82, 1981.
[7] V. McKenny, "A 5V 64K EPROM utilizing redundant circuitry," in ISSCC Dig. Tech. Papers, p. 146, 1980.
[8] T. Mano et al., "A fault-tolerant 256K RAM fabricated with molybdenum-polysilicon technology," IEEE J. Solid-State Circuits, vol. SC-15, p. 865, 1980.
[9] H. A. Schafft, "Second breakdown—A comprehensive review," Proc. IEEE, vol. 55, p. 1272, 1967.
[10] D. H. Pontius et al., "Filamentation in silicon-on-sapphire homogeneous thin films," J. Appl. Phys., vol. 44, p. 331, 1973.
[11] A. S. Grove, Physics and Technology of Semiconductor Devices. New York, Wiley, 1967, p. 102.
[12] C. L. Yaws et al., "Semiconductor industry silicon: Physical and thermodynamic properties," Solid-State Technol., p. 87, Jan. 1981.
[13] F. J. Morin and J. P. Maita, Phys. Rev., vol. 96, p. 28, 1954.
[14] L. Gerzberg et al., "Effect of laser power level in CW laser annealing of polycrystalline silicon," abstract 414, presented at the Electrochem. Soc. Fall Meet., Hollywood, FL, 1980.
[15] G. B. Kenney et al., "Fusing mechanism of nichrome-linked programmable read-only memory devices," in 14th Annual Proc. Reliability Phys. (Las Vegas, NV, 1976), p. 164.
[16] W. E. Armstrong and D. L. Tolliver, "A scanning electron microscope investigation of glass flow in MOS integrated circuit fabrication," J. Electrochem. Soc., vol. 121, p. 307, 1974.
[17] D. L. Crook and B. Meyer, "Redundancy reliability," in 19th Annual Proc. Reliability Phys. (Miami, FL, 1981), p. 1.

Fundamentals of Memory Switching in Vertical Polycrystalline Silicon Structures

VINOD MALHOTRA, STUDENT MEMBER, IEEE, JOHN E. MAHAN, MEMBER, IEEE, AND DANIEL L. ELLSWORTH

Abstract—The fundamentals of memory switching in vertical LPCVD polysilicon structures have been investigated. In the initial state, 4–70 μm^2 devices exhibit effective resistances (at 5 V) in the high megaohm range, with current transport via thermionic emission of electrons over grain boundary potential barriers. An increase in conductance by approximately five orders of magnitude is achieved by a 10–20 V programming pulse of tens of microseconds duration with a few milliamps of current required. A moderately doped filamentary region is created, exhibiting single-crystal silicon transport phenomena. With regard to practical device fabrication, control of thin film interactions is critical. Barrier layers are employed to suppress Al–Si interaction at the top contact and to decrease the effective grain size of the polysilicon film by limiting the epitaxial realignment of the grains near the single-crystal substrate.

I. INTRODUCTION

TO SUPPORT the development of a low-power "fuse-programmable" memory technology utilizing a memory switching transition in polycrystalline silicon (polysilicon), we have investigated the materials basis of electrical switching in vertical polysilicon thin-film structures. More properly termed "anti-fuse," such devices, when properly made, exhibit a permanent conductance increase by a factor of 10^5 when programmed with a suitable voltage pulse.

A 4-kbit MOS electrically programmable read-only memory (PROM) with a vertical polysilicon resistor as the memory element has been reported previously [1]. An electrically induced resistivity decrease is known to result from a structural change in high-resistivity polysilicon, but no physical description of the phenomenon has been given for vertical elements. To our knowledge, the structure has not led to viable commercial products, perhaps because of the large size of the memory cell which incorporates lateral MOS field-effect transistors for supplying the programming current. In the near future, we will report on the design of a compact fully vertical memory cell that merges the polysilicon switching element with a polysilicon-emitter bipolar transistor. This work has demonstrated that the programming behavior of the devices (programming voltage and current and pre- and post-programming conductances) is suitable for such practical applications.

An experimental study of the electronic transport properties of the devices reveals important aspects of the initial microstructure, the nature of the materials transformation accompanying the programming event, and the effects of various fabrication options on current transport and programming behavior. Combined with data from direct structural and compositional probes, the transport data have enabled us to construct a device model of reasonable certainty.

Threshold (reversible) and memory (permanent) switching also have been observed in horizontal [2]–[5] and other vertical [6], [7] polysilicon structures. In the one detailed experimental investigation of horizontal structures known to us, the devices actually were n^+-p-n^+ diodes, with programming initiated by avalanche breakdown [2]. Unfortunately, speculations on switching mechanism(s) and current transport in the vertical structures were not supported by detailed theoretical or experimental investigations.

II. DEVICE FABRICATION

A cross section of the basic device test structure is shown schematically in Fig. 1(a). The devices are rectangular in shape as viewed from the top, having nominal (drawn) areas of $n \times m$ μm^2, with n varying from 2 to 6 μm, and m from 2 to 11 μm. An adjacent low-resistance (n^+) contact to the substrate is present but not shown in the figure.

The fabrication sequence was as follows: n-type silicon wafers were implanted with arsenic through oxide windows to form the lower n^+ regions. After a diffusion/anneal, undoped polysilicon was deposited by low-pressure silane pyrolysis at 625°C to a thickness of either 4000 or 6000 Å. Following a second implant (into the polysilicon), the polysilicon was patterned into pads of varying dimensions. This implant was then annealed at low temperature to control dopant redistribution, as will be discussed.

A barrier layer (as shown in Fig. 1(b)) may be placed between polysilicon and metal (Al–1% Si–0.5% Cu) to allow a contact alloying step which is normally required for low-resistance contacts in an integrated MOS process. The barrier layer is a very thin low-temperature-grown (750°C,

Manuscript received December 11, 1984; revised June 11, 1985. This work was supported by the National Science Foundation under Grant ECS-83-05405.

V. Malhotra and J. E. Mahan are with the Department of Electrical Engineering and the Condensed Matter Sciences Laboratory, Colorado State University, Fort Collins, CO 80523.

D. L. Ellsworth is with the Microelectronics Division, NCR Corporation, Fort Collins, CO 80525.

Reprinted from *IEEE Trans. Electron Devices*, vol. ED-32, no. 11, pp. 2441–2449, November 1985.

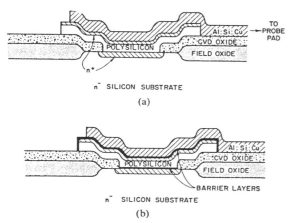

Fig. 1. Schematic cross section of (a) the basic test structure, and (b) a structure with barrier layers.

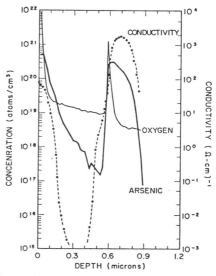

Fig. 2. SIMS impurity depth profiles and a conductivity depth profile obtained from spreading resistance measurements.

2 h) dry oxide. This oxidation step also serves as the diffusion/anneal following the final implant and results in an oxide layer that, in the presence of polysilicon asperities, is too thin to provide a significant electrical barrier. A brief etch in dilute HF is performed prior to aluminum deposition that is not sufficient to remove the barrier layer (about 50-Å final thickness) but does clear the native oxide from other regions on the wafer where low-resistance ohmic contacts are required.

A selectively deposited tungsten film was investigated as an alternative to the oxide contact barrier [8]. With the oxide barrier, a 400°C 90-min alloy in forming gas is used, while with the tungsten barrier, the temperature may be raised to 450°C. Without a barrier layer, alloying results in shorted devices.

An interfacial oxide between the substrate and the polysilicon layer was also found to be advantageous. This very thin oxide was grown chemically (nitric acid, 87°C, 10 min) and left in place for polysilicon deposition. The rationale for this step is based on recent work on the microstructure of the polysilicon-emitter/single-crystal silicon interface in advanced bipolar devices [9]-[11]. It has been shown in these reports that a minimal chemical oxidation step can significantly alter the crystal structure of the polysilicon film by assuring continuity of a native oxide layer under the deposited polysilicon. Its application here is to control the polysilicon grain size. As is detailed below, these barrier layers do not change, in a fundamental way, the conduction properties or the programming characteristics of the devices.

A SIMS impurity depth profile is shown in Fig. 2, together with a corresponding conductivity depth profile (everywhere n-type) obtained from spreading resistance measurements. These measurements were made using large-area unpatterned samples that received the same implantation, deposition, and oxidation treatments as the devices, including contact metal deposition and alloying (contact metal was etched off before the depth profile data were obtained). The two implanted regions are clearly revealed by the SIMS data; the top oxide layer is evident in the high surface oxygen level, and the interface between the polysilicon and the substrate is marked by the second oxygen peak at about 6000-Å depth. The high background oxygen level in the polysilicon and the substrate is an artifact due to the presence of oxygen in the analysis chamber. The imperfect alignment of the SIMS and spreading resistance profiles is within the accuracy of the techniques.

There is considerable spreading of the upper arsenic implant into the undoped polysilicon layer as a result of the 750°C oxidation. The initial-state resistance remains high, however, because of the unique dependence of resistivity on impurity content for polysilicon. The resistivity of polysilicon is in the range 10^5 to 10^6 $\Omega \cdot$ cm and relatively independent of doping level below about 10^{17} to 10^{18} cm^{-3}. The resistivity decreases rapidly with increasing impurity content above 10^{18} cm^{-3} until the curve nearly merges at high impurity concentrations with the single-crystal silicon characteristic [12]-[14]. It is also found that the details of the resistivity curve vary slightly with the grain structure and thermal history of the material and with the identity of the impurity, although the general features are as stated. This behavior is reflected in the very low conductivity values observed in the central region of the polysilicon layer.

A secondary effect of the chemically grown oxide at the polysilicon/single-crystal-silicon interface is revealed in the impurity profile data. A depth profile was also obtained from similar samples from which the chemically grown interfacial oxide had been removed immediately prior to polysilicon deposition. This profile showed a greater amount of arsenic diffusion into the undoped polysilicon from the lower implant. Although some air-grown oxide is present in any case under our conditions, the chemical oxide presents a more uniform and better controlled barrier to the diffusion of the implanted arsenic. The critical function of the chemically grown oxide, however, is suppression of sporadic epitaxial reordering of the fine-grained polysilicon.

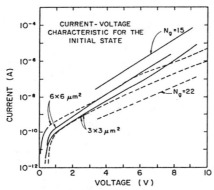

Fig. 3. Semilogarithmic current–voltage characteristic for the initial state for devices of nominal polysilicon thicknesses of 4000 Å (——) and 6000 Å (– – –) and nominal areas as shown; reference slopes corresponding to 15 and 22 grain boundaries are also given.

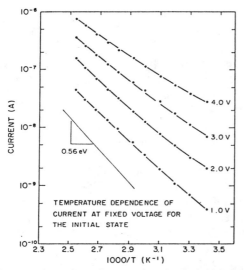

Fig. 4. Current versus reciprocal temperature for the initial state (a 6×8 μm^2 device of 4000-Å polysilicon thickness).

We turn now to a discussion of the electronic transport properties. The devices exhibit some asymmetry with respect to polarity of the applied voltage which is due to a vertically graded grain structure and asymmetric vertical impurity profiles. The fundamental aspects of electronic transport are the same for both polarities, however, and the data for a positive voltage applied to the top contact will be discussed.

III. ELECTRONIC TRANSPORT IN THE INITIAL STATE

In the initial state, the current–voltage characteristic on a semilogarithmic plot is essentially linear over a wide range (Fig. 3). As is evident in Fig. 4, the current is thermally activated, with an activation energy that decreases with applied voltage. The conductance (current/voltage at 3 V applied to the top contact) is, on the average, proportional to the nominal area. This is shown in Fig. 5, where each point represents the mean conductance of four devices. The proportionality between initial state conductance and nominal device area indicates uniformity of current distribution, at least on the macroscopic scale.

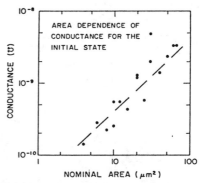

Fig. 5. Low-field initial state conductance versus nominal device area for 4000-Å polysilicon thickness.

These transport properties are consistent with the conduction model based on thermionic emission of majority carriers over grain boundary potential energy barriers [15]. The current–voltage characteristic of a polysilicon resistor has its origin in the following expression:

$$J = J_0 \sinh (qV/2N_g kT) \qquad (1)$$

where J is the current density, q is the magnitude of the electronic charge, V is the applied voltage, N_g is the number of (identical) grain boundaries, k is Boltzmann's constant, and T is the absolute temperature. The prefactor J_0 depends on the band structure of the material and the grain boundary barrier height (qV_b) measured from the Fermi energy

$$J_0 = 2A^*T^2 \exp (-qV_b/kT). \qquad (2)$$

A^* is the effective Richardson constant (120 A/cm$^2 \cdot$ K^2 for free electrons and depending on the details of the band structure for semiconductors [16]).

It should be recognized that (1) and (2) are valid only for (nearly) fixed values of trapped charge at the grain boundaries. It has been shown that this is not generally true, with the amount of trapped charge, and consequently the barrier height, varying with applied voltage and temperature [17], [18].

The data in Fig. 3 are representative for devices of the two nominal areas and thicknesses shown. These data illustrate the basic behavior but, as is often the case, the semilogarithmic current–voltage characteristics are not perfectly linear at high fields and the area dependence of the current is not perfectly consistent. The former may be due to variations in barrier height, as discussed in the preceding paragraph. The latter is to be expected for distributions of grain shapes and sizes such as are found in a real polycrystalline semiconductor thin film [19].

It is possible to estimate an average or *apparent* N_g from the slope of the current–voltage characteristic. The values are approximately 15 and 22 for the two thicknesses, as illustrated by the straight lines drawn in the figure. One may estimate further the effective vertical grain size with N_g and an adjusted thickness value. Although the nominal film thicknesses are 4000 and 6000 Å, these numbers should be corrected by subtracting the thicknesses of the heavily doped regions, which we estimate roughly from Fig. 2 to total 2000 Å. The effective vertical grain size for the 6000-Å film is then 170–200 Å, with somewhat smaller values for the 4000-Å film. These estimates are perhaps lower than expected for LPCVD polysilicon deposited onto oxidized silicon at 625°C, with its generally observed columnar grain structure [20]. However, recent investigations indicate that these values are plausible [21]–[23]. The estimates do increase with film thickness, as expected [20].

The effectiveness of the intentionally grown interfacial oxide layer in reducing the effective vertical grain size is apparent when these results are compared to those for devices having received an HF etch just prior to polysilicon deposition. Devices from another experimental lot with 6500-Å nominal polysilicon thickness, but having no chemical oxide, exhibit an apparent N_g of about 8, as determined by the same procedure. This gives an effective grain size, using the same thickness correction, of 560 Å (over two and one-half times the former value).

The reader might anticipate a resistance increase due to the presence of the oxide barrier alone, even with no change in grain size. However, oxide-dominated conduction would not lead to the temperature effects observed. The thermally activated current is a characteristic of barrier-limited transport. As is apparent in Fig. 4, the value of the activation energy varies slightly with temperature. Similar behavior has been reported previously [24]. Proposed explanations include thermionic field emission [25], detrapping of grain boundary interfacial charge [18], and, most recently, nonuniform grain size [19]. A zero-field value of 0.56 eV was obtained simply by drawing visual "best fit" straight lines through the high-temperature data and extrapolating to zero voltage. A reference line corresponding to that activation energy is shown in Fig. 4. This indicates that the grain boundary Fermi energy is pinned essentially at midgap, as is commonly held [26]–[28].

The current axis intercept of the linear part of the data in Fig. 3, according to (1), should be $J_0/2$ multiplied by the device area. Using nominal area values, a barrier height of 0.56 eV, and an effective Richardson constant of 252 Å/cm² · K² for n-type silicon [29], the current intecepts for the 6 × 6 and 3 × 3 square micron devices should be 1.5 and 0.4 nA, respectively. The measured values are less than this, in spite of the fact that SEM examinations have shown that the actual active area is usually a little larger than the nominal value. There are at leat two possible explanations: 1) the effective Richardson constant may have been overestimated, and 2) only a fraction of the device area may be utilized.

The first explanation originates with previous investigations of metal–semiconductor barriers [30]. It was suggested that a combined thermionic emission-diffusion process is operative. In consequence, the effective Richardson constant contains additional factors to include the effects of carrier backscattering and quantum-mechanical reflection and tunneling. The theory predicts that the value of

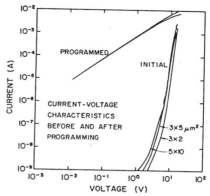

Fig. 6. Logarithmic current–voltage chracteristics comparing the initial and programmed states for devices of 4000-Å polysilicon thickness.

the effective Richardson constant depends on the electric field, which is essentially the built-in field at the grain boundary potential barrier in fine-grained polysilicon. A value of 70 A/cm² · K² gives intercepts (0.4 and 0.1 nA) for the two device sizes that are in basic agreement with the data in Fig. 3.

The second explanation is based on the recognition that there are preferred current paths through the polysilicon that dominate the conductance. The area dependence in Fig. 5 suggests, if this is correct, that the density of preferred paths, or equivalently the fractional active area, is independent of nominal area. Also, Bravman et al. [9], [10] have shown that after high-temperature annealing, the interfacial oxide may break up into included particles that could reduce the effective area of the device.

IV. The Programmed State

The devices may be memory switched (programmed) with a sufficiently large dc voltage or with a voltage pulse. A linear current–voltage characteristic is obtained after programming, except at high fields. Here there is an apparent tendency to saturation (Fig. 6), and a threshold switching transition is often observed as well.

In contrast to the initial state, there is only a weak area dependence of the conductance after programming. This suggests that a filamentary conduction region is created during programming that effectively shorts the rest of the device. Filament formation is a common feature of negative resistance devices of many types [31]. Joule heating and the negative temperature coefficient of resistivity (TCR) of the polysilicon interact, leading to current localization and thermal runaway. Recrystallization occurs in places where the temperature rise is sufficient.

Evidence for the existence of programming filaments is shown in Fig. 7, which is an SEM micrograph of a programmed device. The aluminum contact has been removed with a mixture of phosphoric, nitric, and acetic acids and the underlying polysilicon textured with a dilute Secco ($K_2Cr_2O_7$ and HF) etch. The significant feature is the small nodule, a fraction of a micrometer in lateral extent, left in the active area. Nodules are never found in unprogrammed devices, but are unfailingly seen in pro-

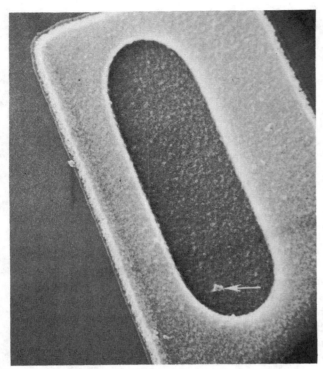

Fig. 7. SEM micrograph of a 2×10 μm^2 programmed device after polysilicon texturing.

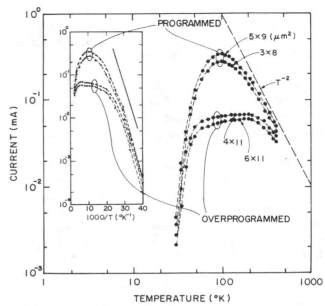

Fig. 8. Current at 0.1 V versus temperature for the programmed state in devices of 4000-Å polysilicon thickness; characteristics for overprogrammed devices, as defined in the text, are also given.

grammed ones. It is likely that the nodule is the remnant of a filament, which etched more slowly than the surrounding fine-grained polysilicon. The original filament itself must be quite small because it cannot be seen until the polysilicon is texture-etched. A similar technique was used to observe filaments formed during memory switching in chalcogenide glass memory devices [32].

The filament is considered to be moderately arsenic-doped single-crystal silicon because of the availability of arsenic in the devices as made, and because of the temperature dependence of post-programming conductance. Data for a series of programmed devices are shown in Fig. 8; the current at constant voltage varies approximately as T^{-2} above the maximum. This is the temperature dependence of the conductivity mobility, with the carrier concentration being fixed. Although the fundamental textbook theory for the carrier mobility in the intraband acoustic phonon scattering regime gives a $T^{-1.5}$ variation [33], well-established experimental data indicate an exponent as large as -2.42 for electrons in this temperature range that is due to a variety of intervalley scattering mechanisms [34]. Intraband charged impurity scattering gives a positive exponent, the classical value being 1.5. This mechanism is dominant at room temperature for doping levels above approximately 10^{18} cm^{-3} [35].

Below about 100 K, carrier freezeout is apparent. The low-temperature data for two selected programmed devices have been replotted in semilogarithmic fashion in the inset in Fig. 8. The thermally activated conductance in this low-temperature regime is characteristic of carrier freezeout. A reference line having the activation energy

for uncompensated arsenic donors in silicon [36] is shown in the inset. The overprogrammed state will be defined below and the data in Fig. 8 pertaining to these devices will be discussed at that time.

Thus, the tendency to saturation that commences around 3 V is attributable to electron drift velocity saturation in single-crystal silicon. The effective field of 5×10^4 V/cm, assuming the nominal thickness of 6000 Å for the filament length, is about where saturation is expected [34].

It should be stated that, although this description of the programmed state generally pertains, there are aspects of the postprogramming behavior that depend on the detailed programming conditions. In Fig. 8, there is a small variation in the value of the programmed state conductance among the different device sizes. This is understandable, because the size, shape, and doping level of a filament reasonably may be expected to depend on the local heat flow conditions. Local programming temperatures at the filament sites are higher in larger devices due to heating of material adjacent to the filament. The higher the peak temperature in the filament locality, the more advanced will be its development [32].

The programmed state is not, therefore, uniquely defined. Both the conductance value and the size and shape of the nodule observed (and therefore probably the filament itself) depend on the extent of programming. A rule of thumb is that a lightly programmed ("underprogrammed") device may not exhibit threshold switching but only velocity saturation, and as the extent of programming increases the negative resistance transition appears and then disappears in an "overprogrammed" device that "turns on" without exhibiting a threshold event.

Three such current–voltage characteristics, obtained with dc instrumentation, are shown in Fig. 9. The programmed device characteristic has a current-controlled

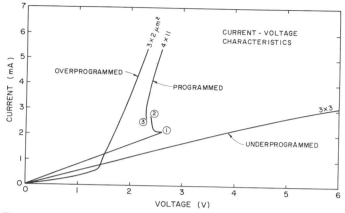

Fig. 9. Current–voltage characteristics for an underprogrammed device, a programmed device exhibiting a current-controlled negative resistance transition, and an overprogrammed device.

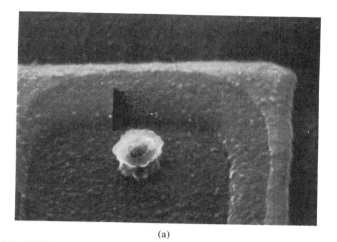

(a)

variable negative resistance region (segment 1–2 of the curve) and a discontinuity (segment 2–3). The former region is accessible with a dc current source, while the discontinuous portion between points 2 and 3 may be a positive incremental resistance region but is not accessible experimentally. A very similar negative resistance characteristic has been reported for lateral polysilicon *fuses* and ascribed to "second breakdown" [37]. This is not an explanation of a fundamental mechanism because second breakdown has come to encompass a wide variety of apparently similar phenomena [38].

One may infer from Fig. 8 that an overprogrammed device has a more heavily doped filament than does a programmed device. For the overprogrammed devices, a maximum in current occurs at around 250 K. We suggest that this is due to a transition from acoustic phonon scattering-limited mobility to charged impurity scattering-limited mobility with decreasing temperature. This transition was not observed with programmed devices because carrier freezeout sets in first and masks any mobility temperature dependence effects.

The filamentary region of an overprogrammed device is shown in the SEM micrograph in Fig. 10(a). A mushroom-shaped structure, much larger than a typical nodule of a programmed device, is present. The relatively large and hollow structure is found frequently in overprogrammed devices and is generally visible even before metal removal. In some cases, multiple nodules and a damaged area in the adjacent oxide are seen (Fig. 10(b)). Compositional analysis of a mushroom by laser microprobe depth profiling indicated no detectable impurities by that technique (which has a resolution on the order of one part per million).

Some further fundamental aspects of the programming transition are revealed in the following description of the transient programming behavior.

V. Programming Behavior

The measured conductance ratio (pulsed/initial conductance at 0.1 V) as a function of programming pulse height is shown in Fig. 11 for five devices of five different sizes (a current-limiting resistance was used to prevent

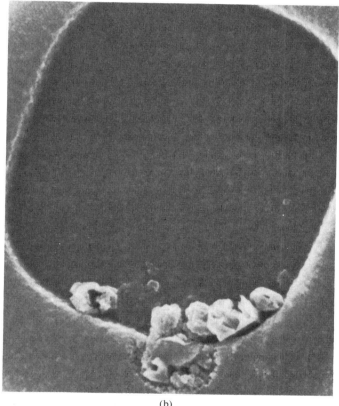

(b)

Fig. 10. SEM micrographs of overprogrammed devices: (a) a mushroom-shaped structure within a $6 \times 6 \ \mu m^2$ device after metal removal, and (b) a damaged area within a $5 \times 6 \ \mu m^2$ device after metal removal and polysilicon texturing.

overprogramming, as discussed below). The pulse width was several tens of microseconds, sufficiently long that there was no pulse-width dependence of the programmed conductance value for the programming circuit employed. The fundamental transition occurs at around 15 V, with essentially no conductance changes below that voltage. The larger conductance ratios observed for the smaller devices are due to the fact that the programmed conductance value increases only slightly with nominal area, while the initial conductance value is basically proportional to area.

Some representative transient programming data are

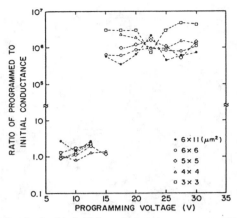

Fig. 11. Ratio of pulsed to initial conductance versus programming voltage for a series of device sizes with 4000-Å polysilicon thickness.

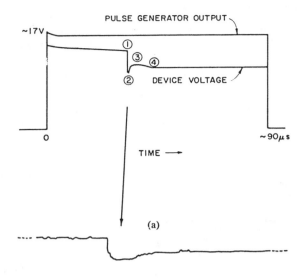

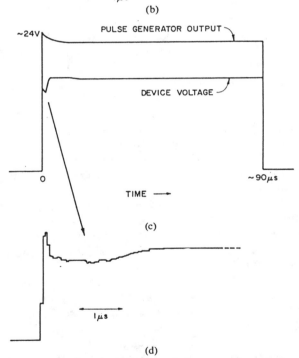

Fig. 12. Pulse generator output pulse and voltage across test device showing transient programming behavior for (a) a "long" delay time, (b) detailed view of the programming event in (a), (c) a "short" delay time, and (d) detail of (c).

presented in Fig. 12. The output voltage of the pulse generator is shown together with the concurrent voltage drop across the device being programmed. Initially, the effective resistance of the unprogrammed device at these rather high voltages is on the order of 10^4 Ω, and the device voltage is a little less than the applied voltage, due to the series resistor. A programming event occurs at point 1 in Fig. 12(a). A delay or "incubation" time of roughly 30 μs is observed. The length of this delay appears to depend on the programming overvoltage, the amount by which the applied pulse exceeds the minimum voltage required for programming. Fig. 12(c) shows a different device programmed with a rather large overvoltage that exhibited a much shorter delay. In each case, the maximum programming current was less than 10 mA.

Care was taken to insure that the devices were not loaded by the measurement circuitry during the transient measurements. As shown in Fig. 13, a high-speed high-input impedance active probe was used to measure the device voltage. The effective input capacitance and resistance of this probe were 0.1 pF and 1.0 MΩ. The output from the probe was displayed with a digital oscilloscope having a resolution of 50 ns/point.

A similar kind of delay has been found for other memory-switching materials, including amorphous chalcogenide glasses [39], [40], for which the most extensive switching literature exists, and amorphous silicon [41], [42]. In the former case, the delay time is on the order of microseconds at threshold and decreases to the order of nanoseconds for a 50-percent overvoltage. In the latter case, a delay in the millisecond to microsecond range is characteristic. It appears that the same descriptive terms may be used for the switching behavior in these very different materials, while the underlying mechanisms must differ greatly.

Once the delay interval has been completed, the device memory-switches very rapidly to a more conductive state (point 2, Fig. 12(a)). This region of the programming transients is shown with an expanded time scale in Fig. 12(b) and 12(d). The switching time appears to be on the order of 100 ns; this would be the minimum programming

time of the devices. For the amorphous chalcogenide glasses, a switching time of less than 1 ns is generally found, and for amorphous silicon, the reported switching times are in tens of nanoseconds.

The detailed shape of the transient after the programming event in Fig. 12(a) is typical of these devices and suggests the following hypothesis regarding the transient behavior and the accompanying materials transformations: The current and power densities are mostly uniform over the device area, but it is inevitable that local hot spots

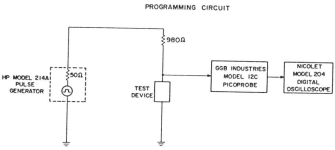

Fig. 13. Programming circuit.

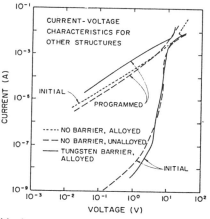

Fig. 14. Logarithmic current–voltage characteristics for $5 \times 5 \ \mu m^2$ devices showing the effects of barrier layers and alloying.

occur due to inhomogeneities; one of these (the one that melts first) will develop into the programming filament. The delay is the time required for a channel through the device, where the filament is to form, to reach its melting point. If the applied voltage is insufficient for melting the channel, the device will not program. The delay is naturally determined by the input power—a large overvoltage gives a short delay. When a molten channel is formed, the device resistance drops because the resistivity of silicon decreases by about a factor of thirty at the melting point; molten silicon is a metallic conductor and the positive TCR of this metallic silicon phase stabilizes the filament [43]. Now the device voltage is somewhat lower and most of the power is delivered to the filament itself because the voltage-dependent effective resistance of the surrounding unprogrammed area increases (see Fig. 3). The filament temperature drops as the surrounding area cools, enough so that the filament solidifies. Since the resistivity of the filament material increases by a factor of 30 upon freezing, the device resistance now increases (the rise at about $\frac{3}{4}$ μs after programming in Fig. 12(b)), but this large change is nearly obscured by the shunting effect of the rest of the device. To account for the additional rise to point 3, we suggest that the semiconducting filament continues to cool, while remaining in the intrinsic regime with a negative TCR. At point 3, the power delivered to the surrounding area has increased because the device voltage is larger; this raises the filament temperature and decreases the total device resistance for a second time (to point 4). The temperature excursions cease rapidly because the system is nearly critically damped.

To our knowledge, this oscillatory thermal behavior has not been observed in the amorphous semiconductor switching materials. A more detailed investigation of the programming transients, to test this hypothesis further, is planned.

VI. ALLOYING AND THE TOP BARRIER LAYER

Some current–voltage characteristics for devices having no top barrier layer are shown in Fig. 14. If the device is not subjected to post-metallization alloying, the conduction properties before and after programming are essentially as given above. However, if the contact is alloyed, the initial current–voltage characteristic resembles that of the programmed state, even exhibiting threshold switching. However, there is no evidence that the threshold

switching mechanism is the same as in a programmed device.

The characteristics of an alloyed device having a selectively deposited tungsten barrier layer are also shown. Here again, the behavior is essentially as given in the previous three sections. SEM examination shows that the tungsten layer retains its integrity after programming; this is further evidence that Al–Si interaction (the formation of an aluminum–silicon eutectic filament) is not the basis of the programming event, as otherwise might reasonably have been supposed [2].

VII. SUMMARY AND CONCLUSIONS

The transport properties data show that current transport in the initial state is by the process of thermionic emission of majority carriers over grain boundary potential barriers, and that a moderately doped single-crystal silicon filament of relatively low resistance is created during programming. The details of the programmed state are not uniquely defined, however. The size and shape of the filament, the post-programming conductance, and the occurrence of threshold switching all depend on the extent of programming as determined by the nominal device area, the programming pulse height and width, and the limiting series resistance used in the programming circuit.

Two types of barrier layers may be incorporated to improve metallurgical aspects of the structure without fundamentally altering the electrical behavior. A chemically grown interfacial oxide between polysilicon and substrate decreases the apparent polysilicon grain size and tends to limit up-diffusion of the lower arsenic implant. The upper barrier layer, which may be either a relatively low-temperature-grown dry oxide or selectively deposited tungsten, impedes Al–Si interaction at the top contact sufficiently to allow a metallization alloy step. It is anticipated that development of this structure will lead to an extremely reliable high-density low-power programmable memory element.

ACKNOWLEDGMENT

The authors (in particular, M. W. Morrissey and R. K. Jones) are grateful to the management of NCR Corporation, Microelectronics Division, for support of this NSF Industry/University Cooperative Research Program. Invaluable assistance was rendered by W. Metz, M. Moll, G. Miller, P. Sullivan, and W. Koldeway. The SIMS analysis and laser microprobe depth profiling were performed by Charles Evans and Associates, and the spreading resistance measurements were made by Solecon, Inc.

References

[1] M. Tanimoto, J. Murota, M. Wada, T. Watanabe, K. Miura, and N. Ieda, "A novel 14V programmable 4 Kbit MOS PROM using a poly-Si resistor applicable to on-chip programmable devices," *IEEE J. Solid-State Circuits*, vol. SC-17, no. 1, p. 62, 1982; M. Tanimoto, J. Murota, Y. Ohmori, and N. Ieda, "A novel MOS PROM using a highly resistive poly-Si resistor," *IEEE Trans. Electron Devices*, vol. ED-27, no. 3, p. 517, 1980.

[2] D. W. Greve and L. V. Tran, "Polysilicon n^+-p-n^+ structures for memory redundancy," *IEEE Trans. Electron Devices*, vol. ED-29, no. 8, p. 1313, 1982.

[3] J. E. Mahan, "Threshold and memory switching in polycrystalline silicon," *Appl. Phys. Lett.*, vol. 41, no. 5, p. 479, 1982.

[4] C. Y. Lu, N. C. C. Lu, C. C. Shih, M. K. Lee, and C. S. Wang, "On resistance switching in polycrystalline silicon resistors," in *Extended Abstracts Electrochem. Soc. Spring Meeting* (San Francisco, CA, May 8–13, 1983), vol. 83-1, p. 627.

[5] P. Kenyon, H. Dressel, and H. Lockwood, "Negative resistance switching in near perfect crystalline silicon film resistors," presented at the Amer. Vacuum Soc. 30th Nat. Symp., Boston, MA, Nov. 1–4. 1983.

[6] H. Kroger, H. A. R. Wegener, and W. M. Shedd, "Memory switching in polycrystalline silicon films," *Thin Solid Films*, vol. 66, p. 171, 1980.

[7] M. Braunstein, A. I. Braunstein, and R. Zuleeg, "Double injection in evaporated silicon films," *Appl. Phys. Lett.*, vol. 10, no. 11, p. 313, 1967.

[8] W. A. Metz, J. E. Mahan, V. Malhotra, and T. L. Martin, "Electrical properties of selectively deposited tungsten thin films," *Appl. Phys. Lett.*, vol. 44, no. 12, p. 1139, 1984.

[9] J. C. Bravman, G. L. Patton, and J. D. Plummer, "Structural aspects of polysilicon emitter contacts," in *Extended Abstracts, Electrochem. Soc. Fall Meeting* (New Orleans, LA, Oct. 7–12, 1984), vol. 84-2, p. 718.

[10] G. L. Patton, J. C. Bravman, and J. D. Plummer, "Characterization of bipolar transistors with polysilicon emitter contacts," in *Dig. Tech. Papers 1984 Symp. VLSI Tech.* (San Diego, CA, Sept. 10–12, 1984), p. 54.

[11] W. J. M. J. Josquin, P. R. Boudewijn, and Y. Tamminga, "Effectiveness of polysilicon diffusion sources," *Appl. Phys. Lett.*, vol. 43, no. 10, p. 960, 1983.

[12] A. L. Fripp, "Dependence of resistivity on the doping level of polycrystalline silicon," *J. Appl. Phys.*, vol. 46, no. 3, p. 1240, 1975.

[13] J. Y. W. Seto, "The electrical properties of polycrystalline silicon films," *J. Appl. Phys.*, vol. 46, no. 12, p. 5247, 1975.

[14] N.C.-C. Lu, L. Gerzberg, C.-Y. Lu, and J. D. Meindl, "A conduction model for semiconductor-grain boundary-semiconductor barriers in polycrystalline-silicon films," *IEEE Trans. Elecron Devices*, vol. ED-30, no. 2, p. 137, 1983.

[15] G. J. Korsh and R. S. Muller, "Conduction properties of lightly doped polycrystalline silicon," *Solid-State Electron.*, vol. 21, p. 1045, 1978.

[16] S. M. Sze, *Physics of Semiconductor Devices*, 2nd ed. New York: Wiley, 1981, p. 255.

[17] G. E. Pike and C. H. Seager, "The DC voltage dependence of semiconductor grain-boundary resistance," *J. Appl. Phys.*, vol. 50, no. 5, p. 3414, 1979.

[18] B. Baccarani, M. Impronta, B. Ricco, and P. Ferla, "*I–V* characteristics of polycrystalline silicon resistors," *Rev. Phys. Appl.*, vol. 13, p. 777, Dec. 1978.

[19] N.C.-C. Lu and C.-Y. Lu, "*I–V* characteristics of polysilicon resistors at high electric field and the non-uniform conduction mechanism," *Solid-State Electron.*, to be published.

[20] T. I. Kamins and T. R. Case, "Structure of chemically deposited polycrystalline-silicon films," *Thin Solid Films*, vol. 16, p. 147, 1973.

[21] G. Harbeke, L. Krausbauer, E. F. Steigmeier, A. E. Widmer, H. F. Kappert, and G. Neugebauer, "Growth and physical properties of polycrystalline silicon films," *J. Electrochemical Soc.*, vol. 131, no. 3, p. 675, 1984.

[22] E. Kinsbron, M. Sternheim, and R. Knoell, "Crystallization of amorphous silicon films during low pressure chemical vapor deposition," *Appl. Phys. Lett.*, vol. 42, no. 9, p. 835, 1983.

[23] S. J. Krause, S. R. Wilson, W. M. Paulson, and R. B. Gregory, "Grain growth during transient annealing of As-implanted polycrystalline silicon films," *Appl. Phys. Lett.*, vol. 45, no. 7, p. 778, 1984.

[24] M. Taniguchi, M. Hirose, Y. Osaka, S. Hasegawa, and T. Shimizu, "Current transport in doped polycrystalline silicon," *Japan. J. Appl. Phys.*, vol. 19, no. 4, p. 665, 1980.

[25] M. L. Tarng, "Carrier transport in oxygen-rich polycrystalline-silicon films," *J. Appl. Phys.*, vol. 49, no. 7, p. 4069, 1978.

[26] C. H. Seager and G. E. Pike, "Grain boundary states and varistor behavior in silicon bicrystals," *Appl. Phys. Lett.*, vol. 35, no. 9, p. 709, 1979.

[27] A. K. Ghosh, A. Rose, H. P. Maruska, T. Feng, and D. J. Eustace, "Interpretation of Hall and resistivity measurements in polycrystalline silicon," *J. Electron. Materials*, vol. 11, no. 2, p. 237, 1982.

[28] W. B. Jackson, N. M. Johnson, and D. K. Biegelsen, "Density of gap states of silicon grain boundaries determined by optical absorption," *Appl. Phys. Lett.*, vol. 43, no. 2, p. 195, 1983.

[29] S. M. Sze, *Physics of Semiconductor Devices*, 2nd ed. New York: Wiley, 1981, p. 257.

[30] S. M. Sze, *Physics of Semiconductor Devices*, 2nd ed. New York: Wiley, 1981, p. 259.

[31] B. K. Ridley, "Specific negative resistance in solids," *Proc. Phys. Soc.*, vol. 82, p. 954, 1963.

[32] C. H. Sie, M. P. Dugan, and S. C. Moss, "Direct observations of filaments in the ovonic read-mostly memory," *J. Non-Crystalline Solids*, vol. 8–10, p. 877, 1972.

[33] R. A. Smith, *Semiconductors*, 2nd ed. Cambridge: Cambridge Univ., 1979, ch. 8.

[34] C. Jacoboni, C. Canali, G. Ottaviani, and A. A. Quaranta, "A review of some charge transport properties of silicon," *Solid-State Electron.*, vol. 20, p. 77, 1977.

[35] S. M. Sze, *Physics of Semiconductor Devices*, 2nd ed. New York: Wiley, 1981, p. 29.

[36] S. M. Sze, *Physics of Semiconductor Devices*, 2nd ed. New York: Wiley, 1981, p. 21.

[37] D. W. Greve, "Programming mechanism of polysilicon resistor fuses," *IEEE Trans. Electron Devices*, vol. ED-29, no. 4, p. 719, 1982.

[38] H. A. Schafft, "Second breakdown—A comprehensive review," *Proc. IEEE*, vol. 55, no. 8, p. 1272, 1967.

[39] S. R. Ovshinsky and H. Fritzsche, "Amorphous semiconductors for switching, memory, and imaging applications," *IEEE Trans. Electron Devices*, vol. ED-20, no. 2, p. 91, 1973.

[40] J. E. Fulenwider and G. J. Herskowitz, "Switching and temperature effects in lateral films of amorphous silicon," *Phys. Rev. Lett.*, vol. 25, no. 5, p. 292, 1970.

[41] W. denBoer, "Threshold switching in hydrogenated amorphous silicon," *Appl. Phys. Lett.*, vol. 40, no. 9, p. 812, 1982.

[42] D. Adler, "Switching phenomena in thin films," *J. Vac. Sci. Tech.*, vol. 10, no. 5, p. 728, 1973.

[43] A. F. Ioffe and A. R. Regel, "Non-crystalline, amorphous, and liquid electronic semiconductors," *Progr. Semicond.*, vol. 4, p. 237, 1960.

AMORPHOUS SILICON ANTIFUSE TECHNOLOGY FOR BIPOLAR PROMS

Brian Cook, Steve Keller
Texas Instruments Incorporated
P.O. Box 1443   M/S 675
Houston, TX   77001

ABSTRACT

In addition to requiring relatively high fusing currents, link technology limits bipolar PROM densities to a practical limit of 64K due to a lack of scalability of the bit cell. A scalable antifuse technology is described which utilizes a thin film of undoped amorphous silicon formed in a contact window that is programmed from a normally open state to a conductive state by the application of a bias with a potential high enough to cause destructive breakdown but at a significantly reduced programming current when compared to existing fusible link technology and avalanche-induced-migration vertical fuse technology. By reducing the bit size and fusing current, this antifuse technology provides the bipolar designer a technique to extend PROM densities to greater than 64K.

DESIGN GOALS

The need for an anti- or vertical fuse is driven by two characteristics of fusible-link technology: the inability to scale the fuse element resulting in larger bit/bar sizes (see Figure 1), and the relatively high currents (>25 mA) required to fuse the link. The vertical fuse presented here is both scalable and has a fusing current less than 10 mA (note that vertical fuses are normally open and are programmed to a conductive state while links are fused open). Other vertical fuse techniques, such as the avalanche-induced-migration or AIM method, offer some scalability but still require relatively high fusing currents [1].

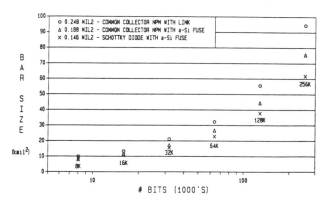

Fig. 1:   PROM bar size versus bit density

Figure 2 defines the electrical design goals required for a vertical fuse element that can be used in a common-collector cell presently used on TI's Series 3 PROM designs. Both the upper and lower limits on fusing current are arbitrarily fixed. The lower limit is to guard against inadvertently stressing the fuse with a transient pulse while fusing another bit. The fusing voltage limits are determined by circuit design with the lower limit determined by the read voltage and the upper limit by the breakdown voltage of the blocking element (base-emitter junction). Pre-fuse and post-fuse resistances are determined by the requirements of the sensing circuitry.

PARAMETER	LIMITS
PRE-FUSE LEAKAGE	< 200 uA at 2.0 V
FUSING VOLTAGE	$3\ Vbe < V_F < BVebo$ $(2.25\ V < V_F < 5.5\ V\ at\ 25\ C)$
FUSING CURRENT	$100\ uA < I_F < 10\ mA$
POST-FUSE RESISTANCE	< 200 ohm at 2.5 mA sense

Fig. 2:   Vertical fuse PROM design goals

PROCESS

Figure 3 illustrates two structures that utilize an amorphous silicon (a-Si) layer sandwiched between two conducting layers. The process required to achieve each structure is modular in the sense that essentially no modification to existing process steps is required, only the insertion of an additional deposition, pattern and etch.

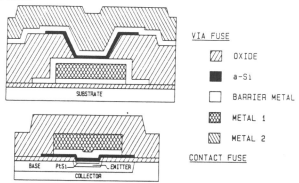

Fig. 3:   "Via" and "Contact" fuse structures

In the case of the "via fuse" structure, after metal 1 has been etched, a barrier layer is deposited, patterned and etched in locations where the fuses will be formed. After depositing the interlevel dielectric, vias are opened exposing both fuse sites as well as metal 1 contact sites. A thin (500 A) undoped a-Si film is then deposited, patterned and etched leaving an a-Si layer in the vias over the fuse sites. After a subsequent 450 degree C anneal step to reduce pre-fuse leakage current, standard metal 2 processing is performed to complete the process.

For the "contact fuse" structure, standard processing is done thru platinum silicide formation and is followed by the a-Si deposition, pattern and etch, leaving the film in selected contact windows. After the anneal step, a standard double level metal process can be done. Both the via and contact fuse structures rely on a Ti:W barrier layer of over 500 A to prevent aluminum spiking. The only critical step in this process is the a-Si deposition since the thickness of the resulting film controls the fusing voltage.

Reprinted from *Proc. IEEE Bipolar Circuits Technol. Meet.*, pp. 99–100, October 1986.

ELECTRICAL CHARACTERISTICS

When measuring the electrical characteristics of the a-Si fuse, several modes of existence are observed as shown in Figure 4. The curve labeled "primary leakage" illustrates the important pre-fuse characteristics as well as defining the point at which destructive breakdown of the a-Si film occurs (programming voltage and current). The curve labeled "secondary leakage" shows evidence of an intermediate transition state of the fuse element between destructive breakdown and the resistive state possibly suggesting the formation of a silicide at the metal-amorphous silicon interface prior to completely shorting the fuse. The final state of the fused bit is represented by the curve labeled "post-fuse". It should be mentioned that the amount of current present at destructive breakdown is not sufficient to reduce the post-fuse resistance to the desired value. Based upon limited data, it appears that 5 - 10 milliamps of current may be required to reduce the final resistance to less than the 200 ohm PROM goal with a typical final value of less than 50 ohms after 10 milliamps of forming or healing current is applied.

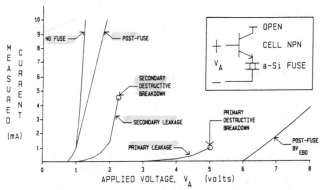

Fig. 4: "Contact" fuse characteristics (2X3 um emitter, 500 A a-Si)

As mentioned earlier, the post-deposition (a-Si) anneal is included in the process to significantly reduce the pre-fuse leakage current as illustrated in Figure 5. Also note that this step results in a slightly higher fusing voltage. Other factors that influence leakage current and fusing characteristics include feature size, temperature (see Figure 6) and a-Si film thickness (see Figure 7).

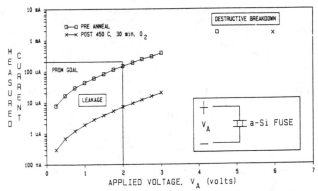

Fig. 5: Effect of anneal on fuse character- (3X3 um via, 500 A a-Si)

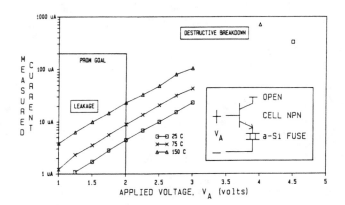

Fig. 6: Temperature effect on fuse characteristics (2X3 um contact, 450 A a-Si)

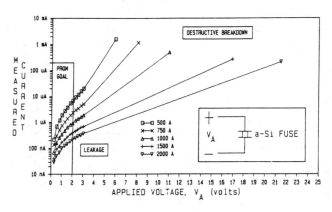

Fig. 7: Effect of a-Si thickness on fuse characteristics (3X3 um via)

FINAL COMMENTS

The a-Si "contact" fuse structure in conjunction with a common-collector NPN cell has been employed in the fabrication of a fully programmable 256 bit PROM. But while the vertical fuse technology described offers several important advantages (scalability, manufacturability, reduced fusing current) over existing link technology for PROM applications, further reductions in leakage current are desirable for PROM designs utilizing a common collector NPN cell and will be required for programmable logic designs. However, by allowing for higher fusing voltages, as would be possible in a Schottky diode cell configuration, thicker undoped a-Si films may be used which will result in lower leakage currents.

ACKNOWLEDGEMENTS

The authors would like to express their appreciation to Sylvia Macejewski and Sandy Ramirez for slice processing and data collection; to Doug Verret, Manolo Torreno and Randy Hollingsworth for their advice and technical support.

REFERENCE

1. "Memory Technology: Nonvolatile Memories" ELECTRONIC DESIGN, Vol 32, No. 16, p. 139 Aug 23, 1984.

A NOVEL ION-IMPLANTED
AMORPHOUS SILICON PROGRAMMABLE ELEMENT

Yosi Shacham-Diamand[*], Alex Sinar, Eric Sirkin,
Ilan Blech and Levy Gerzberg

*Department of Electrical Engineering
Technion - Israel Institute of Technology
Haifa, Israel, 32000.

and

Zoran Corporation
Santa Clara, Ca., 95051
U.S.A.

ABSTRACT

A novel Ion-Implanted Programmable Element (IPEL) suitable for integration with VLSI technology has been developed. The device operation is based on the electrical properties of a metal/amorphous silicon/single crystal silicon structure made by heavy-dose ion-implantation into a contact to a single crystal silicon. The initial resistance of the amorphous silicon is very high ($> 10^{15}$ $\Omega \times cm$) and its dielectric strength is in the $1 \, MV/cm$ range. Its resistance drops over 6 orders of magnitude after switching and the device is transformed irreversibly into its conductive state.

INTRODUCTION

Structures incorporating single crystal and polycrystalline silicon materials dominate the integrated circuit industry today. A third structure of silicon, amorphous, has found only limited applications such as solar cells [1], and image sensors [2]. The most common ways to prepare amorphous silicon are by high-temperature (500°C-580°C) SiH_4 decomposition [3], plasma enhanced chemical vapor deposition [4], sputtering [5] and vacuum evaporation [6]. The use of ion implantation for the conversion of single crystal silicon to amorphous silicon [7] can be an attractive alternative to other amorphous silicon technologies. Variables such as ion type, implant dose, implant energy, surface temperature and surface preparation are controlled and reproduced with today's ion implanter technology. In this technique a directed high dose beam ($> 10^{14} \, cm^{-2}$) of chemically inert medium or heavy mass ions collide with the surface inducing primary and secondary inelastic collisions with the silicon atoms. These collisions destroy the long range order of the crystalline lattice. The amorphous material created by the collisions is well confined to the implanted layer thereby producing a sharp transition at the amorphous/single crystal silicon interface.

The ion-implanted amorphous films undergo a swift phase change to polycrystalline material when an applied potential across the film reaches a critical field strength. The accompanying change in conductivity can in some cases reach more than 6 orders in magnitude making the devices attractive as basic elements for programmable logic devices and memories. A novel self-aligned structure consistent with this intent is described in Fig. 1 [8]. Using standard photolithographic and plasma etching tools a contact is opened through a SiO_2 layer exposing the top surface of a junction isolated single crystal silicon layer. Ions are then implanted over the wafer surface causing amorphization of the exposed silicon region. Figure 2 is a bright field transmission electron micrograph (TEM) showed the cross section of the amorphous silicon/single crystal silicon interface formed by implanting argon ions at a 60 keV accelerating voltage and $10^{16} \, cm^{-2}$ dosage into a single crystal silicon. A metal film is then deposited and standard "backend" IC processing continued. IPELs fabricated in this fashion are easily integrated into standard CMOS, NMOS and bipolar VLSI technologies.

EXPERIMENTAL

Starting material consisted of 100 mm diameter, polished, Czochralsky grown, N type single crystal silicon wafers oriented at <100> crystal plane. The wafers were doped with phosphorus at $5 \times 10^{14} \, cm^{-3}$. The wafers were processed by a conventional CMOS process and therefore there were four doping schemes available for the single crystal part of the IPEL:

A) P^- - Deep boron profile (4-4.5 μm) at a surface concentration of $1-2 \times 10^{16} \, cm^{-3}$.

B) N^- - Deep phosphorus profile (5 μm) at a surface concentration of $2-3 \times 10^{16} \, cm^{-3}$.

C) N^+ - Shallow (.4 - .8 μm) arsenic junction at a surface concentration in the range of $10^{20} \, cm^{-3}$ diffused into P^-.

D) P^+ - Shallow (.7 μm) boron junction at a surface concentration in the range of $10^{20} \, cm^{-3}$ diffused into N^-.

The P^- and N^- profiles were created by implanting the appropriate dopants into the starting material and driving in for 12 hours at 1100°C. The P^+ and N^+ junctions were formed by subsequent implants followed by a 30 minute anneal at 950°C. All four substrate profiles could be achieved within one continuous process flow using the appropriate stepper reticles. After forming the single crystal silicon doping profiles as described above a 100 nm thermal oxide film was grown over the surface under pyrogenic steam ambient followed by chemical vapor deposition of SiO_2 at 450°C. The CVD SiO_2 film was then annealed at 900°C for 30 minutes in N_2 ambient. After standard photolithographic and plasma etching processing an opening was made into the SiO_2 film thereby exposing the surface of the desired silicon substrate material. A blanket ion implant of the wafer induced amorphization of the silicon surface in the exposed contact areas. An additional lithographic and plasma etching step opened other contacts which would permit contact to four different substrate types. Afterwards a metal film was deposited over the wafer surface followed by a photolithography and metal plasma etching step. The wafers were then alloyed at 450°C for 30 minutes in H_2. Where indicated, samples without the final alloy step were also studied.

Species implanted in this study include singly ionized Si, Ar, As and Sb. Except for Ar the atomic species could in principle chemically bind themselves to the crystalline Si lattice, however the post implant processing temperatures were intentionally kept below levels which might induce annealing. Implant energies ranging from 40-180 keV and doses between 5×10^{14} and $1 \times 10^{16} \, cm^{-2}$ were studied.

Two metallization schemes were investigated, Al-Si(1%) and Al-Si(1%) on Ti-W. For the barrier layer metallization the TiW was deposited prior to the Al-Si in the same system without being exposed to the atmosphere. In some cases the devices were measured prior to the alloy cycle, but typically they were exposed to H_2 ambient at 450°C for 30 minutes. For some experiments the wafers were exposed to two alloy cycles. Unless stated otherwise Ar was implanted at 60 keV at a dose of $10^{16} \, cm^{-2}$ in a batch type implanter at currents of 4-6 mA and without flood-gun control.

Reprinted from the *IEDM Tech. Dig.*, pp. 194–197, 1987.

The amorphous silicon material was characterized by TEM, SEM and RBS analysis and electrical I-V and C-V measurements. The current-voltage properties were measured by an automated semiconductor parameter analyzer connected to a desktop computer for equipment control, data storage, retrieval and modeling. Temperature studies were made in the 20-400°C range using a heated chuck installed on a standard probing station.

RESULTS

Typical I-V characteristics of an IPEL are shown in Figure 3. Two distinct regions can be discerned, the initial high resistance "OFF" and final low resistance "ON" states. Both states are separated by an abrupt transition which occurs at the critical or "programming" voltage, Vp. The electrical and physical properties of the IPEL have been investigate as a function of: 1) the single crystal silicon doping type and concentration, 2) the ion energy, dose and type, 3) the metal type and 4) alloying conditions.

The current versus voltage I-V characteristics of the device structure formed by an argon implant of 10^{16} cm^{-2} at accelerations voltages of 40, 50, 60, 90, 120 and 180 keV are shown in Fig. 4. All six experiments exhibited a near linear I-V dependence at low bias and an exponential-like behavior at high bias. Deviations from the exponential I-V characteristics are observed close to the programming voltage where the I-V characteristics start to curve upward. As the implanter acceleration voltage increases the slope of the I-V curves in the exponential dependent region decreases, indicating a decrease in conductivity through the device. At voltages considerably below the programming voltage the difference in device resistances varies by more than an order of magnitude over the acceleration voltages studied. A decrease in programming voltage accompanies the decrease in acceleration voltage and decrease in device resistance.

Current-temperature characteristics at fixed voltage for Al-Si metallization scheme are presented as in Fig. 5. Above 100°C the current follows a straight line characterized by a single "activation energy":

$$I = I_s \times EXP\left[-\frac{qE_0}{kT}\right] \qquad [1]$$

where Is is constant for a given bias applied across the device, q is the unit electron charge, E_0 is the activation energy. k is the Boltzman constant and T is the temperature in degrees K. Is, and therefore I, vary with the applied bias voltage. For devices with Al-Si metallization on N^+ at +0.1V bias $E_0 = 0.6$ eV while at +5V $E_0 = 0.4$ eV.

The I-V characteristics for samples with other substrate doping schemes and different annealing conditions were measured. The results were similar to those presented in figures 4 and 5. The various experimental observations on the IPEL I-V characteristics can be summarized as follows:

(1) I-V characteristics of N^+ or P^+ material have similar behaviors. The N^+ material exhibits a higher high-field current dependence.

(2) For positive biases (silicon diffusion area grounded) the N^+ and N^- material have similar behavior. However at negative biases the N^- substrate shows a significantly reduced current.

(3) There is little difference in temperature dependence of the current between the N^+ and N^- or between P^+ and P^- material.

(4) For positive biases there is little difference in the shape of the I-V curves for Al-Si and Al-Si/Ti-W metallization. The current for the Al-Si/Ti-W structure shows a higher level of conduction. At negative biases the Al-Si devices exhibits significantly lower current vs. positive biases.

(5) Al-Si/Ti-W devices have a higher E_0 than Al-Si.

(6) The greater the time of H_2 annealing at 450°C, the lower the current conduction. There is little effect on the temperature dependence of the I-V curves by the length of the annealing cycle.

The IPEL's switching voltage was found to be very uniform over 100 mm. wafers and it is a monotonous increasing function of the implant energy (Fig.6). The data presented in Fig.6 is based on several runs made with argon implant dose of 10^{16} cm^{-2} and energies range between 40 keV to 180 keV. The switching voltage increased monotonously as the implant energy increased. The average switching electric field was found to be in the 1 MV/cm range and it decreased as the implant energy increased.

The IPEL was integrated with a MOS transistor as drawn in Fig.7. Since it is hidden inside the contact it does not increase the transistor area. Cells with different geometries were made and their pre and postprogramming characteristics were investigated. It is important to note that the MOS characteristics were found to be the same for structures with or without the IPEL. The device's low programming current (<10 mA) and its low final resistance (200 Ω - 10 $k\Omega$) make it attractive for high density fast programmable logic or memories applications (see Fig.8).

DISCUSSION

Ions on impact with the single crystal silicon dislodge Si atoms from their lattice sites causing a disruption in the ordered nature of the crystal. Simultaneous to the amorphization of the silicon layer, the implanted ions lodge themselves within the newly formed film. For example, argon ions implanted into single crystal silicon at a dose and energy of 10^{16} cm^{-2} and 40 keV give rise to an argon atom density of approximately 2×10^{21} cm^{-3} or 10% argon in silicon. Based upon the experimental work described earlier several conclusions can be made regarding the way in which the amorphized layer is formed:

(1) For a given substrate and ion type, the depth of the amorphized layer is determined predominately by the energy of the implanted ions. Empirically, the relationship between argon ion energy (1×10^{16} cm^{-2} and 40-180 keV) and layer thickness as derived from SIMS and RBS analysis of implanted samples:

$$d = A *E^P \qquad [2]$$

where p=0.91, A=2.8, for E in keV and d in nm.

(2) For a given implant energy, the bulk resistivity of the amorphized layer increases with increasing doses until a saturation point is reached when the implanted layer becomes fully amorphized. Intuitively it could be argued that the greater the implant dose, the greater the extent of damage within the layer. After the layer is fully amorphized the resistivity increase with dose is mainly due to the slight increase of the amorphous layer thickness with the dose.

(3) The lateral penetration of the amorphized layer along the perimeter of the device is due to ions passing through the gradually tapered SiO_2 film. As shown in Fig. 2 the lateral extent of the amorphized region underneath the SiO_2 film greater than its vertical dimension. It can be explained either by lateral propagation of the damage or some unusual stress related phenomenon at the thermal SiO_2/Si interface.

The averaged current density as a function of applied bias voltage across the amorphous layer remains constant over device areas ranging from 6×10^{-7} cm^2 to 1×10^{-4} cm^2. This lack of dependence upon the dimensions of the device perimeter suggests that current flowing either through the contact periphery or insulator walls must be negligible, leaving only conduction through the amorphous layer and/or uniformly distributed defects therein as the only likely candidates.

The IPEL's switching initiates an electrothermal forming process. A thin polycrystalline filament is observed in transmission electron micrographs and SEM pictures. The filament shape, as appears on the surface, is irregular. Its diameter is about 200 nm. and it is observed only at the IPEL's periphery. The filament was found to be made of a polycrystalline material and is assumed as the major current path at the IPEL's conducting state. The final resistance of the device is most probably determined by the filament structure, grain size and doping level.

CONCLUSIONS

High dose ion implantation of single crystal silicon causes a phase transformation of the material into a poor electrically conducting amorphous film. The properties of the film can be controllably altered depending upon ion type, energy, dose and substrate type. Electrically programmable devices (IPEL) can be made using the amorphous films. The IPEL programming voltage and current are low, and the device retention time is very long, even at temperatures in the 125°C range. The IPEL is small, compatible with current VLSI technology and is compatible with the scaled ULSI technology.

ACKNOWLEDGEMENTS

The authors wish to thank F. Deadmond and T. Dibiase for technical support in device fabrication and M. Khambatty and I. Beinglas of IMP Corporation (San Jose, CA) for suggestions throughout the course of this work.

REFERENCES

[1] D.E.Carlson, "Amorphous Solar Cells", IEEE trans on Electron Devices, ED-24, 449, (1977).

[2] K.Seki, T. Matsuura, M.Murakami, and T.Tsukada, "Analysis and Design of Large-Scale Linear Image Sensor Using Amorphous Silicon", IEEE Transactions on Components, Hybrids, and Manufacturing Technology, Vol. CHMT-9, No.3, P. 304, 1986. Vol. A 2 (2), p.641, 1984.

[3] P.G.LeComber and W.E.Spear, Phys. Rev. Letters, Vol.25, p.509, 1970.

[4] R.C.Chittick,J.A.Alexander, H.F.Sterling, "The Preparation and Properties of Amorphous Silicon", J. of Electrochemical Society, Vol.116, p.77, 1969.

[5] P.A.Walley, "The Preparation and Properties of Amorphous Silicon", Thin Solid Films, Vol. 2, p.327, 1968. Rev. B1, p.2632, 1970.

[6] A.J.Lewis, G.A.N.Connel, W.paul, J.R.Pawlik, R.J.Temkin, "Tetrahedrally Bonded Amorphous Semiconductor", ed. by M.Brodsky, S.Kirkpatrick, D.Weaire, American Inst. of Physics, p. 27, New-York 1974.

[7] J.Gibbons, Proc. IEEE, Vol.60, p.1062, 1972.

[8] L.Gerzberg, U.S.Patent No. 4590589, May 29, 1986.

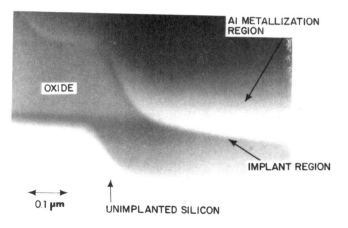

Fig. 2: High-magnification view of the left-hand corner of an IPEL as taken by bright field TEM.

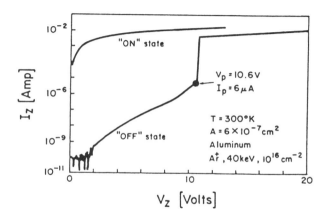

Fig. 3: I-V characteristics of an IPEL before (a) and after (b) programming.

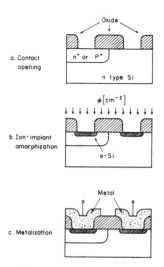

Fig. 1: Schematic cross section of the IPEL process flow.

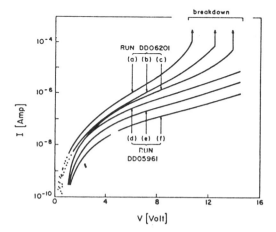

Fig. 4: I-V characteristics for argon implanted IPELs with argon dose of 10^{16} cm^{-2}. and energy of (a) 40 keV, (b) 50 keV, (c) 60 keV, (d) 90 kev, (e)120 keV, and (f) 180 keV.

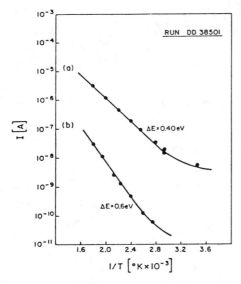

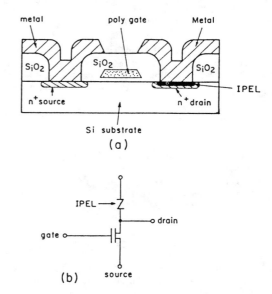

Fig. 5:   Current versus 1/T of IPELs with Al-Si metalization at (a) 5V and (b) 0.1V.

Fig. 7:   Schematic cross section (a) and the equivalent circuit (b) of an IPEL integrated with MOS transistor.

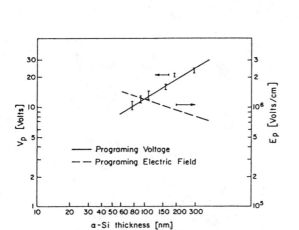

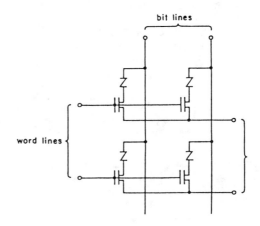

Fig. 6:   The programming voltage and the electric field of argon implanted IPEL as a function of the amorphous layer thickness (the implanted dose is 10^{16} cm^{-2}).

Fig. 8:   Programmable ROM made of IPELs integrated with MOS transistors logic.

A NEW PROGRAMMABLE CELL UTILIZING INSULATOR BREAKDOWN

Noriaki Sato, Takahiro Nawata, and Kunihiko Wada

IC Development Division, Fujitsu Limited
Nakahara-ku, Kawasaki 211, Japan

ABSTRACT

A new programmable cell called the Breakdown-of-Insulator-for-Conduction cell (BIC cell) has been proposed and developed. A BIC cell utilizes the electrical breakdown of an insulator for programming.

A highly refined thin insulator, with a delta-function type of breakdown voltage distribution, is employed in the BIC cell. This cell can be programmed within 1 μsec, making it possible to realize the shortest programming time for PROM cells reported so far. Programmed cell resistance is around 1×10^2 ohms.

Since a BIC cell has a stacked-cell structure, a PROM cell can be formed simply by merging a BIC cell with a MOSFET. Then, a PROM cell array can be formed from these cells. A programming method for a PROM cell array is discussed below.

INTRODUCTION

Recent advances in applications of microprocessors and memories have made it necessary to develop One-Time-PROMs that are field-programmable.

Conventionally, three types of cells- a fuse type cell (1), a junction-shorting type cell (2), and an EPROM cell (3)- are used as programmable cells in One-Time-PROMs as shown in Table I.

A BIC cell is a new type of cell which utilizes insulator breakdown for programming. The advantage of this type of cell is that it can be programmed within 1 μsec. Therefore, a PROM cell, consisting of a BIC cell and a MOSFET, makes it possible to realize the shortest programming time yet reported for PROMs.

This paper describes the BIC cell structure, insulator characteristics, programming and resistance behavior, and a PROM cell array incorporating the BIC cell.

CELL STRUCTURE

As shown in Fig.1, a BIC cell consists of a thin insulator layer which covers a contact area on an N^+-diffusion layer, and an Al electrode connected to the insulator surface.

In the preprogrammed state, the Al electrode is isolated from the N^+-diffusion layer, as shown in Fig.2a (the "0" state). If a pulse is applied to the Al electrode during programming of the BIC cell, the insulator breaks down and a connection is formed between the Al electrode and the N^+-diffusion layer, as shown in Fig.2b (the "1" state).

A BIC cell can be formed on a contact area in a conventional transistor, since it has a stacked-cell structure.

CELL INSULATOR

In order to use insulator breakdown for programming, it is necessary that breakdown voltage be both low and constant.

In a BIC cell, a highly refined thin insulator, with an equivalent SiO_2 thickness of 80 Å, is employed to satisfy these requirements.

As shown in Fig.3, the breakdown voltage of tested samples falls within the 2-volt range from 10 to 12 volts, realizing low breakdown voltage, even when the insulator area is as small as several μm across.

At the same time, the histogram of breakdown voltage shows a delta-function type of distribution. In other words, neither an initial shorting mode nor an intermediate mode (4) is observed in breakdown voltage distribution.

Due to the above-mentioned breakdown voltage characteristics, both programming voltage and read-out voltage are determined as shown in Fig.3.

Reprinted from the *IEDM Tech. Dig.*, pp. 639–643, 1985.

PROGRAMMING CHARACTERISTICS

The number of programming pulses needed to cause a BIC insulator to break down depends on the pulse voltage.

Fig.4 shows the number of programming pulses as a function of pulse voltage. A BIC cell can be programmed with a single pulse if the voltage is higher than 17 volts.

However, the number of programming pulses does not depend on either pulse duration (Fig.5) or duty-factor (Fig.6). Therefore, even when the pulse duration changes from 50 μsec to 1 μsec, the number of pulses shows the same dependence on the pulse voltage (see Fig.4). This is probably because the insulator breaks down almost instantaneously when a programming pulse is applied.

Therefore, programming time was able to be reduced to 1 μsec. This is less than 1/4 the programming time per bit of any PROM cell reported before.

Thus, a PROM cell, consisting of a BIC cell and a MOSFET, makes it possible to realize the shortest programming time yet reported for PROM cells.

CELL RESISTANCE

A preprogrammed cell exhibits a very high resistance of more than 1×10^{13} ohms, as shown in Fig.7. On the other hand, programmed cell resistance is so low, around 1×10^2 ohms, that the read-out delay time due to the cell resistance is negligibly short.

Furthermore, BIC cells have not failed even after 1×10^5 read operations, indicating that read-out operations are reliable enough.

PROM CELL AND CELL ARRAY

As shown in Fig.8, a PROM cell can be formed by connecting a BIC cell to a MOSFET, with the N^+-diffusion layer of the BIC cell acting as the drain in the MOSFET.

This PROM cell has the advantage that it can be made simply by forming a BIC cell on the contact area of a MOSFET, making a new PROM cell array possible, as shown in Fig.9.

In programming of this cell array, normal gate voltage is applied to the decoded X_n line, and a programming pulse, applied to the decoded Y_n line, causes the BIC cell at (X_n, Y_n) (labeled A in Fig.9) to change from a disconnected state to a connected state.

A BIC cell in an unselected PROM cell on the Y_n line, for example, the cell at (X_{n-1}, Y_n) (labeled B in Fig.9), is not programmed.

Since the MOSFET is in the "off" state in the unselected PROM cell, the N^+-diffusion layer of the BIC cell, or the drain in the MOSFET, is transitionally reverse-biased when a programming pulse is applied to the Y_n line.

Therefore, a depletion layer is formed under the N^+-diffusion layer in cell B, so that the programming pulse voltage is divided between the BIC insulator and the depletion layer.

As a result, the effective bias applied to the BIC cell drops below the breakdown voltage. Thus, an unselected PROM cell cannot be programmed.

Fig.10 shows the results of the resistance distribution on both selected and unselected BIC cells.

Only the samples corresponding to the selected BIC cells are programmed. Therefore, it is confirmed that only the selected cell can be programmed in the PROM cell array.

SUMMARY

A new programmable cell utilizing insulator breakdown has been proposed and successfully developed.

This cell has a programming time of 1 μsec, the shortest time yet reported for any programmable cell.

A new PROM cell can be formed simply by merging the BIC cell with a MOSFET.

A PROM cell array can be formed using these PROM cells.

ACKNOWLEDGEMENT

The authors would like to thank R.Togei and M.Nakano for their encouragement.

REFERENCES

(1) R.M.Fisher," A 64K Bipolar PROM," ISSCC Dig. Tech. Papers, p.114, Feb. 1982.
(2) T.Fukushima, K.Ueno, Y.Matsuzaki, and K.Tanaka, "A 40 ns Junction-Shorting PROM," ibid, p.172, Feb. 1983.
(3) K.Okumura, S.Ohya, M.Yamamoto, T.Watanabe, Y.Shimamura, and M.Kikuchi, "A 1 Mb EPROM," ibid, p.140, Feb. 1984.
(4) K.Yamabe and K.Taniguchi, "Time-Dependent Dielectric Breakdown of Thin Thermally Grown SiO_2 Films," IEEE, ED-32 (2), p.423, 1985.

TABLE I
COMPARISON OF CONVENTIONAL PROM CELLS
AND A BIC CELL

Type	Principle	Cell State	Programming Time (sec)
Fuse	Fuse Melting	$1 \rightarrow 0$	$\sim 1 \times 10^{-4}$
Junction Shorting	Junction Breakdown	$0 \rightarrow 1$	$\sim 1 \times 10^{-5}$
EPROM	Avalanche Injection	$1 \leftrightarrow 0$	$\sim 1 \times 10^{-4}$
BIC	Insulator Breakdown	$0 \rightarrow 1$	1×10^{-6}

"0": Disconnected State
"1": Connected State

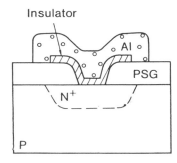

Fig.1. Cross section of the BIC cell.
The cell has a stacked-cell
structure.

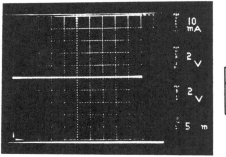

Fig.2(a). I-V characteristic of a BIC
insulator in preprogrammed
state (the "0" state).

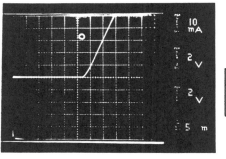

Fig.2(b). I-V characteristic of a BIC
insulator in programmed
state (the "1" state).

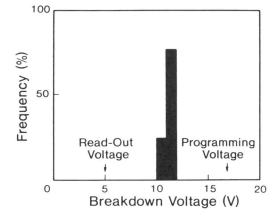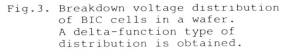

Fig.3. Breakdown voltage distribution
of BIC cells in a wafer.
A delta-function type of
distribution is obtained.

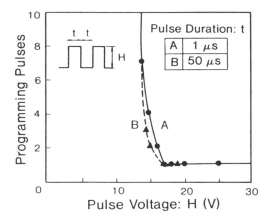

Fig.4. Programming characteristics (1).
The number of programming pulses
as a function of pulse voltage.
A programming time of 1 usec (A)
is obtained.

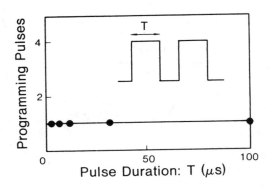

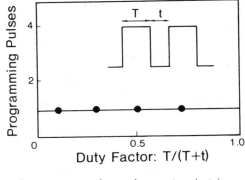

Fig.5. Programming characteristics (2).
The number of programming pulses
as a function of pulse duration.

Fig.6. Programming characteristics (3).
The number of programming pulses
as a function of duty factor.

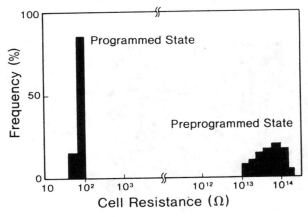

Fig.7. BIC cell resistance distribution
in preprogrammed and programmed
states. Programmed cells have a
low resistance of around 10^2 ohms.

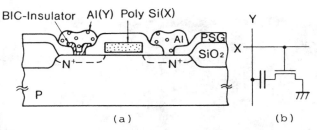

Fig.8(a). Cross section of the PROM cell.
The cell can be formed by
connecting a BIC cell to a
MOSFET.

Fig.8(b). The equivalent circuit of the
cell.

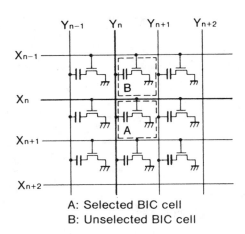

A: Selected BIC cell
B: Unselected BIC cell

Fig.9. BIC PROM cell array.
A BIC insulator in a selected cell
at (X_n, Y_n) is broken down by
programming.

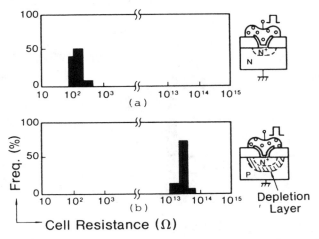

Fig.10. Resistance distribution of selected
BIC cells and unselected BIC cells
after programming. Only the samples
corresponding to the selected BIC
cells are programmed.

DIELECTRIC BASED ANTIFUSE FOR LOGIC AND MEMORY ICs.

Esmat Hamdy, John McCollum, Shih-ou Chen, Steve Chiang,
Shafy Eltoukhy, Jim Chang, Ted Speers, Amr Mohsen

Actel Corporation, 955 East Arques Ave., Sunnyvale CA 94086

ABSTRACT

This paper describes a *Programmable Low Impedance Circuit Element* (PLICE), which is a dielectric based antifuse for use in both logic and memory ICs. The antifuse element offers significant size and performance improvement compared to other programmable cells. A simple thermal model has been developed to predict the antifuse resistance. Each antifuse occupies an area of 1.5 um^2 using 1.2um technology. It can be programmed within 1 msec, and has a tight resistance distribution centered around 500 ohms. The reliability of both the programmed and unprogrammed states is demonstrated to be better than 40 years. The antifuse was used in the design of the first family of desktop-configurable channeled gate arrays and a 64K PROM device.

INTRODUCTION

PROMs and programmable logic devices commonly employ programmable elements such as fusible links, EPROM or EEPROM cells. These programmable elements are either large in area, require high programming current, or are three terminal devices. This paper describes a Programmable Low Impedance Circuit Element (PLICE), which is a dielectric based antifuse that offers significant size and performance improvements over other programmable elements. The antifuse structure, technology, characteristics, thermal model and reliability are described below.

ANTIFUSE STRUCTURE AND TECHNOLOGY

The PLICE antifuse is a dielectric between an n+ diffusion and poly-Si as shown in the SEM cross-section (Fig. (1)) and is compatible with CMOS and other technologies such as bipolar and BIMOS. The PLICE element was integrated in a standard 12 mask, double layer metal twin tub CMOS technology. Three additional masks were required; n+ antifuse diffusion, antifuse poly, and 40 nm oxide mask for the high voltage transistors, bringing the total to 15 masks. Four transistor types (TABLE 1) are used; the low voltage high speed transistors are used for the logic and signal path while

the high voltage transistors are used for the programming path. Fig. (2) is a photomicrograph of a 2000 gate programmable gate array utilizing 186,000 antifuses. There are roughly one hundred antifuses for each logic gate to achieve a high degree of interconnectivity and gate utilization. Each antifuse occupies an area equivalent to a contact or via. The antifuses are incorporated into a cell structure such that when the antifuse is programmed, it connects a metal 1 and metal 2 line [1,2]. The cell structure size is thus limited by the metal 1 and metal 2 pitch. Fig. (3) is a photomicrograph of a 64K PROM designed using the same technology with a typical access time of 35 nsec.

ANTIFUSE CHARACTERISTICS

When 18 volts is applied across the antifuse through X-Y select transistors [1,2], the antifuse is programmed to the conductive state in about 200 usec as shown in Fig. (4). Fig. (5) shows a tight resistance distribution of antifuses programmed with a current of 5 mA.

ANTIFUSE THERMAL MODEL

Once the dielectric is ruptured, the resistance R_l of the conductive state is determined by the size of the conductive conduit (link). The size of the link is determined by the amount of power dissipated in the link which melts the dielectric. Since the temperature of the molten core varies inversely with its radius, the molten core will expand until its temperature drops below the melting point of the dielectric. Since the size of the link is much smaller than the thickness of the conductive silicon layers on both sides of the dielectric, the temperature gradient and the resultant heat conduction can be modelled by a simple sphere. The resultant equation for the link temperature T_l:

$$T_l = I_p V_l / 4 \pi k_{th} r_l \quad \cdots \cdots \cdots (1)$$

Where I_p is the programming current, V_l is the voltage across the link, r_l is the radius of the link, and k_{th} is the thermal conductivity of silicon. The calculation however becomes

Reprinted from the *IEDM Tech. Dig.*, pp. 786–789, 1988.

complicated if the thermal conductivity of silicon is taken into consideration as a function of its temperature [3]. Furthermore, the power dissipation is distributed throughout the sphere. Hence a computer simulation that breaks the sphere into 1 nm thick conductive shells was used to calculate the link temperature T_l and resistance R_l vs programming current I_p. The resultant calculations are plotted in Fig. (6). The link radius r_l is determined by the equilibrium of power dissipation and melting temperature, as expressed in the following equation [4]:

$$r_l = I_p (\sqrt{\rho_l + \rho_{si}/2})/87\pi \dots \dots (2)$$

where ρ_l, ρ_{si} are the resistivities of the link and silicon respectively during programming and the relation between link resistance R_l and link radius r_l can be obtained as follows[4]:

$$R_l = (\rho_l + \rho_{si})/\pi r_l \dots \dots \dots (3)$$

From eqn.(2) and eqn.(3) we derive that R_l is thus inversely proportional to I_p (Fig. (6)), given by the following equation:

$$R_l = (87/I_p) * (\rho_l + \rho_{si})/\sqrt{\rho_l + \rho_{si}/2} \dots (4)$$

This can be further simplified to:

$$R_l = 2.5/I_p \dots \dots \dots \dots (5)$$

At 5 mA, for example, the link radius is about 20 nm and the fuse resistance is 500 ohms - (approximately the impedance of a 20um wide EPROM cell) in its conductive state. The programmed antifuse resistance is a function of the reading current as shown in Fig. (7). The resistance rises at a current just before the programming current, due to heating of the conductive channel; drops when the silicon in the conductive channel melts; and continues to decrease beyond the original resistance as the current exceeds the programming current. This is due to the permanent widening of the conductive link.

ANTIFUSE RELIABILITY

Programmed antifuse reliability was evaluated using discrete antifuses incorporated in a Kelvin structure (Fig. (8)). The structures were stressed with a 5 mA current between two of the terminals 1, 2 at a temperature of 250C. Fig. (9) is a plot of the monitored voltage across the programmed antifuse as a function of stress time. Failure is indicated by an increase in voltage as the structure becomes open. Measurement of the antifuse through the other two terminals 3, 4 indicated that the programmed antifuse did not fail or exhibit any measurable resistance change. Investigation of the failure using SEM indicated that the failure is due to poly contact electromigration. With 0.9 eV activation energy [5] for contacts, the predicted lifetime is more than 40 years. Fig. (10) is a plot of time to breakdown vs 1/electric-field for unprogrammed discrete antifuses. Extrapolation of Fig. (10) indicates that the lifetime of an unprogrammed antifuse under continuous 5.5v stress exceeds 100 years, with a failure rate less than 1 FIT. In addition to the accelerated discrete antifuse device reliability data, 364 product units have accumulated a total of 571,000 device hours of dynamic burn-in at 5.5 volt and 125C (with some units reaching 2500 hours) with no failures or change in a.c. characteristics. This is equivalent to a failure rate of less than 100 FIT.

SUMMARY

In summary we have presented and modelled a reliable high performance dielectric based antifuse which can be programmed with relatively low current and is compatible with CMOS and other technologies. The cell read current, 2 mA at 1 volt, is an order of magnitude higher than that of an EPROM of comparable size. There is no data (charge) retention concern. The unique combination of small size and low resistance has enabled the development of the first family of desktop-configurable channeled gate arrays and a 64K PROM device.

ACKNOWLEDGEMENTS

The authors would like to express their appreciation to Prof. Chenming Hu of the University of California, Berkeley for valuable discussions, to F. Issaq, and M. Rafinejad for collecting the data, and to the technology staff of Data General for their excellent support in manufacturing the chips.

REFERENCES

1) K. El-Ayat, et al, "A CMOS ELECTRICALLY CONFIGURABLE GATE ARRAY", ISSCC Digest of Technical Papers, p.76-77; Feb. 1988.

2) A. El Gamal, et al, "AN ARCHITECTURE FOR ELECTRICALLY CONFIGURABLE GATE ARRAYS", Proceedings of the CICC, 15.4.1; May 1988.

3) THERMOPHYSICAL PROPERTIES OF MATTER, vol.1, Thermal Conductivity-- Metallic Elements and Alloys, ed. by Y. Touloukian, et al (IFT/Plenum, New York, 1970), p.326.

4) to be published

5) ACCELERATED TESTING HANDBOOK, Technology Associates ,D. S. Pech and O. D. Trapp , 1987, p. 5.36-37

TABLE 1
TECHNOLOGY OVERVIEW

PROCESS:TWIN TUB DOUBLE LAYER METAL
CMOS 15 MASKS

TRANSISTOR	OXIDE	LEFF	VOLT
N LOW VOLT	25 nm	1.1 um	5 V
P LOW VOLT	25 nm	1.2 um	5 V
N HIGH VOLT	40 nm	1.5 um	20 V
P HIGH VOLT	40 nm	1.8 um	20 V

ANTIFUSE CHRACTERISTICS:

PROGRAMMING VOLTAGE	18 V
PROGRAMMING TIME	< 1 mS
PROGRAMMING CURRENT	< 10 mA
ON RESISTANCE	< 1K OHMS
OFF RESISTANCE	> 100M OHMS

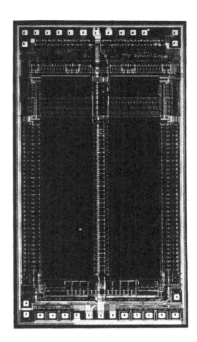

Fig.(3) Photomicrograph of 64K PROM .

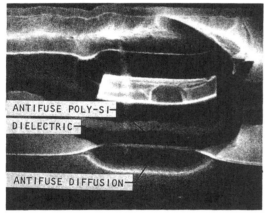

Fig.(1) SEM cross-section of antifuse.

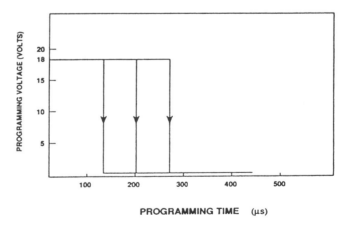

Fig.(2) Photomicrograph of 2000 gate
programmable gate array.

Fig.(4) Programming time of antifuse
with 18V programming voltage.

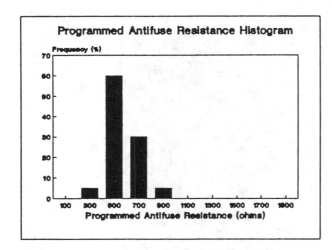

Fig.(5) Programmed antifuse resistance histogram, programmed with 5 mA current.

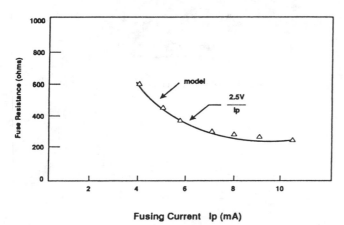

Fig.(6) Programmed antifuse resistance versus programming current.

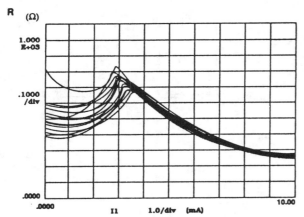

Fig.(7) Programmed antifuse resistance versus reading current, with 100 ohms of parasitic resistance in series.

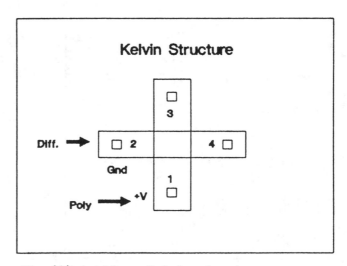

Fig.(8) Antifuse Kelvin structure.

ANTIFUSE ACCELERATED LIFETEST
250C 5mA TEST

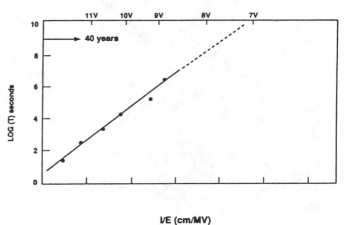

Fig.(9) Voltage across antifuse versus stress time, with 5 mA stress current.

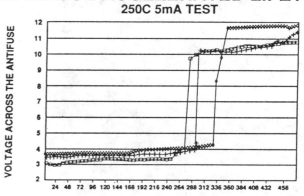

Fig.(10) Time to breakdown versus inverse electric field.

A 40 ns 64 kbit Junction-Shorting PROM

TOSHITAKA FUKUSHIMA, MEMBER, IEEE, KOUJI UENO, YASUROU MATSUZAKI, AND
KAZUO TANAKA

Abstract —A 64 kbit junction-shorting PROM with an access time of 40 ns was developed. The memory is organized as 8192 words×8 bits. A memory cell consists of a programmable element of a p-n junction diode and a vertically connected p-n-p transistor. During programming, the programmable element is changed from a current blocking state of a reverse diode to a current conducting state of a shorted junction diode by using the diffused eutectic aluminum process (DEAP). With a selective power switching dual stage decoder, the power dissipation in the decoder circuit was reduced to 40 percent of a conventional decoder without power switching. The power saved was used to speed up the multiplexers and the output buffers.

I. INTRODUCTION

SINCE the introduction of a 256 bit bipolar PROM in 1970 [1], modern systems have widely used field programmable ROM's. PROM's are commonly used to store microprograms. Fast PROM's with large memory capacities have become especially indispensable in control applications.

Higher languages require more complex sequences of data manipulation. The memory capacity of PROM's has increased by a factor of four every three years. A 64 kbit PROM was developed in 1982.

There are two types of PROM's. One is the fuse-blown PROM, which uses the opening of fuses by programming. The other is the junction-shorting PROM, which uses the shorting of p-n junction diodes by programming. In a fuse-blown PROM, the fuse is deposited horizontally on the Si surface by using materials as Al, NiCr [2]–[6], TiW [7], PtSi [8], or Poly-Si [9]–[12]. In a junction-shorting PROM, the p-n junction diode is a diffused p-n junction diode [13]–[14], fabricated by using the conventional Schottky TTL wafer fabrication process for the peripheral circuitry. Since junction shorting is performed within the Si bulk by using the stable Si-Al eutectic, and the resistivity of the eutectic is unified by the application of additional programming pulses, the junction-shorting PROM has proved to be highly reliable [15]. Furthermore, the vertical structure of the junction-shorting memory cell has been recognized to have the potential for a high packing density. This paper describes considerations in the design of the circuits and the characteristics which were obtained in a 64 kbit junction-shorting PROM.

Manuscript received December 13, 1982; revised April 4, 1983.
T. Fukushima, K. Ueno, and Y. Matsuzaki are with the Memory Division, Fujitsu Ltd., Nakahara-ku, Kawasaki, Japan 211.
K. Tanaka is with the Bipolar Memory Design Division, Fujitsu Ltd., Nakahara-ku, Kawasaki, Japan 211.

II. CIRCUIT DESIGN CONSIDERATION

A. General Description

The 64 kbit PROM consists of a memory cell array, X- and Y-address inverters, decoders, decoder-drivers, multiplexers, output buffers, a chip enable circuit, and a program circuit. The memory is internally organized as 256 words×256 bits. At the output terminals, the memory is observed as being organized as 8192 words×8 bits. The block diagram of the 64 kbit PROM is shown in Fig. 1.

By using the eight X-address inputs, one of the 256 word lines is decoded. With five Y-address inputs, each group of 32 of the 256 bit lines are multiplexed through the multiplexers, and eight out of the 256 bit lines are selected through the program circuit.

During the read operation, the contents of the eight selected memory cells are sensed in the multiplexers and output through the eight output buffers in parallel. During program operation, the eight selected memory cells are programmed serially by applying program current pulses to each of the eight output terminals.

The current, which flows from a selected bit line to a selected word line through a memory cell, changes two to three orders in magnitude corresponding to the read or the program operation. Therefore, to control this widely spread current without affecting the speed or the packing density, sophisticated circuit design technologies and complicated mask-layout techniques were required.

The following features were major considerations in the design: 1) in the read operation, almost all the power should be consumed in the read circuit; 2) in program operation, the power to drive the program circuit and to drain the high program current should be supplied from the chip enable terminal (PV_{CE}) and from the raised supply voltage (PV_{CC}); 3) the power consumption in the decoder circuit should be greatly reduced, and the power saved should be used for speeding up the multiplexers and the output buffers; 4) the Y-address inverters should be separated into two groups, one to drive the high speed multiplexers, and the other to drive the program circuit; and 5) vertical p-n-p transistors should be used as input transistors for the multiplexers and the program circuit for reducing the output load of the Y-address inverters.

To obtain a minimum delay time, the power dissipation in each block was optimized in accordance with transient simulations. Table I shows the component counts and the power dissipation in each block. The power was measured

Reprinted from *IEEE J. Solid-State Circuits*, vol. SC-19, no. 2, pp. 187–194, April 1984.

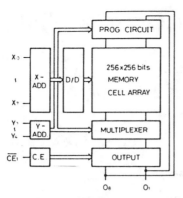

Fig. 1. Block diagram of a 64 kbit PROM with an 8192 word×8 bit organization.

TABLE I
CIRCUIT ELEMENT DISTRIBUTION AND
POWER DISSIPATION IN A 64K PROM

Circuit	Number of elements	Power dissipation (mW)	(%)
X-Add.	185	49.0	6.4
Y-Add.	178	40.5	5.3
D/D	3399	145.5	18.9
Cell matrix	134,680	0.0	0.0
Multiplexer	2098	467.5	60.9
Output	88	64.0	8.3
Prog.	2542	0.0	0.0
Chip enable	14	1.5	0.2
Total	143 184	768.0	100.0

during a read operation at a V_{CC} of 5 V. The device was programmed in a checkerboard pattern. In a high speed read operation, about 69 percent of the total power supply current of 154 mA was dissipated in the multiplexers and in the output buffers.

B. Memory Cell

A partial equivalent circuit of a memory cell array is shown in Fig. 2(a). The upper left and the lower right cells represent preprogrammed states. The upper right and the lower left cells represent postprogrammed states. A memory cell consists of a programmable element of a p-n junction diode and a vertically connected p-n-p transistor. The p-n-p transistor is used to reduce the output load of the decoder-driver and block the reverse current flow toward the programmable element [16]. As shown in Fig. 2(b), the p-n junction diode uses the n^+ and p^+ diffusion layers of an ordinary n-p-n transistor. The p-n-p transistor uses the p^+ diffusion layer, which is common to that of the p-n junction diode, the n epitaxial layer, and the p^- substrate. The aluminum electrode to the cathode of p-n junction diode is a bit line. The common base of the p-n-p transistors acts as a word line.

In programming, the selected word line is pulled down to sink the program current. Reverse current pulses of 125 mA and 11 μs are applied to the selected memory cell

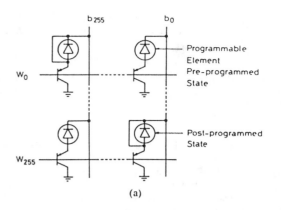

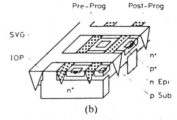

Fig. 2. Partial equivalent circuit and cross section of memory cell array. (a) Combinations of programmable element (p-n diode) and p-n-p transistor. (b) Cross section.

through the single bit line. This increases the temperature at the junction and induces the shorting of the junction using the diffused Al-Si eutectic. This program procedure was thus named "diffused eutectic aluminum process" (DEAP).

In Fig. 3, surface views of preprogrammed and postprogrammed cells are compared. The cells at the right were programmed. Fig. 3(a) shows the surface views of the first aluminum layer, where no deformation is observed between the pre- and the postprogrammed cells. Fig. 3(b) shows the views of the Si surface after the removal of the first aluminum and the doped polysilicon layers. At the edge of the window of the postprogrammed cell, the diffused Al-Si eutectic is observed.

The current blocking state of the reverse diode represents a logical "0." The current conducting state of the shorted junction represents a logical "1." In a read operation, a read current of about 0.5 mA is applied to each of the eight selected memory cells through the eight bit lines. Voltage drops on the bit lines are detected by the eight multiplexers and are output through the eight output buffers.

C. Word Select

Fig. 4(a) shows a schematic diagram of the X-address inverters. To increase the input impedance and to protect against the static charge, p-n-p transistor T_1 is used in the address input. The true and complement address signals, which are fed to the first stage decoders, were shifted upward by D_3 to constrain the voltage swing of the node and to minimize the fall and rise delays. The address signals, which are fed to the second stage decoders, have an ordinary voltage swing of a totem pole output.

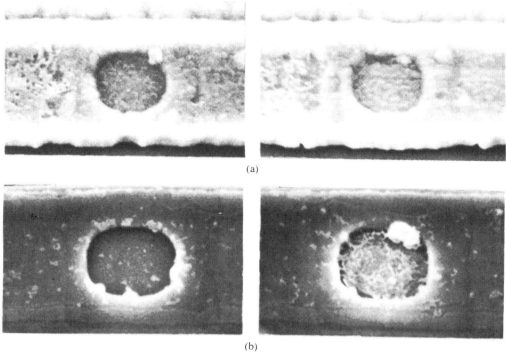

Fig. 3. SEM photomicrograph of memory cells. (a) Surface view of first aluminum layer. (b) Surface view of Si bulk after removal of first aluminum and polysilicon layers. The cells at the right were programmed.

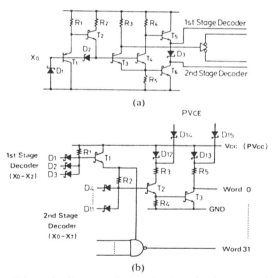

Fig. 4. Schematic diagram of a word select circuit. (a) *X*-address inverter. (b) Selective power-switching dual-stage decoder and driver.

High drive capability, low power dissipation, and high speed access were major considerations for the decoder and decoder-driver circuit. The decoder must supply a sufficient base drive current to the driver to sink the program current in program operation. However, if the base drive current is too large, the excess charge would be stored in the base of the driver, substantially increasing the turn-off time in the read operation.

In conventional decoders, each decoder is supplied power directly from V_{CC}. Therefore, as the number of decoders increases, larger power is dissipated. On the other hand, in a power switching decoder, which uses a lateral p-n-p transistor as a first stage transistor, a sufficiently low power dissipation has been achieved although the access time was sacrificed by the low switching speed of the p-n-p transistor.

By the tradeoff between drive capability, power dissipation, and access time, the selective power switching dual stage decoder shown in Fig. 4(b) was developed.

The decoder and the driver circuit functions as a NAND gate. The first-stage decoder consists of transistor T_1, Schottky diodes D_1, D_2, and D_3, and resistor R_1. The second-stage decoder consists of Schottky diodes D_4 through D_{11} and resistor R_2. The driver consists of transistors T_2 and T_3, Schottky diodes D_{12} through D_{15}, and resistors R_3, R_4, and R_5. Each of the eight first-stage decoders is driven by three out of eight *X*-address inverters for selective power switching. Each group of 32 out of the 256 second-stage decoders are powered through the selected one of the eight first stage decoders. The 256 second-stage decoders are driven by the eight *X*-address inverters. X_0 to X_2 to the first-stage decoder have a higher voltage swing than X_0 to X_7 to the second-stage decoder. As a result, the access time delay induced by the previous power switching dual stage decoder was suppressed. And, the power consumption in the decoder circuit was greatly reduced. In a read operation, a selected word line is pulled down to logical "0" to sink the approximately 0.5 to 4.0 mA read current depending on the number of programmed cells. The remaining 255 word lines are pulled up to V_{CC} through

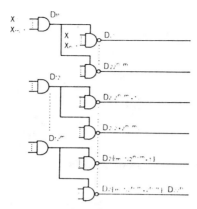

Fig. 5. Generalized logic diagram of the selective power swithing dual-stage decoders.

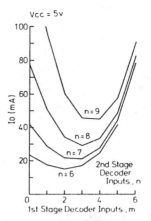

Fig. 6. Relationship between the calculated supply current I_D in a decoder circuit and the number of first-stage decoder inputs m.

TABLE II
COMPARISON OF POWER SUPPLY CURRENT BETWEEN CONVENTIONAL NO POWER-SWITCHED AND SELECTIVE POWER-SWITCHED DECODERS

Supply voltage (V)	4.5	5.0	5.5
Conventional (mA)	69.1	77.5	83.4
Selective power-switched (mA)	26.2	29.1	32.3
Difference (mA) (%)	−42.9 (62.1)	−48.4 (62.5)	−51.1 (61.3)

D_{13} and R_5. To control the base drive current to T_3 accurately, and to suppress the excess charge in the base region, the current was designed to be fed from V_{CC}. In program operation, the selected word line is pulled down to sink the program current, while the remaining 255 word lines are pulled up to PV_{CC} through D_{15}. The sufficient base drive current to T_3 is fed from the raised V_{CC} (PV_{CC}) and PV_{CE}. PV_{CC} increases also the current drain capability of the decoder circuit. This type of base current control circuit resulted in the high speed turn-off of the driver output.

The number of first-stage and second-stage decoder inputs were determined according to the following calculations. (See Fig. 5.) Suppose that each of the 2^m (or M) first-stage decoders is driven by m out of the total n X-address inverters to supply power to 2^{n-m} out of the 2^n (or N) second-stage decoders. Also suppose that each of the 2^n (or N) second stage decoders is driven by the n X-address inverters. The supply current I_D in the decoder circuit can then be expressed as

$$I_D = I_1 + (2^m - 1)I_2 + I_3 + (2^{n-m} - 1)I_4 - (2^{n-m} - 2^n)I_5$$
$$= I_1 + (M - 1)I_2 + I_3 + (N/M - 1)I_4 - (N/M - N)I_5$$

where I_1 is the current flowing through the selected first-stage decoder to the X-address inverters, I_2 the current flowing through the unselected first-stage decoders to the X-address inverters, I_3 the current flowing through the selected first-stage decoder to the selected second-stage decoder, I_4 the current flowing through the selected first-stage decoder to the unselected second-stage decoders, and I_5 the current flowing through the unselected first-stage decoders to the unselected second-stage decoders. The minimum power supply current I_D is calculated at $dI_D/dM = 0$.

Thus, M and m are determined as

$$M = ((I_4 - I_5)N/I_2)^{1/2} \text{ and}$$
$$m = 1/2(n + \log_2(I_4 - I_5)/I_2),$$

respectively.

Fig. 6 shows the relationship between the calculated supply current I_D and the number of the first-stage decoder inputs m. The internal memory organization of 256 words × 256 bits was determined by the chip layout. As a result, the number of X-address inputs n was determined to be 8. According to the equation above, the number of X-address signals m to the first-stage decoder was determined to be 3.

In Table II, the power consumption at the decoder and driver circuit is compared with that of the conventional decoder and driver circuit, which has no power switching function. About 60 percent of the power supply current was saved by the development of the selective power switching dual-stage decoders. The power saved was used to speed up the multiplexers and the output buffers.

D. Bit Select

Fig. 7(a) shows a schematic diagram of the Y-address inverters. The vertical p-n-p transistor T_1 is also used in the Y-address input to increase the input impedance and to protect against the static charge. The Y-address inverters are separated into two groups to increase the switching speed in a read operation. The first two inverters are used to drive the high speed multiplexers, and the second two inverters are used to drive the program circuit.

In Fig. 7(b), a schematic diagram of a multiplexer and a output buffer is shown. The multiplexer constructs a six-input AND gate to drive the input signal to the output buffer. The multiplexer is composed of transistors T_1 through T_6, diode D_1, and resistors R_1 and R_2, and has a conventional

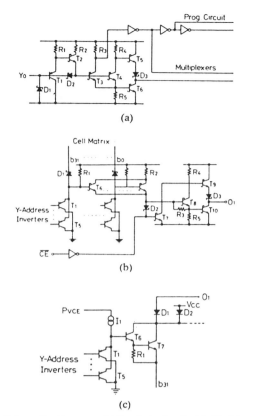

Fig. 7. Schematic diagram of bit select circuit. (a) *Y*-address inverter. (b) Multiplexer and output buffer. (c) Program circuit.

structure to obtain a large amplitude swing at the output. To reduce the output capacitive load of *Y*-address, vertical p-n-p transistors T_1 through T_5 are used in the multiplexer input. Five out of the six inputs receive the *Y*-address signals, and the one remaining input detects the potential difference of one of the 32 bit lines. The presence of the read current, which is drained only through the postprogrammed cell into the selected word line, is sensed as the voltage drop in the multiplexer and results in a logical "1" at the output of the output buffer.

An output circuit is composed of transistors T_8, T_9, and T_{10}, diode D_3, resistors R_3, R_4, and R_5. The three-state function is provided using transistor T_7 and diode D_2 [17].

Fig. 7(c) shows a schematic diagram of the program circuit. The program pulse applied at a output terminal is fed to the one of the 32 bit lines through the program circuit. The critical amplitude 125 mA and the width 11 μs of the program pulse was definitely determined by the size of the memory cell, (the area and the depth of the junction). Therefore, to prevent the current reduction of the program pulses in the program circuit, the base current of 300 μA to the Darlington connection transistors T_6 and T_7 with resistor R_1 shunt is sourced by an independent constant current source I_1, which is supplied power by PV_{CE} [18]. Since the application of PV_{CE} is stopped in the read operation, the Darlington connection transistors turn off, and a high breakdown voltage above 20 V is obtained at the output terminal. This implies the possibility of board programming.

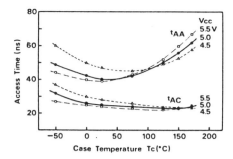

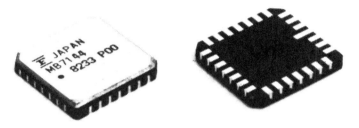

Fig. 8. Temperature dependences of address access time t_{AA} and chip enable access time t_{AC}. Programmed in checkerboard pattern and addressed in galloping pattern.

Fig. 9. Top and bottom views of a 28 pin LCC package.

III. DEVICE CHARACTERISTICS

The device characteristics will be described by the access time temperature dependency, the Schmoo plot measurement, and the speed–power products.

Fig. 8 shows the address access time (t_{AA}), which means that *CE* was previously selected before the address signal transitions, and the chip enable access time (t_{AC}), which means that the address signals were previously defined before the *CE* transitions. The device was measured under the following conditions: 1) the device was housed in a 28 pin LCC package as shown in Fig. 9; 2) the output terminals had a 300 Ω load connected to V_{CC} and a 600 Ω and 30 pF load connected to GND; 3) the memory cells were programmed in a checkerboard pattern; and 4) a galloping pattern was used as an input signal pattern. Fig. 8 shows that the circuit is operable over the full temperature range from -55 to $+175°$C. The typical address and the typical chip enable access times are 40 and 25 ns, respectively. The maximum address and chip enable access times are 45 and 30 ns at a V_{CC} range of 4.75 to 5.25 V and a T_C range of 0 to 75°C. These ac characteristics can be fully guaranteed by using the built-in test circuitry before being programmed [19], [20].

Fig. 10 shows the Schmoo plots of the address access time t_{AA} as a function of the supply voltage V_{CC} at a case temperature of 25°C. It is obvious that the access time exhibits only a small variation with the supply voltage.

The improvement of the speed–power products is shown clearly in Fig. 11, which illustrates the relationships between the address access time and the memory capacity, and the relationships between the power supply current/bit and the memory capacity. By using the saved power by

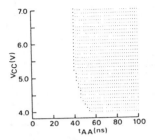

Fig. 10. Schmoo plot figure of supply voltage V_{CC} and address access time t_{AA}. Programmed in checkerboard pattern and addressed in galloping pattern.

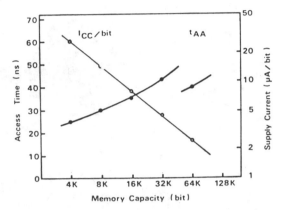

Fig. 11. Memory capacity dependences of address access time t_{AA} and supply current consumption I_{CC}/bit.

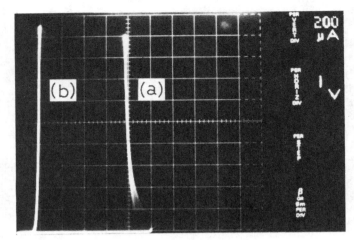

Fig. 12. $I-V$ characteristics of memory cell. (a) Preprogrammed cell. (b) Postprogrammed cell.

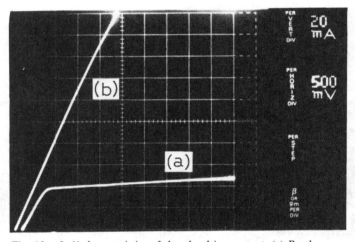

Fig. 13. $I-V$ characteristics of decoder-driver output. (a) Read operation. (b) Program operation.

selective power switching dual-stage decoders to speed up the multiplexers and output buffers, the switching speed could be increased, while the power consumption/bit could be decreased.

The program characteristics will be described by the resistivity transition of the memory cell, the current drive capability of the decoder-driver output, and the waveforms of program pulses.

Fig. 12 shows the $I-V$ characteristics of memory cell, where (a) and (b) indicate the preprogrammed and the postprogrammed states, respectively. By programming, the voltage drop from 5–6 V in the preprogrammed cell is reduced to the forward voltage, 0.8 V, of the p-n-p transistor.

Fig. 13 shows the $I-V$ characteristics of the effective gains of the decoder-driver output. Fig. 13(a) and (b) indicates the gains in the read operation and in the program operation, respectively. The figure shows that the current drive capability in program operation is greatly increased to drive the high program current, while the current drive capability in a read operation is kept low for the high speed turn-off.

One or more program pulses and an additional two successive pulses are required as a full cycle to program a memory cell. The program operation waveforms detected by a digital memory scope, with a minimum resolution of 156 mV, 1.56 mA, and 500 ns are shown in Fig. 14. The address signals which are not displayed in the figure have TTL voltage swings. The top two traces, (a) and (b), show

the waveform of PV_{CC} supplied through V_{CC}, and the waveform of PV_{CE} applied to the $\overline{CE}$ input terminal, respectively. The program current (c) applied at the output terminal was measured using a current probe with a 100 mA/div. vertical scale. Fig. 14(d) shows a trace of the voltage drop at the output terminal. The degradation of the voltage drop within the first pulse width indicates the transition from the preprogrammed state to the postprogrammed state. To obtain a sufficiently stable low resistance in a postprogrammed cell, two additional pulses are required.

Fig. 15 shows a photomicrograph of the chip surface, which contains about 143 200 elements. The die size is 7.14×5.28 mm^2.

IV. Conclusion

By the adoption of the selective power switching dual-stage decoder, the power dissipation in the decoder circuit was reduced to 40 percent of the conventional unit with no power switching decoder. The power saved was used to

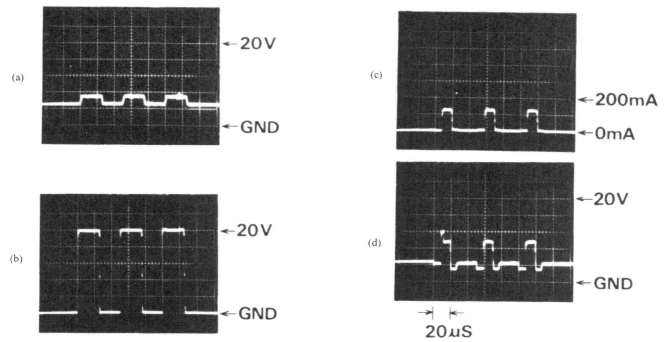

Fig. 14. Waveforms in program operation detected by digital memory scope. Horizontal scale 20 μs/div. (a) PV_{CC} at V_{CC} terminal. Vertical scale 4 V/div. (b) PV_{CE} at $\overline{CE}$ terminal. Vertical scale 4 V/div. (c) Program current at output terminal. Vertical scale 100 mA/div. (d) Voltage drop at output terminal. Vertical scale 4/div.

speed up the multiplexers and the output buffers. The multiplexers and the output buffers consumed about 69 percent of the total power consumption of typical 768 mW.

The typical address access time is 40 ns and is relatively insensitive to variations in either the temperature or the supply voltage.

With the extensive use of these circuit technologies and of advanced wafer fabrication technologies, such as SVG isolation, walled-emitter, and wafer stepper, a high speed 128 kbit PROM may be possible.

ACKNOWLEDGMENT

The authors wish to express their appreciation to J. Mogi, S. Asuma, and Y. Namiki for their encouragement, and to T. Ono for his assistance in this project.

REFERENCES

[1] T. Fukushima, "The bipolar PROM: An overview and history," in *WESCON Conf. Rec.*, 1979, vol. 7/1, pp. 1–5.
[2] P. Franklin and D. Burgess, "Reliability aspects of nichrome fusible link PROM's (programmable read-only memories)," in *Proc. IEEE 12th Annu. Rel. Phys. Symp.*, 1974, pp. 82–86.
[3] J. L. Davidson, J. D. Gibson, S. A. Harris, and T. J. Rossiter, "Fusing mechanism of nichrome thin films," in *Proc. IEEE 14th Annu. Rel. Phys. Symp.*, 1976, pp. 173–181.
[4] P. Franklin, "A reliability assessment of bipolar PROM's," in *Proc. IEEE 14th Annu. Rel. Phys. Symp.*, 1976, pp. 207–218.
[5] R. L. Cline, "Design limitation in bipolar PROM 16K and larger," in *WESCON Conf. Record*, 1978, vol. 9/2, pp. 1–7.
[6] R. M. Fisher, "A 64K bipolar PROM," in *ISSCC Tech. Dig. Papers*, 1982, pp. 114–115.
[7] P. Franklin, "A new generation of bipolar PROM's," in *WESCON Conf. Rec.*, 1978, vol. 9/3, pp. 1–4.
[8] J. Tsantes, "Programmable-memory choices expand design options," *EDN*, vol. 25, no. 1, pp. 81–98, Jan. 5, 1980.

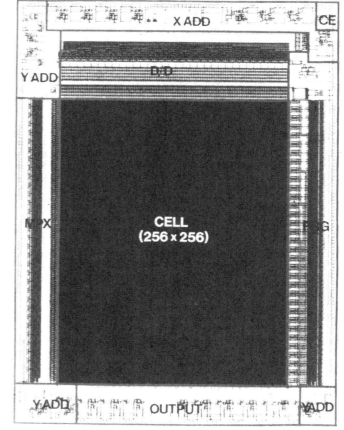

Fig. 15. Photomicrograph of the surface of a 64 kbit PROM chip.

IEEE JOURNAL OF SOLID-STATE CIRCUITS, VOL. SC-19, NO. 2, APRIL 1984

[9] G. H. Parker, J. C. Cornet, and W. S. Pinter, "Reliability considerations in the design and fabrication of polysilicon fusable link PROM's," in *Proc. IEEE 12th Annu. Rel. Phys. Symp.*, 1974, pp. 88–90.

[10] R. C. Smith, S. J. Rosenberg, and C. R. Barrett, "Reliability studies of polysilicon fusible link," in *Proc. IEEE 14th Annu. Rel. Phys. Symp.*, 1976, pp. 193–197.

[11] R. K. Wallace, A. J. Learn, and K. W. Schuette, "A 35 ns 16K PROM," in *ISSCC Tech. Dig. Papers*, 1980, pp. 148–149.

[12] R. K. Wallace and A. J. Learn, "Simple process propels bipolar PROM to 16K density and beyond," *Electronics*, vol. 53, no. 7, pp. 147–150, Mar. 1980.

[13] W. R. Brockhoff, "Electrically shorted semiconductor junctions utilized as programmable read-only memory elements," in *Proc. IEEE 14th Annu. Rel. Phys. Symp.*, 1976, pp. 202–206.

[14] T. Fukushima, K. Ueno, and K. Tanaka, "A high speed Schottky 4 kbit PROM using a diffused eutectic aluminum process (DEAP),"

in *Proc. Int. Conf. Solid-State Devices*, 1979; also in *Japan J. Appl. Phys.*, vol. 19, suppl. 19-1, pp. 175–180, 1980.

[15] T. M. Donnlly, "Reliability evaluation of programmable read-only memories (PROM)," Tech Rep. RADC-TR-75-278, Feb. 1976.

[16] T. Fukushima, "Semiconductor memory devices," U.S. Patent 4287569, Sept. 1978.

[17] T. Fukushima and K. Ueno, "Three-state output circuit," U.S. Patent 4322648, Nov. 1978.

[18] T. Fukushima, K. Koyama, K. Ueno, T. Miyamura, and U. Kawabata, "Programming circuit for permanently storing data in a programmable read only memory," U.S. Patent 4319341, Apr. 1979.

[19] T. Fukushima, "A method of testing a semiconductor device," Japan Patent 1033390, Dec. 1974.

[20] T. Fukushima, K. Koyama, and K. Ueno, "Field programmable device having test provisions for fault detection," U.S. Patent 4320507, Nov. 1978.

Part 3
UV Erasable and One-Time-Programmable EPROM Technologies

UVEPROM is a remarkable device. It is nonvolatile, yet requires only a single transistor in each memory cell. DRAM is well known for its amazingly fast increase in density and delightfully or disgustingly low price, depending on one's perspective. EPROM density has increased at the same or slightly faster rate than DRAM and has recently beaten DRAM in price. EPROM has a smaller cell size and a smaller chip size than DRAM, which requires one transistor and one capacitor per cell. (One might say that EPROM is a three-dimensionally integrated device with the storage capacitor placed over the transistor area.) The edge that EPROM enjoys over DRAM is likely to grow in the future because it is not limited by the alpha-particle soft-error problem and can continue to scale without resorting to trench capacitors or other dramatically new technologies.

Paper 3.1 gives an introduction for the novice. Paper 3.2 describes the first EPROM—a 2-kb memory. It is reprinted here mainly for its historic significance—the beginning of two decades' dominance in nonvolatile memory with no end in sight yet. This first EPROM was quite different from the EPROMs of today. First, it was a p-channel device (n-channel technology had not yet been developed). Each cell had a select transistor and a floating-gate transistor, which had a floating gate but not a control gate. Programming was achieved not by hot-hole injection, as one might expect for a p-channel floating-gate EPROM, but by hot-electron injection, because the hot-hole temperature is only half that of the hot electrons, and the oxide barrier for holes is larger than for electrons. The electrons are created by avalanche impact ionization. Hence, the term avalanche-injection, (i.e., the "A" in FAMOS) was appropriate for the p-channel EPROMs. Today's n-channel EPROM relies on channel hot-electron injection, not avalanche-electron injection, for programming.

Paper 3.3 provides a brief look at EPROMs circa 1980. The next three papers present the physical models of the floating-gate transistor—its I-V characteristics (Paper 3.4), programming (Paper 3.5), and UV light ERASE (Paper 3.6). Paper 3.5 models hot-electron programming with 2-D numerical simulation, while an analytical model was presented in the article by Tam *et al.* [1]. Reference [2] is an excellent experimental study of the hot-electron injection current for a range of device dimensions and bias voltages.

Paper 3.7 was chosen to illustrate the advanced technologies that may be applied to achieve small cell size (3.85 μm^2) and dense memories. They include fine-line lithography (0.6 μm), thin oxide–nitride–oxide stack between the floating gate and control gate to reduce charge leakage, and optimized boron–arsenic doping profile at the drain and to improve punchthrough and programming. It also describes the more novel self-aligned source, contact plug, and polysilicon-shield isolation (for peripheral high-voltage circuits) technologies.

Paper 3.8 presents a potentially important technique to reduce the EPROM cell size. The technique is to eliminate the metal contact in the cell (see Fig. 1 in Paper 3.3). This and other so-called virtual ground array architectures can produce the smallest possible cells measuring minimum linewidth plus space in both directions, or 4 μm^2 using 0.8-μm rule [3]. The EPROM array resulting from this approach is known as a contactless array or a virtual ground array. Asymmetrical source/drain structure can improve READ and PROGRAM disturb robustness [4]. Paper 3.9 reports a three-transistor cell used to achieve a large cell READ current needed for fast access time. It may also be used in programmable logic devices, where high speed is very important.

Reference [5] reports the smallest EPROM cell to date—3.6 μm^2, accomplished through the use of 0.6-μm and trench-isolation technologies. An 85-ns 16-Mb EPROM using this cell has been reported (Paper 8.3). Paper 3.10 reports the smallest cell, 4 μm^2, using the classical EPROM layout. It also reports 5V programming in the very small (0.6 μm technology) EPROMs. Five-volt programming, without requiring an additional high voltage, e.g., 12V, power supply, can be very attractive for flash EPROMs, which, like EEPROMs, may be programmed after installation into circuit boards. In spite of [6], which demonstrated the feasibility of 5V programming in laboratory devices in 1983, there have been no 5V programming EPROM products yet, due to the difficulty of accommodating the worst-case channel length, worst-case temperature, etc. It is all but certain that 5V programming will be a reality in the near future. Paper 3.11 reports a different approach to achieve 5V programming called source-side injection. It provides plenty of margin for channel length and temperature variations, and robustness against READ disturb and very fast programming. Incidentally, fast programming speed will be an important goal of future high-density EPROM technologies, for the purpose of reducing testing and programming time and cost. The source-side-injection concept has been extended to a flash EEPROM cell in Paper 5.4.

Paper 3.12 (as well as Paper 8.4) describes a variation of EPROM of growing importance—one-time-programmable EPROM (OTP). OTPs are EPROMs packaged in opaque plastic packages rather than ceramic packages with transparent quartz windows. This significantly reduces the product cost and package size. For many applications, the users are willing to give up the reprogrammability (of EPROM) for the lower cost and high package density of OTP, which is a PROM. The technology challenge is to find a suitable passivation material, which is the central topic of Paper 3.12. Finally, Paper 3.13 describes the single-poly EPROM technology, which is a variation of EPROM technology popular for ASIC (application-specific ICs) or controller circuits containing "small" EPROM arrays.

Parts 6, 8, and 9 contain additional information on EPROMs. New developments in EPROM technologies and cell concepts are almost always published in the annual *Technical Digest of the International Electron Devices Meeting* (IEDM). There is usually a nonvolatile memories section in the *Digest*.

REFERENCES

[1] S. Tam, P. K. Ko, and C. Hu, "Lucky-electron model of channel hot electron injection in MOSFET's," *IEEE Trans. Electron Devices*, vol. ED-31, pp. 1116–1125, Sept. 1984.

[2] B. Eitan and D. Frohman-Bentchkowsky, "Hot-electron injection into the oxide in n-channel MOS devices," *IEEE Trans. Electron Devices*, vol. ED-28, pp. 328–340, Mar. 1981.

[3] O. Bellezza, D. Laurenzi, and M. Melanotte, "A new self-aligned field oxide cell for multimegabit EPROMs," in *Tech. Dig. Internat. Electron Devices Meet.*, 1989, pp. 579–582.

[4] K. Yoshikawa, S. Mori, K. Narita, N. Arai, Y. Ohshima, Y. Kaneko, and H. Araki, "An asymmetrical lightly doped source cell for virtual ground high density EPROM's," in *Tech. Dig. Internat. Electron Devices Meet.*, 1988, pp. 432–435.

[5] Y. S. Hisamune *et al.*, "A 3.6 μm^2 memory cell structure for 16Mb EPROMs," in *Tech. Dig. Internat. Electron Devices Meet.*, 1989, pp. 583–586.

[6] S. Ohya, M. Kikuchi, and Y. Narita, "Single 5V EPROM with sub-micron memory transistor on on-chip high voltage generator," in *Tech. Dig. Internat. Electron Devices Meet.*, 1983, pp. 570–573.

An E-PROM's integrity starts with its cell structure

A practical understanding of avalanche injection, floating gates, and UV erasure has led to predictable device behavior

by Murray H. Woods, *Intel Corp., Santa Clara, Calif.*

☐ The ultraviolet-light–erasable programmable read-only memory has matured, and its processing become rather routine. This situation was long in arriving. For years, in fact, the right sequence of fabrication steps was elusive because of the E-PROM's many potential failure modes. Owing to the unique structure of the E-PROM, these afflictions can strike during programming, erasing, or reading.

The E-PROM transistor resembles an ordinary MOS transistor, except for the addition of a floating gate, buried in the insulator between the substrate and the ordinary select-gate electrode (Fig. 1). As a result, in an E-PROM, the select-gate voltage must be capacitively coupled in series with the floating gate rather than directly to the underlying channel. Charge stored on the floating gate alters the threshold voltage of the device as seen by the top or select gate.

Figure 1 also shows why very high densities can be achieved with E-PROM cells: the floating storage gate and the select gate are both directly above the transistor's channel. Even higher densities are obtained by self-aligning these two gates and the source and drain regions. This vertical stacking allows the functions of storage and reading—which normally require separate devices—to reside within the space a single field-effect transistor occupies.

The cell is programmed by charging the floating gate via the injection of so-called hot electrons from the drain's pinch-off region (Fig. 2a). It is erased through internal photoemission from the floating gate to the top gate and substrate. The ultraviolet light gives electrons on the floating gate enough energy to surmount the energy barrier between the floating gate and the insulator surrounding it (Fig. 2b).

The charge on the memory cell's floating storage gate changes the threshold voltage of the select gate by an amount $\Delta V_t = -\Delta Q_{FG}/C$, where C is the capacitance between the floating gate and the select gate and ΔQ_{FG} is the change in charge on the floating gate. The drain current versus select-gate voltage transfer characteristics for the programmed and erased states are parallel to each other (Fig. 3). The select-gate voltage during reading lies between these two curves and results in a drain current that reflects the cell's state, the nonconducting programmed state (storing a 0), or the conducting erased state (storing a 1). When the E-PROM cell is pro-

grammed, the negative charge on the floating gate causes the floating-gate-to-source voltage to be negative. This turns the cell off, even with a positive reading voltage applied to the select gate.

Since the floating gate is not tied to a power supply, its voltage is determined by its charge and by capacitive coupling to the voltages of the select gate, the drain, the channel, and the source. The difference between the floating-gate voltage and the voltages of these other cell areas can be used to determine the electric fields in the various oxide regions of the device.

Although the voltage applied to the chip during programming is high—25 volts—the fields across the gate oxide directly above the channel are relatively small, about 2 megavolts per centimeter at the onset of programming and less than 1.5 MV/cm afterward. During all other operations, even when the floating gate is fully charged, this field is ≤ 0.7 MV/cm. This is a typical operating field for a high-performance MOS device.

Programming

The hot electrons get their energy from the voltage applied to the drain of the E-PROM cell. They are accelerated along the channel into the even higher fields surrounding the drain depletion region. While traversing the channel, the electrons enter a region where the electric field in the substrate is about 10^5 V/cm or greater. At this point the rate of energy gained from the electric field can no longer be described by the temperature of the silicon; hence the term "hot." Once these electrons gain sufficient energy they can surmount the energy barrier of about 3.2 electronvolts between the silicon substrate and the silicon dioxide insulator. Because energy loss due to phonon emission increases at higher lattice temperatures, it is actually easier to obtain hot electrons at lower operating temperatures.

In addition to phonon emisson, hot electrons with energies above about 1.8 eV may give up some of this energy in another way: through electron-hole pair creation resulting from impact ionization. This phenomenon is observed in ordinary MOS transistors as the cause of the onset of substrate current at high drain voltages. However, in the case of the E-PROM, significant current multiplication produces substantial substrate current even before a large enough drain voltage is reached to produce hot-electron injection into the oxide.

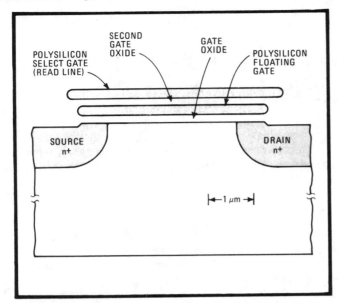

1. Vertical. In the erasable programmable read-only memory, a floating storage gate and a select gate are directly above a MOS FET's channel. The floating gate assumes the select-gate potential during writing. The 1-micrometer scale applies to the 2716.

With positive drain and channel voltages, electrons injected into the oxide of an n-channel E-PROM return to the substrate unless a high positive select-gate voltage is applied to pull the electrons toward the floating gate. Not only does the floating gate have to be positively biased with respect to the source, it must also be positive with respect to the point along the channel where hot-electron injection occurs.

Near the beginning of the injection process, the inversion layer extends almost all the way to the drain, and the field in the oxide is attractive except for a small portion very near the drain (see Fig. 4). Current begins to flow through the oxide at the point where the electrons are their hottest and where the oxide field is most favorable. As the floating gate charges up, the floating-gate-to-source voltage drops and the drain's pinch-off region moves towards the source. The surface field near the drain intensifies and more hot electrons are produced in the substrate.

However, as seen in Fig. 4, in the region where the electrons are their hottest, the oxide field is least favorable for injection and so the injected-electron current begins to subside. Thus, fortunately, the electron injection process is self-limiting. The charging of the floating gate reduces the number of electrons that can be accelerated in the high-field region. As the floating gate becomes fully charged, the oxide current is reduced almost to zero because the oxide field is now repulsive to the electrons injected into the high-field region.

Since the reducing electric field between the floating gate and channel is responsible for shutting off the oxide current, the saturated threshold-voltage shift of the floating gate tracks the select-gate voltage during programming on a volt-per-volt basis. The floating gate charges to the same value relative to the source and the channel. An increase in the select-gate voltage during programming merely increases the charge on the floating gate necessary to abort the injection of hot electrons. The drain voltage does not in general have a major effect on the final programmmed voltage of the floating gate. However, it does affect the speed at which the device is programmed, since injection exhibits an exponential dependence on the electric field in the channel.

The reliability of programming

The high-voltage E-PROM programming process is not without its reliability problems. A major concern is electron trapping in the oxide after several programming cycles. Trapped electrons decrease the rate of programming because the electrons that flow through the oxide now encounter locally repulsive fields.

Owing to their small optical cross section, electrons can easily remain trapped in the oxide even after UV erasure of the floating gate. Therefore, as a result of the field around them, trapped electrons also locally raise the threshold voltage of the channel. Indeed, the erased threshold voltage can, through trapping, rise to a point where cell states are sensed incorrectly. This condition is avoided by proper growth of the first gate oxide to reduce the density of electron traps.

Another programming problem may arise when the select-gate voltage is raised high for a device in a row that contains another device that has already been programmed. This produces the highest field in the upper, or second, gate oxide during any time of operation. The average electric field in the second oxide is only about 1 MV/cm, but pointed asperities on the first polysilicon layer can substantially increase the local electric field to the point where partial erasure of the floating gate occurs. This field emission effect can be eliminated by the right combination of process steps, including the temperature used to form the gate structure.

Another case of erasure through field emission may

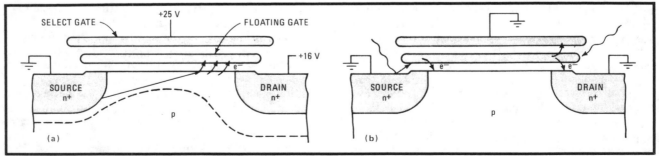

2. To and fro. During programming of the E-PROM cell, electrons are injected onto a floating polysilicon gate (a). During erasure the same electrons receive enough energy from ultraviolet radiation to enter the surrounding silicon dioxide layer (b).

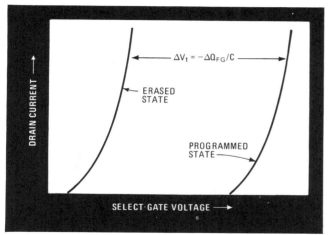

3. Sensible. An E-PROM cell's threshold voltage determines whether it is sensed as a logic 0 (the nonconducting programmed state) or 1 (erased). The change in threshold corresponds to the shift shown in the select-gate voltage to drain current transfer characteristic. This shift depends on the difference in charge on the floating gate in the two states (ΔQ_{FG}), as well as the intergate capacitance (C).

occur when a column is raised high to program a device in another row. The drains of the unselected programmed cells in that column will rise in voltage to create a field of approximately 2.5 MV/cm in the first gate oxide, that between the drain and the floating gate. Fortunately, the bottom of the polysilicon floating gate has a smooth surface so tunneling (Fowler-Nordheim emission) of electrons from the floating gate to the substrate is negligible.

Erase conditions

Complete erasure of an E-PROM is required before the device can be reprogrammed. This is accomplished by exposing the entire array to UV light. Typical sources for erasure are quartz-jacketed mercury arc lamps and mercury vapor lamps, which emit strong radiation with a wavelength of 2,537 angstroms (4.9 eV).

The photons are absorbed by electrons in the conduction and valence bands of the polysilicon floating gate; at this wavelength, most are absorbed within 50 Å of the oxide interface. The excited electrons leave the polysilicon floating gate, enter the oxide, and are swept away to the select gate or substrate by the local field. During erasure, the select gate, source, drain, and substrate are all near ground potential.

With an n-type polysilicon floating gate, electrons can be excited from either the conduction band or the valence band into the oxide. Excitation from the conduction band requires only 3.2 eV, while the barrier height from the valence band is 4.3 eV. Even for heavily doped n-type material there are many more electrons available from the valence band of the polysilicon floating gate than from the conduction band.

The quantum yield and the erasure rate per incident photon follows the square-law dependence upon photon energy shown in Fig. 5. Two distinct threshold energies are apparent. The first, at 3.2 eV, is associated with the photo-excitation of electrons from the conduction band. Its slope is much shallower because of the lower density of electrons. The 4.3-eV threshold corresponds to the

onset of photoemission from the valence band. The much steeper slope is indicative of the much higher density of valence-band electrons.

Unlike earlier p-type floating-gate E-PROMs, the fact that there is a significant density of electrons on the floating gate introduces the potential reliability problem of spurious erasure. Even with atmospheric filtering, sunlight photons having energies as high as 4.1 eV can reach the earth's surface. Also, fluorescent and incandescent lamps emit a minimum wavelength of about 3,000 Å, which corresponds to 4.1 eV. Erasure rates in sunlight or normal room light are much slower—1,000 times or more—than erasure under intense UV exposure because of the lower intensity of illumination and low density of electrons in the conduction band of the floating gate. However, care must still be taken so that programmed E-PROMs are not subjected to prolonged exposure from either sunlight or ordinary room lighting.

Ultraviolet rays are so strongly absorbed that they do not get past the top select gate and the photons can only make their way to the floating gate from the side. In modern self-aligned structures, the edge of the floating gate is directly exposed to the radiation. But in earlier

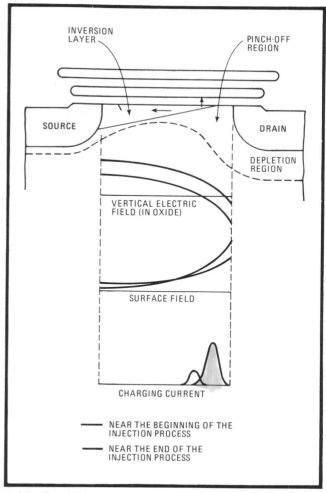

4. Injection. With a positive floating gate, electrons leave the drain and are accelerated along the channel,. They gain enough energy to hop the thin oxide and cling to the attractive floating gate (as implied by the fields shown). This avalanche injection is self-limiting.

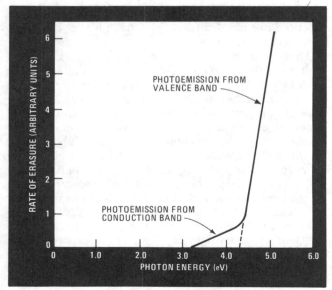

5. Erase rate. Two distinct threshold energies are apparent when erasing an E-PROM cell. The first, at 3.2 eV, corresponds to photoemission from the conduction band of the floating gate. The second point, at 4.3 eV, is associated with the valence band.

n-channel structures in which the floating gate completely overlaps the select gate, erasure is accomplished as the photons travel through the field oxide, under the select gate, and to the floating gate where they are absorbed. This wave-guiding effect is efficient because the reflectivity of silicon to 2,500-Å light is roughly 65%.

An interesting exception exists for very energetic X rays and gamma rays, which can readily penetrate the select gate and then be absorbed throughout the gate oxides, the floating gate, or the substrate. However, a broadband flux on the order of 10^{13} photons per cm from an X-ray tube operated at 100 kiloelectronvolts with a tungsten target is necessary to fully erase an E-PROM; hence X rays are not regarded as a special reliability concern for E-PROMs.

Finally, single ionizing events due to the passage of a cosmic ray or an alpha particle cannot cause spurious erasure because not enough charge is created in the gate oxides around the floating gate to neutralize the charge stored there.

Reading and storage

During reading, the E-PROM cell operates like an ordinary transistor except that the normal gate capacitance is replaced by the series capacitance of the floating-gate structure. Though it might be suspected that some low-level programming could occur during a read operation, as read voltages are applied to both the gate and drain, this has not been observed. One reason is that hot-electron current is an exponential function of drain voltage and the drain voltage used for reading (approximately 3 v) is much lower than that used for programming (over 20 v). In addition, the requirement for electric fields greater than 10^5 v/cm to generate hot electrons—and an energy barrier of greater than 3 eV for injection into the oxide—make spurious programming nonexistent at normal reading voltages.

The key issue for nonvolatile memories is just how well they retain their data. For E-PROM, the answer hinges on how well the charge on the floating gate stays put over the lifetime of the part. The advantage of floating-gate memories is that the gates are surrounded by high-integrity silicon dioxide. This oxide is a nearly ideal insulator because it has a wide bandgap, a very high barrier with reference to silicon and aluminum, a relatively low surface-state density on silicon, low bulk trapping densities and electron trapping levels, and no structural polarization.

For ordinary electric fields from the floating gate to the select gate and substrate encountered during reading and storage, electron emission is negligible. Therefore any charge leakage that occurs must be due to oxide defects. Since this leakage is due to a thermally activated hopping mechanism having an activation energy of 0.6 eV[1], its rate can be accelerated under high-temperature biasing and/or baking conditions. For example, programming all bits and then subjecting the device to a high temperature (150°C) rapidly determines the ability of each floating gate to maintain charge. Additionally, a high-temperature biasing of unprogrammed bits screens out oxide defects that cause current leakage to the floating gate.

By taking advantage of these high-temperature and/or voltage accelerating factors, production screens have been developed that successfully weed out those parts with defective oxides. These screens are the subject of part 2 of this article. □

References
1. R. E. Shiner, J. M. Caywood, and B. L. Euzent, "Data Rentention in E-PROMs," 18th Annual Proceedings, Reliability Physics Symposium (1980).

A Fully Decoded 2048-Bit Electrically Programmable FAMOS Read-Only Memory

DOV FROHMAN-BENTCHKOWSKY, MEMBER, IEEE

Abstract—This paper describes a fully decoded 2048-bit electrically programmable read-only memory implemented with a novel floating-gate avalanche-injection MOS (FAMOS) charge-storage device as the basic nonvolatile memory element. The memory is organized as 256 words of 8 bits, it is fully TTL compatible, and can be operated in both the static or dynamic mode. The memory array was successfully fabricated with silicon gate MOS technology yielding functional devices with access times of 800 ns in the static mode and 500 ns in the dynamic mode of operation. The memory chip is assembled in a 24-lead dual-in-line package.

SEMICONDUCTOR read-only memories (ROM) are presently implemented in a variety of digital system and computer applications. Most available semiconductor ROMs are programmed permanently at the integrated-circuit fabrication stage by a custom mask that defines the desired information pattern. As a result, program changes in microprogramming applications as well as pattern changes during the debugging phase of digital systems involve the generation of a new mechanical mask for every modified ROM pattern. In addition to being an expensive step, it also limits the flexibility of ROM applications because of the delay involved in the production process. These limitations of mask programmable ROMs have led to a growing interest in electrically programmable semiconductor ROMs in which the permanent information pattern is recorded by application of an electrical signal. This allows programming changes to be affected without the expense and time delay involved in generation of a custom mask.

The different proposed electrically programmable ROMs can be divided into two main categories: 1) ROMs in which a permanent (irreversible) change in the memory metal interconnection pattern is affected by an electrical pulse; and 2) alterable ROMs in which a reversible change in active memory device characteristics is induced electrically.

The first category includes fusible-type ROMs, which are mainly bipolar memories with capacities of up to 512 memory bits. Their main disadvantage is that they cannot be reprogrammed, which prevents complete functional testing before shipment, as well as pattern modification in case of programming error or needed change.

The search for alterable (charge storage) ROMs stems from the need for low-cost fully tested field-programmable ROMs as well as an attempt to provide a substitute for the nonvolatile storage capability (retention of stored information without an external power source) of magnetic memories. Most proposed alterable ROMs rely on charge storage in a dielectric that forms part of the gate of an insulated-gate field-effect transistor. Feasibility has been demonstrated for a metal-nitride-oxide-silicon (MNOS) memory [1], [2] a metal-aluminum-oxide-silicon (MAS) memory [3], and a dual-gate MNOS memory [4]. Difficulties in controlling the electrical characteristics of the storage dielectrics and additional fabrication steps required to achieve on-the-chip decoding have limited the realization of these approaches to undecoded memory arrays of up to 256 memory bits.

Recently, feasibility of the ovonic amorphous semiconductor memory device has been demonstrated by fabrication of an undecoded 256-bit memory array [5].

The introduction of a novel MOS memory element—the floating-gate avalanche-injection MOS (FAMOS) charge-storage device—has led to the fabrication of a fully decoded 2048-bit electrically programmable ROM. The memory is organized as 256 words of 8 bits, it is fully TTL compatible and can be operated in both the static or dynamic decoding and sensing mode. The monolithic memory array was successfully fabricated with silicon-gate MOS technology, yielding functional devices with access times below 800 ns in the static mode and less than 500 ns in the dynamic mode of operation. The memory chip is assembled in a 24-lead dual-in-line package.

I. DEVICE STRUCTURE AND OPERATION

A cross section of the FAMOS structure is shown in Fig. 1 with its suggested electrical symbol. It is essentially a p-channel silicon-gate MOS field-effect transistor [6] in which no electrical contact is made to the silicon gate. The floating polysilicon gate is isolated from the silicon substrate by a SiO_2 layer of approximately 1000 Å and from the top surface by 1.0 μ of vapor-deposited oxide. Operation of the FAMOS memory structure depends on charge transport to the floating gate by avalanche injection of electrons from either the source or drain p-n junctions. A junction voltage in excess of -30 V applied to a p-channel FAMOS device (Fig. 2) with 1000 Å of oxide and 5–8-$\Omega \cdot$cm substrate resistivity will result in the onset of injection of high-energy electrons from the p-n junction surface avalanche region to the floating silicon gate. The gate charging current is of the

Manuscript received March 16, 1971. This paper was presented at the ISSCC, Philadelphia, Pa., February 1971.

The author is with the Intel Corporation, Mountain View, Calif.

Reprinted from *IEEE J. Solid-State Circuits*, vol. SC-6, no. 5, pp. 301–306, October 1971.

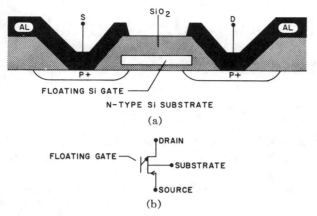

Fig. 1. (a) Cross section of FAMOS structure. (b) Suggested electrical symbol.

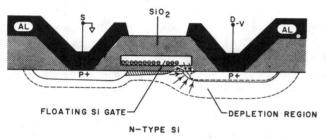

Fig. 2. Cross section of FAMOS device under bias.

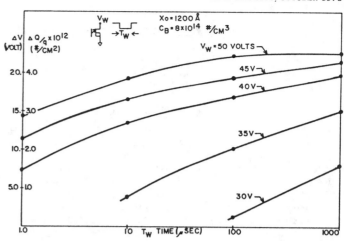

Fig. 3. Charge accumulation on the floating gate as a function of charging pulsewidth for different values of pulse amplitude.

order of 10^{-7} A/cm². Since the silicon gate is floating the electron current through the oxide results in the accumulation of a negative charge on the gate. For a p-channel FAMOS transistor this negative charge will induce a conductive inversion layer connecting source and drain. The amount of charge transferred to the floating gate as a function of the amplitude and duration of the applied junction voltage is shown in Fig. 3. The presence or absence of charge can be sensed by measuring the conductance between the source and drain regions.

Once the applied junction voltage is removed, no discharge path is available for the accumulated electrons since the gate is surrounded by thermal oxide, which is a very low conductivity dielectric. The electric field in the structure after the removal of junction voltage is due only to the accumulated electron charge and is not sufficient to cause charge transport across the polysilicon-thermal-oxide energy barrier. The maximum stored charge of 4×10^{12} electrons/cm² ($V_W = 50$ V, Fig. 3) results in an electric field of approximately 2×10^6 V/cm across the thermal oxide. Assuming current transport by Fowler-Nordheim emission from the polysilicon gate into the oxide, the estimated discharge current (for a polysilicon-SiO₂ energy barrier of at least 3.2 eV) is of the order of 10^{-40} A/cm² at 300°K.

Charge decay plots as a function of time at 125° and 300°C are shown in Fig. 4. The rapid initial decay saturating with time cannot be explained by electron transport across the oxide. Its temperature and electric-field dependence correspond to that of positive-charge buildup at the SiO₂-Si interface that occurs at high electric fields

under negative gate bias conditions [7], [8]. The activation energy of charge decay was measured to be 1.0 eV. An extrapolation of the 300°C charge decay results indicates that 70 percent of the initial induced charge can be retained for as long as 10 years at 125°C.

Since the gate electrode is not electrically accessible, the charge cannot be removed by an electrical pulse. However, the initial condition of no electronic charge on the gate can be restored by two nonelectrical methods. Illumination of the unpackaged device with ultraviolet light will result in the flow of a photocurrent from the floating gate back to the silicon substrate thereby discharging the gate to its initial condition. This erase method allows complete testing of a complex memory array before the package goes through final seal. Once the package is sealed, information can be erased by exposure to X-ray radiation. The radiation dose required is in excess of 5×10^4 rad, which is many orders of magnitude higher than the average yearly atmospheric radiation dose and easily attainable with available commercial X-ray generators.

II. MEMORY CELL

The FAMOS charge-storage device described above can be used as the basic storage element in a large memory array. A circuit schematic of the memory cell and its associated decoding circuitry is shown in Fig. 5. The decode and sense circuits shown are common to both the PROGRAM and READ modes. To select a bit to be programed the address-decode inputs as well as the V_{DD} and V_{GG} lines are energized to -50 V. Programming of a memory bit is accomplished by coincidence selection of the X and Y select lines. The applied programming pulse is transferred to the selected FAMOS device that turns normally on due to the electron charge transferred to its floating gate. All other memory bits are not programmed due to either the lack of a pulse on the Y select line or the absence of a transfer pulse on the X select line. The programming signal V_P is a -50-V 5.0-ms pulse. The amount of charge stored in a memory cell in re-

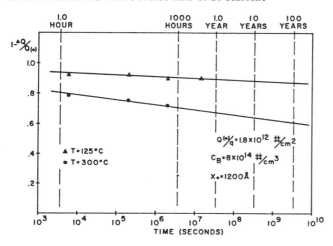

Fig. 4. Charge decay in a FAMOS device as a function of time at 125° and 300°C.

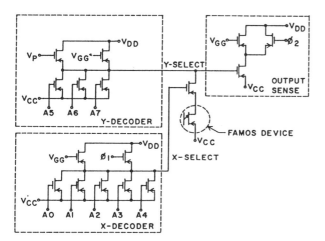

Fig. 5. Memory cell with its associated decode and sense circuits.

sponse to a programming pulse is typically 3.0×10^{-7} C/cm², which is equivalent to 10 V on the gate of a conventional MOS transistor. The load current required to program a memory bit is approximately 5.0 mA. The increase in programming pulse amplitude and duration to charge the memory cell compared to the data presented in Fig. 3 is due to the additional voltage drop across the decode circuits. These high applied voltages in the PROGRAM mode could give rise to parasitic programming paths due to field inversions over the thick oxide regions on the chip. This potential problem was accounted for in both the circuit design and chip layout by providing a highly conductive programming path as compared to the parasitic path as well as careful routing of high-voltage lines on the chip to avoid sensitive circuit nodes.

Memory-cell operation in the READ mode is similar to that of other ROMs. A memory bit is selected by a coincidence of signals on the X and Y select lines. However, compared to the programming mode the READ mode voltages are substantially lower. Since the programming threshold is -30.0 V, the maximum READ voltage of -15 V guarantees a wide margin to avoid disturbing the information during the READ mode. Information in the se-

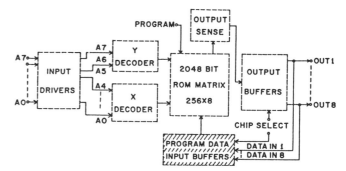

Fig. 6. Block diagram of memory organization.

lected memory cell is sampled by the output sense circuit. If a "0" is stored in the cell (charge on the floating gate) the FAMOS device is ON and the level at the input of the sense circuit is close to V_{CC}. A "1" corresponding to no charge stored in the cell is reflected by a more negative level (close to V_{DD}) at the input of the sense circuit. Information can be decoded and sensed in either the static (no clocks) or dynamic mode (2 clocks). The static mode of operation eliminates the need for clocks at the expense of increased power dissipation and reduced speed, while the dynamic mode offers advantages in both performance categories. The option of the two modes of operation is achieved by parallel load transistors in the decode and sense circuitry, one connected to the clock lines and the other to V_{GG} as shown in Fig. 5. The load device connected to the V_P terminal is connected to ϕ_1 in the dynamic READ mode. Mode selection is done by activating the clocks with V_{GG} connected to V_{CC} in the dynamic mode. V_{GG} is activated in the static mode with the clocks connected to V_{CC}.

III. MEMORY ORGANIZATION AND OPERATION

The electrically programmable memory chip consists of a monolithic array of 2048 FAMOS devices organized as 256 words of 8 bits. A block diagram of memory organization is shown in Fig. 6. All circuit blocks are common to both the PROGRAM and READ modes with the exception of the PROGRAM data input buffers. In the PROGRAM mode the eight output terminals are used as data inputs to determine the information pattern in the eight bits of each word, while word address selection is performed by the X and Y decoders through the input drivers. The PROGRAM data input circuitry for one of eight outputs is shown in Fig. 7. To inhibit the programming of a bit, a negative voltage is applied to the data input terminal. This voltage level is transferred to the inhibit transistor (chip select is enabled), which turns on and overrides the Y select signal. To allow programming of a selected bit, the data input terminal is kept at ground. Initially all 2048 bits are in the "1" state corresponding to normally OFF FAMOS devices (no charge on the floating gate). Information is introduced by selectively programming "0" in the proper bit locations through charging the FAMOS devices from the PROGRAM terminal. The supply (V_{DD}, V_{GG}, V_P), address $(A_0 - A_8)$ and data input $(D_{IN1}$

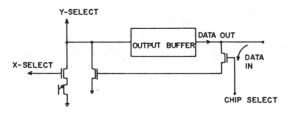

Fig. 7. Circuit description of PROGRAM data input buffers.

APPLIED VOLTAGE (VOLTS) MODE	V_{DD}	V_{GG}	V_P	ϕ_1	ϕ_2	V_{CC}	ADDRESSES DATA IN
PROGRAM	-50.0	-50.0	-50.0	V_{CC}	V_{CC}	0.0	-40.0
STATIC READ	-9.0	-9.0	V_{CC}	V_{CC}	V_{CC}	+5.0	TTL
DYNAMIC READ	-9.0	V_{CC}	-9.0	-9.0	-9.0	+5.0	TTL

Fig. 8. Applied voltage level to the memory in the PROGRAM and READ modes of operation.

— D_{IN8}) voltages in the PROGRAM mode are detailed in Fig. 8. A timing diagram for the applied voltage sequence in the PROGRAM mode is shown in Fig. 9. In the READ mode the PROGRAM data input buffers are inhibited by the chip select signal to cut off the feedback path from the output to the memory array established in the PROGRAM mode. Memory operation in the READ mode is the same as in conventional mask programmable ROMs. The input and output buffers provide for full TTL compatibility and addressing is accomplished by the X and Y decoders operating at the voltage levels detailed in Fig. 8. A selected memory cell with a charged FAMOS device will be reflected by a low "0" TTL level at the output, while a memory bit that is not charged will result in a high "1" TTL level. Both the static and dynamic modes of decoding and sensing are available in a single package through use of parallel load transistors as described in Section II. Mode selection is done by activation of either the clock lines (ϕ_1, ϕ_2) or the V_{GG} terminal in the dynamic and static modes, respectively. Typical access times are 400 ns in the dynamic mode and 700 ns in the static mode. A photomicrograph of the chip with the designation of the different circuit blocks is shown in Fig. 10.

As can be seen from the above description, electrical programming of the memory is conceptually the same as operation in the READ mode with the exception of the voltage levels (Fig. 8). Hence, the memory can be easily programmed from punched paper tape or other data input devices through an electrical programming terminal. Once programmed, the information pattern in the memory can be erased (restored to the all "1" state) by ultraviolet light before packaging or by exposure to X-ray radiation as described in Section I. The ability to erase before packaging allows for complete testing of the memory chip prior to shipment, which is a distinct advantage over once-programmable ROMs. Erasure of information in packaged devices by placing them in a commercially available X-ray generator allows for correction of programming errors as well as unpredictable future pattern modifications.

IV. RELIABILITY

One of the most important performance factors in an electrically programmable ROM (as in all other products) is its long-term reliability. Reliability in this case incorporates both the long-term functionality of the standard MOS transistors and the long-term information retention of the FAMOS devices. Reliability data on sili-

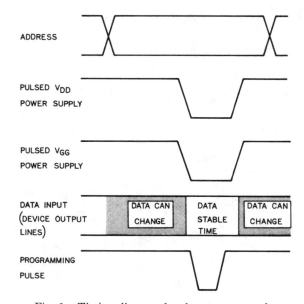

Fig. 9. Timing diagram for the PROGRAM mode.

con-gate MOS memory products have been accumulated over a period of two years, resulting in many device hours without failure. This record is directly applicable to the programmable ROM since it is fabricated with the same silicon-gate MOS technology. As to long-term information retention, the charge-storage programmable ROM has a predictable time-temperature dependence for stored information.

The long-term decay (Fig. 3) has a logarithmic dependence on time with a slope of approximately 1.0 V per 5 decades of storage time at 125°C. This rate of charge decay extrapolates to storage retention times greater than 10 years at 125°C. The predictable time-temperature behavior of stored charge corresponding to an activation energy of 1.0 eV, allows for accelerated life testing of the programmable ROM. To guarantee 10-years retention at 125°C, the device has to be subjected to 300°C storage for only 10 h. This procedure is similar to existing high-temperature stress testing in MOS products to detect potential contamination in the dielectric.

A summary of reliability results on the 2048-bit electrically programmable ROM is shown in Fig. 11. The extrapolation of time from 125° and 200°C to the operating temperature of 85°C is based on an activation energy for charge decay of 1.0 eV. The bias configuration in the temperature/bias test corresponds to worst case operating voltages in the READ mode. No failures have been

Fig. 10. Photomicrograph of the memory chip with designation of the different circuit blocks.

1601 RELIABILITY RESULTS

TEST	T_A	UNITS	HOURS	FAILURES	EQ. TIME AT 85°C
TEMP/BIAS	125°C	15	1500	0	5 YEARS
STORAGE	125°C	10	1500	0	5 YEARS
STORAGE	200°C	10	250	0	100 YEARS

1.0 HOUR AT 125°C ≡ 35 HOURS AT 85°C

Fig. 11. Reliability results for storage retention of the programmable ROM.

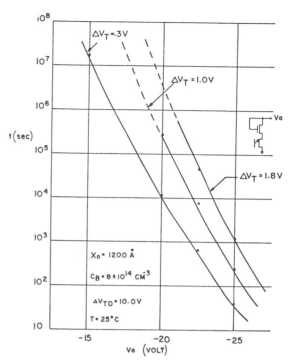

Fig. 12. Retention of the uncharged memory state as a function of applied voltage to the memory cell.

ity and programming, as well as an accelerated high-temperature test to guarantee long-term retention. After the tests are performed, the information pattern is erased and the programmable ROM is shipped with a pattern of all "1" ready for programming.

V. Applications

Despite the attempts of semiconductor manufacturers to lower mask charges and turn-around time for mask-programmable ROMs, the economics and design delay involved have limited the versatility of semiconductor ROM applications. The availability of a low-cost electrically field-programmable ROM opens new application areas, which heretofore have not been economically feasible, mainly those in which relatively small quantities of different ROM patterns are required. For example, the implementation of computer lookup tables that provide a hard-wired means of performing certain routine computer calculations. The variety of possible patterns makes the use of mask-programmable ROMs costly and impractical, while ideally suited for field-programmable ROMs. Other application areas that fall into the same category are binary-sequence generators, microprogramming control of central processors in computer terminals, and programmed logic arrays.

On the other hand, in areas such as code converters, character generators, and other applications in which large quantities of a few patterns are required the field programmable ROM augments the capability of mask programmable ROMs. In these applications, the initial custom mask cost is insignificant compared to the total cost of the high-volume standard ROM pattern. How-

observed in any of the long-term information-retention tests.

An additional reliability factor is the retention of the uncharged "1" memory state. It was pointed out in Section III that operation in the READ mode differs from the PROGRAM mode only in the lowering of the operating voltages from −50 to −14 V. This brings up the question of whether an uncharged memory bit can be slowly charged by repeated selection in the READ mode. Retention of the uncharged memory state as measured on a typical memory cell is shown in Fig. 12. The time for a shift in FAMOS device turn-on voltage as a function of applied voltage to the memory cell is plotted for different values of turnon voltage shift. For an operating voltage in the READ mode of −14 V, a shift of $V_T = 1.0$ V is expected to take place after more than 100 years. A shift of at least 5.0 V is required before the uncharged memory state "1" is interpreted as a "0" by the sense circuitry. Another important aspect of reliability is the extent of preshipment testing. As pointed out in previous sections, because of its reprogrammable feature, the memory array can be completely tested before shipment for functional-

IEEE JOURNAL OF SOLID-STATE CIRCUITS, VOL. SC-6, NO. 5, OCTOBER 1971

ever, in order to finalize a decision on a given high-volume standard pattern a method of debugging is needed to avoid the costly phase of correcting potential errors. In this initial pattern definition phase the electrically programmable ROM is most economical and flexible. Since the flexibility of field-programmable ROMs is generally achieved at the expense of chip area, once the pattern has been defined, the high-volume order is placed for mask-programmable ROMs, which are lower cost in high quantities. Hence the combination of the two programming methods offers both the flexibility and cost incentive required to proliferate the use of semiconductor read-only memories in high-volume applications.

VI. Summary

The introduction of a novel semiconductor memory element—the FAMOS charge storage device—and its implementation in a fully decoded 2048-bit electrically programmable read-only memory constitutes a significant advance in the state of the art of semiconductor memories. It is the first available large-capacity programmable ROM in which the information pattern is recorded electrically by way of a reversible change in memory-device characteristics. This was achieved by a combination of a new charge-storage structure and circuit techniques that allow its implementation in large-scale memory arrays with existing MOS processing techniques.

Acknowledgment

The author wishes to thank L. L. Vadasz, A. S. Grove, and G. E. Moore for many helpful discussions, G. Pasco for fabrication of the memory devices, and G. Greenwood for his help in testing and instrumentation.

References

[1] H. A. Wegener, "MNOS memories," *Digest Intermag. Conf.*, Apr. 1970.
[2] D. Frohman-Bentchkowsky, "An integrated metal-nitride-oxide-silicon (MNOS) memory," *Proc. IEEE* (Lett.), vol. 57, June 1969, pp. 1190–1192.
[3] S. Nakanuma *et al.*, "A read-only memory using MAS transistors," *ISSCC Digest Tech. Papers*, Feb. 1970, pp. 68–69.
[4] H. G. Dill and T. N. Toombs, "A new MNOS charge storage effect," *Solid-State Electron.* vol. 12, 1969, pp. 981–987.
[5] R. G. Neale, D. L. Nelson, and G. E. Moore, "Amorphous semiconductors (Part I)," *Electronics*, Sept. 1970.
[6] L. L. Vadasz, A. S. Grove, T. A. Rowe, and G. E. Moore, "Silicon-gate technology," *IEEE Spectrum*, vol. 6, 1969, pp. 28–35.
[7] B. E. Deal, M. Sklar, A. S. Grove, and E. H. Snow, *J. Electrochem. Soc., Solid-State Sci.*, vol. 114, 1967, p. 266.
[8] S. R. Hofstein, *Solid-State Electron.*, vol. 10, 1967, p. 657.

A 64K EPROM using Scaled MOS Technology

George Perlegos, Saroj Pathak, Alan Renninger, William Johnson, Mark Holler, Joseph Skupnak, Michael Reitsma and Greg Kuhn

Intel Corp.

Santa Clara, CA

THE CONTINUED NEED for higher density, higher performance erasable proms (EPROMs) has been established by the evolution of faster, more dense microprocessors, and their dependence on convenient program storage memories. This need was first served by the 2Kb FAMOS P-channel floating gate EPROM[1,2], implemented by a two-transistor cell. The second generation N-channel microprocessors were served by the 8Kb and 16Kb[3,4], N-channel MOS stacked gate EPROMs which used a one transistor cell.

With the arrival of another generation of microprocessors*, the need for yet higher density and higher performance EPROMs has again become critical. In response to this need, a third-generation 64K EPROM has been developed featuring a scaled stacked cell (cell area = 0.25mil^2), t_{access} <200ns, fully static operation and single 20V pulse programming. Advances in both technology and circuitry were utilized in realizing these characteristics.

The cell, illustrated in Figure 1, is a self-aligned structure fabricated by a dual-layer polysilicon gate process. The first layer of poly (POLY 1) forms the floating gate and the second layer of poly (POLY 2) forms the top select gate.

A cell size of 159μm^2 (0.25mil^2) is achieved through the use of a scaled EPROM technology. Channel lengths of $\sim$3.5μm are obtained in the array and periphery with better Critical Dimension (CD) control and less undercutting. Increased coupling for lower programming voltages and smaller programming times is available by scaling down the first and second gate oxide thickness to approximately 700Å and 800Å, respectively. Additional geometry changes in the cell and periphery are the result of scaling, optimized to account for special EPROM requirements. As demonstrated in Figure 2, the chip size for a 32K density changes from 200mil^2 on a standard EPROM technology to 145mil^2 on a scaled EPROM technology.

The memory cell is programmed by means of hot electrons injected through the oxide to the floating gate[3]. The charge retention characteristics have not changed and are similar to the original FAMOS cell. The cell is 13μm X 12μm and uses 3.5μm gate lengths.

Circuit innovations contributing to the performance of the memory include a differential sensing technique and the use of transfer gates within the x-decoder, as shown in Figure 3. The differential sense amplifier, in conjunction with a special reference circuit, provides increased sensing margin. The transfer gate between x-DECODER and x-SELECT localizes the high voltage during programming, leading to a compact, high speed select design. The 64Kb EPROM shown in Figure 4, is organized 8K X 8, and measures 179 X 181 mil^2. The chip is packaged in a 28-lead package, allowing the use of separate $\overline{OE}$ and $\overline{CE}$ control. The chip automatically powers down to a standby power of <100mW when deselected via $\overline{CE}$. Active power is <500mW, and active read access time <200ns.

The evolution of EPROM devices is summarized in Table 1. The 64K memory does not only achieve a breakthrough in speed and power but new trends in programming voltages, programming speed, and packaging. Higher density and speed were achieved with the use of a scaled MOS technology. The trend to lower programming voltages was adopted with the introduction of arsenic junctions to overcome the lower breakdown voltages.

Acknowledgments

The authors wish to thank W. Morgan and G. Korsh for their technical contributions, P. Salsbury for direction and support and C. Scott for processing support.

---

*8086.

[1] Frohman-Bentchkowsky, D., "A Fully Decoded 2048-Bit Electrically-Programmable MOS-ROM", *ISSCC DIGEST OF TECHNICAL PAPERS*, p. 80-81; Feb., 1971.

[2] Frohman-Bentchowsky, D., "FAMOS — A New Semiconductor Charge Storage Device", *Solid-State Electronics*, Vol. 17, p. 517-529; 1974.

[3] Salsbury, P.J., Morgan, W.L., Perlegos, G. and Simko, R.T., "High Performance MOS EPROMs Using a Stacked Gate Cell", *ISSCC DIGEST OF TECHNICAL PAPERS*, p. 186-187; Feb., 1977.

[4] Stamm, D., Buddy, D. and Morgan, W., "A Single Chip, Highly Integrated, User Programmable Microcomputer", *ISSCC DIGEST OF TECHNICAL PAPERS*, p. 142-143; Feb., 1977.

EPROM Evolution	02	08	16	32	64
• Voltages	+5, −9V	±5, +12	+5	+5	+5
• Program Supplies	−50	+27	+25	+25	+20
• Density	256 × 8	1k × 8	2k × 8	3k × 8	4k × 8
• Access	1ms	450ns	450ns	450ns	200ns
• Devices	P-Channel	N-Channel Enhancement	N-Channel Enhancement Depletion	N-Channel Enhancement Depletion	N-Channel Enhancement Depletion Zero V$_T$ Devices
• High Voltages	Bootstraps	Bootstraps	Depletion Devices	Depletion and Bootstraps OE/V$_{PP}$ Circuits	Depletion Devices
• Programming	1ms-Pulses	100-1ms Pulse/Word	1-50ms Pulse/Word	1-50ms Pulse/Word	1-25ms Pulse/Word
• Power	750mW	1 watt	500mW 50mW (Power Down)	750mW 50mW (Power Down)	500mW 50mW (Power Down)
• Package	24 Pins	24 Pins	24 Pins	24 Pins	28 Pins

TABLE 1—Evolution of EPROM devices.

Reprinted from *IEEE ISSCC Dig. Tech. Pap.*, pp. 142–143, 269, 1980.

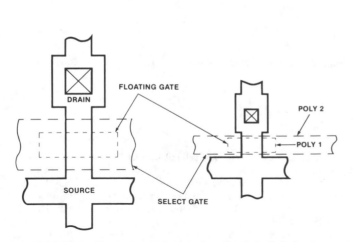

FIGURE 1—Comparison of original and scaled stacked gate cell.

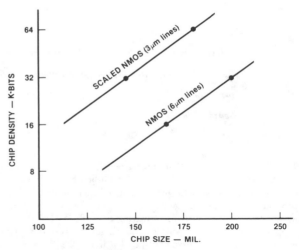

FIGURE 2—Advances in EPROM technology.

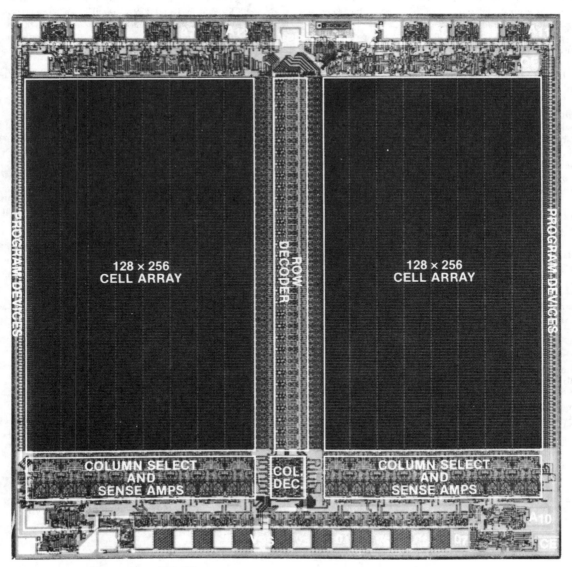

FIGURE 4—Chip photo for 64K EPROM.

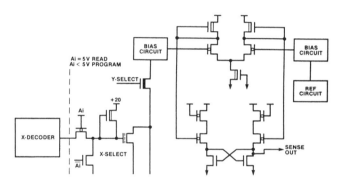

FIGURE 3—Circuit schematic of memory array organization.

On the *I–V* Characteristics of Floating-Gate MOS Transistors

SAMUEL TUAN WANG

Abstract—The effects of capacitive coupling on the *I–V* characteristics of floating-gate MOS transistors are described. A set of modified *I–V* equations for these devices is presented and compared with experimental results.

I. INTRODUCTION

FLOATING-GATE MOS transistors have attracted considerable attention as nonvolatile semiconductor memory devices, such as the EPROM [1]. In a memory-array circuit using these devices the conductivity of the floating-gate transistor determines the nonvolatile information stored in the memory cell. The conductivity of the floating-gate MOS transistor differs from that of a conventional MOS transistor having the same applied terminal voltages due to a capacitive coupling between the drain region and the floating gate. When a voltage is applied to the drain region, capacitive coupling between the drain and the floating gate induces a high electrical potential on the floating gate. This induced field on the floating gate then modifies the conductivity of the underlying channel region. In this paper, the effects of capacitive coupling on the *I–V* characteristics of floating-gate MOS transistors are described. The modified device equations resulting from these effects are presented and compared with experimental results.

II. THEORY

Fig. 1(a) and (b) shows the cross section of a conventional MOS transistor and a floating-gate transistor, respectively. The upper gate in Fig. 1(b) is the control gate and the lower gate, completely isolated within the gate oxide, is the floating gate. C_{FG}, C_{FD}, C_{FS}, and C_{FSub} are the capacitance between the floating gate and the control gate, drain, source, and substrate regions, respectively. Consider the case when the source and substrate are both grounded and potentials V_{GS} and V_{DS} applied to the control gate and drain, respectively. The potential of the floating gate V_F, due to capacitive coupling, is then given by

$$V_F = \frac{C_{FG}V_{GS} + C_{FD}V_{DS}}{C_{FG} + C_{FD} + C_{FS} + C_{FSub}} \qquad (1)$$

or

$$V_F = \frac{C_{FG}V_{GS} + C_{FD}V_{DS}}{C_T}. \qquad (2)$$

Manuscript received July 31, 1978; revised May 10, 1979.
The author was with Hughes Aircraft Company, Newport Beach, CA 92663. He is now with Intel Corporation, Santa Clara, CA 95051.

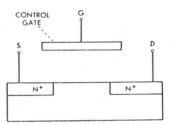

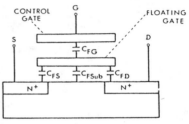

Fig. 1. Cross section of (a) a conventional MOS transistor and (b) a floating-gate MOS transistor.

Here C_T, the total capacitance on the floating gate, is given by

$$C_T = C_{FG} + C_{FD} + C_{FS} + C_{FSub}. \qquad (3)$$

It should be pointed out that (1) is an approximation, since coupling occurs from the channel region as well, the potential of which is nonuniform, increasing from source to drain.

Equation (2) can be rearranged as

$$V_F = \frac{C_{FG}}{C_T}\left(V_{GS} + \frac{C_{FD}}{C_{FG}}V_{DS}\right) \qquad (4)$$

$$= \frac{C_{FG}}{C_T}(V_{GS} + fV_{DS}) \qquad (5)$$

where

$$f = \frac{C_{FD}}{C_{FG}}. \qquad (6)$$

Device equations for the floating-gate MOS transistor can be obtained by replacing V_{GS} with V_F in the conventional MOS transistor equations [2], and transforming the device parameters, such as oxide thickness and threshold voltage, to values measured with respect to the control gate.

Since

$$V_T \text{ (floating gate)} = \frac{C_{FG}}{C_T} V_T \text{(control gate)} \qquad (7)$$

and

Reprinted from *IEEE Trans. Electron Devices*, vol. ED-26, no. 9, pp. 1292–1294, September 1979.

$$\beta \text{ (floating gate)} = \frac{C_T}{C_{FG}} \beta \text{(control gate)}. \qquad (8)$$

The device equations after such replacement and transformation are listed in the following table for a direct comparison with that of the conventional transistor.

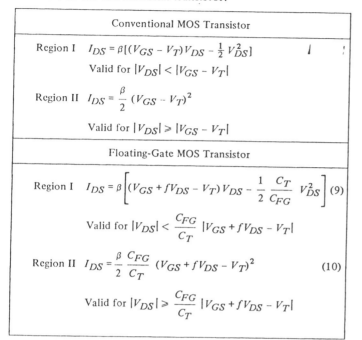

Conventional MOS Transistor
Region I $I_{DS} = \beta[(V_{GS} - V_T)V_{DS} - \frac{1}{2} V_{DS}^2]$
Valid for $\|V_{DS}\| < \|V_{GS} - V_T\|$
Region II $I_{DS} = \frac{\beta}{2} (V_{GS} - V_T)^2$
Valid for $\|V_{DS}\| \geqslant \|V_{GS} - V_T\|$
Floating-Gate MOS Transistor
Region I $I_{DS} = \beta\left[(V_{GS} + fV_{DS} - V_T)V_{DS} - \frac{1}{2}\frac{C_T}{C_{FG}} V_{DS}^2\right]$ (9)
Valid for $\|V_{DS}\| < \frac{C_{FG}}{C_T} \|V_{GS} + fV_{DS} - V_T\|$
Region II $I_{DS} = \frac{\beta}{2}\frac{C_{FG}}{C_T} (V_{GS} + fV_{DS} - V_T)^2$ (10)
Valid for $\|V_{DS}\| \geqslant \frac{C_{FG}}{C_T} \|V_{GS} + fV_{DS} - V_T\|$

β and V_T of (9) and (10) are with respect to the control gate rather than with respect to the floating gate of the stacked gate structure.

Several effects can be observed from these equations:

1) The floating-gate transistor can go into depletion-mode operation and can conduct current even when $|V_{GS}| < |V_T|$. This is because the channel can be turned on by the drain voltage through the fV_{DS} term in (9).

2) Region II for the conventional MOS transistor is the saturation region where I_{DS} is essentially independent of the drain voltage. This is no longer true for the floating-gate transistor in which the drain current will continue to rise as the drain voltage increases and saturation will not occur.

3) The boundary between Region I and Region II for the floating-gate transistor is expressed by the equation

$$|V_{DS}| = \frac{C_{FG}}{C_T} |V_{GS} + fV_{DS} - V_T|$$

compared to the conventional transistor $|V_{DS}| = |V_{GS} - V_T|$.

4) The transconductance in Region II is given by

$$g_m = \frac{\partial I_{DS}}{\partial V_{GS}}\bigg|_{(V_{DS} = \text{constant})}$$

$$= \frac{C_{FG}}{C_T} \beta(V_{GS} + fV_{DS} - V_T)$$

g_m increases with V_{DS} in the floating-gate transistor in contrast to the conventional transistor where g_m is relatively independent of the drain voltage in the saturation region.

5) The capacitive coupling ratio f depends on C_{FD}, C_{FG}

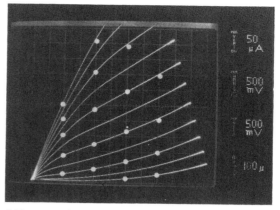

Fig. 2. *I-V* curves of a floating-gate MOS transistor with strong capacitive coupling effect. Curves: experimental, dots: theoretical.

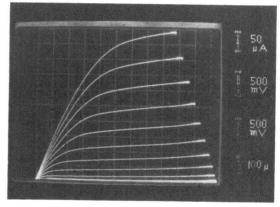

Fig. 3. *I-V* curves of the same transistor as in Fig. 2 but with drain, source interchanged. Capacitive coupling to the floating gate is weak.

only $(f = C_{FD}/C_{FG})$ and its value can be verified by

$$f = -\frac{\partial V_{GS}}{\partial V_{DS}}\bigg|_{(I_{DS} = \text{constant})}$$

in Region II.

III. EXPERIMENTAL RESULTS

N-channel floating-gate transistors with $W/L = 0.3$ mil$/0.3$ mil were designed and fabricated with the drain terminal strongly capacitively coupled to the floating gate ($C_{FD}/C_{FG} = 0.35$) and the source terminal weakly coupled ($C_{FS}/C_{FG} = 0.05$). When fabricated, these transistors exhibited a threshold voltage of $+0.5$ V. Fig. 2 shows the *I-V* curves observed on a Tektronix curve tracer for this device when $+V_{DS}$ is applied on the drain terminal and V_{GS} is increased from 0 to $+5.0$ V in 0.5-V steps. Fig. 3 shows the *I-V* curves for the same device operated under the identical voltage levels, but with the drain and source terminal reversed. With the drain terminal grounded, the coupling effect is weak and the *I-V* curves look similar to those of a conventional transistor. The capacitive coupling ratio f as estimated by $\partial V_{GS}/\partial V_{DS}|_{(I_{DS} = \text{constant})}$ from the lower part of Fig. 2 is about 0.37 in very good agreement with the designed value, 0.35. The lowest curve on Fig. 2 also indicated that the device turned on strongly even for $V_{GS} = 0$ V below $V_T = +0.5$ V. The transconductance in the lower curves indeed increases with both V_{DS} and V_{GS} as predicted. Theoretical value of the drain current as calculated from (9) and (10) for various drain and gate voltages are plotted as dots on Fig. 2 for a direct comparison with the experimental curves. The agreement between theory and experiments is seen to be good.

In summary, the capacitive coupling of the floating gate can strongly distort the *I–V* characteristics of a floating-gate MOS transistor. Device equations for the floating-gate MOS transistors have been presented and shown to be in good agreement with experimental results.

ACKNOWLEDGMENT

The author wishes to thank Dr. T. N. Toombs and Dr. E. Harari for their encouragement and Dr. D. J. McGreivy for reading the manuscript. He also likes to thank the personnel of Hughes Aircraft Advanced I.C. Facility for the preparation of the devices.

REFERENCES

[1] D. Frohman-Bentchkowsky, "A fully-decoded 2048-bit electrically programmable MOS-RAM," in *ISSCC Dig. Tech. Papers*, p. 80, 1971.
[2] R. H. Crawford, *MOSFET in Circuit Design*. New York: McGraw-Hill, 1967.

One-Dimensional Writing Model of n-Channel Floating Gate Ionization-Injection MOS (FIMOS)

SUMIO TANAKA AND MITSUAKI ISHIKAWA

Abstract—A physical writing model for an n-channel floating gate ionization-injection MOS (FIMOS) is described. Strength of accelerating field for the injection is calculated, taking the two-dimensional components near the drain junction into account. A new expression for the channel hot electron injection efficiency is also derived, using Baraff's analytic electron distribution function. The gate current, which shows a complicated dependence on the floating gate and drain voltages, has been reasonably formulated by the model. Integrating the gate current, time behavior of the threshold shift is predicted. The result is in reasonable agreement with experimental results.

I. INTRODUCTION

A N n-CHANNEL erasable and programmable read-only memory (EPROM) has been developed [1], which utilizes the channel hot electron injection just before the avalanche injection starts. Hagiwara *et al.* [2] named this device *floating gate ionization-injection MOS (FIMOS)*. The channel hot electron injection has been studied by direct measurements of the gate injection current, avoiding the electron trapping in the oxide [3], [4], and by the threshold shift measurement using FIMOS structures [5]. The electron injection is found to depend strongly upon applied voltages, channel length, and acceptor concentration.

Various theoretical analyses of the channel hot electron injection have also been reported [2], [6], [7]. However, they are all based on the Shockley model [8] in calculating injection efficiency. The model is not appropriate to be applied to the channel hot electron injection phenomenon, since it assumes a highly peaked distribution function along the accelerating electric field and is only applicable to the impact-ionization problem in the low electric field region [8]. In the channel hot electron injection phenomenon, most electrons are injected making a right angle to the accelerating electric field. Thus the model results in neglecting the major part of the injected electrons, especially in the high electric field region. The field estimation is either too inaccurate to calculate gate current dependence on device parameters [2], [7], or too complicated in two-dimensional analyses [6]. These are the reasons why no clear theoretical explanation of the channel hot electron injection phenomenon has been reported so far.

Manuscript received September 1, 1980; revised May 20, 1981.
The authors are with the Semiconductor Device Engineering Laboratory, Toshiba Corporation, 1, Komukai Toshiba-cho, Saiwai-ku, Kawasaki, 210 Japan.

This paper presents a physical writing model of FIMOS and, more generally, formulates the channel hot electron injection model in IGFET's.

In Section II-A, transistor characteristics of FIMOS structure are derived, considering the floating gate voltage, which is capacitively coupled to the control gate, drain, source, and silicon surface voltages, and channel length modulation [9]. Simple and accurate expression of the accelerating electric field strength in the saturation region is obtained, taking the oxide field and the mobile carrier density near the drain junction into account, as well as the substrate impurity charge density. In Section II-B, a new expression for the channel hot electron injection efficiency into the floating gate is derived, using the Baraff's maximum anisotropy approximation [10] to the electron distribution, instead of Shockley model. In Section II-C, transient characteristics of threshold shift are formulated. In Section III, the fundamental characteristics derived in Section II are calculated numerically as a function of device parameters and applied voltages, and then compared with experimental results. Section IV gives a summary and conclusion.

II. ANALYSIS OF FIMOS CHARACTERISTICS

A. Transistor Characteristics

1) Floating Gate Voltage: In a FIMOS structure, as shown in Fig. 1, the floating gate is capacitively coupled to the control gate, drain, source, and the silicon surface. From charge balance condition, the charge on the floating gate Q_{FG} is given by

$$Q_{FG} = C_1(V_{FG} - \langle \phi_s \rangle - \Phi_{MS}) + C_2(V_{FG} - V_{CG})$$
$$+ C_3(V_{FG} - V_D) + C_4(V_{FG} - V_S) \qquad (1)$$

where $\langle \phi_s \rangle$ is the average silicon surface voltage in the channel region, Φ_{MS} is the difference between the work function Φ_M of the floating gate and the silicon work function Φ_S. C_1, C_2, C_3, and C_4 are capacitances around the floating gate, as shown Fig. 1.

By the parallel plate approximation, capacitances C_1, C_2, C_3, and C_4 are given as

$$C_1 = \frac{K_{OL}\epsilon_0}{t_{ox1}} W_1 L_1 \qquad (2a)$$

$$C_2 = \frac{K_{OL}\epsilon_0}{t_{ox2}} W_2(L_1 + 2x_J) \qquad (2b)$$

Reprinted from *IEEE Trans. Electron Devices*, vol. ED-28, no. 10, pp. 1190–1197, October 1981.

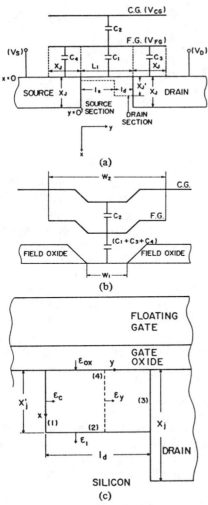

Fig. 1. Cross-sectional view of FIMOS. (a) Along the channel. (b) Across the channel. (c) Definition of the drain section.

$$C_3 = C_4 = \frac{K_{OL}\epsilon_0}{t_{ox1}} W_1 x_J \qquad (2c)$$

where K_{OL}, ϵ_0, t_{ox1} and t_{ox2}, W_1 and W_2, L_1 and x_J are the low frequency dielectric constant of SiO_2 (=3.9), the permittivity of free space, the first and second gate oxide thickness, the channel width and floating gate poly-silicon width, the channel length, and the junction depth, respectively. Normal and lateral diffusion lengths are assumed to be equal.

The surface voltage ϕ_s changes from $(V_S + 2\phi_F)$ to $(V_D + 2\phi_F)$ along the channel, where ϕ_F is the Fermi potential of silicon. Since C_1 is coupled strongly to the source side of the channel, it is assumed that the average surface voltage can be approximated as follows:

$$\langle \phi_s \rangle = V_S + 2\phi_F. \qquad (3)$$

Combining (1) and (3), the floating gate voltage is expressed by

$$V_{FG} = \frac{1}{\eta}\left[V_{CG} + \gamma V_D + \frac{(C_1 + C_4)}{C_2} V_S + \delta(\Phi_{MS} + 2\phi_F)\right. $$
$$\left. + \frac{Q_{FG}}{C_2}\right] \qquad (4)$$

where η, γ, and δ are as follows:

$$\eta = \frac{C_1 + C_2 + C_3 + C_4}{C_2} \qquad \gamma = \frac{C_3}{C_2} \qquad \delta = \frac{C_1}{C_2}. \qquad (5)$$

Transistor characteristics of the FIMOS structure should be those of a conventional IGFET, whose gate voltage is given by (4).

Threshold voltage of the control gate is especially important, because this is the only observable quantity concerning electron injection in a FIMOS structure. The charge density of electrons in the inversion layer, at distance y from the source, is given by [11]

$$Q_n(y) = -C_{ox}Q'_n(y) \qquad (6a)$$

$$Q'_n(y) = V_{FG} - V_{FB} - 2\phi_F - V_y - K_1\sqrt{V_y + 2\phi_F} \qquad (6b)$$

where V_y is the reverse bias between the channel and substrate, $C_{ox}(=K_{OL}\epsilon_0/t_{ox1})$ is the capacitance of the first gate oxide per unit area, $V_{FB}(=\Phi_{MS} - qN_{ss}/C_{ox})$ is the flat band voltage, and $K_1(=\sqrt{2qK_s\epsilon_0 N_A}/C_{ox})$ is the back-bias coefficient. In addition, q, N_{ss}, K_s, and N_A are the electronic charge, the fixed surface state density, the dielectric constant of S_i, and the acceptor concentration under the channel region, respectively. The threshold voltage of FIMOS V_{TC} is defined by the difference between source voltage and control gate voltage, when the charge at the source side of the channel just disappears. Using the condition $Q_n(0) = 0$ and combining (4) and (6), then

$$V_{TC} = (1 + 2\gamma)(\Phi_{MS} + 2\phi_F) - \eta\frac{qN_{ss}}{C_{ox}} - \gamma(V_D - V_S)$$
$$+ \eta K_1\sqrt{V_S + 2\phi_F} - \frac{Q_{FG}}{C_2}. \qquad (7)$$

The last term in (7) corresponds to the threshold shift by electron injection ΔV_T, i.e.,

$$\Delta V_T = -\frac{Q_{FG}}{C_2}. \qquad (8)$$

The threshold voltage of the floating gate is given by [11], similar to the normal threshold voltage of IGFET's

$$V_{T1} = V_{FB} + 2\phi_F + K_1\sqrt{V_S + 2\phi_F}. \qquad (9)$$

Combining (7), (8), and (9), the relation between V_{TC} and V_{T1} is given by

$$V_{TC} = \eta V_{T1} - \gamma(V_D - V_S) + \Delta V_T - \frac{C_1}{C_2}(\Phi_{MS} + 2\phi_F). \qquad (10)$$

V_{TC} is now given as a function of the drain and source voltages, through capacitive coupling between the floating gate and the source-drain regions.

2) Drain Current and Electric Field Near the Drain Junction: Drain current I_{DS} in the triode region is given by [11]

$$I_{DS} = W_1 C_{ox} Q'_n(y) v_y. \qquad (11)$$

Drift velocity v_y depends on the electric field parallel to the surface $\mathcal{E}_y$ and is expressed approximately by

$$v_y = \frac{\mu_s |\mathcal{E}_y|}{1 + \beta \mu_s |\mathcal{E}_y|} \qquad (12)$$

where β is a fitting parameter [9]. The surface mobility at a low drain voltage μ_s is also expressed approximately by

$$\mu_s = \frac{\mu_{s0}}{1 + \theta_m(V_{FG} - V_{T1})} \qquad (13)$$

where μ_{s0} and θ_m are fitting parameters. Solving (11) under the boundary conditions, $y = 0$ and $V_y = V_S$ at the source, and $y = L_1$ and $V_y = V_D$ at the drain, we obtain

$$I_{DS} = \frac{W_1 \mu_s C_{ox} FQ(V_D, V_S, V_{FG})}{L_1[1 + \beta \mu_s(V_D - V_S)/L_1]} \qquad (14)$$

where

$$\begin{aligned} FQ(V_D, V_S, V_{FG}) \equiv &(V_{FG} - V_{FB} - 2\phi_F)(V_D - V_S) \\ &- \tfrac{1}{2}(V_D^2 - V_S^2) - \tfrac{2}{3}K_1\{(V_D + 2\phi_F)^{3/2} \\ &- (V_S + 2\phi_F)^{3/2}\}. \end{aligned} \qquad (15)$$

In (11), I_{DS} is constant, and $Q_n'(y)$ is a monotonically decreasing function. Therefore, electron velocity v_y increases montonically as distance y approaches from the source to the drain. When $Q_n'(y)$ becomes very small in the region of the high reverse bias V_y, and v_y approaches the saturation velocity v_{sat}, (11) loses its validity. Therefore, the total channel region should be divided into two sections, as shown in Fig. 1. One is the source section where (11) is still valid. The other is the drain section, where (11) loses its validity and mobile electrons are running with the saturation velocity v_{sat}. When the lengths of each section are defined as l_s and l_d, then

$$l_s + l_d = L_1. \qquad (16)$$

From (11), drain saturation voltage V_{DSAT} satisfies the following equation:

$$I_{DS} = W_1 C_{ox} Q_n'(V_{DSAT}) v_{sat}. \qquad (17)$$

From (12), critical electric field $\mathcal{E}_c$, which corresponds to the saturation velocity, is given by

$$\mathcal{E}_c = \frac{v_{sat}}{\mu_s(1 - \beta v_{sat})}. \qquad (18)$$

In order to calculate the electric field in the drain section, a one-dimensional model is assumed with uniform mobile electron distribution within the distance $x_J' = x_J/h(h > 1)$ from the surface toward the substrate. Mobile electron density N_{me} is given by

$$N_{me} = \frac{I_{DS}}{q W_1 x_J' v_{sat}}. \qquad (19)$$

From (6b) and (17), N_{me} is given by

$$\begin{aligned} N_{me} = \frac{C_{ox}}{q x_J'}[&V_{FG} - V_{FB} - 2\phi_F - V_{DSAT} \\ &- K_1\sqrt{V_{DSAT} + 2\phi_F}]. \end{aligned} \qquad (20)$$

We model the drain section as a rectangular region which has an area of $l_d x_J'$ as shown in Fig. 1(c). The drain section is surrounded by the four boundaries (Fig. 1(c)) and encloses both mobile and immobile charges. Define $\mathcal{E}_1$, $\mathcal{E}_{ox}$, and $\mathcal{E}_y$ as the electric fields perpendicular to the boundaries 2, 4, and a boundary at a distance y and parallel to 1. The electric field in the oxide $\mathcal{E}_{ox}$ is given by

$$\mathcal{E}_{ox} = \frac{V_{FG} - V_{FB} - \phi_s}{t_{ox1}}. \qquad (21)$$

The electric field $\mathcal{E}_1$ is derived from the depletion approximation, which defines a parabolic potential distribution with x; then

$$\mathcal{E}_1(y) = \frac{q N_A}{K_s \epsilon_0}(x_d(y) - x_J') \qquad (22a)$$

where $x_d(y)$ is the depletion layer width from the surface to the substrate and is given by

$$x_d(y) = \sqrt{\frac{2 K_s \epsilon_0}{q N_A} \phi_s}. \qquad (22b)$$

Applying Gauss's law to the drain section

$$\begin{aligned} \int_0^{x_J'} \mathcal{E}_y \, dx &- \int_{l_s}^y \frac{K_{OL}}{K_s} \mathcal{E}_{ox}(y') \, dy' - \int_0^{x_J'} \mathcal{E}_c \, dx \\ &+ \int_{l_s}^y \mathcal{E}_1(y') \, dy' = -\frac{q}{K_s \epsilon_0} \\ &\cdot \int_{l_s}^y \left\{ \int_0^{x_J'} (N_A + N_{me}(y')) \, dx \right\} dy' \end{aligned} \qquad (23)$$

where the origin of the x-axis is at the interface between the surface, and the direction of the x-axis is toward the silicon, as shown in Fig. 1.

Approximating the surface potential ϕ_s in (21) and (22) by $(V_y + 2\phi_F)$, and differentiating both sides of (23), we have the following relation:

$$\begin{aligned} \frac{d^2 V_y}{dy^2} = \frac{C_{ox}}{K_s \epsilon_0 x_J'} \Bigg[&V_y - V_{DSAT} \\ &+ \frac{K_1(V_y - V_{DSAT})}{\sqrt{V_y + 2\phi_F} + \sqrt{V_{DSAT} + 2\phi_F}} \Bigg]. \end{aligned} \qquad (24)$$

For simplicity, V_y in the square root in (24) is approximated by the average potential $(V_D + V_{DSAT})/2$. Then

$$\frac{d^2 V_y}{dy^2} = A_c^2(V_y - V_{DSAT}) \qquad (25a)$$

$$\begin{aligned} A_c^2 = \frac{K_{OL}}{K_s t_{ox1} x_J'} \\ \cdot \left[1 + \frac{K_1}{\sqrt{(V_D + V_{DSAT})/2 + 2\phi_F} + \sqrt{V_{DSAT} + 2\phi_F}} \right]. \end{aligned} \qquad (25b)$$

Under the following boundary conditions

$$V_y = V_{DSAT}, \&_y = \&_c \text{ at } y = l_s, \text{ and } V_y = V_D \text{ at } y = L_1,$$

we have

$$V_y = \frac{\&_c}{A_c} \sinh [A_c(y - l_s)] + V_{DSAT} \qquad (26a)$$

$$\&_y = \&_c \cosh [A_c(y - l_s)] \qquad (26b)$$

$$l_d = \frac{1}{A_c} \sinh^{-1} \left[\frac{A_c}{\&_c} (V_D - V_{DSAT}) \right]. \qquad (26c)$$

From (26a) and (26b)

$$\&_y = \sqrt{\&_c^2 + A_c^2 (V_y - V_{DSAT})^2} \qquad (27a)$$

$$\simeq A_c (V_y - V_{DSAT}). \qquad (27b)$$

The relation between $\&_y$ and V_y differs from the square root relation by the simple depletion approximation [2].

El-Mansy et al. [9] obtained the empirical expression for V_{DSAT} on short channel devices from their two-dimensional analysis

$$V_{DSAT} = V_S + \frac{V_{DSAT}(0) - V_S}{1 + 30 (t_{ox1}/L_1)} \qquad (28)$$

where $V_{DSAT}(0)$ is the saturation voltage for the long channel devices and is given by

$$V_{DSAT}(0) = V_{FG} - V_{FB} - 2\phi_F$$
$$- \frac{1}{2} [\sqrt{1 + (4/K_1^2)(V_{FG} - V_{FB})} - 1]. \qquad (29)$$

If we determine V_{DSAT} from (28) first, then $A_c, \&_c, l_d, l_s$, and $\&_y$ can be determined from (25b), (18), (26c), (16), and finally (26b), successively. The drain saturation current is given from (14) by replacing V_D and L_1 by V_{DSAT} and l_s, respectively.

B. Injection Efficiency

Baraff presented the maximum anisotropy approximation [10] for the hot electron distribution in both high and low field regions. It is a good analytic approximation to the exact solution by integral equation method, which is also given by Baraff [15]. The distribution function $f(p)$ for electrons with momentum p is given by

$$f(p) = \frac{m_0(E) + m_1(E) \cos \theta}{E} \qquad (30)$$

where $E = p^2/2m$ is the energy of the electron with mass m, and θ is the angle between the field and momentum p. When electron energy E exceed E_i, the threshold energy for impact ionization

$$m_0(E) = (E/E_i)^{-a^*} \exp (-b^*(E - E_i)) \qquad (31a)$$

$$m_1(E) = \alpha m_0(E) \qquad (31b)$$

$$a^* = (1 - 3/\alpha)/(2 + 3/\alpha) \qquad (31c)$$

$$1/b^* = Q(2/3 + 1/\alpha) \qquad (31d)$$

$$\alpha = r + 3(1 - r)E_R^*/2Q$$
$$+ [3r + (r + 3(1 - r)E_R^*/2Q)^2]^{1/2} \qquad (31e)$$

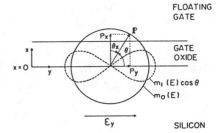

Fig. 2. Hot electron distribution.

$$E_R^* = [(1 - r)^{-1} - 1]/l_n(1 - r)^{-1} \cdot E_R \qquad (31f)$$

$$Q = q\&_y l_i r \qquad (31g)$$

$$r = \lambda/(\lambda + l_i) \qquad (31h)$$

where E_R is the Raman phonon (=0.053 eV at room temperature), λ is the mean free path for optical phonon scattering, and l_i is the mean free path for impact ionization. Contour lines of $m_0(E)$ and $m_1(E) \cos \theta$ are shown in Fig. 2.

The probability for electron–hole pair generation per unit distance, that is, Townsend's alpha coefficient α_T is also given by Baraff [10]:

$$\alpha_T \lambda = \int_{E_i}^{\infty} r m_0(E) \, dE / \frac{1}{3} \int_0^{\infty} m_1(E) \, dE \qquad (32)$$

where $r = 0.5$ and $Q = q\&_y \lambda$ are assumed.

Injection efficiency Γ, the ratio of the gate injection current density in the oxide to the current density in the drain section, is given by

$$\Gamma = \frac{\int v_x f(p) \, d^3 p \text{ (for } E \geq \Phi_B)}{\int v_y f(p) \, d^3 p} \qquad (33)$$

where Φ_B is barrier height energy of SiO_2–Si interface. Assume that the field parallel to the surface is larger, compared to the normal component, integration concerning $m_1(E)$ disappears in the numerator of (33) from the symmetric consideration. Let θ_x denote the angle between the x-axis and p, then integration for $m_0(E)$ in the numerator of (33) is given by

$$\int v_x f(p) \, d^3 p = 2\pi \int_0^{\theta_{max}} d\theta_x \sin \theta_x \int_{\sqrt{2m\Phi_B}}^{\infty} p^2 \, dp$$

$$\cdot \frac{p \cos \theta_x}{m} \cdot \frac{m_0(E)}{E}$$

$$= 2\pi m \int_{\Phi_B}^{\infty} \left(1 - \frac{\Phi_B}{E} \right) m_0(E) \, dE \qquad (34)$$

where $\theta_{max} = \cos^{-1} (\Phi_B/E)^{1/2}$ results from the restriction that the x component energy $p_x^2/2m$ must be larger than the barrier height energy Φ_B. The denominator of (33) has been calculated [10] as follows:

$$\int v_y f(p) \, d^3 p = 8\pi m \cdot \frac{1}{3} \int_0^{\infty} m_1(E) \, dE. \qquad (35)$$

Combining (34) and (35), injection efficiency Γ is given by

$$\Gamma = \frac{1}{4} \int_{\Phi_B}^{\infty} \left(1 - \frac{\Phi_B}{E}\right) m_0(E)\, dE \Big/ \frac{1}{3} \int_0^{\infty} m_1(E)\, dE. \quad (36)$$

On the other hand, the numerator of (32) can be led to a simple form, as shown in the Appendix

$$\int_{E_i}^{\infty} m_0(E)\, dE = 1/b^*. \quad (37)$$

Combining (32) and (37), we have

$$\Gamma = \frac{b^*}{4r} \int_{\Phi_B}^{\infty} \left(1 - \frac{\Phi_B}{E}\right) m_0(E)\, dE \cdot \alpha_T \lambda. \quad (38)$$

Changing the integral variable E to $t_1 = b^*(E - \Phi_B)$, Γ is given by

$$\Gamma = \frac{g}{4r} \exp(-b^*(\Phi_B - E_i)) \cdot \alpha_T \lambda \quad (39a)$$

$$g = \int_0^{\infty} \frac{t_1}{t_1 + b^*\Phi_B} \left(\frac{t_1 + b^*\Phi_B}{b^*E_i}\right)^{-a^*} \exp(-t_1)\, dt_1. \quad (39b)$$

Equation (39) means that injection efficiency is a product of the probability that an accelerated electron gains energy E_i, i.e., $\alpha_T \lambda$, and the probability that the electron further gains barrier height energy Φ_B, i.e., $(g/(4r)) \exp(-b^*(\Phi_B - E_i))$.

Crowell and Sze [12] derive an empirical expression for $\alpha_T \lambda$ from the results of exact integral equation method by Baraff [15], which is given by

$$\alpha_T \lambda = \exp \left\{ \begin{array}{l} (11.5r_I^2 - 1.17r_I + 3.9 \times 10^{-4})x_I^2 \\ + (46r_I^2 - 11.9r_I + 1.75 \times 10^{-2})x_I \\ + (-757r_I^2 + 75.5r_I - 1.92) \end{array} \right\}$$

$$r_I = \frac{E_R}{E_i} \qquad x_I = \frac{E_i}{q \mathcal{E}_y \lambda} \qquad E_i = 1.5 E_g$$

$$\lambda = \lambda_0 \tanh\left(\frac{qE_{R0}}{2k_B T}\right) \qquad E_R = E_{R0} \tanh\left(\frac{qE_{R0}}{2k_B T}\right). \quad (40)$$

$E_g, \lambda_0, E_{R0}, k_B,$ and T are the forbidden band gap energy, the mean free path for optical phonon scattering at absolute zero, the optical phonon energy at absolute zero (=0.063 eV), the Boltzmann's constant, and absolute temperature, respectively.

It can reasonably be assumed that λ is about 62 Å at room temperature, which is measured in the p-n junction measurements [8]. If the value of h can be set properly, in order to calculate field strength $\mathcal{E}_y$ in (26b), probability Γ can be calculated by using (39) and (40).

In Fig. 3, the function $g/(4r) \exp(-b^*(\Phi_B - E_i))$, which is equal to $\Gamma/(\alpha_T \lambda)$, is plotted against electric field $\mathcal{E}_y$ for various barrier height energies Φ_B in case of $\lambda = 62$ Å. Hagiwara et al. [2] assumed that the injection efficiency Γ is expressed by $\Gamma = \text{const} \cdot \alpha_T$. However, Γ/α_T has a strong dependence on the electric field, as shown in Fig. 3, so the assumption is inaccurate.

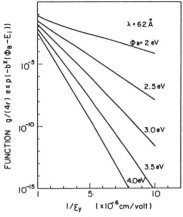

Fig. 3. Function $(g/(4r)) \exp(-b^*(\Phi_B - E_i))$ versus electric field $\mathcal{E}_y$ for various barrier heights Φ_B.

C. Transient Characteristics of Threshold Voltage

In this section, transient characteristics of threshold shift by electron injection into the floating gate is formulated. The current from the floating gate to the control gate and electron trapping in the oxide between the channel and the floating gate, are both assumed to be negligibly small.

Injection efficiency Γ, which was introduced in Section II-B, depends not only upon electric field $\mathcal{E}_y$, but also upon barrier height Φ_B. Electric field $\mathcal{E}_y$ has already been given in (26). When oxide field $\mathcal{E}_{ox} = (V_{FG} - \Phi_s - \Phi_{MS})/t_{ox1}$ is positive, electrons that have enough energy to surmount barrier height Φ_B are injected into the oxide. Barrier height Φ_B is lowered by the Schottky effect [13], as follows:

$$\Phi_B = \chi - \sqrt{\frac{q\mathcal{E}_{ox}}{4\pi K_{OH}\epsilon_0}} - K_{OL}\lambda_T \mathcal{E}_{ox} \quad (41)$$

where χ is silicon electron affinity (=3.05 eV), K_{OH} is the high frequency dielectric constant of SiO$_2$ (=2.15), λ_T is the Thomas-Fermi screening length in the metal (=1 Å).

Therefore, when $V_{FG} > (V_D + \Phi_{MS} + 2\phi_F)$, electrons are injected from the entire channel region. On the other hand, when $V_{FG} < (V_D + \Phi_{MS} + 2\phi_F)$, electron injection does not take place near the drain junction. In both cases, in the source section (see Fig. 1), electric field $\mathcal{E}_y$ is weak and the electron injection can be neglected. As a result, it can be assumed that the actual contribution of the electron injection is limited within a part of the drain section $l_s < y < l_m$. Boundary value l_m is determined by the condition $\mathcal{E}_{ox} = 0$ and (26a)

$$l_m = \frac{1}{A_c} \sinh^{-1} \left[\frac{A_c}{\mathcal{E}_c}(V_{y0} - V_{DSAT})\right] + l_s \quad (42)$$

where

$$V_{y0} = V_{FG} - \Phi_{MS} - 2\phi_F. \quad (43)$$

Combining current density $J_y = I_{DS}/(W_1 x_J')$ and injection efficiency Γ, gate current I_G is given by

$$I_G = W_1 \int_{l_s}^{l_m} J_y \Gamma(\mathcal{E}_y, \Phi_B)\, dy. \quad (44)$$

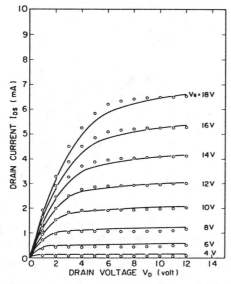

Fig. 4. Drain current characteristics. $W_1/L_1 = 50/6.1 \ \mu m/\mu m$.

From (8), the transient threshold shift ΔV_T is given by

$$C_2 \frac{d(\Delta V_T)}{dt} = \frac{I_{DS}}{x'_J} \int_{l_s}^{l_m} \Gamma(\mathcal{E}_y, \Phi_B) \, dy. \qquad (45)$$

III. COMPARISON WITH EXPERIMENTAL RESULTS

N-channel MOS transistors of conventional and FIMOS structures were fabricated by the standard n-channel Si-gate process. Si wafers used were p-type, (100) oriented, and $6 \ \Omega \cdot$ cm. Boron implantation was performed on the silicon surface to raise surface impurity concentration.

A. Drain Current Characteristics

Circles in Fig. 4 show experimental data of drain currents in a conventional MOS transistor. Device parameters measured are t_{ox1} (gate oxide thickness) = 1000 Å, x_J (source-drain junction depth) = 1.8 μm, V_{T1} (threshold voltage) = 2 V, and W_1/L_1 (channel width/length) = 50/6.1 ($\mu m/\mu m$). Acceptor concentration values N_A were determined to be 2.8×10^{16} cm^{-3} from threshold voltage dependences on the substrate bias voltages.

In order to calculate drain currents using (14), it is necessary to determine, first, the parameters in (12) and v_{sat} in (18). However, since no measured values of β and v_{sat} on MOS transistor were available, the values in bulk Si were used instead. They are $\beta = 7 \times 10^{-8}$ (s/cm) and $v_{sat} = 8.2 \times 10^6$ (cm/s) [14]. The gate voltage dependence of surface mobility on long-channel MOS transistors fabricated on the same chip is best fitted by $\mu_{so} = 620$ cm^2/V $\cdot$ s and $\theta_m = 0.025$ (V^{-1}) over the wide range from $V_{FG} = V_{T1}$ to 20 V.

Solid lines in Fig. 4 show calculated results for $h = 2$. Results agree with the experimental results, indicating that the mobile electrons in the drain section distribute from the surface to half of the junction depth.

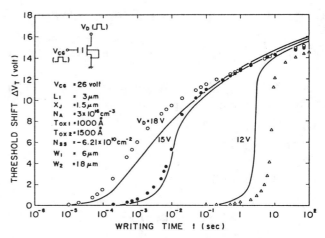

Fig. 5. Threshold shift versus writing time for 3-μm channel length.

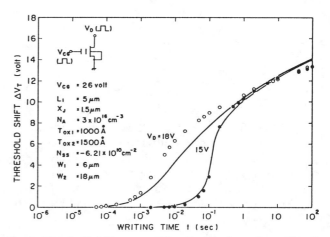

Fig. 6. Threshold shift versus writing time for 5-μm channel length.

B. Time Dependence of the Threshold Shift

For threshold shift measurement of the FIMOS structure, successive pulses were applied synchronously to drain and control gate electrodes. Circles and triangles in Figs. 5 and 6 show the experimental results of the threshold voltage shifts versus the integrated time of the applied pulsewidth. Major device parameters of the samples are listed in the figures. The initial threshold voltage of FIMOS V_{TC} are 4 V in both cases and the threshold of floating gate V_{T1}, calculated by (9) and (10), is 2.64 V. Acceptor concentration N_A and surface state density N_{ss} are determined by the above mentioned method. The threshold shift rate depends strongly upon the drain voltage and channel length. Calculated results, based on the present model, using (45), are also shown in Figs. 5 and 6 by solid lines. The same $h(=2)$ values were used as in MOS transistors. The theoretical results satisfactorily depict threshold shift dependence on drain voltage and writing time.

Comparing the results in Figs. 5 and 6, writing speed in Fig. 5 is faster than that in Fig. 6. The difference is explained theoretically by increase in accelerating field $\mathcal{E}_y$ in (27a) due to a lower saturation voltage V_{DSAT} in a short-channel device (see (28)).

To investigate threshold shift characteristics shown in Figs.

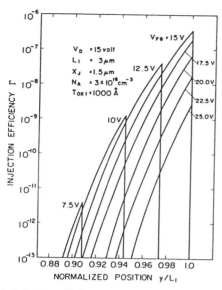

Fig. 7. Injection efficiency versus normalized position.

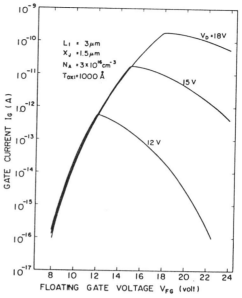

Fig. 8. Gate current as a function of floating gate voltage.

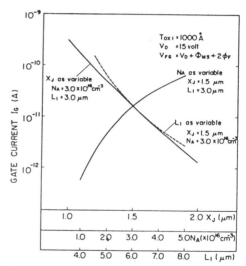

Fig. 9. Maximum gate current versus device parameters.

5 and 6 in detail, gate injection current will be calculated as a function of floating gate and drain voltages in the next section.

C. Gate Current Characteristics

In this section, injection efficiency along the channel and gate injection current are discussed. The device parameters are the same as listed in Fig. 5.

Fig. 7 shows results of injection efficiency calculated at $V_D = 15$ V as a function of a normalized position y/L_1 and floating gate voltage, by using (39a). As described in Section II-C, electrons are injected entirely from the drain section when $V_D + \Phi_{MS} + 2\phi_F \leqslant V_{FG}(\Phi_{MS} + 2\phi_F = -0.18$ V). The highest electron injection occurs at the boundary between the drain and the drain sections ($y/L_1 = 1$). The field at this position is proportional to $A_C(V_D - V_{DSAT})$ from (27b). So, with increase in floating gate voltage, the electron injection rate is reduced, due to increase in V_{DSAT}. On the contrary, when $V_D + \Phi_{MS} + 2\phi_F \geqslant V_{FG}$, electron injection is suppressed near the drain by the field between gate and drain electrodes. The maximum electron injection takes place at a position where the reverse bias voltage V_y is equal to $V_{FG} - \Phi_{MS} - 2\phi_F$ (see (43)). The field at this position is proportional to $A_C(V_{FG} - V_{DSAT} - \Phi_{MS} - 2\phi_F)$ from (27b). Therefore, the electron injection has a strong dependence only on the floating gate voltage.

Fig. 8 shows the gate injection current versus floating gate voltage for three drain voltages $V_D = 12$, 15, and 18 V. With increase in floating gate voltage up to $V_{FG} \simeq V_D$, the gate injection current increases and then decreases rapidly. Fig. 7 confirms that the gate injection current up to $V_{FG} \simeq V_D$ corresponds to the case where the electron injection is limited in a part of the drain section. It is principally independent of the drain voltage.

The gate injection current of $V_{FG} \geqslant V_D$ corresponds to the case where the highest electron injection occurs at the boundary between the drain and the drain section. Therefore, the gate injection current depends strongly on the drain voltage as well as gate voltage, as mentioned before. The result in Fig. 8 explains well the experimental data, which have been reported earlier [3], [4], [5], [7].

The threshold shift dependence on the drain voltage and writing time in Figs. 5 and 6 can be explained by the results in Fig. 8. Within a short writing time, total amount of injected electron into the floating gate is small and the floating gate remains at a higher voltage than V_D. Therefore, the electron injection depends strongly upon drain voltage. When the floating gate voltage is reduced to the drain voltage after a long writing time, the electron injection is no longer sensitive to the drain voltage.

Next, effects of the channel length, junction depth, and acceptor concentration on the gate current has been studied. Fig. 9 shows the calculated results of the gate injection current when $V_{FG} = V_D + \Phi_{MS} + 2\phi_F$, for the three device parameters. Only one device parameter is changed, while others remain at the values listed in Fig. 8. The results in Fig. 9 show qualitatively good agreement with the experimental results published before [2], [3], [4], [7].

IV. Summary and Conclusion

A physical writing model of n-channel FIMOS was formulated. Prediction of the threshold shift is found to be in reasonable agreement with experimental data. The model gives clear explanation to the complicated characteristics of the injected gate current. The model is directly applicable to investigation on the channel hot electron injection phenomena in small geometry MOS devices under normal operating voltages or the unintentional writing phenomena in FIMOS.

Appendix
Derivation of (37)

The relation between $m_0(E)$ and $m_1(E)$ was reported by Baraff [10], as follows:

$$\frac{Q}{3} \frac{dm_1(E)}{dE} + rm_0(E) - (1-r)E_R^* \frac{dm_0(E)}{dE} = 0. \quad \text{(A1)}$$

Integrating $m_0(E)$ in (A1) from E_i to infinity, we can write

$$\int_{E_i}^{\infty} m_0(E)\, dE = \left(\frac{Q}{3} m_1(E_i) - (1-r)E_R^* m_0(E_i)\right) \bigg/ r. \quad \text{(A2)}$$

The ratio of $m_0(E)$ to $m_1(E)$, α, is also given by Baraff [10]:

$$\alpha = \left(3(1-r)E_R^* + \frac{3r}{b^*}\right) \bigg/ Q. \quad \text{(A3)}$$

Substituting the relation $m_0(E_i) = 1$ and $m_1(E_i) = \alpha$ [10] to (A2), and using the relation (A3), yield (37)

$$\int_{E_i}^{\infty} m_0(E)\, dE = 1/b^*. \quad \text{(37)}$$

Acknowledgment

The authors would like to express their appreciation to Dr. H. Hara for valuable comments and discussions and to S. Kohyama for reading this manuscript.

References

[1] G. Gear, "FAMOS PROM reliability studies," *Proc. Int. Reliability Phys. Symp.*, pp. 198–201, 1976.
[2] T. Hagiwara, E. Takeda, M. Horiuchi, R. Kondo, and Y. Ito, "Analysis and experimentation on FIMOS (n-channel FAMOS) devices," Proc. 8th Conf. Solid-State Devices, Tokyo, 1976, *Japan. J. Appl. Phys.*, vol. 16, Suppl. 16-1, pp. 211–214, 1977.
[3] P. E. Cottrell, R. R. Troutman, and T. H. Ning, "Hot-electron emission in N-channel IGFET's," *IEEE J. Solid-State Circuits*, vol. SC-14, pp. 442–455, 1979.
[4] T. H. Ning, P. W. Cook, R. H. Dennard, C. M. Osburn, S. E. Schuster, and H. N. Yu, "1 μm MOSFET VLSI technology: Part IV—hot electron design constraints," *IEEE J. Solid-State Circuits*, vol. SC-14, pp. 268–275, 1979.
[5] S. Kohyama, T. Furuyama, S. Mimura, and H. Iizuka, "Nonthermal carrier generation in MOS structures," Proc. 11th Conf. Solid-State Devices, Tokyo, 1979, *Japan. J. Appl. Phys.*, vol. 19, Suppl. 19-1, pp. 85–92, 1980.
[6] A. Phillips, Jr., R. R. O'Brien, and R. C. Joy, "IGFET Hot Electron Emission Model," *Int. Electron Devices Meeting Tech. Dig.*, pp. 39–42, 1975.
[7] C. Hu, "Lucky-electron model of channel hot electron emission," *Int. Electron Devices Meeting Tech. Dig.*, pp. 22–25, 1979.
[8] A. G. Chynoweth, "Charge multiplication phenomena," in *Semiconductors and Semimetals IV*, R. K. Willardson and A. C. Beer, Eds. New York: Academic, 1968, pp. 263–325.
[9] Y. A. El-Mansy and A. R. Boothroyd, "A simple two-dimensional model for IGFET operation in the saturation region," *IEEE Trans. Electron Devices*, vol. ED-24, pp. 254–262, 1977.
[10] G. A. Baraff, "Maximum anisotropy approximation for calculating electron distribution; application to high field transport in semiconductors," *Phys. Rev.*, vol. 133, pp. A26–A33, 1964.
[11] A. S. Grove, *Physics and Technology of Semiconductor Devices.* New York: Wiley, 1967, pp. 321–333.
[12] C. R. Crowell and S. H. Sze, "Temperature dependence of avalanche multiplication in semiconductors," *Appl. Phys. Lett.*, vol. 9, pp. 242–244, 1966.
[13] C. A. Mead, E. H. Snow, and B. E. Deal, "Barrier lowering and field penetration at metal dielectric interfaces," *Appl. Phys. Lett.*, vol. 9, pp. 53–55, 1966.
[14] E. J. Ryder, "Mobility of holes and electrons in high electric fields," *Phys. Rev.*, vol. 90, pp. 766–769, 1953.
[15] G. A. Baraff, "Distribution functions and ionization rates for hot electrons in semiconductors," *Phys. Rev.*, vol. 128, pp. 2507–2517, 1962.

An Erase Model for FAMOS EPROM Devices

RON D. KATZNELSON AND DOV FROHMAN-BENTCHKOWSKY, SENIOR MEMBER, IEEE

Abstract—A physical model is presented which explains the various features of the UV erase process in FAMOS EPROM devices. An erase sensitivity factor is defined in this model, and correlated with experimental results.

The erase sensitivity factor was found to be proportional to the floating-gate photoinjecting area, and inversely proportional to oxide thickness and total capacitance of the floating gate.

Photoinjection of electrons from thin strips on the floating-gate edges are shown to be responsible for the charge removal from the floating gate. Quantum yields in the order of 10^{-4} were measured for this erase process and correlated with values found in the literature. In addition, the *I-V* and spectral characteristics of photoinjected currents as low as 10^{-15} A from poly-Si to SiO_2 in FAMOS devices were measured and compared to data from Si–SiO_2 structures.

Special features pertaining to the erase of a fully covered floating-gate FAMOS cell were investigated: the decrease in erase rate at low ΔV_t is discussed, as well as the optical access to the floating gate in these devices.

Based on experimental and theoretical grounds, hole injection is discounted as a possible erase mechanism in the structures investigated.

I. INTRODUCTION

EPROM (Erasable Programmable Read-Only Memory) memories employing FAMOS (Floating-Gate Avalanche Injection MOS) [1] devices are in widespread use.

The FAMOS device is electrically programmed by avalanche injection to the polysilicon floating gate and erased by illuminating the device with ultraviolet (UV) light.

The programming mechanism and the structure of these FAMOS devices were studied and described elsewhere [1], [2]. However, very little work was done on the UV erase mechanism [3], [4]. In this study, spectral, electrical, and geometrical erase factors were investigated and correlated with a proposed physical model.

II. ERASE FACTORS AND *I-V* CHARACTERISTICS

A. The UV Erase Model and the Erase Sensitivity Factor for FAMOS Devices

Typical cross sections of three FAMOS devices used in commercial products are shown in Fig. 1. The erase of a FAMOS device is achieved by means of removing the charge on its

Manuscript received July 6, 1979; revised January 15, 1980.

R. D. Katznelson was with the Division of Applied Physics, School of Applied Science and Technology, The Hebrew University of Jerusalem, Jerusalem, Israel. He is now with the Applied Physics and Information Science Department, University of California at San Diego, La Jolla, CA 92093.

D. Frohman-Bentchkowsky is with the Division of Applied Physics, School of Applied Science and Technology, The Hebrew University of Jerusalem, Jerusalem, Israel.

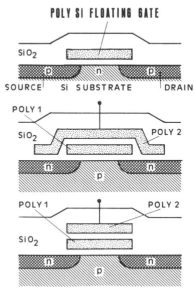

Fig. 1. Cross sections of typical devices used in commercial EPROM products.

floating gate. Charge injected during the programming phase is removed when the poly-Si floating gate is illuminated by UV light of an appropriate wavelength. The incident photons impart sufficient energy to the stored electrons to excite them over the oxide energy barrier with the aid of the built-in field. The photoinjection current to the substrate and/or top gate depends on the oxide field, which is directly related to the charge present on the floating gate. This removal of charge is detected by sensing the change in turn-on voltage V_t of the memory device.

In order to determine the relationship between the charge on the floating gate and time during the erase process, the *I-V* characteristics of photoinjection currents from polysilicon or silicon to silicon dioxide are of interest.

A number of workers have reported on this subject [5]-[9] and the common trend is depicted in Fig. 2. The photoinjection current is nearly linearly dependent on the electric oxide field above $3–4 \times 10^5$ V/cm (Fig. 2). This photoinjection current is also a linear function of the UV light intensity at a given wavelength [9]. For practical purposes, the photoinjection current density J (in A/cm^2) for oxide fields in excess of 4×10^5 V/cm could be modeled as

$$J = F(aE + b) \qquad (1)$$

where F is the UV intensity in W/cm^2, E is the oxide field in V/cm, and a, b are empirical constants depending on wave-

Reprinted from *IEEE Trans. Electron Devices*, vol. ED-27, no. 9, pp. 1744–1752, September 1980.

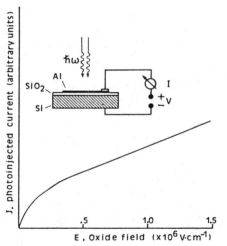

Fig. 2. J-E characteristics of photoinjection currents from Si to SiO$_2$ (taken from [7]).

length and other physical parameters pertaining to the Si-SiO$_2$ interface, affecting the photoyield.

The floating gate is charged with a negative[1] charge Q which sets the floating-gate potential V_{fg} to Q/C_t and the oxide field to V_{fg}/X_o where C_t is the total capacitance of the floating gate and X_o is the effective oxide thickness in the photoinjection area. If the device has a top gate it is biased at substrate potential during the erase period.

The rate of charge removal due to photoinjection current from the floating gate is given by

$$-\frac{dQ}{dt} = A_{\text{inj}} J = A_{\text{inj}} F \left(a \frac{Q}{X_o C_t} + b \right) \qquad (2)$$

where A_{inj} is the effective photoinjecting area on the floating-gate surface.

The solution of this first-order differential equation is given by

$$\left(\frac{Q}{X_o C_t} + \frac{b}{a} \right) = \left(\frac{Q_o}{X_o C_t} + \frac{b}{a} \right) e^{-FKt} \qquad (3)$$

$$K = \frac{a \cdot A_{\text{inj}}}{X_o \cdot C_t} \qquad (4)$$

b/a has the dimensions of field and for oxide fields $Q/(X_o C_t)$ considerably larger than b/a, (3) could be approximated by

$$Q = Q_o e^{-FKt}. \qquad (5)$$

As found experimentally, b/a has a low enough value (2×10^5 V/cm), suggesting that deviations from (5) are possible towards the end of the erase process.

The shift in FAMOS device threshold voltage ΔV_t is proportional to the charge Q on its floating gate. Using (5), ΔV_t is related to time through an exponential relation

$$\Delta V_t(t) = \Delta V_t(0) e^{-FKt}. \qquad (6)$$

[1] Throughout this work, negative charges, currents, and voltages are treated without their negative sign.

The product $F \cdot K$ or $\int_0^\infty K(\lambda) (dF/d\lambda) d\lambda$ for nonmonochromatic source is the erase rate in seconds^{-1}, where $K(\lambda)$ is the erase sensitivity factor defined by (4) and given in s$^{-1} \cdot$ W$^{-1} \cdot$ cm^2, and $dF/d\lambda$ is the UV irradiance spectral density in W $\cdot$ cm$^{-2} \cdot$ Å^{-1}. The EPROM erase time depends both on the erase rate and the threshold voltage set by the sense amplifier of the EPROM array.

B. Spectral Erase Sensitivity—The Dependence of K on Wavelength

The erase sensitivity factor K depends on wavelength through the constant a, which bears the dependence of photoinjection currents on photon energy.

It is well known from early work on photoemission from Si to SiO$_2$ [5], [10]-[13] that the photon energy threshold is about 4.3 eV for photoemission from the valance band of Si to the conduction band of SiO$_2$, regardless of the Si doping. However, in degenerate n-type silicon, an additional lower threshold of about 3.2 eV was observed [11], [13] which corresponds to photoinjection from the conduction band of Si to the conduction band of SiO$_2$. The photoyield was found to be two orders of magnitude lower than that above 4.3 eV [11], [13]. Hence, the spectral erase sensitivity profile is expected to depend on the type (p or n) of floating poly-Si gate and it will have a marked decrease at around 4.3 eV (~2900 Å).

C. Geometrical Aspects of the Erase Sensitivity

It follows from (4) that the erase sensitivity factor is inversely proportional to the oxide thickness X_o and the total capacitance of the floating gate—C_t composed of C_1—the floating gate-substrate capacitance and C_2 the floating gate-top gate capacitance if such control gate is present.

The erase sensitivity is proportional to A_{inj}, which is the effective photoinjection area of the floating gate. It is worth noting that silicon has a large optical-absorption coefficient at 2537 Å (the wavelength commonly used with the mercury UV lamp). $\alpha = 2 \times 10^6$ cm^{-1} [14], [15] corresponds to an absorption depth of about 50 Å at this wavelength. Hence, A_{inj} would only include floating-gate areas, satisfying both the following conditions:

1) Areas optically accessible by either direct paths through the transparent SiO$_2$ [16] or by indirect paths through reflections and diffraction from the silicon substrate and poly-Si gates.

2) Areas around which the oxide electric field supports photoinjection.

Hence, one can deduce that areas of photoinjection would be concentrated around the floating-gate perimeter for which both the above conditions readily apply.

D. I-V Characteristics of Photoinjected Currents in FAMOS EPROM Devices

With no data available on I-V characteristics of photoinjected currents from polysilicon to SiO$_2$, it is desirable to directly confirm the assumed I-V dependence using the FAMOS device

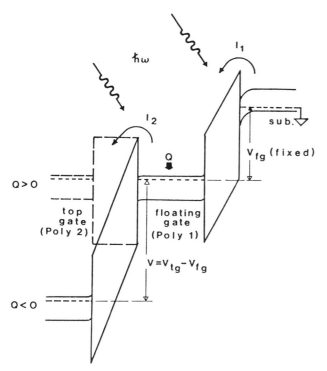

Fig. 3. Energy bands of a FAMOS device under photoinjection I_2-V measurement.

TABLE I

CELL TYPE	L_1 (μm)	L_2 (μm)	Z_1 (μm)	Z_2 (μm)	POLY 1 TYPE
X	8 small 12 large	6	7	20	n
Y_a	6	6	6	18	p
Y_b	6 small 8 large	6 8	6	18	n
W_a	6	12	6	12	n
W_b	6	12	6	12	n

NOTES: 1. All dimensions are within ± 1 μm
2. In all cells top and bottom oxides are 1000 Å thick

gate is I_1 - I_2, thus

$$\frac{dV_{tg}}{dt} = \frac{1}{C_2}\frac{dQ}{dt} = \frac{I_1 - I_2}{C_2} \qquad (7)$$

where C_2 is the capacitance of the floating gate to the top gate. Since the interest is in the functional dependence of I_2-V (where $V = V_{tg} - V_{fg}$), one must let the system scan V_{tg} starting from $V = 0$. As seen in Fig. 3, this condition means that the floating gate must be initially positively charged—a condition one has to provide prior to this measurement. Using the initial condition that when $V_{tg} = V_{fg}$, I_2 vanishes due to the fact that there is no field to support photoinjection, and using (7), one arrives at

$$I_2 = C_2\left[\left(\frac{dV_{tg}}{dt}\right)_{V=0} - \frac{dV_{tg}}{dt}\right] \qquad (8)$$

where $(dV_{tg}/dt)_{V=0}$ is the derivative at the time when $I_2 = 0$.

During this measurement, V_{tg} increases positively until it reaches an asymptotic value where $I_2 = I_1$, thus no current greater than I_1 could be measured with this method. This suggests that a proper value of V_{fg} be chosen and that the device chosen for this measurement be such that photoinjection to the top gate is considerably smaller than that from the substrate to the floating gate, in order to enable a large range of V before reaching the asymptote corresponding to $I_1 = I_2$. Evidently, the device that most lends itself to such measurement is a cell which has no direct optical access to the floating gate, which minimizes photoinjection to the top gate (I_2) with respect to photoinjection to the floating gate (I_1).

itself. In order to perform this measurement, one should keep two terminals under known variable voltage and measure the photoinjected current as a function of the applied voltage. However, difficulties with normal FAMOS device are encountered due to the following factors:

1) Their small area which corresponds to extremely small currents.

2) Although the top gate and the substrate are electrically accessible, the floating gate is not, and its potential is a function of its charge which depends on the photoinjected current time integral.

A simple method to overcome these problems was devised. It incorporates the inherent property of the FAMOS device as an MOS transistor. Photoinjected currents from the floating gate to the top gate only were measured, ensuring no spread in oxide thickness on photoinjection paths. The terminals used are the heavily doped n-type polysilicon gates, in which field penetration is negligible, thus eliminating any significant voltage drop on these terminals.

An electronic feedback system is used to maintain a constant current in the FAMOS channel by controlling the top-gate voltage to compensate for any change in charge on the floating gate—thus keeping its potential fixed. Fig. 3 further clarifies the process: the floating poly-Si gate is kept by the system at some predetermined fixed potential V_{fg} which causes, in the presence of UV light, some fixed photoinjected current I_1 to the floating gate from the substrate. At the same time, photoinjected current I_2 extracts charge from the floating gate. Since V_{tg} (the top-gate voltage) changes during this operation, so does I_2. The rate of charge accumulation on the floating

III. Experimental Results

The FAMOS devices used in this study were n-channel dual-gate memory cells (Table I). Three basic cell structures were investigated: Fig. 4 illustrates these cells. Cell X has a top control gate (poly 2), which leaves the floating gate (poly 1) partially exposed. Cells Y_a and Y_b are self-aligned poly 1–poly 2 cells, leaving direct optical access only to the edges of poly 1. Y_a is processed differently and it has a p-type poly 1 whereas Y_b has an n-type poly 1, like all other cells. Cells W_a and W_b have no direct optical access to their floating gate. The processing of the W_b cell is such that optical access to areas of

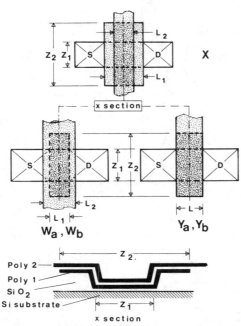

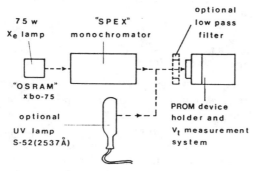

Fig. 4. The structure of FAMOS devices used: cell X has a partially exposed poly 1. Y_a and Y_b cells have self-aligned poly 1–poly 2. Cell Y_a has a p-type floating gate. Cell Y_b is similar to the one used in Intel 2716 type EPROM. Cells W_a, W_b have fully covered poly 1. Cell W_a is similar to the one used in Intel 2708 EPROM.

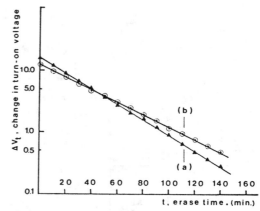

Fig. 6. X cell UV erase. (a) Least exposed cell ($L_1 = 8$ μm). (b) Most exposed cell ($L_1 = 12$ μm). $X_o = 1000$ A.

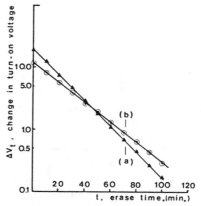

Fig. 5. The experimental setup.

Fig. 7. Y_b cell UV erase. (a) Small cell ($L = 6$ μm). (b) Larger cell ($L = 8$ μm). $X_o = 1000$ A.

poly 1 next to poly 2 is significantly better than that in the W_a cell (see Fig. 13).

Various values of floating-gate width were used in cells X, Y_b, and various misalignments in poly 2 in cell W_a were also investigated. The measurement system is presented in Fig. 5. It incorporates a standard UV lamp (S-52) for the geometrical aspects study. For the spectral sensitivity measurements, an irradiance-calibrated monochromatic light source was used. It is composed of a xenon arc lamp driving a "Minispex" monochromator and an optional low-pass filter (attenuates wavelengths shorter than 3000 Å) to improve the stray UV light rejection of the monochromator when sensitivity to the visible portion of the spectrum was measured.

A. Geometrical Aspects

Devices were electrically programmed, and the change in turn-on voltage ($\Delta V_t(0)$) was measured. During the UV erase process, $\Delta V_t(t)$ decreased exponentially as predicted by (6). This is illustrated in Figs. 6 and 7 for X and Y_b cells, respectively. Note the slower erase rate of the most exposed X cell as compared to the least exposed X cell (Fig. 6). This seeming contradiction will be discussed in Section IV-A. The erase plots of cells W_a and W_b are depicted in Fig. 8. Two W_a cells were tested, one was partially covered with an aluminum strip over the thin-field region, leaving most of the thick-field region uncovered. The ratio between the erase rate of the uncovered cell to that of the partially covered cell was only 1.4, even though about $\frac{2}{3}$ of device area was optically inaccessible. This indicates that optical access through thick-oxide regions has a dominant role in the erase process. Note, also, the change in the erase rate at low ΔV_t (low fields) which is less pronounced in the W_b cell, and hardly detected in the X and Y_a, Y_b cells (Figs. 6, 7). This low-field erase phenomenon in the W_a cell will be discussed in Section IV-D.

In order to investigate how the extent of poly 2 covering poly 1 affects erase rate in a W_a cell, the value of L_x was changed through misalignment of poly 2. The results of the capacitance normalized erase rate $-K \cdot C_t$ versus L_x are presented in Fig. 9. The erase sensitivity of a W_a cell with coincident poly 1 and poly 2 edges is only 2.5 times larger than that

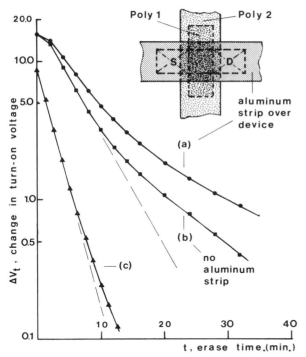

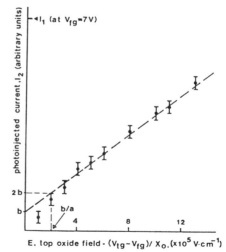

Fig. 8. W_a, W_b cells UV erase. (a) W_a cell with metal strip over thin-field area, thick field mostly exposed. (b) W_a cell. (c) W_b cell. X_o = 1000 Å.

Fig. 10. Experimental photoinjection I-V characteristics. b/a is graphically found to be 2×10^5 V/cm.

not increase significantly, although the exposed area of the floating gate does.

B. The Measurement of Photoinjected I–V Characteristics

According to (8), these characteristics could be obtained by time differentiating the top-gate voltage V_{tg}, and relating it to the voltage $V = V_{tg} - V_{fg}$. The measurement was conducted as follows:

1) The I_D-V_{tg} characteristics of a fully erased FAMOS device ($Q \simeq 0$), were measured and scaled to give the I_D-V_{fg} curve using the capacitance-coupling ratio for this particular device (W_a cell).

2) A fixed floating-gate potential was set (V_{fg} = 7 V) corresponding to I_D = 10 μA at V_{DS} = 0.1 V.

3) The floating gate was positively charged to cause $V_{tg} < $ 7 V when I_D = 10 μA (V_{fg} = 7 V). This was done by applying −20 V to the top gate while using photoinjection to remove negative charge from the floating gate, which was possible due to the fact that photoinjected current from the floating-gate to the substrate was greater than that from the top gate to the floating gate.

4) The feedback system was operated at I_D = 10 μA under UV illumination and V_{tg} started to increase positively, since the floating gate gained negative charges ($I_1 > I_2$). The top-gate voltage V_{tg} was recorded as a function of time, with a strating point at V_{tg} = 7 V (V = 0).

Through the use of (8), and the derivative of the recorded V_{tg} above 7 V, the I-V characteristics were obtained and plotted in Fig. 10, in which the assumption that X_o = 1000 Å is made. It should be noted that the dark current was immeasureably low even under visible light conditions.

The similarity of Fig. 10 to Fig. 2 and the corresponding data in the literature [5]–[9] is good, indicating the similar dependence of photoinjected I-V characteristics in Si–SiO$_2$ and poly-Si–SiO$_2$.

By rapidly blocking any optical access to the device under measurement, it was ascertained that the change due to parasitic photoconductive effects caused the system to shift V_{tg} less than 0.2 V in order to maintain the fixed channel current.

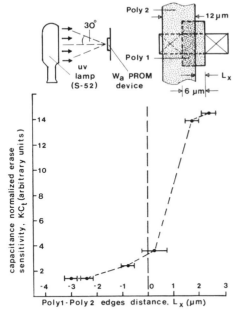

Fig. 9. W_a cell capacitance normalized erase sensitivity ($K \cdot C_t$) as a function of the relative position of poly 1–poly 2.

of a device with poly 1 edge 3 μm away from the poly 2 edge—where light penetrates. For partially exposed poly 1, note the substantial increase in sensitivity around $L_x \simeq 0$, which is due to a transition to a direct optical-access region and an effective increase in A_{inj}, in particular, more photoinjection to the top gate.

The leveling-off of the capacitance-normalized erase rate with increasing exposure of poly 1, indicates that A_{inj} does

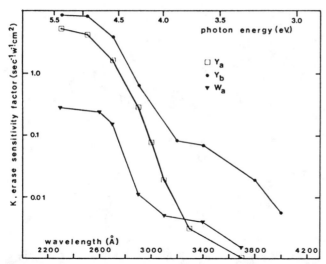

Fig. 11. Spectral erase sensitivity of various FAMOS devices. Note the complete cutoff in sensitivity in the Y_a cell (p-type floating gate).

This indicates that within 0.2 V, this method was free of artifacts related to photocurrents other than the photoinjected currents. It should be emphasized that photoinjected gate currents in the order of 10^{-15} A were measured, suggesting the use of a similar technique in various gate-current measurements.

C. Spectral Sensitivity Measurements

The spectral erase sensitivity factors for cells, Y_a, Y_b, and W_a were measured. The erase sensitivity factor K was obtained by calculating the slopes of the semilog plots of ΔV_t versus time at each wavelength, normalized by the known monochromator irradiance F. The results are displayed in Fig. 11. All devices exhibit a sharp cutoff in their sensitivity around 2900 Å as predicted from data on photoinjection from Si to SiO_2 [5], [10]–[13], whereas cells Y_b and W_a have some residual sensitivity up to 4000 Å, which is two orders of magnitude smaller than that below 2900 Å—this corresponds to emission from the conduction band [11], [13] or shallow traps at that energy level in the n-type poly-Si floating gate. Note, however, that Y_a which has a p-type poly 1, is not sensitive in that spectrum range, suggesting the use of p-type floating silicon gate for minimizing solar erase of EPROM devices.

As seen in Fig. 11, both cells Y_b and W_a have the same spectral behavior, but the absolute value for the latter is smaller by a factor of 30—which is due to the optical losses in the light path to the covered floating gate.

IV. Discussion

A. Quantum Yield and Areas of Photoinjection

The UV erase process is a photoelectric effect. The quantum yield of this process is defined as the ratio of the number of electrons transferred through the oxide per unit time, to the number of photons absorbed by the silicon floating gate in that same period.

Electrically, this process is a discharge of the floating-gate total capacitance

$$V_{fg} = V_{fg}(0)\, e^{-FKt}. \qquad (9)$$

For the sake of simplicity, a uniformly distributed photoinjected current density over the whole area of the device is first assumed. This current density (in A $\cdot$ cm^{-2}) is given by

$$J = C \left| \frac{dV_{fg}}{dt} \right| \qquad (10)$$

where C is the capacitance per unit area of the floating gate. Combining (9) and (10) yields

$$J = J_0\, e^{-FKt}$$

$$J_0 = C V_{fg}(0) FK. \qquad (11)$$

Neglecting optical losses, the quantum yield is related to the photoinjected current density J, the irradiance F (in W $\cdot$ cm^{-2}), and photon energy $\hbar\omega$ (in eV) by

$$Y = \frac{J \cdot \hbar\omega}{F}. \qquad (12)$$

Using (11) and (12), one finds the initial effective quantum yield

$$Y = C \cdot V_{fg}(0) \cdot K \cdot \hbar\omega. \qquad (13)$$

Considering now a Y_b cell (Fig. 4), the thin-oxide capacitance per unit area on both sides of poly 1, neglecting thick-oxide capacitance, is given by

$$C = \frac{\epsilon_o \kappa_o}{X_o}\left(1 + \frac{Z_1}{Z_2}\right) = 4.6 \times 10^{-8} \text{ F/cm}^2 \qquad (14)$$

where $Z_1 = 6$ μm, $Z_2 = 18$ μm, $X_o = 1000$ Å, and $\epsilon_o \kappa_o$ is the dielectric constant of SiO_2. At a wavelength corresponding to photon energy of 4.9 eV, the Y_b cell has a K of 7.5 s^{-1} $\cdot$ W^{-1} $\cdot$ cm^2 (Fig. 11). And if $V_{fg}(0) = 10$ V (oxide field of 10^6 V/cm) (13) yields $Y = 1.7 \times 10^{-5}$.

Bearing in mind that this calculation assumes that the injection area is the whole area of the floating gate (A), thereby overestimating the optical power absorbed by the relevant floating-gate area (A_{inj}) by a factor of A/A_{inj}, the true value of Y is $1.7 \times 10^{-5} \times A/A_{inj}$ which is considerably larger than the effective value found in (13).

Indeed, the quantum yield for photoinjection from Si to SiO_2 as found by Powell [17] is 5×10^{-4} at an oxide field of 3×10^6 V/cm and at the same wavelength.

If a linear relation between photocurrents and oxide field is assumed (which holds for these high fields), the value found by Powell corresponds to $Y = 1.7 \times 10^{-4}$ at a field of 10^6 V/cm.

This low quantum yield is mainly due to processes pertaining to the silicon itself as studied theoretically [18] and verified experimentally for photoemission of electrons from silicon to vacuum [19] where a similar low yield was observed. Scattering in the image force potential well at the Si–SiO_2 interface [6], [20] also has an effect on yield reduction.

Using Powell's data [17] and (13), and neglecting the optical losses, one can find the fraction of active photoinjecting areas in cell Y_b

$$\frac{A_{inj}}{A} = 0.1.$$

Since this area is likely to be along the floating-gate edges of length P next to thin-oxide photoinjection paths, the effective width d of these assumed photoinjecting strips on the floating gate is given by

$$d = \frac{A_{inj}}{P} = \frac{0.1 \times L \times Z_2}{L + 2(Z_1 + Z_2)} = 0.2 \ \mu m \qquad (15)$$

where one covered edge of length L is discarded (see Fig. 4, Y_b cell). This 2000-Å width of photoinjecting strips is comparable to the poly 1 and oxide thickness, which is consistent with an intuitive model of optical penetration to areas within the thin-oxide aperture and on the floating-gate edges.

For FAMOS devices without a top gate, the same active strip width on the poly 1 edge is expected, even though poly 1 is fully exposed, since there could be no other photoinjection oxide path next to that exposed area. Alternatively, considering the possibility of erase through poly 1, the energy loss of hot photoexited electrons generated within the 50-Å absorption depth is likely to be in the range of 1 eV per 200 Å of diffusion length [21]. This means that with no electric field in poly 1, diffusion across the 3000-Å poly 1 thickness is unlikely to contribute to the erase mechanism.

A calculation similar to that of (13)-(15) for the Y_b cell was done for a single-gate cell similar to that in the 1702 EPROM device: the erase sensitivity factor was calculated using the data in [1], the photoinjecting strip width was found to be within 50 percent of the value found in (15).

Additional evidence for thin photoinjecting strips is found in Figs. 6 and 9. Fig. 9 shows that there is a negligible increase in A_{inj} when the floating gate is further shifted outwards once it is exposed. Fig. 6 demonstrates that a device (cell X) with larger exposed poly 1 area erases *slower* than that with a smaller exposed poly 1 area. This seeming contradiction is explained by the fact that A_{inj} is confined to thin strips on the gate perimeter, the relative increase of which, on the most exposed cell, is smaller than the relative increase of the total area which is proportional to the capacitance, thus causing K to decrease.

B. Floating-Gate Capacitance and its Effect on the Erase Sensitivity Factor

According to (4), the erase factor is inversely proportional to the total capacitance of the floating gate. Table II compares calculated and measured ratios of erase sensitivity factors in two pairs of cells. The erase data are taken from Figs. 6 and 7. According to the arguments in the previous section, A_{inj} is the same in the X cell pair (neglecting thick-oxide photoinjection), thus only the capacitance ratio is assumed, while for the Y_b cells, some difference in A_{inj}, due to different photoinjecting strip length, was also accounted for. X_o was kept the same for both pairs (same process, same chip). The experimental results are in excellent agreement with theory.

C. The Optical Acccess to Fully Covered Floating-Gate Devices ($W_{a,b}$ Cells)

The optical absorption coefficient of Si at 2537 Å is about $2 \times 10^6 \ cm^{-1}$ [14], [15]. If one assumes that the optical

TABLE II
THE EFFECT OF C_t ON K

FAMOS CELLS	X	Y_b
Relative erase sensitivity factor calculated according to:	$K \propto \dfrac{1}{C_1 + C_2}$ $\propto \dfrac{1}{L_1 Z_1 + L_2 Z_2 + 0.1 L_1 (Z_2 - Z_1)}$	$K \propto \dfrac{A_{inj}}{C_1 + C_2}$ $\propto \dfrac{L + 2(Z_1 + Z_2)}{L}$
Dimensions (See Fig. 4)	$Z_1 = 7\mu : Z_2 = 20\mu$ $L_2 = 6\mu$ $L_1 = \begin{cases} 8\mu \text{ (least exposed)} \\ 12\mu \text{ (most exposed)} \end{cases}$	$Z_1 = 6\mu : Z_2 = 18\mu$ $L = \begin{cases} 6\mu \text{ (small cell)} \\ 8\mu \text{ (large cell)} \end{cases}$
Calculated Ratio	$\dfrac{K_{least}}{K_{most}} = 1.17$	$\dfrac{K_{small}}{K_{large}} = 1.29$
Measured ratio (Fig. 6, 7)	$\dfrac{K_{least}}{K_{most}} = 1.18$	$\dfrac{K_{small}}{K_{large}} = 1.30$

transmission properties of polycrystalline silicon are similar to those of single-crystal silicon, the optical transmittance of a 3000-Å-thick poly 2 at 2537 Å is about 10^{-26}. This value could not explain the 6×10^{-7} effective quantum yield of cell W_a (being 30 times less sensitive than cell Y_b). Furthermore, it was demonstrated that substantial differences in poly 2 thickness had no effect on erase rate [3]. Even if a 1500-Å poly 2 thickness is assumed, as reported in [4], the 10^{-13} transmittance could not explain the source of optical light that results in 3×10^{-6} effective quantum yield as calculated from the reported erase slope and data in [4].

Based on the above arguments, one can conclude that optical access to the fully covered poly 1 is achieved by means of reflection and diffraction effects confined to the thick-oxide field, as indicated in Section III-A.

A theoretical waveguide erase model based on reflections from the substrate and top gate was proposed to explain the erase in fully covered devices [3]. This model assumes geometrical optics reflections with a reflectance coefficient of 0.6 at the Si–SiO$_2$ interface. An attempt to use the key feature of this model to explain the experimental data in Fig. 9 resulted in the following difficulty. Considering only this waveguide mechanism and the erase conditions used for collecting the data in Fig. 9, the maximal angle of incidence (from the UV lamp ends) was 30°. According to Snells law, the angle θ (Fig. 12) in the SiO$_2$ medium is given by $n \sin \theta = 0.5$, where n is the refractive index of SiO$_2$. For $n = 1.5$ [16], the maximal angle is $\theta \simeq 20°$. Thus for a 1-μm-thick waveguide, at least eight reflections in a 3-μm-long guide are needed to reach the floating gate. The intensity in the optical-guide entrance is then greater by a factor of at least $1/(0.6)^8 \simeq 60$ than that at 3 μm away, under the top gate.

The calculation, therefore, predicts a strong dependence of erase rate on poly 1 location with respect to the edge of poly 2. However, the data in Fig. 9 do not support the above model. A rough calculation using the relative erase rates in

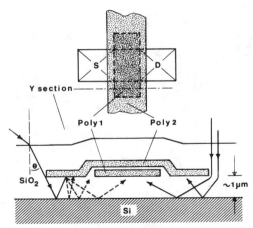

Fig. 12. Optical access to a fully covered floating-gate device.

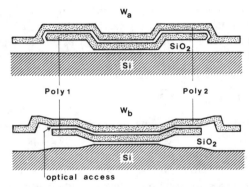

Fig. 13. Cross sections of cells W_a and W_b. Note the larger area exposed to photoinjection to the top gate in cell W_b.

Fig. 9 shows that the ratio between the light intensities of $L_x \simeq 0$ and $L_x = -3$ μm, is no greater than 5, which is twice[2] the corresponding erase rates ratio of $3.5/1.4 = 2.5$ (see Fig. 9).

It should be further noted that the model in [3] assumes optical incidence on the Si substrate at angles up to 90°, which overestimates the intensity reaching poly 1, since the incident angle on the Si substrate could not exceed 42°, which corresponds to a 90° incidence on the SiO_2 surface.

Therefore, it is assumed that, in general, the following optical effects could overshadow the pure reflection effects, especially when only small angles of incidence are present:

1) Diffraction at the poly 2 edge could cause penetration at a favorable angle, thus eliminating additional losses (Fig. 12).

2) Since the grain size in the poly-Si top gate is comparable to the optical wavelength in the oxide ($\lambda_{ox} = \lambda/n = 1690$ Å), its surface could not be modeled as a perfect optical plane, due to different orientations of its grains. This implies that reflections from the top-gate surface are spread over a range of angles which results in the possibility of reaching poly 1 through a small number of reflections (Fig. 12).

D. Low-Field Erase in Fully Covered FAMOS Cells

As can be seen in Fig. 8, at low floating-gate voltages, the W_a cell has a lower erase rate. The transition stage to a lower rate is completed at a floating-gate potential of about 1.0 V. This decrease in erase rate was also observed in [4], and was not present in devices where the edges of the floating gate were partially exposed (cells X, Y_a, and Y_b). However, it was less pronounced in a W_b cell, the floating gate of which is fully covered. The fine structure difference between cells W_a and W_b is depicted in Fig. 13. The processing of the W_b cell is such that optical access to areas of poly 1 next to poly 2 is significantly better than than in the W_a cell. This results in a larger photoinjecting area and a higher erase rate (Fig. 8) as compared to the W_a cell.

It also becomes clear that the common feature of cells that

[2] The introduction of a factor of 2 is due to the fact that "shifting" L_x from -3 μm to $\simeq 0$ causes some loss of light in the other end of poly 1, which is further away from the poly 2 edge.

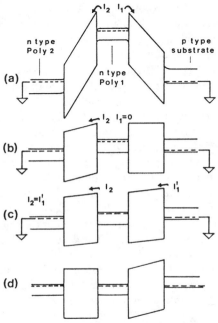

Fig. 14. Stages of UV erase in the W_a cell. (a) Fully programmed cell. (b) Partially erased cell ($\Delta V_t \simeq 1$ V). (c) Fully erased cell. (d) "Virgin" cell.

have a single erase rate is the fact that the dominant photoinjection path is the one to the n-type gate, rather than to the p-type substrate, as in the W_a cell.

This was verified by implementing the procedure and the I–V measurement system described in Section II-D. All devices were tested for the saturation value of their top-gate voltage when illuminated by UV, thus evaluating the relative magnitudes of their I_2 values (Fig. 3). All devices known to have a single erase slope presented a low-saturating top-gate voltage, indicating larger poly 1 areas photoinjecting to the top gate, whereas cell W_a saturated at a much higher voltage compared to the voltage difference between poly 1 and the substrate.

The interpretation of these results to explain the low-field erase rate decrease in cell W_a is presented in Fig. 14.

When cell W_a is programmed, the floating gate is at a high negative potential (Fig. 14(a)) and photoinjection gives rise to currents I_1 and I_2, which sum up to determine a certain erase rate K. When the floating-gate negative potential decreases down to about 1.0 V (Fig. 14(b)) (which is the difference in the Fermi levels of the n-type poly-Si and the p-type Si substrate), the field in the bottom oxide vanishes and starts to change sign. At this stage, UV photoinjection from the substrate to poly 1 competes with the discharge to the top gate. This, in turn, will result in an erase process with a smaller K value due to an effective decrease in A_{inj}.

Equilibrium will be attained when both photocurrents are equal in magnitude (Fig. 14(c)). This could happen before the Fermi levels in all parts of the system align. Fig. 14(d) shows, for comparison, a new cell that was never exposed to UV. As seen, there is a difference in the floating-gate potential between the fully erased cell (Fig. 14(c)) and the virgin cell, which was not subject to UV radiation. This difference is due to residual charge on poly 1 in the fully erased cell, which is indicated by the fact that V_t is a few tenths of volt higher than that of the virgin cell.

Evidently, one can conclude, that according to Fig. 14 the larger the part of I_1 in the total erase current the more pronounced is the underlying effect of erase rate decrease. Since, in cells having partially exposed poly 1, the part of photoinjection to the top gate (I_2) is dominant, these devices exhibit single erase rate characteristics.

E. Hole Injection as a Possible Erase Mechanism

In view of previous attempts to use the concept of hole photoinjection to explain the erase mechanism in fully covered floating-gate EPROM cells, it is worth examining this possibility in light of the following points:

1) The threshold observed for UV erase is about 4.2 eV (Fig. 11), which falls short by about 0.7 eV for any possible hole photoinjection from the poly-Si n-type floating gate. The energy threshold for photoinjection of holes is the energy difference between the conduction band of Si and the valance band of SiO_2 [22].

2) Evidence has been presented in the literature indicating that electrons are, for all practical purposes, the sole charge carriers in the photoinjection at the Si–SiO$_2$ interface. At least three independent methods were used:

a) Williams [10] proved it by the use of a water electrode.

b) Powell [17] used optical interference to determine that the part of holes in photoinjection processes is at most 1 percent of that of electrons.

c) Weinberg et al. [23] used shallow p and n diffusions to determine the sign of the carrier transported across SiO_2 films on Si.

Regardless of the sign of the carrier responsible for erase mechanism, one can use the arguments presented in Section IV-C, that light transmitted through poly 2 could not account for the effective quantum yield observed.

In view of these arguments, it is concluded that in all FAMOS devices the erase mechanism is due only to electron photoinjection from the poly-Si floating gate to other available terminals.

V. Summary

A simple physical model was developed for the UV erase sensitivity of FAMOS EPROM devices, and shown to be in good agreement with experimental results over a wide range of spectral, geometrical, and electrical parameters. It was shown that the erase process can be characterized by an erase sensitivity factor incorporating the effective photoinjection area, oxide thickness, and total capacitance of the floating gate as parameters. Measurements of low-level photoinjection currents and optical access to the floating gate were used to explain the erase process in fully covered, dual FAMOS structures.

Acknowledgment

The authors wish to thank the Intel Corporation for supplying the devices for this study.

References

[1] D. Frohman-Bentchkowsky, *Solid-State Electron.*, vol. 17, p. 517, 1974.
[2] P. J. Salsbury et al., in *ISSCC Dig. Tech. Papers*, pp. 186–187, Feb. 1977.
[3] R. Kondo, E. Takeda, T. Hagiwara, M. Horiuchi, and Y. Itoh, *IEEE Trans. Electron Devices*, vol. ED-25, no. 3, p. 369, 1978.
[4] J. J. Barnes, J. L. Linden, and J. R. Edwards, *Solid-State Electron.*, vol. 21, p. 521, 1978.
[5] A. M. Goodman, *Phys. Rev.*, vol. 144, no. 2, p. 588, 1966.
[6] C. N. Berglund and R. J. Powell, *J. Appl. Phys.*, vol. 42, no. 2, p. 573, 1971.
[7] D. J. Dimaria, Z. A. Weinberg, and J. M. Aitken, *J. Appl. Phys.*, vol. 48, no. 3, p. 898, 1977.
[8] D. J. Dimaria and D. R. Kerr, *Appl. Phys. Lett.*, vol. 27, no. 9, p. 505, 1975.
[9] D. J. Dimaria, F. J. Feigl, and S. R. Butler, *Phys. Rev. B*, vol. 11, no. 12, p. 5023, 1975.
[10] R. Williams, *Phys. Rev.*, vol. 140, no. 2A, p. 569, 1965.
[11] A. M. Goodman, *Phys. Rev.*, vol. 152, no. 2, p. 785, 1966.
[12] B. E. Deal, E. H. Snow, and C. A. Mead, *J. Phys. Chem. Solids*, vol. 27, p. 1873, 1966.
[13] R. J. Powell, *J. Appl. Phys.*, vol. 41, no. 6, p. 2424, 1970.
[14] H. R. Phillip and E. A. Taft, *Phys. Rev.*, vol. 120, no. 1, p. 37, 1960.
[15] H. W. Verleur, *J. Opt. Soc. Amer.*, vol. 58, no. 10, p. 1356, 1968.
[16] *Handbook of Chemistry and Physics.* Cleveland, OH: Cleveland Chemical Rubber Co., 1972.
[17] R. J. Powell, *J. Appl. Phys.*, vol. 40, no. 13, p. 5093, 1969.
[18] E. O. Kane, *Phys. Rev.*, vol. 127, p. 131, 1962.
[19] G. W. Gobeli and F. G. Allen, *Phys. Rev.*, vol. 127, p. 141, 1962.
[20] M. Silver and P. Smejtek, *J. of Appl. Phys.*, vol. 43, no. 5, p. 2451, 1972.
[21] J. F. Verwey and B. J. de Maagt, *Solid-State Electron.*, vol. 17, p. 963, 1974.
[22] A. M. Goodman, *Phys. Rev.*, vol. 152, no. 2, p. 780, 1966.
[23] Z. A. Weinberg, W. C. Johnson, and M. A. Lampert, *Appl. Phys. Lett.*, vol. 25, no. 1, p. 42, 1974.

PROCESS AND DEVICE TECHNOLOGIES FOR 16Mbit EPROMs
WITH LARGE-TILT-ANGLE IMPLANTED P-POCKET CELL

Yoichi Ohshima, Seiichi Mori, Yukio Kaneko, Eiji Sakagami,
Norihisa Arai*, Naonori Hosokawa**, and Kuniyoshi Yoshikawa

Semiconductor Device Engineering Lab. TOSHIBA Corp.
*TOSHIBA MICROELECTRONICS Corp.
**Integrated Circuit Process Engineering Dept. TOSHIBA Corp.
1,Komukai Toshiba-cho,Saiwai-ku,Kawasaki 210,Japan

ABSTRACT

A reliable high-performance process and device technologies for the fabrication of 0.6µm 16Mbit CMOS EPROM have been developed. A novel cell structure (called a LAP cell) is proposed, which yields stable high performance in the 0.6µm regime.

The important processes and device technologies are (a) a Large-tilt-Angle implanted P-pocket (LAP) cell structure with 0.6µm gate length, (b) a Self-Aligned Source (SAS) technology, (c) a poly-Si plugged-contact technology for CMOS devices by novel multi-step poly-Si deposition method, and (d) a 0.8µm poly-Si shield isolation structure for high voltage circuits. These technologies together with advanced lithography techniques will be sufficient for the manufacture of future 64Mbit EPROMs and beyond.

INTRODUCTION

Recently, strong demand for higher densities in nonvolatile memories has arisen in new markets such as IC cards, microcontrollers, and as a replacement for magnetic disks. The EPROM is a device which drives technology in various nonvolatile memory types. Novel processes and device technologies for 0.6µm 16Mbit CMOS EPROMs have been developed.

In order to scale down the cell size and achieve high performance, a LAP cell structure is proposed. To achieve 16Mbit density, SAS technology and poly-Si plugged-contact technology has been developed. Furthermore, by using a poly-Si shield isolation structure, high-voltage circuits using a 0.8µm isolation width can be realized.

This paper describes the key process and device technologies which have realized 0.6µm 16Mbit EPROMs.

LAP CELL STRUCTURE

In order to realize 0.6µm p-pocket Diffusion Self-Aligned (DSA) cells, we propose the LAP cell structure. The cell device designs are based on a previously reported scaling scenario [1]. The new cell structure and fabrication process are shown in Fig.1. After stacked gate definition, arsenic ions are implanted to form an N^+ shallow drain 0.15µm deep. To form halo p-pocket structures, large-tilt-angle boron implantation is carried out. Conventional N^+ deep implants then followed. This is followed by thermal activation. Thus, this new process needs only one photo mask step to cover the peripheral circuit area. On the contrary, in a conventional DSA process, p-pocket implantation and the following annealing step for lateral diffusion length optimization are necessary before N^+ shallow and N^+ deep implantation, so there is an additional photo mask step. Therefore, the LAP structure cell greatly simplifies the overall process.

Figure 2 shows the cell read current characteristics. This LAP cell offers a stable cell read current (around 120µA) in spite of variations in cell gate length, because the effective channel length is mainly determined by the p-pocket layer adjacent to the drain. A sufficient punchthrough voltage is also maintained, down to a 0.4µm gate poly length, as shown in Fig.3. Figure 4 shows the programming characteristics of optimized LAP cells. Programming time variations due to gate length fluctuation are substantially reduced, compared with those of conventional cells, especially in the longer gate length region. EPROM cells with a 0.6µm gate poly length yield 25µsec programming for a threshold voltage shift of more than 3V when Vpp is 10.5V and the drain voltage is 6V.

In addition, to give sufficient read current and programming speed the gate dielectrics are optimized according to a scaling guideline [1]. A 16nm cell gate oxide and optimized 22nm ONO ($SiO_2/Si_3N_4/SiO_2$) inter-poly dielectric [2] are adopted to maintain high reliability.

Reprinted from the *IEDM Tech. Dig.*, pp. 95–98, 1990.

SAS TECHNOLOGY

By adopting a Self-Aligned-Source (SAS) technology, the source area can be formed by removing the field oxide in alignment with the wordlines using the RIE method. Figure 5 shows the resultant cell array observed by SEM. Since this process completely eliminates misalignment of word lines to source active area, it enables a 10% reduction in cell size. As a result, a 3.85 μm^2 (2.2 x1.75μm) cell size is achieved.

We have examined the damage caused by the SAS RIE process to the quality of the oxide which surrounds floating gate. Figure 6 shows the TDDB characteristics of the cell gate oxide under a stress of 11MV/cm. No degradation of cell gate oxide quality is observed. Furthermore, the high temperature(300°C) charge retention characteristics of EPROM cells with and without the SAS process have been investigated. As shown in Fig.7, adequate reliability is retained even when the SAS process is used.

POLY-Si PLUGGED CONTACT

To achieve 16Mbit density, the aspect ratio of the contact hole becomes as high as one, and buried contact technology is necessary to achieve a highly reliable interconnection. A CMOS poly-Si plugged contact technology has therefore been established to achieve 0.6μm^2 area contact holes. The proposed plug technology has low contact resistance characteristics regardless of variations in contact depth, and it uses a newly developed multi-step poly-Si deposition method. Figure 8 shows the sequence of the proposed plug technology, and SEM cross section of EPROM cells. Contact holes are fully filled and metalization topography is very smooth. Figure 9 shows N$^+$ and P$^+$ contact resistance characteristics as a function of contact diameter for poly-Si plugged contacts. Since implanted ions sandwiched between poly-Si 2 and poly-Si 3 can diffuse bi-directionally, the impurity concentration in a poly-Si plug becomes uniform. Thus, low contact hole resistance, 50ohm for N$^+$ and 100 ohm for P$^+$ (with 0.8μm^2 contacts), is realized using this process.

DEVICE TECHNOLOGY

The device/process parameters are summarized in Table 1. The new 16Mbit CMOS EPROMs use an N-well CMOS technology with LDD NMOS and PMOS FETs.

In the peripheral high voltage circuit, a 0.8μm isolation structure is required. Therefore, a shielding poly-Si isolation structure has been developed for N$^+$-N$^+$ and P$^+$-P$^+$ separation. Figure 10 shows the breakdown characteristics of the proposed shield poly-Si isolation as a function of

isolation distance. Note that the shield poly-Si isolation can be formed simultaneously with the peripheral transistors. By optimizing the punch-through prevention implant, shield poly-Si isolation can offer high punchthrough resistance with a sufficiently high breakdown voltage as compared with modified LOCOS isolation. Punchthrough prevention implants can be optimized independently of LOCOS field implant dose. With this technology, the row-decoder area can be reduced without using novel field-isolation technology. The isolation limitations of poly-Si shield technology are smaller than those of modified LOCOS isolation. Figure 11 shows the TDDB characteristics of gate oxide under shield poly-Si under an 11MV/cm stress. The electric field acceleration factor was calculated from various stress TDDB data (~6.3MV/cm). According to this, the lifetime in Vpp operation was estimated at more than 10^5 years. This lifetime indicates that there are no practical limitations due to shield oxide break-down.

Optimized 0.9μm masked LDD NMOS FETs [3] have sufficient hot carrier immunity at 5V operation. Masked LDD PMOS FETs are utilized to prevent the recently reported degradation under off-state stress conditions [4].

The technologies described here have been checked by fabricating 0.6μm 16Mbit CMOS EPROM devices.

SUMMARY

In summary, high-performance process/device technologies for 16Mbit EPROMs have been proposed. The main process and device technologies are the LAP cell structure, the SAS process, poly-Si plugged contact technology and the poly-Si shield structure. These technologies will be important in the further scaling of EPROM devices. Furthermore these technologies are essentially applicable to high-density flash EEPROMs with minor modifications.

ACKNOWLEDGEMENT

The authors wish to thank Dr. S. Shinozaki and M. Wada for their encouragement, and S. Tanaka, J. Miyamoto, N. Ohtsuka, K. Imamiya, N. Tomita, T. Sako, and Y. Iyama for their helpful discussions. They also thank Mr. M. Shiozaki for process development and valuable comments.

REFERENCES

[1] K.Yoshikawa et al.,IEDM, pp.578(1989)
[2] S.Mori et al., Proc.1990 IEEE IRPS, pp.132 (1990)
[3] K.Yoshikawa et al.,IEDM, pp.456(1984)
[4] K.Yoshikawa et al.,Symposium on VLSI Technology, pp.73(1990)

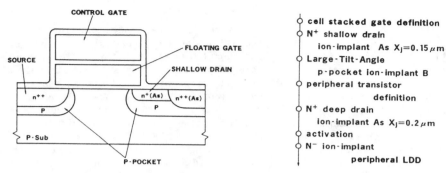

Fig.1 Large-Tilt-Angle implanted P-pocket (LAP) cell cross section and key process sequence.

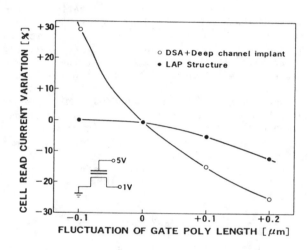

Fig.2 Cell read current variation vs poly gate length. Typical cell read current is around 120μA.

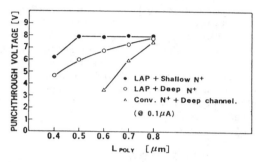

Fig.3 Punchthrough resistance vs gate length

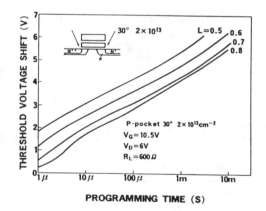

Fig.4 Programming characteristics vs gate length

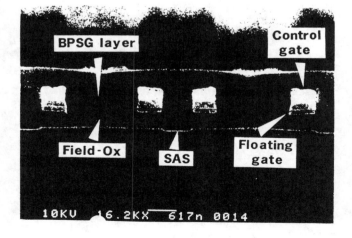

Fig.5 SEM cross section of 16Mb EPROM cells using a Self Aligned Source (SAS) technology

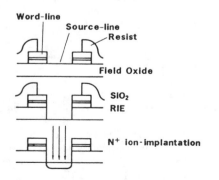

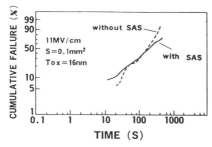

Fig.6 Gate oxide TDDB characteristics, with and without SAS process

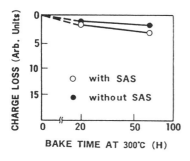

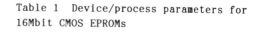

Table 1 Device/process parameters for 16Mbit CMOS EPROMs

PROCESS	N-WELL CMOS	
CELL		
W/L		0.6/0.6 μm
1st GATE OXIDE		16nm
INTER-POLY ONO		22nm
COUPLING RATIO		0.66
JUNCTION DEPTH (DRAIN)		0.15 μm
ISOLATION (MODIFIED LOCOS)		1.2 μm
PERIPHERAL		
GATE LENGTH	NMOS (LDD)	0.9 μm
	PMOS (LDD)	1.0 μm
GATE OXIDE		20nm
JUNCTION DEPTH	N+	0.2 μm
	P+	0.35 μm
ISOLATION (Min.) (POLY-SHIELD)		0.8 μm

Fig.7 Bake retention characteristics with and without SAS process.

Using the SAS process, charge retention characteristics are well preserved.

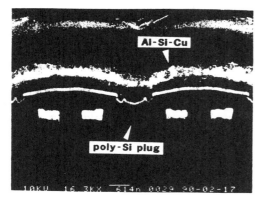

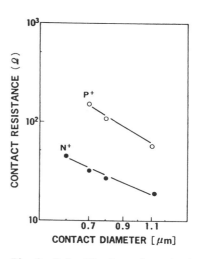

○ contact opening
○ poly-Si 1 deposition
○ ion-implants N+, P+
○ SiN side-wall formation
○ poly-Si 2 deposition
○ ion-implants N+, P+
○ poly-Si 3 deposition
○ activation
○ poly-Si etch-back
○ Al-Si-Cu/TiN/Ti formation

Fig.8 Process sequence in contact plug technology, novel multi-step poly-Si deposition method, and SEM cross section for cells.

Fig.9 Poly-Si plugged contact resistance characteristics

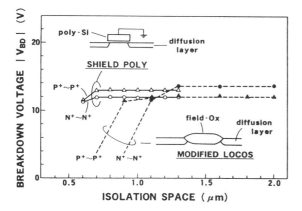

Fig.10 Breakdown characteristics for proposed shielding poly-Si isolation

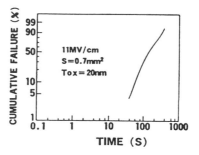

Fig.11 TDDB characteristics for shield poly-Si oxide
Estimated lifetime under V_{pp} operation (~6.3MV/cm) is more than 10^5year which is sufficiently long for device reliability.

A NEW SELF-ALIGNED PLANAR ARRAY CELL FOR ULTRA HIGH DENSITY EPROMS

A.T. Mitchell×, C. Huffman and A.L. Esquivel

Semiconductor Process and Design Center
Texas Instruments Incorporated
Dallas, Texas 75265

ABSTRACT

A novel process technology for producing a true cross-point EPROM cell is described in this paper. Buried N+ diffusions self-aligned to the Floating gate Avalanche injection MOS (FAMOS) transistor are used for the bit lines. These diffusions are covered with a planarized low temperature CVD oxide which isolates them from a perpendicular set of poly word lines. The bit line contacts and LOCOS isolation that are necessary for the industry standard cell have been eliminated. With this technology a 4 um2 cell using 1 um design rules and zero alignment tolerance is feasible. The concept has been tested and verified using a 13.5 um2 test cell.

INTRODUCTION

Traditionally, advances in the reduction of EPROM memories have concentrated on pushing the limits of optical lithography and plasma etching. The cell frequently used by the industry is the cell shown in figure 1a. This cell uses locally oxidized silicon (LOCOS) to isolate individual bits. A half contact per cell is required to connect drain diffusions to the metal bit lines. Though the source/drain diffusions are self-aligned to the polysilicon floating gates, optical registration is required to align the floating gate, word lines and contacts to the field oxide. Recently, a 9 um2 EPROM cell has been reported using this technology (1). However, 0.8 um minimum feature size and stringent alignment tolerances were required for its fabrication. New cell concepts have been suggested in order to reduce the cell size without placing further restrictions on processing limits (2,3). However, these approaches also require array contacts and LOCOS isolation.

This paper presents a process which is used to construct a new FAMOS device (4) which does not require the use of LOCOS isolation or contacts in the array. The cell is fully self-aligned and therefore does not place any alignment restrictions

on conventional optical lithography. The new cell is called SPEAR for Self-aligned Planar EPROM Array. A top view of the SPEAR cell, drawn with a proposed 1 um design rule, is compared to the industry standard cell (also at 1 um design rules) in figure 1. The SPEAR cell is less than half the size of the industry standard cell. A 3-dimensional schematic diagram of the SPEAR cell is shown in figure 2. The SPEAR self-aligned process makes it particularly easy to fabricate. Only two masking levels (bit line and word line) are needed for the fabrication of this cell. Mis-alignment between these two levels has no impact on array performance. In the following sections the process and characterization of the 13.5 um2 test cell which was used to verify the SPEAR technology will be described.

FABRICATION PROCESS

Process steps for the fabrication of SPEAR FAMOS are depicted in figure 3. Two adjacent transistors are shown in these pictures to indicate how the process would be used in an array formation. Samples were fabricated on 12 ohm-cm <100> silicon substrates. Conventional LOCOS isolation was used to isolate peripheral devices, but was not used in

× Now assigned to: Design Automation Division
                   Texas Instruments Incorporated
                   P.O. Box 655303, MS 3668
                   Dallas, Texas 75265

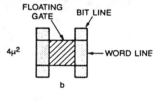

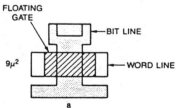

Fig. 1 Comparison of two EPROM cells at 1 um design rules: a) The industry standard cell. b) The idealized Self-aligned Planar EPROM Array cell (SPEAR).

Reprinted from the *IEDM Tech. Dig.*, pp. 548–553, 1987.

the formation of the SPEAR cell. After field isolation, an array implant was performed through a dummy oxide to set the FAMOS threshold voltage. The FAMOS gate oxide (350A) was then grown and polyl deposited and etched to form long continuous polyl slots. The width of the polyl also defines the length of the FAMOS transistor. Next arsenic was implanted in the polyl slots forming the buried N+ bit lines and also acting as the source and drain for the FAMOS transistor (fig. 3a). At this point, standard techniques for siliciding the bit lines could easily be applied. The samples described in this paper were not silicided.

After the buried N+ implant, a conformal CVD TEOS (tetraethyl orthosilicate) oxide was deposited to fill in the slots and a planarizing photoresist was spun on the wafer (fig. 3b). A second resist coat and pattern, applied after the planarization resist coating, was then used to protect the periphery region by opening only the array area. Next a planarizing plasma etch that etches both oxide and photoresist layers at the same rate was used to remove the TEOS oxide over the polyl, thus exposing the polyl surface yet leaving oxide in the slots over the buried N+. This formed a planar surface of alternating oxide and polyl lines (fig. 3c). The planarizing steps are described in more detail in the next section.

Interpoly dielectric with an effective oxide thickness of 350A (consisting of interlevel oxide and interlevel nitride) and poly2 were then deposited. The poly2, interpoly dielectric and polyl were all etched to complete the formation of the polyl floating gate and to form the poly2 word lines (fig. 3d and 2). Standard processing techniques were used to complete the peripheral devices. Figure 4 shows SEM micrographs of the finished device. Figure 4a is a cleave perpendicular to the word lines through the channel and bit line isolation region and shows the stacked gate structure. Figure 4b is a cleave perpendicular to the bit lines through a word line, and shows the planarizing oxide and the source and drain of the SPEAR cell.

PLANARIZATION METHOD

An oxide Resist-Etch-Back (REB) process was used to planarize the interlevel oxide between polyl lines in the array. Shipley 1400-17 resist spun-coated to 0.6 um thickness was used as the planarization medium over 0.6 um of CVD TEOS oxide (fig. 5). To improve the profile over the array a 15 minute white light exposure and a 30 minute 200C convection oven hard bake was employed to insure complete resist flow. Prepared in this way, the resist was almost perfectly planar over the regularly spaced polyl lines.

Using an etch with an oxide:resist selectivity of 1.2:1, the resist surface was transferred into the underlying CVD TEOS oxide. An oxide etch rate 20% faster than the resist etch rate was used to insure that the TEOS oxide was cleared off the top of polyl while leaving a thick oxide between polyl leads. This produced slight depressions in the oxide at the polyl edges as can be seen in figure 4b. Oxide:resist selectivity was controlled by

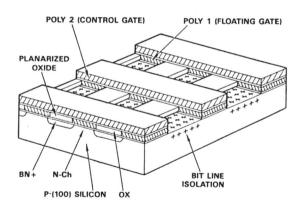

Fig. 2 Three dimensional schematic diagram of a SPEAR EPROM Array.

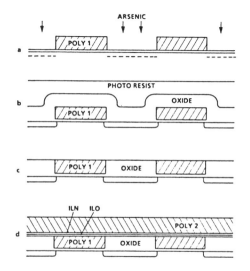

Fig. 3 Schematic representation of the SPEAR fabrication process: a) Bit line formation. b) Photoresist and oxide shown prior to planarization. c) Post planar etch. d) Interlevel oxide (ILO), interlevel nitride (ILN) and poly2 deposition.

adding small amounts of O2 to an etch chemistry of CHF3, C2F6, and He at 1.5 Torr and 280 watts of 13.5 MHz power. Loading effect of resist was held to a minimum since the periphery was covered by a double thickness of resist allowing only the resist from the top of polyl leads in the array to be removed. The small amount of resist removed resulted in a small endpoint signal requiring the use of a timed etch. Etch time was calculated using blanket resist and oxide etch rates and thickness of resist and oxide over the polyl structure.

DEVICE CHARACTERIZATION

In order to economize on the amount of silicon

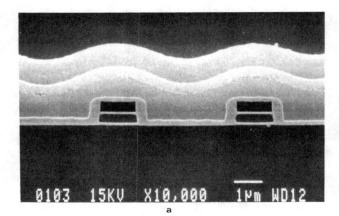

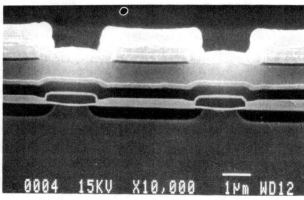

a

b

Fig. 4 SEM micrographs of the SPEAR cell: a) Cross section perpendicular to the poly2 word line showing the stacked poly gate. b) Cross section perpendicular to the bit lines showing the planarized oxide over the buried N+ diffusions.

area used in the SPEAR cell formation, a self-aligned process was implemented as described above. A negative impact of this approach is a reduction in the floating gate to control gate coupling coefficient. As can be seen in figure 1 the industry standard cell has more coupling since the poly1 floating gate overlaps the field oxide. The coupling coefficient (k) for the SPEAR cell is 0.5 while for the industry standard cell it is 0.7. The coupling coefficient k is defined by:

$$k = Cilo / (Cilo + Cgox),$$

where Cilo is the capacitance between poly1 and the control gate and Cgox is the capacitance between the floating gate and the substrate. As will be seen in the following discussion, the penalty paid for more than a factor of two reduction in cell size had little impact on programming performance.

Figure 6 shows the DC programming characteristic of a SPEAR FAMOS with a nominal width/length ratio of 1.5/1.25 um. The effective gate length (Leff) for this transistor is 0.95 um. The gate voltage was held at 12.5 volts while the drain voltage was ramped past BVCEO (9.5 volts), which is the breakdown of the parasitic npn bipolar transistor formed by the source/substrate/drain regions. Resistors (400 ohm) connected in series with the source and drain were used to simulate bit line resistance (see insert). Before programming, the erased Vt was 2.0 volts. After programming, the Vt increased to 11.2 volts.

Programming speed is shown in figure 7 for a SPEAR cell with nominal width/length ratio of 1.5/1.25 um. The source was grounded and 12.5 volts was applied to the gate electrode, while the drain voltage was pulsed at 12.5 volts. Resistors (400 ohm) were again connected in series with the source and drain to simulate bit line resistance. SPEAR transistors with Leff = 0.95 and 1.20 um are displayed. The graph indicates that an increase in threshold voltage up to 4 volts is possible with pulse widths of only 100 usec. A 2 volt shift is possible with a 10 usec pulse. These

characteristics are comparable to those reported by other investigators (1,2,3) and make the SPEAR cell suitable for the fabrication of fast programming memories.

Buried N+ leakage for the SPEAR process is shown in figure 8. The device tested was a 64X64 bit dummy array. It consists of 68 bit lines which were all tied together and ramped to measure bit line leakage to the substrate. The structure therefore has a large amount of perimeter for evaluating edge leakage. This device exhibits very low N+ leakage at the programming voltage of 12.5 volts. Breakdown voltage (at 1 microamp) for the N+ bit lines occurs at 23.5 volts.

Data retention characteristics for the SPEAR FAMOS are shown in figure 9. The devices were baked at 250C for up to 1000 hours. The solid line is a fit to the data assuming a thermionic electron emission model (5), and corresponds to an activation energy of 1.11 eV.

CONCLUSION

A new cross point array technology has been described and it has been demonstrated that the new cell provides, to date, the best utilization of silicon area for non-volatile memories. The self-aligned feature of the source and drain will allow this FAMOS device to be optimized even further for programming speed as has been done by other investigators. By using this self-aligned planarized structure it should be possible to build 4 Mbit and higher density EPROMs which are both easily scalable and easily manufacturable.

ACKNOWLEDGEMENTS

The authors would like to acknowledge the technicians in the Nonvolatile EPROM Branch and the Semiconductor Process Lab personnel for their help in lot processing and characterization. Thanks goes to Tom Bonifield, Bert Riemenschneider and Howard Tigelaar for helpful discussions. Also thanks to Jim Paterson for his support.

REFERENCES

1. "A 120 ns 4Mb CMOS EPROM" S.Atsumi, S.Tanaka, S.Saito, N.Ohtsuka, N.Matsukawa, S.Mori, Y.Kaneko, K.Yoshikawa, J.Matsunaga and T.Lizuka, ISSCC Tech. Digest, 74, (1987).

2. "Characteristics and Reliability of the SEPROM Cell" H.Nozawa, Y.Niitsu, N.Matsukawa, J.Matsunaga and S.Kohyama, IEEE Trans. Electron Devices, ED-31, 1413, (1984).

3. "A New EPROM Cell with a Side-wall Floating Gate for High-Density and High-Performance Device" Y.Mizutani and K.Makita, IEDM Tech. Digest, 635, (1985).

4. US patent 4,597,060.

5. "A Thermionic Electron Emission Model for Charge Retention in SAMOS Structures" H.Nozawa and S.Kuhyama, Japan. J. Appl. Phys., #21, 111, (1982).

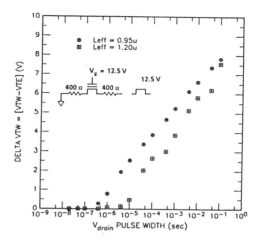

Fig. 7 Programmability versus drain voltage pulse width for a SPEAR FAMOS with Leff = 0.95 and 1.20 um.

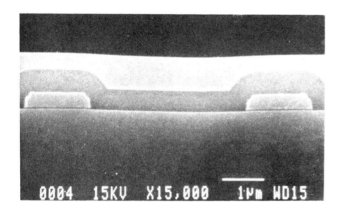

Fig. 5 SEM micrograph of the SPEAR cell just before the planar etch.

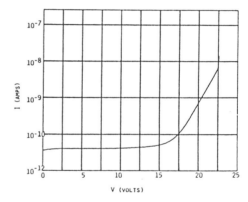

Fig. 8 Leakage current versus bit line voltage for SPEAR buried N+ diffusions, using a 13,056 um perimeter diode.

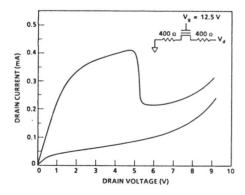

Fig. 6 DC programming characteristics of a SPEAR FAMOS transistor with nominal width/length ratio of 1.5/1.25. Effective gate length (Leff) is 0.95 um.

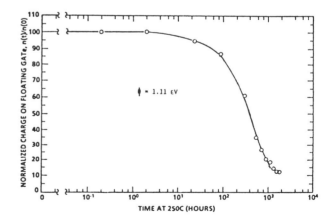

Fig. 9 Data retention characteristics at 250C for a SPEAR FAMOS.

THREE TRANSISTOR CELL FOR HIGH SPEED CMOS EPROM TECHNOLOGY

SANG-SOO LEE, JONG-SUP YOON, GYU-HAN YOON, JI-BUM KIM
YONG-AN HA, AND YOUNG-JUNE PARK.
GOLD STAR SEMICONDUCTOR R&D LAB.
533 HOGAE-DONG, ANYANG, KYUNGGI, 171 KOREA

MIIN WU, TOM YIU, MARK EBEL
SILICON MACROSYSTEMS INC.
2960 N. FIRST STREET, SAN JOSE, CA 95134

ABSTRACT

A high performance 1.5 micron N-well double poly, double metal CMOS process technology has been developed. The patented three transistor cell coupled with this process technology achieved a 25ns 64K high speed EPROM device (8K by 8). The memory core cell with a size of 9.5um x 14.5um was designed to take advantage of maximizing read and write capabilities independently. Seven different types of transistors were generated and optimized to make this possible. A novel interpoly dielectric structure has been developed to simplify the process technology which enhances the manufacturability. High speed (25ns) and small chip size (4.72mm x 3.82mm) were achieved by utilizing a double metal technology.

INTRODUCTION

Over the past years, most of the EPROM cell has been 1-transistor per bit. With this type of design, a rather simple cell layout and high density could be made[1-2]. In this approach, however, it is difficult to achieve high speed EPROM device because of word line delay and low read current.

Since the programming and reading characteristics should be considered in a single transistor simultaneously in the conventional one transistor cell, a rather complicated process sequence is required to obtain the optimum doping concentration profile of the one transistor cell[3-4].

Due to low power consumption and compatible cell size, the EPROM & EEPROM devices begin to be competitive to fusible-link bipolar PROM in the area of high speed PROM. Unlike Bipolar PROM, EPROM offers 100% tested part which is very cost effective.

From this point of view, the authors propose a novel three transistor cell which is suitable for high speed and simple process without any need to compromise between high performance and high voltage by totally separating read and write path in the cell and peripheral circuit.

This paper presents the main considerations in creating the process technology and cell structure, details of how the EPROM cell works and how the high speed is realized.

PROCESS TECHNOLOGY

An N-well double poly, double metal CMOS process is chosen to implement the three transistor cell EPROM device. The n-well is adopted for the compatibility of NMOS EPROM device and high performance requirement. Table-1 shows the key process features. A conventional LOCOS isolation scheme has been used with field oxide of 1 um thickness.

A non-self-aligned double poly stacked gate structure is employed in the EPROM cell to simplify the process without die size penalty. Thin nitride of oxide/nitride/oxide dielectric was the key in growing the 2nd gate oxide with thinner thickness for poly 2 switching transistors. It resulted in the interpoly dielectric film with better uniformity and quality by covering the poly1 gate fully. An anisotropic plasma etching process for poly/nitride/oxide structure has been developed in order to create proper EPROM cell without silicon damage over gate area in the active region of poly2 switching transistors. This process eliminates the complex process to compromise the quality of poly1 oxide edge and 2nd gate oxide thickness as appeared in conventional approach and provides the basis for separating the program and read paths. Figure-1 shows the cross section of the stacked gate structure. In order to maintain good contour structure in the poly1/poly2 cross pattern, the interpoly oxide was grown in dilute gas environment at the temperature higher than $1000^{\circ}C$.

Devices are fabricated on (100) silicon substrate(p-type) with resistivity of 38-63 ohm-cm. After field oxidation, the 1st gate oxide of 350A thickness is grown for the EPROM device. After depositing and defining poly1 structure, 325A poly oxide is grown in 10% dilute oxygen ambient. The nitride film of 200A thickness, then, is deposited and defined to cover all poly1 structure. After masking and threshold voltage adjustment implantation, the 2nd gate oxide of 250A thickness is grown. After poly2 deposition and definition, poly/nitride/oxide film is etched by using the plasma etching technique.

In the double metal process, etch back of inter metal dielectric layer was used by RIE etching technique to achieve better planarization and 2nd metal step coverage. Figure-2 shows the metal step coverage on the planarized intermetal dielectric film.

Seven types of transistors were formed in the process. Table-2 shows the typical transistor par-

Reprinted from the *IEDM Tech. Dig.*, pp. 588-591, 1986.

ameters and their purposes.

THREE TRANSISTOR CELL AND ITS CHARACTERISTICS

The EPROM speed is largely dependent on the sensing speed of bit lines after address decoding. Generally, there are two approaches in high speed EPROM product[5]. One way is to use differential sensing technique as usually used in SRAM. The other way is to raise the bit line voltage and/or read current. The latter approach was chosen in this work. If the bit-line capacitance remains fixed, higher reading current is needed to achieve better speed. The second problem in the conventional single transistor cell comes from high resistive polysilicon. It also suffers from the difficulty in the optimization of programmability and density. Thus, a new three transistor cell has been designed to achieve high speed by using metal word line and optimizing cell transistors with high reading current.

Figure-3 shows the details of designed cell layout and schematics. In the cell, T1 and T2 are stacked gate devices and they are connected by poly1 layer. Once T1 is programmed, T2 is also programmed automatically through poly1 connection. Then T2 and T3 form the reading path in which the state of T2 is detected by selecting the high performance transistor T3 through the metal word line. T2 is designed to obtain high reading current by optimizing the device independently from T1. It has higher W/L ratio and lower Vt than T1.

During the write cycle, high voltage with proper pulse time is applied to the transistor T1 with the read path floating. During the read cycle, the drain of transistor T1 is grounded and control gate (poly2) of stacked gate devices are always kept at high state (around 5V). Through low resistive metal word line, the cell can be read without any further delay.

Figure-4 shows the one shot programming characteristics of the memory cell. Figure-5 shows the programmed threshold voltage as a function of programming pulse width for both write and read transistors. The drain current characteristics of the write and read transistors are shown in Figure-6 before and after programming. As can be seen, both write and read transistors connected by poly1 can be equally programmed. Figure-7(a) and (b) show the leakage current characteristics for interpoly capacitors having four differnt dielectric films with flat and edge intensive patterns, respectively. In the figure, the equivalent thickness for nitride, oxide, nitride/oxide, and oxide/nitride/oxide films are 145A, 1000A, 425A, and 460A, respectively. The flat and the edge intensive capacitors have the area of $2.89 \times 10^{-4} cm^2$ and $1.43 \times 10^{-5} cm^2$, respectively. The edge intensive structure has a perimeter of 2.73cm. It can be seen that O/N/O dielectric comination shows the best leakage characteristics. Also, the edge intensive pattern does not show the appreciable degradation. The charge retention characteristics under both positive and negative stresses and after baking at $200^{\circ}C$ for 40 minutes are summarized in Table-3.

APPLICATION TO 64K BIT EPROM

The process technology and memory cell described above have been applied to 64K BIT (8K by 8) EPROM with the chip size of 4.72mm x 3.82mm. Figure-8 shows the timing waveforms of address input and data output. The chip has been clocked at 22nsec at room temperature from address input to data output. The same technology can be implemented to higher density such as 128K EPROM with similar performance.

CONCLUSION

A three transistor memory cell and 1.5um N-well CMOS process have been developed. The behavior of the cell is compatible to normal single transistor EPROM cell. Most improtantly, the process is very simple and highly manufacturable. Through further scaling of the transistors, the chip speed is believed to be improved.

ACKNOWLEDGEMENTS

The authors would like to thank Drs. C.S.Kim, I.K.Kang, M.S.Choi of GSS and Mr. Phil Siu, Mr. Paul Lui of SMI for their constant encouragement and support. Also the cooperations from GSS wafer processing staffs are highly appreciated.

REFERENCES

[1] Phillip J. Salsbury et al., ISSCC, 1977, pp. 186-187.
[2] Gian Gerosa et al., Technical Digest, 1985, IEEE IEDM, pp. 631-634.
[3] Kuniyoshi YOSHIKAWA et al., Technical Digest, 1984, IEEE IEDM, pp. 456-459.
[4] K.Komori et al., Technical Digest, 1985, IEEE IEDM, pp. 627-630.
[5] Bernard C.Cole, Electronics, August 21, 1986, pp. 47-52.

TABLE-1. PROCESS FEATURES

Leff(min.)	0.8 um
Weff(min.)	1.6 um
Stacked gate transistor	
1st gate oxide	350 A
Interpoly oxide	460 A equivalent
Switching transistor	
2nd gate oxide	250 A
X_j (n^+)	0.23 um
X_j (p^+)	0.35 um
X_j (n-well)	4.5um

TABLE-2. SEVEN TYPE OF TRANSISTORS

	TYPE	Vt	BVDSS	USAGE
1.	Poly-1 PMOS	-1.4V	-16V	program path
2.	Poly-1 NMOS	1.0V	15V	program path
3.	Poly-1 NMOS	0.2V	15V	program path
4.	Poly-2 NMOS	0.8V	11.5V	speed path
5.	Poly-2 PMOS	-0.8V	-13V	speed path
6.	Stacked gate	2.3V	16V	write transistor
7.	Stacked gate	0.5V	16V	read transistor

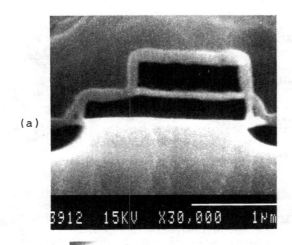

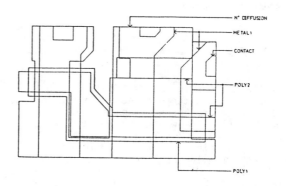

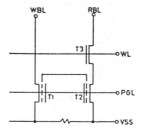

Figure-3. Three transistor cell layout and its schematics

Figure-1. SEM cross-section of the stacked gate structure

    (a) channnel length direction
    (b) channel width direction

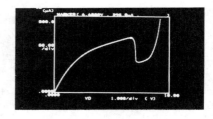

Figure-4. One shot programming characteristics of the write transistor (Vcg = 13V)

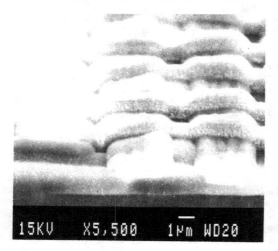

Figure-2. Metal step coverage on the planarized intermetal layer

TABLE-3. Vt OF CELL TRANSISTORS UNDER VARIOUS CONDITIONS

	WRITE TRANSISTOR	READ TRANSISTOR
Before program	2.34 V	0.26 V
After program	5.82 V	3.95 V
After stress		
(Vg=+20V,10sec)	5.73 V	3.90 V
(Vg=−20V,10sec)	5.83 V	3.93 V
After Bake		
(200 C,40MIN)	5.50 V	3.32 V

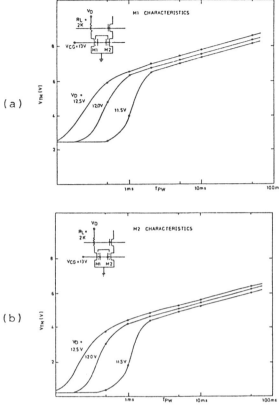

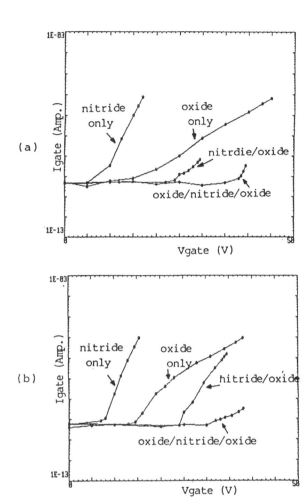

Figure-5. Programmed threshold voltage vs.
programming time for
(a) write transistor and
(b) read transistor

Figure-7. I-V curves of four different
types of interpoly dielectric
films in (a) flat capacitors and
(b) edge intensive capacitors

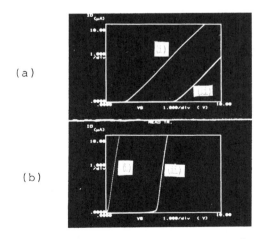

Figure-6. Drain current vs. gate voltage
characteristics in (i) erased and
(ii) programmed states for
(a) write transistor
(b) read transistor

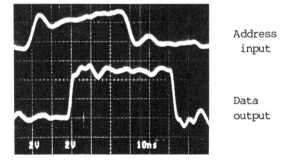

Figure-8. Timing waveforms of address
input and data output

Paper 3.10

0.6μm EPROM CELL DESIGN BASED ON A NEW SCALING SCENARIO

Kuniyoshi YOSHIKAWA, Seiichi MORI, Yukio KANEKO, Yoichi OHSHIMA,
Norihisa ARAI*, and Eiji SAKAGAMI

Semiconductor Device Engineering Laboratory, TOSHIBA Corporation.
* TOSHIBA MICROELECTRONICS Corp.
1, Komukai-Toshiba, Saiwaiku, Kawasaki 210, JAPAN

ABSTRACT

A new scaling guide line is proposed for further scaling of EPROM cells. Lateral and vertical scaling factors are independently introduced to clarify the scaling effects on cell reliabilities and performances. Requiring reliabilities and performances as previous generation devices, a relationship between the two scaling factors are obtained. Based upon this new scaling scenario, device dimensions and operation voltage designs for 16 Mbit EPROM cells are given. 0.6μm EPROM cells have been fabricated and the validity of the new guideline has been experimentally confirmed.

INTRODUCTION

Next generation 16 Mbit EPROMs require less than $4\mu m^2$ cell area for practical die size, which can be realized by a 0.6μm design rule. Up to now, many scaling theories for MOSFETs have been discussed [1-4], including future power supply voltage design. However, EPROM cell scaling methodology has not yet been thoroughly discussed, especially in the submicron regime [5]. Since EPROM cells use hot electron injection phenomenon in programming, triode region operation in reading for avoiding read-disturb failure and inherent stacked gate structure with the floating gate requiring high reliabilities for both interpoly insulator and gate oxide, scaling background is completely different from those for CMOSFETs. Numerical methods for predicting scaled EPROM cell characteristics, utilizing empirical formulas obtained from previous generation devices, has existed [6]. However, their scaling parameter dependencies cannot be seen explicitly.

In this paper, various key issues for EPROM scaling were investigated. A new scaling scenario is proposed by considering simultaneous realization for reliability and performance constraints. Voltage designs for program/read operations and device parameters for 0.6μm cells are proposed. Scaled EPROM cells fabricated with 0.6μm technologies [7], based on this new scaling scheme, were carefully studied. Fabrication technology modules for $3.85\mu m^2$ cell are also discussed.

A NEW SCALING SCENARIO

In order to investigate the scaling effects on cell reliability and performance, two independent scaling factors k (for lateral dimensions, L, W, x_j) and h (for vertical dimensions, tox_1, tox_2) are introduced. We attempt to find a relation between k and h to satisfy the reliability and performance constraints simultaneously. Important key issues for designing scaled EPROM cells are summarized in Table 1, with explicit formulas (symbols and notations, see Tables 1 & 2).

Program-disturb 1 (drain stress)

This disturb refers deprogramming of unselected cells on the same drain (bit) line. This comes from electron tunneling through the cell gate oxide and injected hot holes due to band-to-band tunneling or punchthrough. To avoid this, electric field, Eox_1, should be maintained as the previous generation. Since capacitance coupling ratios, C_1/C_T and C_2/C_T, are unchanged, Eox_1 depends only on $\Delta Vt/tox_1$ and Vdp/tox_1. Therefore, ΔVt and Vdp should be scaled as 1/h.

Program-disturb 2 (gate stress)

This disturb is deprogramming of unselected cells on the same gate (word) line. Electron leakage through interpoly dielectrics is the main cause, which requires maintaining Eox_2. Since Eox_2 is a function of $\Delta Vt/tox_2$ and Vpp/tox_2, ΔVt and Vpp should be scaled as 1/h.

Read-disturb (Soft-write)

Prevention of soft-write for selected "un-injected" cells in reading will be the key for scaling. Longer than 10 years lifetime is required. Assuming the lucky electron model for gate current, soft-write lifetime is a function of 1/Em,r through gate current. Recently, the maximum channel electric field (Em,r) has been found to be proportional to $(Vdr-Vdsat)/(tox_1 \cdot xj)^{1/3}$ [3]. Therefore, Vdr is scaled as $1/(h \cdot k)^{1/3}$ for read-disturb resistance.

Cell read current

For high speed reading and high noise margin, cell read current should be preserved. Since EPROM read operation is usually accomplished in a triode region, reflecting N^+ drain structure for cells, read current is roughly proportional to Vdr/tox_1. Therefore, the Icell will be maintained, preserving $Vdr \cdot h$, as long as Vcc and Vtcell are not scaled. For unscaled Vtcell, channel concentration (N) is scaled as 1/h.

Reprinted from the *IEDM Tech. Dig.*, pp. 587–590, 1989.

Programming

Minimum threshold cell voltage shift (ΔVt) after programming, should be larger than A*Vcc+B*(Vcc-Vtcell) for reliability and noise resistance. If Vcc and Vtcell are not scaled, a slightly enhanced sense amplifier gain (1/B) is necessary to cope with the reduced ΔVt as 1/h. Noting that gate current is an exponential function of -1/Em,p, where Em,p is given as (Vdp-Vdsat)/(tox$_1$*xj)$^{1/3}$, Em,p should be maintained. Since Vdsat in programming decreases faster than 1/(h*k)$^{1/3}$ with Vpp scaling, Em,p is slightly increased, resulting in higher speed programming. Therefore, Vdp should be scaled as 1/(h*k)$^{1/3}$.

Punchthrough

Punchthrough should be strictly prohibited for stable cell operation. However, bulk punchthrough voltage (Vpt) is proportional to (h/k)^2, which leads to degraded resistance if h<k. Drain turn-on leakage for unselected cells on the same drain (bit) line in programming will also be a problem. Since Idl is a exponential function of Vdp, Vdp should be scaled.

Considering these requirements above, as much as possible, a new scaling law is obtained as,

$$h = (k)^{1/2}.$$

It should be noted that constant voltage scaling cannot preserve reliability, while constant field scaling degrades cell performance (program speed and cell read current). This new scaling law concludes that power supply voltage (Vcc) is maintained as the previous generation's, while programming control-gate/drain voltages and read drain voltage should be scaled as 1/(k)$^{1/2}$. Predicted device parameters and operation voltages for 0.6μm 16Mbit EPROM cell are given in Table 2.

0.6μm EPROM CELL CHARACTERISTICS

Scaled 0.6μm cells, based on the scaling law were fabricated to investigate the scenario validity.

Among various issues investigated, only the punchthrough resistance cannot be substantially preserved. Therefore, DSA p-pocket layer structure, surrounding cell drain/source junctions, was introduced for higher punchthrough resistance as well as for programming efficiency increase [8], without increasing cell Vt. Thus, Punchthrough (both bulk-punchthrough and drain turn-on) is completely suppressed, down to 0.5μm poly gate length, as shown in Fig.1.

For program disturb 1, band-to-band tunneling induced deprogramming can be prevented by reducing Vdp to 6V to maintain Vdp/tox$_1$ and ΔVt/tox$_1$. Furthermore, cell gate oxide is reducible down to 10nm, in spite of increasing vertical electric field, as indicated in Fig.2. Note that this deprogramming due to drain stress is greatly enhanced by the onset of punchthrough leakage, as shown in Fig.3. Therefore, punchthrough prevention

is most important, when scaling both the gate oxide thickness and the gate length for EPROM cells. On the contrary, high temperature data retention does not limit the cell gate oxide thickness down to 10nm.

For program-disturb 2, no degradation down to 20nm effective thickness has been observed, since Oxide/Nitride/Oxide (ONO) film has large intrinsic leakage resistance without Vfb shift up to 5MV/cm stress bias. By optimizing ONO composition((B) in Fig.4), superior 300°C bake retention characteristics have been confirmed, as shown in Fig.4.

For read-disturb, predicted voltage for Vdr is around 1V in the 0.6μm regime. Experiments (Fig.5) shows 10 year or longer soft-write lifetime with this Vdr for 0.5μm gate length cells.

For cell read current, Fig.6 indicates that Vdr can be reducible to around 1V for a 0.6μm cell. Above 1V, saturation characteristics are observed and gain (around 12 uA/V) is not so effective. Typically, 80μA cell current is obtained at Vdr=1V. This Vdr value coincides well with that from read-disturb requirement.

For programming, Vdp is expected to be 5.7V in 0.6μm rule from the scaling law. The samples show, however, more enhanced programmability with lower Vdp, such as 4.5V, as shown in Fig.7. This strongly indicates a possible realization for a single 5V Vcc EPROM with internally generated Vpp.

As one of the process modules for 16M EPROMs, the self-aligned source (SAS) process was introduced, which enables realizing a 3.85μm^2 unit cell area. Figure 8 shows typical cell layout, where source diffusion lines are self-alignedly formed with the wordlines by RIE etching of field oxides.

The fabricated EPROM cells reveal substantial operation margin around ± 15% variation for cell gate length and width, which is almost the same as that for previous generation 0.9μm cells, as shown in Fig.9.

SUMMARY

The new scaling scenario has been proposed for the 0.6μm EPROM cell, as well as providing operation voltage designs. The scaled cells based on this scenario showed good reliability and performances, resulting in confirming the validity of the new law. With appropriate modification, this scaling scheme together with the analysis used will be a powerful tool in the beyond 16 Mbit regime.

ACKNOWLEDGEMENT

The authors would like to thank Dr.O. Ozawa and Dr. S. Shinozaki for their encouragements.

REFERENCES

[1] R.H.Dennard et al., IEEE JSSC, p.257, 1974.
[2] G.Baccarani et al., IEEE ED, p.452, 1984.

[3] P.K.Chatterjee et al, IEEE EDL, p.220, 1980.
[4] M.Kakumu et al., IEEE IEDM, p.399, 1986.
[5] J.Chung et al., IEEE IEDM, p.200, 1988.
[6] S.Tanaka, private communication.
[7] S.Mori et al, 10th NVSM Workshop, Vail,1989.
[8] K.Yoshikawa et al., IEEE IEDM, p.456, 1984.

Table 1. Key issues for EPROM scaling.

ISSUES	EXPRESSIONS	SCALING	This Model	Constant Voltage	Constant Field
Lateral dimensions Vertical dimensions	L,W,Xj tox1,tox2	1/k 1/h	1/k 1/√k	1/k 1/k	1/k 1/k
Program-disturb 1 (Drain stress) Program-disturb 2 (Gate stress)	$Eox1 \sim \frac{C2}{CT} \frac{\Delta Vt}{tox1} + \frac{(C1+C2)}{CT} \frac{Vdp}{tox1}$ $Eox2 \sim \frac{C2}{CT} \frac{\Delta Vt}{tox2} + \frac{C1}{CT} \frac{Vpp}{tox2}$	$\sim \frac{(2\Delta Vt+Vdp)*h}{3}$ $\sim \frac{(2\Delta Vt+Vpp)*h}{3}$	1 1	k k	1 1
Read-disturb (Soft-write)	$Igate/W \sim \exp(-C/Em,r)$, $Em,r \sim \frac{(Vdr-Vdsat)}{\sqrt[3]{tox1*Xj}}$ $\ln(T) \sim \ln(LW/tox2)+1/Em.r$	$(Vdr-Vdsat)*\sqrt[3]{kh}$ $\sim 1/Em.r$	1 1	k√k 1/k√k	1/√k √k
Cell read current (Cell Vt)	$Icell \sim \frac{W}{L} \frac{C2}{CT}(Vcc-Vtcell)\frac{Vdr}{tox1}$ $Vtcell \sim tox1*\sqrt{N}$	Vdr*h √N/h	1 1	k 1	1/k 1/k
Program	$\Delta Vt \geq AVcc+B(Vcc-Vtcell)$ $\sim \int \frac{tox1}{L} \frac{Igate}{W}dt$, $Igate/W \sim \exp(-C/Em,p)$, $Em,p \sim \frac{(Vdp-Vdsat)}{\sqrt[3]{tox1*Xj}}$	ΔVt $\sim (\ )^{1/Em,p}$ $(Vdp-Vdsat)*\sqrt[3]{kh}$	1/√k ( ) 1	1 ( )^{k√k} k√k	1/k ( )^{1/√k} 1/√k
Punchthrough (Bulk) (Drain turn-on)	$Vpt \sim N*L^2$ $Idl \sim \frac{W}{L} \frac{1}{N} \sqrt{N} \exp(\frac{q}{kT}VFG+\frac{Vdp}{D})$, $VFG \sim (Xj/L)*Vdp$	N/k^2 $\sim (\ )^{Vdp}$ Vdp	1/k ( )^{1/√k} 1/√k	1 ( ) 1	1/k ( )^{1/k} 1/k

Notation

C_T: Total capacitance of Floating gate.
C_1: Floating gate-sub. capacitance.
C_2: Control gate-Floating gate capacitance.
Vdsat: Drain saturation voltage.
N : Impurity conc. of channel.
Igate: Gate current.
V_{FG}: Floating gate voltage.
Em,r: Maximum channel field in reading.
Em,p: Maximum channel field in programming.
Vtcell: Cell threshold voltage.
DVt: Minimum threshold voltage shift after programming.
Eox_1: Cell gate oxide electric field.
Eox_2: Interpoly ONO electric field.
T: Soft-write lifetime.
1/B: sense amp. gain.
Idl: Drain turn-on leakage current.
A,C,D: constant.

Other meanings, see Table 2.

Table 2. Device parameters and voltage design, based on the new scaling law. Note: Vtcell = 2V for both 4M and 16M.

Parameters/Voltages	4Mb(0.9um)	16Mb(0.6um)	Scaling
Gate length : L(um)	0.9	0.6	1/k
Gate Width : W(um)	0.9	0.6	1/k
Junction Depth : Xj(um)	0.2	0.13	1/k
Cell gate ox. thickness : tox1(nm)	20	16.3	1/√k
Interpoly ONO thickness : tox2(nm)	30	24.5	1/√k
Control gate voltage in program : Vpp(V)	12.5	10.2	1/√k
Drain voltage in program : Vdp(V)	7	5.7	1/√k
Control gate voltage in read : Vcc(V)	5	5	1
Drain voltage in read : Vdr(V)	1.2	0.98	1/√k
Cell threshold voltage : Vtcell(V)	2	2	1

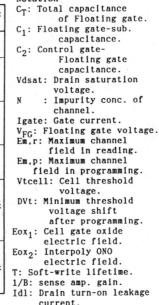

Fig.1. Punchthrough voltage as a function of gate length. DSA p-pocket improves more than 0.15μm minimum length.

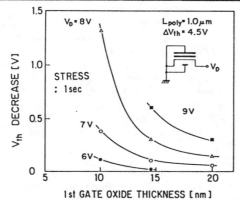

Fig.2. EPROM data de-programming characteristics due to drain stress. To investigate, pure band-to-band tunneling induced degradation, longer gate length(~1μm) devices were used to exclude punchthrough leakage.

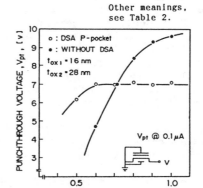

Fig.3. Data deprogramming dependence due to drain stress conditions. (a):Source terminal is grounded. where punchthrough leakage current flows. (b): Source and drains are connected, where punchthrough current does not flow.

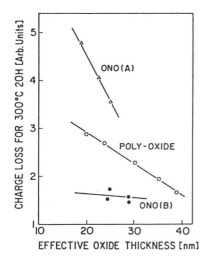

Fig.4. Charge retention characteristics dependence on interpoly insulator composition and thickness. ONO optimization is important for reliability.

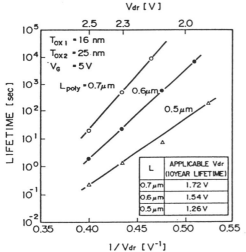

Fig.5. Soft-write immunity for $0.6\mu m$ cells. Lifetime is defined as 10% increase of initial cell threshold voltages.

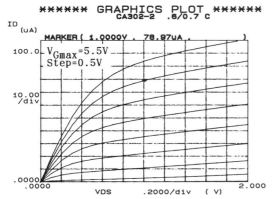

Fig.6. I-V characteristics for $0.6\mu m$ cell. Early velocity saturation is observed, which indicates not so much gain ($12\mu A/V$) can be obtained by applying higher Vdr.

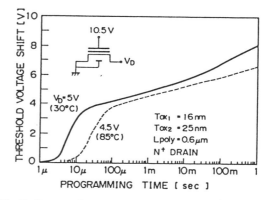

Fig.7. Programming characteristics for $0.6\mu m$ cell. Less than 100usec programming is obtained for Vdp=4.5V at 85C, indicating single 5V programming scheme for EPROM cell.

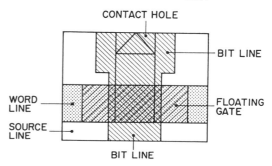

Fig.8. Typical cell layout for 16M bit EPROM cell, using $0.6\mu m$ feature size. Cell size is $3.85~\mu m^2$, with self-aligned source(SAS) technology.

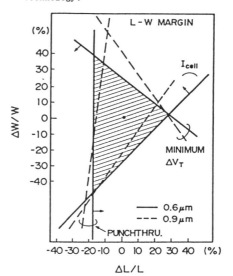

Fig.9. Channel length - width variation margin area for $0.6\mu m$ cell, compared with that for the previous generation 0.9um cells. Margins are well preserved, assuring actual production ease.

Paper 3.11

A NOVEL HIGH-SPEED, 5-VOLT PROGRAMMING EPROM STRUCTURE

WITH SOURCE-SIDE INJECTION

A. T. Wu, T. Y. Chan, P. K. Ko and C. Hu

Department of Electrical Engineering and Computer Sciences
Electronics Research Laboratory
University of California, Berkeley

ABSTRACT

A novel source-side injection EPROM (SIEPROM) structure [1] capable of 5-volt only, high speed programming is described. The cell is an asymmetrical n-channel stacked-gate MOSFET, with a short weak gate-control region introduced close to the source. Under high gate bias, a strong channel electric field is created in this local region even at a relatively low drain voltage. Furthermore, the gate oxide field in this region is favorable for hot-electron injection into the floating gate. As a result, a programming speed of 10 μs at a drain voltage of 5 volts has been demonstrated. Also, a soft-write endurance time of 10 years with a read current larger than 100 μA per μm width can be readily achieved.

I. INTRODUCTION

The conventional EPROMs use drain-side channel hot-electron injection for their programming. The injection current can be enhanced by increasing either the channel field or the gate-oxide field: the former increases the hot-electron population, and the latter enhances the injection probability [2]. However, low gate and high drain voltages are required to generate the high channel field, while exactly the opposite biasing condition-low drain and high gate voltages - is needed to create the high gate-oxide field [2,3]. In practice, very high drain and gate voltages are used as a compromise, such that the device is operating very close to breakdown during programming. This gives a small window between programming and breakdown voltages for device design and process control, not to mention the need for extra power supplies for programming.

In the SIEPROM device, a high channel electric field for generating hot-electrons is created near the source when a large gate voltage is applied. As a result, both high channel and oxide fields exist simultaneously such that hot-electron injection is strongly favored. We have successfully programmed the SIEPROM device with a drain voltage of 5 volts at a programming speed an order of magnitude faster than that achievable in a state-of-the-art EPROM cell programmed with higher voltages.

II. PRINCIPLE OF OPERATION

Figure 1 shows the cross-section SEM of a SIEPROM cell. The cell is a stacked-gate MOSFET with an extra sidewall floating gate, i.e. a poly-Si spacer on the source side of the cell, flanking the stacked gate. A weak gate-control channel region is formed under the spacer oxide between this sidewall gate and the stacked gates. At a high gate bias when the rest of the channel is highly conductive, a channel electric-field peak is created in this weak gate-control region. The two-dimensional device simulation result of a realistic SIEPROM device using PISCES [4] is shown in Figure 2 where the assumed bias voltages are: $V_d = 5$ volts; a floating gate voltage (V_{fg}) of 12 volts; and a sidewall gate potential (V_{swg}) of 4 volts. The 4-volt sidewall gate potential used in this example is the estimated acquired potential due to capacitive coupling between the stacked gate and the sidewall gate. A simple physical model [5] has been developed which qualitatively explains the origin of this mid-channel electric-field.

Since the high channel-field is located near the source, the local gate oxide field is highly favorable for hot-electron injection. Besides, simulation results have also shown that the magnitude of this source-side electric-field peak increases with both the gate and drain voltages. Therefore, by increasing the gate voltage, the drain voltage can be lowered without decreasing the hot-electron population. This makes the gate oxide field even more favorable for electron injection.

The sidewall gate serves several important functions in the programming of the SIEPROM device. It acquires a floating potential through capacitive coupling with the stacked gate and strongly inverts the underlying channel so that very little voltage is dropped in this very short (0.1 μm in our experimental device) sidewall-gate channel region. Also, because of this coupling effect, the peak channel field and thus the hot-electrons injection are controlled by the thickness of the oxide spacer, instead of by drain/source drive-in cycles as in minimum overlap or asymmetrical devices [5]. To study the role of the sidewall gate in programming and reading, its potential was designated as an input for the simulation. Our simulation results show that the peak field is rather insensitive to the sidewall gate potential (Figure 3). Therefore, programming speed is not sensitive to the sidewall gate potential. However, simulation results show that the reading current is rather sensitive to the sidewall gate potential, especially near the channel threshold voltage.

III. EXPERIMENTAL RESULTS

A conventional EPROM process is modified to fabricate the SIEPROM cell. Figure 4 shows the key process steps. A stacked gate is first formed (Fig.4a). An oxide layer is then grown, followed by a thin poly-Si deposition (Fig.4b). The thin poly-Si is anisotropically etched to form poly-Si spacers flanking the stacked gate (Fig.4c). Poly-Si spacer on the drain side is etched away using an extra mask (Fig.4d), followed by drain/source implant. The gate-oxide and the inter-poly oxide thickness in our test devices are 205 Å and 490 Å respectively. The threshold voltage of the cell in the erased state is 0.9 V. The coupling ratio from the control gate to the floating gate is about 0.8. The coupling ratio from the control gate to the sidewall gate is estimated to be between 0.25 to 0.3.

Reprinted from the *IEDM Tech. Dig.*, pp. 584–587, 1986.

The programming characteristics of the SIEPROM cell is shown in Figure 5 where the threshold voltage shift is plotted as a function of programming time. Also shown is the programming characteristics of a state-of-the-art conventional drain-side injection EPROM cell reported by K. Komori et al [6]. The SIEPROM cell has a gate length of 1.0 μm, with programming bias of $V_d = 5V$ and $V_{cg} = 15V$. The conventional cell had a gate oxide thickness of 350 Å and a gate length of 1.2 μm, with programming bias of $V_d = 8V$ and $V_{cg} = 12.5V$. The threshold voltage shift for the SIEPROM is more than 4 volts after only 10 μs programming, at least one order of magnitude faster than that of the conventional cell. If the same drain voltage of 8V is used for both cells, the programming speed of the SIEPROM cell can be three orders of magnitude faster than that of the conventional cell.

Figure 6 shows the one-shot programming characteristics of 10 SIEPROM cells randomly selected from a 4" wafer. The programming is uniform throughout the 4" wafer, and is insensitive to the drain voltage ramping rate between 4×10^2 and 4×10^4 volt/sec, indicating that programming occurs within a narrow drain voltage window of 4 to 5 volts. The device breakdown voltage is about 100% higher than the programming voltage. Figure 7 confirms the sensitivity of the programming speed to the drain voltage variation. For a drain voltage of $5\pm0.5V$, the threshold shift is larger than 4 volts within 40μs. The programming speed is very sensitive to the gate voltage variation as shown in Figure 8. Since the gate current is extremely small, on-chip charge-pumping circuitry can supply a stable high gate voltage for programming, requiring only a 5V power supply.

An ultra-violet EPROM eraser can erase the SIEPROM cell in 20 minutes. The current-voltage characteristics of the memory cell in the erased and programmed states are shown in Figure 9. The erased cell shows identical current-voltage characteristics to that of the fresh cell. One cell has gone through at least 10 program/erase cycles without any degradation in programming speed and current-voltage characteristics. Using a reading voltage of $V_{cg} = 5V$ and $V_d = 2V$, the drain current is 101 μA per μm device width in the erased state. The reading current has a variation of $\pm10\%$ throughout the 4" wafer. In the programmed state, the drain current is less than 70 pA per μm device width at the reading voltage.

To evaluate a possible limitation of the SIEPROM, soft-write endurance time, defined as the time to cause a threshold shift of 0.1 volt, are plotted as a function of $1/V_g$ in Figure 10. Using a drain voltage of 2 volts, a soft-write endurance time of 10 years with a read current larger than 100 μA per μm width can be readily achieved based on extrapolation of measured data.

IV. DISCUSSION

The high-speed, low-voltage programming capability of the SIEPROM structure is due to two facts. First, hot-electron generation under the weak gate-control region increases with increasing gate voltage, as confirmed by the second substrate current hump shown in Figure 11; thereby drain voltage for programming can be decreased while keeping the substrate current high. Secondly, the local oxide field at the point where hot electrons are generated is highly favorable for electron injection. This aiding oxide field comes from the fact that hot-electron generation site is close to the source, and that high gate, low drain voltages are used for programming. The efficient electron injection of SIEPROM is shown in Figure 12 where I_{gate}/I_d is plotted as a function of I_{sub}/I_d. The same characteristics for drain-side injection devices using a model reported by Tam et al [3] are also shown. This figure confirmed that the SIEPROM devices are able to generate strong hot-electrons at a low drain voltage while keeping the gate oxide field strongly favorable for electron injection.

The critical step in fabricating the SIEPROM cell is the removal of the drain-side poly-spacer (Figure 4d), where an alignment error of less than L/2 is required. This is within the alignment specification for a technology with minimum design rule of L. Other device structures using the same source-side injection mechanism without tight alignment requirement are being studied and will be reported.

V. CONCLUSION

The SIEPROM cell structure reported in this paper has several advantages over the conventional EPROM cell. First, the cell can be programmed with drain voltages as low as 5 volt. Such low drain programming voltage has two important impacts on the EPROM technology: (1) it is well below the device breakdown and therefore gives a large tolerance for process control and device design; (2) it is possible to program the cells with a single 5-volt power supply since the gate voltage of 15-volt can be supplied by charge pumping circuitry. Second, even at this low programming voltage, the programming speed for SIEPROM is much faster than that of the drain-side injection EPROMs. This high speed programming is important when the memory size exceeds 1 Mbits per chip.

V. ACKNOWLEDGEMENT

This work is sponsored by DARPA under contract N00039-81-K-0251.

References

[1] A. T. Wu, T. Y. Chan, P. K. Ko and C. Hu, U. S. Patent Pending (1986).

[2] P. E. Cottrell, R. R. Troutman and T. H. Ning, "Hot-Electron Emission in N-Channel IGFET's," IEEE Trans. Solid-State Circuits, vol. SC-14, pp. 442-455, Apr. 1979.

[3] S. Tam, P. K. Ko, and C. Hu, " Lucky Electron Model of Channel Hot Electron Injection in MOSFETs," IEEE Trans. Electron Devices, vol. ED-31, pp. 1116-1125, Sep. 1984.

[4] M. R. Pinto, Ph.D. dissertation, Stanford Electronic Labs., Stanford Univ., Stanford, Ca, 1984.

[5] P. K. Ko, T. Y. Chan, A. T. Wu, and C. Hu "The Effects of Weak Gate-to-Drain(Source) Overlap on MOSFET Characteristics," to be published in 1986 IEDM Technical Digest.

[6] K. Komori, K. Kuroda, S. Meguro, K. Nagasawa, "A High Performance Memory Cell Technology for Mega Bit EPROMs," 1985 IEDM Technical Digest, pp. 627-630.

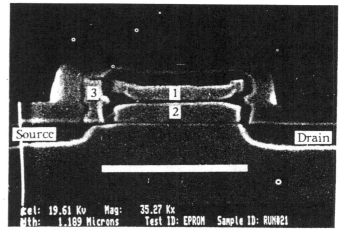

Figure 1: Cross-section SEM of an SIEPROM cell. (1) is the control-gate, (2) is the floating-gate, and (3) is the poly-Si sidewall.

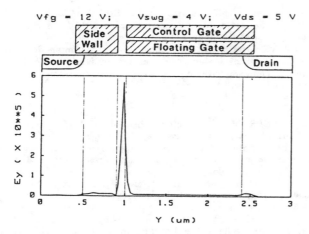

Figure 2: Distribution of channel electric field for an SIEPROM cell under programming condition using 2-D device simulation.

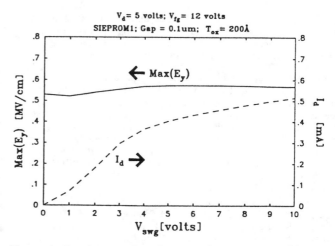

Figure 3: Sensitivity of peak channel field to the sidewall-gate voltage variation using 2-D device simulation.

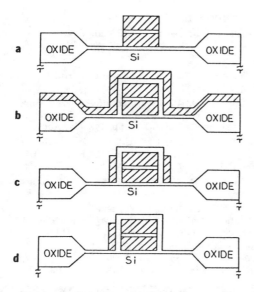

= POLY–SILICON

Figure 4: Key process steps for SIEPROM.

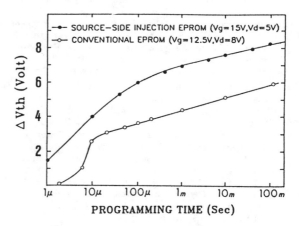

Figure 5: Programming speed of the SIEPROM compared to a state-of-the-art drain-side injection EPROM [6]. Threshold voltage of SIEPROM cell in erased state is 0.9V.

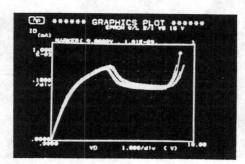

Figure 6: One-shot Programming characteristics of 10 SIEPROM cells randomly selected in a 4" wafer. Gate voltage is 15 volts.

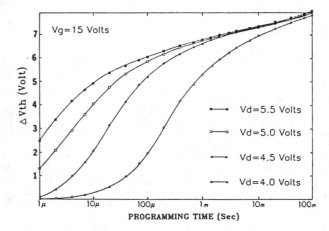

Figure 7: Programming speed of the SIEPROM cell as a function of drain voltage variation.

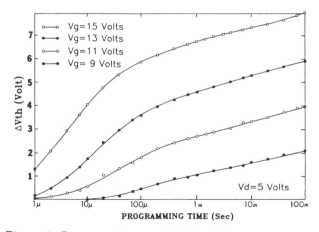

Figure 8: Programming speed of the SIEPROM cell as a function of gate voltage variation.

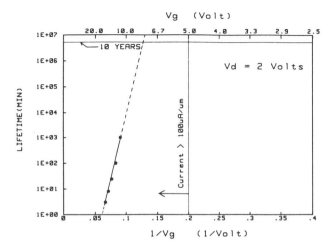

Figure 10: Soft-write endurance time characteristics.

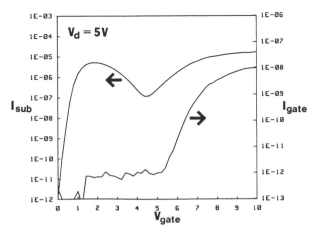

Figure 11: Substrate and gate current characteristics measured with control-gate and floating-gate shorted. W/L=2μm/1μm.

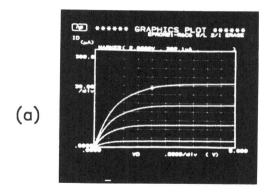

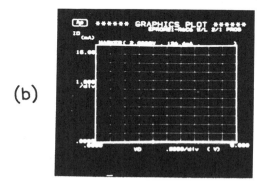

Figure 9: Current-Voltage characteristics in (a) erased and (b) programmed states. Gate voltages sweep from 1V to 5V in steps of 1V.

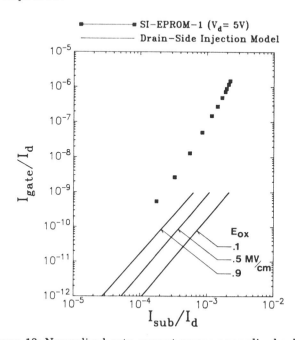

Figure 12: Normalized gate current versus normalized substrate current for SIEPROM and for drain-side injection device using Tam's model [3] with oxide field E_{ox} as a parameter.

MOISTURE RESISTIVE, U. V. TRANSMISSIVE PASSIVATION FOR PLASTIC ENCAPSULATED EPROM DEVICES

Kathryn Alexander, Jeffrey Hicks, Thomas Soukup

Intel Corporation
3065 Bowers Ave.
Santa Clara, Ca. 95051

ABSTRACT

A unique U. V. transmissive passivation process for One Time Programmable EPROMS has been developed which provides moisture resistance for the plastic encapsulated devices and allows erasure of hermetic devices. This passivation, which consists of a two layer film of plasma enhanced CVD oxynitride and phosphorus doped oxide, requires no change in current interlayer dielectric, metal composition or circuit layout. This approach is novel in that it continues to utilize 9% to 10% phosphorus doped CVD oxide as an interlayer dielectric, while most plastic compatable processes require control of phosphorus concentration to approximately 7%. Observed moisture related failure mechanisms, which include single bit charge loss, metal line corrosion and input/output leakage, were investigated and related to specific processing parameters. Processing limits were then determined to eliminate these failure modes.

INTRODUCTION AND GOALS

EPROM devices have traditionally been assembled in hermetically sealed packages with a transparent window in the lid to allow erasure with U.V. light. As the EPROM has come to be used more in a production environment rather than purely as a developmental component, the need for erasability and reprogrammability have become less important than device cost. One way to reduce cost is to assemble the EPROM die in a plastic package. This requires changing the passivation to provide moisture protection for the die. Most of the moisture resistant passivations, however, employ a nitride layer which is opaque to U.V. and thus prevent erasure. For this reason a program was initiated to develop a new passivation process which would provide good protection for plastic encapsulated die as well as allowing U.V. erasure for hermetic encapsulated devices and for electrical and reliability testing on the wafer. The device performance goals that were set out included:

1. Failure rates $\leq$ 0.5% in 1K HRS 85°C/85%RH moisture test.

2. Failure rates $\leq$ 1.0% in 96 HRS 121°C steam test.

3. Erasure comparable to Pyrox (APCVD glass, 4%P) passivated devices.

It was clearly desirable to minimize the processing changes necessary to achieve these goals in order to facilitate implementation and reduce the risk of unanticipated side effects.

Initial discussion in this paper centers on the material aspects of the passivation itself followed by other processing issues of relevance. Finally, the device accelerated moisture test results are presented for the Intel P2764 and P2732A.

BACKGROUND

A variety of different passivation structures were investigated to achieve the performance goals described above. Although it is not particularly fruitful to recount these dead-ends in detail, it is useful to note the nature of their inadaquacies so as to better understand the virtues of the approach ultimately selected.

One of the most physically dramatic of the problems encountered was passivation cracking or delamination (photo's 1,2). These effects can be induced in accelerated moisture testing or temperature cycling. Metalization beneath such passivation disruptions is, understandably, subject to rapid corrosion. The propensity of a particular film to crack or delaminate is a function of its intrinsic stress, brittleness and adhesion to the underlying layer; and its occurance is preferentially disposed towards large planar regions without stress relieving topography.

Many of the films, even some which had good bulk U.V. transmission, prevented erasure of the EPROM cell and were ruled out on these grounds. A number of passivations proved to offer insufficient moisture protection; the dominant failure modes being charge loss in the EPROM cell, interior metal line corrosion and bond pad corrosion. The passivations in these cases were excessively hydrophilic or water permeable or had high densities of critical defects.

Most of the development work centered on plasma enhanced CVD Nitride films, which have a well established suitability for passivating plastic encapsulated I.C.'s[1]. The major hurdle lay with the need to preserve the U.V. erase capability of the device since most plasma nitride films are not transmissive in the near ultra violet region. It was established, however, that oxynitride films could be produced which had >50% U.V. transmission (@253.7nm, 1u thick film) and intrinsic moisture permeability comparable to plasma nitrides[2].

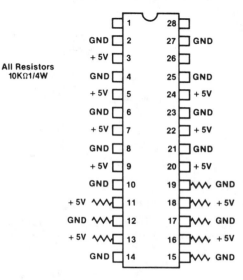

FIGURE 1
85°C/85%RH BIAS DIAGRAM

All Resistors 10KΩ1/4W

Reprinted from *Proc. 22nd IRPS*, pp. 218–222, 1984.

MEASUREMENT TECHNIQUES

Several evaluation techniques were utilized in the course of this project. All moisture evaluations were conducted using the 2764 EPROM assembled in 600 mil packages of flame retardant epoxy with Au eutectic die attach. Moisture performance was measured using alternate bias, minimum power dissipation, 85°C/85%RH and 121°C 2 ATM steam stresses. The 85°C/85%RH bias configuration is illustrated in figure 1. Film stress was measured using an optical lever technique[3]. The diffusion coefficients of moisture were calculated from changes in stress after exposure to 100°C 100%RH for several hours. Film U.V. transmission was measured at 253.7nm on films deposited on 100mm sapphire wafers. Electron dispersive X-RAY technique measured bulk weight percent phosphorus in SiO_2 glass. Refractive index was measured on a Gaertner automatic ellipsometer.

OXYNITRIDE FILM

The oxynitride films were produced in a plasma enhanced CVD reactor in a manner that is very similar to conventional plasma nitrides. Table 1 provides a basic process description. Refractive index "n" was found to be a good indicator for film properties. In particular, a monotonic decrease in U.V. transmission was measured with increasing refractive index as would be expected from previous measurements with nitrides (fig. 2). A severe degradation in device moisture resistance was seen at low refractive index (fig. 3), however, with charge loss being the major failure mechanism. This required a tradeoff between transmission and moisture resistance. At the nominal refractive index transmission is $\geq$25%, allowing U.V. erasure while moisture resistance is suficient to achieve the project goals. A strong dependance of U.V. transmission on deposition pressures was also observed (fig. 4). This dependance on deposition pressure is probably due to structural disorders and excess silicon creating band broadening effects on the stoichiometric silicon nitride absorption edge near 225nm[4].

In order to provide the die with good immunity from the influences of ambient moisture, it was important that the oxynitride retain the inherently low moisture permeability of plasma nitride films. No measurable

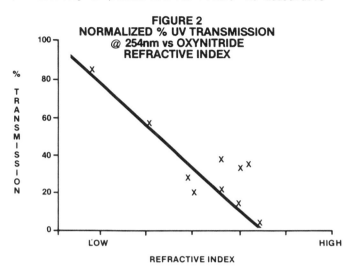

FIGURE 2
NORMALIZED % UV TRANSMISSION
@ 254nm vs OXYNITRIDE
REFRACTIVE INDEX

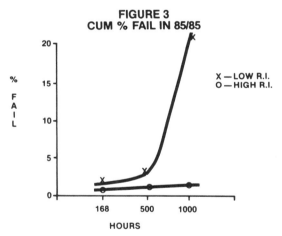

FIGURE 3
CUM % FAIL IN 85/85

X — LOW R.I.
O — HIGH R.I.

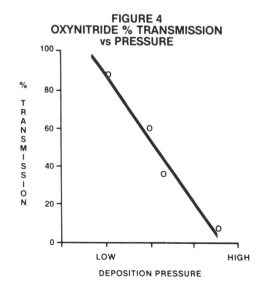

FIGURE 4
OXYNITRIDE % TRANSMISSION
vs PRESSURE

TABLE 1

Type of Film	Plasma Nitride	Plasma Oxynitride
Type of Reactor	Plasma Enhanced Chemical Vapor Deposition	Plasma Enhanced Chemical Vapor Deposition
Reactor Configuration	Quartz Tube with Sled of Vertical Parallel Graphite Plates	Quartz Tube with Sled of Vertical Parallel Graphite Plates
Plasma RF	450KHz	450KHz
Reactant Gasses	SiH₄, NH₃	SiH₄, NH₃, N₂O
Reactor Temp. Range	300-400°C	300-400°C
Deposition Pressure Range	0.5-5.0 Torr	0.5-5.0 Torr

TABLE 2
TABLE OF PASSIVATION PROPERTIES

Film	Film Properties	Diffusion** Coefficient of Moisture	Knoop Hardness	% UV Trans.
NITRIDE	PECVD	$<10^{-18}$cm²/sec	1176	0.55
OXYNITRIDE	PECVD	$<10^{-18}$cm²/sec	1220	52
PLASMA OXIDE	PECVD	$<10^{-18}$cm²/sec	2599	83
PYROX*	APCVD	4×10^{-13}cm²/sec	286	60

*4% Phosphorus SiO₂ Glass
**Measured After 100°C, 100% RH

degradation in moisture permeability was seen as compared with plasma nitride (Table 2). Both plasma nitrides and oxynitrides have many other favorable mechanical properties including high film density[4] and excellent mechanical strength[1], however they can be relatively brittle. It is highly advantageous to minimize the intrinsic stress of passivation layers to avoid film cracking and delamination or disruption of the underlying metalization. 1.2u was selected as the nominal film thickness to provide good step coverage over 1u metal lines while minimizing the intrinsic passivation film forces on underlying layers. No improvement in moisture resistance was seen from increasing the film thickness past this point.

MULTIPLICITY OF FILMS

One recurrent result of the passivation development work was that multiple layer structures improved die moisture resistance compared to passivations of any of their components used singly. In particular a low phosphorus CVD oxide ("pyrox") proved a very effective adjunct to plasma oxynitride. Table 3 gives comparative examples of accelerated moisture test data for multiple layer passivations employing oxynitride and pyrox. The data are in each case from split lots with identical processing except for the noted passivation differences.

TABLE 3
MOISTURE PERFORMANCE IMPROVEMENT DUE TO MULTIPLICITY OF FILMS

EVALUATION	STEAM		
	72 hrs	144 hrs	216 hrs
OXY	1/50[B]	8/50[A,C]	13/50[A]
OXY/PYROX	0/98	0/97	1/97[C]

EVALUATION	STEAM			85/85	
	96 hrs	192 hrs	288 hrs	500 hrs	1000 hrs
LTO/OXY	0/99	5/98[A]	19/98[B,C]	1/245[A]	8/245[A]
LTO/OXY/PYROX	0/99	2/98[A]	5/97[A]	0/149	1/149[C]
PLOX/OXY	25/95[A]	58/95[A,C]	—	0/35	4/35[A]
PLOX/OXY/PYR	0/100	6/100[A]	—	1/99[A]	1/99

FAILURE ANALYSIS:
  A) Single Bit Charge Loss
  B) Bond Pad Corrosion
  C) Metal Line Corrosion

The reasons for the ameliorative effects of the pyrox are not completely clear but substantial reductions in the incidences of corrosion and moisture induced charge loss were observed. One factor is certainly the lower density of critical defects that is a natural consequence of multilayer films provided coincident defects do not form in successive layers. Pyrox offers the additional advantages of improved

scratch protection and low brittleness, thereby providing improved die resistance to handling induced defects. However, since pyrox is relatively hydrophilic, its bond pad openings should be pulled back from those of the oxynitride beneath it (fig 5) to prevent galvanic corrosion under biased high moisture conditions.

FIGURE 5
PASSIVATION OPENING FOR BOND PAD

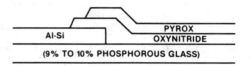

PASSIVATION DEFECTS

Since particle induced defects which form within the passivation films can provide an easy path for moisture diffusion, the reduction of particle densities is critical for consistent moisture performance. Passivation defect sites are associated with charge loss bits in the EPROM array, as well as with metal line corrosion (photo 3). Plasma enhanced CVD films, such as oxynitride, also introduce the added difficulty of forming lumps at preferred nucleation sites on the surface of the wafer. Passivation cracks can readily form around such lumps, reducing overall moisture performance. Particles may also develop in situ should gas phase nucleation occur within the PECVD reactor[1]. This can be avoided only by careful selection of the process parameters. Once such a process is developed, the overall cleanliness of the reactor is the dominant concern in determining defect level.

U.V. ERASE

The oxynitride and pyrox combination permitted normal erasure of the EPROM, as the U.V. transmission measurements would lead one to expect. Thus this passivation is suitable for use with plastic or hermetically encapsulated die. It was discovered, however, that though U.V. transmission ($>20\%$ @ 2537A 1u thickness) is certainly a necessary passivation property for good erasure, it is not in and of itself sufficient. Erasure of the EPROM cell has many structural dependancies and internal reflection in the dielectric layer appears to play an important role for this particular cell configuration, making the optical properties of the interface of concern. The combination of 1.2u of oxynitride atop .45u of plasma oxide illustrates this anomaly. Both films and the combination are highly transmissive in the required spectral region but typical cell erasure times were many times longer than with the oxynitride/pyrox passivation.

PHOSPHORUS CONCENTRATION

The use of a phospho-silicate glass as an interlayer dielectric in MOS devices is desirable for two reasons. First, the phosphorus forms a complex (P_2O_5) which has the ability to getter mobile ionic contaminants that can cause changes in device characteristics[5]. This is particularly important in EPROM devices where the logic state of the memory cell is determined by a small charge on a floating gate[7]. Second, the phosphorus improves the flow chacteristics of the glass, thereby reducing the possibility of poor metal step coverage. When present in a plastic packaged device, however, the phosphorus can combine with moisture entering through the package to form phosphorus acid which corrodes the aluminum metalization (photo 4).

Most plastic compatable processes reduce the incidence of corrosion by controlling the phosphorus to approximatly 7%. In this work, however, it was considered desirable to retain the 9% to 10% phosphorus doped glass thereby preserving the benificial properties of the higher phosphorus concentration an minimizing any changes to the existing process. Pyrox passivated devices showed an unacceptable failure rate from corrosion in moisture testing due to the high intrinsic moiture permeability and defect level. The oxynitride/pyrox combination provides lower permiability and reduced defect density and thereby significantly reduces the failure rate as long as the phosphorus concentration is kept below 10%. These data are shown in figure 6.

DEVICE RELIABILITY RESULTS

Accelerated moisture testing was carried out using the oxynitride/pyrox passivation in conjuction with the Intel 2764 and 2732A. A description of the finalized process is given in Figure 7. 85°C/85%RH and 121°C steam data demonstrate device reliability consistant with the previously stated goals (Table 4). It must be noted that the passivation structure and associated process changes described here, while of paramount importance in achieving these goals, can only be successful when used in combination with a controlled high integrity assembly process. Minimizing the risk of physical damage to the die and its exposure to contamination are two vital aspects of the encapsulation process.

CONCLUSION

It has been demonstrated that a passivation film can be produced which is sufficiently transmissive to allow EPROM erasure. High moisture resistance is also maintained to allow the use of a high (9% to 10%) phosphorus CVD oxide dielectric. Excellent moisture stress results were obtained on plastic encapsulated devices with this passivation.

ACKNOWLEDGEMENTS

The authors wish to thank Mark Pach, Yolanda Singer and Olympia Inciong for their assistance in performing failure analysis and collecting data. We also appreciate the support and assistance provided by R. K. Wallace.

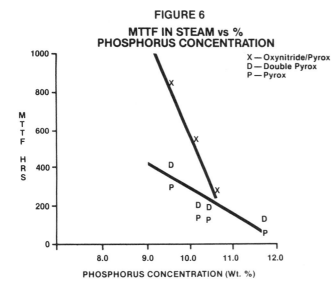

FIGURE 6
MTTF IN STEAM vs %
PHOSPHORUS CONCENTRATION

X — Oxynitride/Pyrox
D — Double Pyrox
P — Pyrox

FIGURE 7
PROCESS FLOW

FRONT END PROCESSING
↓
OXYNITRIDE DEPOSITION
↓
PYROX DEPOSITION
↓
BOND PAD OPENNING
↓
SORT
↓
PLASTIC ASSEMBLY
↓
TEST & FINISH

TABLE 4
2764 AND 2732A RELIABILITY
RESULTS

MOISTURE STRESS RESULTS				
STEAM		85°C/85% RH		
96 hr	168 hr	168 hr	500 hr	1K hr
7/1096	64/1089	0/989	0/989	2/989
(A)	(B)			(C)

ELECTRICAL STRESS RESULTS				RETENTION BAKE		
BURN IN		ELT		140°C		
48 hr	168 hr	500 hr	1K hr	96 hr	500 hr	1K hr
1/8264	1/8263	0/922	2/922	0/432	0/432	0/432
(D)	(E)		(F)			

FAILURE ANALYSIS:
  A) Single Bit Charge Loss, Metal Line Corrosion
  B) Metal Line Corrosion, Pad Corrosion, Charge Loss
  C) Single Bit Charge Loss
  D) Oxide Failure
  E) Single Bit Charge Loss
  F) Single Bit Charge Loss

REFERENCES

1) E. P. G. T. van de Ven, Solid State Technology, September 1981

2) K. Takaski, K. Koyama, M. Takagi, ESC Abs., 1981

3) E. J. McInerney, P. A. Flinn, IRPS 1982

4) M. J. Rand, D. R. Wonsidler, Solid State Science and Technology, J.E.C.S., Jan 1978

5) M. Sega, K. Matsuzaki, ECS Abs., 1981

6) P. Balk, J. M. Eldridge, IEEE, Sept. 1969

7) N. Mielke, IRPS 1983

PHOTO 1

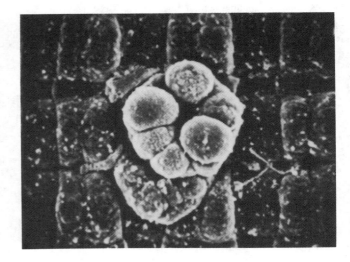

**PHOTO 3
PASSIVATION DEFECT
AT CHARGE LOSS SITE**

**PHOTO 2
PASSIVATION CRACKING AND
DELAMINATION**

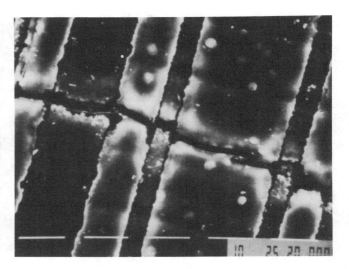

**PHOTO 4
METAL LINE CORROSION UNDER
PASSIVATION CRACK**

A SINGLE-POLY CMOS PROCESS MERGING ANALOG CAPACITORS, BIPOLAR AND EPROM DEVICES

T-I. Liou, D. Farrenkopf, C-M. Shyu, R. Merrill, and C-S. Teng
National Semiconductor Corp., Santa Clara, CA 95052-8090

Introduction

The integration of various integrated circuit fabrication processes into one process is a main stream in current VLSI technology (1). BiCMOS, CMOS/E2, E2/DRAM and mixed analog/digital processes are examples of this trend. However, they are only two processes merged together. The process will become rather complicated and costly when various devices are integrated in the same chip. Therefore, it is important to know how to merge different processes into one manufacturable process with minimum mask count. This paper presents a 1um single-poly CMOS process which merges analog capacitors, NPN bipolar devices and EPROM devices. The bottom plate of capacitors is formed in the silicon by a high-dose phosphorus implant. This capacitor N+ implant also simultaneously forms the collector sinker (or collector plug) region of bipolar devices to reduce the collector resistance. The bipolar devices therefore only require two additional masks (buried layer and base implants). Furthermore, the capacitor implant can also form the buried N+ region which is used as the control gate of single-poly EPROM devices such that only an early N+ implant mask is needed to optimize cell programming characteristics. As a result, only four extra masks are needed to add to the 12-masked CMOS baseline process. The cross section of these devices is shown in Fig. 1.

Analog Capacitors

A masked high-dose phosphorus implant performed before the gate oxidation is used to form the bottom plate of N+poly-to-N+silicon capacitors (2). The oxide between the capacitor N+ poly and the N+ silicon plates is grown simultaneously with the 200A gate oxide to ensure high quality of inter-plate oxide. The phosphorus implant dose and energy must be optimized according to requirements on capacitor oxide thickness and capacitance voltage coefficient. Fig. 2 shows the dependence of capacitor oxide thickness and capacitance voltage coefficient measured at 6V on phosphorus or arsenic implant energy at a dose of 1×10^{16} cm^{-2}. The capacitance voltage coefficient versus voltage applied across two plates of phosphorus-implanted capacitors for different capacitor oxide thicknesses is shown in Fig. 3. The breakdown field for these oxides is around 7MV/cm. The capacitor oxide thickness can be adjusted thicker or thinner depending upon requirements on capacitance per unit area, voltage coefficient, matching properties, oxide quality, and ratio between the parasitic bottom plate junction capacitance and the oxide capacitance.

Bipolar Devices

The formation of NPN bipolar transistor requires two additional masks. One mask is used to define the buried layer and the other defines the base implant. The emitter is formed using the N+ source/drain implant. The sinker region is formed simultaneously with the capacitor implant with the implant dose and energy optimized for the capacitor structure. The thickness of the epitaxial P-silicon of the starting material is increased from 10um for standard CMOS process to 15um so that the collector/substrate capacitance is not affected by the P+ region of the starting material. Another P-epitaxial layer is grown after buried layer mask, implant and drive-in.

Fig. 4 shows a picture of the Ic-Vce family curves of NPN bipolar devices. Table 1 lists several key device parameters. The propagation delay of BiCMOS delay lines is 195 psec/stage. A schematic of the BiCMOS inverter in the delay lines is shown in Fig. 5.

The propagation delay of ECL delay lines for NPN devices with the sinker region is about 10% less compared with that without the sinker. This 10% improvement is obtained as a free by-product of the capacitor implant without any additional process complexity. Since the phosphorus capacitor implant provides a deeper junction (1.5um) than the arsenic junction (0.4um), the phosphorus implant is a better choice to reduce the collector resistance. Besides, the arsenic-implanted capacitors have worse oxide quality and voltage coefficient.

EPROM Devices

The control gate of single-poly EPROM devices can be formed by implanting a buried N+ layer into the silicon. This buried N+ implant mask combined with an early N+ implant mask (3), which is needed to form a conventional n-ch source/drain structure instead of LDD structure to enhance memory cell programming characteristics, are two additional masks for forming EPROM devices in a CMOS process. Fig. 6 shows cell programming characteristics for this type of EPROM devices with coupling oxide thickness of 306A and gate oxide thickness of 200A. Fig. 7 shows the programming characteristics for devices with different coupling ratios and coupling oxide thicknesses. For all these devices, the area ratio between the control gate and the transistor gate is 6. In this merged process, the buried N+ region can be formed by the analog capacitor N+ implant. The capacitor oxide thickness (or coupling oxide thickness) is adjusted based upon requirements on two different devices. A thicker oxide provides a lower voltage coefficient and a lower coupling ratio, and on the other hand, a thinner oxide leads to a higher voltage coefficient and a higher coupling ratio. The area ratio between the control gate and the transistor gate can also be adjusted together with the tuning of coupling oxide thickness to achieve the desirable coupling ratio and die size requirements.

Summary

To merge various devices into a manufacturable process is a challenge and a future trend of process integration. This paper discusses a single-poly process merging analog capacitors, bipolar, CMOS, and EPROM devices with only 4 extra masks adding to the CMOS baseline process.

References

(1) H. Sasaki,1988 VLSI Technology, p.3.
(2) J. L. McCreary, IEEE J. of Solid-State Circuits, SC-16, Dec. 1981, p. 608.
(3) P. Cacharelis et al, IEDM, 1988, p. 60.

Reprinted from the *Dig. 1989 Symp. VLSI Technol.*, pp. 37–38, 1989.

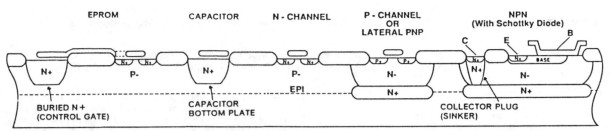

Fig. 1, Cross section of CMOS, bipolar, EPROM devices and an N + poly-to-N + silicon capacitor. The capacitor bottom plate, sinker (or collector plug) of NPN, and buried N + region of EPROM can be formed by one phosphorus implant.

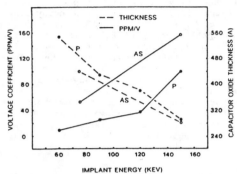

Fig. 2, Capacitance voltage coefficient and capacitor oxide thickness versus capacitor N + implant energy.

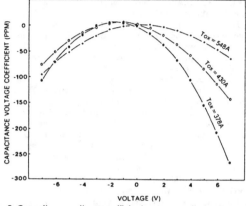

Fig. 3, Capacitance voltage coefficient versus applied voltage between two capacitor plates for different capacitor oxide thicknesses.

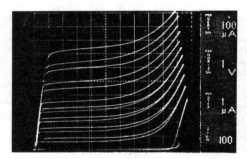

Fig. 4, Ic versus Vce for an NPN bipolar transistor.

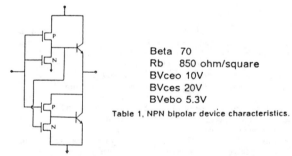

Beta 70
Rb   850 ohm/square
BVceo 10V
BVces 20V
BVebo 5.3V

Table 1, NPN bipolar device characteristics.

Fig. 5, Schematic of a BiCMOS inverter.

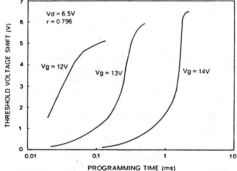

Fig. 6, EPROM cell programming characteristics.

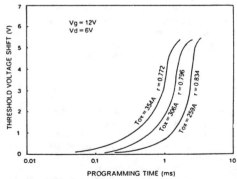

Fig. 7, Cell programming characteristics for EPROM devices with different coupling ratios and coupling oxide thicknesses.

118

Part 4
Floating-Gate and MNOS EEPROM Technologies

THIS PART is concerned with a class of EEPROMs known as byte-erasable or full-featured EEPROMs, which has a current market of about $400M per year. The technologies described here are producing commercial-volume 5V-only parts using on-chip high-voltage generators for programming and erasing. They all use a select transistor in series with a memory transistor in each cell; and this fact is one of the reasons EEPROMs lag behind EPROMs in density. Other EEPROM technologies are discussed in Part 5.

Three EEPROM technologies are included in this section, and Paper 4.1 introduces and compares them. The best known is the floating-gate tunneling-oxide (FLOTOX) EEPROM. The PROGRAM and ERASE operations are carried out by electron tunneling through ~ 100 Å oxide. The oldest EEPROM is the metal–nitride–oxide-semiconductor (MNOS) EEPROM. Note that "MNOS" is meant to include the newer (poly)silicon–oxide–nitride–oxide-semiconductor (SONOS) EEPROM described in Paper 4.7. A third technology, the textured-polysilicon–oxide EEPROM, uses the high conductivity of oxide grown on polycrystalline silicon to achieve programming and erasing.

Paper 4.2 reported the first floating-gate EEPROM product and defined the basic cell and operation of all future FLOTOX EEPROMs. Figure 1 in Paper 4.2 and nearly all cross-sectional drawings of the FLOTOX cell in the literature are slightly misleading in not showing the select transistor in the memory cell. The select transistor is evident in Fig. 3 of Paper 4.2 and its purpose is explained in the text. In contrast, the select transistors of textured-poly and MNOS EEPROMs are almost always included in their cross-sectional drawings, such as Figs. 1(b) and 1(c) of Paper 4.1. In fact, the particular select transistor layout shown in Fig. 1(c) for MNOS EEPROM can be adopted for the textured-poly EEPROM and the FLOTOX EEPROM (see Paper 8.10). Recognizing this similarity may somewhat simplify the task of understanding the differences among the three technologies and between EEPROMs and flash EPROMs.

Paper 4.3 presents a comprehensive model of the PROGRAM and ERASE operations of FLOTOX EEPROM. Paper 4.4 describes a typical state-of-the-art FLOTOX EEPROM technology. A single-poly EEPROM process has been used to fabricate a 256-kb EEPROM [1]. Using a triple-poly process, the most advanced FLOTOX EEPROM cell (Paper 8.10) occupies about 30 μm^2 area. A different approach to reducing the cell size is described in Paper 4.5. A large number (16) of FLOTOX transistors are connected in series and share a single select transistor and contact. The technique, borrowed from high-density mask ROMs, produced a 4-Mb EEPROM [2]. The access time is a very slow 1.6 μs, but is adequate for some applications such as the "smart cards."

Paper 4.6 describes a small textured-poly EEPROM cell. Programming and erasing are carried out by electron tunnel-ing through two separate oxides, both grown on textured polycrystalline silicon. (Papers 7.1 and 7.3 model the en-hanced conductivity of oxides grown on polycrystalline sili-con. Paper 6.1 describes a nonvolatile static RAM based on the same EEPROM cell.) Apparently, textured-poly-oxide conductivity enhancement decreases with decreasing oxide thickness. This and a high rate of electron trapping, which further reduces the oxide conductivity, have required even higher programming voltage for textured-poly cells than FLOTOX cells.

The last three reprints in this chapter are concerned with MNOS (SONOS) EEPROMs [3]. Paper 4.7 describes the newer SONOS cell while Paper 4.8 describes the leading production MNOS technology. Charge-carrier tunneling in MNOS EEPROM is more complicated than in FLOTOX EEPROM because holes as well as electrons and traps are involved. Paper 4.9 is a recent study of charge transport in MNOS. Reference [4] is another recent study of the same subject, which has relevance to a shortcoming of MNOS/SONOS EEPROM relative to FLOTOX EEPROM—the higher rate of charge loss due to tunneling through the very thin (~ 20 Å) oxides. MNOS is sometimes chosen over FLOTOX for its superior cumulative–dose radiation hard-ness. Paper 9.9 models this phenomenon. (The radiation hardness of FLOTOX EEPROM is the subject of Paper 9.8.)

The function of the nitride layer in a SONOS memory transistor is to provide a low-potential site for storing elec-trons. The nitride layer can also serve this function in place of the polysilicon floating gate in an EPROM-like structure as described in Paper 5.5. On the other hand, the nitride layer in the SONOS memory device can be replaced by a conduc-tor layer ([1] of the Prologue), by atomic dopants (traps) such as tungsten in the oxide [5], or, in principle, a potential well (quantum well) formed by heterojunctions [6]. An important attribute of the trap site is that the potential barriers surround-ing the site must be large so that the retention time can be long.

REFERENCES

[1] J-I. Miyamoto, "An experimental 5-V-only 256kb CMOS EEPROM with a high performance single-polysilicon cell," *IEEE J. Solid-State Circuits*, vol. SC-21, no. 5, pp. 852–859, Oct. 1986.
[2] Y. Itoh *et al.*, "An experimental 4Mbit CMOS EEPROM with a NAND-structured cell," *IEEE J. Solid-State Circuits*, vol. 24, no. 5, pp. 1238–1243, Oct. 1989.
[3] J. J. Chang, "Theory of MNOS memory transistor," *IEEE Trans. Electron Devices*, pp. 511–518, May 1977.
[4] C. C. Chao and M. H. White, "Characterization of charge injection and trapping in scaled SONOS/MOMOS memory devices," *Solid State Electron.*, vol. 30, no. 3, p. 307, Mar. 1987.
[5] D. Kahng, W. J. Sundburg, D. M. Boulin, and J. R. Ligenza, "Interfacial dopants for dual-dielectric, charge-storage cells," *Bell Syst. Tech. J.*, vol. 53, no. 9, pp. 1723–1739, 1974.
[6] F. Capasso, F. Beltram, R. J. Malik, and J. F. Walker, "New floating-gate AlGaAs/GaAs memory devices with graded-gap electron injector and long retention times," *IEEE Electron Device Letts.*, vol. 9, no. 8, pp. 377–379, 1988.

COMPARISON AND TRENDS IN TODAY'S DOMINANT E^2 TECHNOLOGIES

S.K. Lai and V.K. Dham
Intel Corporation
3601 Juliette Lane, Santa Clara, CA 95051

D. Guterman
Xicor, Inc.
851 Buckeye Court, Milpitas, CA 95035

ABSTRACT

This paper reviews the three dominant E^2 technologies today, namely the two floating gate approaches of thin tunnel oxide and oxide on textured poly and the dual dielectric approach of MNOS. It evaluates each approach with respect to cell design, operation, manufacturability, compatibility with established process technologies and reliability. It follows with a comparison of the technologies in the areas of development entry cost, scaling and reliability. After a review of the market place, this paper concludes with a projection of the requirements of E^2 technologies to support full function, commodity E^2 memories E^2PROM as well as low cost microcontrollers and ASIC (Application Specific Integrated Circuits).

INTRODUCTION

Electrically alterable non-volatile semiconductor memory has been an area of active research for many years, with the promise that it will be the ultimate silicon memory. The first floating gate memory was proposed in 1967 (1) and MNOS memories were reported at about the same time (2). In 1980, the first 16K E^2PROMs using MNOS (3) as well as floating gate technologies on FLOTOX (4) were reported, while textured poly E^2PROMs were reported in 1983 (5). However, after all these years of development in the laboratory and volume manufacturing, E^2PROMs have yet to become a high volume, widely used memory component compared to EPROMs, the closest equivalent memory with lower functionality. There are many reasons given for the limited growth, ranging from the higher cost of E^2PROM based products to poorly understood reliability of these components. In this paper, we will focus on the technology factors by comparing the three dominant E^2 technologies to date, and giving our own viewpoint on the development in the market place.

DESCRIPTION OF TECHNOLOGIES

FLOTOX (FLOating gate Tunnel OXide)

The cross sectional structure of a FLOTOX cell is shown in Figure 1a. It consists of a floating gate transistor with a thin oxide grown over the drain region. The floating gate is surrounded completely by high quality silicon dioxide, giving its superior retention characteristics. Programming (electrons into floating gate) is achieved by taking the control gate to high voltage while erase (electrons out of floating gate) is achieved by grounding the control gate and taking the drain to high voltage. Because the program and erase coupling conditions are different, they have different design considerations. Electron transfer is through Fowler-Nordheim tunneling mechanism using electric field higher than 10 MV/cm. The IV slope of tunneling is so steep that there is insignificant tunneling under normal read conditions for more than ten years. In order for the cell to properly operate in an array, it has to be isolated by a select transistor. Two cycles are required to load the correct data. All cells in a byte are first programmed, and then selected cells are erased using the drain for data control. The manufacturing process for FLOTOX is an extension of the EPROM technology, which in turn is an extension of the standard single poly silicon gate technology. The critical step in the process is the growth of high quality thin (< 12 nm) tunnel oxide. For reliability, the dominant failure mechanism for FLOTOX is the breakdown of the tunnel oxide due to defects under the high field stress of the program/ erase cycles, resulting in a leaky oxide (6).

Textured Poly Cell

The cross sectional structure of a textured poly cell is shown in Figure 1b. It consists of 3 layers of poly with overlap forming three transistors in series. The floating gate transistor is in the middle formed by poly 2. Again, the floating gate is surrounded by silicon dioxide for high retention. Programming is achieved by electrons tunneling from poly 1 to poly 2 and erase is achieved by electrons tunneling from poly 2 to poly 3. The program and erase coupling again is different. The poly 3 is taken to high voltage in both cases, and the element which tunnels is determined by the voltage applied from the drain and coupled to the floating gate through the channel region. The final data state is determined by the data state on the drain: this is a "direct write" cell with no need to clear before write as is required in the FLOTOX cell. This is possible because there are two active tunnel elements. The tunneling process is fundamentally still Fowler-Nordheim tunneling, with enhancement of local electric field due to the geometrical effect of fine texture at the poly surface. The

Reprinted from the *IEDM Tech. Dig.*, pp. 580–583, 1986.

electric field enhancement factor is in the range of 3 to 5, allowing much thicker oxides (60 to 100 nm) to be used. No extra transistor is required in an array since the poly 3 transistor serves the function of select transistor, giving a much more compact cell layout. The manufacturing process for textured poly is again an extension of the EPROM process with the addition of an extra layer of poly. The critical process step in this process is the growth of the tunnel oxide on poly. Because thicker oxides are used, oxide breakdown is less of a problem compared to FLOTOX. The dominant failure mechanism in a textured poly cell is electron trapping which results in memory window closure (7).

MNOS (Metal Nitride Oxide Silicon) Cell

The cross sectional structure of a MNOS cell is shown in Figure 1c. It consists of a single transistor with a dielectric stack of silicon nitride on top of a thin layer of oxide (1.5 to 2.0 nm) on silicon. Typically, the transistor resides in a well so that the channel potential can be controlled. Unlike the floating gate, charge is stored in discrete traps in the bulk of nitride. Because of the discrete nature of traps, charge transfer has to occur over the large area of the channel region. This is different from floating gate devices where charge transfer can occur over a small area removed from the channel region. On the other hand, any dielectric defect fatal to floating gates will only discharge local traps in MNOS. Programming is achieved by applying high voltage to the top gate whereas erase can be achieved by grounding the top gate and taking the well to high voltage. The program and erase coupling is symmetrical. Because of the very thin oxide, charge is being leaked off continuously due to the internal field, giving an ever diminishing window. In an array, select transistor is required to operate the cell properly. The select transistor may be separate (3) or integrated (8) in which case a more compact cell layout can be realized. Two cycles are again required to load the correct data. Furthermore, the well potential has to be controlled during data change, which makes the array operation more complex. The manufacturing process for MNOS is an extension of single poly silicon gate technology. The memory transistor is fabricated after the first poly periphery transistors are formed to maintain the integrity of the dual dielectric storage element. The important steps include thin oxide growth, nitride deposition and post nitride temperature cycles. The biggest reliability concern is cell retention and its degradation with cycling (9).

COMPARISON

The three different approaches have their technical merit and difficulties. Any one of these technologies can be made to work if they are given sufficient effort and focus. As a result, other considerations ranging from "comfort factors" to compatibility with available technologies tend to determine the choice.

Development Entry Cost

Entry cost is the amount of extra effort required to bring up a new technology. To an EPROM manufacturer, it is relatively easy to take the FLOTOX approach. The cell concept is simple and the tunnel oxide process is a straight forward variation of a standard high quality oxide furnace cycle. This is why the majority of companies have opted for this approach for their E^2 effort. The textured poly approach, on the other hand, depends on a tunneling process which is not generally understood and is believed to require tighter process control. The cell concept is more complex and the use of three layers of poly imply higher wafer cost. These factors have limited the popularity of developing this approach. Finally, MNOS approach requires the mastering of a number of difficult process steps. The growth and control of the ultra thin oxide, as well the quality of nitride are critical issues. As a result, despite gaining initial momentum, MNOS has not achieved dominance as an E^2 technology.

Scaling

There are many factors that determine the size of a memory cell, and generally cell design represents finding the optimum compromise of a number of tradeoffs. Furthermore, as these technologies approach fundamental physical or practical material limits, scaling will become increasingly difficult. For FLOTOX, there is large area requirement for layout of the two transistors plus the tunnel oxide area, dictated by minimum design rules. The select transistor is limited by high voltage. Given the high oxide capacitance of thin tunnel oxide, large poly to poly area is required for the sense transistor. Scaling of the tunnel dielectric is also limited by direct tunneling at 6 nm and yield and reliability issues at 8 to 10 nm. Typically, relatively high voltages (15 to 20V) are required to operate the cell. As a result, FLOTOX cell does not scale well.

In the case of textured poly, the three poly layers are integrated resulting in a compact layout. Cell size is limited more by lithographic registration of poly layers than by ability to resolve space between poly lines as is the case with FLOTOX. Furthermore, the thick tunnel oxide requires smaller coupling capacitor area to give the required coupling. Given the same performance and reliability requirement, it is estimated that a textured poly cell is about a factor of two smaller compared to a FLOTOX cell for a given generation of technology. Textured poly does require higher operating voltage (> 20V) and thus needs a high voltage technology to support it. Finally, scaling of the poly oxide involves more than thinning down the oxide as the field enhancement factor changes with oxide thickness.

The basic MNOS memory cell can be very small and highly scaleable. The select transistors, whether separated (3) or integrated (8), will limit scaling. However, in either case, the cell size is better than FLOTOX, and competitive with triple poly for a given generation of technology. One major problem is the requirement of well voltage control. Full byte function is only possible with separate well, giving a large effective cell size. Page function (8) can be used to partially circumvent the well problem but limits endurance. For oxide thicknesses, there is little or no room to scale the ultra thin tunnel oxide, so most of the emphasis has been on scaling the nitride. Charge leakage from the scaled nitride to top gate has been solved by oxidizing the nitride to give a MONOS stack. Low program and erase voltages have been demonstrated at the expense of smaller operating window.

Reliability

One general problem for E^2PROM is the limited information on the reliability of the technologies due to sample size or correlation problems. For floating gate technologies, there is no intrinsic problem with data retention, and because the technologies are designed to handle high voltage, there is very low failure rate due to normal 5V operation. Reliability problems occur during program and erase cycles in part because very high voltages are used. For FLOTOX, there is random single bit failure due to oxide defect resulting in a leaky oxide that loses charge over time. For textured poly, the average electric field across the tunnel oxide is 3 to 5 times lower compared to FLOTOX. As a result, oxide breakdown failure is reduced significantly. On the other hand, there are more electron traps in the oxide, and the impact of electron trapping is magnified by the 3 to 5 times field enhancement factor. Consequently, electron trapping is the dominant failure mechanism, showing up as a failure to program or erase. The failure can be projected real time with margining techniques and since trapping is an intrinsic property, failure probability can be easily projected. In MNOS, charge retention is the dominant reliability issue. The charge loss process is time dependent, resulting in continuous loss of cell margin and performance. The degradation based on short term data is difficult to predict. The ultra thin oxide is stressed by electric field comparable to FLOTOX and retention is further degraded with program and erase cycles. So far, wide variation in retention and endurance are being reported based on limited sampling (9).

THE MARKET PLACE

Though E^2PROMs have been available for the last five years, their usage has not grown to the volumes projected. A host of new and established companies have become active in the field, but lack of technology and product feature standardization, together with high cost and reliability concerns have limited the growth in the market place. The major issues for 16K have been 5V only, address/data latch vs no latch, ready busy vs data polling, 24 pin vs 28 pin, 1 mSec vs 10 mSec program, self timed vs user timed, with and without Vcc lockout and 10K vs 1 Million cycles endurance. Byte vs page function and page size are issues at 64K density level. In addition, one can choose oxynitride vs oxide for FLOTOX, textured poly vs FLOTOX for floating gate, and MNOS vs floating gate for E^2. The reliability claims are difficult to

understand and verify due to the link of failure to endurance cycling. Different methods are used in reliability evaluation, and no standard exists to allow a meaningful comparison. For example, high temperature cycling is worse case for FLOTOX but may be best case for textured poly. Nevertheless, there has been continued growth in the E^2PROM market, sustained by a wide, diversified application base. The driving force is end-user, in-the-field customization capability offered to microprocessor based products, which is either unavailable, unreliable or not cost effective using other techniques. As a result, standards are now established following 5V-only RAM-like functionality, and the cost and density gap to competing solutions continues to close.

FUTURE TRENDS

There are two major driving forces in the development of E^2 technologies for the future. One of them is high density memories, requiring small memory cell size for the lowest cost per bit. The second requirement is low density non-volatile memories in microcontrollers and programmable logic type applications. In the latter case the absolute cell size is not as important as process simplicity and low cost of the overall technology. MNOS based E^2 memories will continue to be used in low density memory as well as military applications requiring high radiation tolerance. However, it has only enjoyed limited popularity for use in high density memory and the trend will continue. A majority of companies have opted for FLOTOX as their first E^2 technology because of the simple device physics and the low entry cost for development. Recently, many Japanese companies have announced 64K E^2PROMs based on FLOTOX for the smart card market. A number of companies have applied FLOTOX in ASIC and programmable logic array applications. In fact, some have developed single poly versions of FLOTOX for synergy with random logic technology. However, for stand alone high density E^2 memories, FLOTOX will be increasingly limited by defect oxide breakdown problems (10), giving unacceptable failure rate above the 64K level, unless thicker oxides or new dielectrics can be used in new approaches. Error correction codes can also be used but at the expense of additional die cost (11). Finally, textured poly inherently gives a smaller memory cell and suffers least from the oxide breakdown problem. Electron trapping is an intrinsic property that can be predicted and easily screened. Consequently, textured poly technology is expected to be most reliable and cost effective for 256K and above densities, while the higher cost of a three layer poly process may limit its use in logic applications.

The non-volatile memory technology is an ever evolving field. Memories (12,13,14) based on hybrid operation of programming by EPROM and erase by tunneling have gained interest. The erase function is generally limited to the full array and thus it is called FLASH erase. Recent approaches offer cell size and technology complexity comparable to EPROMs, and the functionality of electrical erase. If such technologies are proven to be reliable and manufacturable, they will fill the need of a special market segment and become another major force in the developing non-volatile memory market.

SUMMARY

We have reviewed the three dominant E^2 technologies today. MNOS is used in low density memories as well as military applications, but enjoyed only limited popularity for high density memories. FLOTOX has been the most popular approach because of its simplicity and is most suited for low density memories and programmable logic type application. Textured poly gives the smallest memory cell size and is the most cost effective and reliable approach for high density memories.

REFERENCES

(1) D. Kahng and S.M. Sze, "A Floating Gate and Its Application to Memory Devices", Bell Syst. Tech. J., 46, 1283 (1967).

(2) H.A.R. Wegener et al., "The Variable Threshold Transistor, a New Electrically Alterable Nondestructive Read-Only Storage Device", presented at the IEEE Electron Devices Meeting, Washington, D.C., 1967.

(3) T. Hagiwara et al., "A 16Kbit Electrically Erasable PROM Using n-Channel Si-Gate MNOS Technology", IEEE J. of Solid State Circuits, SC-15, 346 (1980).

(4) W.S. Johnson et al., " A 16Kbit Electrically Erasable Non Volatile Memory", ISSCC Tech. Digest, p. 152 (1980).

(5) S. Jewell-Larsen et al., "A 5 Volt RAM-like Triple Poly Silicon EEPROM", Proc. 2nd Annual Phoenix Conf., p. 508 (1983).

(6) R.E. Shiner et al., "Characterization and Screening of SiO2 Defects in EEPROM Structures", 21st Annual Proc. Reliability Physics, p. 248 (1983).

(7) H.A.R. Wegener, "Endurance Model for Textured-Poly Floating Gate Memories", IEDM Tech. Digest, p. 480 (1984).

(8) A. Lancaster et al., " A 5V-Only EEPROM with Internal Program/Erase Control", ISSCC Tech. Digest, p. 164 (1983).

(9) W.D. Brown, "MNOS Technology- Will it Survive?", Solid State Tech., p. 77 (July 1979).

(10) A. Bagles, "Characteristics and Reliability of 100 Å Oxides", 21st Annual Proc. Reliability Physics, p. 152 (1983).

(11) S. Mehrotra et al., "A 64Kb CMOS EEROM with On-Chip ECC", ISSCC Tech. Digest, p. 142 (1984).

(12) D. Guterman et al., "Electrically Alterable Hot-Electron Injection Floating Gate MOS Memory Cell with Series Enhancement Transistor", IEDM Tech. Digest, p.340 (1978).

(13) F. Masuoka et al., "A New Flash E^2PROM Cell Using Triple Polysilicon Technology", IEDM Tech. Digest, p. 464 (1984).

(14) S. Mukherjee et al., "A Single Transistor EEPROM Cell and its Implementation in a 512K CMOS EEPROM", IEDM Tech. Digest, p. 616 (1985).

FLOTOX DEVICE STRUCTURE

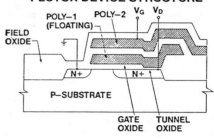

Figure 1a: Cross sectional structure of a FLOTOX memory cell.

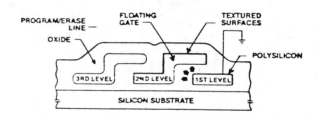

Figure 1b: Cross sectional structure of a textured poly memory cell.

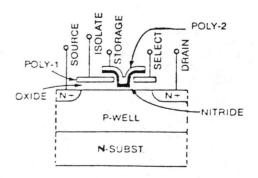

Figure 1c: Cross sectional structure of a MNOS memory cell (8).

A 16Kb Electrically Erasable Nonvolatile Memory

William S. Johnson, George Perlegos, Alan Renninger, Greg Kuhn and T. R. Ranganath[†]

Intel Corp.

Santa Clara, CA

FLOATING GATE STRUCTURES have been highly successful as nonvolatile devices because of their compatibility with silicon gate processing and their excellent charge retentivity with applied voltage at operating temperature. The accepted method of erasure in the commercial marketplace is ultra-violet light (EPROM)[1], although proposals have been made to erase electrically by avalanche injection of holes[2], electron tunneling[3,4], or a combination of both[5]. These methods, however, have typically suffered from poor reproducibility and very fast wearout during program/erase cycling.

To realize nonvolatile devices which can be erased electrically with high program/erase endurance, many have resorted to MNOS structures[6] which are programmed and erased by direct tunneling through a thin oxide. In this approach, charge is stored in traps within the nitride dielectric. A major problem with this approach is that the properties of the nitride/oxide dielectric are difficult to control and are adversely affected by normal silicon gate processing. Furthermore, the threshold voltages of these structures are vulnerable to disturbance by even small applied voltages and data retention is not easily guaranteed for long periods (years).

The device reported (FLOTOX, for *f*loating gate *t*unnel *ox*ide) retains the processing and the retention advantages of floating gate over MNOS while solving the traditional endurance problem. This is accomplished by utilizing an oxide less than 200Å thick between a floating poly gate and an N^+ region, as shown in

Figure 1. In FLOTOX both program and erase are accomplished by tunneling[7] of electrons through the tunnel oxide using voltages of less than 25V. A typical endurance plot for a single cell appears in Figure 2. This shows that the threshold window remains open beyond 100,000 cycles. Also by keeping voltages low during read, this structure can retain charge over 10 years under full power, at operating temperatures. There is no refresh requirement no matter how many read accesses are made.

The FLOTOX cell configuration, shown in Figure 3, uses two devices, a select transistor and a memory transistor. Cell area is 0.85mil^2. Clearing of the memory is accomplished by programming every device in a row. This is done by selecting a row and raising the program line to VPP, which attracts electrons to the floating gate. Writing is accomplished by erasing selected bits within a word. This is done by again selecting a row, but now the program line is held at zero volts while selected columns go to VPP. Electrons are thus removed from the floating gates of the selected devices.

Figure 4 shows the 16K chip, which is arranged as 2K/8b words. It is packaged with 24 leads with a pinout identical to the 16K EPROM*. The chip is automatically powered down until selected ($\overline{CE}$ low). Read is accomplished by selecting the part and enabling the output buffers ($\overline{OE}$ low). On the other hand, selecting the part and taking VPP to 20V for 10ms puts the chip in write mode and writes a word. If the incoming data are all 1's, then the chip automatically goes into clear mode and clears the addressed word. Thus, a clear-write sequence requires merely two 10ms writes, first all 1s, then the data desired. If clearing of the entire chip is desired, this can be accomplished with one 10ms pulse by applying VPP to $\overline{OE}$ as well as the VPP pin with the chip selected. This approach allows a wide variety of functions while maintaining simple control and complete EPROM compatibility.

FLOTOX utilizes a new high performance N-channel two-level-poly silicon gate technology with channel lengths of 3.5μ. Access times for the 16K FLOTOX E^2PROM are below 200ns as shown in Figure 5. This allows use of the device with the newer microprocessors which operate in the 5-8MHz range without wait states. Other features of the 16K E^2PROM are listed in the table.

[†]Current Address: Hughes Research, Malibu, CA

*2716.

[1]Salsbury, P.J., Morgan, W.L., Perlegos, G. and Simko, R.T., "High Performance MOS EPROMs Using A Stacked Gate Cell", *ISSCC DIGEST OF TECHNICAL PAPERS*, p. 186; Feb., 1977.

[2]Gosney, W.M., "DIFMOS — A Floating-Gate Electrically Erasable Nonvolatile Semiconductor Memory Technology", *IEEE Transactions on Electron Devices*, ED-24, p. 594; May, 1977.

[3]Gulterman, D.C., Rimari, I.H., Halvorson, R.D., McElroy, D.J. and Chan, W.W., "Electrically Alterable Hot-Electron Injection Floating Gate MOS Memory Cell With Series Enhancement", *IEDM Technical Digest*, p. 340; Dec., 1978.

[4]Harari, E., Schmitz, L., Troutman, B. and Wang, S., "A 256-Bit Nonvolatile Static RAM", *ISSCC DIGEST OF TECHNICAL PAPERS*, p. 108; Feb., 1978.

[5]Scheibe, A. and Schulte, H., "Technology of a New N-Channel One-Transistor EAROM Cell Called SIMOS", *IEEE Transactions on Electron Devices*, ED-24, p. 600; May, 1977.

[6]Hagiwara, T., Kondo, R., Yatusuda, Y., Minami, S. and Itoh, Y., "A 16Kb Electrically Erasable Programmable ROM", *ISSCC DIGEST OF TECHNICAL PAPERS*, p. 50; Feb., 1979.

[7]Lenzlinger, M. and Snow, E.H., "Fowler-Nordheim Tunnelling into Thermally Grown SiO_2", *J. of Applied Physics*, 40, p. 278-283; Jan., 1969.

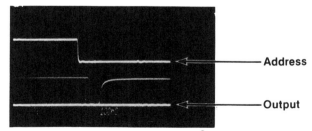

FIGURE 5—Access time for E^2PROM.

Reprinted from the *IEEE ISSCC Dig. Tech. Pap.*, pp. 152–153, 271, 1980.

	16K E²PROM	16K EPROM
Configuration	2K X 8	2K X 8
Package	24 pin	24 pin
Power Supplies		
read mode	+5	+5
clear/write	+5, +20	+5, +25
Write		
method	tunnel injection	hot electron injection
time/word	10ms	50ms
Clear		
method	tunnel ejection	UV light
time/word	10ms	—
time/chip	10ms	30 min
Access Time	200ns	450ns
Power Dissipation		
active	500mW	550mW
standby	100mW	100mW
Data Retention	10 years	10 years
Refresh Requirement	None	None

TABLE 1

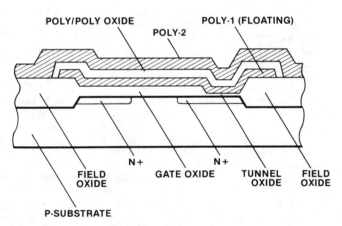

FIGURE 1—Cross section of memory transistor.

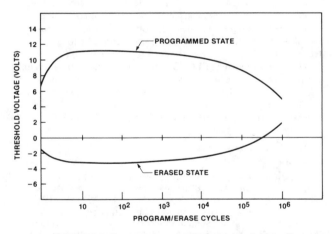

FIGURE 2—Program/erase endurance for single cell.

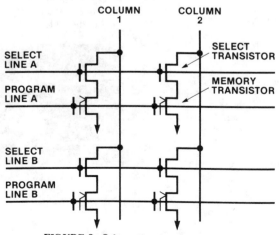

FIGURE 3—Schematic of memory cells.

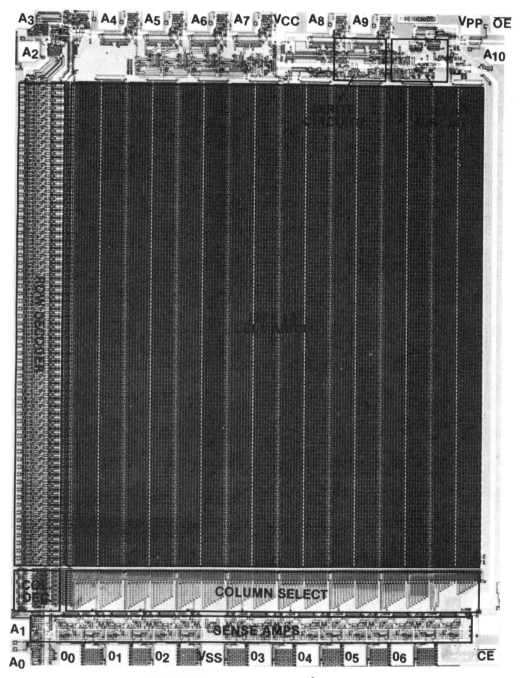

FIGURE 4—Photograph of 16Kb E^{2}PROM.

Analysis and Modeling of Floating-Gate EEPROM Cells

AVINOAM KOLODNY, SIDNEY T. K. NIEH, BOAZ EITAN, MEMBER, IEEE,
AND JOSEPH SHAPPIR, MEMBER, IEEE

Abstract—Floating-gate MOS devices using thin tunnel oxide are becoming an acceptable standard in electrically erasable nonvolatile memory. Theoretical and experimental analysis of WRITE/ERASE characteristics for this type of memory cell are presented. A simplified device model is given based on the concept of coupling ratios. The WRITE operation is adequately represented by the simplified model. The ERASE operation is complicated due to formation of depletion layers in the transistor's channel and under the tunnel oxide. Experimental investigation of these effects is described, and they are included in a detailed cell model.

In certain cell structures, a hole current can flow from the drain into the substrate during the ERASE oepration. This effect is shown to be associated with positive charge trapping in the tunnel oxide and threshold window opening. An experimental investigation of these phenomena is described, and a recommendation is made to avoid them by an appropriate cell design.

I. INTRODUCTION

ELECTRICALLY erasable nonvolatile memory (EEPROM) technology has emerged in recent years as a promising approach for implementing sophisticated VLSI systems [1]–[5]. Among the various devices that have been used to realize such a memory, floating-gate MOS transistors that employ a thin insulator for electron tunneling (FLOTOX) have been dominant [1]–[4]. This paper presents a theoretical analysis and experimental data of the programming and erasing of FLOTOX memory cells.

The general device structure is depicted schematically in Fig. 1. This is an n-channel double-poly transistor in which the first polysilicon is floating. A thin (~ 100 Å) dielectric layer between the floating gate and the drain enables the flow of electrons into and from the floating gate during WRITE/ERASE operations, by means of Fowler–Nordheim tunneling [6], [7].

In the WRITE operation the floating gate is charged negatively with electrons tunneling from the drain through the thin oxide. This is achieved by applying a positive voltage pulse to the top gate of the cell, while the source, drain, and substrate are grounded. The stored negative

Manuscript received March 13, 1985; revised December 31, 1985.
A. Kolodny was with Intel Corporation, Santa Clara, CA 95051. He is now at the Intel Israel Design Center, Haifa, Israel.
S. Nieh was with Intel Corporation, Santa Clara, CA 95051. He is now with Intel Corporation, Portland, OR.
B. Eitan is with WaferScale Integration, Inc., Fremont, CA 94538.
J. Shappir is with the Hebrew University of Jerusalem, Jerusalem, Israel.
IEEE Log Number 8608243.

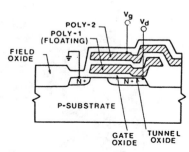

Fig. 1. Cross section of an EEPROM cell.

charge on the floating gate shifts the transistor's threshold voltage, as measured on the top gate, toward a more positive value. In a subsequent READ operation the transistor will not conduct channel current.

The ERASE operation removes electrons from the floating gate by applying a positive high-voltage pulse at the drain, while the source is floating and both the top gate and the substrate are grounded. The threshold voltage is shifted in the negative direction, and channel current would flow during subsequent READ operations.

During READ operations the voltages used are low enough such that tunnel current is negligible, and the floating gate is practically insulated. Charge retention in excess of 10 years can readily be obtained on the floating gate under normal operating conditions [9].

In memory circuits, a two-transistor cell is used [1]–[5]; the additional transistor is necessary in order to isolate the cell from adjacent cells during WRITE/ERASE operations.

This work focuses on analysis and modeling of the WRITE/ERASE operations, considering effects that occur during ERASE, which have not been discussed in the literature [9], [10]. An understanding of these effects is of major importance in cell design and optimization.

II. SIMPLIFIED DEVICE MODEL

A. Calculation of Tunnel Current

The tunneling current density through the tunnel oxide is approximated by the well-known Fowler–Nordheim equation [6], [7].

$$J_{tun} = \alpha E_{tun}^2 \cdot (\exp(-\beta/E_{tun})) \qquad (1)$$

where E_{tun} is the electric field in the oxide, and α and β

Reprinted from *IEEE Trans. Electron Devices*, vol. ED-33, no. 6, pp. 835–844, June 1986.

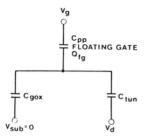

Fig. 2. A simplified capacitive equivalent circuit of the EEPROM cell.

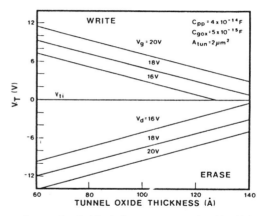

Fig. 3. WRITE/ERASE threshold window versus tunnel oxide thickness, calculated with the approximation of (8), (9), assuming that $V'_{tun} = 1 \times 10^7 \cdot X_{tun}$ at the end of the operation.

are constants. The thin-oxide field E_{tun} is given by

$$E_{tun} = \frac{|V_{tun}|}{X_{tun}} \qquad (2)$$

where V_{tun} is the voltage drop across the oxide and X_{tun} is its thickness. V_{tun} can be calculated from a capacitive equivalent circuit of the cell.

B. Calculation of V_{tun}

In order to gain insight into the basic device operation, a simplified equivalent circuit, shown in Fig. 2, is used. A more detailed analysis is given in Section V. In Fig. 2, C_{pp} is the interpoly capacitance, C_{tun} is the thin oxide capacitance, and C_{gox} is the capacitance of the gate oxide between the floating gate and the substrate. Q_{fg} is the stored charge on the floating gate. V_{tun} can be expressed for an electrically neutral floating gate in terms of simple coupling ratios

$$|V_{tun}|\text{WRITE} = V_g \cdot K_w \qquad (3)$$

where

$$K_w = \frac{C_{pp}}{C_{pp} + C_{gox} + C_{tun}} \qquad (4)$$

and

$$|V_{tun}|\text{ERASE} = V_d \cdot K_- \qquad (5)$$

where

$$K_e = 1 - \frac{C_{tun}}{C_{pp} + C_{gox} + C_{tun}}. \qquad (6)$$

The coupling ratios K_w and K_e denote the fraction of the applied voltage that appears across the tunnel oxide. Note that (3) and (5) are applicable only when $Q_{fg} = 0$. During WRITE operation buildup of negative stored charge of the floating gate will reduce the tunnel-oxide voltage according to

$$|V_{tun}|\text{WRITE} = V_g \cdot K_w + \frac{Q_{fg}}{C_{pp} + C_{gox} + C_{tun}}. \qquad (3')$$

In the ERASE operation, the initial negative stored charge on the floating gate will increase the tunnel-oxide voltage according to

$$|V_{tun}|\text{ERASE} = V_d \cdot K_e - \frac{Q_{fg}}{C_{pp} + C_{gox} + C_{tun}}. \qquad (5')$$

at the end of the ERASE operation when positive charge is built up on the floating gate, the last term in (5) will reduce the tunnel-oxide voltage.

C. Calculation of Threshold Voltages

The initial threshold voltage of the cell, corresponding to $Q_{fg} = 0$ is denoted by V_{ti}. Stored charge shifts the threshold according to the relation

$$\Delta V_t = -\frac{Q_{fg}}{C_{pp}}. \qquad (7)$$

Using (3') and (5') for Q_{fg} at the end of the WRITE/ERASE pulse, the cell's threshold voltages are

$$V_{tw} = V_{ti} - \frac{Q_{fg}}{C_{pp}} = V_{ti} + V_g\left[1 - \frac{V'_{tun}}{K_w \cdot V_g}\right] \qquad (8)$$

$$V_{te} = V_{ti} - \frac{Q_{fg}}{C_{pp}} = V_{ti} - V_d\left[\frac{K_e}{K_w} - \frac{V'_{tun}}{K_w \cdot V_d}\right]. \qquad (9)$$

Here V_{tw} is the threshold of a written cell, and V_{te} is the threshold of an erased cell. V_g and V_d are the WRITE/ERASE pulse amplitudes, respectively, and V'_{tun} is the tunnel-oxide voltage at the end of the pulse. Assuming that the WRITE/ERASE pulse is sufficiently long, the thin-oxide field will be reduced to below about 1×10^7 V/cm, when tunneling practically "stops." An approximation of V'_{tun} can be calculated from (2), and substituted in (8), (9) to give the approximate programming window of the cell and its dependence on cell parameters and programming voltage. Typical results are shown in Fig. 3.

In order to maximize the cell's window at a given tunnel-oxide thickness and WRITE/ERASE voltage, the coupling ratios should approach unity. Both coupling ratios can be increased by reducing C_{tun} and increasing C_{pp}. At a given tunnel-oxide thickness, this is usually achieved by minimizing the thin oxide area and adding extra poly-poly overlap area on the sides of the cell transistor. Typical coupling ratios are about 0.7 (K_e is always higher than K_w). Increasing the gate-oxide capacitance C_{gox} improved K_e but lowers K_w.

D. Dependence of Thresholds on WRITE/ERASE Time

An analytic expression for the cell's threshold versus programming time is obtained by solving the differential equation

$$\frac{dQ_{fg}}{dt} = A_{tun} \cdot J_{tun} \tag{10}$$

using the expressions in (1), (2), (3'), (5'), and (7). The resultant solutions are

$$V_{tw}(t) = V_{ti} + V_g - \frac{1}{K_w} \cdot \frac{B}{\ln(A \cdot B \cdot t + E_1)} \tag{11}$$

$$V_{te}(t) = V_{ti} - V_d \frac{K_e}{K_w} + \frac{1}{K_w} \cdot \frac{B}{\ln(A \cdot B \cdot t + E_2)}. \tag{12}$$

where

$$A = \frac{A_{tun} \cdot \alpha}{X_{tun} \cdot (C_{pp} + C_{gox} + C_{tun})}$$

$$B = \beta \cdot X_{tun}$$

$$E_1 = \exp\left[\frac{B}{K_w \cdot (V_g + V_{ti} - V_t(0))}\right]$$

$$E_2 = \exp\left[\frac{B}{V_d \cdot K_e + K_w \cdot V_t(0) + K_w \cdot V_{ti}}\right].$$

$V_t(0)$ is the cell's threshold at $t = 0$, which should not be confused with V_{ti}, the threshold of a neutral cell. A_{tun} is the tunnel-oxide area.

Note in (11) that the threshold voltage remains virtually constant at $V_t(0)$ if V_g is applied for a period that is less than a characteristic "time constant" τ defined by

$$\tau = \frac{1}{AB} \exp\left[\frac{B}{K_w(V_g + V_{ti} - V_t(0))}\right]. \tag{13}$$

For longer time t, the threshold asymptotically approaches the curve

$$V_{tw}(t) = V_{ti} + V_g - \frac{B}{K_w \cdot \ln(A \cdot B \cdot t)}. \tag{14}$$

Similar expressions are derived from (12) for the ERASE operation. These approximations are useful for cell design, and can be employed to evaluate the tradeoffs between programming time, retention time, threshold window, and operating voltages for any given set of cell parameters (A, B, V_{ti}, K_w, K_e). An example is given in Fig. 4, showing that a gate voltage of 5 V does not change the threshold even within several years. However, a pulse amplitude of 20 V can achieve a window of several volts within 1 ms.

III. Experimental Results and Comparison with the Simplified Model

In order to simulate the device performance, its physical parameters have to be measured. Some of the parameters (gate oxide thickness, poly-poly-oxide thickness) can

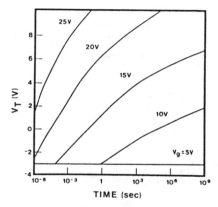

Fig. 4. Simulated threshold voltage versus time, for several WRITE pulse amplitudes (11). $V_t(0) = -3$ V, $V_{ti} = 0$ V, $C_{total} = 1 \times 10^{-13}$ F, $X_{tun} = 120$ Å, $A_{tun} = 2\ \mu m^2$, $K_w = 0.7$.

be measured directly on large structures by well-known techniques (C–V or ellipsometry). However, most of the parameters are more difficult to measure and need special consideration for the floating-gate EEPROM device.

To measure the gate coupling ratio K_w (see (4)), a floating-gate device is compared with the equivalent MOS device (an identical device with direct contact to the first polysilicon gate). The coupling ratio can be obtained by comparing thresholds, body coefficients, or transconductances. In the latter two techniques, the coupling is calculated as the ratio of the body coefficient or transconductance of the MOS device and the EEPROM cell. However, these parameters are sensitive to short-channel effects, mobility degradation, and threshold-adjust boron profile. Care should be taken to measure the two devices at the same operating point. In the first technique, the coupling ratio is calculated as

$$K_w = \frac{V_t(\text{MOS}) - V_{fb}(\text{MOS})}{V_t(\text{EEPROM}) - V_{fb}(\text{EEPROM})}. \tag{15}$$

For accurate results it is important to ensure that $Q_{fg} = 0$. This is achieved by UV light erasure of the EEPROM cell. The drain coupling ratio K_e (see (6)) is calculated from the slope of the V_t versus V_d characteristics. The threshold voltage as a function of the drain voltage can be measured by defining threshold as an arbitrary current level in the weak-inversion region. A significant fraction of the "coupling ratio" measured by this technique is actually due to drain-induced barrier lowering [11]. This short-channel effect is measured similarly on the equivalent MOS device, and subtracted from the slope of the EEPROM device

$$K_e = 1 - K_w[\text{slope}(V_t \text{ versus } V_d(\text{EEPROM}))$$

$$- \text{slope}(V_t \text{ versus } V_d(\text{MOS}))]. \tag{16}$$

The large coupling between the drain and the floating gate has a substantial effect on the I–V characteristics as is shown in Fig. 5. The slope of the I–V characteristics in the saturation region is mainly due to the increase in the floating gate voltage with V_d.

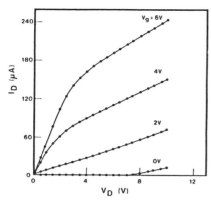

Fig. 5. I_d–V_d characteristics of the EEPROM cell, demonstrating the strong coupling from the drain to the floating gate. $W/L = 5/3.5$ μm, $X_{tun} = 120$ Å, $K_w = 0.72$, $K_e = 0.88$.

Extraction of the tunneling parameters α and β from the tunnel I–V characteristics is difficult and is a subject of controversy in the literature [7]. There are two major problems in determining the tunneling parameters; the first is the accuracy in which the tunnel-oxide thickness can be measured and the second is the change of the tunnel I–V characteristics with charge flow through the oxide due to positive and negative charge trapping [12], [13]. For simplicity, a compromise is made in which the oxide thickness is measured by the C–V technique assuming 3.9 for its relative dielectric constant, and tunnel coefficients are measured from an I–V taken after 0.1-C/cm^2 charge flowed through the oxide. This last decision is based on the fact that the positive charge trapping has saturated after this amount of charge has passed through the oxide, and the negative charge trapping is relatively small for the rest of the relevant device endurance [13]. Based on the above assumptions, it is found that

$$\alpha = 1.88 \times 10^{-6} \text{ A/V}^2$$

$$\beta = 2.55 \times 10^{8} \text{ V/cm}$$

for X_{tun} in the range 100–150 Å.

The calculated and measured results for the WRITE operation are compared in Fig. 6(a),(b). In Fig. 6(a) the threshold voltage as a function of WRITE time and in Fig. 6(b) the threshold voltage as a function of WRITE pulse amplitude are shown. For both examples the simulation results fit the measured data closely.

Trying to extend the same simplified model to the ERASE operation is shown in Fig. 7. The discrepancy between the simulated and measured results clearly demonstrates that the ERASE operation does not follow the simple model.

The main physical effects which cause the deviation of the ERASE characteristics from the simple model are: deep depletion under the gate, deep depletion under the tunnel oxide, and a current path for holes from under the tunnel oxide into the substrate. The detailed discussion of these mechanisms, along with the techniques to incorporate their effect in the device simulation, is the subject of the following sections.

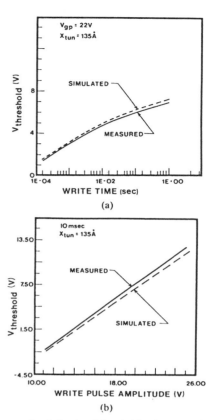

Fig. 6. (a) Measured and simulated threshold voltage as a function of WRITE time for a fixed pulse amplitude. (b) Measured and simulated threshold voltage as a function of WRITE pulse amplitude, for a fixed WRITE time.

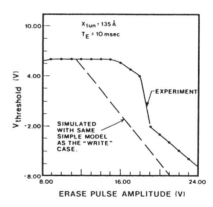

Fig. 7. Measured and simulated ERASE characteristics, using the simplified model. The discrepancy between the two curves is due to formation of depletion layers in the channel and under the tunnel oxide, and due to hole flow to the substrate.

IV. MECHANISMS AFFECTING THE ERASE OPERATION

The "anomalous" behavior of the cell during ERASE is related to the formation of a depletion region in the channel and under the tunnel oxide, and to a hole current to the substrate. These three effects are shown schematically in Fig. 8 and will be analyzed below in more detail.

A. Deep Depletion in the Channel

During the ERASE operation the floating gate potential becomes positive due to the coupling of the positive drain voltage into the floating gate and the reduction in the neg-

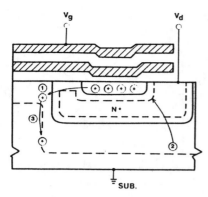

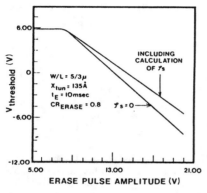

Fig. 8. Schematic illustration of three mechanisms affecting the ERASE operation: ① Deep depletion in the channel. ② Deep depletion under the tunnel oxide. ③ Current path for holes from under the tunnel oxide to the substrate.

Fig. 9. Simulated ERASE characteristics with and without the effect of channel depletion. This effect reduces the efficiency of the ERASE operation.

ative stored charge. As a consequence, a depletion-layer is formed in the channel (region① in Fig. 8), reducing the effective capacitance between the floating gate and the substrate, causing a reduction in the ERASE coupling ratio of the cell. In order to avoid channel current, which can overload the on-chip high-voltage generator supplying V_d, the source is floated. As a result the source is pulled up, tracking the floating-gate potential. This further reduces the ERASE coupling ratio.

Calculation of the channel depletion effect on ERASE characteristics is given in Section V. A typical example of simulated erased threshold as a function of ERASE drain voltage is shown in Fig. 9. The effect of the deep depletion in the channel is becoming more pronounced as the cell threshold is reduced, since the channel surface potential (ϕ_s) is becoming more and more positive and the ERASE coupling ratio is reduced.

B. Deep Depletion Under the Tunnel Oxide

1) The Origin of Deep Depletion: An electric field intensity above 1×10^7 V/cm is required for significant tunneling current. At this field, the n$^+$ region beneath the tunnel oxide is inverted or depleted, depending on its doping level and the availability of holes in this region. Hence, there is a voltage drop across the depletion layer in the n$^+$ region (denoted by② in Fig. 8).

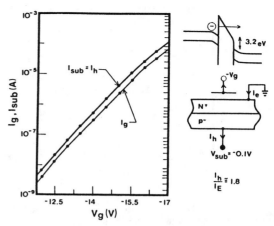

Fig. 10. Measurement of impact ionization by tunnel electrons, entering the silicon from the SiO$_2$ with the high energy (>3.2 eV, as shown in the insert). Electrons and holes are separated by the p $-$ n$^+$ junction: from the ratio of the two currents, the ionization rate is 1.8 pairs per tunnel electron.

This voltage drop ϕ_{sn} is usually more than the equilibrium value of $2\phi_f$ since thermal equilibrium cannot be reached during the short ERASE operation. The holes in the depletion layer can be generated by any one of the following four mechanisms [14]–[16]:

1) thermal generation;
2) avalanche multiplication;
3) band-to-band tunneling in the n$^+$ Si; and
4) pair generation by tunnel electrons from the floating gate.

The first mechanism is very slow and for a typical ERASE operation (in the range of a few milliseconds) its effect is negligible.

The avalanche multiplication and band-to-band tunneling are fast generation mechanisms. Avalanche multiplication is dominant for doping levels below about 5×10^{17} cm^{-3}, and band-to-band tunneling for higher doping levels. The voltage drop across the depletion layer under the tunnel oxide is pinned to a value denoted by ϕ_{gen} that is determined by the onset of a fast hole generation by either one of the above mechanisms [14].

Yet another source of holes in the depletion layer under the tunnel oxide, are the pairs generated by the tunnel electrons entering the silicon [15], [16]. These electrons are very energetic (hot) in the Si conduction band due to the 3.2-eV energy difference between the Si and the SiO$_2$ conduction bands and their kinetic energy in the oxide conduction band (see insert in Fig. 10). A measurement of both the electron tunneling and the impact ionization hole current into the substrate is shown in Fig. 10. It is found that on the average every tunneling electron generates 1.8 hole electron pairs [17]. This measurement is done on a capacitor configuration in which the hole and electron currents in the substrate are separated [18]. The mechanism of hole generation accelerates the collapse of the deep depletion under the tunnel oxide into inversion.

2) The Effect of the Deep Depletion under the Tunnel Oxide on ERASE Characteristics: The deep depletion un-

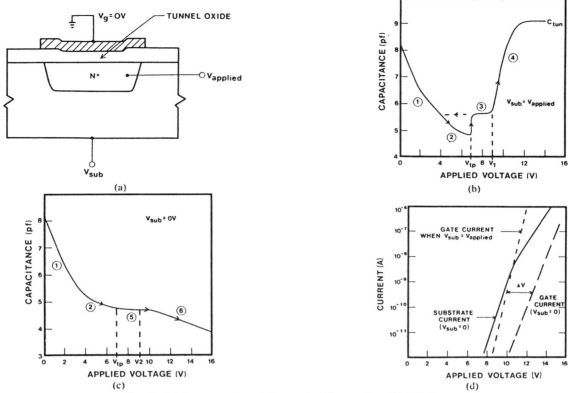

Fig. 11. (a) A cross section of the tunnel oxide capacitor. (b) A $C-V$ curve measured with the substrate connected to the n$^+$ region. (c) A $C-V$ curve measured with the substrate connected to the gate (grounded). (d) Gate and substrate currents measured on the same device.

der the tunnel oxide is associated with a potential drop ϕ_{sn} in the n$^+$ region. The effective ERASE voltage at the Si-tunnel oxide interface is $V_d - \phi_{sn}$. This is equivalent to a shift of the horizontal axis by ϕ_{sn} in the V_t versus V_d characteristic.

For practical modeling purposes, ϕ_{sn} is assumed to be constant throughout the ERASE operation. In a typical EEPROM cell where the n$^+$ concentration is higher than 1×10^{18} cm^{-3}, the initial ϕ_{sn} is equal to ϕ_{gen}, corresponding to hole generation by band-to-band tunneling. More holes are generated by impact ionization of the tunnel electrons (mechanism 4) until ϕ_{sn} is reduced from ϕ_{gen} to $2\phi_f$. An average value of ϕ_{sn} is used in the model. This value is actually a fitting parameter, typically between 1 and 1.5 V.

C. Hole Flow into the Substrate

A surface channel from the inversion layer in the drain region beneath the tunnel oxide to the substrate might be turned on allowing the flow of holes into the substrate. This is the case in the cell structure shown in Fig. 8, where the path of hole flow is denoted by ③ . Continuous removal of holes from the inversion layer forces a deep depletion condition, in which holes are continuously generated and accelerated toward the surface. It is experimentally shown that this effect enhances positive charge trapping in the tunnel oxide and alters the Fowler-

Nordheim characteristic. The discussion of hole flow into the substrate starts with its manifestation in the $C-V$ and the $I-V$ curves of a tunnel capacitor, followed by its effect on positive charge trapping in the oxide, and concluded by its effect on the ERASE characteristics.

1) Investigation of a Tunnel Oxide Capacitor: The effects of deep depletion under the tunnel oxide and hole flow to the substrate have been investigated by $C-V$ and $I-V$ measurements on the test structure shown in Fig. 11(a). This device is a 20 μm $\times$ 180 μm thin-oxide capacitor fabricated on an ion-implanted n$^+$ region in a p-type substrate, which is equivalent to the tunnel-oxide capacitor in the EEPROM cell.

A typical $C-V$ measurement with a grounded gate is shown in Fig. 11(b). Bias is applied to the n$^+$ and the substrate terminals, which are connected together. This $C-V$ curve reveals the existence of a surface channel for holes under the thicker oxide at the edge of the tunnel capacitor. The various segments of the $C-V$ curve are:

1) Depletion: The n$^+$ surface under the tunnel oxide is depleted of electrons.

2) Deep depletion: The voltage drop across the depletion layer exceeds $2\phi_f$ due to the shortage of holes and the relatively fast ramping (10 V/s).

3) Collapse of the deep depletion to inversion at $V = V_{tp}$ the depletion voltage under the thicker oxide in the edges of the capacitor reaches $2\phi_f$, and a surface channel

is formed for holes. The p-type substrate acts as a source, and the inversion layer under the tunnel oxide acts as a virtual drain of a p-channel transistor. The measurement corresponds to equilibrium inversion high-frequency capacitance.

4) Strong conduction in the surface channel: At about $V = V1$ the conductivity of the surface channel is high enough to short-out the depletion capacitance, so that the full thin-oxide capacitance is observed (i.e., the transit time for holes to and from the inversion layer becomes shorter than the period of the measurement ac signal). This is similar to low-frequency behavior.

The surface channel described above has an important effect on the ERASE characteristics of the EEPROM cell. To simulate the ERASE conditions, a $C-V$ measurement is performed on the same device with the substate grounded together with the gate, and bias applied to the n^+ region. The $C-V$ curve is shown in Fig. 11(c). It coincides with the previous result up to $V = V_{tp}$. At this point, when the surface p-channel is turned on, the substrate acts as a drain for the p-channel transistor, and the inversion layer of holes beneath the tunnel oxide acts as a virtual source. In the range denoted by (5), the capacitance is clamped to a value C_{gen}, corresponding to a potential drop ϕ_{gen} in the depletion region. The generated holes are continuously removed into the substrate through the surface channel so that equilibrium cannot be reached. Above $V = V2$ (range (6)), the potential barrier at the virtual source is reduced beyond ϕ_{gen}, and the capacitor is forced into deeper depletion with increasing bias voltage.

The interpretation of $C-V$ curves is confirmed by $I-V$ measurements on the same device, shown in Fig. 11(d). With a grounded substrate, a large substrate current appears at voltage above V_{tp} (as more and more holes are generated under the tunnel oxide and collected by the substrate).

By comparing the $I-V$ curves of the gate current, one with grounded substrate and the second with substrate connected to the n^+ region, a voltage difference ΔV is observed. This voltage drop is the additional drop across the deep-depletion layer in the n^+ region when the substrate is grounded. Surface potentials ϕ_{sn} extracted from capacitances in Fig. 11(c) agree very well with $\Delta V + 2\phi_f$ as measured on Fig. 11(d).

In summary, the edge transistor can be understood analyzing the $C-V/I-V$ characteristics of the tunnel capacitor. The main consequences of this edge transistor are: deep depletion under the tunnel oxide which reduces the tunneling current, and hole flow into the substrate.

2) Positive Charge Trapping in the Tunnel Oxide: Enhanced positive charge trapping in the tunnel oxide, correlated with the above hole current flow to the substrate, has been observed in $C-V$ measurements on capacitor structures. Positive charge trapping in thin oxide has been previously discussed in the literature [12], [13] as a side effect of tunneling; it is exhibited experimentally by hysteresis in the $I-V$ and $C-V$ curves.

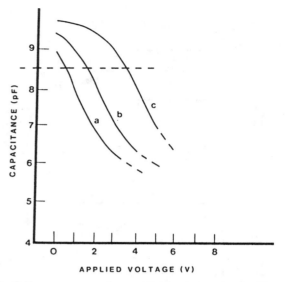

Fig. 12. $C-V$ curves measured around flat band on a tunnel oxide capacitor: (a) Before stress, (b) After stress without hole flow to the substrate ($t = 20$ s, $J = 3.1 \times 10^{-2}$ A/cm², $V_{sub} = V_n^+$). (c) After stress with hole flow to the substrate ($t = 20$ s, $J = 3.1 \times 10^{-2}$ A/cm², $V_{sub} = V_g = 0$). Enhanced positive charge trapping is indicated by the flatband shift in curve *c*.

The $C-V$ curves of a tunnel capacitor around flat band are shown in Fig. 12. Curve *a* is the initial $C-V$ before any stress. The second (curve *b*) is the $C-V$ after tunneling only (substrate connected to the n^+ region). There is a flat-band shift which indicates positive charge trapping. However, repeating the $C-V$ measurement after tunneling with the substrate connected to the gate, results in a large flat-band shift due to enhanced positive charge trapping (curve *c*). The enhanced trapping is the result of hot-hole injection in the deep depletion layer under the tunnel oxide, which is also manifested by hole current to the substrate (see previous section). Effective interface charge densities up to 1×10^{13} cm⁻² have been observed, in correlation with the depth of the depletion region as measured from the capacitance during the stress. The observation of positive charge trapping in oxides due to hot-hole injection is well established in the literature [7], [19]. In this work, however, the hole injection is not over the oxide potential barrier since the total voltage drop in the silicon is less than the potential barrier for holes. A possible explanation for the injection involves a two-step mechanism: energetic holes are injected toward the interface and tunnel into trapping levels in the oxide. The positive charge in the oxide is very unstable and can be annihilated by electron injection or annealed by a high-temperature cycle [20].

3) The Effect of Hole Flow on the ERASE Characteristics: The result of an experiment done on an EEPROM cell with a structure permitting hole flow into the substrate is shown in Fig. 13. The cell is written and erased repetitively, and the threshold voltage is measured after each operation. For writing the cell, fixed conditions are used ($V_g = 20$ V, $t = 10$ ms). For erasing the cell, the pulse

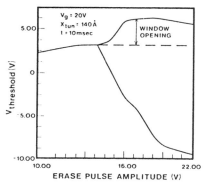

Fig. 13. Cell's threshold window measured versus ERASE pulse amplitude, with a constant WRITE pulse amplitude. The data exhibits window opening due to positive charge trapping, associated with hole flow into the substrate.

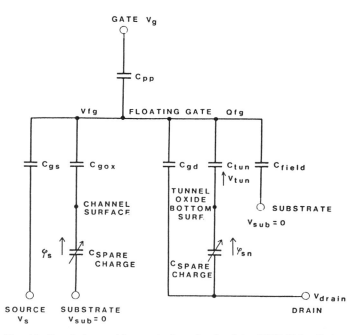

Fig. 14. Detailed capacitive equivalent circuit of the EEPROM cell, including space charge and parasitic capacitance.

amplitude applied to the drain is gradually increased at each cycle. The first WRITE operation shifted the cell's threshold from ϕ V to about 2.5 V. The first few ERASE pulses did not cause any change in threshold, because the amplitude of the ERASE pulse was still too small, and the repetitive WRITE operations slightly moved the threshold voltage upward. With ERASE pulse amplitude above 14 V, a measurable threshold window could be observed. The important feature in this experiment is the window opening on the WRITE side. The written cell threshold was increased by about 3 V when the ERASE pulse amplitude reached approximately 16 V, instead of following the dashed line, as would be expected with fixed amplitude of the WRITE pulses. This window opening is a result of positive charge trapping in the tunnel oxide, which enhances the tunnel current by increasing the oxide electric field at the injecting electrode [8]. The window opening was found to be correlated with the appearance of a current spike in the substrate during the ERASE operation, verifying the relation between hole injection and the positive charge trapping. Note also the nonlinear shape of the V_{te} curves in Figs. 13 and 7. This is an indication of the voltage drop across the deep-depletion layer in the n^+ region, as well as the increase in tunneling field after the enhanced positive-charge trapping begins. The positive charges associated with window opening can be removed either by high-temperature anneal or by cycling the cell at low ERASE pulse amplitude.

The hole flow to the substrate in the ERASE operation is associated with an unpredictable and unstable threshold window. Furthermore, the current flow from the high drain voltage to the substrate may prevent the use of an on-chip charge pump for "5 V only" application. Therefore, it is important to avoid hole flow into the substrate in a good cell design. This is accomplished by isolating the tunnel area from the substrate by a thick gate oxide overlapping the n^+ region, so that the virtual p-channel transistor cannot be turned on when the cell is erased. In the case that a thin oxide is intentionally used over a n^+-p junction [2], the undesirable consequences of the hole flow to the substrate cannot be avoided.

V. DETAILED DEVICE MODEL

A. Calculation of Floating Gate and Channel Potentials

An equivalent circuit for the EEPROM cell, including parasitic capacitances and depletion-layer capacitances, is shown in Fig. 14. The effect of hole flow into the substrate is excluded from the model, assuming that the cell is appropriately designed (see Section IV-C). C_{gs} and C_{gd} are overlap gate-oxide capacitances, C_{fld} is a field-oxide capacitance from the floating gate to the substrate. The voltage drop on the depletion-layer capacitances is ϕ_s and ϕ_{sn} for the channel and the n^+ region, respectively. The stored charge on the floating gate Q_{fg} is the sum of all capacitor charges

$$Q_{fg} = C_{pp}(V_{fg} - V_g) + C_{gd}(V_{fg} - V_d) + C_{fld}(V_{fg} - V_{sub})$$
$$+ C_{tun}(V_{fg} - (V_D - |\phi_{sn}|)) + C_{gs}(V_{fg} - V_s)$$
$$+ C_{gox}(V_{fg} - (V_{sub} + |\phi_s|)). \quad (17)$$

During the WRITE operation, the n^+ region is accumulated and ϕ_{sn} is assumed to be zero. The channel is formed so that the channel surface and the floating source assume the voltage of the drain $V_d = 0$. Thus, V_{fg} can be solved explicitly from (17).

During the ERASE operation, ϕ_{sn} is assumed to be constant, as discussed in Section IV-B above. The condition of the channel surface is determined in the following manner for any given Q_{fg}: First, depletion is assumed, and the last term in (17) is replaced by

$$Q_{dep} = A_{ch} \cdot \sqrt{2q \cdot \epsilon_{si} \cdot \epsilon_0 \cdot N_b \cdot \phi_s}. \quad (18)$$

For this assumed condition, V_{fg} is related to ϕ_s by

$$V_{fg} = V_{fb} + \phi_s + \frac{A_{ch}}{C_{gox}} \sqrt{2q \cdot \epsilon_{si} \cdot \epsilon_0 \cdot \phi_s}. \quad (19)$$

135

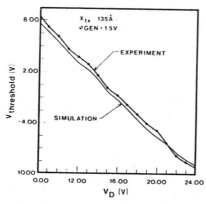

Fig. 15. A comparison between measured and simulated ERASE characteristics for a cell without hole flow path to the substrate using the detailed model.

This expression is inserted into (17), and the resultant quadratic equation is solved for $\sqrt{\phi_s}$. If there is no positive solution, the channel surface is accumulated and ϕ_s is taken as zero. The voltage V_s at the floating source is equal to ϕ_s. Equation (17) is then solved for V_{fg} with the appropriate value of ϕ_s.

B. Calculation of WRITE and ERASE Characteristics

Once all the internal voltages are determined, the tunnel current density can be calculated from (1). Starting from an initial stored charge $Q_{fg}(0)$, the differential equation

$$dt = \frac{a Q_{fg}}{A_{tun} \cdot J_{tun}} \quad (20)$$

is integrated numerically, to obtain the floating-gate charge as a function of time. Each step in the integration involves the calculation of voltages and tunnel current as outlined above.

The cell's threshold voltage is related to Q_{fg} by

$$V_t = V_{ti} - \frac{Q_{fg}}{C_{pp}} \quad (21)$$

where V_{ti} is the neutral cell threshold. V_{fb} is adjusted in (17) to yield $Q_{fg} = 0$ when $V_g = V_{ti}$ accounts for any fixed surface charges in the double-poly structure.

Using (21) and the solution of (20), the dependence of threshold on programming time is simulated for any set of device parameters and programming waveforms. An example is shown in Fig. 15 for ERASE characteristics of a cell without hole flow into the substrate, exhibiting a reasonable fit to measured data.

VI. Conclusions

A simplified model for FLOTOX EEPROM cells based on the concept of coupling ratios has been presented. The principal considerations in cell design can be derived from the simplified model. However, this model cannot be used for accurate simulation of the ERASE operation. Physical effects which complicate the ERASE operation have been presented and analyzed. Depletion in the transistor's channel reduces the coupling ratio during erasure. Deep depletion in the n^+ region under the tunnel oxide causes a voltage drop that leads to a further reduction in the threshold shift. The role of these depletion layers has been included in a detailed cell model.

A flow path for holes from under the tunnel oxide into the substrate during erasure leads to further detrimental consequences. On-chip generation of the drain voltage by charge pumps may not be possible due to the large substrate current. Enhanced positive charge trapping in the oxide, associated with the hole flow, has been observed. The role of hot-hole injection in this process has been discussed. Unstable opening of the cell's threshold window has been shown to occur as a result of the enhanced positive charge trapping. It is concluded that hole flow into the substrate can be avoided by an appropriate cell design.

Acknowledgment

The authors are indebted to J. Lee, N. Mielke, S. Lai, G. Gongwer, and E. Hellman for their contribution to this work.

References

[1] W. Johnson, G. Perlegos, A. Renninger, G. Kuhn, and T. Ranganath, "A 16K bit electrically erasable non-volatile memory," in Dig. Tech. Papers IEEE Int. Solid-State Circuits Conf., p. 152, Feb. 1980.

[2] C. Kuo, J. R. Yeargain, W. J. Downey, K. A. Ilgenstein, J. R. Jorvig, S. L. Smith, and A. R. Bormann, "An 80-nS 32-K EEPROM using the FETMOS cell," IEEE J. Solid-State Circuits, vol. SC-17, p. 821, 1982.

[3] G. Yaron, S. J. Prasad, M. S. Ebel, and B. M. K. Leong, "A 16K EEPROM employing new array architecture and designed-in reliability features," IEEE J. Solid-State Circuits, vol. SC-17, p. 833, 1982.

[4] A. Gupta, T. L. Chiu, M. S. Chang, A. Renninger, and G. Perlegos, "A 5V-only 16K EEPROM utilizing oxynitride dielectrics and EPROM redundancy," in Dig. Tech. Papers IEEE Int. Solid-State Circuits Conf., p. 184, Feb. 1982.

[5] T. Hogiwara, Y. Yatsuda, R. Kendo, S. I. Minami, T. Aoto, and Y. Itoh, "A 16 Kbit electrically erasable PROM using n-channel Si-gate MNOS technology," IEEE J. Solid-State Circuits, vol. SC-15, p. 346, 1980.

[6] M. Lenzlinger and E. H. Snow, "Fowler-Nordheim tunneling into thermally grown SiO," J. Appl. Phys., vol. 40, p. 278, 1969.

[7] Z. A. Weinberg, "On tunneling in metal-oxide-silicon structures," J. Appl. Phys., vol. 53, p. 5052, 1982.

[8] B. Euzent, N. Boruta, J. Lee, and C. Jenq, "Reliability aspects of a floating gate EEPROM," in Proc. Int. Reliability Physics Symp., 1981.

[9] P. I. Suciu, B. P. Cox, D. D. Rinerson, and S. F. Cagnina, "Cell model for EEPROM floating-gate memories," in IEDM Tech. Dig. (San Francisco), p. 737, 1982.

[10] S. T. Wang, "Charge retention of floating-gate transistors under applied bias conditions," IEEE Trans. Electron Devices, vol. ED-27, p. 297, 1980.

[11] L. D. Yau, "A simple theory to predict the threshold voltage of short channel IGFET's," Solid-State Electron., vol. 17, pp. 1059-1063, 1974.

[12] Y. Nissan-Cohen, D. Frohman-Bentchkowsky, and J. Shappir, "Characterization of simultaneous bulk and interface high-field trapping effects in SiO₂," in IEDM Tech. Dig. (Washington, DC), paper 8.2, 1983.

[13] M. Itsumi, "Positive and negative charging of thermally grown SiO₂ induced by Fowler-Nordheim emission," J. Appl. Phys., vol. 52, pp. 3491-3497, 1981.

[14] E. H. Nicollian and J. R. Brewz, MOS Physics and Technology. New York: Wiley, 1982, ch. 9.

[15] E. Suzuki and Y. Hayashi, "Transport processes of electrons in MNOS structures," Appl. Phys., vol. 50, pp. 7001-7006, 1979.

[16] M. S. Liang, C. Chang, Y. T. Yeow, C. Hu, and R. W. Brodersen,

"Creation and termination of substrate deep depletion in thin oxide MOS capacitors by charge tunneling," *IEEE Electron Device Lett.*, vol. EDL-4, pp. 350-352, 1983.

[17] E. O. Kane, "Electron scattering by pair production in silicon," *Phys. Rev.*, vol. 159, pp. 624-631, 1967.

[18] B. Eitan and A. Kolodny, "Two components of tunneling current in metal-oxide-semiconductor structures," *Appl. Phys. Lett.*, vol. 43, pp. 106-108, 1983.

[19] J. M. Aitken and D. R. Young. "Avalanche injection of holes into SiO$_2$," *IEEE Trans. Nucl. Sci.*, vol. NS-24, pp. 2128-2134, 1977.

[20] C. Jenq *et al.*, "High-field generation of electron traps and charge trapping in ultra-thin SiO$_2$," in *IEDM Tech. Dig.*, pp. 388-391, 1981.

[21] Y. Tarui, Y. Hayashi, and K. Nagai, "Electrically programmable nonvolatile semiconductor memory," in *Proc. 5th Conf. Solid State Devices*, supplement to *J. Japan Soc. Appl. Phy.*, vol. 43, 1974.

[22] Y. N. Hsieh, R. A. Wood, and P. O. Wang, "Electrically alterable programmable logic array," in *IEDM Tech. Dig.*, pp. 598-601, 1980.

[23] H. Schaver *et al.*, "A high-density, high performance EEPROM cell," *IEEE Trans. Electron Devices*, vol. ED-29, p. 1178, 1982.

A 256K HIGH PERFORMANCE CMOS EEPROM TECHNOLOGY

Ling Chen, Scott W. Owen, Ching S. Jenq and Alan R. Renninger

SEEQ Technology, Inc
San Jose, CA 95131

ABSTRACT

A high performance CMOS technology has been developed for a 256K EEPROM. Using this technology, a 54um² EEPROM cell has been realized. The high coupling ratio of the cell, together with the use of an ultrathin oxynitride layer as a tunneling dielectric, allows cell programming voltages as low as 17 volts at a programming time of 0.1 msec. The intrinsic cell endurance has been improved to greater than 10^8 cycles. The utilization of an optimized interpoly dielectric process and low temperature reflow glass prevent the degradation of tunneling dielectric. A special gettering technique reduces tunneling dielectric defects as well as junction leakage, thus paving the way to 5 volt-only operation over full military temperature range.

INTRODUCTION

Over the last five years tremendous progress in EEPROM technology has been made, which has resulted in cost-effective 64K NMOS parts exhibiting excellent reliability and circuit performance. A CMOS 256K EEPROM represents the next natural step in this evolution because of the advantage in power consumption and noise margin of CMOS over its NMOS counterparts.

For high density EEPROM circuits, cell size is the most important factor in determining the die size and thus the manufacturing yield. In order to maintain the same level of program/erase threshold, a scaled EEPROM cell requires, in most cases, a thinner tunneling dielectric. A thinner tunneling dielectric, however, usually causes the defect density to increase (1), resulting in higher infant mortality failures or lower cell and array cycling endurance. Oxynitride films of 90-100Å thickness have been proven to be extremely reliable for EEPROM cells, due to their low charge trapping, long time-to-breakdown characteristics and low defect density (2,3). For further scaling, oxynitride films with thickness of 70-90Å are required which preserve these critical qualities for EEPROM cell application.

In this paper a CMOS process will be reported with emphasis on the development of a high quality thin oxynitride dielectric that results in a production-worthy EEPROM cell occupying an area of 54um²

PROCESS TECHNOLOGY

The N-well double polysilicon gate CMOS process is based on a p-type substrate of resistivity 10-15 ohm-cm. LOCOS isolation is used with a 9000Å field oxide. Table I shows the key process features.

The tunneling dielectric is the heart of the EEPROM process technology. Extensive investigation and development of thin oxynitride films has been made. These films are fabricated by annealing a thermally grown dry SiO_2 in diluted-ammonia ambient at high temperature. Films of thicknesses ranging from 70 to 90Å have been developed with characteristics comparable to those reported for the 90 to 100Å oxynitride films of previous generation EEPROMs (4).

These films have a charge trapping rate of about 0.5mv/sec and a time-to-breakdown characteristic that is longer than 100 sec. Fig. 1 shows typical charge trapping characteristics of an 80Å oxynitride capacitor under a 100mA/cm² constant-current stress. Using oxynitride, the single cell endurance is higher than one hundred million cycles, as shown in Fig. 2. Fig. 3 shows the low breakdown frequency of these films as measured on 250um x 250um capacitors indicating their high manufacturability. Defects and impurities in thermal SiO_2 have previously been shown as the main sources of electron traps (5). Therefore, in order to obtain high quality tunneling dielectrics, pre-existing defects and impurities in the substrate surface must be eliminated, and process-induced defects and contamination must be prevented. Experiments comparing different gettering techniques

Reprinted from the *IEDM Tech. Dig.*, pp. 620–623, 1985.

were carried out. As shown in Table II, desirable improvement can be seen in the controlled process. This controlled process also gives a 10-20% reduction in junction leakage current.

For speed performance, a shallow n+ as well as p+ junction was chosen. A double-diffused graded-drain high voltage transistor was used for programming circuitry. To ensure high data retention of the floating gate EEPROM cell, an optimized low temperature interpoly dielectric process was developed. Also included is the use of borophosphosilicate glass for low temperature backend process. The use of these low temperature thermal cycles after tunneling dielectric formation has proven to be beneficial to the integrity of the tunneling dielectric.

CELL DESIGN AND PERFORMANCE

Over the last four years, the size of EEPROM cells has been scaled almost by a factor of two per year as shown in Fig. 4. This scaling trend would not be possible if not for the better understanding of cell physics and design, the improvement in thin oxynitride technology, and the advancements in fine-line lithography and dry etching technologies. In the current process the in-line two-transistor EEPROM cell (6) is further scaled to a size of 54um². Fig. 5 shows the SEM cross-section of the cell. The desired coupling ratio is maintained through corresponding reduction in the thickness of interpoly dielectric and improvement in layout design. The tunneling dielectric is also scaled slightly by utilizing an oxynitride film of approximately 80Å.

The performance of the cell is shown in Fig. 6 and Fig. 7. From Fig. 6, it can be seen that the cell will work under a programming voltage of 15V, resulting in an acceptable threshold window of approximately 4V. At a worst-case chip programming voltage of 17V, the cell has a very usable threshold window of 8V. The programming speed of the cell is shown in Fig. 7. The cell is found to operate down to below 1 msec, providing the basis for high programming-speed circuit design. With the use of oxynitride, the endurance of the cell has reached one hundred million cycles before breakdown, as was shown earlier in Fig. 3.

High cell endurance is one of the most important factors for achieving a high EEPROM array endurance. Using this cell and proper design techniques, a 256K memory array should be capable of meeting a one million cycle endurance specification.

SUMMARY

An N-well double-polysilicon gate CMOS technology has been successfully developed for a 256K EEPROM. A high quality thin oxynitride tunneling dielectric and thin interpoly dielectric make it possible to scale the cell size to 54um². This scaling is accomplished without sacrificing coupling ratio, and the programmability of the cell is thereby maintained. The cell has been shown to operate within a programming voltage as low as 17V and programming times as short as 0.1 msec. The use of an optimized interpoly dielectric process, a low temperature reflow glass, and special gettering techniques improve the tunneling dielectric characteristics and enable EEPROM cell endurance beyond 100 million cycles. Based upon the integrity of the oxynitride film and the performance of the scaled EEPROM cell, a cost-effective 256K EEPROM capable of 1 million cycles of endurance is expected.

ACKNOWLEDGMENT

The authors would like to thank Dinesh Tandan, Tien Lin, Jone Vrhel, Mark Chang, Dumitru Cioaca and Ed Mitchell for their technical assistance and helpful discussions, and Arleen Conner, Sharon Kitta, Lina Luna and the entire Fab staff for wafer processing. They also would like to thank Dr. Phil Salsbury for his encouragement and support.

REFERENCES

(1) A.C. Adams, T.E. Smith and C.C. Chang, J. Electrochem. Soc. 127, 1787 (1980).

(2) Ching S. Jenq, Te-Long Chiu, Bharati Joshi and Jim Hu, IEDM Tech. Digest, 811 (1982).

(3) Ching S. Jenq, Ting Wong, Bharati Joshi and Chenming Hu, IEDM Tech. Digest, 585 (1983).

(4) A. Gupta, T-L. Chiu, M.S. Chang, A. Renninger and G. Perlegos, ISCCC Tech. Digest, 184 (1982).

(5) D.J. DiMaria, "The Physics of SiO₂ and Its Interfaces", edited by S.T. Pantelides, 160 (1978).

(6) Sanjay Mehrotra, Tsung-Ching Wu, Te-Long Chiu and Gust Perlegos, ISSCC Tech. Digest, 142 (1984).

Table I. Key Process Features (nominal)

L_{eff} (min.)	1.6 um
W_{eff} (min.)	0.8 um
Field oxide	9000Å
Gate oxide	~400Å
Interpoly dielectric	~400Å
Tunnel dielectric	~80Å
x_j (n+)	0.4 um
x_j (p+)	0.5 um
x_j (n-well)	4.0 um
V_{tn}	0.6 volts
V_{tp}	-0.85 volts

Table II. Tunneling Dielectric Characteristics Dependence on Gettering Process

	Time to Breakdown (T_{BD} in sec)	% of Defects ($T_{BD} < 50$ sec)
Controlled process	138 ± 40	10%
Phosphorus backside diffusion process	125 ± 41	30%
Epi-wafer	123 ± 52	40%

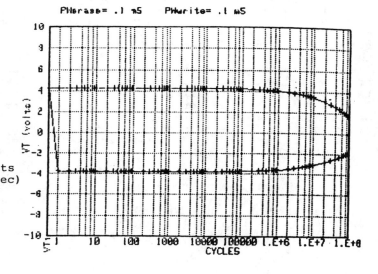

Fig. 2 Endurance characteristics of a single EEPROM cell

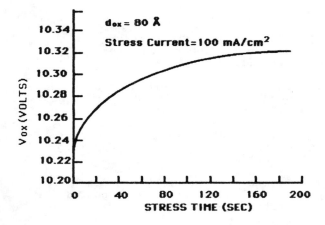

Fig. 1 Charge trapping of an oxynitride capacitor under constant current stress

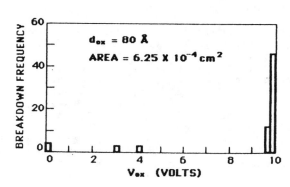

Fig. 3 Breakdown frequency of oxynitride capacitors under a constant current stress of 100 mA/cm²

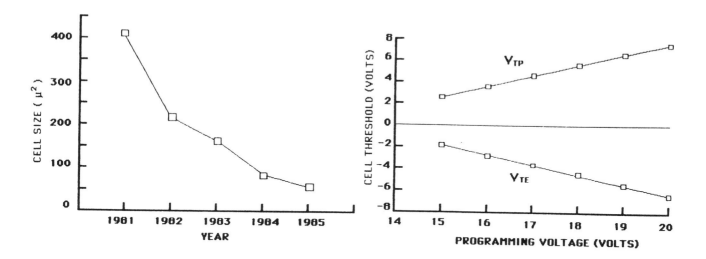

Fig. 4   Scaling trend of EEPROM cell
         sizes

Fig. 6   Cell threshold as a function of
         programming voltage

Fig. 5   SEM cross-section of the EEPROM
         cell

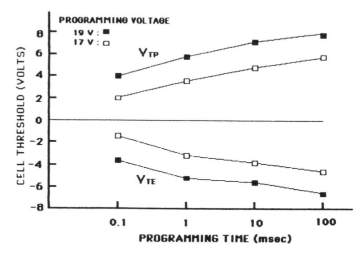

Fig. 7   Cell threshold as a function of
         programming time

Paper 4.5

NEW DEVICE TECHNOLOGIES FOR 5V-ONLY 4Mb EEPROM
WITH NAND STRUCTURE CELL

M.Momodomi, R.Kirisawa, R.Nakayama, S.Aritome, T.Endoh, Y.Itoh,
Y.Iwata, H.Oodaira, T.Tanaka, M.Chiba, R.Shirota and F.Masuoka

ULSI Research Center
Toshiba Corporation, Komukai 1,Saiwai-ku,Kawasaki 210,Japan

ABSTRACT

A NAND structure cell is most promising as an ultra high density EEPROM to replace magnetic memories. This paper describes a new device technology to realize a high performance 4Mb EEPROM with NAND structure cell. The main features of the technology are a new NAND structure cell to realize wide threshold window and high reliability, and a high voltage CMOS process to realize program and erase operations,which require high voltage pulses,such as 22V.

By using 1.0um design rules, the unit cell area per bit is 12.9um^2, which is small enough to realize a 4Mb EEPROM.

INTRODUCTION

In order to replace magnetic memories by solid state devices, a high density EEPROM has been required. Conventional 5V-only EEPROMs, utilizing Fowler-Nordheim tunneling, occupy a very large cell area, which make it difficult to achieve high density EEPROMs[1],[2]. Flash EEPROMs, utilizing channel hot electron injection, occupy a very small cell area. However, they require external high voltage power supply[3],[4]. In order to realize 5V-only power supply for programming and erasing without external Vpp and to achieve a small cell area, a NAND structure cell has been proposed[5]. This NAND structure cell is now considered one of the most promising to realize a 5V-only EEPROM beyond 4M bits.

A 5V-only EEPROM with NAND structure cell is realized by using several new device technologies. Main features of technology are as follows. (a) A wide threshold voltage window for the NAND cell can be achieved by new programming operation. (b) Successive program/erase operations can be realized by high voltage CMOS process. This paper presents a new programming operation for the NAND structure cell , reliability and high voltage CMOS process for the 4Mb EEPROM.

NAND STRUCTURE CELL AND ARRAY

The NAND structure cell arranges 8 memory transistors in series between 2 select transistors, as shown in Fig.1. The first select transistor(SG1) ensures the selectivity. The second one(SG2) prevents current from passing during programming operation. The cell has only one memory transistor, 1/4 select transistor and 1/16 contact hole area per bit,which realizes a small cell area without scaling down the device dimensions. This NAND structure cell is fabricated by conventional self-aligned double poly Si gate technology. The dimensions of 8 memory cells and two select transistors are 4.0 x 25.8 um,therefore,the cell size is 12.9 um^2 per bit. The gate length of the memory transistor is 1.0um and the gate oxide thickness under the floating gate is 100 A.

This 4Mb EEPROM is composed of 256 x 2048 NAND structure cell arrays. Figure 2 shows the NAND structure cell array.

CELL OPERATION

This cell can be programmed and erased by F-N tunneling mechanism. Therefore, current dissipation during these operations is very small. High voltage pulses are generated on the chip from an external single-5V power supply.

In an erase operation, 17V is applied to the control gates and bit lines are grounded. All cells in a block are erased simultaneously. The threshold voltage (Vth) of erased cells become an enhanced mode at approximately 2V after 1msec erasing time.

In a programming operation, 22V is applied to the unselected control gates and the selected bit lines ,and the selected control gate is grounded. Half of the programming voltage (11V) is applied to the unselected bit lines in order to keep Vth of unselected cells. Figure 3 shows the programming characteristics in a NAND array. Vth of the programmed cell are pushed into depletion

Reprinted from the *IEDM Tech. Dig.*, pp. 412–415, 1988.

mode at approximately -3V after 2msec programming time,and Vth of unselected cells is maintained at 2V. Furthermore, in order to prevent interference between selected and unselected cells , programming begins from the source side cell to the bit line side cell sequentially (from cell-1 to cell-8). Control gates of the previously-programmed cells are always kept at 0V. Figure 4 shows the sequential programming characteristics. Vth of the previously-programmed cells does not shift. Only the selected cell can be programmed in an array. Thus, the threshold voltage window of the NAND cell reaches more than 5V,which is the same as the current EPROM.

In a read operation, 5V is applied to the control gates of unselected cells and the control gate of selected cell is grounded. The unselected cells act as transfer gates. If the selected cell is a depletion mode, 20uA typical cell current flows. If the selected cell is an enhanced mode, no cell current flows.

FABRICATION PROCESS

This 4Mb EEPROM is fabricated by the high voltage CMOS process, which achieves high voltage structures in 2.0um N-well CMOS technology.

A charge pump circuit on chip generates high programming voltage (22V). Figure 5 shows the relation between Vth of N-channel field transistor and field isolation length. Because half of the programming voltage(11V) is applied to unselected bit lines, Vth of N-channel field transistor in a memory cell array is over 24V at 2.4um field isolation length. In the peripheral circuitry, p^+ layer under the field oxide are separated from the drain regions ,which consist of n^- and n^+ regions. Furthermore, n^+ regions of drain are separated from field regions. Also, in order to achieve high voltage N- and P-channel MOS transistors, a masked LDD technology and N-well with an approximately 5E16cm^{-3} doping concentration are introduced. The threshold voltage of N-channel field transistor , junction breakdown voltage and punch-through voltage of N- and P-channel devices are over 24V, as shown in Fig.6. This high voltage process make it possible to achieve high voltage programming.

The peripheral circuitry is fabricated by using triple poly-Si, single metal process. The gate oxide thickness is 400A. The gate lengths of NMOS and PMOS are 2.0um and 2.5um,respectively. The main device parameters are shown in Table 1.

RELIABILITY

The endurance of NAND structure cell

has been found to be greater than 10000 program/erase cycles, as shown in Fig.7. In endurance characteristics, closure of the cell window has not been found. This phenomena is strongly dependent on drain concentrations. Hole traps in the thin gate oxide during programming steps of the cycle is suppressed by the optimization of drain concentration. Vth of the erased cells goes up from 1V to 3V by 20 program/erase cycles. As a result, Vth of the programmed cell goes up from -3V to -2V, because the programming high voltage can not be sufficiently transferred.

It has been confirmed that the NAND structure cell has good read retention characteristics as shown in Fig.8. (i.e. 10 year life time with read retention of 7.1V) In a 4Mb EEPROM, the control gate voltage of unselected cell is limited to below 5.5V in a read mode for high reliability.

CONCLUSION

New device technologies for 5V-only EEPROM with a NAND structure cell have been described. By applying half of the programming voltage to unselected bit lines and a successive programming sequence, the NAND structure cell keeps a wide threshold margin. A high voltage CMOS process realize a reliable programming characteristics. Reliability of the cell has been confirmed experimentally.

A 5V-only 4Mb EEPROM has been successfully developed by using the new device technology.

ACKNOWLEDGMENT

The authors would like to thank K.Ohuchi for his helpful discussion on this work. Appreciation is extended to Dr.H.Iizuka for his support and encouragement.

REFERENCES

[1] G.Yaron, M.Ebel, J.Prassad and B.Leong, ISSCC DIGEST OF TECHNICAL PAPERS, pp108-109,1982.
[2] J.R.Yeargain and C.Kuo,IEDM TECHNICAL DIGEST,pp.24-27,1981.
[3] F.Masuoka, M.Asano, H.Iwahashi, T.Komuro and S.Tanaka,IEDM TECHNICAL DIGEST,pp552-555,1987.
[4] F.Masuoka, M.Momodomi, Y.Iwata, R.Shirota,IEDM DIGEST TECHNICAL DIGEST ,pp552-555,1987.
[5] R.Shirota, Y.Itoh, R.Nakayama, M.Momodomi,S.Inoue, R.Kirisawa, Y.Iwata, M.Chiba and F.Masuoka, Proc.Symp.VLSI Tech.,p33-34, 1988.

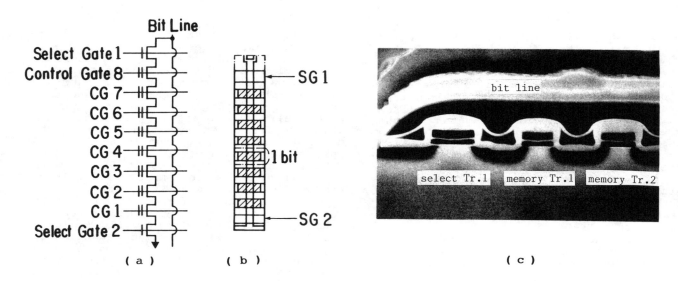

Fig.1 NAND structure cell (a) Equivalent circuit (b) Layout
(c) Cross-sectional view

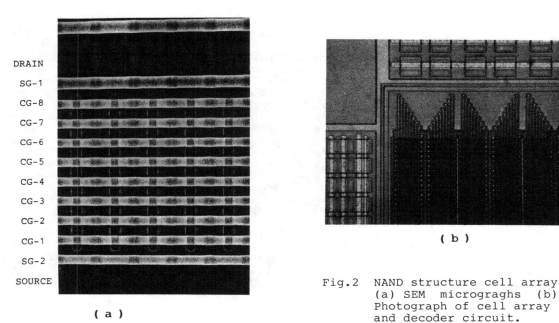

Fig.2 NAND structure cell array
(a) SEM micrograghs (b)
Photograph of cell array
and decoder circuit.

Table 1 Process and device parameters of 4M bit EEPROM

TECHNOLOGY	;	N-WELL CMOS	
		TRIPLE LEVEL POLY Si	
		SINGLE ALUMINUM LAYER	
GATE LENGTH	;	MEMORY CELL	1.0um
		SELECT GATE	1.5um
		NMOS	2.0um
		PMOS	2.5um
OXIDE THICKNESS	;	TRANSISTOR	400A
		MEMORY CELL	100A

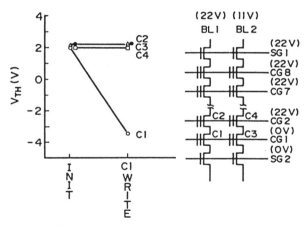

Fig.3 Selective programming in a NAND cell array. Only the selected bit (C1) is programmed.

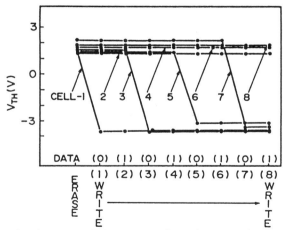

Fig.4 Sequential programming characteristics of single NAND cell (8 bit). Programming data is "01010101".

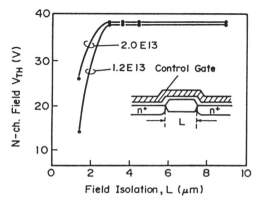

Fig.5 N-ch. Field Vth vs. field isolation length as a function of field dose.

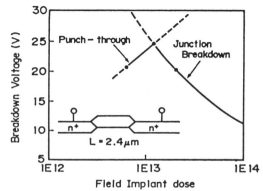

Fig.6 Junction breakdown voltage and punch-through voltage as a function of field implant dose.

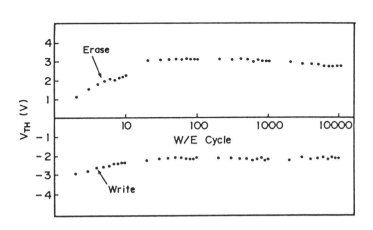

Fig.7 Endurance characteristics. Closure of the cell threshold window has not been found up to 10000 write/erase cycles.

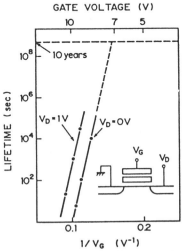

Fig.8 Read retention characteristics. Control gate voltage for 10 year life time is 7.1V.

Paper 4.6

NEW ULTRA-HIGH DENSITY TEXTURED POLY-SI FLOATING GATE EEPROM CELL

D. Guterman, B. Houch, L. Starnes and B. Yeh

Xicor, Inc., Milpitas, California

This paper describes a new, highly scaled cell structure, the smallest full function EEPROM cell reported to date. It utilizes the textured triple-poly-si technology, exploiting the high degrees of structural and functional integration, to achieve a cell size of $31u^2$. A top view of the cell built with 1.2 micron rules is shown in Figure 1, with cell cross-section and equivalent circuit shown in Figures 2 and 3, respectively.

Very small memory cell size is achieved by exploiting the vertical integration of the three poly layers to form a merged gate single transistor cell. This cell is made possible through the dual functions incorporated within various key components; specifically, (1) the poly 3 element, which functions as both word line select transistor and erase tunneling anode (2) the poly 1 electrode which served the dual role of cell ground isolation transistor and programming cathode during write operation, and (3) the poly 2 floating gate transistor whose channel region establishes both the floating gate charge-conditional current path for reading and the input-data conditional steering capacitor for writing. Charge transport to and from the floating gate is through Fowler-Nordheim tunneling, established by the geometrically enhanced fields at the textured poly interfaces between poly-si layers. This allows tunneling injection and transport to occur across oxides of thickness greater than 500Å at voltages less than 15 volts. In comparison to ultrathin (100Å) EEPROM technologies, the thicker interpoly oxides result in lower parasitic capacitance of the tunneling element, improved dielectric reliability because of the 3-5x lower average fields in the oxide, and an easier path to oxide scaling.

Because of the simultaneous incorporation of the poly 2 to 1 programming and poly 3 to 2 erase tunneling elements, data storage is a direct, single pass operation, involving the following sequence (See Table I). First the poly 1 line, common to the entire array, is brought low, cutting off the conduction path from bit line through the cell to array ground. Next, the bit lines are set up to either 0v for an erased state or about 16v for a programmed state. Finally, the poly 3 word line is ramped up to about 22 volts in 1 msec to drive the nonvolatile charge transport. To erase, the bit line is grounded, whereupon the channel under poly 2 capacitively steers the floating gate towards ground. This induces sufficient voltage across the poly 3/2 tunneling element to remove electrons from the floating gate. When the bit line is high for programming, the channel potential steers the floating gate positively. This induces sufficient voltage across the poly 2/1 tunneling element to inject electrons onto the floating gate.

Following up on the present 256K product experience, a number of fundamental factors are incorporated into the technology to maintain a high degree of reliability with scaling. Dielectric integrity and excellent charge retentivity is preserved through the use of thick, high quality thermal SiO_2 dielectrics, throughout. Direct write cell operation provides shorter write time by eliminating the unconditional clear before write. As in previous floating gate EEPROMs, 5-volt-only capability via on-chip voltage multiplication is possible because of the efficient Fowler-Nordheim tunneling mechanism.

Small test arrays of the $31u^2$ cell, shown in the SEM top view of Figure 4, have been built and operated successfully for endurances of 1 million writes. Figure 5 shows a representative extended endurance plot, demonstrating erased state cell currents of greater than 40uA and programmed cells having thresholds of greater than 5v, thereby remaining in cutoff.

In conclusion, this paper reports the smallest full function EEPROM cell described to date. Small size is a result of a cell in which elements serve multiple functions and a technology which is conducive to scaling. This approach will serve as foundation for developing future generation EEPROMs beyond today's 256K density.

Reprinted from the *IEDM Tech. Dig.*, pp. 826-828, 1986.

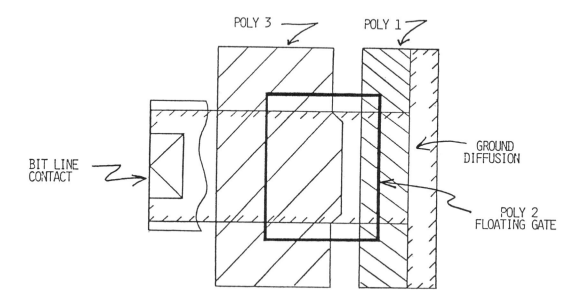

POLY 3

POLY 1

BIT LINE
CONTACT

GROUND
DIFFUSION

POLY 2
FLOATING GATE

FIGURE 1. CELL TOP VIEW

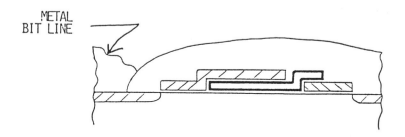

METAL
BIT LINE

FIGURE 2. CELL CROSS-SECTION

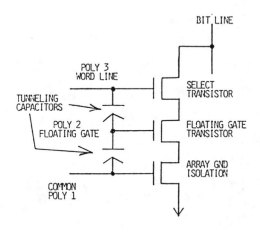

FIGURE 3. CELL EQUIVALENT CIRCUIT

OPERATION	BIT LINE	POLY 2	POLY 3
STANDBY	2v	0	5v
READ	2v	5v	5v
WRITE ERASED STATE	0	~22v	LOW
PROGRAMMED STATE	~16v		

TABLE I. OPERATING CONDITIONS

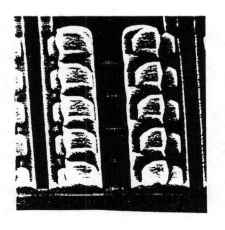

FIGURE 4. SEM TOP VIEW

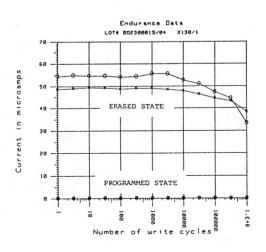

FIGURE 5. ENDURANCE PLOT

148

A 5V-Only EEPROM with Internal Program/Erase Control

Art Lancaster, Bob Johnstone, Jeff Chritz, Gerry Talbot, David Wooten

Inmos Corp.

Colorado Springs, CO

AN 8K X 8 EEPROM with internal high voltage generation for 5-volt-only operation, will be discussed. Double-poly, N-channel silicon gate Nitrox technology has been used to achieve a very small cell area. External interface hardware is eliminated for most applications by an internal program/erase controller. Latched program/erase commands free the system from waiting. Parallel row programming results in a 64 times decrease in programming time, compared to other EEPROMs, and provides single or multiple byte modify capability.

The memory cell is shown in Figure 1a. The cell's operational biases are shown in Figure 1b. The central poly-2 gate, with its nitride-oxide (Nitrox) dielectric, forms the nonvolatile storage region. The poly-1 isolation gate allows the source diffusion to be common to all memory cells in the array. This avoids an extra ground line for every column of memory cells; as required in a previous EEPROM[1]. The result is a cell area of $167\mu^2$ with 3μ design rules. The entire memory array is in a P-well which is isolated from a second P-well in which all peripheral circuitry is built.

Parallel row programming is implemented; 64 bytes can be programmed in one 10ms operation. As shown in Figure 2, the array consists of 128 rows of 64 bytes each. There is a single row (64 bytes) of column latches. These latches store the data used to program a row. These data can be written directly from the data-in pins in random access fashion under control of column addresses AO -A5. This is done in the LOAD-BYTE cycle. During a PROGRAM operation, the data in these column latches are programmed in parallel into all 64 bytes of the row selected by addresses A6 - A12. This results in a 64 times programming time decrease compared to single-byte programming.

The latches can also be used to store in parallel all data in a selected row, before erasure of that row. This is called a LOAD-LATCHES-ROW-ERASE operation. Any combination of the 64 bytes in these latches can then be modified via LOAD-BYTE cycles so as to achieve single byte or multiple byte modify capability, all within a single erase, and single program operation. Another operation called ROW-ERASE is available, which simply erases the selected row without saving contents in the column latches. The entire memory array can also be erased with the FULL-ARRAY-ERASE operation.

Control of the EEPROM is illustrated in the timing diagrams of Figure 3. Timing specifications are listed in Figure 4b. The part is clocked, with addresses $\overline{PE}$ and $\overline{CS}$ latched by $\overline{CE}$. Note that both the $\overline{CE}$ active and inactive times have no maximum

limit. To load bytes into the column latches, the part is written like a clocked RAM. $\overline{WE}$ latches the data to be written.

The minimum LOAD-BYTE cycle time is the same as for a READ cycle. Figure 5 shows a photograph of the output accessing in under 200 ns.

All PROGRAM/ERASE operations are latched and internally controlled, freeing the system to perform other tasks. The internal P/E controller also shown in Figure 2, is a microprogrammed sequencer. Its instructions are routed on a 5b internal bus to the high voltage generator and to the many other timing circuits.

To initiate a program or erase operation, a single 300 ns PE-INITIATE cycle is executed as shown in Figure 3c. One of the four PROGRAM/ERASE operations is selected by the status of column addresses A4 and A5 as shown in Figure 4a. This method of control is possible since only row selection is done during these operations. After the PE-INITIATE cycle, the part internally controls the requested operation. Programming or erasure continues until the user instructs it to stop with the PE-TERMINATE cycle shown in Figure 3d. This approach eliminates the need for a READY/BUSY pin, and the corresponding uncertainty as to when programming will be complete.

The die (6.38 x 5.28mm) is shown in Figure 6. Two redundant row pairs and two redundant column quartets are selectable with electrically blown fuses in the same manner as described earlier[2]. Retention of greater than 10 years with in excess of 10^4 program/erase cycles is extrapolated from measurements. No read disturb effects are observed. The part is packaged in a 28 lead DIP, compatible with the industry standard pin-out.

Acknowledgments

The authors wish to acknowledge the major contributions of T. Anderson, D. Preedy, R. Sokel, J. Adams, and G. Derbenwick, which have been crucial to the success of this project.

[1]Hagiwara, T., Yatsuda, Y., Kondo, R., Minami, S., Aoto, T., and Itoh, Y., *IEEE Journal of Solid State Circuits*, SC-15, p. 346; 1980.

[2]Eaton, S., Wooten, D., Slemmer, W. and Brady, J., *ISSCC DIGEST OF TECHNICAL PAPERS*, p. 84; Feb., 1981.

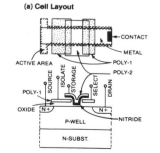

FIGURE 1—Nitrox memory cell.

Reprinted from the *IEEE ISSCC Dig. Tech. Pap.*, pp. 164–165, 302, 1983.

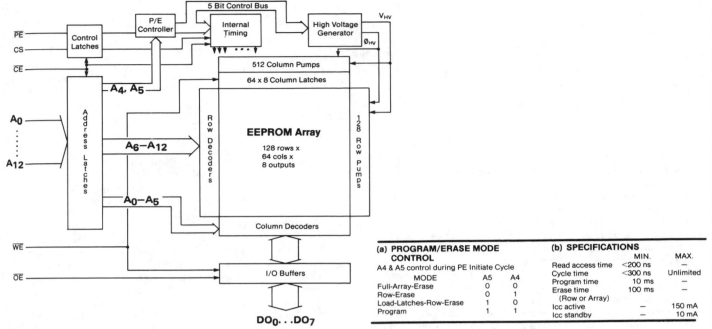

FIGURE 2—Functional block diagram.

(a) PROGRAM/ERASE MODE CONTROL

A4 & A5 control during PE Initiate Cycle

MODE	A5	A4
Full-Array-Erase	0	0
Row-Erase	0	1
Load-Latches-Row-Erase	1	0
Program	1	1

(b) SPECIFICATIONS

	MIN.	MAX.
Read access time	<200 ns	—
Cycle time	<300 ns	Unlimited
Program time	10 ms	—
Erase time	100 ms	—
(Row or Array)		
Icc active	—	150 mA
Icc standby	—	10 mA

FIGURE 4—Program/erase control and specifications.

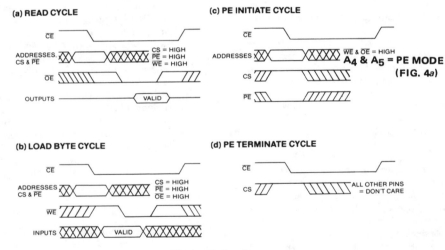

FIGURE 3—Timing diagrams.

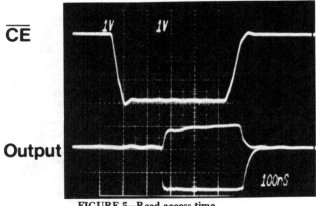

FIGURE 5—Read access time.

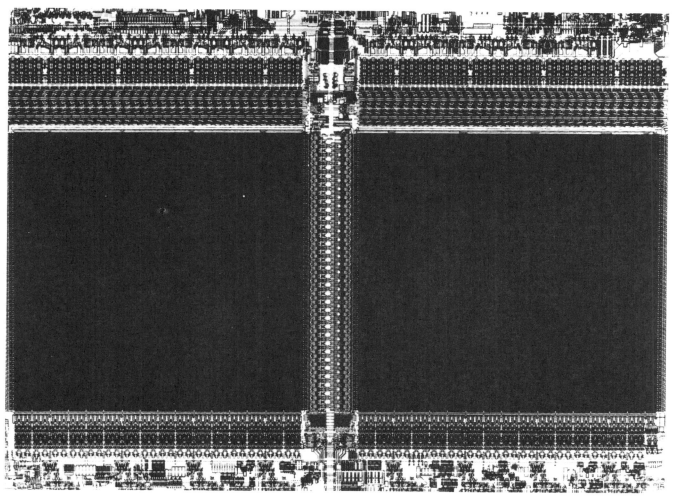

FIGURE 6—Chip photograph of 64K EEPROM.

Hi-MNOS II Technology for a 64-kbit Byte-Erasable 5-V-Only EEPROM

YUJI YATSUDA, SHINJI NABETANI, KEN UCHIDA, SHIN-ICHI MINAMI,
MASAAKI TERASAWA, TAKAAKI HAGIWARA, HISAO KATTO, AND
TOKUMASA YASUI

Abstract —Improved high-performance MNOS (HiMNOS II) technology has been developed for application to a byte-erasable 5-V only 64-kbit EEPROM. A minimum feature size of 2 μm and scaling theory implementation for the MNOS device have led to the realization of a small cell size of 180 μm², a low programming voltage of 16 V, and a high packing density of 64 kbits. The high-voltage structure of the MNOS device, as well as the high-voltage circuit technology, has been developed to eliminate dc programming current in the memory array and the high-voltage switching circuits for the use of on-chip generated programming voltage. This voltage is regulated with an accuracy of ±1 V by using a Zener diode formed in a p-type well. Moreover, in order to accomplish reliable byte erasing, high-voltage switching circuits and their control logic have been carefully designed so as to eliminate the possibility of erroneous writing or erasing due to a timing skew of the high-voltage application to the memory cells. The obtained 64K EEPROM chip shows such superior characteristics as a fast access time of 150 ns, low power dissipation of 55 mA, high-speed write and erase times of less than 1 ms, and high endurance of less than 1-percent failure after 10^4 write/erase cycles.

I. INTRODUCTION

SINCE the advent of the first new-generation 16-kbit electrically erasable programmable ROM [1] compatible with up-to-date high-speed microcomputers, EEPROM's have been the subject of extensive pursuit. The need for EEPROM's has grown rapidly with the expansion in the electronic market in recent years and each system designer has come to require EEPROM's having higher density, more functions, and higher quality.

This paper accordingly describes a higher performance byte-erasable 5-V-only 64K EEPROM of which the basic cell structure and memory array configuration were already presented [2] in 1982. Since that time, other kinds of EEPROM's having such advanced features have been developed [3]–[5].

As things now stand, three kinds of EEPROM's which have different memory cells from each other (MNOS [1]–[3], FLOTOX [5]–[7], and textured poly Si [8]) seem to represent the state of the art on the EEPROM market. MNOS, however, features a simple cell structure which results in small cell size and high reliability [9]. Moreover, even with the FLOTOX type, nitrided oxide thin film is used as a tunnel insulator to obtain better endurance characteristics [5], [7]. From these facts, nitride seems to be superior for use as a film to which a high field is applied, and MNOS seems to be the most suitable device for realization of highly integrated EEPROM's.

The EEPROM described in this paper has been developed using Hi-MNOS II technology, which is the advanced one of *n*-channel Si-gate MNOS technology [1].

This new technology mainly concerns the following.

1) Accommodation of a program voltage supply on-chip. This requires elimination of dc programming current. The high-voltage switching circuit and the memory cell, where a large quantity of current flow in the conventional 16K EEPROM [1], should be improved. Although a high-voltage switching circuit which operates without flowing dc current was already introduced by Gupta *et al.* [7], it will be shown in this paper that the circuit should be more carefully designed, especially when the "well" is used. A conventional fully self-aligned MNOS memory device [1] has a lower drain breakdown voltage than a program voltage. It causes quantities of current flow. Therefore, a new high-voltage structure should be developed.

2) Byte-mode erasure. Two approaches of memory array configuration will be possible for a byte-mode erasure in an MNOS-type EEPROM. One is the page-mode-based approach [3] and the other is the byte-mode-based approach, which will be shown in this paper. The page-mode features a fast load time in programming, but has a drawback in that it reduces the number of effective write/erase cycles per byte compared with the byte-mode. The byte-mode approach can be extended to the page-mode operation.

The programming voltage also has to be applied to the substrate or well in MNOS-type EEPROM's [1]–[3]. This makes their programming operations more complex than those in other types of EEPROM's. Therefore, it should be carefully designed to eliminate the possibility of erroneous writing or erasing due to a timing skew as well as a latchup phenomenon.

Manuscript received July 2, 1984; revised September 27, 1984.
Y. Yatsuda, S.-I. Minami, and T. Hagiwara are with the Central Research Laboratory, Hitachi Ltd., Kokubunji, Tokyo 185, Japan.
S. Nabetani, K. Uchida, H. Katto, and T. Yasui are with the Musashi Works, Hitachi Ltd., Kodaira, Tokyo 187, Japan.
M. Terasawa is with the Hitachi Microcomputer Engineering Ltd., Kodaira 187, Japan.

II. MEMORY CELL

The memory cell of the 64-kbit EEPROM consists of two transistors. An MNOS memory transistor and a select

Reprinted from *IEEE J. Solid-State Circuits*, vol. SC-20, no. 1, pp. 144–151, February 1985.

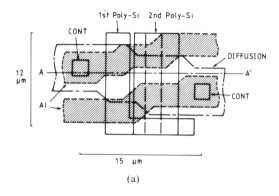

(a)

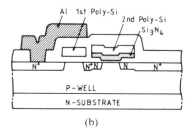

(b)

Fig. 1. Memory cell (a) layout pattern and (b) cross section for 64-kbit EEPROM.

transistor are connected in series. The layout pattern and cross section of the memory cell are shown in Fig. 1. This configuration is the same as for the 16-kbit EEPROM [1]. The new cell features reduced dimensions and a new high-voltage structure. Using a 2-μm process technology which takes advantage of stepper lithography and dry etching, the cell size is reduced to less than 50 percent (180 μm^2) of that for the old cell which employed a 3-μm process [1]. The MOS transistor was scaled down, based on the usual scaling theory, and the MNOS memory transistor was designed based on the principle [10]

$$T_n \propto V_p \propto T_{ox} \tag{1}$$

$$t_e \propto \exp(T_{uto}/\lambda_{ox}). \tag{2}$$

Here, T_n is the nitride thickness, T_{ox} the oxide thickness of the MOS transistor, T_{uto} the thickness of ultrathin oxide (UTO), V_p the programming voltage, t_e the erasing time, and λ_{ox} the de Broglie constant of oxide.

As can be seen in these equations, the programming voltage is reduced by decreasing the nitride thickness, and the erasing time is shortened by decreasing the UTO thickness. $T_n = 30$ nm, $T_{uto} = 1.7$ nm, and $V_p = 16$ V were used in this 64K EEPROM, while in the 16K EEPROM $T_n = 50$ nm, $T_{uto} = 2.1$ nm, and $V_p = 25$ V had been used. Consequently, high-speed erasing (typically less than 1 ms) was realized as shown in Section IV.

The use of an on-chip program voltage supply requires elimination of dc program current because it cannot provide large current. However, in a conventional memory cell where the MNOS memory transistor has a fully self-aligned structure, large program current flows, because the drain breakdown voltage with the gate kept grounded is lower than the program voltage (see Fig. 2). To get the break-

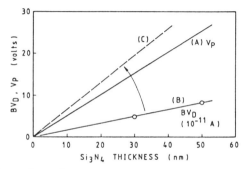

Fig. 2. Comparison of program voltage with drain breakdown voltage, showing both as function of Si$_3$N$_4$ thickness. Curve (*a*) shows program voltage, curve (*b*) shows drain breakdown voltage for conventional self-aligned MNOS device, and curve (*c*) is a target for high-voltage-structure MNOS device.

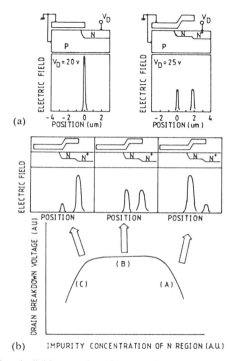

Fig. 3. Electric-field strength under gate electrode. (a) Comparison between conventional MNOS device and high-voltage-structure MNOS device. (b) Drain breakdown voltage versus impurity concentration of n-region, in conjunction with electric-field strength.

down voltage up to where it was larger than the program voltage (curve *C* in Fig. 2), a new high-voltage structure was developed. As shown in Fig. 1, this structure features n–n$^+$ offset drain (source) structure and a thick oxide layer of about 40 nm between the n-layer and the gate. This results in a reduction of the maximum surface electric-field strength through separation of the electric-field concentration into two regions under the gate electrode edge and at the n-layer edge, as shown in Fig. 3(a). This result was obtained using the device simulator "CADDET" [11].

In this high-voltage-structure MNOS, when the impurity concentration of the n-region increases, the field at the n-region edge increases and it results in the low drain breakdown voltage (see (A) in Fig. 3(b)). On the other hand, when the concentration decreases, the field under the

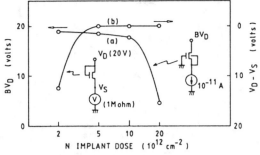

Fig. 4. n-implant dose dependence of (a) breakdown voltage, and (b) voltage drop through MNOS device.

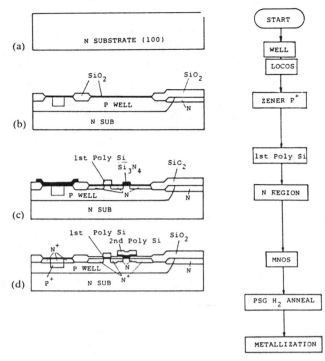

Fig. 5. Fabrication steps for 64-kbit EEPROM.

gate electrode edge increases and it also results in the low drain breakdown voltage (see (C)). Therefore, it is obvious that an optimal concentration for the n-region exists. Moreover, as another factor in deciding the n-region's impurity concentration, the voltage drop through the region should be considered. Fig. 4 shows these two relations in curve a between the breakdown voltage and the n-region's implant dose, and in curve b between the voltage drop through the MNOS transistor and n-region's implant dose. From these results in Fig. 4, the optimal n-region dose was decided to be from 3×10^{12} cm^{-2} to 1×10^{13} cm^{-2}.

III. FABRICATION PROCESS

The Hi-MNOS II fabrication process features

1) effective use of Si$_3$N$_4$ at a lot of process steps,
2) formation of a Zener diode in a p-type well,
3) formation of a high-voltage-structure MNOS memory device,
4) high-temperature H$_2$ annealing, and
5) 2-μm fine-pattern processing.

The key steps for an MNOS memory device are as follows. 1) UTO is formed at 850 °C by using a diluted oxygen ambient (O$_2$/N$_2$ = 10^{-3}). 2) Si$_3$N$_4$ is deposited at about 750 °C under low pressure using mixed SiH$_2$Cl$_2$ and NH$_3$ gases. 3) High-temperature H$_2$ annealing is performed at 900 °C after the PSG deposition.

The main process steps for the 64-kbit EEPROM are shown in Fig. 5. The starting wafer is n-type (100). After the well and LOCOS process steps, a p$^+$ region for a Zener diode is formed. Then, the MOS gates are prepared by patterning the first-level poly-Si layer. Next, n-regions are formed by implanting phosphorus ions using Si$_3$N$_4$ film as a mask for the channel region of the MNOS memory device during implantation and oxidation.

After removing the Si$_3$N$_4$ film, UTO, Si$_3$N$_4$, and the second-level poly-Si layers are successively formed and patterned to make the MNOS gates. Then, the n$^+$ layer is formed through implementation of self-aligned phosphorus ion implantation. Finally, the high-temperature H$_2$ annealing and metallization process are executed.

IV. BASIC FEATURES OF THE MEMORY DEVICE

This section provides a look at the characteristics of the new discrete high-voltage-structure MNOS device used in the 64K chip. Write and erase characteristics are shown in Fig. 6. Typical write and erase times are about 10 and 200 μs, respectively, with applied voltage of 15 V. They can be defined as the times necessary to shift the threshold voltage from the extreme to the reference level. The erase time is about 1.5 orders shorter than that for the conventional 16K EEPROM MNOS device. The erase mechanism involves direct tunneling. Thus as was shown in Section II and [10], it was possible to obtain a shorter erase time through decreasing the UTO thickness. On the other hand, the write time is almost the same as for the 16K device. As the write mechanism is modified Fowler–Nordheim tunneling, the write time scarcely depends upon the UTO thickness [10].

Retention characteristics at 125 °C for the two memory devices with 1.6- and 2.1-nm-thick UTO's are shown in Fig. 7. As can be seen in the figure, a thinner UTO film does not cause any deterioration in memory retention. Consequently, it was possible to confirm ten-year nonvolatility at 125 °C.

Fig. 8 shows a comparison of the Si$_3$N$_4$ thickness margin between conventional and scaled-down (Hi-MNOS II) MNOS devices. Taken into consideration here are retention characteristics and the electric field of the Si$_3$N$_4$ film. When programming voltage increases, retention time becomes longer because the threshold voltage window for write and erase characteristics becomes larger, but failure rate also increases because the electric field in the Si$_3$N$_4$ film becomes stronger. It can be seen from this result that

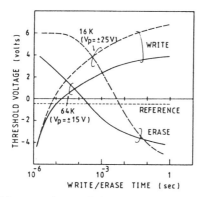

Fig. 6. Write-erase characteristics for MNOS memory devices.

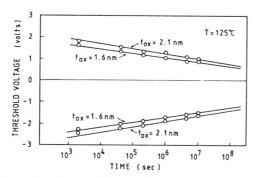

Fig. 7. Retention characteristics for high-voltage-structure MNOS devices having 1.6- and 2.1-nm-thick UTO films.

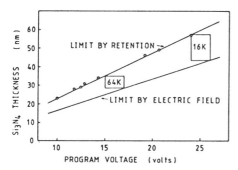

Fig. 8. Comparison of Si_3N_4 thickness margin between conventional and the scaled-down MNOS devices.

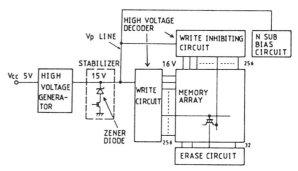

Fig. 9. High-voltage system and memory array for 64K EEPROM.

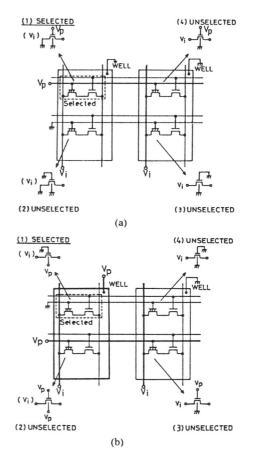

Fig. 10. Bias conditions for (a) byte writing and (b) byte erasing.

the Si_3N_4 thickness should be more precisely controlled in the Hi-MNOS II process. The low-pressure CVD technique is responsible for this requirement because its controllability for Si_3N_4 film thickness is much better than that of the atmospheric pressure CVD.

V. DESIGN OF THE 64K EEPROM

A. General Description

The memory organization is 8192 words × 8 bits. Cells are placed to form a 256 × 256 matrix. This 64K device is fully pin-compatible with EPROM's, except that pin 1 is not connected because the programming voltage is gener-

ated on-chip. In addition, pin 22, called the $\overline{OE}$ pin, is also used for selection of the erase mode by byte or chip.

B. Memory Array Configuration

A memory cell array is formed in 32 wells and each well consists of 8×256 memory cells. Eight bits are placed in the direction of the word line in each well correspond to one byte, or eight sense amplifiers and eight input/output buffers. This array configuration differs from that for the 16K EEPROM where byte erase was not available [1].

The whole high-voltage system and the memory cell array in the 64K chip are shown in Fig. 9. An external 5V (V_{cc}) is supplied to the chip and boosted at a high-voltage

155

generator. This high voltage is regulated at 15 V using the stabilizer of a Zener diode and provided to the high-voltage switching circuits. This voltage is boosted to about 16 V in these switching circuits and applied to the memory devices.

Byte-mode writing and write inhibiting are accomplished, as shown in Fig. 10(a). This is the same way as in the 16K device, except that the programming voltage is reduced and generated on-chip.

In the byte-mode erasing shown in Fig. 10(b), a selected high-voltage row line is grounded, and the generated high voltage is applied to unselected row lines and a selected well. In the three states, (2), (3), and (4) in the figure, the following reliability measures were necessary.

State (2): This is the erase-inhibit state. Instantaneous erasing or writing can occur if the order of high-voltage application is in error. In order to avoid this, the erase operation is started in the order n-substrate bias circuit, write inhibiting circuit, write circuit, and then erase circuit. The operation is terminated according to the opposite order.

State (3): In this write-inhibiting state, $V_p - V_i$ (programming voltage − write inhibiting voltage) is applied between the gate and the channel. Therefore, the voltage levels of V_p and V_i should be carefully chosen. When all the bits except any single particular byte are erased by repeated byte erasures, the total time (t_{pi}) during which this particular bit is in the inhibit state ($V_p - V_i$ is applied) can be very great. As the memory array consists of 32 wells, and each well has 256 bytes of memory cells, and if 10^4 rewrites are guaranteed, t_{pi} can be expressed as follows:

$$t_{pi} = 31 \times 255 \times 10^4 \times t_e \qquad (3)$$

where t_e is the erase time for 1 byte. In the 64K EEPROM, $t_e = 10$ ms and t_{pi} is approximately nine days, which is long compared to the 50 min in the 16K EEPROM. Such a long application of $V_p - V_i$ between the gate and the channel causes a reliability problem if $V_p > V_i$. Therefore, $V_p = V_i$ is used here.

State (4): Here, the problem is the breakdown voltage for the n^+-p junction under the gate electrode kept grounded. This bias situation arises in more memory cells for the write mode than for the erase mode (see Fig. 10). The total leakage current in the memory array should then be less than the output current for the on-chip high voltage generator, such that

$$I_l \times 255 \times 31 \times 8 \leqslant I_{out}. \qquad (4)$$

Here, I_l is the leakage current per memory device, and I_{out} is the output current for the generator. I_{out} is determined by the frequency of clock pulse and the capacitance which are used in the high-voltage generator. In order that the generator circuit should occupy a small area, I_{out} should be designed to be less than about 10 μA.

In order to be satisfied with (4) with a sufficient margin, the total leakage current was designed to be less than 1 μA, or I_l should be less than 1.58×10^{-11} A. Therefore, the breakdown voltage BV_d is defined as the voltage applied to

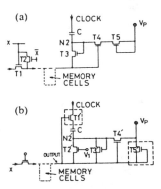

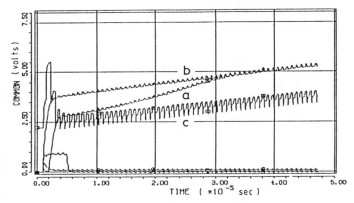

Fig. 11. High-voltage switching circuits. (a) Basic circuit which operates without flowing dc current, and (b) improved high-reliability, high-voltage switching circuit.

Fig. 12. Computer-simulated timing of high-voltage application. (a) High-voltage word line, (b) write-inhibit line, and (c) V_p line.

the drain when I_l is 10 pA, (see Figs. 2 and 4). It has been ensured that BV_d is more than V_p in the newly developed high-voltage structure using this definition.

C. High-Voltage Generation and Switching

Two major issues in using an internally generated program voltage are 1) achieving a voltage multiplier circuit using stabilization with a small fluctuation, and 2) realizing a high-voltage switching circuit through which no current flows.

An on-chip multiplier circuit was first reported by Dickson [12]. In the present 64K EEPROM chip, a similar circuit with a Zener diode for voltage stabilization has been used. The characteristic fluctuation due to voltage stress for the Zener diode is small compared with the use of source–drain breakdown voltage BV_{DS} for an MOS transistor. In addition, the temperature coefficient of the breakdown voltage for the Zener diode is approximately 13 mV/°C, which is sufficiently small for reliable voltage stabilization.

The basic configuration for the high-voltage switching circuit conventionally used in the 16K device is an E/D inverter, through which a large current flows. A basic high-voltage switching circuit which can do the decoding without causing a flow of current has been reported by

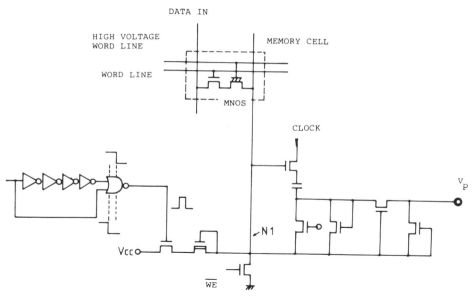

Fig. 13. Write-inhibiting circuit.

Gupta *et al.* [7] (Fig. 11(a)). This circuit, however, has the following drawbacks preventing its use for our 64K EEPROM.

1) When the high-voltage output is 0 V, node N2 swings negative. Since wells are used for substrate isolation in this EEPROM with the MNOS device, the negative swing causes various problems, including a latchup.

2) Each word line and data line needs to have a Zener diode for voltage stabilization. This is difficult from the occupied area point of view.

In order to overcome these drawbacks, the circuit shown in Fig. 11(b) was developed. A feature of this circuit is that issue 1) is solved by addition of $T1'$. In other words, when the high-voltage output is 0 V, this $T1'$ comes off and prevents $N2'$ from going negative. Also, issue 2) is solved by adding $T5'$. When the high-voltage output is $V_p + V_{th}$, $T5'$ comes on, preventing a further increase of voltage.

To increase the current supply capability of this switching circuit, a sufficiently large capacitor is used. As a result, the high voltage applied to each part of each memory device in the memory array increases in approximately the same way and at the same speed as the rise speed for the output voltage of the multiplier circuit. This eliminates the possibility of erroneous writing or erasing due to a timing skew during high-voltage application. Computer simulation results are shown in Fig. 12. This figure shows the rising behavior for high voltage applied to the gate (high-voltage word line) and source (write-inhibit line or data line) of the MNOS device in an unselected byte when one byte is in the write state, which is supposedly the worst condition. In the figure, the slight voltage difference at the onset is due to the fact that since the V_p output line is usually held at V_{cc} (around 2 V is assumed in the calculation), write voltage is applied to the memory cell array at the onset with the timing described in Section V. This timing is such that erroneous writing or erasing will be prevented, and therefore there will be no reliability problem.

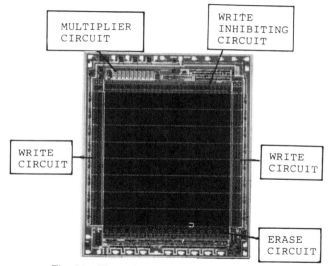

Fig. 14. Photomicrograph of 64-kbit EEPROM.

Fig. 13 shows the write-inhibiting circuit. In the other high-voltage switching circuits, the output nodes of the circuits are charged to about 5 V at the beginning, when the high voltage should be output. In this write-inhibiting circuit, however, the output node $N1$ is opened when any memory cell belonging to it is not selected. In order to charge this node to about 5 V at the beginning of the operation of the write-inhibiting circuit, a short pulse is applied to the gate of the switching transistor, which is placed between V_{cc} and node $N1$.

VI. CHARACTERISTICS OF THE 64-kbit EEPROM

A chip photomicrograph for the 64K EEPROM is shown in Fig. 14. The multiplier circuit is placed in the top left corner of the chip, the write-inhibiting circuit is under the multiplier circuit, the write circuit on both sides of the memory array, and the erase circuit at the bottom. This

TABLE I
CHARACTERISTICS OF 64-kbit EEPROM

Configuration	8K words X 8 bits
Cell area	180 μm^2
Chip area	5 X 6.3 mm^2
Supply voltage	5 V
Access time	200 ns
Current dissipation(operation)	55 mA
(standby)	20 mA
Write/erase voltage	16 V (internal)
Write/erase time	10 ms
Erase mode	byte / chip
Retention	10 years (85 °C)
Endurance	10000 times

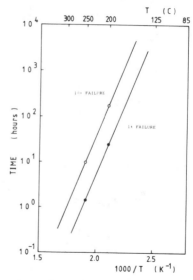

Fig. 16. Dependence of retention time on temperature for 64K chip.

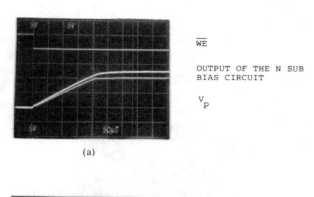

(a)

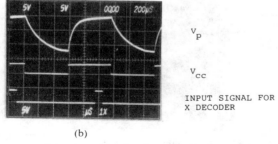

(b)

$\overline{WE}$

OUTPUT OF THE N SUB
BIAS CIRCUIT

V_p

V_p

V_{cc}

INPUT SIGNAL FOR
X DECODER

Fig. 15. (a) Output waveforms of voltage multiplier and n-substrate bias circuit, and (b) output waveform of voltage multiplier when signal input for X decoder is varied.

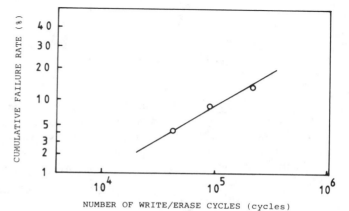

NUMBER OF WRITE/ERASE CYCLES (cycles)

Fig. 17. Endurance characteristics of 64K chip.

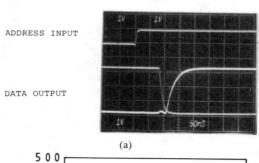

ADDRESS INPUT

DATA OUTPUT

(a)

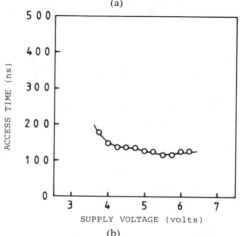

(b)

Fig. 18. (a) Single-bit address access waveforms for room temperature at $V_{cc} = 5$ V, and (b) dependence of address access time on supply voltage.

voltage is then applied to the memory array. Characteristics of this device are summarized in Table I.

Illustrated in Fig. 15(a) is behavior whereby the output of the multiplier circuit increases to roughly 15 V with a setting of the program mode, and where the output of the substance bias circuit increases more rapidly and to a larger value. Fig. 15(b) shows that the output of the multiplier circuit does not change at all when the signal input to the address buffer for X decoder switching is varied. The obtained minimum write time is about 0.2 ms, and minimum erase time is about 0.4 ms. Thus, it was confirmed that there is no problem in on-chip high-voltage generation (around 15 V) and switching, and in write and erase operation.

The retention characteristics of the 64K chip are shown in Fig. 16. As was expected from measurements of the discrete MNOS device, a ten-year nonvolatility at 85 °C could be confirmed with a sufficient margin. Endurance characteristics are shown in Fig. 17. Endurance goes beyond 10^4 write/erase cycles per byte with less than a 1-percent failure. Finally, read characteristics for the 64K chip are shown in Fig. 18. A disadvantage of the memory array configuration mentioned in Section V is the increase in parasitic capacitance of the common data line., However, in order to ensure high-speed sensing of the small signal there, a differential amplifier is used. Therefore, as can be seen from these data, a typical access time of about 150 ns has been obtained.

VII. CONCLUSION

Advanced n-channel Si-gate MNOS (Hi-MNOS II) technology for process, device, and circuit has been developed to realize a highly reliable byte-erasable 5-V-only 64K EEPROM. Both 2-μm fine-pattern processing and scaling of the MOS and MNOS devices have reduced memory cell size to 180 μm^2 (about half the size of the conventional cell) and chip size to 5×6.3 mm^2.

A high-voltage-structure MNOS memory device, a highly reliable high-voltage switching circuit, and a high-voltage stabilizer of a Zener diode have realized the 5-V-only operation. To ensure highly reliable execution of byte-erase operations, the values of the write voltage and write-inhibiting voltage were made equal, and timing was set for each high-voltage switching circuit as the operation is started in the order of n-substrate bias circuit, write-inhibiting circuit, write circuit, and erase circuit.

Test results for the 64K EEPROM have shown a fast access time of 150 ns, first write/erase time of less than 1 ms, good endurance going beyond 10^4 write/erase cycles, and 10-year data retention at 85 °C.

ACKNOWLEDGMENT

The authors wish to thank Dr. M. Kubo, Dr. S. Yoneyama, Dr. S. Asai, and Dr. T. Makimoto for their constant encouragement during this work, as well as Dr. M. Shiota for his device fabrication efforts. They also appreciate the support of N. Satoh, K. Ujiie, and A. Furuno at the Musashi Works.

REFERENCES

[1] T. Hagiwara, R. Kondo, Y. Yatsuda, S. Minami, Y. Itoh, and K. Uchiumi, "A 16Kb electrically erasable programmable ROM," in *ISSCC Dig. Tech. Papers*, pp. 50–51, 1979.
[2] Y. Yatsuda, S. Minami, T. Hagiwara, T. Toyabe, S. Asai, and K. Uchida, "An advanced MNOS memory device for highly-integrated byte-erasable 5V-only EEPROM's," in *IEDM Tech. Dig.*, pp. 733–736, Dec. 1982.
[3] A. Lancaster, B. Johnstone, J. Chritz, G. Talbot, and D. Wooten, "A 5V-Only EEPROM with Internal Program/Erase Control," in *ISSCC Dig. Tech. Papers*, pp. 164–165, Feb. 1983.
[4] D. D. Donaldson, E. H. Honnigford, and L. J. Toth, "+5V-Only 32K EEPROM," in *ISSCC Dig. Tech. Papers*, pp. 168–169, Feb. 1983.
[5] S. Mehrotra, T. C. Wu, T. L. Chiu, and G. Perlegos, "A 64Kb CMOS EEROM with on-chip ECC," in *ISSCC Dig. Tech. Papers*, pp. 142–143, Feb. 1984.
[6] W. S. Johnson, G. Perlegos, A. Renninger, G. Huhn, and T. R. Ranganath, "A 16Kb electrically erasable nonvolatile memory," in *ISSCC Dig. Tech. Papers*, pp. 152–153, Feb. 1980.
[7] A. Gupta, T. Chiu, M. Chang, A. Renninger, and G. Perlegos, "A 5V-only 16K EEPROM utilizing Oxynitride Dielectrics and EPROM Redundancy," in *ISSCC Dig. Tech. Papers*, pp. 184–185, Feb. 1982.
[8] G. Landers, "5-volt-only EEPROM mimics static-RAM timing," *Electronics*, pp. 127–130, June 1982.
[9] K. Uchiumi, H. Wakimoto, S. Nabetani, and T. Hagiwara, presented at Electro 82, Professional Program Session, Record Session no. 30, Boston, MA, 1982.
[10] Y. Yatsuda, T. Hagiwara, S. Minami, R. Kondo, K. Uchida, and K. Uchiumi, "Scaling down MNOS nonvolatile memory devices," *Japan J. Appl. Phys.*, vol. 21, Suppl. 21-1, pp. 85–90, 1982.
[11] T. Toyabe, K. Yamaguchi, S. Asai, and M. S. Mock, "A numerical model of avalanche breakdown in MOSFET's," *IEEE Trans. Electron Devices*, vol. ED-25, pp. 825–832, July 1978.
[12] J. F. Dickson, "On-chip high-voltage generation in MNOS integrated circuits using an improved voltage multiplier technique," *IEEE J. Solid-State Circuits*, vol. SC-11, pp. 374–378, June 1976.

Hole and Electron Current Transport in Metal-Oxide–Nitride-Oxide–Silicon Memory Structures

EIICHI SUZUKI, KATSUHIRO MIURA, YUTAKA HAYASI, MEMBER, IEEE, RE-PENG TSAY, AND DIETER K. SCHRODER, FELLOW, IEEE

Abstract—The carrier transport properties in metal–oxide (top oxide)–nitride-oxide (tunnel oxide)–silicon (MONOS) memory structures have been investigated in steady-state conditions under negative gate bias voltage by separating carriers into holes and electrons utilizing an induced junction of the p-channel MONOS transistors. Two-carrier transport is confirmed in the structure at negative gate polarity. It is found that the relatively thick top oxide acts as a potential barrier to the holes injected from the Si into the thin nitride. In addition, it is found that a portion of the electrons injected from the gate at negative gate polarity recombine with the holes injected from the Si even in such a thin nitride and/or at the top-oxide-nitride interface.

I. INTRODUCTION

NONVOLATILE semiconductor memories, especially electrically erasable and programmable read-only memories (EEPROM's), are expected to become very important devices in VLSI's for flexible use of highly integrated circuits [1]. If EEPROM's could be embedded in VLSI's, one could change or determine the performance of VLSI's by programming the EEPROM's. From this point of view, it is strongly necessary to realize EE-PROM's with low program voltage and high endurance. The former requirement is essential for VLSI's composed of small-sized MOS devices with thin gate silicon oxides, and, therefore, low WRITE and ERASE (W/E) voltage will be desirable for the embedded EEPROM's. The latter is a common technological target for EEPROM's. For these demands, some novel memory structures have been proposed [2]–[7].

Among them, the thin oxide–nitride-oxide multiple-gate insulator layer is of high technological interest [8], [9]. It is quite difficult for conventional MNOS memory structures to reduce the nitride thickness to less than about 200 Å, which results in a limitation for the reduction of the program voltage [10]. However, a thin oxide (top oxide) layer on a chemically vapor deposited nitride is expected

to act as a potential barrier to carriers injected into the nitride and consequently is useful for the realization of low program voltages by reducing the nitride thickness in metal–oxide(top oxide)–thin-nitride-oxide(tunnel oxide)–silicon structures. A very low program voltage of 6 V has been already demonstrated in early MONOS memory transistors [9]. In addition, generation of a large number of electron traps predominantly at the top-oxide–nitride interface acting as memory sites have been found by the authors [11], [12]. However, the understanding of the behavior of the top oxide and of carrier transport in such thin MONOS structures is insufficient.

In this paper, we describe carrier transport properties in the MONOS structures measured by the induced junction technique, i.e., the measurement method of a separation of hole and electron flow utilizing an induced junction formed between the inversion layer and the substrate in an MOS-type field-effect transistor structure [13], [14]. For the p-channel MONOS memory transistors, we show the dependence of the carrier transport on the thickness difference of the thin nitride and the top oxide, and discuss the electron and hole transport in the MONOS structures.

II. EXPERIMENTAL PROCEDURES

The test devices were p-channel MONOS memory transistors listed in Table I. The MNOS memory transistors were also fabricated as reference devices. Substrates were phosphorous-doped n-type (100) oriented CZ Si wafers with a resistivity of 2–5 Ω-cm. The tunnel oxide was thermally grown at 900°C by an O_2/N_2 partial-pressure method using mass-flow controllers. A control device was also grown at the same time to confirm the tunnel-oxide thickness. A thin nitride of 50–70 Å was deposited at 700°C with an ammonia : silane ratio of 1400 : 1 in a hot-wall reactor by the conventional atmospheric pressure CVD method in N_2. The thicknesses of the deposited thin nitride and the thermally grown tunnel oxide were measured by ellipsometry. The Si wafers were then thermally oxidized in a steam atmosphere at 900°C for 2–4 h by pyrogenic oxidation to grow a top oxide on the deposited thin nitride. The pyrogenic oxidation rate of the nitride was about 1/10 of the dry oxidation rate of the Si. The actual thickness of the thin nitride after the oxidation was estimated by chemically etching the top oxide on the thin

Manuscript received August 6, 1988; revised January 14, 1989. The review of this paper was arranged by Associate Editor P. K. Ko.

E. Suzuki and Y. Hayashi are with the Electrotechnical Laboratory, 1-1-4, Umezono, Tsukuba-shi, Ibaraki 305, Japan.

K. Miura is on leave with the Electrotechnical Laboratory, 1-1-4, Umezono, Tsukuba-shi, Ibaraki 305, Japan. He is with Nihon University, Funabashi, Chiba, Japan.

R.-P. Tsay was with the Center for Solid State Electronics Research, Arizona State University, Tempe, AZ 85287. He is now with EG&G Reticon Inc., San Jose, CA.

D. K. Schroder is with the Center for Solid State Electronics Research, Arizona State University, Tempe, AZ 85287.

IEEE Log Number 8927653.

Reprinted from *IEEE Trans. Electron Devices*, vol. 36, no. 6, pp. 1145–1149, June 1989.

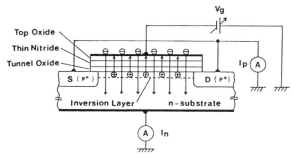

Fig. 1. Schematic drawing of the induced junction technique used in the hole and electron separation measurements of the MONOS structures.

TABLE I
THE p-CHANNEL MONOS MEMORY TRANSISTORS USED IN THE EXPERIMENTS

Sample	Tunnel–Oxide (A)	Nitride (A)	Top–Oxide (A)
A1	23.3	32	34
A2	21.9	30	33
A3	21.9	28	50
A5	21.9	49	48
A6	21.9	48	32
A7	23.3	51	33

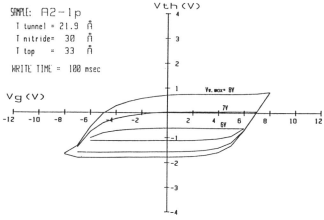

Fig. 2. Typical memory hysteresis loops of the p-channel MONOS memory transistor A2.

nitride, measuring by ellipsometry, and analyzing with a two-layer model. The thickness of the top oxide was estimated by repeated C-V measurements before and after chemical etching of the top oxide on the thin nitride by assuming that the dielectric constants of the top oxide and the thin nitride are equal to those of a bulk oxide and nitride. The volume ratio of the top oxide and nitride was 1.6, which is in good agreement with the value reported in the literature [15]. After that, H_2 annealing was performed at 400°C for 30 min to reduce the Si–SiO_2 interface state density. Finally, evaporated Al contacts completed the MONOS memory transistors. The length and width of the p-channel MONOS transistors are 6 and 64 μm, respectively.

The steady-state carrier transport in the MONOS structures was measured using the induced junction method [13] as shown in Fig. 1. In the case of a p-channel field-effect transistor, a negative gate voltage is applied to form a field-induced junction between the inversion layer and the substrate immediately underneath the gate insulator layer, similar to the shallow p-n junction structure [16], [17]. The positive hole current I_p injected from the inversion layer into the multiple insulator layer is measured through the source and drain, which are connected together. Electrons are injected from the gate, transported in the multiple insulator layer, and occasionally recombine with holes. The electron current I_n, which reaches at the Si–SiO_2 interface, flows to the substrate through the extremely thin inversion layer and the thin depletion layer and is measured as a substrate current. Recombination of electrons with holes at the Si surface region is negligible, since the diffusion length of electrons in the p-type region (the inversion layer in this case) is much larger than the inversion layer thickness, and also the surface electric field accelerates the electrons toward the substrate. There-

fore, we can easily distinguish between the hole current and the electron current through the induced junction. This induced junction method has been utilized for carrier separation experiments with an MNOS memory structure [13], [14] and a dual electron injector structure [18], [19].

To measure the steady-state current–voltage characteristics, a prescribed maximum negative gate bias voltage was applied for 5 min at first, and then the amplitude of the gate bias voltage was gradually reduced until the currents fell into the 10^{-13} A range. After each gate voltage change, the currents were measured for 2 min, which was sufficiently long to ensure steady-state conditions. Keithley 410A picoammeters were used for the current measurement. The measurement accuracy of the currents was about 0.2 pA. To compare the hole and electron current at the same contact electric field at the Si–SiO_2 interface, the gate threshold voltage $V_{th}(V_g)$ of the memory transistors at each gate voltage V_g were also measured under the same gate bias voltage conditions as in the current measurements with a method similar to that described in the literature [20]. $V_{th}(V_g)$ was measured within 15 ms after finishing each gate voltage application. All the measurements were performed at room temperature.

Typical memory hysteresis loops of one of the p-channel MONOS transistors are shown in Fig. 2. This figure shows that 6-V WRITE/ERASE operation is possible. The relatively long 100-ms WRITE time is due to the thick tunnel oxide of 22 Å. It is easy to reduce the WRITE time by optimizing the tunnel-oxide thickness. For higher or longer WRITE gate pulses, the memory hysteresis window extends further, mainly in the positive gate voltage direction.

III. EXPERIMENTAL RESULTS AND DISCUSSION

A. Gate Threshold Voltage for Negative Gate Bias

Fig. 3 shows typical experimental results of the gate threshold voltage $V_{th}(V_g)$ of sample A2 after application of each gate voltage V_g for 2 min. Some holes injected from the Si are captured at the trapping sites in the thin nitride and/or at the top-oxide–nitride interface, and con-

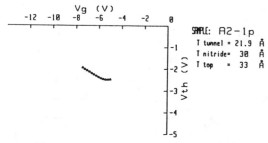

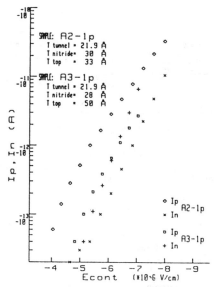

Fig. 3. Typical experimental results of the gate threshold voltage of sample *A*2. The gate bias voltage conditions are the same in the current-voltage measurements as described in the text.

Fig. 4. Hole and electron currents of samples *A*2 and *A*3 with different top-oxide thicknesses as a function of the contact electric field E_{cont} in the tunnel oxide. The thicknesses of the thin nitride and tunnel oxide are 28–30 and 22 Å, respectively.

sequently the threshold voltage shifts in the negative voltage direction. This is apparent also from Fig. 2. Fig. 3 indicates, however, that the negative threshold voltage reverses toward the positive direction at strong negative gate voltages of around -6 V. This phenomenon is associated with either recombination of some trapped holes at the top-oxide–nitride interface and/or that in the thin nitride with electrons injected from the gate into the multiple insulator layer, or by discharging of trapped holes to the gate at high electric fields. From the viewpoint of the memory action, this reversal of the threshold voltage shown in Fig. 3 is not desirable, and excess negative WRITE voltages should be avoided for this device.

This kind of threshold voltage reversal is not observed for positive gate voltages where the threshold voltage increases with increasing positive gate bias slowly and monotonically. This means that the injection of the opposite type of carriers, i.e., holes from the gate, is restricted by the top oxide under positive gate bias. This behavior is quite important for effective WRITE operation at positive gate voltages and for reduced degradation of the MONOS memory structure [9].

B. Dependence of the Hole and Electron Current on Top-Oxide Thickness

The hole current injected from the Si into the thin nitride is considered to be mainly governed by the contact electric field in the tunnel oxide. The contact electric field E_{cont} for an applied gate voltage V_g is given by

$$E_{\text{cont}} = \left(V_g - V_{th}(V_g) \right)/t_{eq} + 4qN_D\phi_F\epsilon_s/\epsilon_{ox} \quad (1)$$

where

$$t_{eq} = t_{\text{tunnel}} + (\epsilon_{ox}/\epsilon_N) * t_N + t_{\text{top}}. \quad (2)$$

t_{tunnel}, t_N, and t_{top} are the thicknesses of the tunnel oxide, nitride, and top oxide, respectively, ϵ_s, ϵ_{ox}, ϵ_N are permittivities of the Si, oxide, and nitride, respectively, ϕ_F is the Fermi level of the Si measured from the intrinsic energy level, and $V_{th}(V_g)$ is the variable threshold voltage including the effect of trapped charge in the multiple insulator layer as a function of V_g. The other variables have their usual meanings. We use the values of $3.8\epsilon_0$ and $7.6\epsilon_0$ for ϵ_{ox} and ϵ_N.

Figs. 4 and 5 show a comparison of the hole and electron currents of samples with different top-oxide thicknesses and with almost the same nitride thickness. As the

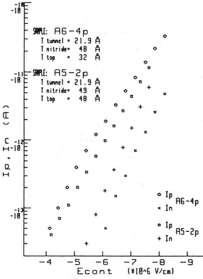

Fig. 5. Hole and electron currents of samples *A*5 and *A*6 with different top-oxide thicknesses as a function of E_{cont} in the tunnel oxide. The thicknesses of the thin nitride and tunnel oxide are 48–49 and 22 Å, respectively.

contact electric field at the metal–top-oxide interface is unknown, the electron currents are plotted as a function of E_{cont} for convenience. It is evident from Figs. 4 and 5 that two-carrier transport takes place in the MONOS structures, and the dominant carrier species are holes for negative gate voltage. Figs. 4 and 5 also indicate that the hole current injected from the Si into the multiple insulator layer is smaller in the thicker top-oxide samples than in the thinner top-oxide samples. Similar properties were observed by using other samples with the same thickness parameters. Therefore, these properties are reproducible. These are not due to sample scattering by defect sites or lateral nonuniformities but due to the thickness difference of the top oxide. These observations can be explained as follows. The relatively thick top oxide acts as a potential barrier to the holes injected from the Si into the thin nitride, and consequently the holes remain temporarily in the nitride, especially near the top-oxide–nitride interface. Hence, the hole transport is greatly impeded at the top-oxide–nitride interface for negative gate voltages in the case of the thicker top-oxide samples.

The barrier behavior of the relatively thinner top oxide is weak and more holes can flow through the thin top oxide. The holes temporarily remaining in the vicinity of the top-oxide–nitride interface increase the electric field in the top oxide and some of the holes recombine with the electrons injected from the gate. This mechanism may be the reason why the electron current observed at the Si side is larger in the thicker top-oxide samples than in the thinner top-oxide samples. The reversal of the threshold voltage for strong negative gate bias shown in Fig. 3 is also explained by the recombination of trapped holes with electrons injected from the gate. However, there is some possibility that the thicker top oxide is slightly electron-conductive compared with the thinner one due to the long oxidation time of the thin nitride, or that such a thin nitride is slightly uneven [11], [21]. The electrical quality of the top oxide is not fully understood. It is presently under further study.

C. Dependence of the Hole and Electron Current on Nitride Thickness

In Figs. 6 and 7, the hole and electron currents of the samples with the thicker nitride are compared with those of the samples with the thinner nitride. The remarkable feature in these data is that the electron currents in the thicker nitride samples are smaller than those in the thinner nitride samples, in spite of almost the same hole currents in both samples. This is also reproducible and not due to sample scattering. It should be noted that the electron current originally injected from the gate is observed only at the Si side after transport in the multiple insulator layer. These experimental results indicate that the recombination of electrons and holes takes place even in such a thin nitride in the MONOS structure and/or at the top-oxide–nitride interface. As discussed in Section III-B, the holes temporarily remain in the nitride at negative gate polarities. This results in an increased recombination rate of the holes and the electrons. It is obvious that the recombination probability of electrons injected from the gate with holes is higher in the thicker nitride than in the thinner nitride. It is well known that there are many deep electron traps in bulk nitride [22] that may act as recombination centers [14]. Of course, some electron traps located mainly at the top-oxide–nitride interface [11], [12] act as recombination centers. From this discussion, it is evident that two-carrier transport occurs in the thin MONOS structure at negative gate polarity accompanied by carrier recombination in the thin nitride and/or at the top-oxide–nitride interface.

From the viewpoint of WRITE operation in MONOS de-

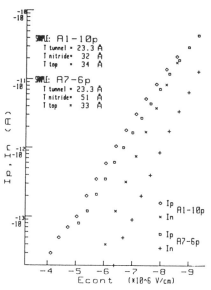

Fig. 6. Hole and electron currents of samples A1 and A7 with different nitride thicknesses as a function of E_{cont} in the tunnel oxide. The thicknesses of the top oxide and tunnel oxide are 33–34 and 23.3 Å, respectively.

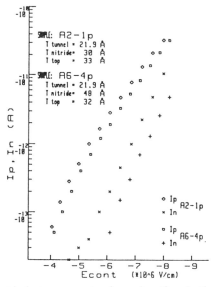

Fig. 7. Hole and electron currents of samples A2 and A6 with different nitride thicknesses as a function E_{cont} in the tunnel oxide. The thicknesses of the top oxide and tunnel oxide are 32–33 and 22 Å, respectively.

vices, electron injection from the gate and carrier recombination for negative gate voltages is undesirable. Therefore, the negative WRITE pulse height or duration should be reduced to optimum values for the sake of effective negative-voltage WRITE action.

IV. CONCLUSIONS

The basic carrier transport properties under steady-state conditions in thin MONOS memory structures have been investigated by measuring the hole and electron current simultaneously and separately. The experimental results show that two-carrier transport is confirmed in the structure at negative gate polarity. The dominant carriers are holes injected from the Si. It is found from the dependence of the hole and electron currents on the top-oxide thickness that the relatively thick top oxide acts as a potential barrier for the holes. This behavior of the top oxide is quite useful for effective negative gate pulse writing in the MONOS memory. In addition, we observed that some of the electrons injected from the gate for negative gate polarity recombine with holes injected from the Si in the thin nitride and/or at the top oxide–nitride interface when the top oxide exists, even if the nitride is very thin.

ACKNOWLEDGMENT

The authors would like to thank Dr. T. Tsurushima for his continuous encouragement and also Dr. H. Hiraishi and K. Ishii for their support with sample fabrication.

REFERENCES

[1] S. K. Lai and V. K. Dham, "VLSI electrically erasable programmable read only memory," in *VLSI Handbook*, N. G. Einspruch, Ed. Orlando, FL: Academic, 1985, ch. 13, p. 167.

[2] M. Horiuchi and H. Katto, "FCAT—A low-voltage high-speed alterable n-channel nonvolatile memory device," *IEEE Trans. Electron Devices*, vol. ED-26, no. 6, p. 914, 1979.

[3] T. Ito *et al.*, "Low-voltage alterable EAROM cells with nitride-barrier avalanche-injection MIS (NAMIS)," *IEEE Trans. Electron Devices*, vol. ED-26, no. 6, p. 906, 1979.

[4] D. J. DiMaria, K. M. DeMeyer, and D. W. Dong, "Electrically-alterable memory using a dual electron injector structure," *IEEE Electron Device Lett.*, vol. EDL-1, no. 9, p. 179, 1980.

[5] Y. Yatsuda *et al.*, "A proposition to scale down MONOS non-volatile memory devices," *Japan. J. Appl. Phys.*, suppl. 21-1, p. 85, 1982.

[6] M. Kamiya, Y. Kojima, Y. Kato, K. Tanaka, and Y. Hayashi, "EPROM cell with high gate injection efficiency," in *IEDM Tech. Dig.*, 1982, p. 741.

[7] E. Suzuki, Y. Hayashi, K. Ishii, and H. Hiraishi, "A low-voltage alterable metal-oxide-nitride-oxide-semiconductor memory with nanometer thick gate insulators (NM-MONOS)," *Japan. J. Appl. Phys.*, suppl. 22-1, p. 581, 1983.

[8] C. C. Chao and M. H. White, "Characterization of charge injection and trapping in scaled SONOS/MONOS memory devices," *Solid-State Electron.*, vol. 30, no. 3, p. 307, 1987.

[9] E. Suzuki, H. Hiraishi, K. Ishii, and Y. Hayashi, "A low-voltage alterable EEPROM with metal-oxide-nitride-oxide-semiconductor (MONOS) structures," *IEEE Trans. Electron Devices*, vol. ED-30, no. 2, p. 122, 1983.

[10] F. L. Hampton and J. R. Cricchi, "Space charge distribution limitations on scale down of MNOS memory devices," in *IEDM Tech. Dig.*, 1979, p. 374.

[11] E. Suzuki, Y. Hayashi, K. Ishii, and T. Tsuchiya, "Traps created at the interface between the nitride and the oxide on the nitride by thermal oxidation," *Appl. Phys. Lett.*, vol. 42, no. 8, p. 608, 1983.

[12] E. Suzuki and Y. Hayashi, "On oxide-nitride interface traps by thermal oxidation of thin nitride in metal-oxide-nitride-oxide-semiconductor memory structures," *IEEE Trans. Electron Devices*, vol. ED-33, no. 2, p. 214, 1986.

[13] A. S. Ginovker, V. A. Gritsenko, and S. P. Sinitsa, "Two-band conduction of amorphous silicon nitride," *Phys. Status Solidi*, vol. (a)26, p. 489, 1974.

[14] E. Suzuki and Y. Hayashi, "Carrier conduction and trapping in metal-nitride-oxide-semiconductor structures," *J. Appl. Phys.*, vol. 53, no. 10, p. 8880, 1982.

[15] T. Enomoto, R. Ando, H. Horita, and H. Nakayama, "Thermal oxidation rate of a Si_3N_4 film and its masking effect against oxidation of silicon," *Japan. J. Appl. Phys.*, vol. 17, no. 6, p. 1049, 1978.

[16] Z. A. Weinberg and R. A. Pollack, "Hole conduction and valence-band structure of Si_3N_4 films on Si," *Appl. Phys. Lett.*, vol. 27, no. 4, p. 254, 1975.

[17] D. K. Schroder and M. H. White, "Characterization of current transport in MNOS structures with complementary tunneling emitter bipolar transistors," *IEEE Trans. Electron Devices*, vol. ED-26, p. 899, 1979.

[18] D. J. DiMaria *et al.*, "Charge transport and trapping phenomena in off-stoichiometric silicon dioxide films," *J. Appl. Phys.*, vol. 54, no. 10, p. 5801, 1983.

[19] D. J. DiMaria *et al.*, "Electron heating in silicon dioxide and off-stoichiometric silicon dioxide films," *J. Appl. Phys.*, vol. 57, no. 4, p. 1214, 1985.

[20] L. Lundkvist, I. Lundstrom, and C. Svensson, "Discharge of MNOS structures," *Solid-State Electron.*, vol. 16, no. 7, p. 811, 1973.

[21] K. K. Young, W. G. Oldham, and J. Rose, "Preparation and characterization of 100 Å oxide/nitride/oxide stacked films," in *Proc. Symp. Silicon Nitride and Silicon Dioxide Thin Insulating Films*, V. J. Kapoor, and K. T. Hankins, Eds. Pennington, NJ: The Electrochemical Soc., 1987, p. 471.

[22] V. J. Kapoor and S. B. Bibyk, "Energy distribution of electron trapping defects in thick-oxide MNOS structures," in *The Physics of MOS Insulators*, G. Lucovky, S. T. Pantelides, and F. L. Calecner, Eds. New York: Pergamon, 1980, p. 117.

Part 5
Flash EEPROM Technologies

A FLASH EEPROM is an electrically erasable non-volatile memory that achieves a smaller cell size than an EEPROM by giving up the byte-ERASE capability and often other features such as 5V-only operation. The conventional EEPROMs described in Part 4 are sometimes referred to as the *full-featured* EEPROMs in order to be clearly distinguished from the flash EEPROMs. The smallest flash EEPROM cells are only slightly larger than the EPROM cells—therein lies the attractiveness of the flash EEPROM memory. Flash EPROM is another name for flash EEPROM, especially those flash EEPROMs with characteristics similar to EPROMs such as lower PROGRAM/ERASE endurance cycle capabilities. This additional terminology is not widely accepted nor considered useful at this time.

All byte-ERASE EEPROM cells have an independently controllable select gate in addition to the control gate. The purpose of the select gate or the select transistor is twofold. First, a select transistor is needed to accomplish PROGRAM and ERASE by byte. Eliminating this select transistor, one obtains a single stacked-gate transistor—identical to an EPROM. This stacked-gate transistor can be programmed by hot-electron injection, just as an EPROM transistor, and can be erased through Fowler–Nordheim tunneling by applying a high voltage to the drain or source. However, the entire EPROM array (or a large section of the array) will be erased by this application of high voltage. The resultant memory is a flash EEPROM, and Paper 5.1 and [1] describe such a stacked-gate flash EEPROM.

The select transistor in the EEPROM cell has a second purpose. Unlike UV ERASE, which is self-terminated when the floating gate becomes approximately neutral (see Paper 3.6), electrical ERASE can proceed until the floating gate is positively charged (see Paper 4.3). Thus, electrical ERASE can and usually does result in a negative threshold voltage; i.e., it turns the floating-gate transistor into a depletion-mode transistor. Without a select transistor to isolate such a depletion mode transistor from the bit line, READ and PROGRAM operations cannot be carried out on the other cells sharing the same bit line.

The stacked-gate flash EEPROM cell described earlier avoids over-erasure (into a negative threshold voltage) by an algorithm of ERASE–READ iterations. Another approach is to let the floating gate control only half of the channel and let the other half of the channel be controlled by the control gate. In this manner, the transistor would be off even if the floating gate is positively charged. Such a cell is known as a split-gate cell and is to be found in Papers 5.3 and 5.8–5.10.

The reader should take note of an opinion that the technologies of flash EEPROM and full-feature EEPROM may become difficult to distinguish. Paper 5.5 for example, points

out how byte ERASE can be achieved in this cell through the use of negative voltage on the word line, while flash ERASE can be accomplished without this additional requirement. Many flash EEPROM cells use the gate oxide as the thin tunneling oxide to save cell area. This has been tried but not widely used for full-feature EEPROM [2] because of a leakage current problem (see Paper 5.7). The fact is that the floating-gate EEPROM community adopted the current standard byte-ERASE EEPROM cell concept rather quickly in the 1979–1981 period. The flurry of new ideas being proposed for flash EEPROMs may result in new byte-ERASE EEPROMs as well.

Paper 5.1 compares flash EEPROM with EPROM and EEPROM. It describes the incentives and the potential rewards for developing flash EEPROMs. Paper 5.2 describes a stacked-gate flash EEPROM using an adaptive ERASE algorithm to avoid over-ERASE. In this and many other instances, an older article was chosen for the reprint volume in favor of more recent articles on the same subject because the older article contains a clearer or more self-contained description. The development group responsible for Paper 5.2 has reported much more advanced devices, specifically a 90-ns, one-million-ERASE/PROGRAM cycle, 1-Mb flash memory [3]. ERASE is carried out at the source diffusion, whose doping profile can be optimized separately from the drain. There is yet an even earlier article on this flash cell in [1].

Paper 5.3 describes an alternative cell—the split-gate cell, which automatically protects against over-erasure. The longer channel length, however, results in somewhat longer programming times and/or higher bit-line voltage during programming and may increase the cell size. (Papers 5.8–5.10 also adopt the split-gate cell.)

Paper 5.4 describes a compact cell that actually has two separately controlled gates, one of which is a polysilicon "spacer" line running along one side of the stacked gate. Five-volt programming using low programming current is achieved through source-side injection (see Paper 3.11).

Paper 5.5 describes a novel single-transistor EEPROM using channel-hot-electron injection for programming without a floating gate—the electrons are stored in a nitride layer. ERASE through tunneling or hot-hole injection can only cause localized net positive charge trapping near the drain. Therefore, over-erasure is prevented. *X-Y* addressing for erasing may be accomplished. Paper 5.6 highlights the potential of using the contactless array architecture (see Paper 3.8) to reduce cell size. Of course, all the different flash EEPROM cell structures presented in this section can benefit from the use of the contactless array architecture.

One common problem experienced by all cells employing high-voltage application to a source or drain diffusion under a thin-gate oxide (for ERASE) is excessive junction leakage even at voltages considerably below the avalanche breakdown voltage. This excess leakage is explained in Paper 5.7 as a band-to-band tunneling current. Additional information on this mechanism may be found in [4] and [5].

The next two papers avoid the band-to-band tunneling leakage current by erasing the flash cell via tunneling through oxide between polysilicon layers. Paper 5.8 or its predecessor [6] can claim credit for being responsible for the recent interest in flash EEPROM, although one should trace the idea of an EPROM cell erasable through poly-to-poly tunneling to much earlier reports such as [7]. Paper 5.9 introduces a new concept of achieving 5V programming.

Paper 5.10 achieves 5V-only operation by using tunneling for both PROGRAM and ERASE (as EEPROMs do) and on-chip high-voltage generation. Significantly, this flash EEPROM introduces negative voltage to the word line. If widely accepted, it will be a powerful new circuit technique in the development of new EEPROMs and flash EEPROMs. Paper 5.11 describes the use of negative gate voltage for erasing in a $3.6\text{-}\mu\text{m}^2$ flash EEPROM cell, as small as the smallest EPROM cell (Paper 3.7) that uses hot-electron programming and tunneling erase.

Reference [8] is a general introduction to the flash EEP-ROM technologies and applications. It projects that, by the year 2000, a 256-megabyte flash EEPROM memory will be available on a die 1.8 cm on one side for $1 per megabyte. This pretty much sums up the lure of flash EEPROMs.

REFERENCES

[1] S. Mukherjee, T. Chang, R. Pang, M. Knecht, and D. Hu, "A single transistor EEPROM cell and its implementation in a 512K CMOS EEPROM," in *Tech. Dig. Internat. Electron Devices Meet.*, 1985, pp. 616–619.

[2] J. R. Yeargain and C. Kuo, "A high density floating-gate EEPROM cell," in *Tech. Dig. Internat. Electron Devices Meet.*, 1981, pp. 24–27.

[3] V. N. Kynett *et al.*, "A 90 ns one million erase/program cycle 1-Mbit flash memory," *IEEE J. Solid-State Circuits*, vol. 24, no. 5, pp. 1259–1264, Oct. 1989.

[4] T. Y. Chan, J. Chen, P. Ko, and C. Hu, "The impact of gate-induced drain leakage current on MOSFET scaling," in *Tech. Dig. Internat. Electron Devices Meet.*, 1987, pp. 710–713.

[5] K. Kurimoto, Y. Odake, and S. Odanaka, "Drain leakage current characteristics due to the band to band tunneling in LDD MOS devices," in *Tech. Dig. Internat. Electron Devices Meet.*, 1989, pp. 621–624.

[6] F. Masuoka *et al.*, "A new flash EEPROM cell using triple polysilicon technology," in *Tech. Dig. Internat. Electron Devices Meet.*, 1984, pp. 464–467.

[7] D. Gutman *et al.*, "Electrically alterable hot-electron injection floating gate MOS memory cell with series enhancement," in *Tech. Dig. Internat. Electron Devices Meet.*, 1978, pp. 340–343.

[8] R. D. Pashley and S. K. Lai, "Flash memories: The best of two worlds," *IEEE Spectrum*, pp. 30–33, Dec. 1989.

Endurance Brightens the Future of Flash

Flash memory as a viable mass-storage alternative

Kurt Robinson, Product-Line Architect
Intel Corp., Flash Memory Operation
Folsom, California

Imagine the ideal memory. It would be infinitely and randomly rewritable at static-RAM speeds and with dynamic-RAM capacity. All memory technologies, in reality, demand concessions from their users, and both ROM and RAM solutions incur higher system costs to circumvent their respective drawbacks. Various types of E^2PROM and "shadow" NVRAM offer features closest to ideal, but at a lower density and higher cost than RAM.

The distinguishing characteristic of "RAM" is random write capability at read speeds (i.e. "symmetrical read/write"). The chief drawback of both dynamic- and static-RAM technologies is volatility. Typically, DRAM is backed by magnetic disk, while low-power CMOS SRAM is supported by auxiliary battery power.

In contrast, ROMs are inherently nonvolatile. They excel at storing code, as long as one does not need to change it. EPROMs offer more flexibility by allowing electrical reprogramming—after a long exposure to ultraviolet light performed outside of the computer system. EPROMs are generally treated as user programmable, but not reprogrammable. Frequently updated code creates logistical problems for EPROM users due to the cumbersome UV erase procedure.

Intel's ETOX™ flash technology could well strike the optimum balance between ROM and RAM. From a semiconductor processing standpoint, ETOX technology evolved from EPROM just as its acronym implies: "EPROM-Tunnel Oxide". It has the smallest read/write memory cell for any given photolithography and true nonvolatility, trading off fast rewrite for slower write and block-clear functionality. Based on observations of other electrically erasable (E^2) technologies, ETOX has a theoretical limitation in the total number and success rate for successive erase/write operations, or write cycle endurance. In actual practice, most applications exhibit

virtually infinite endurance: no "hard" memory-cell failures due to catastrophic oxide breakdown have been seen on thousands of devices tested. Neither has the E^2 "window closing" wear-out effect been found significant after tens of thousands endurance of cycles.

Looking more closely at typical applications, even the most frequent code updates only number in the realm of tens per year. Also, code is updated "en masse", all at once. For these reasons, the functional tradeoffs (e.g. the lack of single-byte alterability) made by flash technology are not issues for code storage.

Data storage, on the other hand, automatically evokes the image of DRAM and disk. This results from the desire for very high capacity for archival data storage. Secondly, data is generally rewritten more frequently than code. Nonvolatile memories, namely E^2PROMs, have struggled for years to improve write endurance. Ironically, the stated endurance ratings are not the primary issue. Closer inspection reveals that most systems typically need far fewer write cycles over their lifetimes than the number currently offered by chip makers.

The success rate for E^2PROM cycling is the bigger issue. Failure rate specifications of up to 5% for 10,000 write cycles is common. Another limiter for widespread E^2PROM or NVRAM adoption is low

capacity arising from complex transistor structures and fabrication processes.

ETOX flash technology provides essential E^2PROM capability with unprecedented density, quality, and reliability. Its simple, stacked-gate, one-transistor cell affords two to four times the capacity, or cost savings per bit, of comparable E^2PROM technologies. Ninety-five-percent process compatibility with EPROM allows ETOX to tap a proven manufacturing base (Figure 1). Equally important is the ETOX breakthrough in high-quality cycling endurance: 10,000-cycle failure rates are specified at less than 0.1%, and endurance of well over 50,000 cycles is typical—without failures. Data retention and lifetime reliability statistics are equivalent to those of EPROM. Typical endurance far exceeds the E^2PROM-standard 10,000-cycle minimum.

ETOX versus E^2PROM

The E^2PROM, like the EPROM, was invented by Intel in the 1970's. The principle of Fowler-Nordheim electron tunneling drives electrical erasure, eliminating the UV-erasure requirement of EPROM. ETOX flash memories are erased in the same way, but they use the EPROM's channel hot electron-injection (CHE) programming method. E^2PROMs employ tunneling for both the write (program) and erase operations.

EPROM is programmed and erased by depositing and removing electrons from a "floating" gate. Floating-gate cells differ from normal transistors only in having an extra, unconnected gate sandwiched between the normal (control) gate and the channel region between the source and drain. The cell is turned on by the capacitive coupling between the gates, whereby the "floating" gate provides a gate voltage similar to that of a standard single-gate transistor. This is the case for an "erased" or "ones state" EPROM cell.

Programming the cell to the "zero" or "off" state deposits electrons on the floating gate, resulting in a net negative charge.

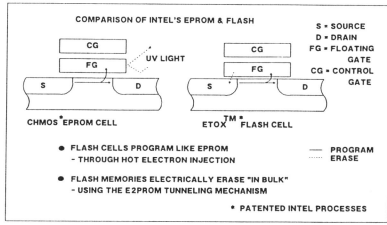

COMPARISON OF INTEL'S EPROM & FLASH

S = SOURCE
D = DRAIN
FG = FLOATING GATE
CG = CONTROL GATE

CHMOS* EPROM CELL — UV LIGHT

ETOX™* FLASH CELL

● FLASH CELLS PROGRAM LIKE EPROM
  - THROUGH HOT ELECTRON INJECTION

● FLASH MEMORIES ELECTRICALLY ERASE "IN BULK"
  - USING THE E2PROM TUNNELING MECHANISM

— PROGRAM
······ ERASE

* PATENTED INTEL PROCESSES

Figure 1: Intel's ETOX™ (EPROM-tunnel oxide) flash technology is 95% compatible with EPROM process technology. ETOX cells are programed like EPROM, using channel hot-electron injection, and erased in bulk-array fashion via the Fowler-Nordheim electron-tunneling mechanism used for E^2PROM.

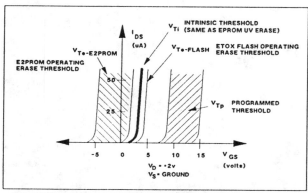

Figure 2: *Tunneling erasure, used by both E²PROM and flash memory, is an active process, with the potential for producing negative erase thresholds. E²PROM's higher erasure voltage produces a wide scattering of cell thresholds.*

The control gate must be taken to a much higher voltage in order to get a net floating-gate potential sufficient to turn the cell on. A typical off-state threshold voltage is 9 V or higher, versus the original on-state threshold of around 2 V. Within the standard logic voltage range, 0 to 5 V, an off-state cell cannot be turned on. The effect is identical to that of writing to a ROM, where a process masking step disables transistors for "zeros" coding.

The programmed EPROM cell is highly stable because a quantum-mechanical energy barrier holds the floating-gate charge. Only a high energy input can dislodge the excess electrons. This property provides nonvolatility—in contrast to the volatility inherent in DRAM because it has electrical connections through which its charge-storage capacitors leak. Both flash and byte-alterable E²PROMs are the same in this respect.

EPROMs employ ultraviolet light to supply sufficient energy to dissipate floating-gate electrons for erasure. This is a "passive", self-limiting process; UV erasure leaves the "intrinsic" amount of charge the floating gate had upon its creation. Thus, UV-erased cells have the same threshold voltage they had after initial wafer processing.

Tunnel erasure, used by both E²PROM and flash memory, is an active process, with erasure performed electrically through external control. The inverse of programming, erasure actively pulls electrons off the floating gates. When more electrons are removed than were added, leaving floating gate with less than the intrinsic number, cell thresholds go below their intrinsic level. If erasure is not carefully controlled, the highly efficient tunneling process can cause some cells to be erased very quickly, leaving some cells are depleted before others are sufficiently erased. (Figure 2 plots floating gate-transistor characteristics as a function of stored charge.) E²PROM's fast, higher-voltage erase procedure produces a wide scattering of cell thresholds. A threshold below 0 V creates an "al-

ways on" cell, or a depletion-mode transistor. Most of the E²PROM cell population ends up with negative thresholds after being erased, which in turn requires that extra transistors or control gates be employed to turn these cells off.

In contrast, ETOX flash combines lower-voltage operation with an advanced tunnel oxide process to implement controlled erasure. All cells tunnel-erase uniformly to produce a very tight cell threshold distribution very close to the UV-erase intrinsic threshold. ETOX technology produces the closest possible analogy to the UV-stimulated operation and compact cell size of EPROM. E²PROM's need for select devices adds to cell size, and hence cost. Figure 3 shows the program/erase mechanisms and compares the relative memory-cell sizes for ETOX flash and triple-poly E²PROM technologies.

The single-transistor barrier

E²PROM vendors have long sought to eliminate

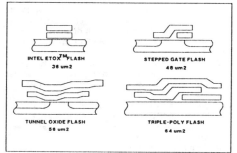

Figure 4: *The ETOX cell's simple structure makes it smaller than other flash-type cells. This comparison is for a common 1.5-μm lithography.*

the extra control gate or transistor for the obvious cost advantage this would bring. Ironically, the byte-alterability feature E²PROMs offer is made possible by the key barrier: single-byte erasure is facilitated by the deselect capability required for detaching erased cells from columns. Byte alterability also creates a performance constraint. If the contents of memory is changed one location at a time, the change must happen quickly for the chip-rewrite time to be reasonable. E²PROM makers commonly specify byte-rewrite times between 1 ms and 10 ms. The internal voltages used for these faster program/erase times are in the 20-V range (charge-pumped internally from the 5-V supply).

Since flash memories erase in bulk-array fashion, the per-bit time constraint is relaxed to thousands of milliseconds (i.e. seconds). (E²PROMs also have block-clear modes, but that does not remove the single-byte performance constraint.) Consequently, flash memories use a far lower internal erase voltage. This is a primary factor in erase control without control gates. Lower voltage also yields better reliability and cycling endurance. The 12-V supplies used with today's flash memories drastically reduce the electric field across the thin tunnel oxides inside each transistor, with the difference on the order of 2 MV/cm. This eliminates the catastrophic oxide-breakdown failures commonly observed in cycling of E²PROMs.

The ETOX cell's physical construction is another key reliability contributor. ETOX's EPROM-like structure allows defect-free oxide growth on undoped silicon. The cleaner oxide lacks the impurities linked to dopants. Furthermore, ETOX uses a small active tunnel oxide area, which results in fewer "active" defects and charge-trapping sights, and thus a reduced chance of failure. Since triple-poly E²PROM uses two oxide regions for tunneling, it has larger active area, as shown in Figure 3.

Other roads to flash

There are three keys to ETOX cell operation: 1) a very high-quality oxide, 2) unique drain and source structures, optimized for program and erase respectively, and 3) the use of complementary, adaptive program and erase algorithms. This combination supports well-controlled erasure and reprogramming of the simple stacked-gate ETOX cell.

The use of a truncated floating gate, or stepped-gate cell, also provides a flash E²PROM capability. The truncated floating gate's voltage must be accompanied by a select-gate voltage for turning on the cell. The programming operation and read function are identical to those used in EPROM and ETOX flash cells.

The stepped-gate structure's primary drawback is an electrical-stress-induced charge loss during programming known as "program disturb", whereby floating-gate charge is lost through the drain region of the cell. This and various other stresses are present with all floating-gate technologies and must be designed and processed out. Very tight stepped-gate process control can provide a sufficient "operating window", but in any case, electrical stresses are significant factors in cycle-related programming failures. Furthermore, the problem is exacerbated by slower programming, caused by a longer cell channel.

ETOX flash cells use separate program and erase junctions to ensure against these stresses. These separate operating regions are optimized for reprogramming speed.

Two other "flash" approaches have been developed. These are effectively hybrid technologies and have many of the same cost and reliability issues of

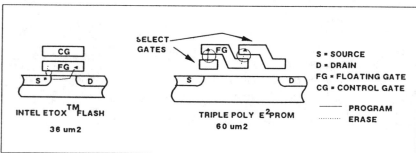

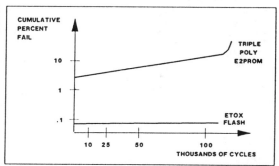

Figure 3: *The ETOX cell is less complex, and therefore smaller, than the triple-poly E²PROM cell, shown here for a 1.5-μm lithography. The circle areas are the active tunnel regions: ETOX's smaller tunnel area reduces the chance of failure.*

Figure 5: *The failure rate of ETOX through 10,000 cycles is specified as less than 0.1% by statistical round-up from zero observed failures.*

their byte-alterable E²PROM counterparts. Figure 4 shows what the relative cell sizes of all the "flash" technologies would be for a common 1.5-μm photolithography.

Endurance rooted in technology

Other functional differences aside, extended write cycling is important for both byte-alterable and flash E² memories. Various technologies all respond differently to this need. Conventional lifetest and data-retention reliability testing indicates dependability after successful reprogramming. This compares favorably among them all. The E²-specific need for cycling is where they differ.

Triple-poly E²PROMs have been observed to cycle well over the 10,000-cycle minimum before a substantial number of devices fail, with the failure rate remaining flat until failure occurs. When they do fail, triple-poly E²PROMs tend to fail from charge "trap-up". Like triple-poly, ETOX flash is theoretically trap-up limited but this has not caused failures in 256-kbit devices taken out to 100,000 cycles (no data is available yet beyond that due to the newness of the technology). Most importantly, the failure rate of ETOX through the normal life of 10,000 cycles, specified as less than 0.1% by statistical round-up from zero observed failures, is substantially lower than that of byte-alterable E²PROMs (Figure 5). The triple-poly E²PROM cell has a much larger tunneling area exposed to high voltage compared to ETOX flash. Oxide breakdown is virtually nonexistent in ETOX flash compared with triple-poly E².

The lower voltages and relatively defect-free oxides used by ETOX memories prevent cycle-related damage. Trap-up causes a slowdown of the ETOX memory's program and erase operations as a function of cycling, but not hard failure.

Temperature and programming voltage (V_{pp}) also affect reprogramming rates. A 1-V change in V_{pp} makes almost an order-of-magnitude difference in program/erase performance. Elevated temperature slows down programming (due to reduced carrier mobility) and speeds erasure. These effects are shown in Figure 6.

The programming-voltage effect explains Intel's different 256K product offerings. The 28F256 is available with either 12.0 -V (± 5%) programming or an EPROM-compatible 12.75-V (± 0.25 V) programming voltage. The latter's worst-case V_{pp} is 1 V higher than the former's nominal V_{pp} to ensure successful reprogramming beyond the 10,000-cycle minimum. The 12.0-V version provides a minimum of 100 cycles to service designs with existing 12.0-V supplies. There is no difference in cycle-related failures, just in write performance. However, 12.0-V versions cycled over several thousand times may see a slowdown to where the reprogramming algorithms stop before erasure or programming is complete, but these are not hard failures.

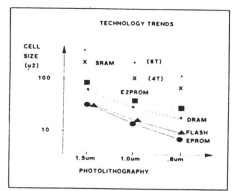

Figure 7: ETOX memory has the smallest read/write cell of any memory, including DRAM.

The volatile or nonvolatile choice

Many designers achieve system-level non-volatility using volatile-memory chips. Battery-backed SRAMs can provide a cost-effective solution in low-reliability environments. On the other hand, this is often unacceptable in reliability-critical environments. A battery is guaranteed to fail, and there are few reliable estimates as to when.

High-capacity systems often employ DRAM and magnetic or magneto-optical disks. Bulky, stationary equipment can employ disks without problems. Rugged, portable equipment cannot live with mechanical media like disks, at least not where a high degree of reliability is required. Electrically erasable memories, either flash or byte alterable, provide the ability to update their contents, along with

ruggedness.

Designers have the hardest time choosing between alternatives where the reliability and density boundaries are less clear. For example, battery-backed SRAM is less expensive than flash due to greater volumes and cost learning. When ETOX flash hits mature volumes, it could easily be cheaper on a per-bit basis. In fact, ETOX memory has the smallest read/write cell of any memory, including DRAM (Figure 7). System-level costs for flash solutions are often cheaper than for disk-and-DRAM implementations — even though flash is more expensive on a per-bit basis — because the latter incur a fixed cost for the disk, independent of capacity. Since flash memory is added in single-component increments, it is cheaper overall than disk/DRAM up through a few megabytes of capacity (Figure 8). Furthermore, the cost crossover point between disk/DRAM and ETOX systems will increase because flash technology currently has a much steeper slope on its cost learning curve.

The primary barrier perceived by designers considering flash memory is cycle endurance. This issue deserves a closer look. Code storage for embedded controller programs or standard computer applications is infrequently updated; twenty-year system lifetimes rarely generate even 100 rewrites. The next level of write cycles is seen in routinely-changed data tables. Examples include updates to navigational-computer parameters, black-box recorders, or even automobile-engine parameters that can be modified for changes in the composition of each tank of gas. These data, changed typically on a weekly basis, require about 1000 write cycles over a twenty-year period.

One might think that archival data storage in general-purpose computers must exceed ETOX write

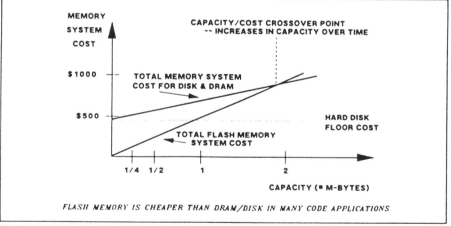

CAPACITY/COST CROSSOVER POINT -- INCREASES IN CAPACITY OVER TIME

FLASH MEMORY IS CHEAPER THAN DRAM/DISK IN MANY CODE APPLICATIONS

Figure 8: Flash memory can be less expensive than DRAM-and-disk systems.

endurance. Again, this is more a perception than reality. The most prolific PC user might store several letters, a couple large documents, a few spreadsheets, and dozens of graphics files in a given week. Including five-minute backup intervals, this barely reaches 2 Mbyte stored per week. Even with fairly inefficient "cycle management" (i.e., spreading cycling uniformly among all the flash devices), a 10-Mbyte flash-memory array would see less than 500 write cycles in 20 years. And since flash memories are directly, randomly accessible, the user sees instant response (instant writes, too, since writes can be handled as background tasks during subsequent file reads).

The bottom line is that computers read much more frequently than they write. This exactly matches the asymmetrical read/write performance of flash memory.

ETOX flash memory enables designers to create systems which are significantly more reliable, lighter, and faster than those based on other technologies. This could create a demand which far exceeds that for earlier nonvolatile memories. That, in turn, would drive volumes which might lever its small cell size into the lowest-cost alternative, and even the greatest skeptic would find low cost hard to ignore.

For more information on ETOX memory, contact Intel Corp., Literature Dept., P.O. Box 58065, Santa Clara, CA 95052-8065. (800) 548-4725.

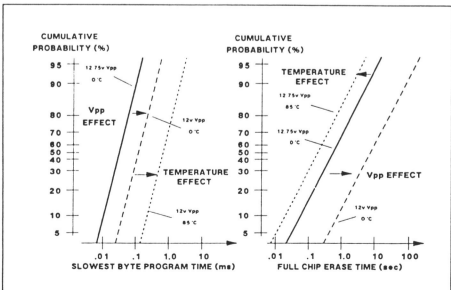

Figure 6: Temperature and programming voltage affect reprogramming rates. Intel offers EPROM-compatible 12.75-V programming flash memories which ensure successful reprogramming beyond the 10,000-cycle minimum endurance.

An In-System Reprogrammable 32K×8 CMOS Flash Memory

VIRGIL NILES KYNETT, ALAN BAKER, MICK LEE FANDRICH, GEORGE P. HOEKSTRA, OWEN JUNGROTH, MEMBER, IEEE, JERRY A. KREIFELS, STEVEN WELLS, AND MARK D. WINSTON

Abstract —This paper describes the design and performance of a 192-mil² 256K (32K×8) flash memory targeted for in-system reprogrammable applications. Developed from a 1.5-μm EPROM-base technology with a one-transistor 6×6-μm² cell, the device electrically erases all cells in the array matrix in 200 ms and electrically programs at the rate of 100 μs/byte typical. The READ performance is equivalent to comparable density CMOS EPROM devices with a chip-enable access time of 110 ns at 30-mA active current consumption. Electrical erasure and programming are controlled through a command port that receives instructions from a microprocessor or microcontroller utilizing standard bus timing. These instructions include erase, erase verify, program, program verify, and READ. The device employs on-chip circuitry to provide margin-voltage generation reducing typical EPROM external power supply requirements. Cycling endurance experiments have demonstrated that the device is capable of greater than 10 000 erase/program cycles.

I. Introduction

ADVANCES in tunnel oxides have driven the development of a double-poly, single-transistor, electrically erasable, programmable flash memory. Reliable reprogramming capability is accomplished with the addition of a 12-V power supply for erase and program instead of the 18 V or greater normally associated with FLOTOX technologies.

The 256K flash memory described here electrically erases all cells in the array matrix simultaneously. Electrical byte programming is achieved through hot-electron injection which is the same programming mechanism currently utilized by EPROM's. Other flash memories have been previously described without in-system reprogrammable capabilities [1]–[3]. This device is the first high-density nonvolatile CMOS flash memory optimized for microprocessor-controlled reprogramming capability by providing a command port interface, internal erase and program margin-voltage generation, address and data latches, and no high-voltage multiplexed pins. The 32K×8 flash memory exhibits READ times equivalent to comparable density CMOS EPROM's with chip-enable access times of 110 ns typical. The one-transistor cell and good array efficiency yields a die that measures 5156×4598 μm².

Manuscript received March 30, 1988; revised May 16, 1988.
The authors are with Intel Corporation, Folsom, CA 95630.
IEEE Log Number 8822443.

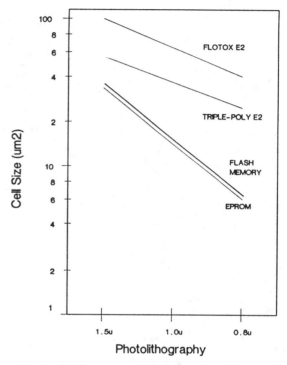

Fig. 1. Flash-memory cell size versus photolithography.

II. Technology

The flash-memory technology is derived from a standard CMOS EPROM technology base. Using an advanced CMOS 1.5-μm technology, a 32 768×8-bit flash memory has been developed with a 6×6-μm² single-transistor cell which affords an array density nearly equivalent to the comparable EPROM technology (Fig. 1) [4]. The cell typically generates 100-μA READ current, erases in 200 ms, and programs at the rate of 100 μs/byte. SEM cross-sectional microphotographs of the flash-memory EPROM tunnel oxide (ETOX™) cell and an equivalent EPROM cell are shown in Fig. 2(a) and (b), respectively. The flash-memory cell structure is similar to the EPROM cell structure.

The cell features an electrical erase capability achieved by the utilization of a high-quality tunnel oxide under the single floating poly gate cell. All cells in the array matrix

Reprinted from *IEEE J. Solid-State Circuits*, vol. 23, no. 5, pp. 1157–1162, October 1988.

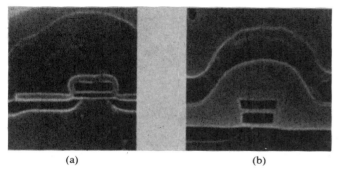

Fig. 2. Array cell cross sections: (a) flash cell, and (b) EPROM cell.

TABLE I
TECHNOLOGY PARAMETERS

Technology	Cell	Periphery
1.5um Lithography	Area = 6um x 6um	Tox = 400 Å
Double–Polysilicon	Gate Oxide ≈ 100 Å	Leff N+P = 1.4 um
N-Well CMOS	Read Current = 100 uA	Xjn = 0.3 um
	Terase = 200mS	Xjp = 0.4 um
	Tprogram = 100uS	

erase simultaneously through Fowler–Nordhiem tunneling by applying 12 V on the source junctions and grounding the select gates. The entire array erasure occurs in 200 ms typical. Programming is accomplished in the standard EPROM manner of hot-electron injection from the cell drain junction to the floating gate. This is initiated by bringing both the select gate and the cell drain to high voltage.

The periphery remains unchanged from the parent EPROM technology. Peripheral devices, which utilize a standard single-metal technology, are fabricated with a L_{eff} of 1.4 μm and a 400-Å gate oxide. Table I summarizes the key technology features.

III. CHIP ARCHITECTURE

A simplified device block diagram is illustrated in Fig. 3. The die photo, with functional blocks identified, is shown in Fig. 4. The feature differentiating this device from a standard memory is its command-port architecture. The command port allows easy microprocessor control of erase, erase verify, program, program verify, and READ modes without the need for additional or high-voltage multiplexed pins. On-chip address and data registers minimize the system interface logic required for erase and program functions while leaving the system bus free. The 12-V program and erase voltage required on the V_{PP} supply pin for reprogramming enables the command port. The command port is set to READ mode by loading the READ code into the command register or by dropping V_{PP} below 5 V, allowing standard EPROM READ operation (Fig. 5).

The command port consists of the command register, command decoder and state latch, the data-in register, and the address register. The command-decoder outputs control signals that direct the operations of the high-voltage flash erase switch, program voltage generator, and the erase/program verify generator. Functions are selected via the command port in a WRITE cycle controlled by the $\overline{WE}$ and $\overline{CE}$ pins. Contents of the address register are updated on the falling edge of $\overline{WE}$. The rising edge of $\overline{WE}$ latches the command register and the data register, decodes new internal modes, and initiates operations.

Erase is achieved by a two-WRITE sequence with the erase code written to the command register on the first WRITE cycle, and the erase confirm code written on the second cycle. The confirm code initiates erasure upon the rising edge of $\overline{WE}$. The command decoder triggers a high-voltage flash erase switch which connects 12 V to the source of all array cells and grounds all word lines. Fowler–Nordheim tunneling results in the simultaneous erasure of all array cells. Writing the erase verify code to the command register terminates erase, latches the address of the byte to verify, and sets up the internal erase verify voltages through the erase/program verify generator. A microprocessor can then access the output from the addressed byte using standard READ timings. The verify procedure is repeated for all addresses. Should some bytes require more time to reach the erased state, the entire erase sequence is iterated until all bytes in the array are erase verified. The algorithm outlined above is illustrated in Fig. 6. Reliable erasure of the one-transistor cell array matrix is insured when the algorithm is followed.

Programming is executed in a similar manner. The program command is entered in the command register on the first WRITE cycle. A second WRITE cycle is then required to load the address and data latches. The second WRITE initiates programming by applying high voltage to the gate and drain of the addressed byte via the program voltage generator. Writing the program verify command terminates programming and sets the internal verify voltages for verification of the newly programmed byte. Again, the addressed byte can be accessed using standard microprocessor READ timings. Should a byte require more time to reach the programmed state, the program sequence is repeated until the addressed byte is program verified.

IV. VERIFY CIRCUIT

Verify voltages, which guarantee program and erase margins, are derived from V_{PP} and are applied to the word lines through the X decoder. The memory employs a unique circuit to generate erase verify and program verify voltages on-chip. Fig. 7 shows a simplified version of the circuit used. The circuit consists of the high-voltage switch and the verify generator. Transistors $M1-M4$ constitute the high-voltage switch that disconnects V_{PP} from the resistor when not in verify mode. The verify generator includes a resistor divider and a buffer. This feature main-

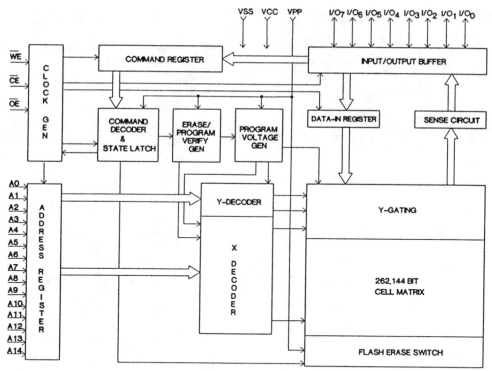

Fig. 3. Chip block diagram.

tains microprocessor compatibility by eliminating the need for additional external power supplies to provide the required verify voltages as needed with EPROM programming.

The simple resistor divider generates the verify voltages for this flash-memory application. Transistor $M5$ is a source follower that has been added to quickly pull the verify voltage to the specified level. Transistor $M6$ prevents the variations in fabrication process from affecting the final verify value. The matched transistors $M5$ and $M6$ form a buffer driving the large internal capacitance with the voltage:

$$\text{verify voltage} = V_{PP} \cdot (R2)/(R1 + R2 + R3).$$

Two of these verify circuits are used, one for erase verify and the other for program verify.

V. FLASH-MEMORY ERASE SWITCH

To erase the cell, a high voltage is placed on the source and the gate is grounded. The voltage across the thin first gate oxide causes tunneling of electrons off the floating gate, reducing the cell threshold. The higher the voltage on the source, the faster the erase time. Though tunneling current is small, breakdown voltage of the source junction is low enough to cause a substantial current load.

When the array starts out programmed, the gate-aided breakdown of each bit is reduced due to the negative voltage on the gate. This breakdown current pulls against the erase path and reduces the voltage on the source junction. But as the array is erased, this negative charge is removed and the gate-aided breakdown voltage is increased, reducing the current load on the erase path, and the source junction voltage increases. To get shorter erase times, the flash-memory erase circuits must be designed to handle this load current and maintain the high source junction voltage.

The high-voltage flash erase switch is shown in Fig. 8. Transistors $M1-M4$ and the inverter constitute a high-voltage latch that enables the erase path. The signal ERASE is an output from the command decoder and controls the erase function. During the erase mode, the zero threshold device $M5$ pulls the array source to 12 V. Transistor $M6$ prevents leakage through transistor $M5$ when the part is not in erase mode. Transistor $M7$ connects the source junctions of the array to ground in READ and program modes. Since ground drop is critical, transistor $M7$ is made appropriately large. Transistor $M8$ has been added to lock out the erase function should the voltage on the V_{PP} be at 12 V before V_{CC} powers up. The signal LOW VCC originates from a circuit that detects this condition.

VI. PROGRAM LOAD LINE

The values of the bit-line and the word-line voltages are critical during programming. If the word-line voltage is too low during programming, the program time will increase and the program threshold saturation level will be lowered. High bit-line voltage may cause electrons to tunnel from the floating gate to the drain, and lead to reduced cell threshold voltages. This effect is termed program disturb

IEEE JOURNAL OF SOLID-STATE CIRCUITS, VOL. 23, NO. 5, OCTOBER 1988

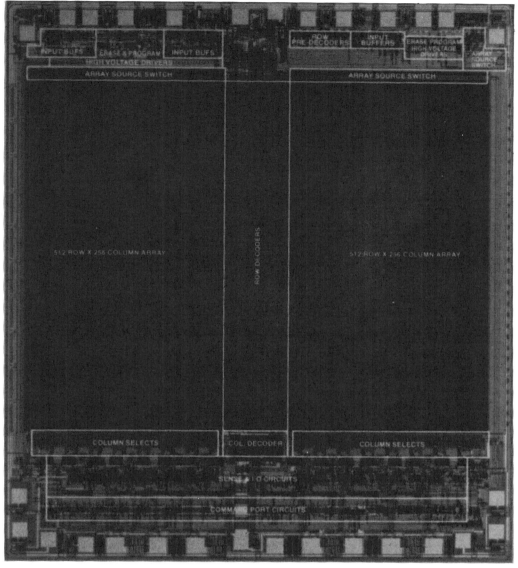

Fig. 4.   Die microphotograph.

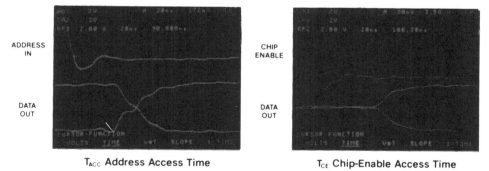

T_{ACC} **Address Access Time** T_{CE} **Chip-Enable Access Time**

Fig. 5.   READ access-time waveforms.

[5]. A bit-line voltage that is too low will lengthen the program time.

The program load-line circuit is illustrated in Fig. 9. The simplest method to generate the signal WREF would be to use a resistor divider. The problem with this approach is that variations in the gate–source voltage of the W select device, $M6$, can shift the load line outside of the acceptable limits. The circuit shown is similar to the erase/program verify generator previously described. The voltage on $V1$ is:

$$V1 = (V_{PP})(R1 + R3)/(R1 + R2 + R3).$$

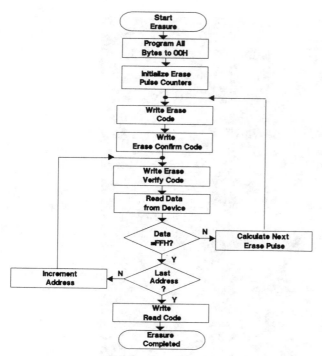

Fig. 6.   Erase algorithm.

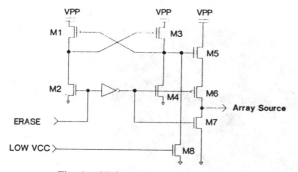

Fig. 7.   Erase/program verify generator.

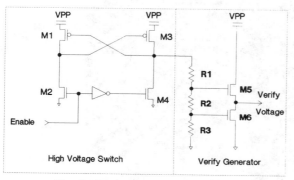

Fig. 8.   High-voltage flash erase switch.

The size of $M1$ is chosen to source the nominal current of 500 μA. The resistor tap points are selected such that $V1 = 6.5$ V. If $M2$ is matched to the W select device $M6$, and $M3$ is matched to the Y select device $M7$, then the voltage on the column should be equal to $V1$ when the programming current is 500 μA, independent of the fabrication process variation in the W or Y select devices.

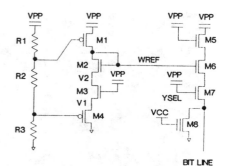

Fig. 9.   Program load circuit.

TABLE II
FLASH CYCLING

LOT ID	100 ERASE/WRITE CYCLES	# OF ERASE/WRITE CYCLES	EXTENDED FUNCTION CYCLING
Q1	0/198		
Q2	0/225		
Q3	0/225	100	0/200
Q4	0/247	1000	0/200
Q5	0/301	10,000	0/200
TOTAL	0/1196	20,000	0/100

VII.   CHIP RELIABILITY

The internal verify values have been defined that will provide reliable device operation. UV EPROM's are known to have excellent data-retention properties. The typical margin shift for EPROM's is 0.3 V after 250°C/168-h bakes. These data represent more than 20 years of continuous use in a system at an ambient temperature of 55°C. Flash memories, with one to two reprogramming cycles, have comparable shifts. However, after extended cycling, margin shifts of up to 1 V are seen [5]. The internal verify voltages have been set to guarantee 1.25-V higher program thresholds than the required 5.5 V to ensure data-retention properties equivalent to EPROM's.

Oxide integrity has proven excellent, with no oxide breakdown exhibited over more than 10 000 erase/program cycles (Table II). This contrasts with many EEPROM's which suffer 1–5-percent failure rate in 10 000 erase/program cycles due to oxide breakdown. The improvement seen can be attributed to several factors.

First, the oxide area in which tunneling occurs is at the gate–source junction. This area is small. Therefore, the flash-memory ETOX cell can tolerate a higher oxide defect density. Secondly, flash-memory reliability is substantially better than standard FLOTOX EEPROM. In addition to improved process technology, choosing to relax the erasure time to 200 ms allowed a reduction in electric field-induced stress across the tunnel oxide. EEPROM requires a 18-V supply and has a cell coupling ratio of 70 percent yielding 12.6-V internal voltage applied to the tunnel oxide. The flash ETOX cell requires a 12-V supply with a cell coupling ratio of 90 percent yielding a 10.8-V internal voltage applied to the tunnel oxide. The difference is about 2 V, leading to approximately 2-MV peak electrical field across the oxide. Reliability figures indicate that 2 MV

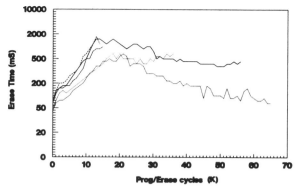

Fig. 10.   Flash erase time versus cycling.

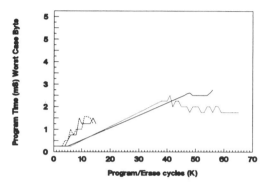

Fig. 11.   Flash program time versus cycling.

corresponds to greater than four orders of magnitude longer time to oxide breakdown.

The primary limitation to flash-memory cell erase/program cycling is an increase in erase and program time

caused by electron and hole trapping in the tunnel oxide. Window closing, which is commonly associated with EEPROM, does not occur when using the erase and program sequences outlined previously in the architectural description. These procedures allow for increasing erase and program time since the bytes are verified to the verify voltage. Erase and program times as a function of cycles are shown in Figs. 10 and 11, respectively.

VIII.   SUMMARY

In summary, the development of a 110-ns 256K electrically erasable flash memory based on a standard CMOS 1.5-μm floating-gate technology has been described. A command-port interface facilitates microprocessor-controlled reprogramming capability. Device reliability has been increased over byte-alterable EEPROM's by reducing the program power supply to 12 V. Reliable operation has been demonstrated, even after 10 000 erase/program cycles.

REFERENCES

[1]   F. Masuoka et al., "A new flash EEPROM cell using triple polysilicon technology," in IEDM Tech. Dig., Dec. 1984, pp. 464–467.
[2]   G. Samachisa et al., "A 128K flash EEPROM using double polysilicon technology," in ISSCC Dig. Tech. Papers, Feb. 1987, pp. 76–77, 345.
[3]   G. Samachisa et al., "A 128K flash EEPROM using double polysilicon technology," IEEE J. Solid-State Circuits, vol. SC-22, pp. 676–683, Oct. 1987.
[4]   F. Mukherjee et al., "A single transistor EEPROM cell and its implementation in a 512K CMOS EEPROM," in IEDM Tech. Dig., Dec. 1985, pp. 616–619.
[5]   G. Verma and N. Mielke, "Reliability performance of ETOX based flash memories," presented at the IEEE Electron Devices and Reliability Societies Conf., Apr. 1988.

A 128K Flash EEPROM Using Double-Polysilicon Technology

GHEORGHE SAMACHISA, MEMBER, IEEE, CHIEN-SHENG SU, MEMBER, IEEE, YU-SHENG KAO,
GEORGE SMARANDOIU, MEMBER, IEEE, CHENG-YUAN MICHAEL WANG, STUDENT MEMBER, IEEE,
TING WONG, MEMBER, IEEE, AND CHENMING HU, SENIOR MEMBER, IEEE

Abstract—A highly manufacturable 128K flash EEPROM was developed based on a new cell. Programming is achieved through hot-electron injection and erasing through electron tunneling from the floating gate to the drain. The cell is 20 percent larger than an EPROM cell and contains an integral series transistor which ensures self-limited erasing, reduces leakage, and increases the cell current. The flash EEPROM device can withstand thousands of program/erase cycles. Endurance failures are due to threshold window closing caused by electron trapping in the gate oxide. Typical erase time is 1 s to clear the entire memory.

I. INTRODUCTION

THE EPROM, when introduced in the mid-70's, was perceived as a tool for system prototyping before a design is committed to ROM. But the EPROM became widely used in mass-produced systems and today it is the second largest memory market, second only to the DRAM. An important reason for EPROM's popularity is its small cell size and hence high density and low cost. The cell is a single MOS transistor structure with a double-polysilicon gate. The cell is programmed by channel hot-electron injection. It is programmed only when both drain and gate are raised to high voltages. Therefore $X-Y$ addressing of a cell in an array is simple and no byte select transistors are required.

One shortcoming of the EPROM is that its ceramic package with a quartz window adds significantly to the cost. One-time-programmable (OTP) EPROM's packaged in plastic packages do not have this cost problem, but cannot be fully tested after assembly.

The floating-gate tunneling oxide (FLOTOX) EEPROM technology was introduced as an improved EPROM. The advantage of EEPROM over EPROM is significant system flexibility due to on-board programming and erasing and high endurance [1]. The disadvantage is its large cell size. The EEPROM cell relies on the Fowler–Nordheim tunneling mechanism for both programming and erasing. A separate select transistor per cell is needed when implemented in a memory array. Because of this, the FLOTOX cell size is two to three times the size of an EPROM cell

[1]–[3]. Other EEPROM technologies are available but all have drawbacks besides the cell size disadvantage [4]. MNOS EEPROM's have limited data storage time. Textured-poly EEPROM's require triple-poly technology and high internal programming voltage.

Flash EEPROM technology offers nearly the same cell size as EPROM and provides electrical erasability. It can be housed in an inexpensive plastic package and still be fully tested. "Flash" refers to the fact that the entire memory array, or at least a large block of it, is erased at the same time during the erase operation. It is not possible to erase only a single byte. Small cell size is achieved through the use of channel hot-electron injection for programming, like EPROM's. Erasing is accomplished by Fowler–Nordheim tunneling.

Different flash EEPROM cell concepts have been proposed [5]–[7] but none has been successfully implemented in a flash EEPROM product until now.

This paper describes a flash EEPROM device based on a new cell structure [8] that combines the strengths of previously investigated cell concepts. The cell size is small and shrinkable and the operation is reliable. A 128K flash EEPROM has been designed, tested, and transferred to production. The device is highly manufacturable.

II. CELL STRUCTURE

Fig. 1 shows a drawing and an SEM photograph of the cross section of the new flash EEPROM. As shown on the figure, the first- (lower) level polysilicon is the floating gate. The second-level polysilicon forms the control gates and the word lines in an array. One edge of each gate is etched with a self-aligned etching process. The diffusion adjacent to the floating gate is the drain. The gate oxide thickness is around 200 Å. The dielectric between the polysilicon gates is an oxide–nitride–oxide (ONO) stack with a capacitive equivalent oxide thickness of 450 Å. ONO has low leakage current and low defect density, providing superior charge retention performance. Devices reported in this paper have about 2-μm effective channel length.

Cell layout is shown in Fig. 2. The cell can be thought of as two transistors in series. One is a floating-gate memory transistor, similar to an EPROM cell. The other is a simple

Manuscript received April 14, 1987; reivsed June 16, 1987.
G. Samachisa, C.-S. Su, Y.-S. Kao, G. Smarandoiu, C.-Y. M. Wang, and T. Wong are with SEEQ Technology, Inc., San Jose, CA 95131.
C. Hu is with the Department of Electrical Engineering and Computer Sciences, University of California, Berkeley, Ca 94720.
IEEE Log Number 8716433.

Reprinted from *IEEE J. Solid-State Circuits*, vol. SC-22, no. 5, pp. 676–683, October 1987.

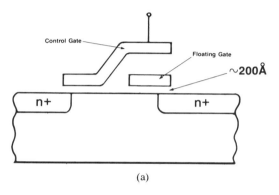

(a)

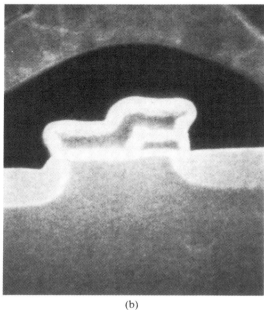

(b)

Fig. 1. (a) Cross section of the flash EEPROM cell. (b) SEM cross section.

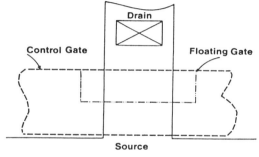

Fig. 2. Layout of the flash EEPROM cell.

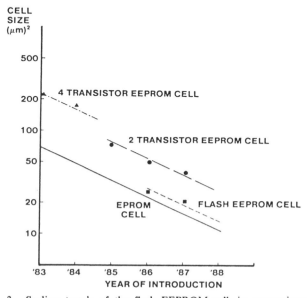

Fig. 3. Scaling trends of the flash EEPROM cell, in comparison to other EPROM and EEPROM cells.

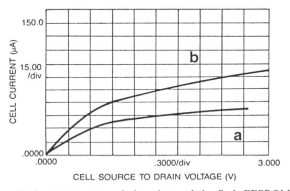

Fig. 4. Drain current versus drain voltage of the flash EEPROM cell (*a*) after UV erase, and (*b*) after electrical erase. The gate voltage is 3.5 V for both characteristics.

enhancement transistor controlled by the control gate, i.e., the word line. Unlike ultraviolet (UV) light erasing, electrical erasing is not self-limiting. Electrical erasing can (and usually does) leave the floating gate positively charged, thus turning the memory transistor into a depletion-mode transistor. The series enhancement transistor is needed to prevent current flow under this condition.

Due to the presence of the series enhancement transistor, the control gate is wider in a flash EEPROM cell than in an EPROM cell. For this reason, this flash EEPROM cell size is about 20 percent larger than the size of an EPROM cell for the same set of design rules and is scalable as shown in Fig. 3.

III. Cell Performance

The purpose of the series enhancement transistor in this flash EEPROM cell is to prevent the leakage current in a memory array during programming and/or reading caused by an overerased cell. This structure eliminates the need for adaptive erasing [7], which may be difficult to implement in a high-density memory.

The extra cell size added by the series enhancement transistor in Fig. 1 can also be justified on the basis of improved cell current and programming characteristics even without considering the benefit of electrical erasability. The improvement is a result of the high gain of the series transistor and the shorter floating gate length that

177

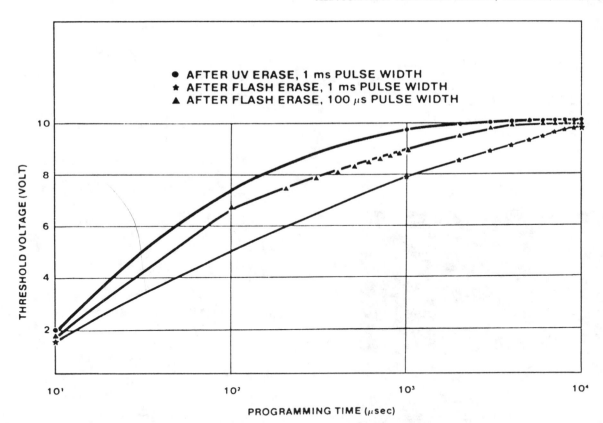

Fig. 5. Programming characteristic of the flash EEPROM cell with different programming algorithms. The gate and drain voltages during programming are 16 and 9 V, respectively.

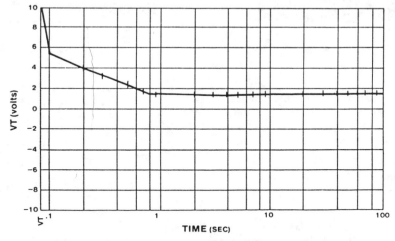

Fig. 6. Erase characteristic of the flash EEPROM cell. The drain is at 19 V and the source and the gate are grounded.

can be used without causing current leakage due to punchthrough. The read current improvement in an electrically erased cell is even greater (about 60 percent higher than an EPROM cell for the same design rules) due to the positive charge on the floating gate. The difference in cell current after UV and electrical erasures is shown in Fig. 4.

A fresh flash EEPROM cell can be programmed at a speed comparable to an EPROM cell. It is known, however, that the initial programming rate dV_T/dt deteriorates after an electrical erase [5]. This is attributed to the positive charge on the floating gate which causes the maximum rate of hot-electron injection to occur at a lower control gate voltage than before the electrical erase. Previously proposed solutions were to increase the drain voltage [5] or dope the channel heavily [9]. Instead of one long programming pulse, many shorter 100-μs pulses are used in this EEPROM so that efficient hot-electron injection can take place in periods of lower gate voltage during the word-line

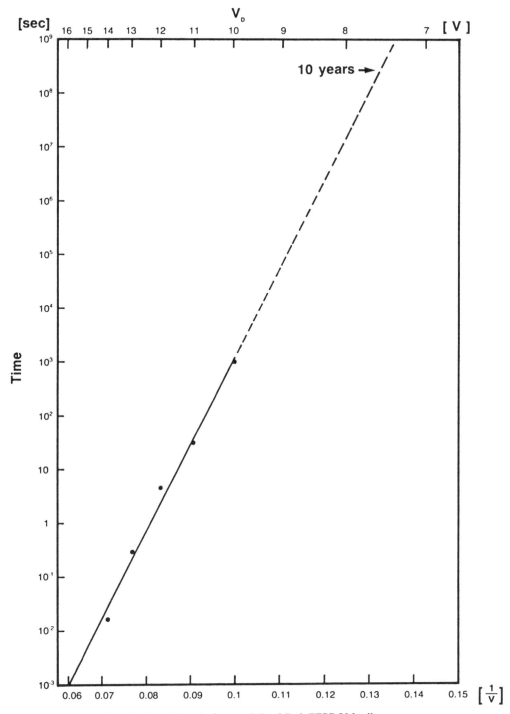

Fig. 7. Read disturb characteristic of flash EEPROM cell.

ramp-up. Fig. 5 shows the programming characteristic of the flash EEPROM cell with different programming algorithms.

Erasing is the result of Fowler–Nordheim tunneling of electrons from the floating gate to the drain diffusion. Erasing is completed in about 1 s with 19 V applied to the drain as shown in Fig. 6. Further erasing only increases the positive charge on the floating gate and V_T remains at the threshold of the series enhancement transistor. The initial

seemingly very rapid drop of V_T in Fig. 6 is an artifact of data presentation as $t = 0$ cannot be represented on the logarithmic time scale.

Read disturb is examined in Fig. 7. During read, a small voltage is applied to the drain and one must ensure that data are not disturbed by slow "erasing" over a long period of time. Fig. 7 plots the time it takes for V_T to decrease by 0.5 V. A read disturb time of longer than ten years can easily be achieved at 2-V reading voltage.

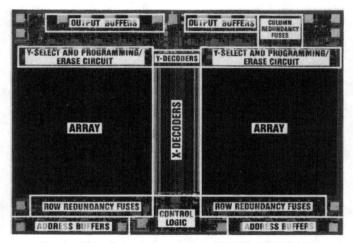

Fig. 8. Chip photomicrograph of the 128K flash EEPROM.

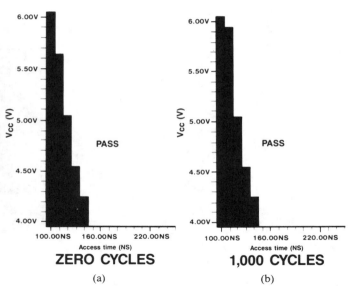

Fig. 10. Access time versus V_{cc} for the 128K flash EEPROM at room temperature: (a) before cycling and (b) after 1000 program/erase cycles.

TABLE I
V_{cc} MARGIN VERSUS NUMBER OF PROGRAM/ERASE CYCLES FOR THE 128K FLASH EEPROM

CYCLE	1	10	100	200	500	1000	2500	5000
V$_{CC}$ MAX (volts)	9	9	9	9	8.4	7.5	6.4	5.6
V$_{CC}$ MIN (volts)	3.6	3.6	3.6	3.6	3.6	3.6	3.6	3.6

This flash EEPROM has a typical access time of 140 ns as shown in Fig. 10 and an excellent speed distribution as a result of the large cell current (Fig. 4). The manufacturing yield is comparable to its EPROM counterpart.

V. PROGRAM/ERASE ENDURANCE

The 128K flash EEPROM can withstand thousands of program/erase cycles. The wearout mode is a decrease in V_{cc} margin as shown in Table I (9 V in Table I is a tester limit). Speed is not degraded until the V_{cc} margin fails as shown in Fig. 10.

The wearout mechanism is believed to be electron trapping in the gate oxide near the drain. Electrons may be trapped in the oxide on their way to the floating gate during programming. The density of trapped electrons increases with increasing program/erase cycles. Trapped electrons induce a field that slows down the programming speed, thus causing a gradual reduction of V_T after programming as illustrated in Fig. 11. The rate of V_T reduction in this cell is comparable to that observed when erasing was achieved by tunneling between the polysilicon gates [5]. This suggests that the high field in the gate oxide during erasing does not significantly increase the rate of V_T window closing. One may suspect that electron trapping takes place in UVEPROM's to a comparable degree.

Fig. 12 illustrates two facts. First, useful program/erase cycles can be increased simply by increasing the initial V_T after programming. Fig. 12(a) shows that quite a large V_T

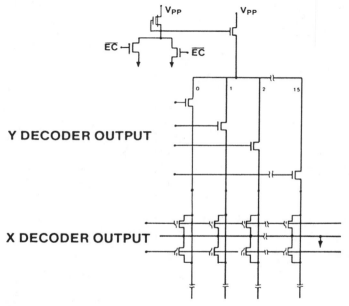

Fig. 9. Erase control circuit of the 128K EEPROM.

IV. CIRCUIT DESIGN

A 128K flash EEPROM has been designed, tested, and transferred to production. The circuit design was derived from a production 128K EPROM and utilizes most of the peripheral circuit layout of the original EPROM. Thus, the cell size (43 μm^2) and chip size (4.6 × 3.4 mm²) are identical to those of earlier EPROM's using 2.5-μm NMOS technology. The gate oxide thickness in the peripheral circuit is 600 Å. A die photograph is shown in Fig. 8. The pinout is compatible with the 128K EPROM.

The flash EEPROM requires a 21-V power supply for programming and erasing. Erasing is accomplished by applying high voltage to all of the bit lines through an erase control circuit shown in Fig. 9. During flash erase, the erase control signal $\overline{EC}$ is low, all Y-decoder outputs are high, and all X-decoder outputs are low. About 19 V are applied to the bit lines. The erase time is below 1 s (Fig. 6) to clear the entire memory.

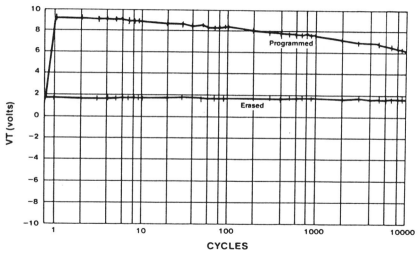

Fig. 11. The program/erase characteristic of a single flash EEPROM cell.

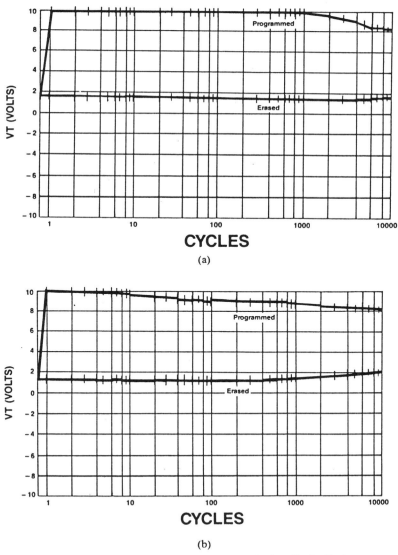

(a)

(b)

Fig. 12. (a) Endurance characteristic of a fresh cell. (b) Endurance characteristic of the same cell as in (a) after it was cycled for 10 000 program/erase cycles and baked at 350°C for 5 h in N_2.

181

IEEE JOURNAL OF SOLID-STATE CIRCUITS, VOL. SC-22, NO. 5, OCTOBER 1987

window is still available at 10 000 cycles because of an increased initial V_T. $V_T = 10$ V is a tester limit. Second, the V_T window can be restored by a 350°C bake, further supporting the electron trapping model. After 10 000 cycles, the cell was baked at 350°C for 5 h in nitrogen ambient. Afterwards it was cycled again and the results are plotted in Fig. 12(b). V_T was raised from 8 V before the bake to over 10 V after the bake.

VI. RETENTION

128K flash EEPROM devices were baked at 250°C for 1000 h in the programmed state. The voltage margin of the cells was measured before and after bake. No drop in voltage margin was found for experiments done on fresh devices or on devices cycled for 1000 cycles. These results confirm the good quality of the oxides as grown and also show that the high quality and integrity of oxides is preserved after a certain number of cycles.

VII. CONCLUSION

A 128K flash EEPROM has been developed and reported. The essence of this development is a simple and reliable cell design. The integral select transistor in series with the floating-gate transistor makes the cell about 20 percent larger than an EPROM cell for the same design rule. This transistor eliminates the need for adaptive erasing, greatly reduces the leakage current during programming and/or read, and increases the cell read current. The result is a highly manufacturable flash EEPROM with a die size comparable to that of an EPROM.

The problem of slow programming of electrically erased cells was overcome by using a pulse programming scheme. Advanced gate oxide technology makes reliable erasing possible through Fowler–Nordheim tunneling of electrons from the floating gate to the drain. The erase time is less than 1 s. Electron trapping in gate oxide occurs during hot-electron-injection programming. This causes the threshold window to close. The 128K flash EEPROM can withstand thousands of program/erase cycles.

Compared with EPROM's, this flash EEPROM technology offers higher erase speed, in-system reprogrammability, and potentially lower cost due to reduced testing and package costs. Compared with one-time-programmable EPROM, this flash EEPROM technology offers reprogrammability and full testability after assembly.

ACKNOWLEDGMENT

The authors would like to thank Dr. A. Renninger for his contribution to process development, D. Laughlin for test and characterization, and Dr. P. Salsbury for his encouragement and support.

REFERENCES

[1] D. Cioaca et al., "A million cycle CMOS 256K EEPROM," in ISSCC Dig. Tech. Papers., Feb. 1987, pp. 78–79.
[2] S. Atsumi et al., "A 120ns 4Mb CMOS EPROM," in ISSCC Dig. Tech. Papers, Feb. 1987, pp. 74–75.
[3] S. K. Lai et al., "Design of an EEPROM memory cell less than 100 μm using 1 micron technology," in IEDM Tech. Dig., Dec. 1984, pp. 468–471.
[4] S. K. Lai and V. K. Dham, "Comparison and trends in today's dominant EE technologies," in IEDM Tech. Dig., Dec. 1986, pp. 580–583.
[5] D. C. Guterman et al., "An electrically alterable non-volatile memory cell using a floating gate structure," IEEE J. Solid-State Circuits, vol. SC-14, pp. 498–508, Apr. 1979.
[6] F. Masuoka et al., "A new flash EEPROM cell using triple polysilicon technology," in IEDM Tech. Dig., Dec. 1984, pp. 464–467.
[7] S. Mukherjee et al., "A single transistor EEPROM cell and its implementation in a 512K CMOS EEPROM," in IEDM Tech. Dig., Dec. 1985, pp. 616–619.
[8] G. Samachisa et al., U.S. patent pending, 1986.
[9] F. Masuoka et al., "A new phenomenon of flash EEPROM," presented at the 8th IEEE Nonvolatile Semiconductor Memory Workshop, Vail, CO, Aug. 18–20, 1986.

A NEW FLASH-ERASE EEPROM CELL
WITH A SIDEWALL SELECT-GATE ON ITS SOURCE SIDE

K. Naruke, S. Yamada, E. Obi, S. Taguchi, and M. Wada

Semiconductor Device Engineering Laboratory, Toshiba Corporation
1, Komukai-Toshiba-cho, Saiwaiku, Kawasaki, 210, Japan.

ABSTRACT

A new flash-erase EEPROM cell is described, which consists of a stacked-gate MOSFET with a SIdewall Select-gate On the Source side of the FET (SISOS-cell). Three layers of polysilicon are employed. The cell has a self-aligned structure which makes it possible to realize small cell area of $4.0\times3.5\mu m^2$ with $1.0\mu m$ technology, and has a select-gate which prevents undesirable leakage current due to over-erasing. The cell is programmed by channel hot electron injection at the source side, and erased by Fowler-Nordheim tunneling of electrons from the floating-gate to the drain. The programming by source-side-injection makes it possible for drain junction to be optimized independently of hot electron generation, and possible to achieve the erasure with no degradation in programmability.

1. INTRODUCTION

A flash-erase EEPROM is expected to be a most promising device for expanding a next generation nonvolatile memory market, because of its advantages such as low-cost and high-density.

Among the different structures of flash-EEPROM cells reported in the literatures[1-7], the tradeoff has been between a small cell area with self-aligned structure[1-3] and a relief from over-erasing problem with a select-transistor[4-7]. Since the cells with a select-transistor usually have a split-gate structure, the scalability of total cell area is limited by a mask alignment tolerance.

A new flash-erase EEPROM cell proposed in this paper satisfies both two demands as follows,
(1) small cell area,
(2) relief from the over-erasing problem,
and has following advantages additionally,
(3) independent optimization of drain junction,
(4) programming with single 5-volts power supply,
(5) erasure with no programmability degradation.

2. CELL STRUCTURE

The cross-sectional view of a SISOS-cell is shown in Fig.1. The cell consists of a stacked-gate MOSFET with a sidewall select-gate on its source side. Three layers of polysilicon are employed. The cell has a self-aligned structure which makes it possible to realize a small cell area, and has a select-transistor which prevents undesirable leakage current due to over-erasing, as shown in Fig.2.

Fig.3 shows the key process steps of the SISOS-cell used in this work. A stacked-gate is first formed, followed by a drain N- implant using a mask (Fig.3a). An oxide layer is then grown, followed by third polysilicon deposition (Fig.3b). The third polysilicon is anisotropically etched to form sidewall select-gate (Fig.3c), using a mask to remain contact area (not indicated). Then it is followed by source/drain N+ implant (Fig.3d). The sidewall gate remains also on the drain side of the cell as shown in Fig.4, though it could be etched away using an extra mask. A small cell area of $4.0\times3.5\mu m^2$ could be accomplished with $1.0\mu m$ technology.

3. PRINCIPLE OF OPERATION

The programming of the SISOS-cell is achieved by source-side-injection of channel hot electrons similar to PACMOS[8] and SIEPROM[9], where the source-side-injection means the injection from the weak gate-controled channel region under the oxide between the select-gate and the stacked-gate, as shown in Fig.1. And the erasure is achieved by Fowler-Nordheim tunneling of electrons from the floating-gate to the drain. Typical operation voltages are listed in Table-1. Since the hot electrons for programming are generated at the source side, the drain junction could be optimized independently of programmability.

In order to explain the fundamental injection mechanism of the SISOS-cell, a simulated typical three-dimensional potential profile during programming is shown in Fig.5. Under the select-gate, an inversion layer is formed and the surface potential is to be the source potential. On the other hand, under the floating-gate, a deep depletion layer is formed and the surface potential is to be the drain potential. As a result, a large potential gap is created in the weak gate-controled channel region.

The conditions to obtain a large potential gap are summarized as follows[8].
(a) Select-gate voltage is around Vth.
(b) Drain voltage is large.
(c) Control-gate voltage is large.

Fig.6 shows a three-dimensional schematic energy band diagram during programming. A channel electron which drifts from the select-gate edge:X1 to the floating-gate edge:X2 without energy loss is to be hot obtaining the energy corresponding to the potential gap ΔV between X1 and X2. For programming by the source-side-injection, the potential gap ΔV is required to be greater than the potential barrier hight ϕ of the oxide.

Reprinted from the *IEDM Tech. Dig.*, pp. 603-606, 1989.

4. EXPERIMENTS

Using the dual gate MOS transistor which consists of a directly-connected floating-gate and a sidewall select-gate, the floatng-gate current:IFG and the substrate current: IB were measured. Fig.7 shows these characteristics as a function of floating-gate voltage, where the select-gate voltage VSG= 1V and the drain voltage VD=5V. The rapid increase in the gate current is observed corresponding to the second hump of the substrate current. This result shows that the hot electron injection occurs at the source side. Since increasing the floating-gate voltage enhances the hot electron generation, the SISOS-cell would not be degraded in programming speed even if it would be over-erased.

The threshold voltage shift ΔVth of the SISOS-cell is plotted as a function of the programming drain voltage in Fig.8. This result shows that the SISOS-cell has a capability of 5V only programming. A negligible small ΔVth in lower VD than 3V is explained by that the channel electrons could not become hot enough to jump the potential barrier of the oxide.

The threshold voltage shift ΔVth of the SISOS-cell is also a strong function of the programming select-gate voltage VSG, as shown in Fig.9. The maximum ΔVth is obtained at about the threshold voltage of the select-transistor which is 0.9V. The increase in the select-gate voltage over its threshold voltage increases the channel current and thereby the potential drop along the channel under the floating-gate. It results in the reduction of the potential gap ΔV and the decrease of the hot electron generation rate. As a result, ΔVth is reduced. In other words, low channel current is required to achieve the programming by source-side-injection.

Fig.10 shows the one shot programming ID-VD characteristic of the SISOS-cell, where the VSG=1.5V and VCG=17V which are the conditions to obtain the maximum ΔVth in Fig.8. The programming current is only about 20μA. The low programmimg current is realized due to that the channel current is limited by select-transistor of which gate voltage is set to around Vth.

According to the literature[9], the programming speed of the cell using source-side-injection is faster than that using the drain-side-injection, because of its high injection efficiency. Programming speed of the SISOS-cell is shown in Fig.11, where the VSG=1.5V, VCG=17V and VD=5V. The threshold voltage of the erased cell is about -2V. The threshold voltage shift of the SISOS-cell is more than 4 volts after 10μs programming.

Fig.12, shows endurance characteristics. The cell withstands at least ten thousands of write(program)/erase cycles. The increase in the write-state Vth is explained by the electrons trapped in the gate oxide at injection region during programming. The increase in the erase-state Vth is owing mainly to the reduction of electron tunneling efficiency due to the electrons trapped in the oxide at tunneling region during erasing. In addition, the increase in the channel conductance of the cell was observed with increasing the write/erase cycles. It is explained by that the effective channel length under the floating-gate becomes short due to the holes trapped in the gate oxide near the drain junction, which are generated by band-to-band tunneling effect at a deep-depleted drain n+ surface undernearth the gate oxide during erasing. Though the trapped holes degrade the programmability in the cell using drain-side-injection[10], the degradation is not observed in the SISOS-cell because the hot electrons are generated at the source side.

5. SUMMARY

A new flash-erase EEPROM cell has been developed, which features a stacked-gate MOSFET with a sidewall select-gate on source-side of the FET.
We have demonstrated that the cell has following advantages on its structure and principle of operation.
(1) small cell size and shrinkability,
(2) freedom from over-erasing problem,
(3) independent optimization of drain junction,
(4) 5 volts only programming,
(5) erasure without disturbance in programmability.
These advantages are adequate for implementation in reliable Mbits flash-erase EEPROM chips.

ACKNOWLEDGMENT.

The authors would like to thank Dr.S.Sinozaki, H.Yamada and K.Maeguchi for their continuous encouragement, and D.Tohyama, K.Yoshikawa, Dr.J.Miyamoto and S.Tanaka for their fruitful discussions.

References

[1] J.Kupec et al, "TRIPLE LEVEL POLY SILICON E²PROM WITH SINGLE TRANSISTOR PER BIT", Tech. Digest, 1980, IEDM, pp.602-606.
[2] S.Mukherjee et al, "A SINGLE TRANSISTOR EEPROM CELL AND ITS IMPLEMENTATION IN A 512K CMOS EEPROM", Tech. Digest, 1985, IEDM pp.616-619.
[3] V.N.Kynett et al, "An In-System Reprogrammable 256K CMOS Flash Memory", Tech. Digest, 1988, ISSCC, pp.132-133.
[4] F.Masuoka et al, "A NEW FLASH E²PROM CELL USING TRIPLE POLYSILICON TECHNOLOGY", Tech. Digest, 1984, IEDM, pp.464-467.
[5] G.Samachisa et al, "A 128K Flash EEPROM using Double Polysilicon Techonogy", Tech. Digest, 1987, ISSCC, pp.76-77.
[6] M.Gill et al, "A 5-VOLT CONTACTLESS ARRAY 256KBIT FLASH EEPROM TECHNOLOGY", Tech. Digest, 1988, IEDM, pp.428-431.
[7] R.Kazerounian et al, "A 5 VOLT HIGH DENSITY POLY-POLY ERASE FLASH EPROM CELL", Tech. Digest, 1988, IEDM, pp.436-439.
[8] M.Kamiya et al, "EPROM CELL WITH HIGH GATE INJECTION EFFICIENCY", Tech. Digest, 1982, IEDM, pp.741-744.
[9] A.T.Wu et al, "A NOVEL HIGH-SPEED 5-VOLT PROGRAMMING EPROM STRUCTURE", Tech. Digest, 1986, IEDM, pp.584-587.
[10] S.Haddad et al, "Degradations Due to Hole Trapping in Flash Memory Cells", IEEE Electron Device Lett., vol.10, no.3, 1989, pp.117-119,

Table-1. Typical operation voltages.

	PROGRAM	ERASE	READ
DRAIN	5V	14V	1V
CONTROL-GATE	17V	0V	0V
SELECT-GATE	1.5V	0V	5V
SOURCE	0V	open	0V

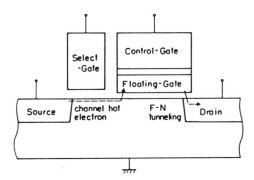

Fig.1. Schematic cross sectional view of the proposed flash EEPROM cell.

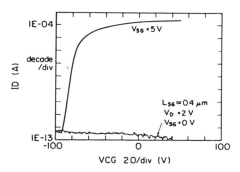

Fig.2. Cut off characteristics of sidewall select-gate transistor.

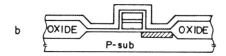

a

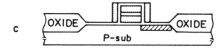

b

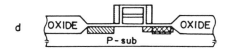

c

d

Fig.3. Key process steps for SISOS-cell.

Fig.4. Cross sectional SIM of a SISOS-cell used in this work. Stacked-gate length is 1.2 μm.

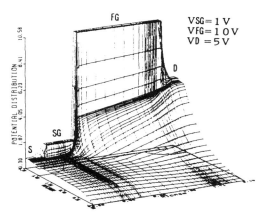

VSG = 1 V
VFG = 1 0 V
VD = 5 V

Fig.5. Simulated typical three dimensional potential profile during programming.

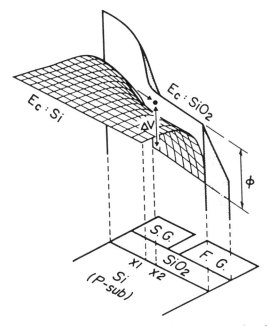

Fig.6. Schematic three-dimensional energy band diagram during programming.

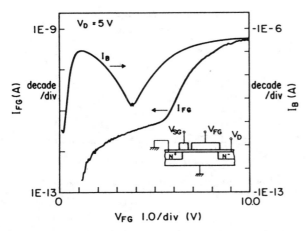

Fig.7. Substrate and gate current characteristics measured with dual-gate MOS transistor. Floating-gate W/L=1.2μm/1.2μm.

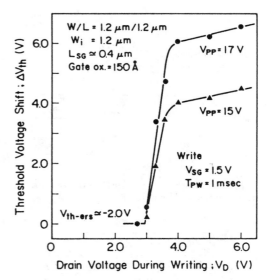

Fig.8. Threshold voltage shift ΔVth of the cell as a function of programming drain voltage VD and control-gate voltage VCG.

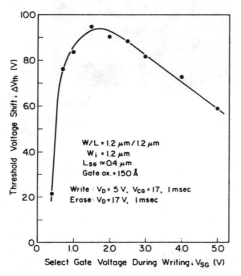

Fig.9. Threshold voltage shift ΔVth of the cell as a function of programming select-gate voltage VSG.

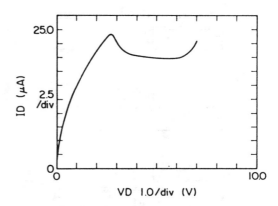

Fig.10. One shot programming ID-VD characteristic of the cell.

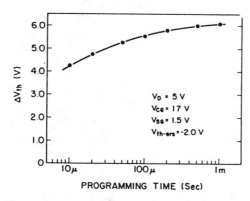

Fig.11. Programming speed of the SISOS-cell.

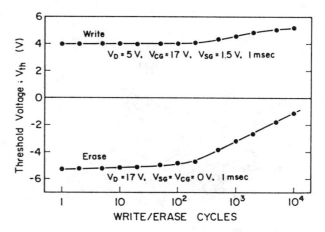

Fig.12. Cell endurance characteristics.

A True Single-Transistor Oxide–Nitride–Oxide EEPROM Device

T. Y. CHAN, K. K. YOUNG, AND CHENMING HU, SENIOR MEMBER, IEEE

Abstract—A novel single-transistor EEPROM device using single-polysilicon technology is described. This memory is programmed by channel hot-electron injection and the charges are stored in the oxide-nitride–oxide (ONO) gate dielectric. Erasing is accomplished in milliseconds by applying a positive voltage to the drain plus an optional negative voltage to the gate causing electron tunneling and/or hot-hole injection due to the deep-depletion-mode drain breakdown. Since the injection and storage of electrons and holes are confined to a short region near the drain, the part of the channel near the source maintains the original positive threshold voltage even after repeated erase operation. Therefore a select transistor, separate or integral, is not needed. Because oxide layers with a thickness larger than 60 Å are used, this device has much better data retention characteristics than conventional MNOS memory cells. This device has been successfully tested for WRITE/ERASE endurance to 10 000 cycles.

I. Introduction

THE basic floating-gate [1] and MNOS conventional EEPROM cell consists of a memory transistor in series with a select or isolation transistor. After being erased, the memory transistor can become over-erased, i.e., become a depletion-mode device. Therefore a select transistor is needed to prevent current flow. This two-transistor structure limits the density of EEPROM memories. In addition, the MNOS EEPROM cells require 20-Å-thin tunneling oxides for fast PROGRAM/ERASE, with the undesirable consequence of shorter data retention time [2]. Therefore single-transistor structures are very attractive and different forms have been suggested before. However, they involved complex circuits or structures with viabilities yet to be proven. Other structures [3] have been referred to as single-transistor EEPROM devices but actually have integral select transistors defined by lithography. In this study, a true single-transistor EEPROM device using an oxide–nitride–oxide (ONO) gate dielectric for charge storage is presented.

II. Device Structure and Fabrication

This EEPROM cell uses the gate dielectric as the storage medium as shown in Fig. 1. An LPCVD nitride layer is sandwiched between two thin layers of oxide (60–100 Å). The bottom oxide was grown by low-temperature dry oxidation. High-temperature wet oxidation (at 1000°C) was performed to convert a portion of the nitride into the top oxide. The effective thickness of ONO stacked film in the test cell is about

Manuscript received October 16, 1986; revised December 15, 1986.

The authors are with the Department of Electrical Engineering and Computer Sciences, Electronics Research Laboratory, University of California, Berkeley, CA 94720.

IEEE Log Number 8613232.

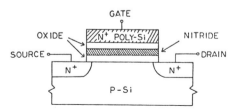

Fig. 1. The cross section of the single-transistor ONO EEPROM device. This cell uses a multilayer insulator structure.

230 A. The effective channel length is 1 μm. Only devices with 5-μm channel width have been tested so far.

III. Operation Principles and Experimental Results

For writing the cell, hot electrons generated in the high-field region near the drain junction are injected into, trapped, and stored in the nitride in a ~1000-Å-long region. Stored electrons do not spread much laterally because of the low conductivity of the silicon nitride and the direction of the lateral field. In floating-gate EPROM's and EEPROM's, stored electrons reduce the potential of the entire floating gate. This causes the channel current to decrease as programming proceeds and degrades the programming speed. In the new EEPROM device, the electron injection efficiency during writing is not degraded as much and lower gate voltage may be used due to the localization of electron trapping. Fig. 2(a) demonstrates the programming characteristics of the ONO EEPROM with $V_g = 10$ V and $V_d = 9$ V. The threshold voltage is 6.8 V after 10-ms programming, where the threshold voltage is defined as the gate voltage at which $I_D = 10^{-7} \times W/L$ with $V_d = 0.05$ V. The drain current measured at $V_g = 3$ V and $V_d = 1$ V is reduced to less than 1 nA/μm after writing. The writing speed is comparable to a conventional EPROM device. This writing method requires both drain and gate voltage to be present and hence provides a method for writing only selected cells.

The erasing mechanism is self-limiting. Hot holes are injected through the bottom oxide, again locally near the drain, by using the deep-depletion-mode drain breakdown [4]. The cell can be erased in 1 ms although the threshold voltage continues to drop slowly until it saturates at the threshold voltage of a fresh cell as shown in Fig. 2(b). Since an excessive amount of stored holes due to prolonged erasing only affects the inversion threshold voltage of a very small region near the drain, a larger portion of the channel (near the source) still retains the threshold voltage of a fresh cell. In a sense, this structure is a two-transistor cell with an integral

Reprinted from *IEEE Electron Device Lett.*, vol. EDL-8, no. 3, pp. 93–95, March 1987.

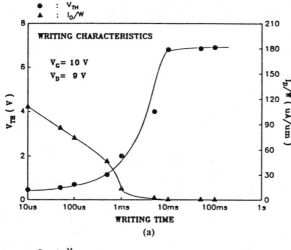

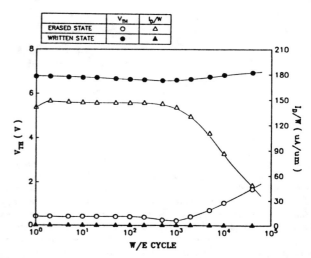

	V_{TH}	I_D/W
ERASED STATE	○	△
WRITTEN STATE	●	▲

Fig. 3.   The WRITE/ERASE characteristics of the ONO EEPROM cell.

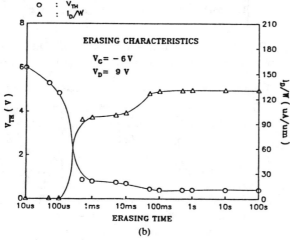

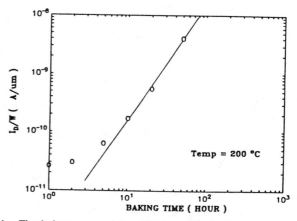

Fig. 2.   (a) The writing characteristics of the cell with writing voltages of V_g = 10 V and V_d = 9 V. (b) The erasing characteristics of the cell with erasing voltages of V_g = −6 V and V_d = 9 V. I_D is measured at V_g = 3 V and V_d = 1 V.

Fig. 4.   The drain current variation of a programmed cell versus baking time at 200°C. Current is measured at room temperature at V_d = 1 V and V_g = 3 V. It will take 10^4 h for the drain current to increase to 1 $\mu A/\mu m$ by extrapolation.

select transistor, but without the cell size penalty. This explains how the self-limiting erasing feature is achieved. Selective erasing is accomplished by applying −6 V to the gate and 9 V to the drain (Fig. 2(b)). The deep-depletion-mode drain breakdown voltage is lowered by the negative V_g [4]. This requirement of both a gate and a drain voltage, as in the case of writing, provides a convenient means of erasing only selected cells. Erasing an entire memory array can be performed under the same conditions or by grounding the source and gate and applying high voltage to the drain. Other methods of hole injection [5] or electron tunneling to the drain may be applied in this device structure and erasing would still be self-limited.

Since the effective gate dielectric thickness of this device is thinner than that of a floating-gate EPROM or EEPROM cell, high read current can be obtained. A read cell current of more than 140-$\mu A/\mu m$ channel width is conducted at V_g = 3 V and V_d = 1 V. This low V_d in contrast to the 2 V commonly used for reading EPROM can greatly improve the soft-write or read-disturb endurance. The soft-write endurance has been projected by extrapolating the measured read time at larger V_d's before causing 10-percent reduction in cell current. A

soft-write endurance time much larger than ten years is expected.

The WRITE/ERASE characteristics of this EEPROM cell are shown in Fig. 3. Both the threshold voltage and the drain current under reading condition are presented. No device performance degradation is observed for the first 1000 cycles. Even at 40 000 cycles, only the erased state or ON-state characteristics are degraded. The reading current decreases due to electron trapping and/or interface trap generation, but is still larger than 40 $\mu A/\mu m$ after 40 000 WRITE/ERASE cycles.

Unlike MNOS memory cells employing 20-Å bottom oxide in order to obtain sufficient tunneling current for writing and erasing, this new device can easily accommodate 60 Å or thicker bottom oxide. Furthermore, the top oxide of similar thickness, isolating the nitride layer from the polysilicon gate, greatly improves the data retention characteristics. Fig. 4 shows the cell leakage current of a programmed cell versus baking time at 200°C. It will take about 10^4 h for the drain current to increase to 1 $\mu A/\mu m$ from extrapolation. The data retention times at several different temperatures have been taken and a data retention time far exceeding ten years can be extrapolated for room temperature.

IV. Conclusion

This novel memory cell has several attractive features compared to conventional EEPROM's. Injected electrons and holes are only trapped and stored in the nitride locally near the drain. Excessive holes injected during prolonged erasing only affect the surface inversion voltage locally and a large portion of the channel retains the threshold voltage of a fresh cell. A self-limited erasing feature is thus achieved and a separate select transistor is not needed. Deep-depletion-mode drain breakdown is utilized to generate hot holes for erasing. The drain breakdown voltage is lowered by applying a negative gate voltage. Hence, selective erasing is possible in addition to bulk erasing. The charge storage medium, the nitride layer, is sandwiched between two thick oxide layers (>60 Å). Therefore the data retention performance is superior to MNOS memory cells. Since no select or floating-gate transistor is needed, an ONO EEPROM cell would occupy the same area as an EPROM cell and less than half the area of a conventional EEPROM. Hot-electron programming does not preclude single 5-V supply operation [6]. This and many other issues relating to the operation and reliability of this new EEPROM cell require further investigation.

References

[1] W. S. Johnson, G. Perlegos, A. Renninger, G. Kuhn, and T. R. Ranganath, "A 16Kb electrically erasable nonvolatile memory," in *ISSCC Dig. Tech. Papers*, 1980, p. 152.

[2] H. Yamamoto, H. Iwasawa, and A. Sasaki, "Discharging process by multiple tunnelings in thin oxide MNOS structures," *IEEE Trans. Electron Devices*, vol. ED-29, pp. 1255–1260, Aug. 1982.

[3] F. Masuoka, M. Asano, H. Iwahashi, T. Komuro, and S. Tanaka, "A new flash EEPROM using triple polysilicon technology," in *IEDM Tech. Dig.*, 1984, p. 464.

[4] W. S. Feng, T. Y. Chan, and C. Hu, "MOSFET drain breakdown voltage," *IEEE Electron Device Lett.*, vol. EDL-6, p. 449, July 1986.

[5] M. S. Liang and T. C. Lee, "A hot-hole erasable memory cell," *IEEE Electron Device Lett.*, vol. EDL-7, p. 463, Aug. 1986.

[6] A. T. Wu, T. Y. Chan, P. K. Ko, and C. Hu, "A source-side injection erasable programmable read-only-memory (SI-EPROM) device," *IEEE Electron Device Lett.*, vol. EDL-7, p. 540, Sept. 1986.

189

A NOVEL MEMORY CELL USING FLASH ARRAY CONTACTLESS EPROM (FACE) TECHNOLOGY

B.J.Woo, T.C.Ong, A.Fazio, C.Park, G.Atwood, M.Holler, S.Tam, & S.Lai

Intel Corporation
P.O.Box 58125, Santa Clara, CA 95052

ABSTRACT

A new single transistor Flash memory cell which utilizes channel hot electron injection for programming and Fowler-Nordheim tunneling for erase is described. This Flash memory technology employs a "buried" N^+ bitline to connect the memory transistors rather than metal and contacts. Elimination of contacts results in a 45% cell area shrink of the conventional ETOX™ cell (based on 1.0 μm design rules). A 4.48 μm² cell area is also realized by using a 0.8 μm technology. In addition to this tremendous cell scalability, the diffusion corner induced erase threshold "bimodality" can be reduced due to the intrinsic stripe geometries in the memory array. Furthermore, the Contact/Metal related layout rules can be relaxed which allows this contactless approach to be extended to future generations without requiring complicated contact processing. Hence, the Flash Array Contactless EPROM (FACE) technology lends itself to a very compact cell as well as a more manufacturable process.

INTRODUCTION

Nonvolatile PROM memories can be divided into two groups: EPROMs and E^2PROMs. EPROMs use channel hot electron injection for byte-programming, and apply ultraviolet light exposure for erase. E^2PROMs employ Fowler-Nordheim (F-N) tunneling for both electrical programming and erase. Due to the small cell size and simple cell design/process, EPROMs can be produced with higher density and lower cost when compared to E^2PROM. On the other hand, E^2PROMs offer the capability of byte-erase as well as the convenience of in-system electrical erasability. Recently, the Flash memory has gained significant attention as it promises to combine the advantages of EPROM density with E^2PROM electrical erasability.

For high density nonvolatile memories, many innovative technologies and new cell structures have been proposed in recent publications, mainly based on "contactless" technology [1,2]. The advantage of this contactless approach in memory applications is that it can provide a significant cell area reduction without further stretching the device limits. However, the complicated fabrication steps involved with these reported cell structures may result in a loss of cost competitiveness in the memory market. This paper describes a new Flash contactless cell which satisfies both small cell size and good manufacturability requirements for high density Flash memories.

The FACE memory technology utilizes the buried bitline approach [3] where the half contact per bit requirement of the conventional ETOX Flash memory is essentially eliminated [4]. Instead, the FACE array has one contact for every 16 rows (Fig.1). The stripe layout in the FACE array also reduces the erase threshold bimodality [5] observed in the ETOX array. In this paper, the FACE process flow is described and the intrinsic cell characteristics are evaluated through a 64K memory array. Comparison of the cell performance between the FACE and the ETOX cells is also made.

FACE CELL TECHNOLOGY

An N-well CMOS double poly process has been developed to fabricate the FACE array. A modified LOCOS isolation with field oxide up to 6500Å is used for periphery devices as well as for the array blocking. A 1500Å Self Aligned Thermal Oxide (SATO) between the tungsten silicide wordline and the bitline is also provided by the modified LOCOS process. Prior to the gate oxidation, a sacrificial oxidation (seal ox) is employed to alleviate the Kooi effect which is inherent to the LOCOS technology. A shallow drain junction and a graded source junction are optimized for hot electron programming and F-N tunneling erase, respectively. The lack of the thick field oxide isolation and field implant across the buried bitlines leads to a multiple isolation implant sequence in order to suppress any "bitline to bitline" punchthrough. This is followed by a 115Å tunnel oxide and the standard ETOX double poly and single metal process. The cross sections of the FACE cell using 1.0 μm design rules are shown in Figure 2. The cell area of 8.4 μm² represents 55% that of the conventional ETOX cell [4]. Using the

Reprinted from the *IEDM Tech. Dig.*, pp. 91–94, 1990.

same process flow but 0.8 μm lithography rules, a 4.48 μm² FACE cell is also fabricated.

FACE CELL CHARACTERISTICS

A) Programming

The FACE cell is programmed by channel hot electron injection at the drain edge. Figure 3 shows the typical programming characteristics of FACE cells (both 8.4 and 4.48 μm²). With 11.4V on the control gate, both types of cells can be programmed to 6V threshold voltage using a 10μs, 6V drain pulse. This fast programming speed also reduces any gate/drain disturbs, and therefore, better charge retention performance.

B) Erase

The electrical erase of the FACE cell is accomplished by F-N tunneling with a high voltage at the source and ground potential at the gate. Unlike the conventional Flash cell, the erase speed of the FACE cell exhibits strong dependences on arsenic ion implant (S/D implant) and seal oxidation conditions. Such behaviors are believed to be caused by two mechanisms: source junction surface depletion effect and tunnel oxide thickening effect.

C) Depletion Effect

During erase, the source junction near the tunnel oxide interface is highly depleted up to or even into the arsenic region due to the high erase voltage applied to the source. The depletion region near the interface reduces the voltage across the tunnel oxide and thus degrades the erase performance of the FACE cell. This kind of depletion effect also exists in the conventional Flash cell but is more pronounced in the FACE cell as its source/drain junctions are formed at an earlier stage of the process. The severe dopant segregation through many later thermal cycles, such as SATO, seal ox, tunnel ox,...etc., leads to a significant reduction in surface dopant concentration at S/D junctions. Therefore, increasing the surface concentration via heavier implant dose and lower implant energy can readily lead to an improved erase performance (Fig. 4). The existence of the depletion layer also can enhance the hot hole injection into the tunnel oxide which will negatively affect the program/erase cycling endurance [6]. Shown in Figure 5 are 10K cycling results for both high and low energy implanted FACE cells, and poor cycling behavior is observed only on the high implanted energy cells.

D) Oxide Thickening Effect

A key difference between the FACE and the ETOX process flow is the sequence of tunnel oxide growth and S/D implant. In the FACE process flow, the S/D dopants can laterally diffuse into the channel during the seal oxide step. The tunnel oxide above the source region, where the tunneling erase is to take place, is then grown out of the heavily-doped arsenic area. As a result of impurity enhanced oxidation, the tunnel oxide above the source region is thicker than that of the channel area. This thickening effect causes a reduction of electric field across the tunnel oxide and results in a degradation of tunneling efficiency. Decreasing the seal oxide oxidation time or temperature will reduce the heavy dopant lateral diffusion and therefore, improve the erase performance (Fig. 6).

E) Read

The channel width of the FACE cell is determined by the width of the wordline, and is not affected by the isolation bird's beak. Therefore, for a given drawn dimension, the effective channel width (Weff) will be larger compared to that of the conventional cell, and it is a distinct advantage for the FACE cell. The read current of an erased cell can be as high as 100 μA under the normal read operation (Fig. 7) which allows a less than 50 nsec access time to be achieved in the 64K array.

F) Program Disturb

The FACE cell shows similar behavior as the conventional cell in gate and drain disturbs. The gate disturb characteristic is shown in Figure 8. For the FACE cell, although the tunnel oxide is grown on the arsenic area, the oxide quality is equivalent to that of ETOX cell as the gate disturb induced Vt shift is the same for both cells. Due to the cell layout difference, the FACE array is more susceptible to the parasitic programming than the conventional ETOX array. Programming a selected cell may possibly disturb the unselected cells under the same wordline. To prevent this parasitic programming, a debias scheme is employed in the 64K FACE array. The concern about the drain disturb associated with the debias architecture has been evaluated. Figure 9 shows that there is only 0.5V shift even after 1000 seconds of drain disturb which is comparable to the conventional cell.

CONCLUSION

A Flash contactless technology has been developed and demonstrated on a 64K FACE memory array. The intrinsic FACE cell characteristics have been examined. The mechanisms affecting erase performance and cycling behavior are proposed and the possible solutions for improvement are also suggested. For the deep-submicron (<0.5 μm) generation, contact printing, definition and associated contact filling, barrier metal and planarization techniques will become more complicated. Therefore this contactless technology, which allows simpler contact/metal process yet offers improved device performance, promises to be ideally suitable for high density Flash memories.

ACKNOWLEDGEMENTS

We would like to acknowledge the contributions of Betty Buck, Ken Buckmann and Rick Dodge for wafer processing, E-test and sort supports.

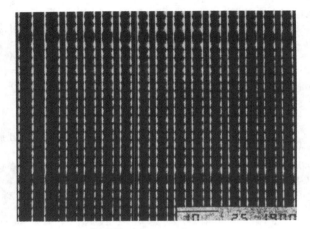

Fig.1 FACE array top view

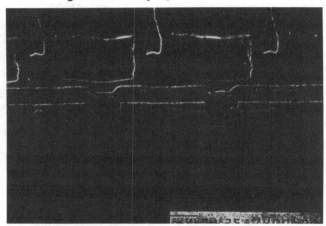

Fig.2(a) FACE array SEM cross section
along wordline

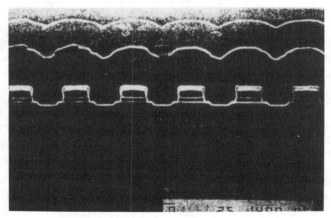

Fig.2(b) FACE array SEM cross section
along bitline

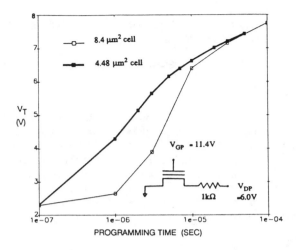

Fig.3 FACE cell programming characteristics

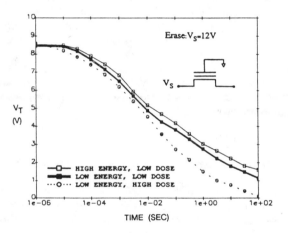

Fig.4 Erase performance as a function
of S/D implant dose/energy

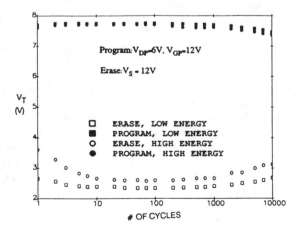

Fig.5 The effect of S/D implant energy on
P/E cycling window

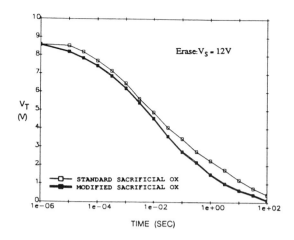

Fig.6 The impact of tunnel oxide thickening effect on erase performance

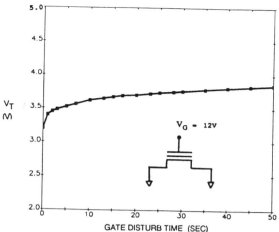

Fig.8 Gate disturb characteristics of FACE cell after 10 P/E cycles

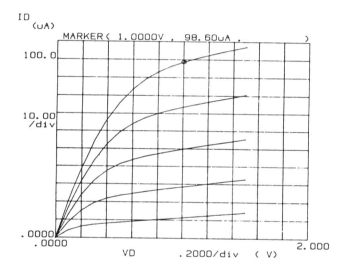

Fig.7 I-V characteristics of 8.4 μm^2 cell Vgmin=3.0V, step=0.5V

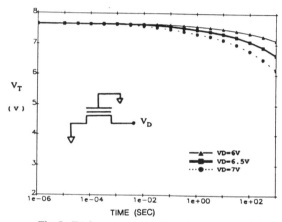

Fig.9 FACE cell drain disturb characteristics

REFERENCES

[1] M.Gill et al., "A 5-Volt Contactless Array 256K Bit Flash EEPROM Technology," IEDM Tech. Dig., Dec.1988, pp 428-431.

[2] O.Bellezza et al., "A New Self-Aligned Field Oxide Cell For Multimegabit EPROMs", IEDM Tech. Dig., Dec. 1989, pp 579-582.

[3] J.Esquivel et al., " High Density Contactless, Self Aligned EPROM Cell Array Technology", IEDM Tech. Dig.,Dec. 1986, pp 592-595.

[4] V.Kynett et al., "A 90ns 100K Erase/Program Cycle Megabit Flash Memory", ISSCC Tech. Dig., Feb. 1989, pp 140-141.

[5] D.Tang et al., " One Micron Flash Technology ", IPTC, 1988, pp 11-14.

[6] G.Verma et al., "Reliability Performance Of ETOX Based Flash Memories", IRPS, 1988, pp 158-166.

Subbreakdown Drain Leakage Current in MOSFET

J. CHEN, T. Y. CHAN, I. C. CHEN, P. K. KO, AND CHENMING HU, SENIOR MEMBER, IEEE

Abstract—Significant drain leakage current can be detected at drain voltages much lower than the breakdown voltage. This subbreakdown leakage can dominate the drain leakage current at zero V_G in thin-oxide MOSFET's. The mechanism is shown to be band-to-band tunneling in Si in the drain/gate overlap region. In order to limit the leakage current to 0.1 pA/μm, the oxide field in the gate-to-drain overlap region must be limited to 2.2 MV/cm. This may set another constraint for oxide thickness or power supply voltage.

I. INTRODUCTION

IN A MOSFET with a thin gate oxide and with the gate grounded, significant drain leakage current can be observed at drain voltages much below what is usually considered the "breakdown voltage" [1]. We shall refer to this as the subbreakdown leakage current. This subbreakdown leakage current is also observable in the subthreshold I_D–V_G characteristics of thin-oxide devices. Fig. 1 shows the typical subthreshold characteristics for a 88-Å gate oxide n-MOSFET. The large leakage current near zero V_G is another manifestation of the subbreakdown leakage. It increases with increasing V_D and decreasing V_G. A good understanding and control of this MOSFET subbreakdown leakage current is very important to thin-oxide VLSI MOSFET's and some high-voltage devices such as nonvolatile memory cells or programming circuits.

Deep-depletion breakdown in MOS capacitors has been studied in detail [2]. In [1], Feng *et al.* have studied the effect of scaling oxide thickness and channel doping concentration on the drain avalanche breakdown voltage. This paper explores the mechanisms responsible for the MOSFET drain subbreakdown leakage current.

II. EXPERIMENT

Measurements were performed on n-channel MOSFET's fabricated with conventional n-type polysilicon gate technology. The p-bulk was doped at 10^{16} cm^{-3} and the source/drain diffusions were 0.4-μm As junctions. The channel was 20 μm long and 20 μm wide. Gate oxide thicknesses ranging from 55 to 350 Å were examined.

Fig. 2 shows the measured drain current at $V_G = 0$ V for several oxide thicknesses. These currents flow from the drain to the substrate. For the 155-Å gate oxide device, data are presented for three different temperatures, 25, 100, and 150°C. As temperature increased, a V_D-independent leakage

Manuscript received August 12, 1987; revised August 18, 1987. This work was supported by AMD, Hughes, and Rockwell International under the State of California MICRO program and JSEP under Contract F49620-84-C-0057.

The authors are with the Electronics Research Laboratory and the Department of Electrical Engineering and Computer Science, University of California, Berkeley, CA 94720.

IEEE Log Number 8717412.

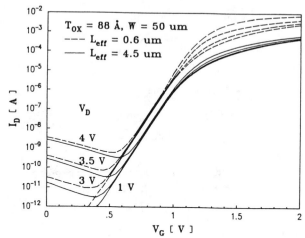

Fig. 1. Subthreshold characteristics for two n-MOSFET's with $T_{ox} = 88$ Å, $W = 50$ μm, and $L = 4.5$ and 0.6 μm. Significant drain leakage current can be observed when V_{DG} is high.

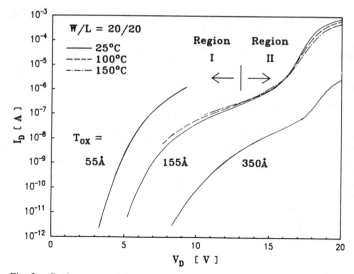

Fig. 2. Drain current characteristics for n-MOSFET's at different temperatures with gate grounded. A V_D-independent leakage current, believed to be the thermal generation current, has been subtracted for clarity. The drain current characteristics for devices with $T_{ox} = 55$ and 350 Å at room temperature are also included.

current (2.28 × 10^{-9} at 100°C and 1.17 × 10^{-7} at 150°C), believed to be the thermal generation currents collected by the drain junction, appeared as expected. The data shown in Fig. 2 have this current component subtracted for clarity.

III. MODEL AND DISCUSSION

One may attempt to attribute the subbreakdown leakage current to thermal current amplified by impact ionization. The

Reprinted from *IEEE Electron Device Lett.*, vol. EDL-8, no. 11, pp. 515–517, November 1987.

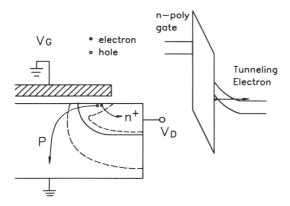

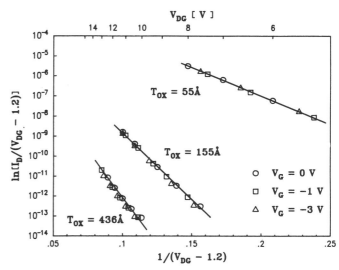

Fig. 3. A deep-depletion region is formed in the gate-to-drain overlap region. The energy-band diagram illustrates the band-to-band tunneling process and the flow of carriers. Valence-band electrons tunnel into the conduction band and are collected at the drain. The holes created flow to the substrate.

Fig. 4. Plot of ln $(I_D/(V_{DG} - 1.2))$ versus $1/(V_{DG} - 1.2)$, where V_{DG} is the voltage difference between the drain and gate. All measured data with the same oxide thickness fall on a straight line, which is in agreement with the band-to-band tunneling model.

data at different temperatures show that this leakage current is insensitive to temperature while the thermal leakage current varies by more than 10^5 times over the temperature range. This indicates that the subbreakdown drain current is not amplified thermal leakage current. Another possible origin of this subbreakdown current is the amplification of the electron tunneling current from the gate. However, the drain current is more than three orders of magnitude larger than the gate current which rules out this possibility.

We interpret the subbreakdown current as due to the band-to-band tunneling process in the gate-to-drain overlap region as illustrated in Fig. 3. Drain current is due to the tunneling of valence-band electrons into the conduction band. The holes created by the tunneling of electrons flow to the substrate. Note that tunneling is only possible in the presence of a high electric field. The field in silicon at the Si–SiO₂ interface depends on the doping concentration in the diffusion region and the difference between V_D and V_G, i.e., V_{DG}.

Band-to-band tunneling current density is the highest where the electric field is the largest and the band bending is larger than the energy bandgap E_g. A simple expression for the surface electric field at the tunneling point in the gate-to-drain overlap region can be obtained as follows:

$$E_s \simeq \frac{V_{DG} - 1.2}{3 \, T_{ox}} \qquad (1)$$

where E_s is the vertical electric field at silicon surface, 3 is the ratio of silicon permittivity to oxide permittivity, and T_{ox} is the oxide thickness in the overlap region. A band bending of 1.2 eV is the minimum necessary for band-to-band tunneling to occur. The theory of tunneling current predicts [3]

$$I_D = A E_s \exp\left[-\frac{\pi m^{*1/2} E_g^{3/2}}{2\sqrt{2}q\hbar E_s}\right] = A E_s \exp\left(-B/E_s\right) \quad (2)$$

where A is a preexponential constant and $B = 21.3$ MV/cm with $m^* = 0.2m_o$ [4]. According to (1), E_s is proportional to

$V_{DG} - 1.2$. Fig. 4 shows that measured ln $(I_D/(V_{DG} - 1.2))$ plotted against $1/(V_{DG} - 1.2)$ is linear in agreement with (2). Measured data yield an experimental value of $B = 18$ MV/cm. This is in reasonable agreement with the theoretical value of $B = 21.3$ MV/cm, which has never been verified to this accuracy. Fig. 4 also verifies that the tunneling current only depends on the vertical field, namely, the difference between drain and gate voltages as in [1]. These facts strongly support our interpretation that the currents are due to band-to-band tunneling. Using measured A and B, a drain leakage current of $I_D = 0.1$ pA/μm can be created when E_s is 0.75 MV/cm and the oxide field is about 2.2 MV/cm. Empirically, we have found $I_D = 0.1$ pA/μm when $V_{DG} \cong 1.2 + T_{gox} \times E_{crit}$ with E_{crit} ranging from 2.2 to 3 MV/cm for a wide range of MOSFET technologies, where T_{gox} is the measured gate (channel) oxide thickness. The fact that E_{crit} is larger than 2.2 MV/cm suggests that the oxide near the gate edge is thicker than T_{gox} due to polysilicon gate reoxidation. This sets another limit to the minimum oxide thickness or the maximum power supply voltage.

As seen in Fig. 2, there is a noticeable kink in the drain I–V characteristics. So far we have only addressed Region I, to the left of the kink. In Region I, I_D increases slightly with increasing temperature probably due to a decrease in E_g in (2). In Region II, I_D rises above the predicted tunneling current. We attribute the rise to the amplification of the tunneling current by avalanche impact ionization. I_D in Region II is characterized by a negative temperature coefficient due to the decrease of the impact ionization coefficient at higher temperature and by the sensitivity to the substrate bias (not presented here), of which I_D in Region I is independent.

IV. Summary

Subbreakdown leakage is the significant drain leakage current observable at below-breakdown voltage. The dominant mechanism for this current is band-to-band tunneling at the Si–SiO$_2$ interface in the gate-to-drain overlap region. At higher drain voltages, impact ionization amplifies this current and results in even larger leakage currents until breakdown occurs.

In thin oxide devices, the OFF-state drain current often increases with decreasing V_G measurably due to the same mechanism (Fig. 1). The voltage required to cause band-to-band tunneling will decrease when oxide thickness decreases. This may be another barrier to VLSI MOSFET scaling. Possible solutions to the problem are the use of lightly-doped drain devices which have lower E_s, or graded gate oxide devices [5] in which the oxide is thicker in the gate-to-drain overlap region than that in the channel.

ACKNOWLEDGMENT

The authors would like to thank M.-C. Jeng for assistance in preparation of one sample.

REFERENCES

[1] W. S. Feng, T. Y. Chan, and C. Hu, "MOSFET drain breakdown voltage," *IEEE Electron Device Lett.*, vol. EDL-7, p. 449, 1986.
[2] E. H. Nicollian and J. R. Brews, *MOS Physics and Technology.* New York: Wiley, 1982, p. 378.
[3] J. L. Moll, *Physics of Semiconductor.* New York: McGraw-Hill, 1964, p. 253.
[4] S. M. Sze, *Physics of Semiconductor Devices*, 2nd ed. New York: Wiley, 1981, p. 525.
[5] P. K. Ko, S. Tam, and C. Hu, "Enhancement of hot-electron currents in graded-gate-oxide (GGO)-MOSFETS," in *1984 IEDM Tech. Dig.*, p. 88.

A 256-kbit Flash E²PROM Using Triple-Polysilicon Technology

FUJIO MASUOKA, MASAMICHI ASANO, HIROSHI IWAHASHI, TEISUKE KOMURO, NORIYOSHI TOZAWA, AND SHINICHI TANAKA

Abstract —A high-density 256-kbit flash electrically erasable PROM (E²PROM) with a single transistor per bit has been developed by utilizing triple-polysilicon technology. As a result of achieving a new compact cell that is as small as 8×8 μm², even with relatively conservative 2.0-μm design rules, a small die size of 5.69×5.78 mm² is realized. This flash E²PROM is fully pin compatible with a 256-kbit UV-EPROM without increasing the number of input pins for erasing by introducing a new programming and erasing scheme. Programming time is as fast as 200 μs per byte and erasing time is less than 100 ms per chip. A typical access time of 90 ns is achieved by using new sense-amplifier circuitry.

I. INTRODUCTION

RECENTLY, the memory capacity of EPROM's has been increasing two times every year. Now 256-kbit UV-EPROM's are being rushed into mass production and 1-Mbit EPROM's have been reported [1]–[3]. Conventional electrically erasable PROM's (E²PROM's), on the other hand, have many advantages that include ease of use, but because the memory cells consist of two transistors per bit, development of a large-capacity device has been very difficult, the largest under present production being only 64 kbit [4].

It is desirable for E²PROM's to have small die size, fast programming and erasing time, and high-speed operation. A new idea for a compact E²PROM cell with a single transistor per bit was presented at the 1981 and 1984 IEDM's [5], [6]. Using this new E²PROM cell and introducing a new erasing system and new circuitry, which consists of a new program circuit and a high-speed sense amplifier, a high-performance 256-kbit "flash E²PROM" has been successfully developed. This new E²PROM can simultaneously and instantly erase the contents of all the memory cells.

Section II provides a comparison of the characteristics of the new device and current devices, and explains the advantages of the flash E²PROM. Section III describes the memory cell design and the circuit design of the 256-kbit flash E²PROM. Section IV shows the typical characteristics of the device and the conclusion is presented in Section V.

Manuscript received June 10, 1985; revised January 21, 1987.

The authors are with the Microelectronics Center, Integrated Circuit Division, Toshiba Corporation, Komukai 1, Toshiba-cho, Saiwai-ku, Kawasaki 210, Japan.

IEEE Log Number 8715081.

TABLE I
COMPARISON BETWEEN NEW DEVICE AND CURRENT DEVICES

	CURRENT DEVICE			NEW DEVICE
	UV-EPROM	ONE TIME PROM	CURRENT E²PROM	FLASH E²PROM
PACKAGE	CERAMIC WITH WINDOW ✕	PLASTIC ○	PLASTIC ○	PLASTIC ○
ERASE TIME	20 min ✕	NO ERASE ✕	1 msec ○	100 ms ○
PROGRAM TIME	< 1 msec ○	< 1 msec ○	< 1 msec ○	200 μsec ○
CELL AREA (2μm ground rule)	64 μm² ○	64 μm² ○	270 μm² ✕	64 μm² ○
CHIP AREA 256K BIT (2μm rule)	32.9 mm² ○	32.9 mm² ○	≃98 mm² ✕	32.9 mm² ○
RELIABILITY	SCREENING ○	NO SCREENING ✕	SCREENING ○	SCREENING ○
ERASER	UV LIGHT ✕	NO NEED ○	ELECTRI-CALLY ○	ELECTRI-CALLY ○
STRUCTURE	DOUBLE POLY-Si	DOUBLE POLY-Si	DOUBLE POLY-Si	TRIPLE POLY-Si

II. ADVANTAGES OF THE NEW FLASH E²PROM

Table I compares the characteristics of the new device with current devices. In this case, the current devices are listed as a UV-EPROM, one-time PROM, and current E²PROM.

Conventional UV-EPROM's are expensive because of their ceramic package with a window, compared to a plastic package. In addition, UV-EPROM's take a longer time for erasing the memory cell contents than E²PROM's; it takes over 20 min for UV erasing. Of course, the one-time PROM cannot be erased after programming. Programming times are generally less than 1 ms for all devices. Therefore E²PROM's have large advantages. On the other hand, current E²PROM cells consist of two transistors per bit. This results in a very large cell size, for example, 270 μm². Thus, the estimated chip size for 256 kbits with a 2-μm design rule is about 98 mm².

Obviously, it is always important to reduce the chip area as much as possible. The flash E²PROM has an answer. The cell size of a flash E²PROM is 64 μm² and the chip size measures 32.9 mm², which is the same as a UV-EPROM. It should also be noted that a one-time PROM

Reprinted from *IEEE J. Solid-State Circuits*, vol. SC-22, no. 4, pp. 548–552, August 1987.

197

in a plastic package is cheaper but cannot confirm cell reliability by screening test before shipment, unlike the other devices including the flash E²PROM. Finally, a UV-EPROM needs both a large UV-light eraser and a programmer.

As noted above, current devices have some disadvantages. Therefore the new flash E²PROM which overcomes these defects is the preferable device to replace the UV-EPROM.

III. DEVICE TECHNOLOGY OF A 256-KBIT FLASH E²PROM

A new type of E²PROM cell which is available for high-density E²PROM's is applied to a $32K \times 8$-bit flash E²PROM. Triple-polysilicon technology is combined with new circuit techniques for achieving fast programming and erasing time and high-speed operation. A unique erasing system makes this new E²PROM pin compatible with a 256-kbit UV-EPROM.

A. Memory Cell Design

The basic structure of the flash E²PROM cell is shown in Fig. 1(a)–(c). This single transistor per bit memory cell consists of three polysilicon layers including the selection transistor. The erase gate is made of the first polysilicon layer which is located on the field oxide. The floating gate is made of the second polysilicon layer and partially located on the erase gate. The control gate is made of the third polysilicon layer and functions as a word select line during programming and reading. The bit line consists of metal and the ground line of n^+ diffusion. The memory cell unit area is shown by a dashed line labeled A, B, C, and D. The cell is programmed by the same channel hot-carrier injection mechanism as that used in UV-EPROM's. The flash erasing is achieved by using field emission of electrons from the floating gate to the erase gate. In order to capture hot electrons efficiently, the floating gate is located near the drain where hot carriers are generated. The cell configuration prevents the cell from being pushed into the depletion mode as a result of over-erasing, by utilizing the enhancement-type selection transistor. The cell size is 8×8 μm^2 and is as small as a UV-EPROM cell using 2-μm design rule.

Fig. 2 shows an SEM photograph of the flash E²PROM cell in an array. The right-hand side illustrates the photograph on the left. Two cells have one erase-gate polysilicon in common to minimize the cell area. As a result, the same area as a UV-EPROM can be realized by using proper cell layout.

B. Circuit Design

1. Erasing: The concept of erasing without any additional pins is shown in Fig. 3. An internal erase voltage is generated by the on-chip charge pump circuit. The erase operation is performed by supplying the A_{10} address input with 12 V. A high erase voltage V_E is supplied to the erase

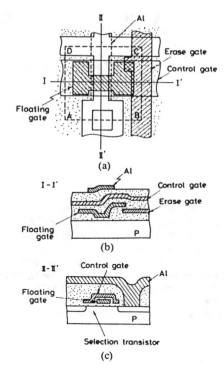

Fig. 1. Cell structure consisting of three levels of polysilicon: (a) top view of flash E²PROM cell; (b) cross section along I–I′ line in (a); and (c) cross section along II–II′ line in (a).

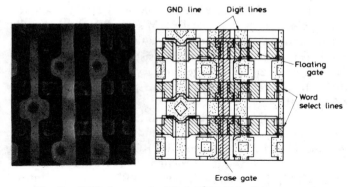

Fig. 2. SEM photograph of flash E²PROM cell in an array.

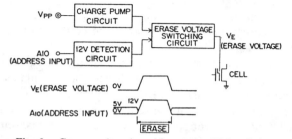

Fig. 3. Concept of erasing without any additional pins.

gate from the charge pump circuit through the erase-voltage switching circuit, which controls the output voltage V_E corresponding to an erase signal. As a 12-V detecting circuit is introduced to receive the erase signal, the number of input pins does not increase. Thus, pin compatibility with a UV-EPROM can be achieved. The erase system of

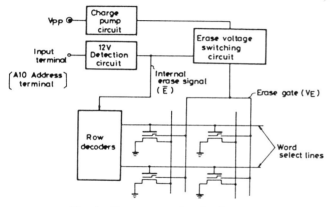

Fig. 4. Erase system of flash E^{2}PROM.

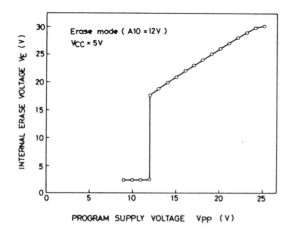

Fig. 5. Program supply voltage versus internal erase voltage.

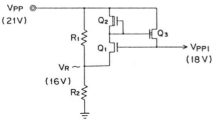

Fig. 6. Program voltage regulator.

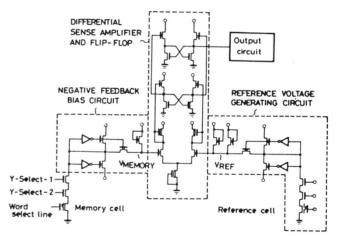

Fig. 7. Schematic of sense amplifier.

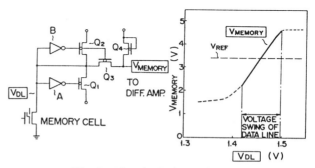

Fig. 8. Negative feedback bias circuit.

the flash E^{2}PROM is shown in Fig. 4. In the erase mode, in response to the internal erase signal, all of the word select lines become 0 V and a high erase voltage is applied to the all erase gates in the array. Fig. 5 shows the internal erase voltage as a function of the program supply voltage V_{pp}. The erase function is engaged when the V_{pp} supply voltage is raised above 12 V, and an erase voltage is generated. In this figure, when 21 V is applied to V_{pp}, an erase voltage as large as 27 V has been obtained.

2. Programming: A program supply voltage of 21 V has been adopted to make this flash E^{2}PROM compatible with 21-V 64K and 128K UV-EPROM's. In order to get the proper voltage for these small devices, a new program voltage regulator was used as shown in Fig. 6. This circuit consists of a reference-voltage generating circuit, whose output voltage V_R is made by dividing V_{pp} voltage through the polysilicon resistors R_1 and R_2, and a feedback circuit which is composed of the transistors Q_1–Q_3. The internal program supply voltage V_{pp_I} is fixed at 18 V and can supply up to 30 mA of output current, when V_{pp} is 21 V.

3. New Sense-Amplifier Circuitry: The schematic of the sense amplifier is shown in Fig. 7. In order to realize high-speed operation with a wide margin of READ operation, a negative feedback bias circuit and differential sense amplifier were used. The reference voltage of this amplifier is generated by a reference circuit with a reference cell.

Fig. 8 shows the operation of the negative feedback bias circuit. In response to the stored data of the cell, the feedback circuit, composed of inverters A, B and transistors Q_1, Q_2, restricts the voltage swing of the data line V_{DL} to within 0.1 V. Then, by transistors Q_3 and Q_4, the voltage swing of the output voltage V_{MEMORY} is amplified to about 2.5 V. The reference voltage V_{REF} was designed to be one-half of the voltage swing of V_{MEMORY}. Fig. 9 shows the operation of the differential sense amplifier and the flip-flop circuits. The differential amplifier quickly detects the data logic ZERO or ONE at the point where the voltage of V_{MEMORY} crosses the reference voltage V_{REF}. Two flip-flop circuits sufficiently amplify the data signal from the differential amplifier, and the high- or low-level voltage on node A is transmitted to the output circuit. Then, the output voltage V_{OUT} quickly swings to full level. In this

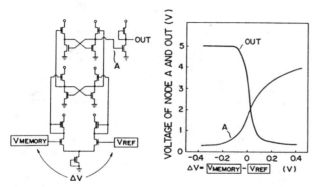

Fig. 9.   Differential sense amplifier and flip-flop circuit.

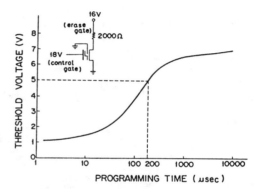

Fig. 12.   Programming characteristics.

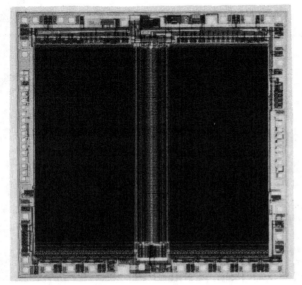

Fig. 10.   Photomicrograph of the 256-kbit flash E²PROM.

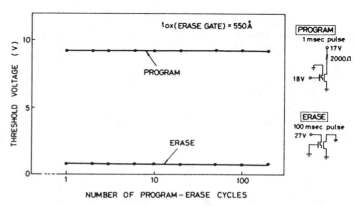

Fig. 13.   Characteristics of program–erase endurance.

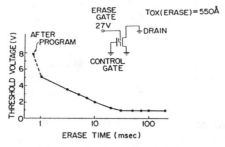

Fig. 11.   Erasing characteristics.

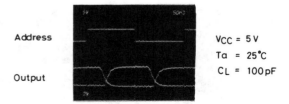

Fig. 14.   Operating waveforms.

way, a high-speed sense circuit with wide operating margin has been obtained.

A photomicrograph of the 256-kbit flash E²PROM is shown in Fig. 10. The memory cell area occupies about 51 percent of the whole chip area. The chip size is 5.69×5.78 mm².

IV.   Characteristics

The erase time versus threshold voltage of the cell is shown in Fig. 11. During erase, the drain, the source, and the control gate are grounded and 27 V is applied to the erase gate. The cell is completely erased by a pulse width of less than 100 ms. Programming time versus threshold voltage is shown in Fig. 12. The control gate is supplied with 18 V and the drain of the cell is supplied with 16 V through the 2-kΩ resistance which is equivalent to the load transistor. A threshold voltage of 5 V has been achieved with programming time as fast as 200 μs, similar to that of a UV-EPROM. Fig. 13 shows the typical program and erase cycle characteristics. Program and erase conditions are shown on the right. After 200 cycles, the threshold-voltage window remains constant. Fig. 14 shows an oscillograph of the address input and the data output waveforms. The access time from an address input signal change of 90 ns is achieved under the typical conditions. The features and the typical characteristics of the 256-kbit flash E²PROM are listed in Table II.

TABLE II
FEATURES OF THE 256-KBIT FLASH E^{2}PROM

○ PROCESS	: NMOS TRIPLE POLYSILICON TECHNOLOGY
○ ORGANIZATION	: 32K WORD × 8 BIT
○ CHIP SIZE	: 5.69 × 5.78 mm²
○ CELL SIZE	: 8 × 8 μm²
○ ACCESS TIME	: 90 ns (5V, 25°C)
○ PROGRAM TIME	: 200 μs /BYTE
○ ERASE TIME	: 100 ms /CHIP
○ POWER DISSIPATION	: OPERATING 60 mA (5V, 25°C) STANDBY 10 mA (5V, 25°C)
○ POWER SUPPLY	: READ ----- SINGLE 5V PROGRAM / ERASE 21V
○ PACKAGE	: 28 PIN 600 MIL DIP
○ COMPATIBILITY	: FULLY PIN COMPATIBLE WITH 256K UV-EPROM

V. CONCLUSION

A 256-kbit flash E^{2}PROM has been developed by intro-ducing a triple-polysilicon technology. A small cell size of 8×8 μm^2 is achieved even with relatively conservative 2-μm design rules. This flash E^{2}PROM is fully pin com-patible with a 256-kbit UV-EPROM without increasing the number of pins by introducing a unique erasing sys-tem. Fast access time and wide operating margin have been achieved by using the negative feedback sense-ampli-fier circuitry. The new compact cell is successfully incorpo-rated into a die size comparable with that of UV-EPROM's.

This approach appears to be very promising, and could be an industry standard E^{2}PROM technology.

ACKNOWLEDGMENT

The authors would like to thank K. Suzuki and M. Ueno for their continuous encouragement throughout this work. The authors are also thankful to H. Minagawa for the cooperative effort and T. Tsushima for his contribution to this work.

REFERENCES

[1] K. Okumura et al., "A 1Mb EPROM," in 1984 ISSCC Dig. Tech. Papers, THAM 10.3, pp. 140–141.
[2] S. Saito et al., "A programmable 80ns 1Mb CMOS EPROM," in 1985 ISSCC Dig. Tech. Papers, THPM 13.8, pp. 176–177.
[3] T. Hagiwara et al., "Page mode programming 1Mb CMOS EPROM," in 1985 ISSCC Dig. Tech. Papers, THPM 13.7, pp. 174–175.
[4] D. H. Oto et al., "High-voltage regulation and process consideration for high-density 5 V-only E^{2}PROM's," IEEE J. Solid-State Circuits, vol. SC-18, no. 5, pp. 532–538, Oct. 1983.
[5] F. Masuoka, "Bit by bit erasable E^{2}PROM with single transistor per bit," in 1981 IEDM Tech. Dig., 2.1, pp. 20–23.
[6] F. Masuoka et al., "A new flash E^{2}PROM cell using triple polysili-con technology," in 1984 IEDM Tech. Dig., 17.3, pp. 464–467.

Paper 5.9

A 5 VOLT HIGH DENSITY POLY-POLY ERASE FLASH EPROM CELL

R. Kazerounian, S. Ali, Y. Ma, and B. Eitan

WaferScale Integration, Inc.
47280 Kato Road, Fremont, California 94538

ABSTRACT

A 5 volt only Flash EPROM cell is described which is programmed by channel hot electron injection and erased through poly-poly oxide. The cell consists of a self-aligned split gate EPROM and a polysilicon erase line. A charge pumping technique which takes advantage of very low programming current is employed to ensure fast programming at worst case condition of 125°C and 4.5V supply. An overerase technique is used to achieve a uniform erase, high read current, and extended endurance. The Flash cell is implemented in a staggered virtual ground array which yields a cell size of 18µm with 1.2µm design rules in a double poly CMOS EPROM process.

INTRODUCTION

The increasing demand for high density low cost, on-board programmable non-volatile memory devices has resulted in the introduction of Flash EPROM devices. The conventional Flash devices disclosed so far have the disadvantage of requiring a 12V supply in addition to a 5V supply for read operation [1,2,3,4]. In this paper, a new Flash EPROM cell concept is introduced which requires a single 5 volt supply for both programming and erase. This concept relies on a self-aligned split gate EPROM structure [5,6], and poly-poly erase mechanism.

Programming of EPROM devices directly from Vcc supply is not feasible due to low efficiency of hot electron injection. To overcome this problem a new concept of 5 volt only programming is developed which is based on reduction of channel programming current to below 1µA level. The low programming current allows on-chip generation of a high voltage on bit lines to ensure reliable programming at the worst case condition of 4.5 volt supply and 125°C. The cell is erased through poly-poly oxide which has a low erase current and makes it possible to generate the erase voltage from a 5 volt supply.

To meet the high density requirement of Flash EPROM a new staggered virtual ground array architecture is employed which yields 18µm^2 cell size with 1.2µm design rules. With 1.0µm design rules a cell size of 11 µm^2 can be achieved which is very competitive with dense EPROM technologies.

CELL STRUCTURE

The Flash cell consists of a single self-aligned split gate EPROM device and a shared poly erase gate. Cell layout and cross sections are shown in Figures (1a, 1b). The erase gate is formed from the second layer of polysilicon and overlaps part of the floating gate to form the erase area. The erase area, which is defined by the crossings of floating gate and erase gate is misalignment insensitive which yields a uniform erase over the entire array.

To achieve a small cell size, a new staggered virtual ground array architecture is developed which takes advantage of asymmetrical self-aligned split gate EPROM (Figure 2). In this array one erase line is shared between two word lines and runs across the whole array. To increase packing density drain of Flash cells are alternating between odd and even word lines. The cell size in this array is 18 µm^2 with 1.2 µm design rules. The memory array is flash erased by raising the voltage on erase lines while keeping word and bit lines at zero volts.

The Flash cell is implemented in a double poly CMOS process which is the same as split gate EPROM process with no modifications.

Reprinted from the *IEDM Tech. Dig.*, pp. 436-439, 1988.

PROGRAMMING

To program conventional EPROM devices by channel hot electron injection, a drain voltage of more than 5V is usually required. Lowering the voltage to 5 volts, especially at high temperatures (125 °C), reduces hot electron injection and increases the programming time to a level which is impractical for most on board applications. The only solution to 5V programming proposed in the literature uses source side injection and requires a complicated spacer technology which is not suitable for low cost EPROM technology [7]. To enhance programming efficiency at low voltages, doping concentration can be increased to the range of 10^{17} to 10^{18} cm^{-3}. Above this doping level, junction avalanche breakdown and surface band to band tunneling limit the maximum bit line voltage below 6V. Figure (3) shows low voltage programming characteristics of an optimized cell with high doping concentration and short channel length. The results at high temperature indicate that straight forward optimization of the cell is not a solution to 5 volt programming. Further reduction of effective channel length was found to have little effect on programming rate in the case of heavily doped channel.

To overcome the low voltage programming problem, the Flash cell is optimized such that hot electron injection efficiency (Ig/Id) is by a factor of over 1000 higher compared to a typical EPROM. As a result, the required channel current during programming is reduced below 1μA as can be seen from the one shot programming characteristics of the cell, Figure (4). This low current allows a high bit line voltage up to 8 volts to be supplied to the cell by using an on chip charge pump. To keep the cell programming current during charge pumping below 1 μA level, a current controlled technique is employed which relies on application of a back bias voltage to the cell [8]. Figure (5) shows the equivalent circuit diagram of the cell as implemented in the array. Programming characteristics of the cell in this configuration is shown in Figure (6). A programming time of less than 1 mS at the worst case condition of 125 C is achieved which is no longer limited by the minimum supply voltage of 4.5 volts. To avoid read disturb, the maximum bit line voltage is kept below 1.5V during read.

ERASE

The cell is electrically erased through a 450 Å poly-poly oxide. The required erase voltage is above 27 volts which is generated using an on-chip charge pump. Special high voltage devices with N-well junction and double poly gate are used in charge pump circuitry to prevent extra processing steps. The poly-poly erase offers two advantages over the conventional drain or source bit line erase. First, poly erase current (<1 μA per 256K cells) is much smaller than the band to band tunneling induced current of bit line erase(~1e-8 A per cell) which makes it easier to generate the erase voltage from a 5 volt supply. Second, the poly-poly erase path is completely isolated from the programming path which was found essential to optimize the cell for 5 volt programming. In addition, with bit line erase a complicated optimization of two junctions for programming (N+/P+) and erase (N+/N-) is needed which can be avoided by using poly erase.

The erase coupling is less than 0.15 which results in good erase characteristics. An example of the cell erase is shown in Figure (7), where erase time is less than 100mS. In practice, the inherent select device in split gate cell makes it immune to overerase. As a result, the cell can be overerased to achieve a high read current and a uniform erase which depends only on the select device. The overerase characteristics of the cell is shown in Figure (8). Increase of the erase gate voltage forces the floating gate into depletion and results in a higher read current controlled by the select device.

A recognized problem with poly-poly oxide is electron trapping which slows down erase and results in premature cycling window closure [9]. To compensate for electron trapping in the Flash cell an overerase method is employed which can ensure as high as 10000 cycles. The overerase feature is implemented in a 256K Flash device by the use of a programmable charge pump regulation scheme [10].

RELIABILITY

Endurance behavior of the Flash cell is shown in Figure (9) where a 10000 cycle is achieved. The retention characteristics of the poly-poly erase is studied on 256K Flash devices and 10-year lifetime is guaranteed.

SUMMARY

Poly-poly erase and split gate structure were two essential elements which made it possible to develop a 5 volt only Flash EPROM cell. A new concept for 5 volt only programming is developed to ensure reliable performance over the worst case conditions. An over erase method is employed to achieve 10000 cycles. A staggered virtual ground array is introduced to achieve a small cell size. The cell is implemented in a double poly EPROM process with no process changes which preserves the low cost nature of Flash EPROM.

REFERENCES

[1] S. Mukherjee, et al., "A Single Transistor EEPROM Cell and Its Implementation in a 512K CMOS EEPROM", IEDM, 26.1, 1985.

[2] H. Kume, et al., "Flash Erase EEPROM Cell with an Asymetric Source and Drain Structure", IEDM, 25.8, 1987.

[3] S. Tam, et al., "A High Density 1-T Electrically Erasable Non- Volatile (Flash) Memory Technology", 4-4, Symposium on VLSI Technology, 1988.

[4] F. Masuoka, et al., "A New Flash EEPROM Cell using Triple Poly- silicon Technology", IEDM, 17.3, 1984.

[5] S. Ali, et al., "A 50 NS 256K CMOS Split Gate EPROM", IEEE J. of Solid State Circuits, p. 122, 1988.

[6] B. Eitan, U.S. Patent #4639893.

[7] A. T. Wu, et al., "A Novel High Speed, 5 Volt Programming EPROM Structure with Source Side Injection", IEDM, 26.2, 1986.

[8] R. Kazerounian and B. Eitan, patent pending.

[9] S. K. Lai, et al., "Comparison and Trends in Today's Dominant EEPROM Technologies", IEDM, 26.1, 1986.

[10] R. Kazerounian, S. Ali, B. Eitan, patent pending.

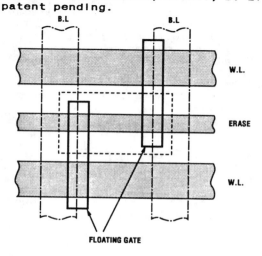

FLOATING GATE

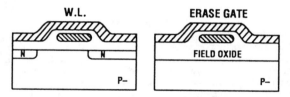

Figure (1) (a) Layout of Flash cell(not to scale), (b) Cross-sectional views of the cell.

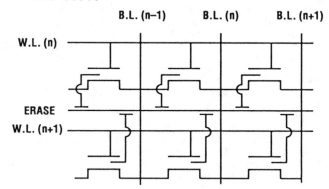

Figure (2) Schematic diagram of staggered virtual ground array.

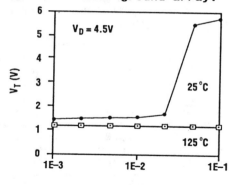

Figure (3) Programmed threshold voltage of optimized cell under low drain voltage.

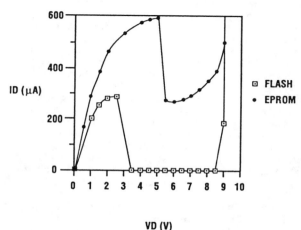

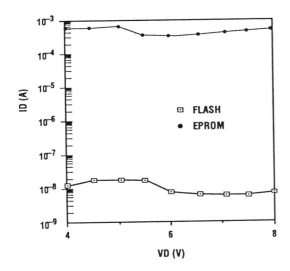

Figure (4) (a) One shot I-V's of Flash and Typical EPROM cell, (b) An expanded portion of 4(a) on logarithmic scale.

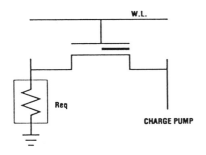

Figure (5) Equivalent circuit diagram of cell in the array.

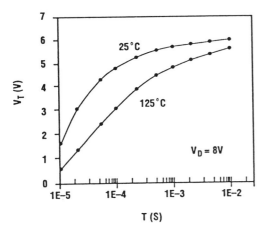

Figure (6) Programming characteristics of the Flash cell at room and high temperature.

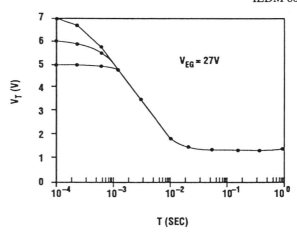

Figure (7) Erase threshold voltage of the cell as a function of time.

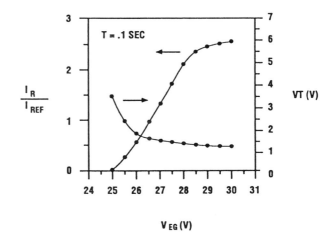

Figure (8) Overerase characteristics.

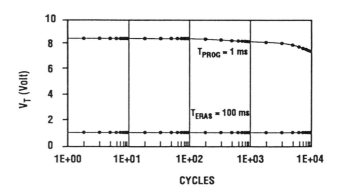

Figure (9) Cell endurance characteristics.

Paper 5.10

A 5V-Only 256k Bit CMOS Flash EEPROM

Sebastiano D'Arrigo, Giuliano Imondi, Giovanni Santin, Manzur Gill, Rinn Cleavelin, Stefano Spagliccia,
Elvio Tomassetti, Sung Lin, Arthur Nguyen, Pradeep Shah, Guiseppi Savarese, Dave McElroy
Texas Instruments Incorporated
Houston, TX

THIS PAPER DESCRIBES A Flash EEPROM device which requires only 5V for program, erase, and read operations and has performance and cost comparable to that of the recently-reported dual-power-supply flash EEPROMs which require 12V for programming and erase, and 5V for read[1]. Figure 1 shows the cross section of the 256k bit flash EEPROM memory cell, which consists of a floating-gate transistor and a merged-pass-gate transistor. The process is array-contactless EEPROM (ACEE), with buried source/drain for the bit lines with a tunnel oxide module and a 20V CMOS module.

The program and erase operations employ the Fowler-Nordheim current tunnelled through 100A oxide, when the proper electrical voltages are applied to the selected bit (Fig. 2). To program bit 21, a pulse of 18V amplitude and 10ms duration is applied to word line 2 (WL2) with source S1 tied to ground and drain D1 floating. During the same timeframe, to prevent bit 2 from programming, source S2 is tied to 7V with drain D2 floating, so that the total voltage across the tunnel region is not adequate to start the tunnelling current. During programming of bit 21, bit 12 is stressed and could be de-programmed because source S2 is at 7V. This stress is avoided by applying a pulse of 7V to the de-selected WL1. Consequently, the de-selected bit 11 cannot program because the voltage across the tunnel region (7V) is inadequate to start the tunnelling current.

All operating voltages, +18V for program, +7V for program inhibit, -11V for erase, are internally generated from the 5V supply through charge-pump circuits. The bulk erase operation is performed by applying a negative high-voltage pulse to all the word lines and 5V to all the bit lines at the same time. The negative pulse is generated with a cascade of 4 P-channel-only voltage multiplier stages. Figure 3 shows the multiplier stage circuit and the 4 non-overlapping phases required for operation. When the 4 phases become active, node B discharges to node A through T4 and node C discharges to node B through T6, so that a negative voltage is established at node C. T3 and T5 enhance the conduction performance of T4 and T6 and the multiplication efficiency of the stage. Figure 4 shows the negative pulse waveform.

Figure 5 shows the electrical schematic of the level shifter driving the word line to +18V (program) or to -11V (erase) or to +3V (read selected word line) or to 0V (de-selected word line). The P-channel transistor P1 prevents the negative voltage from being clamped by the drain junction of transistor N1 and the P-channel transistor P2 permits driving all the word lines to -11V during erase and isolating one word line from the rest during programming. Figure 6 shows the measured access time. Memory alteration is not possible if the program or the erase mode is not accessed through a specified sequence of 3 commands for programming and 6 commands for erase. Both sequences are loaded in an internal register. Only after the proper sequence of commands has been detected by the device are the programming and erase operations enabled. These sequences and command timings can be easily generated by software in a microprocessor. Protection against inadvertent alterations during power-up or power-down is also provided. Figure 7 shows the typical VTH distribution of the 256k bits after erase and programming. Figure 8 shows the endurance of the cell. Figure 9 is the chip micrograph and Table 1 summarizes the device and technology parameters.

Acknowledgement

The authors thank M. Smayling for technical advice.

[1]Kynette, V.N., et. al., "An In-System Reprogrammable 256K CMOS Flash Memory", ISSCC DIGEST of TECHNICAL PAPERS, p.132-133; Feb. 1988.

PROCESS	ACEE – CMOS; ILO = 350A; TOX = 100A PERIPHERY GOX = 250A/500A
PROGRAM	FOWLER-NORDHEIM TUNNELING
ERASE	FOWLER-NORDHEIM TUNNELING
MINIMUM FEATURE	1.5 UM
CELL SIZE	40 UM2
CHIP SIZE	46 KMILS2
ORGANIZATION	32KX8
ACCESS TIME	170 NS
PROGRAMMING TIME	150 US/BYTE EQUIVALENT (PAGE MODE)
ERASE TIME	10MS

TABLE 1 — Device characteristics

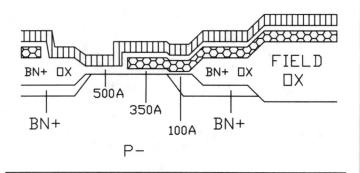

FIGURE 1 — Cross sectional diagram of 5V memory cell

Reprinted from the *IEEE ISSCC Dig. Tech. Pap.*, pp. 132–133, 313, 1989.

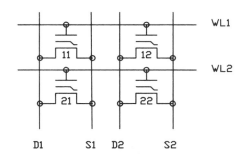

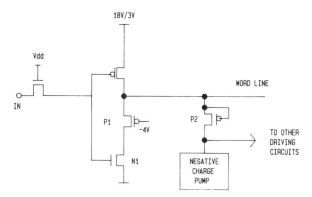

FIGURE 5 — Word line driving circuit

CELL '21' OPERATING CONDITIONS

	WL1	WL2	S1	D1	S2	D2
ERASE	−11V	−11V	5V	FLOAT	5V	FLOAT
PROGRAM	7V	18V	0V	FLOAT	7V	FLOAT
READ	0	3	0	1V	0	1V

FIGURE 2 — 5V cell operating conditions

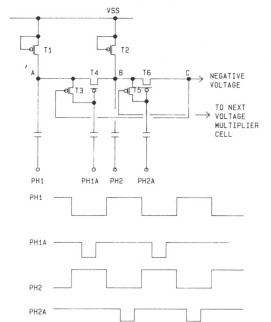

FIGURE 3 — Negative charge pump multiplier stage and 4 non-overlapping phases

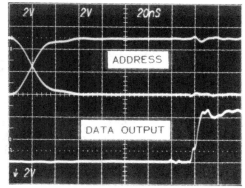

FIGURE 6 — Access time

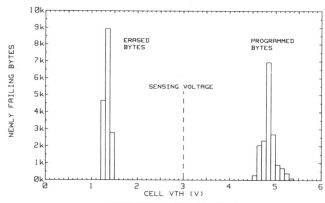

FIGURE 7 — V$_{th}$ distribution

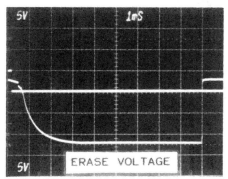

FIGURE 4 — Negative erase pulse wave form

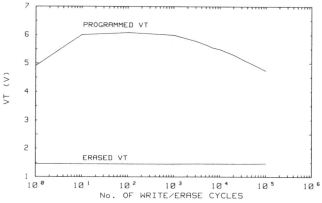

FIGURE 8 — Cell endurance

207

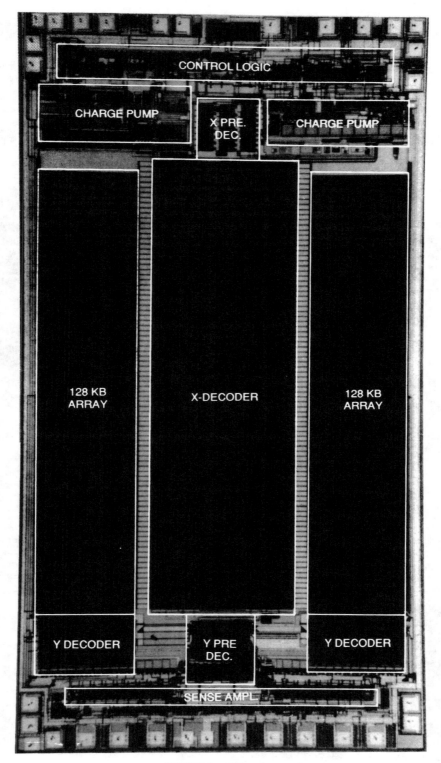

FIGURE 9 — Chip micrograph

A 5 VOLT ONLY 16M BIT FLASH EEPROM CELL WITH A SIMPLE STACKED GATE STRUCTURE

N. Ajika, M. Ohi, H. Arima, T. Matsukawa and N. Tsubouchi

LSI Research and Development Laboratory
Mitsubishi Electric Corporation
4-1 Mizuhara, Itami, Hyogo, Japan

ABSTRACT

We obtain a 3.6 μm^2 5 volt only 16 mega bit flash EEPROM cell using a simple stacked gate structure and conventional 0.6 μm CMOS process.

We realize a single 5 volt power supply operation of simple stacked gate cell by optimizing the well impurity concentration, drain structure and using a gate negative biased erasing operation.

It is also shown that the gate negative biased erasing operation mode is very effective to improve the cell endurance characteristics.

INTRODUCTION

In recent years, developments of high density nonvolatile memories, especially flash EEPROMs have been successfully carried out[1]-[6]. However, further high density and low cost are still needed to get the huge market of the external data storage devices of computers.

While several kinds of cell structures for flash EEPROMs are reported[1]-[6], the cell which has a self-aligned double polysilicon stacked gate structure without a select transistor is one of the most promising device for high density low cost nonvolatile memories[2]. However 5 volt single power supply operation is not yet realized using this cell structure, because the drain voltage during the programming operation and source voltage during the erasing operation cannot be obtained by using an on-chip high voltage generator. Tehrefore rather complicated cell structures for 5 volt only flash EEPROMs are proposed previously[5][6].

We obtain a 3.6 μm^2 5 volt only 16 mega bit flash EEPROM cell with a simple stacked gate structure by optimizing the drain structure, well impurity concentration and using gate negative erasing operation[7].

PROCESS TECHNOLOGY

This cell uses a twin well, double level polysilicon and double layers of metal, based on 0.6 μm CMOS process. A modified LOCOS isolation is used with a 600 nm thick field oxide adequate to 12 volts programming voltage. The CMOS peripheral circuits have 15 nm gate oxides, an LDD structure for n-channel transistors and 25 nm gate oxides for high voltage transistors. The floating gate oxide is 10 nm thick and oxide equivalent thickness of the inter polysilicon dielectric (oxide-nitride-oxide layers) is 20 nm. The key process technologies are listed in Table 1.

Technology	Twin well CMOS Double level polysilicon Double layers of Metal
Leff (min)	Nch 0.6 μm Pch 0.8 μm
Field Oxide	600 nm
Tunnel Oxide	10 nm
Peripheral Gate Oxide	15 nm
High Voltage Gate	25 nm
Inter Poly Dielectric	20 nm (effective)

Table 1. Major process technology of the proposed cell.

CELL STRUCTURE

Figure 1 shows a schematic drawing of the cell. This cell has an area of 3.6 μm^2 (1.8 μm X 2.0 μm) and uses the simple self-aligned double polysilicon stacked gate structure.

The first polysilicon layer is used as the floating gate and the second is used as the control gate and peripheral gates. The first aluminum layer forms the bit line and the second aluminum layer stitches the polysilicon word line to reduce the word line resistance for high speed performance. Figure 2 shows a cross sectional SEM micrograph of the finished cell.

Reprinted from the *IEDM Tech. Dig.*, pp. 115–118, 1990.

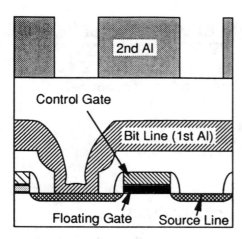

Figure 1. Schematic drawing of the cell.

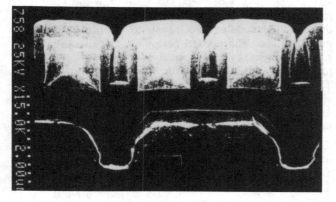

Figure 2. Cross sectional SEM micrograph of the cell.

CELL CHARACTERISTICS

[Program]

Figure 3 shows the program characteristics of the obtained cell. Nominal programming drain voltage of 5 volts with an acceptable pulse width of 10 µsecs can be realized by the optimization of the drain structure and well impurity concentration.

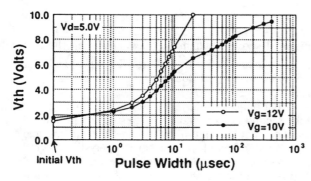

Figure 3. Program characteristics of the cell. Programming of Vd=5V is realized.

[Erase]

It is very important for 5 volt only operation of stacked gate type flash EEPROM to reduce the source voltage during the erase operation as well as the drain voltage during the programming operation. High impurity concentration of the well, to obtain the high hot electron generation efficiency and 0.6 µm transistor operation, causes a low breakdown voltage of the source junction and a high leakage current during the erase operation. So that the high voltage applied to the source region during the erasing operation cannot be obtained by an on-chip high voltage generator. We adopt the gate negative biased erasing condition[7] to realize a 5 volt single power supply operation.

Figure 4 shows the cell erase characteristics. By using the gate negative (-12V) erasing, acceptable erase characteristics with source voltage of 5 volts is obtained instead of the conventional source 10 volts biased erasing. Because of low current requirements, the high voltage applied to the control gate, which is required during the programming and erase operation, can be generated internally from a single external 5 volt supply. The conditions for various operations are summarized in Table 2.

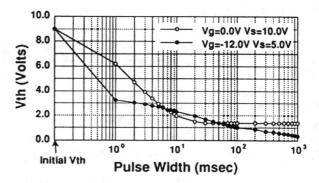

Figure 4. Erase characteristics of the cell. Erasing of Vs=5V is realized by using gate negative (-12V) erasing condition.

	Bit Line	Control Gate	Source Line
Write	5V	12V	GND
Erase	Floating	−12V	5V
Read	1V	5V	GND

Table 2. Operational conditions for the cell.

[Endurance]

Another advantage of the gate negative erasing operation is to suppress the hole generation, because of the reduction of lateral electric field at the source edge[7][8]. Figure 5 shows the gate current and source current versus source voltage characteristics of the memory cell whose control gate and floating gate are

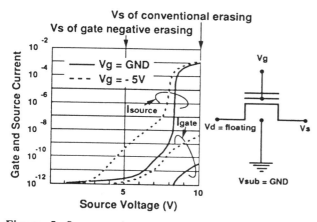

Figure 5. Source and gate current versus source voltage characteristics. The control gate and floating gate of this transistor are connected electrically. Solid lines show the I-V characteristics of gate grounded condition and broken lines show those of gate negative biased condition. A -5 volts gate biased condition of this transistor coincides with -12 volts biased condition of the memory cell.

connected electrically. Solid lines show the I-V characteristics of gate grounded condition and broken lines show that of the gate negative biased condition. Since the well impurity concentration is rather high, junction breakdown voltage of the source region is low (about 8V). Using gate negative erasing, as the erasing begins to take place at much lower source voltage (5V) than that of junction breakdown, gate current consists mainly not of the holes generated by avalanche breakdown but of the F-N tunneling electrons. Since hole injection causes serious degradation to the gate oxides [7][9], this gate negative erasing operation may lead to high endurance characteristics.

A single cell endurance is shown in figure 6. Compared with conventional gate grounded erasing operation, the gate negative erasing improves the endurance characteristics remarkably.

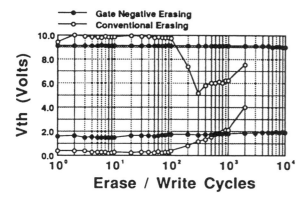

Figure 6. Endurance characteristics of the cell. Gate negative erasing operation improves the endurance characteristics remarkably.

[Disturb]

This type of cell suffers the disturb phenomena because of its structure that has no select gate transistor. There are four types of disturb phenomena which are
(1) drain disturb which is an undesired erasing of the unselected cell during programming of the other cells on the same bit line,
(2) gate disturb (poly/poly mode) which is an undesired erasing of the unselected cell through the inter-poly dielectric during programming of the other cells on the same word line,
(3) gate disturb (tunnel SiO_2 mode) which is an undesired programming of the unselected cell through the tunneling oxide during programming of the other cells on the same word line and
(3) read disturb which is an undesired programming during read operation.

All kinds of disturb characteristics are shown in figure 7. The number of cells connected to a word line or a bit line is about the order of 1000, for 16 mega bit flash EEPROMs. That means the longest disturbing time is about the order of 10 msecs for the drain and gate disturb. The longest disturbing time for read disturb is 10 years. Figure 7 clearly shows that all these disturb characteristics are acceptable for actual device operation.

(a)
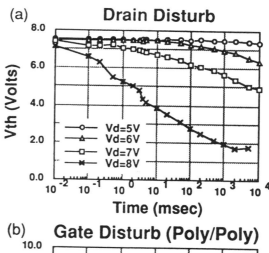

(b)
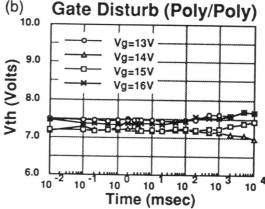

(c)

Gate Disturb (Tunnel SiO2)

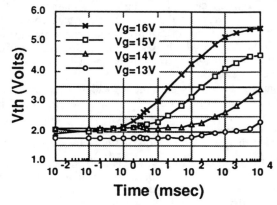

(d)

Read Disturb

Vd=1.0V

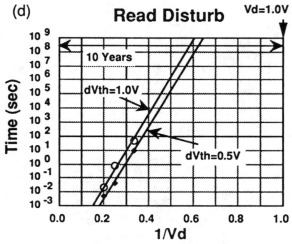

Figure 7. Disturb characteristics of the cell. (a) Drain disturb. (b) Gate disturb (poly/poly mode). (c) Gate disturb (tunnel oxide mode). (d) Read disturb. All these disturb characteristics are acceptable for actual device operation.

CONCLUSION

A simple stacked gate cell which has an area of 3.6 μm^2 using 0.6 μm conventional CMOS process has been developed. Obtained cell can be programmed and erased by a 5 volt single power supply by using the gate negative erasing operation. Using the currently available process technology and the proposed operation condition, a high performance, high reliability and low cost 16 mega bit 5 volt only flash EEPROM will be realized.

ACKNOWLEDGEMENTS

The authors would like to thank Dr. Y. Terada and Messrs. T. Nakayama, S. Kobayashi, Y. Miyawaki, M. Akazawa and T. Katayama for their technical assistance and helpful discussions. They also wish to thank Drs. T. Yoshihara, T. Nakano and H. Komiya for their encouragement and support.

REFERENCES

(1) F. Masuoka, M. Asano, H. Iwasaki, T. Komuro and S. Tanaka, "A New Flash EEPROM Cell Using Triple Polysilicon Technology," IEDM Tech. Dig., (1984) pp. 464.

(2) S. Mukherjee, T. Chang, R. Pang, M. Knecht and D. Hu, "A Single Transistor EEPROM Cell and its Implementation in a 512K CMOS EEPROM," IEDM Tech. Dig., (1985) pp. 616.

(3) G. Samachisa, C. Su, Y. Kao, G. Samarandoiu, T. Wang and C. Hu, "A 128K Flash EEPROM Using Double Polysilicon Technology," ISSCC Dig. Tech. Papers, (1987) pp. 76.

(4) F. Masuoka, M. Momodomi, Y. Iwata and R. Shirota, "New Ultra High Density EPROM and Flash EEPROM with NAND Structure Cell," IEDM Tech. Dig. (1987) pp. 552.

(5) R. Kazerounian, S. All, Y. Ma and B. Eltan, "A 5 Volt High Density Poly-Poly Erase Flash EPROM Cell," IEDM Tech. Dig. (1988) pp. 436.

(6) B. Riemenschneider, A. L. Esquivel, J. Raterson, M. Gill, S. Lin, J. Schrech, D. McElroy, P. Truong, R. Bussey, B. Ashmore, M. McConnell, H. Stiegler and P. Shah, "A Process Technology for 5-Volt Only 4MB Flash EEPROM with an 8.6 μm^2 Cell," Symp. on VLSI Tech. Dig. Tech. Papers, (1990) pp. 125.

(7) S. Haddad, C. Chang, B. Swaminathan and J. Lien, "Degradations Due to Hole Trapping in Flash Memory Cells," IEEE Electron Device Lett. vol.10 (1989) pp. 117.

(8) Y. Odake, K. Kurimoto and S. Odanaka, "Three-Dimensional Numerical Modeling of the Indirect Band-to-Band Tunneling in MOSFET's," Extended Abstracts of the 22nd Conference on SSDM, (1990) pp. 131.

(9) H. Kume, H. Yamamoto, T. Adachi, T. Hagiwara, K. Komori, T. Nishimoto, A. Koike, S. Meguro, T. Hayashida and T. Tsukada, "A Flash-Erase Cell with an Asymmetric Source and Drain Structure," IEDM Tech. Dig., (1987) pp. 560.

Part 6
Floating-Gate and Ferroelectric Nonvolatile RAM Technologies

IT IS OFTEN desirable to store data, not just microcodes, in a nonvolatile memory. For example, critical data should be saved in the event of power failure. In a "smart card," financial, personal, or medical data can be stored and easily carried on a person. The traditional nonvolatile data storage medium, the magnetic disk, is widely used for data storage. The disk drive, however, is bulky and power hungry, especially unattractive for portable electronic equipments.

Many of these needs can be met with battery back-up. There can be a system-level battery that provides power to SRAM or DRAM for data storage. Or, there can be a dedicated battery mounted in the sample package as an SRAM chip to save the data. The cost and battery reliability of these schemes are acceptable for many applications but not entirely satisfactory for others. Battery back-up is not a subject of this reprint volume. Instead, we examine the role that nonvolatile semiconductor memories can play.

The simplest scheme would be to use an EEPROM as a main memory in place of DRAM or SRAM. That way, all the data will be stored in nonvolatile memory automatically. Unfortunately, EEPROMs are expensive. Therefore flash EEPROMs are more attractive. However, (flash) EEPROMs are not adequate as a data memory because the 10 ms (or even the 0.1 ms) program time is several orders of magnitude slower than DRAM and SRAM speed and the 10 000 (or even the 1 000 000) cycle limit on WRITE/ERASE endurance is much less than the practical requirement.

To overcome the WRITE speed/cycle limitations, a special type of nonvolatile memory has evolved. These memories operate as RAMs with WRITE/READ speed and endurance characteristic of RAMs. Upon command (as in magnetic disk storage) or upon detection of power failure (power supply voltage dropping below a certain critical level) the memory content is stored into nonvolatile form. So far, this is accomplished by combining an SRAM array and a FLOTOX EEPROM array of equal bits on the same chip and the memory content can be transferred from SRAM into EEPROM or recalled from EEPROM into SRAM within milliseconds. Such memories are known as nonvolatile RAMs (NOVRAMs).

NOVRAM cells are many times larger than EEPROM cells and NOVRAM density and price are inferior to those of EEPROMs and battery-backed RAMs. Newer NOVRAM concepts based on DRAM (instead of SRAM) or MNOS may bring a new generation of higher density NOVRAMs. Table 1 lists a 4K ferroelectric NOVRAM with 10^{12} nonvolatile WRITE cycles. Ferroelectric nonvolatile memories make use of the permanent polarization of a ferroelectric thin film. The polarity of the permanent polarization is alterable by a 5V pulse in 10 ns, to represent the data. At the very early stage

TABLE 1
COMPARISON OF TYPICAL 1990 NOVRAMs WITH EEPROMs AND BATTERY-BACKED RAMs FROM MANY DIFFERENT MANUFACTURERS

		Price ($)	WRITE Speed/Cycles	Nonvolatile Store Cycles
1K	EEPROM	1.40	10ms/10^4	10^5
4K	EEPROM	3.77	1ms/10^4	10^4
16K	EEPROM	5.27	10ms/10^4	10^4
64K	EEPROM	12.00	2ms/10^4	10^4
1M	EEPROM	750	10ms/10^4	10^4
1K FLOTOX	NOVRAM	7.00	200ns/infinite	10^4
4K FLOTOX	NOVRAM	23.00	200ns/infinite	10^4
4K	Ferroelectric NOVRAM	?	200ns/10^{12}	10^{12}
64K MNOS	NOVRAM	48.75	35ns/infinite	10^5
64K	Battery-RAM	15.00	150ns/infinite	infinite
1M	Battery-RAM	99.00	70ns/infinite	infinite

of development now, it may be the basis of a revolutionary new memory, one that can potentially provide cost-effective nonvolatile main memory—an ideal memory.

Paper 6.1 describes the first commercially produced NOVRAM. The SRAM/EEPROM combination has also been adopted by many other NOVRAM designs such as the 4K NOVRAM described in Paper 6.2. A NOVRAM based on SRAM/MNOS combination was reported in [1]. Paper 6.3 is a detailed description of an 8K MNOS-based NOVRAM.

SRAM-based NOVRAMs require large cell sizes because each bit consists of an SRAM cell and two nonvolatile memory cells. Future megabit-density NOVRAMs may be DRAM-based, with each bit consisting of a DRAM cell and a single nonvolatile memory cell. Paper 6.4 reports the latest achievement in DRAM-based NOVRAM technology. The DRAM capacitor is a part of the control-gate-to-floating-gate capacitor of the EEPROM. Depending on whether 0V or 5V is stored on the (DRAM) capacitor at the time of nonvolatile programming of the EEPROM, the EEPROM threshold voltage after programming may be higher or lower. Using 0.8-μm technology, 35 μm^2 cell size was achieved. Other DRAM-based NOVRAM cells were reported in [2] and [3].

The idea of using the polarization of a ferroelectric film to modulate the surface conductivity of a semiconductor was proposed in the 1950s. Paper 6.5, published in 1974, is thus a "recent" report on such a memory device. The gate oxide of a silicon MOSFET is substituted with a ferroelectric thin film. The state of the ferroelectric polarization can change the threshold voltage of the transistor by many volts. The ferroelectric polarization can be programmed or erased in nanoseconds. The problem is the poor quality of the ferroelectric–semiconductor interface. If a thin-oxide film is inserted between the ferroelectric film and silicon, the pro-

213

gramming voltage rises dramatically due to the voltage-divider effect and the large permittivity of the ferroelectric film. Spontaneous depolarization (data retention) may present a problem; and a select transistor is probably necessary to avoid stressing the memory transistor gate during READ, i.e., to avoid the READ disturb problem. These problems have reduced the development activity in this NOVRAM device to nearly nil. Future materials improvements may change the situation, of course.

In recent years, a new ferroelectric memory cell, described in Paper 6.6, has given ferroelectric memory new hope and inspired the notion of an "ideal memory"—a memory that can be read and written with RAM speed, that is as compact as or more compact than DRAM in cell size, and is nonvolatile, too.

The compactness stems from the fact that the cell is in principle identical to a DRAM cell with the capacitor dielectric replaced by a ferroelectric film. Because the ferroelectric film permittivity can be higher than 1000, only a very small capacitor area, perhaps the area of a contact via, is needed.

The major problem with this memory today is the limited READ or WRITE cycles ($\sim 10^{12}$ cycles). Each READ or WRITE operation involves the switching of the ferroelectric polarization, which causes the ferroelectric material to lose its desir-

able characteristics, notably the loss of polarizability with time (aging, in ferroelectrics terminology). Materials improvement is needed to raise the endurance (fatigue, in ferroelectrics terminology) to 10^{16} cycles. Paper 6.7 suggests a way to overcome the READ cycle limitation and move closer to the "ideal" memory.

Reference [4] gives a comprehensive account of the current development efforts. Paper 6.8 addresses the switching kinetics of ferroelectric thin films. The radiation effects on the same ferroelectric films are the subject of [5].

REFERENCES

[1] Y. Uchida, S. Saito, M. Nakane, N. Endo, T. Matsuo, and Y. Nishi, "1-K-bit nonvolatile semiconductor read/write RAM," *IEEE Trans. Electron Devices*, vol. ED-25, p. 1066, 1978.

[2] Y. Terada *et al.*, "A new architecture for the NVRAM—An EEP-ROM backed-up dynamic RAM," *IEEE J. Solid-State Circuits*, vol. 23, pp. 86–90, Feb. 1988.

[3] Y. Yamauchi *et al.*, "A novel NVRAM cell technology for high density applications," in *Tech. Dig. Internat. Electron Devices Meet.*, 1988, pp. 416–419.

[4] D. Bondurant and F. Gnadinger, "Ferroelectrics for nonvolatile RAMs," *IEEE Spectrum*, pp. 30–33, July 1989.

[5] J. F. Scott *et al.* "Radiation effects on ferroelectric thin-film memories: Retention failure mechanisms," *J. Appl. Phys.*, vol. 66, no. 3, pp. 1444–1453, 1 Aug. 1989.

A Single 5V Supply Nonvolatile Static RAM

Joseph Drori, Steven Jewell-Larsen, Raphael Klein, William Owen,

Richard Simko, Wallace Tchon

Xicor, Inc.

Sunnyvale, CA

Mougahed Darwish and Hans Dill

MEM-EBAUCHES Electroniques

Marin, Switzerland

A TTL-COMPATIBLE, single 5V supply, nonvolatile RAM utilizing a three-layer polysilicon process and a low-current floating gate tunneling approach will be described.

The device is organized as a conventional 1024b static RAM overlaid bit-for-bit with a nonvolatile 1024b electrically-erasable PROM (E[2]PROM). At each memory-bit location, two bits of memory storage exist: one in the RAM and one in the nonvolatile E[2]PROM; Figure 1. All data I/O occurs through the RAM memory, while in the background the E[2]PROM nonvolatile memory looks like a shadow ROM. Data is written into the non-volatile E[2]PROM by copying the entire RAM array (1024b) in parallel by applying a TTL STORE signal. Data is read out of the nonvolatile memory by first transferring the data into the RAM by applying a TTL ARRAY RECALL signal. Once data is in the RAM it can be read or modified as in any RAM.

A significant result is that all inputs and outputs are directly TTL-compatible with a single 5V supply requirement. The device eliminates drawbacks in present devices, such as the need for high voltages, quartz lids, and unsocketing. The ability to simply change electrically nonvolatile data affords the possibility for practical *in-the-circuit* programming in which the writing, erasing and reading of nonvolatile data are accomplished without removing the device from the circuit.

The nonvolatile RAM uses a triple polysilicon process utilizing electron tunneling properties between layers of polysilicon for programming and erasing electrically a new nonvolatile floating-gate memory element. The floating gate is programmed by tunneling electrons onto the floating gate. The floating gate is erased by tunneling electrons off the floating gate. The enhanced tunneling is due to a textured surface on polysilicon which produces field-aided emissions[1,2]. All necessary internal voltages are generated on chip from a single 5V external supply.

The nonvolatile static RAM results from mating a standard six-transistor depletion load static RAM cell and a nonvolatile

element: Figure 2. The interfacing of the nonvolatile element to the cell is via the floating gate which is either on or off. The nonvolatile data in the cell is read by first setting the potential of VCCA to ground which equilibrates nodes N1 and N2. If the floating gate is at a positive potential transistor, T8, will be turned ON and capacitor C2 will load node N2. Node N2 will have a larger capacitance than node N1. Now as VCCA is raised from ground to +5V, node N2 will rise more slowly than node N1, and the cell will latch by regenerative action with node N2 low and node N1 high. Data can then be read out of the latched cell. Similarly, if the floating gate is at a negative potential, transistor T8 will be turned OFF and the capacitive load on N1 will be larger than the capacitive load on N2, and the cell will latch in the opposite state. VCCA is an internal signal developed by on-chip circuits.

Data is written into the nonvolatile memory by sensing the state of the static RAM and then programming or erasing the floating gate to represent the sensed data. The state of the static RAM is sensed by the condition of transistor T7 which is controlled by the potential of node N1. If N1 is low, the floating gate is programmed by electrons tunneling in the C_p area from poly 1 to poly 2. If N1 is high, the floating gate is erased by electrons tunneling in the C_E area from poly 2 to poly 3.

If node N1 is low, T7 is turned OFF; then the control line which is floating is allowed to go high during a store operation. During a store operation, the store terminal is brought to a high level by the on-chip generator shown in Figure 3. A schematic of the programming operation is shown in Figure 4. Since CC3, CC2, and C_E are large compared to C_p and C_{FG}, the floating gate is pulled high as the store line is raised, developing a voltage across C_p sufficient to cause electrons to tunnel from the grounded poly 1 line to the floating gate. The floating gate will have a net negative potential when the store voltage is returned to ground, leaving T8 turned OFF. The floating gate is therefore left in the programmed state.

If node 1 is high, T7 is turned ON; this grounds the control line. A circuit schematic of the erasing operation is shown in Figure 5. Since C_E is small compared to CC2, the floating gate voltage remains close to ground as the store line is raised, developing a voltage across C_E sufficient to cause electrons to tunnel from the floating gate (poly 2) to the store line (poly 3). The floating gate will have a net positive potential when the store voltage is returned to ground, leaving T8 turned ON. The floating gate is therefore left in the erased state. The programmed or erased state of the floating gate is read as previously described.

It is interesting to note than when data is read from the nonvolatile memory, nodes N1 and N2 take on the potentials identical to those used to write the nonvolatile data. The RAM cell recovers noninverted data directly.

The chip size of the device is 119 x 164mils using typically 5μm design rules. Typical access time is 250ns and power dissipation is 200mW. The maximum time required to transfer all bits in parallel from static RAM to E[2]PROM is 10ms. Maximum recall time for all bits from E[2]PROM to RAM is 1.5μs.

---

[1] Lenzlinger, M. and Snow, E. H., "Fowler-Nordheim Tunneling into Thermally Grown SiO$_2$," *J. Appl. Phys.*, Vol. 40, p. 278-283; 1969.

[2] DiMaria, D. J. and Kerr, D. R., "Interface Effects and High Conductivity in Oxides Grown from Polycrystalline Silicon," *Appl. Phys. Lett.*, Vol. 27, p. 505-507; 1975.

Reprinted from the *IEEE ISSCC Dig. Tech. Pap.*, pp. 148–149, 1981.

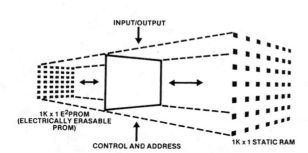

FIGURE 1—Nonvolatile static RAM is organized as 1K static RAM overlaid bit-for-bit with a nonvolatile 1K Electrically-Erasable PROM (E^{2}PROM).

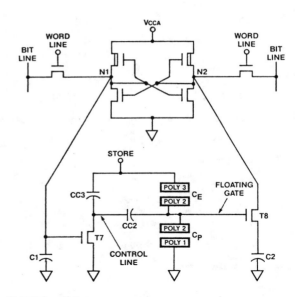

FIGURE 2—Complete circuit schematic of nonvolatile static RAM cell.

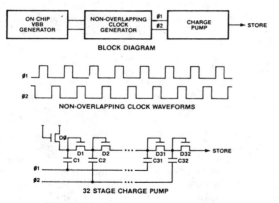

FIGURE 3—Store voltage generation.

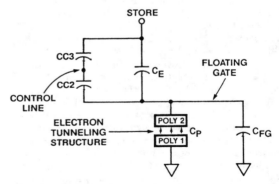

FIGURE 4—During programming electrons are added to floating gate by tunneling, resulting in net negative gate potential.

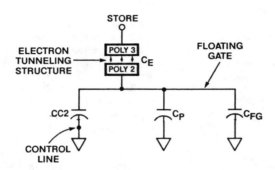

FIGURE 5—During erasing electrons are removed from floating gate by tunneling, resulting in net positive gate potential.

A 5V-Only 4K Nonvolatile Static RAM

Neil J. Becker, Vinod K. Dham, Douglas J. Lee, Andrew L. Schlafly, Joseph A. Skupnjak

Intel Corp.

Santa Clara, CA

FIVE-VOLT ONLY OPERATION is now an industry standard for electrically erasable and programmable nonvolatile memories. A 4K nonvolatile static RAM (NVRAM) with on-chip high-voltage generation and regulation was designed with high density and future scalability as key design parameters. Using wafer stepper HMOS I dual poly FLOTOX[1] technology and a restructured cell, a die size of 30,268 mils[2] (19.53mm[2]) was achieved: Figure 1. Single pulses control the data transfers: STORE (static RAM to E[2]PROM) and RECALL (E[2]PROM to static RAM). Typical electrical characteristics are shown in Table 1.

The array cell is a nine-transistor structure consisting of a standard six transistor depletion load static RAM cell, an E[2]PROM transistor, and two additional transistors used as gating devices: Figure 2. While a smaller cell is possible, the gating devices are necessary to eliminate the dc current path from the high voltage source.

The STORE operation occurs in two-timed 10ms steps. During the first half of the STORE cycle, the entire E[2]PROM array is erased to a low threshold by holding the CLK and PRO lines at zero volts and raising the CLR line to the internally generated high voltage (VPP). During the second half of the cycle, CLR is lowered to zero volts, CLK is set to VCC and PRO to VPP. Diode connected transistor T9 enables node D to retain high voltage by trapping charge when the CLR line is lowered from VPP to zero volts. The state of the static RAM cell determines whether the transfer gate controlled by CLK is conducting, which discharge the trapped charge on node D, or nonconducting which leaves the trapped charge intact. The former condition causes the E[2] element to program, the latter, to inhibit programming, which leaves the E[2] element erased. The state of the RAM cell is thereby stored in the E[2] element.

The RECALL operation requires control of the internal array power supply (VVD). The static RAM depletion loads have an inbalance to allow the RAM cell to latch in a desired state during VDD ramping. During RECALL, the CLK, PRO, and CLR lines are held high, and VDD is ramped to ground and back to VCC. The E[2] element determines the state of the static RAM cell during the ramping. A high threshold, or programmed, E[2] element is nonconductive and allows the imbalance on the loads to be dominant; a low threshold, or erased, E[2] element is conductive and overcomes the imbalance of the loads, pulling the static RAM cell to the opposite state. Typical waveforms for STORE and RECALL sequencing are shown in Figures 3 and 4.

The proper operation of the cell during STORE and RECALL data transfers requires complex sequencing of high (VPP) and low (VCC) voltages. Since the design required TTL level signals to initiate STORE and RECALL operations, these complex control functions were integrated on chip. A single-control pin differentiates between standard static RAM operation and nonvolatile (STORE/RECALL) operations. When this pin is high, the NVRAM operates as a conventional static RAM; when low, a static RAM READ operation initiates a RECALL cycle, and a static RAM WRITE operation initiates a STORE cycle. Control logic on chip latches the given state and internally times the appropriate STORE or RECALL function. Figure 5 illustrates the basic logic configuration for the nonvolatile functions. An on-chip VCC level detector (VLKO) disables the state machines when the power supply falls below the lockout voltage (4.4V) so that an inadvertent STORE or RECALL cannot occur. On power up, the VLKO circuit initiates an automatic RECALL, placing valid data into the RAM. The RECALL state machine controls the ramping of the VDD line and the switching of the CLR, PRO, and CLK lines both during power up RECALL and user initiated RECALL. The STORE state machine controls the high voltage generation circuitry, the internal self-timer, and sequences high voltage (VPP) to the array during the STORE cycle. Simultaneous operation of STORE and RECALL cannot occur.

Acknowledgements

The authors wish to gratefully acknowledge K. Gudger for early cell development work, D. Oto for the design of the charge pump and regulation circuitry, D. Burton for the organization and layout of the NVRAM, Y.W. Hu and J. Olund for the process development, and B. Lusk for the testing support.

[1] Johnson, W., et. al., "A 16Kb Electrically Erasable Nonvolatile Memory," *ISSCC DIGEST OF TECHNICAL PAPERS*, p.152; Feb., 1980.

PHYSICAL CHARACTERISTICS	
Cell Size	2.86 mil[2]
Die Size	30,268 mil[2]
Organization	512 × 8
Package	28 pin
ELECTRICAL CHARACTERISTICS	
Power Supply	+ 5V
Active Power	500 mW
Standby Power	250 mW
READ Cycle Time	200 ns
WRITE Cycle Time	200 ns
STORE Cycle Time	20 ms
RECALL Cycle Time	1500 ns
CELL CHARACTERISTICS	
Data Retention	10 years
STORE Endurance	10[4] cycles
RECALL Endurance	unlimited
READ Access	unlimited

TABLE 1—Physical, electrical and performance characteristics.

Reprinted from the *IEEE ISSCC Dig. Tech. Pap.*, pp. 170–171, 1983.

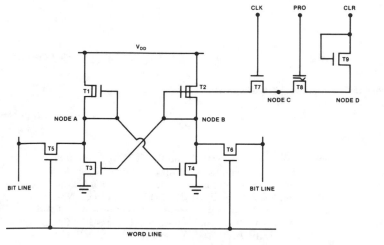

FIGURE 2—NVRAM array cell.

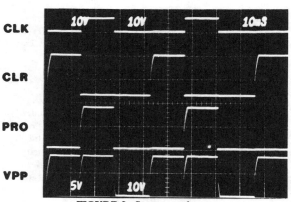

FIGURE 3—Store waveforms.

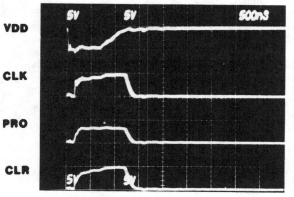

FIGURE 4—Recall waveforms.

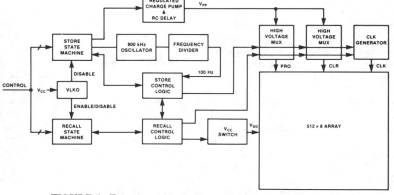

FIGURE 5—Functional block diagram of nonvolatile portion.

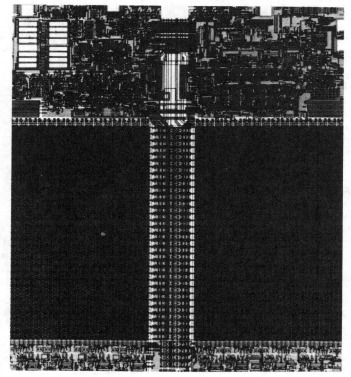

(Right)
FIGURE 1—Photograph of 5V-only
4K nonvolatile static RAM.

218

SNOS 1K × 8 Static Nonvolatile RAM

DARREL D. DONALDSON, MEMBER, IEEE, MICHAEL D. EBY, MEMBER, IEEE, ROY FAHRENBRUCK, MEMBER, IEEE, AND EDWARD H. HONNIGFORD, MEMBER, IEEE

Abstract—Using an advanced n-channel, double level polysilicon SNOS technology, a 1K × 8 bit nonvolatile static RAM has been designed. Typical RAM access time is 300 ns, with typical active power dissipation of 300 mW, and standby power of 160 mW. Endurance of 10^4 erase/store cycles has been demonstrated. The ability to measure erased and written memory thresholds allows prediction of retention lifetime. For the 8K NVRAM, the minimum retention lifetime is 1 year following a 10 ms erase and store.

TABLE I
SNOS PROCESS PARAMETERS

Gate Length	4 μm
Gate Oxide	700 Å
Xj	1.3 μm
Memory Oxide	20 Å
Memory Nitride	380 Å
Field Threshold	>30 V
Diode Breakdown	>30 V
Sheet Resistance	
n⁺	13 Ω/□
Poly I	30 Ω/□
Poly II	50 Ω/□
Poly Resistors	10 MΩ/□

I. INTRODUCTION

THE nonvolatile RAM or NVRAM is a new type of n-channel EEPROM that is gaining recognition. These devices combine the nonvolatility of an EEPROM with the ease of use and fast alterability of a static RAM.

Until now the highest density NVRAM available was a 4K bit device. This paper reports on a new 8K bit NVRAM. Internally it has 8K bits of static RAM and 8K bits of EEPROM for a total of 16K bits of usable memory. Fully operational 8K parts have been manufactured and tested over a 0–70°C temperature range with ±5 percent power supplies. Table I shows some typical process parameters.

II. SNOS NVRAM CELL

The schematic of the 8K NVRAM cell is shown in Fig. 1. It is a standard six element static RAM cell utilizing polysilicon resistors for loads. Two EEPROM memory elements, comprised of $C1$, $M1$, and $M2$ have been added to implement nonvolatility in an otherwise volatile RAM cell. Referring to Fig. 2, $C1$ is an alterable threshold capacitor and provides the means for retaining the last stored state of the RAM cell. $M1$ shares a common gate with $C1$ and is a poly II depletion transistor. $M2$ is a poly I depletion transistor with its gate strapped to V_{SS}. It serves as a decoupling transistor during store operations.

Fig. 3 shows the cross sections of the two EEPROM memory elements in a single cell and below them are the simplified surface potential profiles for the different regions of the elements. This figure serves to illustrate how the two memory capacitors may be programmed to retain the state of the volatile RAM cell. The A and $\bar{A}$ nodes in Fig. 3 are also shown in the cell schematic. Node A is set high and node $\bar{A}$ is therefore grounded.

In Fig. 3(a) the $V_{E/S}$ line is at 0 V and the cell is operating as a volatile RAM. The surface potentials for $M1$ and $M2$ on the A side of the cell have risen to a potential equal in magnitude

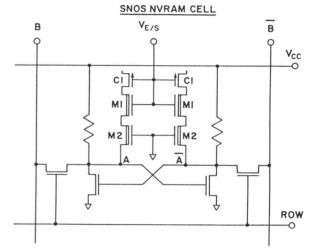

Fig. 1. Schematic of SNOS NVRAM cell.

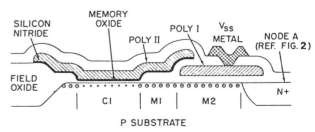

Fig. 2. Cross section of nonvolatile memory element.

to the threshold of $M2$. At that time $M2$ is turned off, decoupling $M1$ and $C1$ from node A. The surface potential for $C1$ is determined by the last state stored in $C1$ and is therefore shown as indeterminant. On the other side of the cell the grounded node $\bar{A}$ holds $M2$ turned on and the surface poten-

Manuscript received March 17, 1982; revised June 4, 1982.

The authors are with the Microelectronics Division, National Cash Register, Miamisburg, OH 45342.

Reprinted from *IEEE J. Solid-State Circuits*, vol. SC-17, no. 5, pp. 847–851, October 1982.

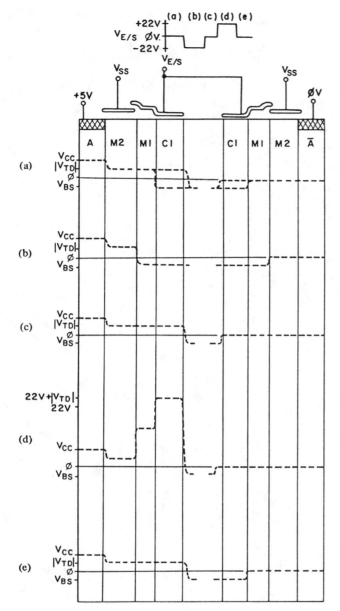

Fig. 3. Surface potential profile (a) during volatile RAM use, $V_{E/S}$ = 0 V; (b) during erase operation, $V_{E/S}$ = –22 V; (c) after erase operation, $V_{E/S}$ = 0 V; (d) during store operation, $V_{E/S}$ = +22 V; (e) after store operation, $V_{E/S}$ = 0 V. $|V_{TD}|$ is magnitude of poly I depletion transistor threshold.

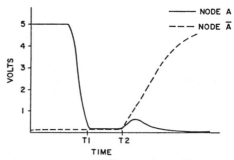

Fig. 4. Recall of data from EEPROM back into RAM cell. Both sides of the cell are grounded at time t_1 and released at time t_2.

tials of $M1$ and $M2$ are zero. Again $C1$ has an indeterminant surface potential.

When the EEPROM memory elements are to be erased, $V_{E/S}$ is pulsed to –22 V. This forces the silicon surface of the $M1$ transistors and the $C1$ capacitors into accumulation and their surface potentials go to the same potential as the substrate bias. Fig. 3(b) shows this condition. With V_{BS} at –2.5 V, 19.5 V of the –22 V applied to the $V_{E/S}$ line appear across the memory dielectric of the $C1$ capacitors. This voltage across the memory dielectric causes a net positive charge to be stored in the memory nitride of $C1$. The mechanism by which the charge reaches the nitride is described in [1].

After the erase pulse, the positive charge stored in the memory nitride shifts the threshold of the two $C1$ capacitors to about –6 V. On the node A side of the cell, the surface potentials of $M1$ and $C1$ rise to that of $M2$ and $M2$ turns off as in

Fig. 3(a). $M2$ on the other side of the cell is held on by the grounded $\bar{A}$ node resulting in a surface potential of zero for $M1$ and $C1$. These surface potentials are shown in Fig. 3(c).

The memory capacitors are now ready to receive the data from the volatile RAM cell when $V_{E/S}$ is pulsed to +22 V. On the rising edge of the $V_{E/S}$ pulse, with $M2$ off, the surface potentials of $M1$ and $C1$ on the A side of the cell are free to follow $V_{E/S}$. The dielectric thicknesses and composition along with the doping concentrations in the substrate regions of $M1$ and $C1$ determine how well their surface potentials follow $V_{E/S}$. In this structure the surface potential of $C1$ follows $V_{E/S}$ very closely. This prevents any of the $V_{E/S}$ potential from dropping across the memory dielectric and leaves the threshold of $C1$ unaltered. This process of preventing the $C1$ threshold from changing is referred to as deep depletion channel shielding. The name comes from the fact that the high surface potential creates a very deep, approximately 5 μm, depletion layer in the silicon below the $C1$ gate and all of the $V_{E/S}$ potential is dropped across this depletion layer. $M1$, with its 1200 Å thick gate oxide, has a lower surface potential but because it is not an alterable threshold device it is not as important to have its surface potential follow $V_{E/S}$.

On the other side of the cell, $M2$ is on and the surface potentials of $M1$ and $C1$ are held to zero by node $\bar{A}$. All of the $V_{E/S}$ potential is dropped across the $C1$ memory dielectric and causes negative charge to replace the positive charge that was stored in the memory nitride. This negative charge shifts the $C1$ threshold from its –6 V erased level to a +6 V written level. Fig. 3(d) shows the surface potentials during the $V_{E/S}$ store pulse.

When $V_{E/S}$ returns to 0 V, $C1$ on the $\bar{A}$ side of the cell turns off and its surface potential is equal to the substrate bias potential. This is shown in Fig. 3(e).

After the store pulse the EEPROM memory element on the A side of the cell, with $C1$ still turned on, provides a heavier capacitive load than does the memory element on the $\bar{A}$ side with $C1$ turned off. In this cell design an erased $C1$ capacitor accounts for about 30 percent of the total nodal capacitance of node A or node $\bar{A}$. If both nodes, A and $\bar{A}$, are simultaneously grounded and then released node $\bar{A}$ will have an RC time constant that is 70 percent of that for node A. Node $\bar{A}$ will therefore charge to the threshold of the grounding transistor of node A before node A charges very far. Once this happens node A is pulled to ground and node $\bar{A}$ continues to charge to V_{CC}. This process of grounding both sides of the cell and then releasing them is how data are recalled from the EEPROM memory elements back into the RAM cell. Fig. 4

illustrates the voltages on nodes A and $\bar{A}$ during the recall. The data in the cell after the recall are opposite to the data that were in the cell during the store. There is circuitry in the NVRAM to compensate for this inversion and it is discussed in the circuitry section of this paper.

III. CIRCUIT DESIGN

A block diagram of the 8K NVRAM is shown in Fig. 5. The memory matrix consists of two arrays, separated by the row decode. Each array feeds 4 bits of data through the column decode to the data I/O buffers. Circuitry in the row and column buffers and decoders, as well as data I/O circuits, are powered down during either a deselected state, or when a nonvolatile operation is in progress. This is accomplished by gating zero threshold transistors on or off with the output of the chip select buffer, yielding low standby power dissipation. Logic is present to control row address buffers, row decode, and bit line precharging during a nonvolatile operation, as indicated by the NV control block. This block also controls data path direction in the I/O buffers. An on-chip bias generator provides -2.5 V substrate bias.

The $\overline{NV}$ input is the control signal which determines whether the NVRAM is in the volatile or nonvolatile mode of operation. A high TTL logic level on the $\overline{NV}$ input designates a volatile RAM operation. A low logic level designates a nonvolatile operation. There are three nonvolatile modes of operation associated with the NVRAM: erase, store, and recall. The erase would be performed first, followed by the store, and at some later time, the recall. Erase and store operations transfer static RAM data to the nonvolatile EEPROM portion of the cell, without disturbing the existing RAM data. A recall operation transfers data from EEPROM back into static RAM, with no effect on existing EEPROM data. Only the data which are in the static RAM at the time may be accessed by the user. All nonvolatile operations are block functions, operating on all 8K bits at the same time.

The erase operation is performed by first applying a low logic level to the $\overline{NV}$ pin, which prevents any RAM operations, and then applying a -22 V pulse to the $V_{E/S}$ line. A store operation occurs when the $\overline{NV}$ pin is again at a low logic level, and the $V_{E/S}$ line is pulsed to $+22$ V. Following these two operations, the static RAM data have been copied into the nonvolatile EEPROM section, and the part may now be powered down or RAM data altered without altering the copy of data in EEPROM.

To access data which have been stored in nonvolatile EEPROM, a recall must be performed to transfer the data into static RAM. The following describes the recall sequence. The $\overline{NV}$ signal and $\overline{WE}$ signal are both pulled to low logic levels. This turns off the bit line prechargers, grounds all bit lines and selects all rows, which grounds the internal nodes of all of the memory cells. As described previously, this prepares the cells for the actual recall operation. The $\overline{WE}$ line is now pulled to a high logic level, immediately turning off all rows, and floating the bit lines. The cells are now allowed to recall data by the method discussed in the section describing the cell operation. Following this, the $\overline{NV}$ signal is returned to a high logic level, turning on the bit line prechargers, and allowing normal static RAM operation.

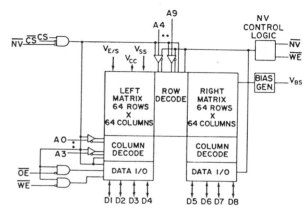

Fig. 5. Block diagram of 8K NVRAM.

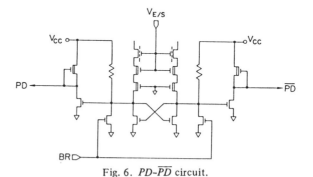

Fig. 6. PD–$\overline{PD}$ circuit.

Data Correction Circuitry

After the recall operation, the data in the cell are the inverse of the originally stored data. To recover original data, the data must be inverted again between the cell and the output pin. An inversion must also be performed on input data to write correct data into the cells. Data correction circuitry to perform the necessary inversion on-chip is shown in Figs. 6 and 7. Fig. 6 shows the PD–$\overline{PD}$ circuit which is basically a duplication of the memory cell structure. The PD–$\overline{PD}$ circuit data are recalled by switching the BR transistors on and off, allowing the same method of recall described previously. Since the PD–$\overline{PD}$ circuit is a duplication of the memory cell, it will also recall data which are the inverse of the stored data. This means that following each erase-store-recall cycle, the PD–$\overline{PD}$ outputs will switch to a state opposite that of the state prior to the cycle, in the same manner as the memory cell. Since the PD–$\overline{PD}$ outputs switch in sequence with the memory cell, the PD and $\overline{PD}$ outputs can be used to steer the data through the I/O buffer as shown in Fig. 7. The two groups of four transistors controlled by PD–$\overline{PD}$ perform the necessary inversions. The data path preceding the correction circuitry will always remain the same. Output data progress through a differential amplifier, level shifter, and then to the data correction transistors. These four devices will steer the data to the necessary path according to the state of PD and $\overline{PD}$. The corrected data are again level shifted and passed on to the output driver. Input data must also be corrected, so that they will correspond to the output. This correction is performed by the four transistors between the input buffer and the internal data bus. By doing the necessary inversions on chip, no external circuitry is required, and the user will not see the effect of the data inversion after erase-store-recall.

221

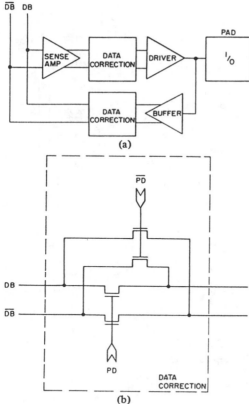

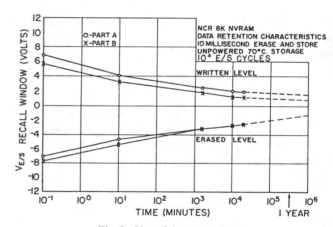

Fig. 8. Plot of data retention.

Fig. 7. (a) Block diagram of I/O buffer. (b) Schematic of data correction circuit.

Three circuit elements are used on the NVRAM to prevent data disturbance during high voltage erase and store pulsing. First, an on-chip series poly II resistor and high internal capacitance on the programming line provides an RC time constant to shape the rising and falling edges of the erase and store pulses. Second, an on-chip bias generator clamp prevents the substrate from charging below −3 V. Third, an external capacitor attached to the V_{BS} pin prevents substrate bounce during the programming operations.

IV. NVRAM Performance

The 8K NVRAM is word organized in 1K bytes, with a memory matrix organized 64 rows × 128 columns. The memory cell measures 66.5 × 34.5 μm (3.56 mils^2) resulting in an overall die size of 215 × 234 mils. Figs. 9 and 10 show the die and an SEM of the cell, respectively.

Measured operating characteristics are shown in Table II.

The 8K NVRAM is used as a normal static RAM in all microprocessor operations, it is only when data must be retained over an intentional or inadvertent power down that the part is operated in a nonvolatile mode. As is true in all electrically alterable processes, there is a limitation on the number of nonvolatile operations. After 10^4 erase/store cycles the NVRAM is guaranteed to retain stored data up to one year. There are, of course, no limitations on the number of RAM operations.

The recall operation leaves the contents of the EEPROM memory elements unaltered allowing for an unlimited number

Fig. 9. Photomicrograph of 8K SNOS NVRAM.

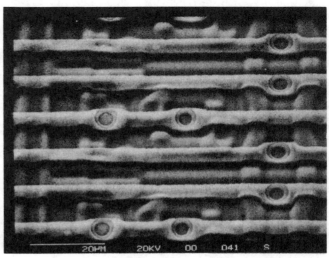

Fig. 10. SEM photomicrograph of memory cell.

TABLE II
TYPICAL OPERATING CHARACTERISTICS

Supply Voltage	+5 V
Active Power Dissipation	300 mW
Standby Power Dissipation	160 mW
I/O Voltage Levels	TTL
Address Access Time	300 ns
Output Enable	110 ns
Bulk Erase Voltage	−22 V
Erase time	10 ms
Bulk Store Voltage	+22 V
Store Time (10 1 ms pulses)	10 ms
Minimum Data Retention (unpowered)	1 year

of recalls. This and the fact that the $V_{E/S}$ line is directly accessible from the outside allows the threshold of the $C1$ capacitors to be measured at anytime, simply by putting different voltages on $V_{E/S}$ and performing a recall. When $V_{E/S}$ reaches the threshold of the written (or off) capacitor, this capacitor will turn on. At that point both sides of the cell will have the same capacitance and wrong data will be recalled. Similarly, as $V_{E/S}$ reaches the threshold of the erased (or on) capacitor, this capacitor will turn off, and again both sides will have equal capacitance resulting in wrong data after a recall.

The data retention characteristic is shown in the curve of recall voltage limit as a function of increasing time. The positive voltage is the maximum window at which data 1's will be recalled and the negative voltage is the maximum voltage for data 0's to be recalled. The recall window voltage shows an exponential decay with time. Measured data from the 8K NVRAM in Fig. 8 show data retention greater than two years for 70°C storage and after 10^4 erase/store cycles.

V. SUMMARY

The design and performance of an 8K NVRAM, that was manufactured utilizing SNOS technology, has been described. Using conservative 4 μm gate lengths, a 3.56 mil^2 cell was achieved. The process is based on standard NMOS technology and lends itself to scaling techniques. Reliability has been improved by removal of nitride from under all nonmemory gates.

With the capability of margining the memory threshold window, data retention has been extrapolated to over 2 years at 70°C and after 10^4 erase–write cycles.

ACKNOWLEDGMENT

The authors would like to thank T. Humbert and C. Stermer for chip and cell layout, and D. Langer, C. Bair, and R. Shreve for test software. They would also like to thank J. Stewart for processing, and J. Waldroup for typing of the original manuscript.

REFERENCES

[1] J. A. Topich, "Charge storage model for SNOS memory devices," *Electrochem. Soc. Extended Abstracts*, vol. 81, no. 1, abstract 268, p. 672.
[2] D. G. Craycraft *et al.*, "Static volatile/non-volatile RAM cell," U.S. Patent 4 271 487, June 2, 1981.

A VERSATILE STACKED STORAGE CAPACITOR ON FLOTOX CELL FOR MEGABIT NVRAM APPLICATIONS

Yoshimitsu Yamauchi, Hiroshi Ishihara, Kenichi Tanaka,
Keizo Sakiyama and Ryuichiro Miyake

A1136 Project Team, Sharp Corporation
2613-1, Ichinomoto-cho, Tenri-shi, Nara 632, Japan

ABSTRACT

A versatile stacked Storage Capacitor on FLOTOX (SCF) cell is proposed for full featured megabit nonvolatile DRAMs. The SCF cell structure achieves a cell area of 35.02 μm^2 with 0.8 μm features and enables an innovative flash store/recall (DRAM to EEPROM / EEPROM to DRAM) operation that does not disturb the original data in DRAM or EEPROM). This store operation is completed in less than 10 msec. and store endurance for a single cell is greater than 10^6 cycles. In addition, data retention time sufficient for megabit DRAMs (greater than 10 sec. at R.T.) is obtained by use of a stacked capacitor structure.

INTRODUCTION

Nonvolatile RAM (NV-RAM) has emerged as a high performance nonvolatile memory which combines the advantages of RAM with EEPROM nonvolatility. However, conventional nonvolatile SRAM (NV-SRAM) combining a six-transistor SRAM with an EEPROM requires a very large cell size because of its complicated cell structure, which makes it difficult to achieve high density. Recently, several studies [1, 2] on nonvolatile DRAM (NV-DRAM), which combine a DRAM instead of an SRAM with an EEPROM, have been reported to reduce the cell size.

This paper describes a versatile NV-DRAM cell named the SCF cell suitable for megabit density, which enables an innovative flash store/recall operation that does not disturb the original data in DRAM or EEPROM.

CELL STRUCTURE

The SCF cell structure is shown in Fig. 1. The cell consists of two transistors (T_1, T_2), a FLOTOX EEPROM transistor (MT) and a stacked capacitor (C) on the floating gate (FG). T_1 is the word-line select transistor, whose drain (D) is connected to the bit line (BL). T_2 is the recall mode select transistor and turns on only in the recall operation.

The key process features are shown in Table 1. The SCF cell structure is fabricated using a 0.8 μm triple polysilicon technology. The select gate (SG), the recall gate (RG) and the floating gate (FG) are fabricated from the first polysilicon, the DRAM storage node polysilicon (NP) is fabricated from the second polysilicon and the capacitor gate (CG) is fabricated from the third polysilicon. The node NP is connected to the n+ diffusion between the SG and RG. The tunnel dielectric (TD) of approximately 8nm is the heart of this process technology and is fabricated by post-oxidation annealing of thermally grown oxide at high temperature. The interpoly dielectric equivalent oxide thickness of the oxide-nitride-oxide stacked films are 20 nm over the first polysilicon and 14 nm over the second polysilicon.

By utilizing the above technologies, a 35.02 μm^2 cell size with a DRAM storage capacitance of 50 fF has been developed. This is a reasonable cell size for realizing 1 megabit NV-DRAM.

OPERATION

The new concept for data transfer from DRAM to EEPROM (store operation) is shown in Fig. 2. In the store cycle the EEPROM is programmed or erased by Fowler-Nordheim tunneling current through the tunnel oxide, the

Reprinted from the *IEDM Tech. Dig.*, pp. 595–598, 1989.

timing diagram of which is shown in Fig. 3(A). The store cycle is completed in two-timed steps with a Vp voltage pulse.

The EEPROM of this cell has an asymmetrical capacitive coupling ratio for programming and erasing as shown in Fig. 4. The capacitive coupling ratio of the EEPROM for programming is smaller than that for erasing.

During the first half of the store cycle, if the DRAM is in the "0" state, then the EEPROM is erased to the low threshold state by applying a high Vp voltage pulse to the source and grounding the CG. However, if the DRAM is in the "1" state, the EEPROM is inhibited from being erased, since the voltage applied between source and NP is reduced to Vp-Vcc due to the positive charge stored in the DRAM. During the second half of the store cycle, if the DRAM is in the "1" state, then the EEPROM is programmed to the high threshold state by applying a high Vp voltage pulse to the CG and grounding the source, since the node NP potential is increased more than Vp due to the positive charge stored in the DRAM, regardless of the low capacitive coupling ratio of the EEPROM. However, when the DRAM is in the "0" state, the EEPROM is inhibited from being programmed due to its low capacitive coupling ratio.

As a result, the EEPROM is programmed or erased depending on whether the DRAM state is "1" or "0". The DRAM data is not disturbed even after the store operation, since the two transistors T_1 and T_2 are turned off during the store operation. In addition, this cell enables on-chip generation of high voltage Vp from an external single 5-volt power supply due to the very small current dissipation during the store operation.

In the recall operation shown in Fig. 3 (B), the DC current path from the Vcc is blocked by the two transistors T_1 and T_2.

These new concepts for store and recall operations enable simultaneous transfer of the entire chip data between the DRAM and the EEPROM.

EXPERIMENTAL RESULTS

The measured store characteristics of this cell are shown in Fig. 5 and Fig. 6. The EEPROM threshold voltage Vt is defined as the drain (D) voltage for the drain current of 1 μA under applying 8 volts to the select gate (SG) and the recall gate (RG). Fig. 5 shows the store pulse voltage (Vp) dependence of Vt after a store

operation. An acceptable Vt window of approximately 4 volts is obtained with a Vp of 13.5 volts. Fig. 6 shows the store pulse time (Tp) dependence of Vt after a store operation. The state of the DRAM is stored in the EEPROM in less than 10 ms with a Vp of 13.5 volts.

The store endurance for a single cell is shown in Fig. 7. The closure of the Vt window of EEPROM is less than 10 % after 10^6 store cycles. This high endurance is achieved by use of an optimized POA technology. The endurance of the EEPROM in this cell is extended further, because when the data states in the DRAM and EEPROM are equal prior to the store operation, then the EEPROM is inhibited from being programmed or erased.

The data retention time (Tret) of the DRAM was evaluated. Fig. 8 shows the EEPROM Vt after the store operation as a function of Tret. The EEPROM Vt window after a store operation is determined by the charge stored in the DRAM during the store operation. The EEPROM Vt window shows no decrease during a very long retention time of 10 sec. at R.T., even after 5×10^6 store cycles, which is sufficient for megabit DRAMs. This excellent data retention time is obtained by use of a stacked capacitor structure.

CONCLUSIONS

A SCF cell has been developed for megabit NV-DRAMs. The SCF cell, with a small cell area of 35.02 μm^2, provides an innovative flash store/recall operation and improves reliability. In addition, data retention time sufficient for megabit DRAMs is obtained by use of a stacked capacitor structure.

The newly developed 5-volt only SCF cell is a most promising candidate for implementation into full featured 1 megabit NV-DRAM.

REFERENCES

[1] Yasushi Terada et al., " A New Architecture for the NVRAM- An EEPROM Back-up Dynamic RAM ", IEEE J. Solid-State Circuits, vol. 23, pp. 86-90, Feb. 1988
[2] Yoshimitsu Yamauchi et al., " A Novel NVRAM Cell Technology for High Density Applications", in IEDM Technical Digest, pp. 416-419, Dec. 1988

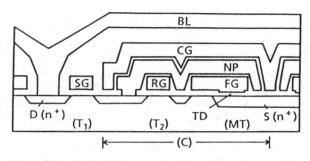

(A) SCHEMATIC CROSS-SECTIONAL VIEW

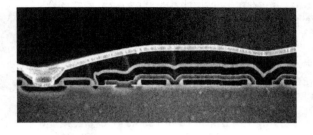

(B) SEM CROSS-SECTIONAL VIEW

FIG.1 Cross-sectional view of SCF cell.

TABLE 1 Key process features of memory cell.

PROCESS	0.8μm TRIPLE POLYSILICON TECHNOLOGY
GATE LENGTH (MIN.)	1.1 μm
GATE WIDTH (MIN.)	1.0 μm
GATE OXIDE	35 nm
TUNNEL DIELECTRIC	8 nm
INTERPOLY DIELECTRIC	20 nm / 14 nm (POLY1-POLY2 / POLY2-POLY3)
CELL SIZE	3.4 X 10.3 = 35.02 μm^2

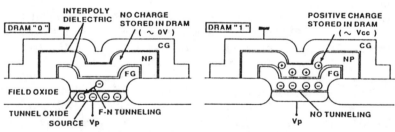

(A) ERASE (THE FIRST HALF OF STORE CYCLE)

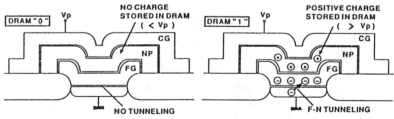

(B) PROGRAM (THE SECOND HALF OF STORE CYCLE)

FIG.2 New concept for data transfer from DRAM to EEPROM (STORE).

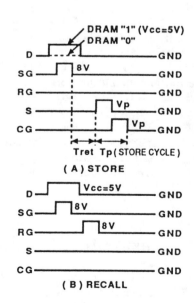

(A) STORE

(B) RECALL

FIG. 3 Timing diagrams for store and recall operations.

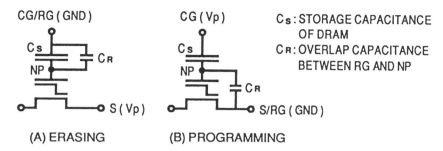

(A) ERASING (B) PROGRAMMING

FIG. 4 Asymmetrical capacitive coupling ratio of
EEPROM for programming and erasing.

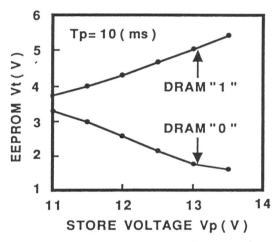

FIG.5 EEPROM threshold voltage Vt after
data transfer from DRAM to EEPROM as a
function of store pulse voltage Vp.

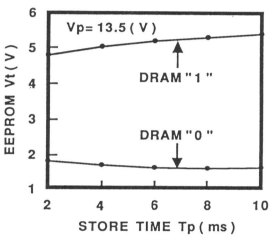

FIG.6 EEPROM threshold voltage Vt after
data transfer from DRAM to EEPROM as a
function of store pulse time Tp.

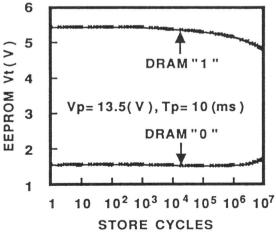

FIG. 7 Store endurance characteristics.

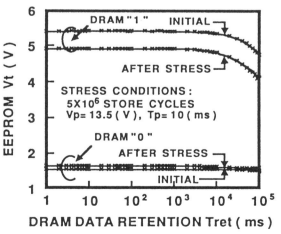

FIG. 8 EEPROM threshold voltage Vt after
data transfer from DRAM to EEPROM as a
function of DRAM data retention time Tret.

A New Ferroelectric Memory Device,
Metal-Ferroelectric-Semiconductor Transistor

SHU-YAU WU, MEMBER, IEEE

Abstract—The ferroelectric field effect has successfully been demonstrated on a bulk semiconductor (silicon) using a thin ferroelectric film of bismuth titanate ($Bi_4Ti_3O_{12}$) deposited onto it by RF sputtering. A new memory device, the metal-ferroelectric-semiconductor transistor (MFST), has been fabricated. This device utilizes the remanent polarization of a ferroelectric thin film to control the surface conductivity of a bulk semiconductor substrate and perform a memory function. The capacitance–voltage characteristics of the metal-ferroelectric-semiconductor structure were employed o study the memory behavior. The details of the study together with a preliminary result on the MFST are presented.

I. INTRODUCTION

THE ferroelectric field effect, which is the modulation of conductivity by electrostatic charges induced by ferroelectric polarization, has attracted much attention again recently. The idea of using a ferroelectric material to modulate the surface conductivity of a bulk semiconductor was proposed originally nearly 16 years ago [1]-[4]. The ferroelectric material used was a crystal of guanidinium aluminum sulfate hexahydrate (GASH), placed in intimate contact with the surface of a semiconductor crystal. The air gap between the two surfaces was minimized either by carefully polishing the surfaces, or by filling the gap with a liquid dielectric such as ethylene cyanide or nitrobenzene. The experimental results, however, were not very successful, apparently due to the poor modulation efficiency of the ferroelectric polarization, and a low spontaneous polarization ($P_s \sim 0.35$ μC/cm²) of the GASH crystal.

Observations of ferroelectric conductivity modulation have been reported in recent years by several workers in devices using thin metal films deposited on ferroelectric $BaTiO_3$ or TGS crystals [5], or semiconducting films deposited by vacuum evaporation on ferroelectric crystals [6]-[12] or on ferroelectric ceramic (PZT) substrates [13], [14]. These ferroelectric field effect devices in general can be divided into two categories. One is the adaptive resistor and the other the adaptive transistor. The former is fabricated by depositing a semiconducting layer, and the latter by fabricating a semiconductor thin film transistor, on a bulk ferroelectric substrate. All of the work was based on bulk ferroelectrics and the conductivity

modulation was only observed in thin films. These devices, however, all suffered from an electrical instability associated with the thin film semiconducting material. The electrical conductivity and the transconductance in either ON or OFF state would drift and decay into an intermediate state with time.

With advances in vacuum technology, RF sputtering has become one of the most promising techniques for deposition of thin films. Attempts to grow ferroelectric $BaTiO_3$ films by RF sputtering were reported [15]-[18], but the films all showed little evidence of ferroelectric behavior. Values of spontaneous polarization were very small and the films did not have the ferroelectric tetragonal structure. Epitaxial ferroelectric films of bismuth titanate ($Bi_4Ti_3O_{12}$) were first successfully grown by RF sputtering in our laboratories [19]-[21]. The films deposited on (110) $MgAl_2O_4$ crystals are single-crystal layers of (010) orientation which show essentially the electrooptic behavior of bulk single crystals [21]. Atkin [22] also succeeded in growing films of a complex perovskite-type ferroelectric involving oxides of Pb, Bi, La, Fe, Nb, and Zr. Films deposited on platinum film substrates exhibited spontaneous polarization of about 22 μC/cm² with loop squareness values as high as 0.9. These successes in growing films prompted us to study the ferroelectric field effect in the bulk semiconductor utilizing a ferroelectric thin film, and to explore possible device applications [23].

In this paper, we present experimental observations of the ferroelectric field effect in a bulk semiconductor using a ferroelectric thin film, and propose a new memory device called the metal-ferroelectric-semiconductor transistor (MFST). The device structure is similar to the conventional metal-insulator-semiconductor (MIS) field-effect transistor with the exception that the gate insulating layer is replaced by an active ferroelectric thin film. Fig. 1 shows the cross-sectional view of the device. The ferroelectric material is bismuth titanate, which is deposited by RF sputtering on the semiconductor (silicon) substrate. Results of the preliminary study on this device will be described.

II. EXPERIMENTAL TECHNIQUES

The bismuth titanate films were deposited on (100) silicon wafers by RF sputtering. The techniques used to

Manuscript received November 22, 1973; revised March 22, 1974.
The author is with the Research Laboratories, Westinghouse Electric Company, Pittsburgh, Pa. 15235.

Reprinted from *IEEE Trans. Electron Devices*, vol. ED-21, no. 8, pp. 499–504, August 1974.

228

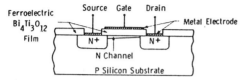

Fig. 1. Cross-sectional view of N-channel MFST structure.

prepare the films were similar to the epitaxial growth of bismuth titanate films described in detail in [19], [20]. The ceramic targets contained an excess of Bi_2O_3 in order to compensate for the loss of this component in the films during sputtering. The target composition used was 0.8 $Bi_4Ti_3O_{12}$ + 0.2 $Bi_{12}TiO_{20}$. This gave a convenient "stoichiometric temperature range" of ~500° to 700°C in which the desired compound could be obtained. The films were deposited in an argon–oxygen ambient at a sputtering pressure of about 6 mtorr. The depositions were done at temperatures slightly higher than the Curie temperature 675°C. Heating of the substrates for the depositions was achieved by clamping them to boron nitride slabs which were heated by a platinum strip heater.

The silicon wafers were mechanically lapped, polished, and finally "Syton" polished. Source and drain islands were formed by high-temperature diffusion processes in either PH_3 (for p-type wafers) or BBr_3 (for n-type wafers) with thermally grown SiO_2 as the diffusion mask. The source-drain distance was 76 μm and the width was 780 μm. Prior to deposition of the bismuth titanate layer the SiO_2 layer was removed. The gold metal gate electrode, which was 127 μm wide, was deposited by dc sputtering and delineated with photolithographic techniques. Contact windows in the bismuth titanate layers over the source and drain regions were removed by etching in concentrated HCl acid.

The film orientations were determined from X-ray diffraction patterns obtained with a Weissenberg single crystal camera. Ferroelectric hysteresis studies were usually made at 60 Hz with a modified Sawyer and Tower bridge. The capacitance–voltage measurements on MFS capacitors were made at 1 MHz.

III. RESULTS AND DISCUSSION

The basic principle of the MFST device is to utilize the remanent polarization of the ferroelectric ($Bi_4Ti_3O_{12}$) thin film to control the surface conductance of a bulk semiconductor (silicon) and to perform the memory function. This will be described using the metal-ferroelectric-semiconductor (MFS) structure.

Ideally (assuming no interface states and no bound charges in the ferroelectric), when a positive external field whose magnitude is larger than the coercive field of the ferroelectric material is applied to the metal electrode, the polarization in the ferroelectric will be aligned toward the ferroelectric–semiconductor interface. When the external field is removed, the remanent polarization will induce a field which attracts negative compensation charge to the semiconductor surface. For an n-type semiconductor this will create an accumulation layer. The energy bands of the

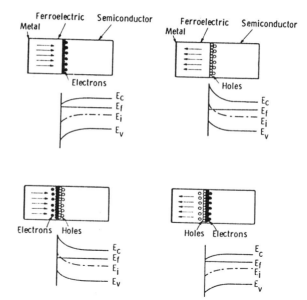

Fig. 2. Surface energy band diagrams at ferroelectric-semiconductor interface after external field is removed. (a) Ideal case: positive remanent polarization state, electrons accumulated at semiconductor surface (left); negative remanent polarization state, holes accumulated at semiconductor surface (right). (b) Carrier injection case: positive remanent polarization state, holes accumulated at semiconductor surface (left); negative remanent polarization state, electrons accumulated at semiconductor surface (right).

semiconductor at the interface will bend downward, as shown in the left side of Fig. 2(a). When a negative field is next applied to the metal electrode, the polarization in the ferroelectric will be reversed. The field induced by the remanent polarization, in this case, will attract positive compensation charge to the semiconductor surface. The carrier density of a p-type semiconductor at the interface will be enhanced, and that of an n-type will be depleted or inverted. The semiconductor energy bands at the interface will bend upward, as shown in the right side of Fig. 2(a).

In actual devices, however, when an external field is applied to the metal electrode, injection of carriers (either electrons or holes, depending on the polarity of the applied field, as also being observed by Chu et al. [24] in Si_3N_4 films) from the semiconductor into the ferroelectric occurs, as can be seen from the results of capacitance–voltage measurements shown later. These injected charges will be attracted by the remanent polarization field and bound to ferroelectric domains when the applied field is removed. Because of the bound charge in the ferroelectric, a charge of opposite polarity will be induced at the semiconductor surface. The semiconductor surface will be depleted, inverted or enhanced, depending on the polarity and amount of the bound charges. The surface energy band diagrams after the external field is removed for the case of carrier injection are shown in Fig. 2(b). If electrons are injected into the ferroelectric (as shown on the left) positive charges will be induced at the semiconductor surface and the surface energy bands bend upward. For the hole injection case (on the right) the surface energy bands bend downward.

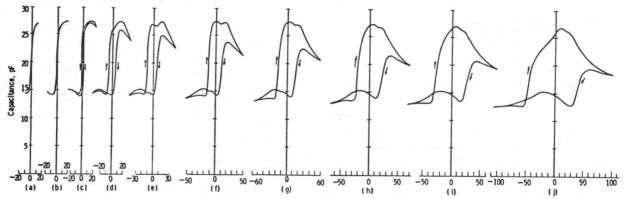

Fig. 3. Typical capacitance–voltage curves of $Bi_4Ti_3O_{12}$ film deposited on n-type silicon wafer measured at 1 MHz with different dc sweep voltages applied to metal electrode.

The injection of carriers and the memory effect observed in the capacitance–voltage measurements will be described next. Bismuth titanate films were both deposited on n- and p-type (100) silicon wafers. The resistivity of the n-type wafers was 0.25 Ω·cm and that of the p-type was 0.4 Ω·cm. Fig. 3 shows a family of the capacitance–voltage curves obtained from a film deposited on an n-type wafer. The measurements were made at a signal frequency of 1 MHz. The thickness of the film was 3.6 μm and the area of the gold metal electrode was 5.8×10^{-4} cm². The sample that was as-grown and electrically unpoled before was first cycled back and forth with a low frequency sweep generator at voltages between −10 and +10 V [Fig. 3(a)]. The voltage range was then increased in steps to a maximum of between −100 and +100 V [Fig. 3(j)].

When the sample was cycled at a maximum voltage smaller than 20 V, as shown in Fig. 3(a) and 3(b), the measured capacitance–voltage curves were similar to those of conventional MIS capacitors. The capacitance approached a maximum for positive voltages, which corresponded approximately to the capacitance of the ferroelectric. As the voltage was reduced and became negative, a depletion layer was formed near the semiconductor surface. The total capacitance which was a series combination of the capacitances of the ferroelectric and the semiconductor depletion layer decreased. If the voltage was further decreased the semiconductor surface became inverted. The capacitance went through a minimum and then increased again at low signal frequencies, or approached a constant at high frequencies. The maximum capacitance C_{max} measured was about 27.5 pF. The dielectric constant of the ferroelectric calculated from this value was about 193. The measured minimum capacitance was about 14.3 pF. This value agreed closely with that calculated from the equation of the high frequency minimum capacitance [25]

$$C_{min}' = C_{max} \left[1 + \left(\frac{\epsilon_F}{\epsilon_S}\right) \left\{ \frac{4\epsilon_S kT \ln (N_D/n_i)}{q^2 N_D} \right\}^{1/2} \right]^{-1} \quad (1)$$

where ϵ_F and ϵ_S are the permittivities of the ferroelectric and the semiconductor, respectively, n_i the intrinsic carrier concentration, and N_D the donor impurity concen-

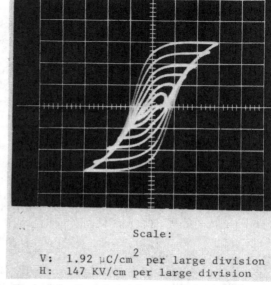

Scale:

V: 1.92 μC/cm² per large division
H: 147 KV/cm per large division

Fig. 4. Typical family of step-by-step opened hysteresis loops obtained from 3.4-μm thick film deposited on p-type wafer.

tration. The minimum capacitance calculated from (1) was 14.8 pF.

When the voltage applied to the metal electrode was higher than 20 V, injection of carriers from the semiconductor into the ferroelectric occurred. This was reflected from the shift of flat-band voltage, as shown in Fig. 3(c) to 3(j). The higher the applied voltage, the larger the shift in flat-band voltage. The direction of the shift was the same as the polarity of the applied voltage (positive shift by positive applied voltage and vice versa), indicating that both holes and electrons were participating in the effect. Furthermore, the amounts of the shifts in both directions were almost the same if the sample was cycled back and forth with a symmetrical voltage. Once shifted in one direction, the flat-band voltage would remain there and not shift back into other direction unless an opposite polarity voltage higher than 20 V was applied again.

Another interesting phenomenon associated with the shift of the flat-band voltage was a decrease in the total

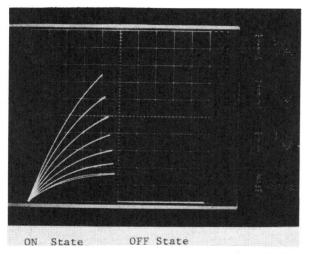

Fig. 5. Drain characteristics of *N*-channel MFST device—ON state (left) after metal gate electrode was poled with −20 V; OFF state (right) after poled with +20 V.

capacitance at higher voltages, which was never observed in conventional MIS capacitors. The decrease was quite noticeable, particularly on the right-hand side of the capacitance–voltage curves, as shown in Fig. 3(c) to 3(j), (or on the left-hand side for p-type wafers). This was due to the fact that the dielectric constant of the ferroelectric $Bi_4Ti_3O_{12}$ film decreased with increasing electric field. On the left-hand side, since the semiconductor depletion layer capacitance dominated, the decrease in the total capacitance was not much. Presumably, the charges injected into the ferroelectric were bound to boundaries of ferroelectric domains where the polarization was not continuous. They induced a depolarization field, opposed the dominating polarization, and caused the dielectric constant to decrease. This decrease in dielectric constant with increasing electric field has also been observed in RF sputtered $SrTiO_3$ films [26]. The dielectric constant of the bismuth titanate was reduced to about 130 at 100 V (average applied electric field of 280 kV/cm). The calculated effective surface charge density due to the bound charges in the ferroelectric after this field was removed was about $8.28 \times 10^{12}/cm^2$, where use was made of a flat-band voltage of 40 V and ferroelectric capacitance of 19.2 pF. The two humps at about +20 (upper curve), and −20 V (lower curve), as clearly seen in Fig. 3(f), were due to polarization reversals of the ferroelectric film.

The ferroelectric hysteresis studies were made on films deposited on low-resistivity n- and p-type wafers. The film thicknesses usually ranged between 3 and 4 μm. Fig. 4 shows a typical family of the hysteresis loops obtained from a 3.4-μm thick film deposited on a p-type wafer. The photograph, which shows the step-by-step opened hysteresis loops, was taken by snapping the camera each time the applied field was increased slightly. The loop squareness was about 0.85. The coercive field was about 130 kV/cm and the switched polarization was 5.7 μC/cm² at a field of 440 kV/cm. The switched polarization might increase slightly at higher fields, but it was not attempted to saturate the polarization for fear that the film might

break down. The measured polarization was slightly higher than the *c*-axis polarization of 4 μC/cm² observed in bulk $Bi_4Ti_3O_{12}$ single crystals [27] and epitaxial films [19], [20], but it was small compared with the *a*-axis polarization of 50 μC/cm². X-ray diffraction studies on this film indicated that it was polycrystalline with a (001) *c*-axis fiber texture. The formation of the (001) fiber texture is not surprising, since (001) orientation is the natural growth morphology as displayed by bulk crystals [28]. From a device point of view, this is the preferred orientation, since the coercive field along the *c*-axis is much smaller than that along the *a*-axis (about 15 times smaller in bulk crystals [27] and 8 times in epitaxial films [20]), so the device can be operated with a lower switching field.

The MFST's were fabricated on 10 to 40 $\Omega \cdot$cm p- and n-type (100) silicon wafers. After being mounted on TO-5 headers, they were examined with a Tektronix 576 curve tracer. The devices all exhibited memory effect. Fig. 5 shows typical drain characteristics of an n-channel device. The characteristics shown on the left were obtained a few minutes after the device was poled with a pulse of −20 V (between the gate and the source). The drain current at zero gate voltage was about 80 μA. This current would be higher if a higher negative poling voltage was employed. When the device was poled with a pulse of +20 V, it was completely cut off, as shown on the right with a horizontal line. The drain current was not detectable even when the gate voltage was increased in five steps to +5 V. The device seemed to be stable in both ON and OFF states. The drain currents of the ON and the OFF states at zero gate voltage varied less than 5 percent in 2 hours after the poling field was removed. Detailed studies on the switching and stability properties of the device will be discussed in the future.

IV. CONCLUSIONS

In this paper, we described observations of the ferroelectric field effect in a bulk semiconductor (silicon) using a ferroelectric bismuth titanate ($Bi_4Ti_3O_{12}$) film. The MFST, a new ferroelectric memory device, was successfully fabricated. This device utilizes the remanent polarization of the ferroelectric film to control the surface conductivity of a bulk semiconductor and perform the memory function. The ferroelectric bismuth titanate film was deposited by RF sputtering in an argon–oxygen atmosphere on silicon substrates. Good quality films with a low coercive field had *c*-axis fiber texture with a polarization slightly higher than 4 μC/cm². MFS structure was employed to study the memory effect. Injection of carriers, both electrons and holes, from the semiconductor into the ferroelectric was observed. This was found from the shifts of flat-band voltage on the measured capacitance-voltage curves. The charges injected into the ferroelectric were presumably attracted by the remanent polarization and bound to ferroelectric domains after the external field was removed. Preliminary studies indicated that the device in the ON and OFF states was relatively stable. Results of the detailed study on the device characteristics will be discussed in another paper.

The MFST device has a number of advantages over other memory devices. It has a higher surface charge density. The transconductance and the amplification gain are also higher than the conventional MIS transistor, because of the high dielectric constant of the ferroelectric film. It is much more stable than the ferroelectric field effect device incorporating a semiconductor thin film transistor. It can operate with a lower switching voltage due to the use of a thin film ferroelectric, instead of a thick bulk ferroelectric substrate. It also has a higher field effect mobility. The fabrication processes are simpler and also compatible with planar silicon technology. Because of its capability of retaining memory in the absence of external field, ability for continuous and nondestructive readout, low switching power requirements, and relatively rapid switching speed, it has a significant potential for use in memory, counting, and switching circuit applications.

ACKNOWLEDGMENT

The author wishes to thank Dr. M. H. Francombe and Dr. J. R. Szedon for helpful discussions during this study; also Dr. W. J. Takei for making X-ray diffraction measurements. Technical assistance by G. A. Ferguson, C. M. Pedersen, J. Chedrick, P. E. Barbarich, and J. C. Neidigh is also acknowledged.

REFERENCES

[1] D. H. Looney, "Semiconductive translating device," U. S. Patent 2 791 758, May 7, 1957.
[2] W. L. Brown, "Semiconductive device," U. S. Patent 2 791 759, May 7, 1957.
[3] I. M. Ross, "Semiconductive translating device," U. S. Patent 2 791 760, May 7, 1957.
[4] J. A. Morton, "Electrical switching and storage," U. S. Patent 2 791 761, May 7, 1957.
[5] H. L. Stadler, "Changing properties of metals by ferroelectric polarization charging," Phys. Rev. Lett., vol. 14, pp. 979–981, 1965.
[6] J. L. Moll and Y. Tarui, "A new solid state memory resistor," IEEE Trans. Electron Devices (Solid-State Res. Conf. Abs.), vol. ED-10, pp. 338–339, Sept. 1963.
[7] R. Zuleeg and H. H. Wieder, "Effect of ferroelectric polarization on insulated-gate thin film transistor parameters," Solid-State Electron. vol. 9, pp. 657–661, 1966.
[8] P. H. Hyman and G. H. Heilmeier, "A ferroelectric field effect device," Proc. IEEE, vol. 54, pp. 842–848, June 1966.
[9] P. Buckman and H. Diamond, "Effect of ferroelectric polarization fields on semiconductor films," in Proc. Int. Meet. Ferroelectricity, (V. Dvorak, A. Fouskova, and P. Glogar, Eds., Prague, Czechoslovakia), vol. 2, pp. 313–325, 1966.
[10] S. S. Perlman and K. H. Ludewig, "An adaptive thin film transistor," IEEE Trans. Electron Devices, vol. ED-14, pp. 816–821, Dec. 1967.
[11] J. H. McCusker and S. S. Perlman, "Improved ferroelectric field-effect devices," IEEE Trans. Electron Devices (Corresp.), vol. 15, pp. 182–183, Mar. 1968.
[12] G. G. Teather and L. Young, "Non-destructive readout of ferroelectrics by field effect conductivity modulation," Solid State Electron., vol. 11, pp. 527–533, 1968.
[13] J. C. Crawford and F. L. English, "Ceramic ferroelectric field effect studies," IEEE Trans. Electron Devices, vol. ED-16, pp. 525–532, June 1969.
[14] J. C. Crawford, "Ferroelectric field effect studies at low temperatures," Ferroelectrics, vol. 1, pp. 23–30, 1970.
[15] T. Putner, "A small scale radio frequency sputtering apparatus," Thin Solid Films, vol. 1, pp. 165–169, 1967.
[16] R. Vu Huy Dat and C. Baumberger, "Ferroelectricity of barium titanate thin films of less than one micron thickness," Phys. Status Solidi, vol. 22, pp. K67–K70, 1967.
[17] I. H. Pratt and S. Firestone, "Fabrication of rf-sputtered barium titanate thin films," J. Vac. Sci. Technol., vol. 8, pp. 256–260, 1971.
[18] S. Iida and S. Kataoka, "$BaTiO_3$ films prepared by rf sputtering on to InSb or GaAs," Appl. Phys. Lett., vol. 18, pp. 391–392, 1971.
[19] W. J. Takei, N. P. Formigoni, and M. H. Francombe, "Preparation and epitaxy of sputtered films of ferroelectric $Bi_4Ti_3O_{12}$," J. Vacuum Sci. Technol., vol. 7, pp. 442–448, 1970.
[20] S. Y. Wu, W. J. Takei, M. H. Francombe, and S. E. Cummins, "Domain structure and polarization reversal in films of ferroelectric bismuth titanate," IEEE Trans. Sonics Ultrason., vol. SU-19, pp. 217–224, Apr. 1972.
[21] S. Y. Wu, W. J. Takei, and M. H. Francombe, "Electro-optic contrast observations in single-domain epitaxial films of bismuth titanate," Appl. Phys. Lett., vol. 22, pp. 26–28, 1973.
[22] R. B. Atkin, "Performance of sputtered $Pb_{0.92}Bi_{0.07}La_{0.01}$ $(Fe_{0.405}Nb_{0.325}Zr_{0.27})O_3$ ferroelectric memory films," IEEE Trans. Sonics Ultrason., vol. SU-19, pp. 213–215, Apr. 1972.
[23] M. H. Francombe, "Ferroelectric films and their device applications," Thin Solid Films, vol. 13, pp. 413–433, 1972.
[24] T. L. Chu, J. R. Szedon, and C. H. Lee, "The preparation and C-V characteristics of $Si-Si_3N_4$ and $Si-SiO_2-Si_3N_4$ structures," Solid-State Electron., vol. 10, pp. 897–905, 1967.
[25] S. M. Sze, Physics of Semiconductor Devices. New York: Wiley, 1969, p. 437.
[26] W. B. Pennebaker, "RF sputtered strontium titanate films," IBM J. Res. Develop., vol. 15, pp. 686–695, 1969.
[27] S. E. Cummins and L. E. Cross, "Electrical and optical properties of ferroelectric $Bi_4Ti_3O_{12}$ single crystals," J. Appl. Phys., vol. 39, pp. 2268–2274, Apr. 1968.
[28] L. G. Van Uitert and L. Egerton, "Bismuth titanate, a ferroelectric," J. Appl. Phys., vol. 32, p. 959, May 1961

An Experimental 512-bit Nonvolatile Memory with Ferroelectric Storage Cell

JOSEPH T. EVANS, MEMBER, IEEE, AND RICHARD WOMACK, MEMBER, IEEE

Abstract —An experimental 512-bit random access memory based on ferroelectric-capacitor storage cells has been successfully fabricated and tested. The device was designed solely for use in process development and electrical characterization and includes on-board test circuitry for that purpose. The internal timing of the memory is controlled externally to allow experimentation with timing algorithms, hence the name 512 externally controlled device, or 512 ECD. This paper will discuss the properties of the ferroelectric ceramics used in integrated circuit memories, the operation of a destructively read ferroelectric memory cell, and the organization of the 512 ECD die, including its on-board test circuitry. The paper will close with a discussion of the retention and wear-out properties of ferroelectric capacitors as they relate to design requirements.

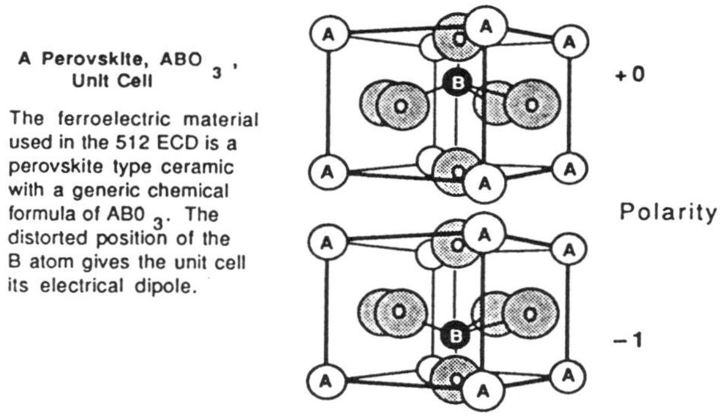

I. FERROELECTRIC PROPERTIES

A FERROELECTRIC capacitor has a highly nonlinear dielectric with permanent charge retention after application of a voltage by an external circuit. The permanent charge originates from a net ionic displacement in unit cells of the material resulting from the external voltage application (see Fig. 1). The individual unit cells interact constructively with their neighbors to produce domains within the material. As the voltage is removed, the majority of the domains will remain poled in the direction of the applied electric field, requiring compensating charge to remain on the plates of the capacitor. This compensating charge causes a hysteresis in the standard charge versus voltage plot of the capacitor as it is cycled through positive and negative voltage applications (see Fig. 2). A measured hysteresis is shown in Fig. 3. From a digital point of view, if a voltage is applied to a ferroelectric capacitor in a direction opposite of the previously applied voltage, remanent domains will switch, requiring compensating charge to flow onto the capacitor plates. If the field is applied in the direction of the remanent domains, no remanent switching takes place, no change occurs in the compensating charge, and a reduced amount of charge will flow into the capacitor. This property can be used by a properly designed external circuit to sense the last state of the capacitor or write a desired state into the

Manuscript received April 4, 1988; revised May 24, 1988.
J. T. Evans was with Krysalis Corporation, Albuquerque, NM 87109. He is now with Radiant Technologies, Albuquerque, NM 87109.
R. Womack is with Krysalis Corporation, Albuquerque, NM 87109.
IEEE Log Number 8822498.

A Perovskite, ABO_3, Unit Cell

The ferroelectric material used in the 512 ECD is a perovskite type ceramic with a generic chemical formula of ABO_3. The distorted position of the B atom gives the unit cell its electrical dipole.

Fig. 1. A unit cell of the 512 ECD ferroelectric material.

capacitor. Note that the remanent charge does not generate a detectable voltage on the capacitor after the removal of the applied field. In fact, unlike a DRAM capacitor, the plates of the ferroelectric capacitor can be shorted without affecting the remanent charge internally and the charge requires no refresh. More complete descriptions of the properties and applications of ferroelectric materials are given in works listed in the reference section of this paper [1]–[4].

The thin ferroelectric film capacitor is a rugged, highly reliable device which can withstand a wide range of extremes in temperature and radiation. The ferroelectric ceramic used in the 512 externally controlled device (ECD) has a Curie temperature in excess of 300°C with a diffuse phase transition allowing for excellent data retention and storage over the full military temperature range from −55 to 125°C. The Curie temperature is the point at which the unit structural cell loses its distortion and the ferroelectric properties, as well as any stored data, disappear. There is a nondestructive change in the amount of remanent charge in the capacitor generated as a function of temperature. The 512 ECD ferroelectric capacitors have a dynamic signal range of two over the military temperature range. The designer must ensure that his sensing techniques operate over that dynamic range. A conservative technique used on the 512 ECD is the double-ended sense architecture where two ferroelectric cells are matched for each bit. Single-ended sense techniques are certainly possible with the technology if a temperature-compensated reference or dummy cell is generated by the designer.

Reprinted from *IEEE J. Solid-State Circuits*, vol. 23, no. 5, pp. 1171–1175, October 1988.

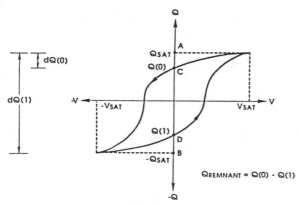

Fig. 2. Hysteresis of ferroelectric capacitor.

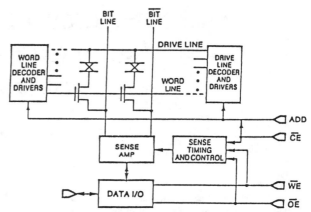

Fig. 4. 512 ECD block diagram.

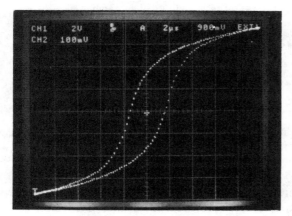

Fig. 3. Measured hysteresis of 100×100-μm^2 ferroelectric capacitor. Y scale/div $= 10$ μC/cm^2; X scale/div $= 2$ V.

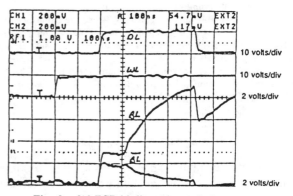

Fig. 5. 512 ECD bit-line voltages during READ.

II. FERROELECTRIC MEMORY OPERATION

The very nature of the charge storage mechanism in the ferroelectric material, i.e., ionic displacement, makes the capacitor naturally radiation hard. High-energy particles, gamma radiation, or neutrons must physically move ions in the lattice to erase the stored polarization state and this requires extremely high doses. Radiation tests conducted by the Naval Surface Warfare Center, Sandia National Laboratories, and Raytheon Corporation confirm this model. The radiation hardness of a ferroelectric-based memory will ultimately depend on the hardness of the underlying control circuitry. There are several reports available to the public concerning radiation hardness and test results of ferroelectric capacitors [5], [6].

Unlike a linear capacitor, the switching speed of a ferroelectric capacitor is limited by the domain switching speed. This is much slower than the electronic displacement common in linear capacitors. The modified lead titanate materials used in the 512 ECD can switch at speeds tested above 50 MHz. The limit may be in the gigahertz range. However, we have not been able to determine the maximum switching speed of the ferroelectric material used in the 512 ECD. In a useful CMOS circuit, the response of the ferroelectric material is such that the speed of the circuit will be determined by the circuit's intrinsic ability to deliver charge, not by the speed of the ferroelectric capacitor.

The memory cell utilized in the 512 ECD consists of a pass-transistor/ferroelectric-capacitor combination. Two cells are used in a double-ended sense scheme to create a self-referencing signal differential across a regenerative sense amp. A block diagram is shown in Fig. 4. The data bit consists of a word line (WL) controlling two pass transistors, a bit line (BL) and bit-bar line (BLb) to collect charge from the capacitors, and a common drive line (DL) to actively drive the capacitors. A sense amp resides between BL and BLb. For a WRITE, the sense amp is set to the desired state driving BL and BLb to the opposite voltage values of V_{drive} and ground. The drive line is then pulsed such that the high drive line against the grounded bit line writes the $Q(0)$ state into that capacitor. When the drive line drops to ground after the pulse, the other capacitor has a $Q(1)$ written in it by its high bit-line voltage. V_{drive} is derived directly from V_{cc2}. The state written into the capacitor on BL represents the polarity of the stored datum.

The READ operation is best understood by examining the photograph of the 512 ECD bit-line signals in Fig. 5. A voltage step is applied to the drive line with the bit lines floating and the sense amp OFF. Since the capacitors are in opposite states, BL and BLb will collect different amounts of charge and produce a voltage differential of a polarity determined by the stored data. The capacitor that is flipped

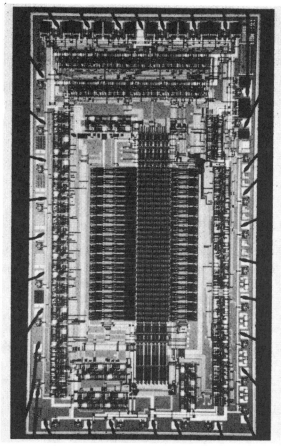

Fig. 6. Die photograph of 512 ECD.

TABLE I
CRITICAL STATISTICS

Technology	N-well CMOS
Critical Feature Size	3 micron
Die size	3.2mm x 6mm
Vcc1	5 volts
Vcc2	5 volts -> 10 volts
Active Power	30mW
Bit Area	1300 μ^2
Capacitor Size	5 μ x 9 μ
Read/Write Access Speed	550ns
Tested Read Accesses per byte (50°C)	10^{12}
Tested Write Accesses per byte (50°C)	10^{11}

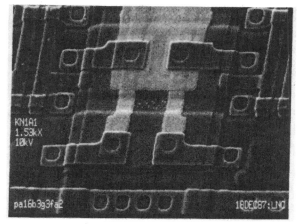

Fig. 7. SEM photograph of 512 ECD capacitors.

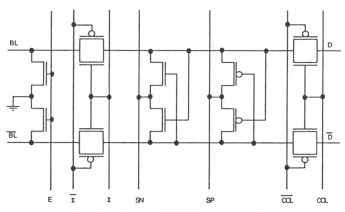

Fig. 8. Circuit of 512 ECD sense amplifier.

during the READ will generate the higher bit-line voltage. When the sense amplifier turns on, it will drive that particular bit line to the high rail while the other bit line will be driven to ground. This situation recreates the original WRITE condition and restores both capacitors to their original states. The restore is invisible to the user and occurs in parallel with the output gating of the READ data to the I/O ports. Note the 1-V differential generated on the bit lines in Fig. 5 by the two capacitor states.

III. 512 ECD ORGANIZATION

Fig. 6 is a die photograph of the 512 ECD and its internal organization. Table I reflects its critical statistics. The device is arranged as a 64×8 memory. The memory array consists of 64 rows of 8 bits apiece with no column decode. One row consists of 16 capacitors sharing a common WL and DL and arranged as eight double-ended memory bits. The capacitors are approximately $5 \times 9 \mu m^2$, less than 1 μm thick, and have a nominal capacitance of 1 pF apiece. The upper half of the photograph in Fig. 7 shows the two matched capacitors of a single bit. As noted in Table I, a single bit occupies approximately 1300 μm^2, a very large area. The part was never intended for production, so large tolerances were provided for in the layout rules to ensure operable parts on first silicon. The 3-μm

technology and double-ended architecture also contributed to the memory cell area.

The DL drivers and WL drivers are located on either side of the memory array. Eight regenerative feedback amplifiers similar to those in DRAM's constitute the sense amps. A circuit diagram of one of the sense amps, including equalization, isolation, and output gate controls, is shown in Fig. 8. The device has standard three-state I/O functions. The die size is 3.2×6 mm².

The WL, DL, sense amp, and equalization functions are controlled from buffered inputs. In combination with the I/O controls, the 512 ECD requires seven timing inputs to actively control the device in normal operation. The individual control lines allow separate switching of:

1) word lines,
2) drive lines,
3) sense amplifiers,
4) equalization of the bit lines,
5) output ports of the sense amplifiers,
6) output enable, and
7) WRITE enable.

Additionally, the isolation between the memory array and the sense amplifiers can be controlled externally. The part has two separate internal power grids with a common ground. V_{cc1} supplies standard voltages to the control circuitry. V_{cc2} supplies the second power grid consisting of the memory array, sense amplifiers, word-line drivers, and drive-line drivers. Voltage translation circuits convert the control signals, data, and addresses between the two voltages. The flexibility of the separate control lines allows examination of various timing algorithms on the ferroelectric-capacitor performance. The dual power system provides the same flexibility in examining the effects of various drive voltages across the capacitors in the memory array. The memory has operated with V_{cc2} as low as 5 V and as high as 10 V. The seven control lines are unique to the 512 ECD. Products based on this technology may be designed with standard SRAM three-line control using a synchronous chip enable to compensate for the destructive READ mechanism.

The performance of 512 ECD is severely limited by the use of buffered control signals to drive the internal operation. Also, its primary mission is to study the ferroelectric capacitors under realistic conditions. Consequently, no attempt to formally characterize the speed performance of the device has been made. The various test programs used on the part have operated as fast as 550-ns access time and 1-μs cycle time to as slow as 1700-ns access time and 2.4-μs cycle time. The part has operated as high as 125°C using these timing algorithms.

The top 20 percent of the die is occupied by special analog test circuitry consisting of source followers connected to the bit lines. A circuit diagram of a source-follower pair connected to one bit-line pair is shown in Fig. 9. There is a source-follower pair for each bit-line pair in the 512 ECD and all 1024 capacitors of the part can be measured individually. Note that one source follower serves both the bit and bit bar of a single column and that the output of the source follower is routed to the associated output pad. The user can select either bit or bit bar for measurement via the TAP control line. The TEST control line disconnects the source followers from the memory array for normal digital operation. A pull-up resistor to an external reference voltage is connected to each I/O pad. In the TEST mode with a voltage on the bit line under observation, the source follower produces a voltage at the I/O pad related to the bit-line voltage. Circuitry is included which allows calibration of the I/O pad voltage relative to the bit-line voltage generating it before starting

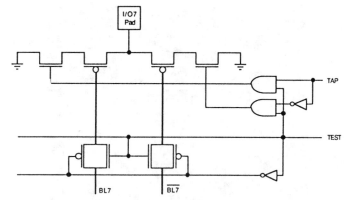

Fig. 9.   512 ECD source-follower circuit.

the test. External computer-controlled analog-to-digital converters are used to measure the bit-line signals generated by the ferroelectric capacitors in the array.

Using the analog test system, capacitor uniformity after production can be examined. The part can then be subjected to different types of operations under varying environmental conditions to examine the long-term effects on capacitor performance. This is probably the most important feature of the 512 ECD. Wear-out and retention characteristics of the ferroelectric capacitors in an actual digital memory can be objectively quantified over a wide range of operating conditions. It is necessary to measure these characteristics since they must be compensated for in design to produce the longest lifetime and widest temperature margins for a product. Without this information, it is presently impossible to design a product with long-term reliability.

IV. RETENTION

Ferroelectric capacitors poled into a specified state will depolarize over time. The rate of depolarization is a function of temperature, intrinsic stress, WRITE voltage, and ferroelectric material composition. The sense-amp design used in the 512 ECD has a minimum limit below which the internal threshold imbalances of the sense amp will overcome the READ signal and an error may occur. The time required for the signal level generated by the capacitor to be reduced through the effects of natural depolarization represents the retention capability of the device under the stated conditions of temperature, WRITE voltage, and previous history. The minimum signal level targeted by the designer to ensure a correct READ operation is determined by the product specification and must take into account the radiation and noise environment the part is intended to operate in as well as the level of sense-amp bias resulting from design and process rule variations.

Projections based on analog measurement of retained signals in the 512 ECD at room temperature indicate more than 30 years retention after 10^8 WRITE/READ/invert accesses. The retention capability drops off with temperature and number of accesses.

V. Wear-Out

Thin ferroelectric film capacitors do wear out from being accessed. The access lifetime of the device is determined by the retention period desired by the user. At the beginning of that retention period, the capacitor must retain enough charge to equal the minimum signal required at the end of the retention period to overcome the sense-amp bias in the specified noise environment plus the expected signal loss over the stated retention period. The number of accesses allowed on the capacitor prior to the last desired retention period must not exceed a number that will wear out the capacitor signal below that required to successfully complete the retention period as noted above.

The design of the 512 ECD is such that access limits apply per byte and not to the memory as a whole. Due to the experimental nature of the device, its actual specifications have not been determined. However, the experience gained from extensive testing has been used to determine design rules for follow-on products. The goal for the Krysalis 16K products are for ten years retention after 10^{12} WRITE/READ/invert accesses over the industrial tempera-ture range. This constitutes a 3-kHz access rate per byte constantly for ten years followed by ten years retention.

VI. Conclusion

The 512 ECD represents the first completely integrated CMOS-based ferroelectric memory. It was designed to be used as a test bed for measuring ferroelectric-capacitor performance in realistic conditions and it has proven valuable for that purpose. The results of testing the 512 ECD have significantly improved the chance of success for developing future products using ferroelectric-based memory cells.

References

[1] M. E. Lines and A. M. Glass, *Principles and Applications of Ferroelectrics and Related Materials*. Oxford: Clarendon, 1977.

[2] B. Jaffe, W. R. Cook, and H. Jaffe, *Piezoelectric Ceramics*. London: Academic, 1971.

[3] J. M. Herbert, *Ceramic Dielectrics and Capacitors*. New York: Gorden and Breach, 1985.

[4] J. C. Burfoot and G. W. Taylor, *Polar Dielectrics and Their Applications*. Berkeley: Univ. of Calif. Press, 1979.

[5] T. F. Wrobel, J. A. Bullington, and L. J. Schwee, "Radiation hardness evaluation of thin film ferroelectric capacitors," in *Govt. Microcircuit Applications Conf. Dig. Papers*, Oct. 1987, p. 267.

[6] J. A. Ballington, "Ferroelectric radiation hardness for nonvolatile memory applications," Krysalis Corp., Albuquerque, NM, Tech. Rep., Nov. 1987.

A Ferroelectric DRAM Cell for High-Density NVRAM's

REZA MOAZZAMI, CHENMING HU, FELLOW, IEEE, AND WILLIAM H. SHEPHERD

Abstract—The operation of a ferroelectric DRAM cell for nonvolatile RAM (NVRAM) applications is described. Because polarization reversal only occurs during nonvolatile store/recall operations but not during read/write operations, ferroelectric fatigue is not a serious endurance problem. For a 3-V power supply, the worst-case effective silicon dioxide thickness of the unoptimized lead zirconate titanate film studied here is less than 17 Å. This cell can be the basis of a very high-density NVRAM with practically no read/write cycle limit and at least 10^{10} nonvolatile store/recall cycles.

I. Introduction

THE LARGE charge storage density requirement for future generations of DRAM's has generated significant interest in high dielectric constant materials such as tantalum pentoxide and yttrium oxide. However, because of the lower dielectric breakdown strengths of these materials, the net gain in charge storage density has been a factor of 2 or 3 at best. Recently, nonvolatile memory cells exploiting the large polarization and ferroelectric hysteresis loops of materials such as lead zirconate titanate ($PbZr_xTi_{1-x}O_3$, commonly called PZT) have been proposed [1]. However, because these memories suffer from fatigue, a gradual loss of polarizability following repeated read/write cycling, ferroelectric materials have also been considered as a direct replacement for oxide/nitride/oxide structures in conventional volatile DRAM's [2]. In this case, the ferroelectric is not cycled between the two polarization states during read/write operation, thus possibly avoiding significant fatigue. In this letter we describe a ferroelectric nonvolatile RAM (FNVRAM) which normally operates as a conventional DRAM yet also exploits the hysteresis loop of ferroelectric materials for nonvolatile operation.

II. Material Properties and Preparation

Metal–ferroelectric–metal (MFM) capacitors were fabricated using lead zirconate titanate as the ferroelectric material. Polycrystalline 4000-Å PZT films were prepared by sol gel deposition [3] and subsequent annealing at 650°C in an oxygen ambient. Platinum was used for both top and bottom electrodes. In addition to the conventional Sawyer–Tower measurement, large-signal quasi-static capacitance (voltage

Manuscript received May 23, 1990; revised July 12, 1990. This work was supported by the Joint Services Electronics Program under Contract F49620-87-0041. R. Moazzami is supported by an IBM Doctoral Fellowship.

R. Moazzami and C. Hu are with the Department of Electrical Engineering and Computer Science, University of California, Berkeley, CA 94720.

W. H. Shepherd is with the National Semiconductor Corporation, Santa Clara, CA 95052.

IEEE Log Number 9038779.

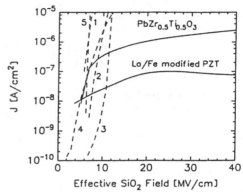

Fig. 1. The conduction characteristics of PZT films are superior to other dielectric structures (1: SiO_2/Si_3N_4 [6], 2: Ta_2O_5/Si_3N_4 [7], 3: Y_2O_3/SiO_2 [8], 4: Ta_2O_5/SiO_2 [9], 5: 60-Å SiO_2).

ramp rate: 1 V/s) and small-signal high-frequency capacitance (1 MHz, 10 mV rms) measurements were used to obtain the ferroelectric capacitor polarization. Fig. 1 is a plot of the current density versus effective electric field [4] (defined as the equivalent silicon dioxide field needed to obtain the same capacitor polarization) for a $PbZr_{0.5}Ti_{0.5}O_3$ film and a $PbZr_{0.5}Ti_{0.5}O_3$ film prepared from a lanthanum-iron modified sol gel. The electrical conductivity of PZT films is influenced significantly by impurities. Adding the proper impurities compensates for the enhanced conductivity arising from oxygen and lead vacancies [5]. Because of the large polarization of the PZT films (the relative dielectric constant calculated from the large-signal capacitance is approximately 1300), a 2-V drop across a PZT film corresponds to an effective SiO_2 field of 17 MV/cm. At these high fields, the PZT films exhibit superior leakage characteristics compared to other dielectric films [6]–[9] (see Fig. 1). However, the leakage current needs to be reduced further to meet the refresh time requirements for high-density DRAM's.

III. Memory Cell Operation

A. Nonvolatile Mode

The FNVRAM cell is a simple one-transistor DRAM cell with a ferroelectric capacitor as shown in Fig. 2. A conductive diffusion barrier is required as the storage node contact to prevent interdiffusion of silicon with the ferroelectric material during high-temperature annealing. Two different bias schemes for the operation of the FNVRAM cell are described. In the first scheme, the cell plate is always held at half of the supply voltage ($V_{DD}/2$). During DRAM operation, the storage node is at either $V_{DD}/2$ or V_{DD} such that

Reprinted from *IEEE Electron Device Lett.*, vol. 11, no. 10, pp. 454–456, October 1990.

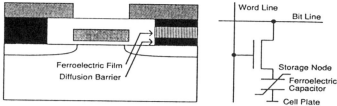

Fig. 2. The FNVRAM cell is a conventional DRAM cell with a ferroelectric capacitor dielectric. Since the ferroelectric material has a very large polarization, it is possible to incorporate the capacitor in the contact hole of the select transistor.

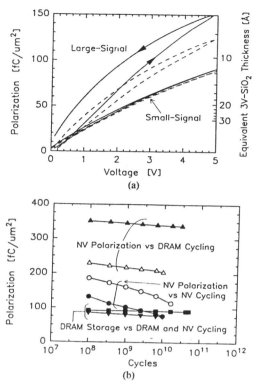

Fig. 3. (a) DRAM read/write cycling causes a significant loss in detectable polarization during DRAM operation (large-signal capacitance). However, the small-signal capacitance provides a lower limit for the available polarization. This limit is approximately 60 fC/μm^2 for a 3-V swing across the ferroelectric capacitor. (Fresh curves: solid lines; polarization after 10^{10} read/write cycles: dashed lines.) (b) Endurance characteristics of PbZr$_{0.5}$Ti$_{0.5}$O$_3$ (closed symbols) and lanthanum-iron modified films (open symbols). Capacitance measurements from -5 to 5 V and 0 to 5 V are used to determine the nonvolatile polarization and DRAM storage capacity, respectively.

the ferroelectric capacitor is not cycled between opposite polarization states. In the second scheme, the cell plate is held at V_{DD} during DRAM operation and the storage node is at either 0 V or V_{DD}. Upon command or power failure, a nonvolatile store operation is executed: the state of the cell is read and written back as one of the two permanent polarization states of the ferroelectric film. In the first scheme, if the DRAM datum is ZERO, i.e., the storage node is at $V_{DD}/2$, the word line is selected and the bit line is grounded. The ferroelectric is now polarized in one direction (nonvolatile ZERO). In the second scheme, a DRAM ZERO (storage node at V_{DD}) is stored as a nonvolatile ZERO by selecting the word line, driving the bit line to V_{DD}, and grounding the cell plate. The recall operation [1] is performed similarly to a DRAM read: the remanent polarization of the ferroelectric film is sensed and restored as one of the two DRAM states.

In this manner, the ferroelectric film is only cycled between opposite polarization states during nonvolatile store/recall operations, not during DRAM read/write operations. Even after 10^{10} store/recall cycles (corresponding to 10 store/recall cycles per second for 30 years), there is sufficient detectable ferroelectric polarization. Therefore, fatigue from store/recall cycling is not a serious limitation to the nonvolatile operation of this cell. Since the ferroelectric polarization is not reversed during DRAM read/write operation, there is almost no loss in nonvolatile polarization even after 10^{10} read/write cycles. At this rate, the FNVRAM cell is expected to tolerate orders of magnitude higher nonswitching read/write cycles than the 10^{12} switching cycles demonstrated for PZT films [10].

B. DRAM Mode

DRAM read/write cycling still causes degradation in the DRAM capacitor polarization. This degradation is observed in the measured large-signal capacitance and can be attributed to the effect of space-charge accumulation in the PZT film on the detectable ferroelectric polarization. Very little degradation is observed in the small-signal capacitance after 10^{10} read/write cycles (see Fig. 3(a)) since the small-signal capacitance is attributed primarily to nonferroelectric ionic and electronic polarizability. Even if there is no detectable ferroelectric polarization, the nonferroelectric polarization, characterized by a small-signal capacitance, is available for DRAM capacitor polarization. In this worst case, the DRAM capacitor polarization for a 3-V supply is effectively a 17-Å silicon dioxide film subjected to a 3-V voltage swing (see Fig. 3(a)).

The endurance properties of the FNVRAM cell are summarized in Fig. 3(b). The top two curves show that the nonvolatile polarization is virtually unaffected by DRAM read/write cycling (0 to 5 V) but fatigues significantly after nonvolatile store/recall cycling (-5 to 5 V) (see the two curves in the middle). The two curves on the bottom represent the worst-case polarization (small-signal capacitance limit) available for DRAM operation following read/write cycling (square symbol) and store/recall cycling (triangular symbol).

The characteristics presented above represent an unoptimized 4000-Å PbZr$_{0.5}$Ti$_{0.5}$O$_3$ film. Improved performance and reliability are possible by modifying the composition of the film: a lanthanum-iron modified PZT film has comparable storage capacity but much higher resistivity than PbZr$_{0.5}$Ti$_{0.5}$O$_3$ and exhibits less fatigue as shown in Figs. 1 and 3(b), respectively. Further increase in DRAM storage density is possible by scaling the ferroelectric film thickness: for a 1.5-V power supply, a 2000-Å film has an equivalent SiO$_2$ thickness of less than 9 Å [11].

IV. SUMMARY AND CONCLUSIONS

The operation and endurance of the FNVRAM cell are discussed. Ferroelectric fatigue does not pose a serious endurance problem for this cell since polarization reversal only occurs for nonvolatile operation but not for DRAM operation. A loss in the detectable polarization is observed even during DRAM operation. However, a lower limit for the available polarization can be obtained from the small-signal capacitance of the ferroelectric film. For the unoptimized 4000-Å PZT films studied here, this lower limit is 60 fC/μm^2 for a 3-V power supply equivalent to a 17-Å silicon dioxide film. The resistivity and endurance properties of ferroelectric films can be optimized by modifying the composition of the film. This cell can be the basis of a very high-density NVRAM with practically no read/write cycle limit and at least 10^{10} nonvolatile store/recall cycles.

References

[1] J. T. Evans and R. Womack, "An experimental 512-bit nonvolatile memory with ferroelectric storage cell," *IEEE J. Solid-State Circuits*, vol. 23, no. 5, p. 1171, Oct. 1988.

[2] J. Carrano, C. Sudhama, J. Lee, A. Tasch, and W. Miller, "Electrical and reliability characteristics of lead-zirconate-titanate (PZT) ferroelectric thin films for DRAM applications," in *IEDM Tech. Dig.*, 1989, p. 255.

[3] G. Yi, Z. Wu, and M. Sayer, "Preparation of Pb(Zr, Ti)O$_3$ thin films by sol gel processing: Electrical, optical, and electro-optic properties," *J. Appl. Phys.*, vol. 64, no. 5, Sept. 1, 1988.

[4] R. Moazzami, C. Hu, and W. H. Shepherd, "Electrical conduction and breakdown in sol-gel derived PZT thin films," in *Proc. Int. Rel. Phys. Symp.*, 1990, p. 231.

[5] B. Jaffe, W. R. Cook, and H. Jaffe, *Piezoelectric Ceramics*. New York: Academic, 1971, ch. 10, pp. 237–242.

[6] Y. Ohno *et al.*, "Reliability of SiO$_2$/Si$_3$N$_4$ dielectric films on MoSi$_2$ and WSi$_2$," in *Tech. Dig. Symp. VLSI Tech.*, 1989, p. 23.

[7] H. Shinriki, Y. Nishioka, Y. Ohji, and K. Mukai, "Oxidized Ta$_2$O$_5$/Si$_3$N$_4$ dielectric films for ultimate-STC DRAMs," in *IEDM Tech. Dig.*, 1986, p. 684.

[8] L. Manchanda and M. Gurvitch, "Yttrium oxide/silicon dioxide: A new dielectric structure for VLSI/ULSI circuits," *IEEE Electron Device Lett.*, vol. 9, no. 4, p. 180, Apr. 1988.

[9] H. Shinriki, M. Nakata, Y. Nishioka, and K. Mukai, "Leakage current reduction and reliability improvement of effective 3 nm-thick CVD Ta$_2$O$_5$ film by two-step annealing," in *Tech. Dig. Symp. VLSI Tech.*, 1989, p. 25.

[10] W. I. Kinney, W. Shepherd, W. Miller, J. Evans, and R. Womack, "A non-volatile memory cell based on ferroelectric storage capacitors," in *IEDM Tech. Dig.*, 1987, p. 850.

[11] R. Moazzami, C. Hu, and W. H. Shepherd, to be published.

Switching kinetics of lead zirconate titanate submicron thin-film memories

J. F. Scott

Symetrix Corporation, 1873 Austin Bluffs Parkway, Colorado Springs, Colorado 80918 and Condensed Matter Laboratory, Department of Physics, University of Colorado, Boulder, Colorado 80309-0390

L. Kammerdiner, M. Parris, S. Traynor, and V. Ottenbacher

Ramtron Corporation, 1873 Austin Bluffs Parkway, Colorado Springs, Colorado 80918

A. Shawabkeh and W. F. Oliver

Condensed Matter Laboratory, Department of Physics, University of Colorado, Boulder, Colorado 80309-0390

(Received 29 October 1987; accepted for publication 21 March 1988)

We have measured coercive field and switching voltage versus thickness in $PbZr_{0.54}Ti_{0.46}O_3$ thin (0.15–0.50 μm) films, together with switching times and current transient shapes versus field and temperature. The results show activation fields of order 120 kV/cm at room temperature, threshold voltages below 1.3 V, and switching speeds faster than 100 ns, demonstrating that fast, nonvolatile memories can be constructed that are compatible with standard silicon or GaAs integrated circuit voltage levels, without the need for an internal voltage pump. The displacement current transient data yield 2.5 as the dimensionality of domain growth if one-step intial nucleation rate is assumed, and are compatible with the theory of Ishibashi, yielding $i_{max}t_{max}/P_s = 1.65 \pm 0.23$, in comparison with the predicted 1.646. The switching time exhibits an activation field dependence upon both voltage and temperature through a single reduced parameter $(T_C - T)(VT_C)^{-1}$, in accord with the theory of Orihara and Ishibashi.

I. INTRODUCTION

The use of lead zirconate titanate (PZT) thin films and related alloys (such as PLZT) for computer memories has been under investigation for approximately 15 years.[1,2] However, early technology emphasized relatively thick ceramic devices with intrinsically large access voltages and relatively high costs and slow speeds. Thinner films have been prepared with good ferroelectric properties,[3] but at the cost of very high substrate temperatures (600 °C or above), which precludes application to may devices and processes. Alternative schemes, such as sol-gel deposition, also generally produce films in the 1 μm thickness range and resulting access voltages that are too high to be compatible with standard silicon or GaAs integrated circuit operating levels. (Note that for fast switching applied fields E_a must generally be of order $2E_C$, where E_C is the coercive field.) Although the design of nonvolatile memories with two power supplies or with an internal high-voltage pump is possible to circumvent the limitations that imposes on application of this technology, a superior device would be a submicron sputtered PZT film, deposited at low temperatures (~ 200 °C), whose thickness was sufficiently thin to permit fast (less than 100 ns) operation with a single 4.5 V (for Si) or 3 V (for some GaAs devices) power supply. We report in the present paper the device characteristics of such sputtered films.

II. SPECIMENS

The films described in this report were sputtered onto oxidized single-crystal silicon substrates. Processing details are proprietary.

III. EXPERIMENT

A. Coercive fields

In general, ferroelectrics do not exhibit well-defined coercive fields.[4] Their apparent thresholds strongly depend

TABLE I. Switching characteristics of $d = 350$-nm $PbZr_{0.54}Ti_{0.46}O_3$.

E (kV/cm)	t_m (ns)	t_0 (ns)	P_s (μC/cm^2)	$i_m t_m/P_S$	n
			High-temperature anneal		
$T = 294$ K					
142	74	30.3	14	1.29	2.8
284	64	21.1	20	1.54	3.0
425	55	17.7	21	1.47	2.8
$T = 423$ K					
142	71	24.7	8	1.46	2.3
284	63	17.7	10	1.76	2.5
425	58	15.0	10	1.65	2.4
$T = 468$ K					
142	73	20.2	6	1.80	2.3
284	64	13.4	5	2.15	2.2
425	57	14.9	5	1.69	2.6

Average values: $u = 0$; $n = 2.55 \pm 0.25$; $i_m t_m/P_S = 1.65 \pm 0.23$.
Theoretical value for $u = 0$ and $n = 2.5$ from Ishibashi and Takagi: 1.646.

E (kV/cm)	t_m (ns)	t_0 (ns)	P_s (μC/cm^2)	$i_m t_m/P_S$	n
			Lower-temperature anneal		
$T = 294$ K					
200	115	33	3.8	1.51	3.1
284	113	30	4.2	1.45	2.6
484	88	27	11.8	1.64	3.4
568	87	27	9.6	1.81	3.8
710	81	15	5.0	2.11	2.6
852	80	16	8.8	2.09	2.7
1000	82	22	14.6	1.68	3.1
1142	80	15	15.4	2.08	2.7

Average values: $u = 0$; $n = 3.0 \pm 0.13$; $i_m t_m/P_S = 1.80 \pm 0.27$.
Theoretical value for $u = 0$ and $n = 3.0$ from Ishibashi and Takagi: 2.054.

upon the length of time over which the field is applied. (The same is also true for breakdown fields.) As a result, it is important to distinguish between hysteresis data, typically obtained at a very slow rate (50 or 60 Hz), and displacement current transient data $i(t)$ obtained from switched capacitors on a 10–100 ns time scale. Except where otherwise noted, data reported here assumes driving voltages in the form of square pulses 30 μs wide, repeated approximately every 100 μs.

The coercive fields specified below are the threshold fields required to see a nonlinear current response differing from the linear (nonswitching) response by more than 5% within 1 μs. Figure 1 plots the coercive fields E_c we measure versus film thickness d. Open circles in this figure are earlier data on thicker films from Japan[1]; crosses are present work. The solid curve is the theoretical prediction of Kay and Dunn,[5] valid for relatively low fields (thick films).

In Fig. 2 these same data are multiplied by thickness to yield access (switching) voltage $V_s(d)$. The "processing window" of film thicknesses compatible with standard CMOS silicon logic levels is shown by the horizontal dashed line: it ranges from 0.15 to 1.5 μm. Devices in the thinner part of this range will be faster for a given voltage. The increase in V_s below 0.15 μm is similar to that found in other ferroelectrics, including TGS (triglycine sulfate), KNO$_3$, and BaTiO$_3$. There is no published analytic theory for $V_s(d)$ in this range, but empirically it is found that $E_c(d)$ varies approximately as $d^{-1.3}$, so that $V_s(d)$ varies approximately as $d^{-0.3}$, in contrast to the thick-film regime in which $V_s(d)$ varies as $d^{+0.67}$.

Breakdown voltages for 1-μs pulses are also shown in Fig. 2. They are generally one to two orders or magnitude above the threshold switching levels.

B. Switching times

We now use below a theory of switching developed by Ishibashi[6,7] from an earlier model of domain growth due to Avrami.[8] It is assumed that the rate of nucleation is a con-

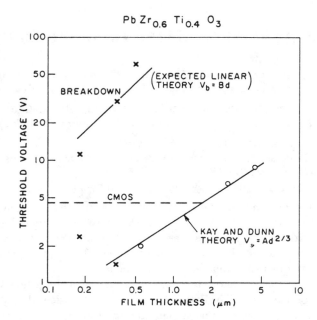

FIG. 2. Threshold switching voltage $V_s(d)$. Circles are data (Ref. 1) from Nakagawa; crosses, present work. The increase below $d = 0.2$ μm is also observed in TGS (Ref. 21) and KNO$_3$ (Ref. 12).

stant throughout the switching process [this is qualitatively different from the assumption in Fatuzzo's theory[9,10] that all nucleation occurs initially as a single step (e.g., inhomogeneous nucleation at the surfaces) and is not followed by forward or sideways domain growth until the nucleation is essentially complete]. The characteristic switching time t_0 is defined from equations describing switched charge as a function of time t

$$Q(t) = Q_0 - Q_0 \exp[-(t+t_c)^n t_0^{-n} + (t_c/t_0)^n]$$

$$\cong Q_0\{1 - \exp[-(t/t_0)^n]\} \quad \text{if } t_c \ll t_0, \quad (1a)$$

$$i(t) = 2P_s \frac{A dQ(t)}{dt}, \quad (1b)$$

whence

$$i(t) = (2P_s An/t_0)(t/t_0)^{n-1} \exp[-(t/t_0)^n], \quad (2)$$

where P_s and n are the spontaneous polarization and the dimensionality of the domain growth ($n = 1$ implies needle-like growth; $n = 2$, planar growth; and $n = 3$, spherical growth). A further simplifying assumption of the theory is that domain-wall velocities are independent of domain size. This is genereally untrue and is one source of noninteger values of dimensionality that result from least-squares fits of $i(t)$ data to Eq. (2).

A parameter of importance in the theory is the dimensionless ratio $u = t_c/t_m$, where t_m is the time at which the current $i(t)$ is maximum. t_m is typically of order 50% of the true switching time t_s, defined as the time required to transfer 90% of the charge from one side of the nonlinear capacitor to the other. t_c has no simple relationship to t_m or t_s; it can be significantly larger or smaller than t_m.

Table I summarizes t_0 values and other parameters observed for a single set of data at 294 K on PbZr$_{0.54}$Ti$_{0.46}$O$_3$ for $d = 350$ nm.

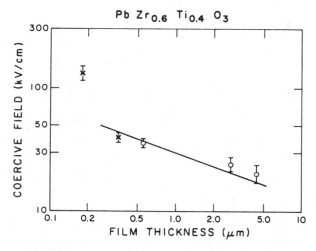

FIG. 1. Coercive field E_c vs film thickness d for PbZr$_{0.6}$Ti$_{0.4}$O$_3$ at $T = 294$ K. Solid curve is theory of Kay and Dunn (Ref. 5) in the thick film, low-field regime. Crosses are present data given the smallest value of $E_c(d)$ observed at each d.

Figure 3 illustrates the actual fits to $i(t)$ from the three-parameter theory described above. The dimensionality of domain growth, n, is found to be 3.0. This result is compatible with either continuous nucleation at a constant rate with true dimension $D = n - 1 = 2.0$ (two-dimensional domain growth perpendicular to the applied field, i.e., in the plane of the film) or with inhomogeneous nucleation all at once from existing defects (for which $D = n = 3.0$, i.e., three-dimensional growth). The theory does not differentiate between these two models, although independent evidence[11] favors the $n = 2.0$ model of continuous nucleation. We find in Table I that for $n = 3.0$, the dimensionless ratio $i_m t_m / P_S = 1.80 \pm 0.27$, in reasonable agreement with the value 2.054 predicted theoretically.[6,7] For high-T anneal, the dimensionality is 2.55 and $i_m t_m / P_S = 1.65 \pm 0.23$, in even better agreement with the predicted[6,7] 1.646. The data in Table I are for a single set of pulses (one current transient at each specified field), not averaged over many pulses at a given E. Because the number of domains switching each time is subject to random fluctuations, the measured values of $P_S(E)$ do not increase monotonically with applied field E. However, when P_S is low (P_S is the area under each curve in Fig. 3), the peak current $i_m(t_m)$ is also low by the same ratio, so that there is no effect, to first order, on the quantity of interest ($i_m t_m / P_S$). Note also that the area of the film does not enter this ratio. One might note that ratios of ($i_m t_m / P_S$) greater than 1.0 imply a sharply peaked (t) curve, whereas ratios much less than unity imply a broad (and usually asymmetric) current $i(t)$.

Note in Fig. 3(a) that there are four curves at each tested field value. The large positive curve arises when the film is initially polarized negatively ($-P_S$) and a positive switching voltage is applied. For this case the displacement current $D = 2P_S + \epsilon E$. The smaller positive curve is the current transient that results when the film is already polarized positively and a second positive (nonswitching) pulse is applied. In this case $D = \epsilon E$. Since ϵ is of order 500 in our films, as shown in Fig. 4, the nonswitching component of $i(t)$ is very large, larger than that due to $2P_S$. Hence, in comparing $i(t)$ with theory in Fig. 3(b), we have subtracted the nonswitching transient from the switching transient and fitted only the difference to the appropriate theory. This subtraction procedure was unnecessary in our earlier work[12,13] on KNO$_3$ films, because in that material $\epsilon = 17$.

The subtraction also eliminates the complications due to the fact that $\epsilon(t)$ changes substantially during the time over which switching occurs.

To our knowledge, detailed fitting of current transients

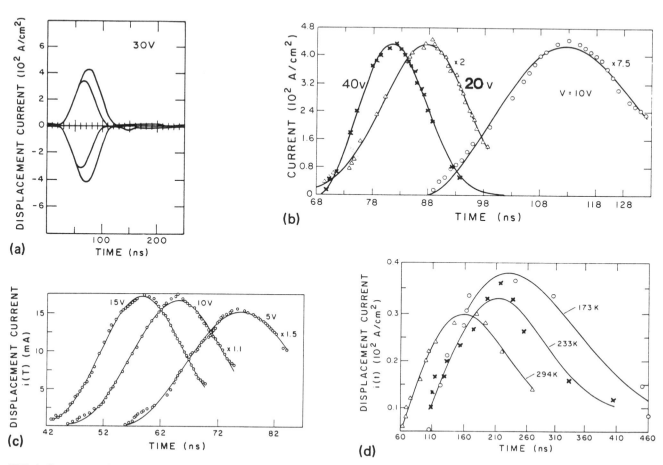

FIG. 3. Current transients $i(t)$ for PbZr$_{0.54}$Ti$_{0.46}$O$_3$ at $T = 294$ K. (a) Raw data, showing both switching and nonswitching responses to positive and negative voltage pulses; (b) subtracted data, with nonswitched pulses digitally subtracted from switched pulses. The solid curves are fits to Eq. (2) with parameters summarized in Table I. (c) As in (b) but for higher temperature anneal. (d) As functions of T at a constant field of $E = 1.71 \times 10^5$ V/cm [this is a different film from that in (b) with slightly slower speeds].

$i(t)$ for multiaxis ferroelectric ceramic materials such as PZT has not been made before. In this material the large number of nearly equivalent polar directions permits the realignment of ferroelectricity on a unit cell basis, rather than via reorientation of large grains. However, as shown in Fig. 5, the voltage dependence of switching time yields an activation field[14] α of 272 kV/cm, about the same as that in uniaxial ferroelectrics[15] such as KNO_3. This field decreases with temperature as $(T_C - T)$ and also depends on annealing procedures, with lower values of α at higher annealing temperatures.

C. High-temperature performance

Above room temperature the differences between current transients $i(t)$ produced by switching and nonswitching voltage pulses (e.g., positive and negative pulses, respectively, applied to a negatively polarized cell) become small, except at high voltages. This is due to an increase in the nonswitching response, probably from the time-dependent contribution to dielectric constant $\epsilon(t)$ from domain walls, as described[16] by Fouskova. Our results are shown in Fig. 6 for t_0 at an applied voltage of 6 V across a 350 nm film. It is interesting to note in Fig. 6 that $t_s(T)$ extrapolates to zero near $T_C = 390$ °C. The same unexplained linear dependence was also observed[7] in KNO_3. Qualitatively this is reasonable because the free energy difference to be overcome by polar-

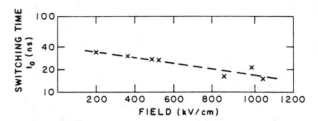

FIG. 5. Switching time t_0 [see Eqs. (1) and (2)] vs applied voltage V. Solid curve is a fit to Eq. (3), yielding an activation field of 272 kV/cm.

ization reversals becomes smaller as T_C is approached from below, but quantitatively it is not accounted for in existing theories.

The activation field α is defined as

$$t_0(V) = Ae^{\alpha d/V}. \qquad (3)$$

At sufficiently high fields this exponential dependence is expected to give over[17] to an E^{-1} or $E^{-3/2}$ dependence.[12]

The inference that the domain growth kinetics are two dimensional ($D = 2.0$) and that the Avrami model is valid for PZT is compatible with earlier observations by Mehta, Silverman, and Jacobs[11] in which lead zirconate alloys that sidewise domain-wall motion is the rate limiting parameter and that domain overlap is in the Avrami limit of large random overlap.

It is interesting to note that in Fig. 3(a) the nonswitching current transient $j(t)$ which results when two successive voltage pulses of the same polarity are applied is much greater than that predictable from the static dielectric constant. This was also noticeable in our work[15] on KNO_3, although smaller in magnitude in that case, and arises from domain wall contribution to ϵ during the switching, and in particular, to sideways growth.[16]

D. Static scaling

Ishibashi has shown[18] that switching times t as functions of field E and reduced temperature $\tau = (T_C - T)/T_C$ scale in ferroelectric TGS and DOBAMBC. That is, switch-

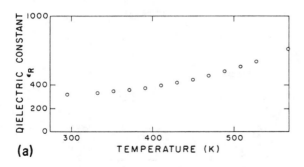

(a)

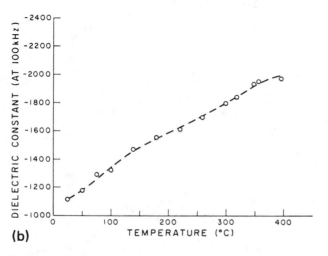

(b)

FIG. 4. (a) Dielectric constant vs temperature for $d = 350$ nm $PbZr_{0.54}Ti_{0.46}O_3$ film. (b) For higher-temperature anneal the room temperature value rises to 1150.

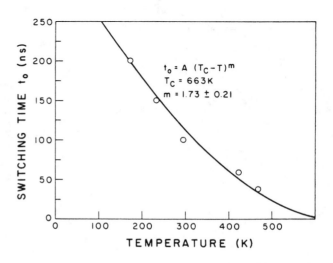

FIG. 6. Switching time t_0 vs temperature for 6 V across a 350-nm PZT film. The temperature exponent of 1.73 agrees quite closely with that obtained by Ishibashi and Orihara for TGS (Ref. 18 and private communication).

ing times may be described as functions of a single reduced variable $E\tau^{-n}$, where n is a dimensionless parameter of order unity. This theory applies to our earlier results[7] in KNO_3, since we established separately that $t_s = A\tau$ and $t_s = BE^{-3/2}$. Hence,

$$t_s = Cf(E\tau^{-n}), \qquad (4)$$

with $f(x) = x^{-3/2}$ and $n = \frac{2}{3}$; i.e., $t_s = C\tau E.^{-3/2}$

In PZT, as discussed above, we find $t_s = A_1\tau$, as in KNO_3; but instead of Stadler's high-field power law of $-3/2$ for the field dependence,[17] we find an activation field dependence

$$t_s = De^{\alpha/E}. \qquad (5)$$

Hence,

$$t_s = C_1 f(E\tau^{-n}), \qquad (6)$$

with $f(x) = e^{\alpha/x}$; i.e., $t_s = De^{\alpha\tau n/E}$. Some switching times for different E and τ values are graphed together in Fig. 7.

It is useful to relate these observations with the empirical observation of Lines and Glass[19] that activation fields are often of form

$$\alpha = FP_S^3/T. \qquad (7)$$

In mean-field approximation, $P_S^3 = G\tau^{3/2}$, so that Eq. (7) becomes

$$\alpha = F_1\tau^{3/2}T^{-1}. \qquad (8)$$

For large applied fields E, we can expand the exponential in Eq. (5) as[20]

$$t_s \approx 1 + \alpha/E + \cdots = 1 + F_1\tau^{3/2}E^{-1}T^{-1}. \qquad (9)$$

This may be rewritten as

$$t_s = Cf(E\tau^{-n}), \qquad (10)$$

with $f(x) = x^{-1}$ and $n = 3/2$, as in Eq. (4) above.

We are unaware of any microscopic derivation of these forms, but we note that switching time below T_C should be proportional, in lowest order, to the inverse of the hopping probability per unit time

$$p \propto \tanh(qV/\Delta G) \approx qV/\Delta G, \qquad (11)$$

where ΔG is the difference in free energy between states polarized parallel and antiparallel to the applied field. This term ΔG is proportional to τ in mean field. Hence, for large V and E,

$$t_s \approx 1/p \approx A\tau/E, \qquad (12)$$

which is very nearly the form given in Eq. (9), differing only by a factor of $\tau^{1.5}$ compared with $\tau^{1.0}$.

E. Relationship to Ishibashi's theory

Ishibashi *et al.*[6,18] have assumed a switching time dependence of form

$$t_0 = BE^{-j}\tau^{+k} \qquad (13)$$

and empirically find j and k of order 1–2.

If we expand Eq. (5) for large E, we obtain

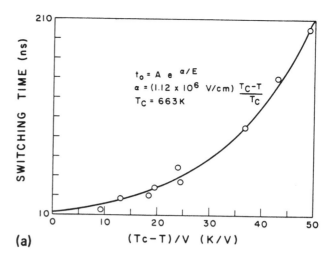

(a)

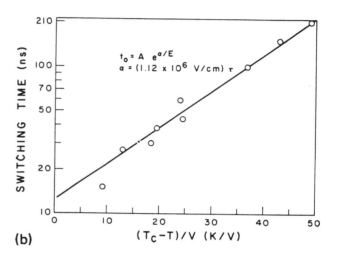

(b)

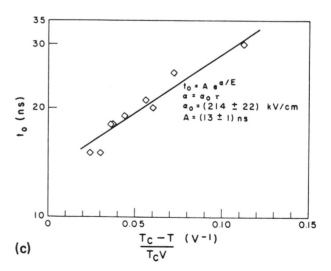

(c)

FIG. 7. (a) $PbZr_{0.54}Ti_{0.46}O_3$. $t_0(\tau/E)$ for different fields and temperatures. Temperatures plotted include 173, 233, 294, 423, and 468 K; fields include 1.42, 2.83, 4.25, 5.68, and 11.4×10^5 V/cm. The theoretical form plotted linearly in Fig. 9(a) and semilogarithmically in (b) is $t_0 = Ae^{\alpha/E}$ with $\alpha = (1.12 \pm 0.04) \times 10^6$ V/cm $\times [(T_C - T)/T_C]^{1.0}$, as in Eqs. (5) and (12). (c) As in (a) but for higher-T anneal. Here the activation field is much lower: $\alpha = \alpha_0\tau$ with $\alpha_0 = (214 \pm 22)$ kV/cm, so that α(ambient) = 120 kV/cm.

245

$$t_0 = D + D\alpha/E + D(\alpha/E)^2 \qquad (14)$$

or

$$t_0 = D + D\alpha_0\tau/E + D\alpha_0^2(\tau/E)^2. \qquad (15)$$

Now if one empirically fitted t_0 data as[18]

$$t_0 = D + (D\alpha_0)(\tau/E)^j, \qquad (16)$$

one will obtain a value of j such that $1 \leqslant j \leqslant 2$, since the second term in (16) involves an average over linear and quadratic terms in (15).

Note that Eq. (15) involves fewer adjustable parameters (D, α^0) than does (16), (D, α_0, j). Hence, it might be useful to refit TGS and DOBAMBC data[18] to Eq. (15).

IV. CONCLUSIONS

Our data shows that sputtered films of PZT thinner than 1 μm are compatible with memory fabrication for CMOS logic levels. Switching kinetics are characterized by two-dimensional domain growth and an activation field of order 120 kV/cm at room temperature for optimally annealed specimens.

ACKNOWLEDGMENTS

Work at the University of Colorado was supported by NSF industry-university Grant No. DMR86-06666; work at Symetrix and Ramtron was supported by US Naval Surface Warfare Center and Naval Weapons Support Center Contracts Nos. N00164-87-C-0240 and N60921-87-C-0198.

[1] T. Nakagawa, J. Yamaguchi, T. Usuki, Y. Matsui, M. Okuyama, and Y. Hamakawa, Jpn. J. Appl. Phys. **18**, 897 (1979); D. W. Chapman, J. Appl. Phys. **40**, 2381 (1969); R. B. Atkin, Ferroelectrics **3**, 213 (1972).

[2] M. Sayer, in *Proceedings of the 6th Symposium on Applied Ferroelectricity* (IEEE, New York, 1986), p. 559.

[3] M. Ishida, H. Matsunami, and T. Tanaka, J. Appl. Phys. **48**, 952 (1977); Appl. Phys. Lett. **31**, 433 (1977).

[4] E. Fatuzzo and W. Merz, *Ferroelectricity* (North-Holland, Amsterdam, 1967).

[5] H. F. Kay and J. W. Dunn, Philos. Mag. **7**, 2027 (1962).

[6] Y. Ishibashi and Y. Takagi, J. Phys. Soc. Jpn. **31**, 506 (1971); Y. Ishibashi, Jpn. J. Appl. Phys. **24**, 126 (1986).

[7] K. Dimmler, M. Parris, D. Butler, S. Eaton, B. Pouligny, J. F. Scott, and Y. Ishibashi, J. Appl. Phys. **61**, 5467 (1987).

[8] M. Avrami, J. Chem. Phys. **7**, 1108 (1939; **8**, 212 (1940); **9**, 177 (1941).

[9] E. Fatuzzo, Phys. Rev. **116**, 1999 (1962).

[10] C. Araujo, J. F. Scott, R. B. Godfrey, and L. McMillan, Appl. Phys. Lett. **48**, 1439 (1986).

[11] R. R. Mehta, B. D. Silverman, and J. T. Jacobs, J. Appl. Phys. **44**, 3379 (1973).

[12] R. B. Godfrey, J. F. Scott, H. B. Meadows, M. Golabi, C. Araujo, and L. McMillan, Ferroelectrics Lett. **5**, 167 (1986); J. F. Scott, R. B. Godfrey, C. A. Araujo, L. D. McMillan, H. B. Meadows, and M. Golabi, in *Proceedings of the 6th Symposium on Applied Ferroelectricity* (IEEE, New York, 1986), p. 569

[13] J. F. Scott, B. Pouligny, M. Parris, K. Dimmler, D. Butler, and S. Eaton, J. Appl. Phys. **62**, 4510 (1987).

[14] This value compares poorly with that of 12 kV/cm at lower fields in ceramic $PbZr_{0.54}Ti_{0.46}O_3$ by M. Takahashi, Jpn. J. Appl. Phys. **9**, 1236 (1970).

[15] J. F. Scott, H. M. Duiker, P. D. Beale, B. Pouligny, K. Dimmler, M. Parris, D. Butler, and S. Eaton, Physica B/C (in press).

[16] A. Fouskova, Czech. J. Phys. B **20**, 790 (1970); J. Phys. Soc. Jpn. **20**, 1625 (1965).

[17] H. L. Stadler and P. J. Zachmanidis, J. Appl. Phys. **34**, 3255 (1963); **33**, 3487 (1962); **29**, 1485 (1958).

[18] H. Orihara and Y. Ishibashi, Jpn. J. Appl. Phys. **24**, 902 (1985).

[19] M. E. Lines and A. M. Glass, *Principles and Applications of Ferroelectrics and Related Materials* (Clarendon, Oxford, 1977).

[20] Unlike the case (Ref. 19) of DOBAMBC or TGS, it is not possible to approximate t_s over a wide range of fields E as $t_s = AE^{-n}\tau^{+m}$, because the effective exponent n depends strongly upon temperature; i.e., the field dependence and temperature dependence are not separable. However, a temperature exponent can be obtained, as in Fig. 6, if field E is kept constant.

[21] A. Hadni and R. Thomas, Ferroelectrics **59**, 221 (1984).

Part 7
Interpoly Dielectrics, Thin, and Novel Tunneling Oxides

IN THIS part, we will be mainly concerned with the dielectrics involved in floating-gate memories. The dielectrics in MNOS memories are briefly discussed in Papers 4.8, 4.9, and 9.9. The dielectrics in floating-gate nonvolatile memories serve two somewhat conflicting functions—to prevent the stored charge from leaking off the floating gate during READ and storage and to allow charge carriers to flow to and from the floating gate during PROGRAM and ERASE at a high rate.

In order not to lose a significant amount of charge from the floating gate in 10 years means that the oxide leakage current must be lower than approximately one electron per hour. It is so difficult to accomplish this requirement that nearly every paper in Part 9, "Nonvolatile Memory Reliability," addresses this charge retention problem to a varying degree. Part 9 is primarily concerned with the defects in the oxide or electrical-stress-induced effects while the present section is basically concerned with the "intrinsic" time-zero properties of the oxides.

There are two oxides in a floating-gate memory device: the thermal oxide between the substrate and the floating gate, often called the (first) gate oxide, and the oxide (dielectric) between the floating gate and the control gate, often called the interpoly oxide. Charge leakage is more likely to occur through the interpoly oxide than the gate oxide because the asperities at the rough floating polysilicon gate surface create field enhancement at the tips of the asperities [1]. This reduces the average electric field or voltage that is required to produce a certain Fowler–Nordheim tunneling current [2] by a factor of two to five. Paper 7.1 presents an electrostatic model for the field and conduction enhancements.

Enhanced conduction through interpoly oxide is unfortunate for it limits one's freedom to employ very thin interpoly oxides, which is desirable for obtaining large coupling ratios (see Papers 3.4, 3.5, and 4.3). Paper 7.2 reports the effects of oxidation temperature and phosphorous concentration on the interpoly oxide conduction. Paper 7.3 provides additional information on the interpoly-oxide technology and presents a technique for smoothing the floating-gate surface—deposition of amorphous silicon instead of polycrystalline silicon. Paper 7.4 describes the most significant interpoly dielectrics improvement—the use of oxide–nitride–oxide (ONO) stacked dielectrics in lieu of a simple oxide. ONO is so effective a solution that interpoly dielectrics thinner than 350 Å are almost universally of the ONO construction. One might expect the DRAM-stacked capacitor technology to accelerate the development of future high-quality thin ONO films over polysilicon floating gate. An intriguing finding in [13] of Paper 7.4 is that CVD interpoly oxide may be less conductive than thermal oxide. The optimal partition of ONO thickness among the three dielectric layers is the subject of a recent study [3].

Thin-tunneling oxide is an essential part of FLOTOX EEPROMs. Paper 7.5 (and Paper 9.2) describe the problem of electron trapping and breakdown in thin oxides. Electron-trap generation is probably a result of electron-hole recombination in the oxide [4], where the holes are either generated in the oxide or injected from the anode under high field stress. Breakdown occurs after a certain amount of electron charge, measured in C/cm^2, known as Q_{BD}, has passed through the oxide. This Q_{BD} limits the PROGRAM/ERASE cycles of FLOTOX EEPROMs. Paper 7.6 presents a model for oxide breakdown, including a model for Q_{BD}. The PROGRAM/ERASE endurance of large EEPROM circuits is limited by the presence of defects in the oxide (see Papers 9.2–9.5). Reference [5] presents a model of the oxide defects. Defect breakdown and the resultant random single-bit failure is such a serious reliability limitation to high-density FLOTOX EEPROM that error-correction circuits are standard features (see Papers 8.10, 8.11, and 8.12). Defect reduction will continue to be a high-priority goal of nonvolatile memory process development.

Thin oxides are prone to defects, stress-induced leakage (see Paper 9.5), and direct tunneling [6]. For these reasons, textured-polysilicon-oxide EEPROMs and flash EEPROMs do not use the thin-tunneling oxide, but opt for much thicker interpoly oxide as the tunneling medium (see Papers 4.5, 5.8, and 5.9). Here, the enhanced conductivity of interpoly oxide is a desirable characteristic. The larger oxide thickness and the smaller conduction area (near the tips of the asperities), however, increase the electron-trapping rate and hence the rate of PROGRAM/ERASE threshold-voltage-window closing. The electron-trapping phenomenon is empirically modeled in Paper 7.7.

Paper 7.8 describes a study of texturing the single-crystalline silicon surface by dry etching before growing thermal oxide to achieve enhanced conductivity. Very good combination of high conductivity, lower trapping rate (than interpoly oxide), higher Q_{BD}, and lower defect density (than thin oxide) was obtained in this laboratory study. Paper 7.9 reports another approach to creating field-enhancing conductor geometries—using silicon globules in silicon-rich CVD oxide. In both these field-enhancing techniques, Q_{BD} and breakdown-limited endurance are improved over FLOTOX EEPROMs. This can be explained by the reduced electric field in the bulk of the oxide and therefore a lower rate of oxide wearout (see Paper 7.6).

Paper 7.10 reports the use of a graded bandgap dielectric as yet another means of achieving electron injection at reduced field. Finally, Paper 7.11 describes the empirical observation of high conductivity in oxides grown on heavily doped silicon. The reason is not yet understood.

References

[1] R. M. Anderson and D. R. Kerr, "Evidence for surface asperity mechanism of conductivity in oxide grown on polycrystalline silicon," *J. Appl. Phys.*, vol. 48, no. 11, p. 4834, 1977.

[2] M. Lazlinger and E. H. Snow, "Fowler–Nordheim tunneling into thermally grown SiO_2," *J. Appl. Phys.*. vol. 40, p. 278, 1969.

[3] S. Mori, E. Sakagami, H. Araki, Y. Kaneko, K. Narita, Y. Ohshima, N. Arai, K. Yoshikawa, "ONO inter-poly dielectric scaling for nonvolatile memory applications," *IEEE Trans. Electron Devices*, vol. 38, no. 2, pp. 386–391, 1991.

[4] I. C. Chen, S. Holland, and C. Hu, "Electron trap generation by recombination of electrons and holes in SiO_2," *J. Appl. Phys.*, vol. 61, no. 9, p. 4544, 1987.

[5] J. Lee, I. C. Chen, and C. Hu, "Modeling and characterization of oxide reliability," *IEEE Trans. Electron Devices*, vol. 35, no. 12, pp. 2268–2278, 1988.

[6] C. Chang, R. W. Brodersen, M. S. Liang, and C. Hu, "Direct tunneling in thin oxide MOSFETs," *IEEE Trans. Electron Devices*, vol. ED-30, no. 11, pp. 1571–1572, 1983.

ELECTRON TUNNELING IN NON-PLANAR
FLOATING GATE MEMORY STRUCTURE

R.K. Ellis, H.A.R. Wegener, and J.M. Caywood

Xicor, Inc.

ABSTRACT

Until recently, detailed understanding of tunneling from a textured surface through a thick oxide layer for the non-volatile write mechanism has been limited by poor agreement between theory and experimentally observed emission currents. A recent paper which modelled the structure with an emitting surface of varying curvature combined with a planar collecting surface succeeded in obtaining a good fit to the current-voltage characteristic for electron emission from the non-planar surface. In real textured memory structures, the deposited poly on which the oxide is grown has convex structures. The poly deposited on top of the thermally grown oxide has topological features which are concave and of lesser curvature. These differences lead to asymmetric tunneling characteristics. The previous model for the one-sided case has been extended to the more complex double non-planar case and is able to quantitatively describe the observed characteristics.

Introduction

Quantum mechanical tunneling of electrons through a potential barrier thinned by an applied electric field was first described by Fowler and Nordheim in 1928. (1) With the advent of semiconductor memories which rely on Fowler-Nordheim tunneling for non-volatile data storage, there has been an increased interest in characterization of this phenomenon. (2-4) For that class of device which employs a textured emitting surface for enhanced current emission, these efforts produced measured current-voltage curves which agreed poorly with existing theory. (5) In a very recent paper, good agreement between theory and experiment has been obtained for Fowler-Nordheim emission from a textured polysilicon surface by modeling the problem as emission from a non-planar surface with collection at a planar surface. (6) In reality, none of the surfaces involved in poly-to-poly tunneling are planar. This paper will extend the analysis of the single non-planar surface case to that case in which neither emitting nor collecting surface is planar. The results of this extension will be compared with data, and the effect of the non-planar collecting surface on the observed current will be discussed.

Structures

The tunneling structures to be discussed in this paper are made by depositing polysilicon on an insulating surface, thermally growing the SiO_2 layer through which tunneling will take place on the deposited polysilicon, and finally, depositing another layer of polysilicon upon the thermally-grown tunnel oxide. After the first layer of polysilicon is deposited and oxidized, its surface is covered with a large density of small, low-relief bumps.

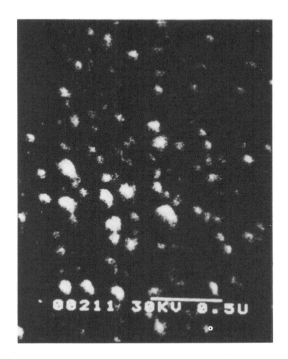

Figure 1. Scanning electron micrograph of the top surface of a poly layer which has been oxidized with the oxide subsequently removed.

Reprinted from the *IEDM Tech. Dig.*, pp. 749–752, 1982.

For the deposition and oxidation conditions employed in fabricating the structures utilized in the study reported here, the texture of the top surface of the bottom poly consists of bumps 1000A across the base and a few hundred angstroms high. A scanning electron photomicrograph of this surface (hereafter referred to as "surface #1") is shown in Figure 1. Note the dense array of topological features which are convex, have a small height-to-base ratio, and are of similar size. The horizontal bar in the photo is 0.5 um long.

The thermal oxide grown on the first silicon surface tends to be conformal to surface 1, but the oxidation process does result in an oxide whose top surface is somewhat smoother than the polysilicon surface which it overlies. When the next layer of polysilicon is deposited upon the oxide layer, the bottom surface of this layer (hereafter referred to as "surface #2"), forms a negative replica of the top oxide surface so that surface 2 has concave features where surface 1 has convex features.

Figure 2 is a high-resolution SEM photograph of a cross section through a tunneling structure. In this photograph, the

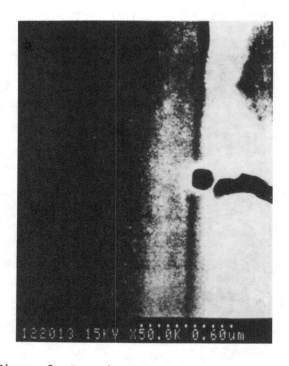

Figure 2. Scanning electron micrograph of a cross section through a tunnel structure. The bottom layer of poly is on the left; top poly layer is on the right; the black above the '15KV' represents the oxide layer.

bottom layer of polysilicon is on the left and the top layer is on the right. Note the three bumps seen on surface 1 with corresponding depressions on surface 2. The distance between the measurement ticks at the bottom of the photograph is 600 A. From this it can be seen that the oxide layer is 800 A thick and that the bumps are 1200 A across the base and 300A in height.

Mathematical Model

The analysis performed in this model assumes that the current density at any point on the emitting surface is given by the Fowler-Nordheim equation

$$J_{FN} = \left(\frac{q \; E^2}{8 \; h\phi_B}\right) \; \exp\left(\frac{-4\sqrt{2m} \; \phi_B^{3/2}}{3\sqrt{h} \; q \; E}\right) \tag{1}$$

where E is the field normal to the emitting surface increment and the other symbols have their customary significance. The total current is found by integrating the current density over the emitting surface.

The nub of the problem is to find E. For cases in which the radius of curvature is a constant, the value of E has been long known. However, as is obvious from Figures 1 and 2, the radius of curvature of the emitting surface is not a constant for real surfaces. This problem has been solved by utilizing differential geometry to transform Poisson's equation onto a metric in which it reduces to a one-dimensional case. Following this approach, it may be shown that the current between an array of curved surfaces is given by

$$J_{collected} = \tag{2}$$

$$\frac{\left[\int_S \frac{q^3 E^2}{8 \; h\phi_B} \exp\left\{\frac{-4(2m)^{1/2}\phi_B^{3/2}}{3\;\hbar\;q\;E}\right\} dS\right]_{emitting}}{\left[\int_S dS\right]_{collecting}}$$

where

$$E = \frac{V_A}{\xi(S_2) - \xi(S_1)}\left(\left(\frac{d\theta}{dr}\right)^2 + \frac{1}{r^2}\right)^{1/2} \frac{d\xi}{d\theta}$$

and where $\xi = \frac{1}{\left|\frac{d\vec{r}}{d\theta}\right|} \frac{d}{d\theta}(\vec{e}_t)$,

$\vec{r}$ is the position vector, and $\vec{e}_t$ is the unit tangent vector.

Experimental

The current-voltage characteristics were measured for structures of the type described above. The emitting structure had an area of $960u^2$. To prevent trapping effects from distorting the results, floating gate techniques were used as described by Hu et al.(5) The characteristics were measured for both electron emission from surface 1 and for electron emission from surface 2. The characteristics are very asymmetric. Emission is many orders of magnitude greater for the same applied voltage for the case in which the convex surface (surface 1) is the emitting surface. By analogy from diodes, the case of current emitted from surface 1 and collected by surface 2 is called the forward tunneling direction; the opposite case is called the reverse tunneling direction.

Figure 3 compares the currents calculated using equation (2) and two conformal

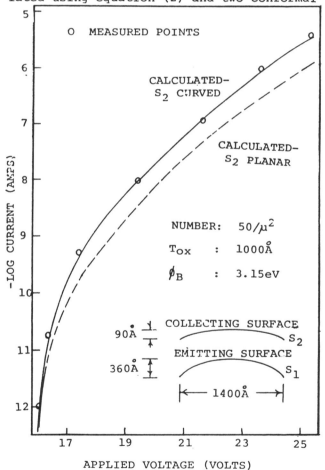

Figure 3. Forward tunneling characteristic comparing the measured data with curves calculated for a concave and planar collecting surface.

curved surfaces with measured data. The parametric values used in the calculation are shown in Figure 3. For comparison, the current which would be expected if surface 2 were planar rather than curved was calculated and is shown as the dashed line in Figure 3. Although the current in this case is depressed by about 3x from the case of the curved collecting surface, the solid and dashed curves have the same shape and, if displaced vertically, lie atop one another.

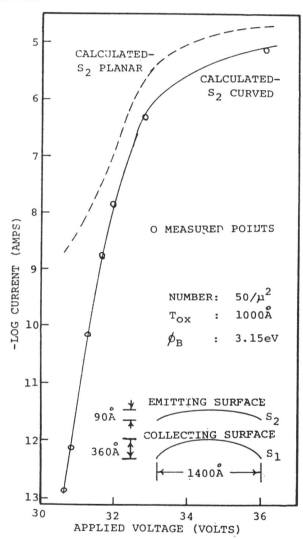

Figure 4. Reverse tunneling characteristic comparing the measured data with curves calculated for a concave and planar emitting surface.

Figure 4 makes similar comparisons for the reverse current direction for the same sample. Note the differences in horizontal scale between figures 3 and 4. Good agreement is obtained between experimental and calculated results for the two curved surfaces in this direction also. However, the calculated current for the case of planar surface 2 is now higher than the curved case, but also has a different shape. While the currents calculated for the two cases vary by only about 3x at high current values, they differ by four orders of magnitude at low current values.

Discussion

Figure 5 illustrates schematically the reason for the results shown here. The field enhancement increases with the radius of curvature. In the case of a curved surface, current emission occurs initially from the points of greatest curvature. As the applied field increases, other areas of lesser curvature begin contributing to the current. The rapid increase in current at low fields in the reverse tunneling case is a result of this increase in emitting area.

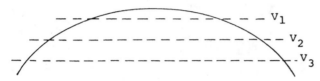

Figure 5. Schematic illustration of emitting feature illustrating the increase of emission area with increasing applied voltage.

Several observations may be made about tunneling in a structure with textured surfaces. First, the asymmetry of the characteristic between the bias direction in which the convex surfaces are emitting and that in which the concave surfaces are emitting must be emphasized. Secondly, the current emitted from surface 1 is not too sensitive to the shape of surface 2. However, when surface 2 is the emitter, the current voltage characteristic is very sensitive to the shape of surface 2. Thus, by measuring both forward and reverse characteristics, information can be extracted about the shape of both surfaces. Finally, the understanding gained about the influence of surface topology on tunneling characteristics opens the door to the improvement of memory performance by the fabrication of surface topologies designed to optimize the characteristics.

References

1. R.H. Fowler and L. Nordheim, Proc. Royal Soc. London, Ser. A, 119, 173 (1928)

2. M. Lazlinger and E.H. Snow, J. App. Phys. 40, 278 (1969)

3. D.J. DiMaria and D.R. Kerr, Appl Phys Lett., 27 (9), 505 (1975).

4. R.M. Anderson and D.R. Kerr, J. Appl Phys., 48 (11), 4834 (1977).

5. C. Hu, Y. Shum, T. Klein and E. Lucero, Appl Phys Lett., 35(2), 189 (1979).

6. R.K. Ellis, IEEE Electron Device Lett., in press.

STUDIES OF THIN POLY Si OXIDES FOR E AND E^{2}PROM

Takashi Ono, Tadashi Mori, Tsuneo Ajioka, and Tetsuya Takayashiki

Electronic Devices Group, OKI Electric Industry Co., Ltd.
550-1 Higashiasakawa, Hachioji, Tokyo 193, Japan

ABSTRACT

Electrical conductivity of thin poly Si oxides, 400-600A thick, has been investigated. Using an annealing prior to the oxidation, the relationship between electrical conductivity and the phosphorus concentration in the oxide has been estimated for the same poly Si asperity. The leakage current through the poly Si oxide increases with increasing phosphorus concentration in the oxide. The redistributed phosphorus concentration strongly depends on the oxidation conditions. This can be explained by segregation and transportation at the poly Si-SiO$_2$ interface.

INTRODUCTION

The poly Si oxide in E and E^{2}PROM is a very important factor which influences the data programming and retention. It is generally known that the poly Si oxide has a high conductivity because of the asperity of the poly Si-SiO$_2$ interface[1][2]. So far, in order to obtain a smooth interface, the poly Si with a high phosphorus concentration has often been oxidized at a high temperature (>1050 °C)[3][4][5]. On the other hand, it is required to oxidize the poly Si at a lower temperature because of increasing integration scale . In this study, characteristics of the poly Si oxide grown at low temperature(<1000 °C) were investigated. In particular, effects of phosphorus redistributed in the oxide are described.

EXPERIMENTAL

1st poly Si, 3500A thick, was deposited on oxidized silicon substrate by using LPCVD. The film was doped with phosphorus using POCl$_3$. Then, the samples were split in two types. One was annealed in dry O$_2$ ambient and this oxide was then removed. The annealing temperature was 1000 °C. The other one was not annealed.

Then, interpoly oxidation was performed on both types at the same time . These oxidation conditions were in the range 900-1000 °C, dry O$_2$ or O$_2$/N$_2$, and oxide thicknesses were 400-600A on 1st poly Si. Subsequently, upper electrodes were formed by phosphorus doped poly Si. Electrical conductivity of the inter poly Si oxides was measured with two types of patterns, as shown in figure 1. Positive voltage was applied to the 2nd poly Si. Then, leakage electric fields E$_1$ were determined at current density of 2x10^{-11} A/mm^2.

RESULTS AND DISCUSSION

Figure 2 shows the SEM photographs of the cross section and 1st poly Si surface. It is observed in the cross sections that the patterned edge of the 1st poly Si with 7x10^{20} cm^{-3} is rounder than the one with 4x10^{20} cm^{-3} . Similarly, the surface photographs with 7x10^{20} cm^{-3} is smoother than those with 4.3x10^{20} cm^{-3} . It is known that silicon self-diffusion coefficient is enhanced by increasing the phosphorus concentration in the poly Si[6][7]. Therefore, it is considered that the patterned edge and the 1st poly Si surface become smoother, and the stress during the thermal oxidation is decreased.

Figure 3 shows the relationship between the phosphorus concentration in the 1st poly Si and the leakage electric field E$_1$ measured with the two methods described in Figure 1. E$_1$ on the overlap type is lower than the one on parallel plate type because of the local electric field enhancement at the patterned edge. Since these two curves have a similar shape, it can be considered that the E$_1$ of both types is basically determined by the same mechanism. Therefore, only the parallel plate type was used in this evaluation. It is thought that decrease of E$_1$ in the lower concentration region is caused by rougher interface. And, it is considered that decrease of E$_1$ in the higher concentration region is due to poorer oxide integrity.

Reprinted from the *IEDM Tech. Dig.*, pp. 380–383, 1985.

Previously only the effect of the asperity has been discussed in detail, but the oxide integrity has hardly been reported.

In this report, the electrical conductivity of poly Si oxide, especially the effects of the oxide integrity were investigated.

Figure 4 shows the relationship between the phosphorus concentration in the 1st poly Si and the leakage electric field E_1 for various oxidation temperatures. It is found that the E_1 is decreased by lowering oxidation temperature. This fact has only been explained by the effect of the 1st poly Si asperity, and the influence of the oxide integrity has not been discussed so far.

The normalized electric field enhancement versus the radius of the 1st poly Si protrusions is shown in figure 5. A spherical approximation was used for this calculation. The degree of the enhancement is low when the radius of protrusions is large enough compared with the oxide thickness. Therefore, in order to increase the grain size and the radius of protrusions, the 1st poly Si with a high phosphorus concentration was annealed at 1000 °C in O_2 ambient prior to the interpoly oxidation. The final radii of the protrusions were greater than 0.2um, and the 1st poly Si morphology, analyzed by SEM, was almost identical after the various oxidations. This makes it possible to evaluate different poly Si oxides with similar poly Si asperity.

Figure 6 shows the E_1 under the various oxidation temperatures and O_2 partial pressure, measured by the above method. It is found that the E_1 decreases with lower temperature and higher O_2 partial pressure. This indicates that there are other factors than asperity which influence E_1. In order to clarify these factors, the phosphorus concentration in the oxides was measured by SIMS. Figure 7 shows an example of these results. It is found that more phosphorus is redistributed in the oxide for lower temperature and higher O_2 partial pressure.

Next, using these SIMS data, the relationship between the phosphorus concentration in the oxides and the E_1 is plotted in figure 8. The average value in the oxide is taken as this phosphorus concentration. It is clearly found that E_1 only depends on the phosphorus concentration in the oxide.

Subsequently, the relationship between oxidation time and E_1 is replotted in figure 9 using the data of figure 6. In this figure, longer oxidation times means lower oxidation rates, because the final oxide thickness of each point is almost the same. Leakage electric field E_1 increases with increasing oxidation times, but tends to saturate.

Additionaly, saturation value of E_1 depends on the oxidation temperature. These results can be explained by segregation and transportation[8][9]. Namely, phosphorus concentration in the oxide depends on oxidation time because of the effects of the transportation. For high oxidation rates, the phosphorus at poly $Si-SiO_2$ interface can not be transported into the poly Si. Therefore, a lot of phosphorus is included in the oxide. On the other hand, for low oxidation rates, the phosphorus concentration in the oxide is only determined by the segregation. The fact that saturated phosphorus concentration depends on temperature indicates that the segregation coefficient depends on the oxidation temperature.

SUMMARY

Using the O_2 annealing method, it has been shown that increasing phosphorus concentration in the poly Si oxides increases the electrical conductivity of the oxides. The phosphorus concentration in the oxide strongly depends on the oxidation temperature and the O_2 partial pressure. The redistribution of phosphorus in the oxide is explained by segregation and transportation at the poly $Si-SiO_2$ interface. Since the asperity has less influence on thinner poly Si oxide, the effects of phosphorus in the oxide become very important in advanced E and E^2PROM.

ACKNOWLEDGEMENT

We would like to thank I.Aikawa for SIMS measurement and K.Sakamoto, M.Ino, K.Uchiho for valuable discussions.

REFFERENCE

(1) P.A.Heimann, S.P.Murarka, and T.T.Sheng, J.Appl.Phys., 53, 6240 (1982)
(2) G.Groeseneken, and H.E.Maes, IEDM Tech. Dig., 84, 476 (1984)
(3) F.kiyosumi, M.Ino, and Y.Mizokami, Electrochem. Soc. Extended Abs., 82-1 , 316 (1982)
(4) K.Anraku, M.Honda, and M.Ino, JST News, 1, 4, Aug. (1982)
(5) K.Shinada, Y.Nagakubo, K.Yoshikawa, and K.Kanzaki, Electrochem. Soc. Extended Abs., 83-2, 354 (1983)
(6) Y.Wada, and S. Nishimatsu, J. Electrochem. Soc., 125, 1499 (1978)
(7) L.Mei, M.Rivier, Y.Kwark, and R.W.Dutton, J. Electrochem. Soc., 129, 1791 (1982)
(8) R.B.Fair, and J.C.C.Tsai, J. Electrochem. Soc., 125, 2050 (1978)
(9) D.Fuoss, and J.A.Topich, Appl. Phys. Lett. 36, 275 (1980)

parallel plate type

overlap type

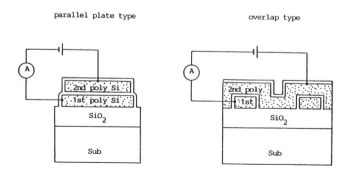

Fig.1 Measurement patterns.

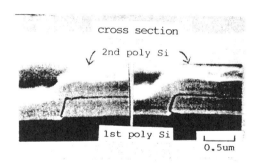

cross section

2nd poly Si

1st poly Si

0.5um

1st poly Si surface

3.0um

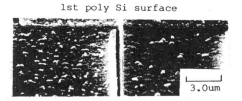

phosphorus conc.

$4.3 \times 10^{20} cm^{-3}$ $7.0 \times 10^{20} cm^{-3}$

Fig.2 SEM of the cross section and the 1st poly Si surface : non annealing, oxidation temp. = 1000°C.

left   : $4.3 \times 10^{20} cm^{-3}$

right   : $7.0 \times 10^{20} cm^{-3}$

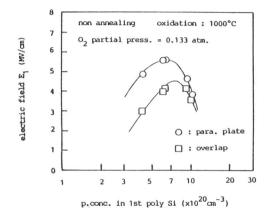

Fig.3 The relationship between the phosphorus concentration in 1st poly Si and leakage electric field E_1 on two measurement patterns.

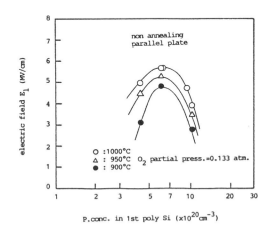

Fig.4 The relationship between the phosphorus concentration in 1st poly and leakage electric field E_1 at various oxidation temperature.

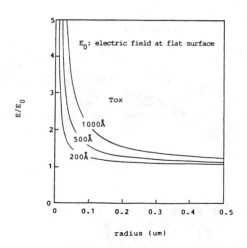

Fig.5 The normalized electric field enhancement depended on the radius of 1st poly Si protrusion.

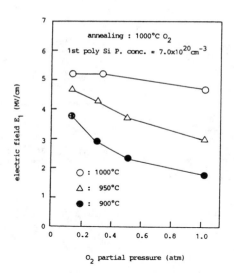

Fig.6 E_1 under different oxidation temperature and dilution ratios : 1000°C O_2 annealing.

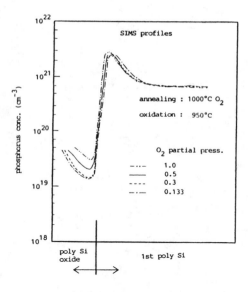

Fig.7 An example of the profile of the phosphorus concentration measured by SIMS.

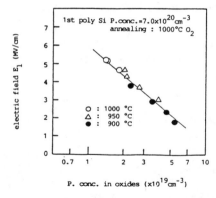

Fig.8 The relationship between phosphorus concentration in the oxide and E_1.

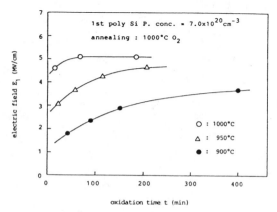

Fig.9 The relationship between the oxidation time t and E_1.

Characterization of Thermally Oxidized n⁺ Polycrystalline Silicon

LORENZO FARAONE, MEMBER IEEE, ROBERT D. VIBRONEK, AND JOSEPH T. McGINN

Abstract—The properties of thermally grown silicon dioxide films on n⁺ polysilicon are studied using cross-sectional TEM, and electrical measurements to evaluate conduction, electron trapping, destructive breakdown and wearout mechanisms. All of the above electrical parameters are found to be degraded by any increase in the degree of surface roughness at the oxide–polysilicon interface. Our results suggest that a significant improvement in the insulating properties of the SiO₂ films can be achieved if the polysilicon is initially deposited in the amorphous phase at 560°C rather than the polycrystalline phase at 620°C. For example, for dry-oxidized diffusion-doped films, there is an increase in oxide breakdown field from 3.0 MV · cm⁻¹ to 6.2 MV · cm⁻¹, and a reduction in leakage (Fowler–Nordheim) current of two orders of magnitude. Furthermore, it is shown that the long-term reliability of n⁺ polysilicon/SiO₂/n⁺ polysilicon structures is directly related to the degree of interface texture; i.e., a smoother interface will result in a significant reduction in electrical wearout and an increase in time to failure.

I. INTRODUCTION

LAYERS OF polycrystalline silicon (polysilicon) are extensively used in the fabrication of silicon MOS devices. In general, these films are heavily doped to minimize their electrical resistance, and are used to form gate electrodes and interconnections in MOS integrated circuits and charge-coupled devices. In order to increase the packing density of large-scale integrated circuits, multilevel polysilicon structures consisting of doped polysilicon layers separated by an insulating dielectric are used. Commonly, the polysilicon layers are deposited by low-pressure chemical-vapor deposition (LPCVD) at temperatures of approximately 620°C, and the interlevel dielectric consists of SiO₂ thermally grown from the underlying polysilicon.

The ever-present drive toward smaller device dimension requires a concomitant decrease in the thickness of both polysilicon and insulating layers. Furthermore, many EPROM and EEPROM device structures rely on thin interlevel dielectrics for improved capacitive coupling between conducting layers. Consequently, an increasing concern in multilevel polysilicon technology is the reliability of the interlevel structure with regard to minimizing interlevel leakage current and maximizing the destructive breakdown voltage of the interlevel dielectric. It has previously been shown that the insulating properties of SiO₂ thermally grown from polysilicon are inferior to those of SiO₂ grown from monocrystalline bulk silicon [1]. In particular, oxides grown from polysilicon (poly-

oxides) have a lower dielectric strength and exhibit enhanced Fowler–Nordheim (F–N) tunneling current for any given applied field. These effects have generally been attributed to nonuniformities in the SiO₂ film thickness [2] and to the texture (surface roughness) of the polysilicon–SiO₂ interface which leads to localized electric field being greater than the average applied field [3].

Because of the technological importance of multilevel polysilicon structures, there has recently been a large research effort to understand and characterize the relationship between various fabrication techniques and the resulting interface texture and electrical properties of the completed double-polysilicon devices. The initial surface topology of the polysilicon film can be affected by deposition temperature [4]–[7] and by polysilicon grain size which is a function of deposition temperature, doping conditions and annealing sequence [6], [8], [9]. The insulating properties of thermally grown SiO₂ have been shown to be a function of the particular doping sequence used prior to thermal oxidation [10]–[13]. The situation is further complicated by the fact that thermal oxidation itself is a "surface-roughening" process due to enhanced oxidation at polysilicon grain boundaries [2], [14], [15]. In addition, the oxidation ambient and temperature has a strong influence on the polysilicon–oxide interface texture and the corresponding electrical properties of double-polysilicon structures [3], [10]–[12], [16].

The aim of this study was to determine whether the initial surface topology of LPCVD silicon films had any influence on the resulting interface texture and insulating properties of thermally grown SiO₂ thin films. In particular, we investigated the use of LPCVD silicon deposited in the amorphous phase which has recently been shown to result in extremely smooth layers in the As-deposited state [4]–[7].

II. DEVICE FABRICATION

Fig. 1 shows the n⁺ polysilicon/thermal SiO₂/n⁺ polysilicon capacitor structures that were fabricated by the following process sequence. The starting substrates consisted of ⟨100⟩-oriented n-type silicon wafers that were thermally oxidized to a thickness of 3000 Å and patterned to allow contact to the lower polysilicon layer from the back of the wafer (Fig. 1). The first, 0.75-μm-thick polysilicon layer was then deposited by LPCVD from the decomposition of SiH₄ at a pressure of approximately 500 mtorr, and at a temperature of either 560°C (amorphous) or 620°C (polycrystalline). Doping of the silicon films was achieved by either ion implantation of phosphorus

Manuscript received July 16, 1984; revised September 17, 1984.
The authors are with RCA, Research and Engineering, David Sarnoff Research Center, Princeton, NJ 08540.

Reprinted from *IEEE Trans. Electron Devices*, vol. ED-32, no. 3, pp. 577–583, March 1985.

257

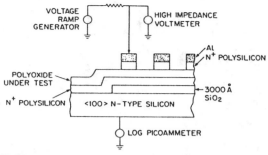

Fig. 1. Device structure used in this study and experimental setup for measuring ramped I–V curves.

TABLE I
LIST OF DEVICE-TYPES USED IN THIS STUDY AND SOME
EXPERIMENTAL PARAMETERS

LOWER POLY T_{dep} (°C)	LOWER POLY DOPING	OXIDATION PROCESS	AVERAGE OXIDE THICKNESS (Å)	LOWER POLY Ω/□	PULSED J(Acm⁻²) +3MV cm⁻¹	FIELD (MVcm⁻¹) FOR 10⁻⁷ Acm⁻² AT 0.1 MV cm⁻¹ sec⁻¹ +	FIELD (MVcm⁻¹) FOR 10⁻⁷ Acm⁻² AT 0.1 MV cm⁻¹ sec⁻¹ −	OXIDE–LOWER POLY INTERFACE ROUGHNESS (Å)
560	POCl₃ 950°C 15 min	850°C STEAM	1115	11.2	1×10⁻³	1.0	2.6	220
620			790	17.2	4×10⁻³	1.0	2.8	350
560		1000°C DRY O₂	1590	9.3	7×10⁻⁶	2.4	5.3	200
620			1295	11.5	8×10⁻⁴	1.1	3.5	480
560	PHOSPH. ION–IMPLANT 10¹⁶ cm⁻²	850°C STEAM	735	60	1×10⁻⁵	2.4	6.1	120
620			760	55	1×10⁻⁵	2.4	4.3	310
560		1000°C DRY O₂	1155	35	1×10⁻⁴	1.9	6.7	180
620			1020	37	1×10⁻²	1.2	3.0	420

at 120 keV to a density of 10^{16} cm^{-2} or POCl₃-diffusion at 950°C for 15 min. The interlevel thermal SiO₂ layers were subsequently grown for 20 min at 850°C in an ambient of pyrogenic steam plus 3-percent gaseous HCl, or for 90 min at 1000°C in an ambient of dry oxygen plus 3-percent HCl. The upper polysilicon electrodes were formed by LPCVD at 560°C followed by POCl₃ diffusion at 950°C for 15 min. After aluminum deposition, circular electrodes of 8.11×10^{-3} cm² were photolithographically defined. The composite Al/n⁺ polysilicon upper conducting layer was etched with a sequence of wet chemical etching and dry plasma etching for the aluminum and polysilicon layers, respectively. After deposition of the back-side metal contact, the completed devices were annealed at 450°C in forming gas for 20 min. A complete list of the device-types used for this study is shown in Table I.

III. EXPERIMENTAL RESULTS AND DISCUSSION

The sheet resistivity and oxide thickness values listed in Table I were determined by four-point probe and 1-MHz capacitance measurements, respectively. It should be pointed out that the oxide thicknesses represent an average value calculated from $d_{ox} = \epsilon_{ox}/C_{ox}$, where C_{ox} is the measured capacitance per unit area. As evident from the results in Table I, the sheet resistivity was not degraded when the polysilicon deposition temperature was reduced from 620° to 560°C; in fact, for POCl₃-doped samples there appears to be a slight improvement with the polysilicon deposited in the amorphous phase.

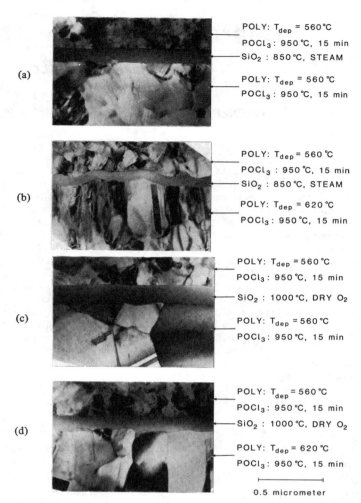

(a) POLY: T_{dep} = 560 °C
POCl₃: 950 °C, 15 min
SiO₂ : 850 °C, STEAM
POLY: T_{dep} = 560 °C
POCl₃ : 950 °C, 15 min

(b) POLY: T_{dep} = 560 °C
POCl₃ : 950 °C, 15 min
SiO₂ : 850 °C, STEAM
POLY: T_{dep} = 620 °C
POCl₃: 950 °C, 15 min

(c) POLY: T_{dep} = 560 °C
POCl₃ : 950 °C, 15 min
SiO₂ : 1000 °C, DRY O₂
POLY: T_{dep} = 560 °C
POCl₃: 950 °C, 15 min

(d) POLY: T_{dep} = 560 °C
POCl₃ : 950 °C, 15 min
SiO₂ : 1000 °C, DRY O₂
POLY: T_{dep} = 620 °C
POCl₃: 950 °C, 15 min

0.5 micrometer

Fig. 2. Cross-sectional TEM's for samples with diffusion-doped lower polysilicon.

A. Cross-Sectional TEM's

For TEM examination, cross-sectional samples were cut vertically along the (011) plane and prepared by standard techniques [17]. All micrographs were taken with the silicon substrate in a symmetric [011] orientation which allowed the interfaces to be viewed edge-on. Figs. 2 and 3 contain typical micrographs of the interlayer oxide formed by each of the eight different fabrication processes.

Unique morphological features within the microstructure of these films were left by each of the processing steps used to fabricate the oxide layers. The two different polysilicon deposition temperatures may be easily distinguished by the shape of the resultant interlayer oxide. In 560°C-deposited samples, the oxide is seen as a relatively straight ribbon separating the two levels of polysilicon, while the interlayer oxide grown from the 620°C-deposited samples forms a meandering path. These variations are a result of differences in the surface morphology between polysilicon films deposited at the two temperatures [4], [6], [7], [18]. Low-temperature LPCVD films are deposited in an amorphous or mixed amorphous-crystalline state which results in relatively smooth layers with a surface

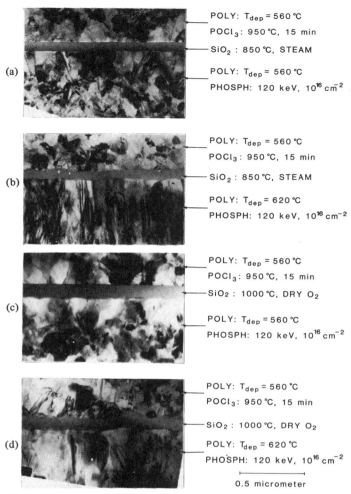

(a)
- POLY: $T_{dep} = 560\,°C$
- POCl$_3$: 950 °C, 15 min
- SiO$_2$: 850 °C, STEAM
- POLY: $T_{dep} = 560\,°C$
- PHOSPH: 120 keV, 10^{16} cm^{-2}

(b)
- POLY: $T_{dep} = 560\,°C$
- POCl$_3$: 950 °C, 15 min
- SiO$_2$: 850 °C, STEAM
- POLY: $T_{dep} = 620\,°C$
- PHOSPH: 120 keV, 10^{16} cm^{-2}

(c)
- POLY: $T_{dep} = 560\,°C$
- POCl$_3$: 950 °C, 15 min
- SiO2: 1000 °C, DRY O$_2$
- POLY: $T_{dep} = 560\,°C$
- PHOSPH: 120 keV, 10^{16} cm^{-2}

(d)
- POLY: $T_{dep} = 560\,°C$
- POCl$_3$: 950 °C, 15 min
- SiO2: 1000 °C, DRY O$_2$
- POLY: $T_{dep} = 620\,°C$
- PHOSPH: 120 keV, 10^{16} cm^{-2}

0.5 micrometer

Fig. 3. Cross-sectional TEM's for samples with ion-implanted lower polysilicon.

roughness of less than 20 Å [4]. The 620°C-deposited films are crystalline with a resultant columnar grain structure in which each of the columns terminate at the free surface in a dome-like feature. Consequently, the surface has irregularities with lateral dimensions governed by the polycrystalline grain width. For the fabrication conditions described in this paper, the earlier-described difference between the As-deposited free surface topologies remained recognizable through the doping and oxidation processes.

Doping of the polysilicon using POCl$_3$ at 950°C for 15 min resulted in significant grain growth throughout the polysilicon film. The 560°C-deposited films developed a well defined equiaxed grain structure, while the 620°C-deposited films often retained regions with column-like grains. These grains, though column-like, were wider and more equiaxed than in the As-deposited films. In comparison, ion implantation gave rise to a nonuniform distribution of grain sizes through the final polycrystalline film. This effect was strongly noticeable in the 560°C-deposited films, where the grains which form near the top of the implanted films were significantly larger than those at the base of the lower polycrystalline silicon (Fig. 3(c)). In

the 620°C-deposited films, the effect was subtle, but detectable (Fig. 3(b)). It is assumed that the grain size differences were the result of a nonuniform distribution of phosphorus in the early stages of oxidation. In addition, ion implantation at the dose and energy used in this study would have resulted in the near-surface region of the 620°C-deposited film being rendered amorphous [19]. Recrystallization of this near-surface region may have also attributed to the change in grain structure.

Except for a slight degree of grain boundary grooving, steam oxidation at 850°C resulted in a lower oxide–polysilicon interface which approximated the original preoxidation surface topology. A notable exception to this was the steam oxidation of 560°C-deposited POCl$_3$-doped samples where silicon inclusions and isolated protrusions were seen to mar an otherwise excellent replica of the original surface (Fig. 2(a)). Dry oxidation at 1000°C resulted in a poorer replica of the original surface. Large irregularities, such as the mound evident in Fig. 3(d), were leveled during oxidation. In addition, dry oxidation resulted in more extensive grain boundary grooving and a rougher lower oxide–polysilicon interface. This can be seen by comparing the upper and lower interfaces of the interlayer oxides in Figs. 2 and 3.

Roughness measurements of each of the lower oxide–polysilicon interfaces were made from a number of micrographs. For simplicity, the measurements were made by determining the separation between a pair of lines in which one line passed though the peaks of the two highest mounds on that interface, while the second connected the two deepest valleys. An average separation taken over four regions for each sample-type is given in Table I. Some irregularities in the microstructure were noted during TEM examination. For example, interoxide precipitates and protrusions of silicon were found extensively in the 560°C-deposited POCl$_3$-doped, and steam-oxidized samples. These precipitates and protrusions would undoubtedly adversely affect the dielectric properties of the interlevel SiO$_2$.

B. Conduction and Electron Trapping

The high-field conduction properties of SiO$_2$ films on silicon can be described by the Fowler–Nordheim equation

$$J = 2.84 \times 10^6 \, (E^2/\varphi_B) \exp \left[(-48.3/E) \, \varphi_B^{3/2} \right]. \quad (1)$$

where E is the electric field in MV · cm^{-1} at the injecting electrode (negative electrode for electron injection), φ_B is the barrier height in volts at the injecting electrode, and the electron effective mass within the oxide bandgap has been taken as 0.5 m_o [20]. To use (1) to describe conduction through polyoxides is rather inappropriate due to the high degree of surface roughness of both oxide–polysilicon interfaces, and a considerable nonuniformity in oxide thickness. As a consequence, the electric field at the injecting interface can differ substantially from the average applied field as calculated from the applied voltage and the average oxide thickness. In addition. the localized electric field at the injecting interface is nonuniform, which can lead to localized current density nonuniformities of many orders of magnitude. With the above reservations, however, (1) can be used to compare and evaluate the insulating qualities of polyoxides by using the average applied field E and determining the "effective" barrier height, $\varphi_{B_{eff}}$.

When attempting to determine the conduction properties of polyoxides, several technical difficulties were encountered due to the strong time dependence of the measured current. For example, when measuring ramped I-V curves, the current for a given applied voltage was found to decrease with decreasing voltage ramp rate. The problem was also found to occur with pulsed-voltage measurements, where the current may decay by several orders of magnitude within a few seconds. The above effects are a result of the highly nonuniform current flow through the oxide which occurs for the reasons described earlier. Consequently, the electron trapping rate is enhanced in the regions where the localized current density is very high. Since trapped electrons will build up a negative space charge with a resultant electric field within the oxide which opposes the applied field at the injecting electrode, the injected Fowler-Nordheim current will decrease. In other words, the measured current at any given voltage and/or time will be a strong function of the integrated current (i.e., charge) that has passed through the oxide. We have found that the difficulties in determining the device current with no trapped charge can be minimized by using a pulsed constant-current source and measuring the induced voltage. As suggested by (1), the device current is approximately an exponential function of voltage; thus for a given electron trapping rate the constant-current-induced voltage is a much weaker function of time than the device current under constant-voltage conditions. This technique facilitates determination of the pulsed response by a simple extrapolation to $t = 0$. A similar technique has been described by Korma et al. [15], in which a constant voltage was used and the resultant log I versus Q plot was extrapolated to $Q = 0$.

C. Ramped J-E Results

The instrument setup illustrated in Fig. 1 was used to measure all experimental I-V curves. The results plotted in Fig. 4 show some typical J-E curves as a function of voltage ramp rate and polarity. The constant value of current measured for low applied fields is simply the capacitive charging current equal to ramp rate times capacitance, whereas the monotonically increasing portion of the curves represents the situation when the Fowler-Nordheim current exceeds the charging current. In an attempt to minimize the effects of variations in average oxide thickness from sample to sample, the ramp rates were always adjusted so as to achieve a particular *field* ramp rate rather than *voltage* ramp rate. Although the results in Fig. 4 were obtained from dry-oxidized samples in which the lower polysilicon was deposited at 560°C and diffusion doped at 950°C, the following comments in this section are applicable to all the sample types listed in Table I. The previously discussed dependence on ramp rate is evident from the data shown in Fig. 4(a). It should be noted, however, that although the device current for a given applied field decreases with decreasing ramp rate, the destructive breakdown field was found to be essentially independent of ramp rate. In this case, destructive breakdown was defined as the point at which a

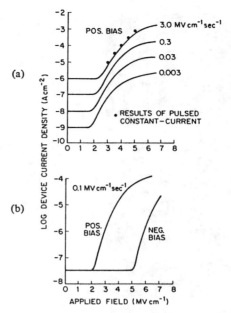

Fig. 4. Ramped J-E curves for dry-oxidized diffusion-doped samples in which the lower polysilicon was deposited in the amorphous phase: (a) effect of ramp rate for positive bias, (b) effect of bias polarity for a ramp rate of $0.1\ MV \cdot cm^{-1} \cdot s^{-1}$.

concurrent decrease in device voltage and increase in device current occurred. The results of pulsed constant-current measurements are also shown in Fig. 4(a) and, for all sample types, were found to be in good agreement with ramped I-V data when the ramp-rate was $\geq 3\ MV \cdot cm^{-1} \cdot s^{-1}$.

The curves in Fig. 4(b) are typical of the polarity dependence that was observed for all samples. In agreement with previous workers [1], [11] [16], we found that all polyoxides were far more "conductive" when the polarity of the applied bias was such that electron injection occurred across the lower oxide-polysilicon interface (i.e., upper electrode biased positive). This would be expected from a simplistic point of view in which the thermal oxidation process increases the surface roughness due to enhanced oxidation at polysilicon grain boundaries [2], [14]. In other words, with increasing oxidation time (and oxide thickness) the lower oxide-polysilicon interface will have a progressively lower effective barrier height due to increasing surface roughness [15], [21]. On the other hand, the upper oxide-polysilicon interface will more closely approximate the initial polysilicon surface topology prior to thermal oxidation.

Listed in Table I are the values of electric field (leakage field) for $10^{-7}\ A \cdot cm^{-2}$ at a ramp rate of $0.1\ MV \cdot cm^{-1} \cdot s^{-1}$, and for both polarities of applied bias. These results illustrate the earlier described polarity dependence of the conduction properties of polyoxides. This is also evident from an examination of the cross-sectional TEM's in Figs. 2 and 3. In general, it can be stated that the upper oxide-polysilicon interfaces are smoother than the corresponding lower interfaces. Furthermore, samples in which the lower polysilicon was deposited in the amorphous phase at 560°C exhibit comparatively smooth interfaces for the upper oxide-polysilicon interface and result in correspondingly higher leakage fields for

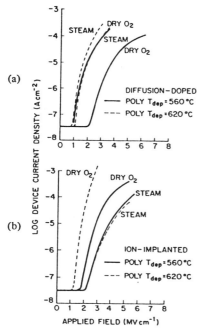

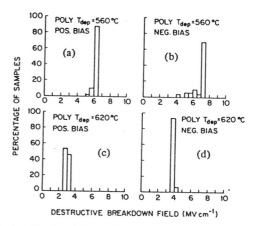

Fig. 6. Destructive breakdown field histograms for dry-oxidized diffusion-doped samples.

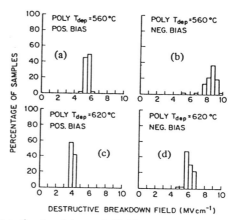

Fig. 7. Destructive breakdown field histograms for dry-oxidized ion-implanted samples.

Fig. 5. Ramped J-E curves for each sample type for positive bias and a ramp-rate of 0.1 MV $\cdot$ cm^{-1} $\cdot$ s^{-1}: (a) diffusion-doped samples, (b) ion-implanted samples.

negative polarity on the upper electrode (see Table I). This is a consequence of the relatively smooth surface prior to oxidation for amorphous-deposited films [4]–[7].

Fig. 5 illustrates a direct comparison of all sample types with regard to polyoxide conduction for positive applied bias and at a ramp rate of 0.1 MV $\cdot$ cm^{-1} $\cdot$ s^{-1}. It should be noted that for low-temperature steam-oxidized samples, there does not appear to be any significant effect with regard to the polysilicon deposition temperature; that is, the resultant electron injection properties across the lower polysilicon–oxide interface are determined by the oxidation process rather than the preoxidation surface topology. On the other hand, for high-temperature dry-oxidized samples, the current was found to be a strong function of the deposition conditions. For example, at any given applied field the measured device current was approximately two orders of magnitude lower when the polysilicon was deposited in the amorphous phase. Similar results were obtained for pulsed constant-current measurements (see Table I). Although it is difficult to see a direct one-to-one correspondence between the electrical results shown in Fig. 5 and the cross-sectional TEM's in Figs. 2 and 3, some correlation is still evident. For example, dry-oxidized diffusion-doped films with amorphous-deposited polysilicon, and steam-oxidized films with ion-implanted polysilicon, generally result in comparatively smooth lower interfaces with correspondingly higher leakage fields.

D. Destructive Breakdown Field

As stated previously, destructive breakdown is defined as the point on a ramped I-V measurement at which a concurrent decrease in device voltage and increase in device current occurs. The breakdown field histograms shown in Figs. 6 and 7 were determined with a ramp rate of 1.0 V $\cdot$ s^{-1} and by testing

at least 50 devices per sample type. For the sake of brevity, only the results for dry-oxidized samples are presented since measurements on steam-oxidized devices produced histograms that were similar to some of those presented in Figs. 6 and 7.

The histograms of destructive breakdown field E_{bn} for diffusion-doped samples are shown in Fig. 6. These results illustrate the improvement that can be attained by using polysilicon films that are initially deposited in the amorphous phase. For example, for both polarities of bias there is an increase in the average E_{bn} by approximately a factor of two. On the other hand, steam-oxidized samples produced results that were virtually identical to Fig. 6(c) and (d) for positive and negative polarity, respectively; i.e., no substantial improvement was obtained with amorphous-deposited polysilicon. It should be noted that there is good correlation between the E_{bn} histograms in Fig. 6, and the leakage field and pulsed constant-current results in Table I. It is evident that the more "conductive" polyoxides exhibit the lowest breakdown fields.

For dry-oxidized ion-implanted samples, the breakdown field histograms are shown in Fig. 7. In this case the amorphous-deposited polysilicon films exhibited a 40-percent increase in E_{bn} for both polarities of bias when compared to polycrystalline-deposited films. Once again, little improvement was observed for steam-oxidized samples, and the results were similar to Fig. 7(a) and (d) for positive and negative polarity, respectively. Correlation between the conduction properties listed in Table I and the breakdown characteristics in Fig. 7 is also evident, though not as conclusive as for diffusion-doped samples.

E. Interface Texture, Electron Trapping, and Wearout

The large variation of electrical characteristics between the different sample types makes a direct comparison of the long-term reliability of polyoxides rather difficult. In particular, we are interested in the relationship between interface texture and various wearout mechanisms such as electron trapping in the oxide and time-dependent breakdown, which are usually studied under constant-field conditions. Because of the large differences in oxide thickness uniformity, interface texture, and conduction properties between sample-types, however, a constant-field stress would result in large differences in localized field and current density. Consequently, the resultant electron trapping and related wearout mechanisms would be difficult to interpret in terms of sample-to-sample comparisons.

In an attempt to circumvent the preceding difficulties, experimental results were taken on only one device type: dry-oxidized diffusion-doped samples in which the lower polysilicon was deposited in the amorphous phase. This choice was made since, in this case, *both* polysilicon electrodes were deposited and doped under identical conditions, and both polarities of bias resulted in relatively high breakdown fields (see Fig. 6(a) and (b)). On the other hand, the conduction properties were strongly polarity-dependent (Fig. 4(b) and Table I) due to roughening of the lower oxide–polysilicon interface during thermal oxidation which resulted in slight differences in interface roughness of the upper and lower electrodes (see Fig. 2(c)). Consequently, any observed polarity dependence of wearout phenomena can be directly attributed to differences in interface texture. With regard to electrical measurements, a constant-current rather than a constant-field stress was chosen since this condition should result in comparable localized fields and current densities.

Using a constant-current stress of $\pm 1.23 \times 10^{-5}$ A $\cdot$ cm^{-2}, the average field measured across the device was found to increase with time as shown in Fig. 8. This is due to electron trapping within the bulk of the oxide which builds up a negative space charge and an internal field which opposes the applied field; i.e., as time proceeds, an increasing voltage magnitude is required to maintain the constant current. The observed higher trapping rate for positive polarity (i.e., electron injection across lower oxide–polysilicon interface) is a direct consequence of the relatively rough lower interface compared to the upper interface (see Fig. 2(c)). This is also evident from the fact that a lower initial device field is required for electron injection across the lower oxide–polysilicon interface. In other words, a rough interface results in a greater field enhancement and more localized current flow which, in turn, leads to an apparently higher electron trapping rate.

Also evident from Fig. 8, is the fact that the mean time to failure (and, consequently, charge density to failure) for negative bias on the upper electrode is approximately 50 times greater than for positive polarity, even though the average field is much higher. This would suggest that the *dominant failure mechanism is determined by the localized current density*

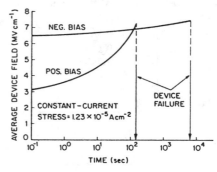

Fig. 8. Time-dependence of average device field under a constant-current stress for dry-oxidized diffusion-doped samples in which both polysilicon layers were deposited in the amorphous phase.

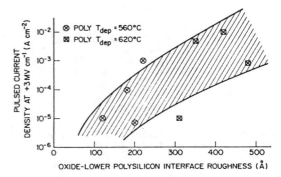

Fig. 9. Relationship between pulsed constant-current at 3 MV $\cdot$ cm^{-1} and interface roughness as determined from cross-sectional TEM's.

(and, consequently, localized charge density), rather than the average applied field. Since practical integrated circuits under normal use would result in constant-voltage stresses to be applied to multilevel structures, an even greater dependence of interlevel dielectric reliability on polysilicon interface texture would be expected. This is due to the fact that under constant-voltage conditions the localized charge density injected into the oxide can vary by orders of magnitude depending on the polysilicon interface topology present in the final device structure.

The motivation for using 560°C LPCVD silicon stems from the improved surface smoothness inherent to these amorphous-deposited films. To determine if indeed the resultant smoothness of the oxide–polysilicon interface yields improved dielectric properties, the pulsed constant-current results and the leakage field for 10^{-7} A $\cdot$ cm^{-2} at a ramp rate of 0.1 MV $\cdot$ cm$^{-1} \cdot$ s^{-1} were plotted against the roughness measurements obtained from TEM (see Table I, and Figs. 9 and 10). Although a one-to-one correlation does not exist, nor should one be expected given the differences in the processing parameters and the technique for measuring roughness, a clear trend towards improved electrical properties is observed with reduced surface roughness. The data in Figs. 9 and 10 may be divided into two subgroups in each of these plots, with improved dielectric properties associated with the smoother polysilicon films deposited in the amorphous phase.

IV. Conclusions

The properties of silicon dioxide films thermally grown from the underlying n$^+$ polysilicon have been studied using cross-sectional TEM and electrical measurements. The effects of

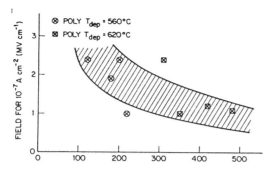

Fig. 10. Relationship between average field for 10^{-7} A $\cdot$ cm^{-2} at a ramp-rate of 0.1 MV $\cdot$ cm^{-1} $\cdot$ s^{-1} and interface roughness as determined from cross-sectional TEM's.

REFERENCES

[1] D. J. DiMaria and D. R. Kerr, "Interface effects and high conductivity in oxides grown from polycrystalline silicon," *Appl. Phys. Lett.*, vol. 27, pp. 505–507, 1975.

[2] E. A. Irene, E. Tierney, and D. W. Dong, "Silicon oxidation studies: Morphological aspects of the oxidation of polycrystalline silicon," *J. Electrochem. Soc.*, vol. 127, pp. 705–713, 1980.

[3] R. M. Anderson and D. R. Kerr, "Evidence for surface asperity mechanism of conductivity in oxide grown on polycrystalline silicon," *J. Appl. Phys.*, vol. 48, pp. 4834–4836, 1977.

[4] G. Harbeke, L. Krausbauer, E. F. Steigmeier, A. E. Widmer, H. F. Kappert, and G. Neugebauer, "High quality polysilicon by amorphous low pressure chemical vapor deposition," *Appl. Phys. Lett.*, vol. 42, pp. 249–251, 1983.

[5] E. Kinsbron, M. Sternheim, and R. Knoell, "Crystallization of amorphous silicon films during low pressure chemical vapor deposition," *Appl. Phys. Lett.*, vol. 42, pp. 835–837, 1983.

[6] G. Harbeke, L. Krausbauer, E. F. Steigmeier, A. E. Widmer, H. F. Kappert, and G. Neugebauer, "LPCVD polycrystalline silicon: Growth and physical properties of *in-situ* phosphorus doped and undoped films," *RCA Rev.*, vol. 44, pp. 287–312, 1983.

[7] M. T. Duffy, J. T. McGinn, J. M. Shaw, R. T. Smith, R. A. Soltis, and G. Harbeke, "LPCVD polycrystalline silicon: Growth and physical properties of diffusion-doped, ion-implanted, and undoped films," *RCA Rev.*, vol. 44, pp. 313–325, 1983.

[8] Y. Wada and S. Nishimatsu, "Grain growth mechanism of heavily phosphorus-implanted polycrystalline silicon," *J. Electrochem. Soc.*, vol. 125, pp. 1499–1504, 1978.

[9] L. Mei, M. Rivier, Y. Kwark, and R. W. Dutton, "Grain-growth mechanisms in polysilicon," *J. Electrochem. Soc.*, vol. 129, pp. 1791–1795, 1982.

[10] H. R. Huff, R. D. Halvorson, T. L. Chiu, and D. Guterman, "Experimental observations on conduction through polysilicon oxide," *J. Electrochem. Soc.*, vol. 127, pp. 2482–2488, 1980.

[11] P. A. Heimann, S. P. Muraka, and T. T. Sheng, "Electrical conduction and breakdown in oxides of polycrystalline silicon and their correlation with interface texture," *J. Appl. Phys.*, vol. 53, pp. 6240–6245, 1982.

[12] D. K. Brown and C. A. Barile, "Ramp breakdown study of double polysilicon RAM's as a function of fabrication parameters," *J. Electrochem. Soc.*, vol. 130, pp. 1597–1603, 1983.

[13] M. Sternheim, E. Kinsbron, J. Alspector, and P. A. Heimann, "Properties of thermal oxides grown on phosphorus *in-situ* doped polysilicon," *J. Electrochem. Soc.*, vol. 130, pp. 1735–1740, 1983.

[14] K. C. Saraswat and H. Singh, "Thermal oxidation of heavily phosphorus-doped thin films of polycrystalline silicon," *J. Electrochem. Soc.*, vol. 129, pp. 2321–2326, 1982.

[15] E. J. Korma, J. Snijder, and J. F. Verweij, "SiO$_2$ layers on polycrystalline silicon," in *Insulating Films on Semiconductors*, J. F. Verweij and D. R. Wolters, Eds. Amsterdam, The Netherlands: North-Holland, 1983, pp. 278–281.

[16] M. Conti, G. Corda, and R. Gastaldi, "Electric conduction and charge distribution in poly-oxide-poly silicon structures," in *Insulating Films on Semiconductors*, G. G. Roberts, Ed. England: Inst. of Physics, 1980, pp. 55–61.

[17] M. S. Abrahams and C. J. Buiocchi, "Cross-sectional specimens for transmission electron microscopy," *J. Appl. Phys.*, vol. 45, pp. 3315–3316, 1974.

[18] J. T. McGinn, H. F. Kappert, L. Krausbauer, J. M. Shaw, and A. E. Widmer, in *Proc. Electrochem. Soc. Spring Meeting*, Abstract 414, San Francisco, CA, 1983.

[19] D. J. Mazey, R. S. Nelson, and R. S. Barnes, "Observation of ion bombardment damage in silicon," *Phil. Mag.*, vol. 17, pp. 1145–1161, 1968.

[20] Z. A. Weinberg, "On tunneling in metal-oxide-silicon structures," *J. Appl. Phys.*, vol. 53, pp. 5052–5056, 1982.

[21] L. Faraone, RCA Labs., Princeton, NJ 08540, unpublished.

[22] J. M. Shaw, RCA Labs., Princeton, NJ 08540, private communication.

various fabrication processes were investigated, including LPCVD of polysilicon in the amorphous or polycrystalline phase, either ion implantation or diffusion doping of the n$^+$ polysilicon, and SiO$_2$ formation by thermal oxidation in low-temperature steam or high-temperature dry O$_2$. Cross-sectional TEM's suggest that comparatively smooth oxide–polysilicon interfaces can be obtained if the lower polysilicon is deposited in the amorphous phase. Furthermore, for dry-oxidized samples there was a significant improvement in the insulating properties of polyoxide grown from amorphous-deposited polysilicon. Although electrical measurements of low-temperature steam-oxidized samples showed only a marginal improvement for amorphous-deposited films, it should be emphasized that this study was only concerned with relatively thick polyoxides ($\geqslant 750$ Å). For thinner SiO$_2$ films, the interface texture and insulating properties would be expected to be more dependent on the preoxidation surface topology of the polysilicon and less dependent on the oxidation conditions. In another study [21], it has been found that for SiO$_2$ thickness $\leqslant 500$ Å, the use of amorphous-deposited polysilicon results in significant improvements even for low-temperature steam oxidation.

In summary, extensive characterization of double-level polysilicon structures suggests that the use of amorphous-deposited films can lead to significant improvements in oxide–polysilicon interface texture, and in the insulating properties of thermally grown interlevel SiO$_2$. To date, the only disadvantage appears to be the lower silicon film growth rate for amorphous deposition, which is approximately 2 to 4 times slower when comparing LPCVD at 560°C (amorphous) to 620°C (polycrystalline) [6], [22].

ACKNOWLEDGMENT

The authors wish to thank M. T. Duffy, G. Harbeke, and A. E. Widmer for many helpful discussions, and D. L. Patterson, J. M. Shaw, and IC Center personnel for device fabrication.

Reliability study of thin inter-poly dielectrics
for non-volatile memory application

Seiichi Mori, Yukio Kaneko, Norihisa Arai*, Yoichi Ohshima, Hitoshi Araki,

Kazuhito Narita, Eiji Sakagami,and Kuniyoshi Yoshikawa

Semiconductor Device Engineering Laboratory
TOSHIBA Corporation
*TOSHIBA Microelectronics Corporation
1,Komukai Toshiba-cho,Saiwai-ku, Kawasaki 210,JAPAN

ABSTRACT

This paper presents the results obtained from a systematic study on thin inter-poly dielectrics, especially for   non-volatile memories with floating gate structures. First, the key factors, which dominate the leakage current in poly-oxide, are reviewed and intrinsic limitation in thinner poly-oxide to device application were investigated considering defect densities and edge leakage current. Second, the ONO(Oxide/Nitride/Oxide) structure, overcoming poly-oxide thinning limitations, will be described. This stacked film reveals superior electric field strength due to the inherent electron trapping assisted self limiting process. UV erase characteristics for EPROM cells with ONO structure will be considered. Finally, how the ONO inter-poly dielectrics should be scaled down is discussed, considering memory cell charge retention capability.

INTRODUCTION

Scaling down inter-poly dielectric thickness is one of the most important subjects for non-volatile memories, such as EPROM, EEPROM, and Flash EEPROM with stacked gate structure. In addition, inter-poly dielectrics are currently used for stacked capacitor cells for DRAM. For DRAM, low leakage current, low defect density, and long Mean Time To Failure(MTTF) are key issues to be considered. However, for non-volatile memories, memory cells charge retention capability would also be an important issue that has to be considered.

Poly-oxide has been used for inter-poly dielectric layer in non-volatile memories for a long time. In thinner film region, however, ONO structure has begun to be widely used, due to its lower defect density and lower leakage current. This paper first clarifies the intrinsic limitations of thin poly-oxide for device applications. ONO film properties will be discussed, compared with those for poly-oxide film. ONO superiority and the origin will be reported. ONO application to UV EPROMs generally results in longer UV erase time. Some experimental data concerning this phenomena are shown. Finally, ONO scaling methodology for non-volatile memories will be discussed, mainly considering charge retention capability.

1.POLY OXIDE CHARACTERISTICS

1.1 Leakage Current for Thick Poly-Oxide

It is well known that poly-oxide is more conductive than oxide grown on single-Si substrate and that leakage current for poly-oxide, thermally grown on phosphorus doped poly-Si, depends on phosphorus concentration in oxidized 1st poly-Si(poly1)[1]-[5]. In this section, leakage current characteristics for poly-oxide in a relatively thicker(~50nm) film region are reviewed.

Figure 1 shows typical poly-oxide critical field strength (defined as $10^{-7}A/cm^2$ leakage current in plane capacitors)dependence on phosphorus concentration in poly1, when positive bias is applied to 2nd poly-Si(poly2). Oxide thicknesses are around 50nm. Oxidation was accomplished at 950^oC in dry O_2 atmosphere. An optimum phosphorus concentration, which provides the highest critical field strength, exists at around $4-6x10^{20}cm^{-3}$. In Figs.2, (A)to(C) show the I-E(current versus electric field) characteristics for poly-oxide, corresponding to lower(A), optimum(B), and higher(C) phosphorus concentration in poly1 for both gate bias polarities. SEM photographs of surface texture are also shown in Figs.3(A)to(C).

In lower phosphorus concentration case (A), leakage current, when positive bias is applied to poly2, is larger than that when negative bias is applied. Leakage current, when negative bias is applied to poly2, is mainly affected by the poly2/poly-oxide interface texture, which reflects poly1 surface texture before oxidation. Positive bias leakage current is affected by the final (after oxidation) poly-oxide/poly1 interface texture. In a low phosphorus concentration case, since asperities grow on poly1 due to thermal oxidation, the enhanced electron emission from the asperities   causes the asymmetrical I-E characteristics. This enhanced growth of asperities must be due to the stress during oxidation. In a low phosphorus concentration region, poly-Si grain sizes are relatively small and many grain boundaries exist. Thus, large amounts of phosphorus are segregated at such boundaries. Therefore, actual phosphorus concentration in individual Si grains must be lower than the value evaluated by SIMS. In these regions, stress induced oxide thinning and "horn" formation have been observed in shaped Si oxidation study [6][7][8]. For poly-oxide formation, surface roughness can be gener-

Reprinted from the *Proc. 28th IRPS*, pp. 132–144, 1990.

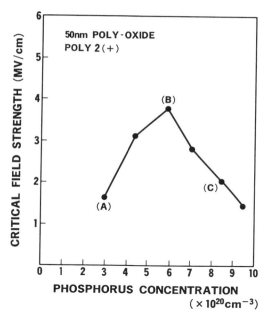

Fig.1 Typical poly-oxide critical field strength (defined as $10^{-7} A/cm^2$ leakage current) dependence on phosphorus concentration in poly1: E-I curves and surface texture corresponding to (A),(B), and (C) are shown in Figs.2 and 3.

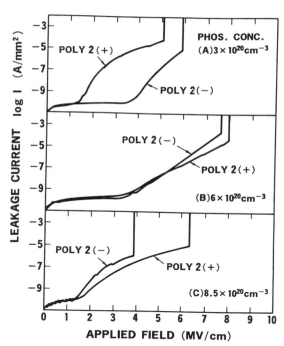

Fig.2 Leakage current characteristics for poly-oxide, as a parameter of phosphorus concentration for both gate bias polarities

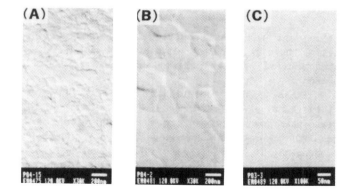

Fig.3 SEM photographs showing poly1 surface texture after oxidation. (A) corresponding to $3 \times 10^{20} cm^{-3}$ phosphorus concentration. (B) corresponding to $6 \times 10^{20} cm^{-3}$ phosphorus concentration. (C) corresponding to $8.5 \times 10^{20} cm^{-3}$ phosphorus concentration.

ated by similar mechanisms. Moreover, enhanced oxidation at grain boundaries also enhances the surface roughness. Oxidation rate at grain boundaries becomes higher, compared with that on Si grains, due to the segregated phosphorus at the boundaries. Surface roughness can, therefore, be enhanced by the differences in oxidation rates.

With the increase in phosphorus concentration, leakage current decreases and surface roughness becomes smaller. Phosphorus effects on thermal oxidation of silicon with geometrical nonplanarity were investigated. It was reported that phosphorus incorporation prevented the generation of "horn"[6]. This phenomena was attributed to the shorter reaction controlled region, stress relaxation due to the introduced vacancies, and SiO_2 viscous flow enhancement. These models can also be applicable to the poly-Si oxidation case. Larger grain size also contributes the improvement in surface roughness.

In a higher than $6 \times 10^{20} cm^{-3}$ phosphorus concentration region(C), critical field strength decreases with increasing phosphorus concentration, regardless of the smoother interface texture. In this region, since leakage current increases for both gate bias polarities, this must be owing to the degradation in oxide quality, caused by the phosphorus incorporation into poly-oxide.

Intrinsic leakage current for poly-oxide is mainly affected by two factors. One is poly-Si surface texture. The other is poly-oxide quality. These two factors are strongly correlated to phosphorus concentration in oxidized poly-Si.

In addition, poly-oxide defect density is strongly affected by contamination in poly-Si and the defect

levels are usually higher than for oxide grown on single-Si substrate especially in thinner film region[13].

1.2 Leakage Current for Thin Poly-Oxide

To form thin poly-oxide on phosphorus doped poly-Si with good controllability, a conventional dry O_2 oxidation method cannot be used, because of the high oxidation rate. Therefore, a diluted oxygen oxidation method is one of the most promising methods to form thin poly-oxide. The authors have already reported the increase in critical field strength by diluted oxidation for a relatively thicker oxide region[4]. In that case, a two-step oxidation method was proposed to form a relatively thick oxide with applicable oxida-

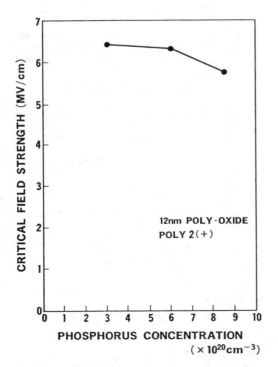

Fig.4 Typical 12nm poly-oxide critical field strength dependence on phosphorus concentration in poly1

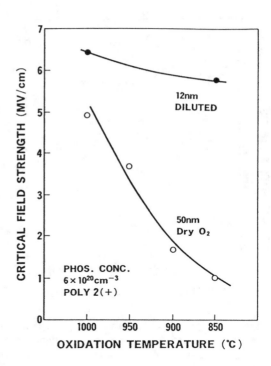

Fig.5 Typical thin poly-oxide critical field strength dependence on oxidation temperature and oxide thickness, including the oxidation method difference

tion time for mass production. To form a thinner oxide, however, only the 1st step oxidation(with less than several percent oxygen concentration) can be used.

Figure 4 shows the critical field strength for thin(-12nm) poly-oxide grown by diluted oxidation(with less than several percent oxygen concentration) method at 1000°C and their dependence on poly1 phosphorus concentration. The critical field strength absolute value becomes high, compared with those shown in Fig.1, and dependence on phosphorus concentration becomes smaller. The reasons for this improvement are as follow. Field enhancement effect is moderated in a thin oxide region, because asperities grown by thermal oxidation are not enhanced so much in thin oxide region. Moreover, a slow oxidation rate, due to diluted oxidation, can relax the stress during oxidation and suppresses asperity growth.

Field enhancement factor due to the asperity is described by

$$1 + Tox/r \quad (1)$$

where Tox is oxide thickness and r is curvature radius for an asperity. This factor becomes smaller with decreasing oxide thickness. Tox becomes smaller and r becomes larger, for the reasons described above in the thin oxide region. As a result, field enhancement effect becomes smaller with decreasing oxide thickness. Therefore, critical field strength reduction in the lower phosphorus concentration region disappears.

In a high phosphorus concentration region, the main reason for the improvement must be the reduction in phosphorus concentration in poly-oxide by the diluted oxidation method. Reduced phosphorus concen-

tration, due to slow oxidation rate, has been confirmed by SIMS measurements[4][5].

Figure 5 shows the critical field strength dependence on oxidation temperatures for 12nm oxide, formed by diluted oxidation method, and for 50nm oxide, formed by dry O_2 oxidation method. Low temperature oxidation enhances the stress during oxidation and segregation of phosphorus at grain boundaries. Thus, surface roughness is enhanced by low temperature oxidation. For 50nm oxide grown by dry O_2 oxidation, a marked lowering in critical field strength can be observed with reducing the oxidation temperature. On the contrary, by using diluted oxidation method, 12nm thin poly-oxide with high critical field strength can be formed, even at low oxidation temperature, such as 850°C.

In this way, thin poly-oxide with high critical field strength can be formed by the diluted oxidation method. The dependence on phosphorus concentration and oxidation temperature can be reduced.

1.3 TDDB for Thin Poly-Oxide

As shown in Fig.4, critical field strength dependence on phosphorus concentration becomes small for 12nm poly-oxide formed by the diluted oxidation method. To investigate the oxide quality dependence on phosphorus concentration in detail, TDDB(Time Dependent Dielectric Breakdown) characteristics at the constant electric field stress conditions have been investigated.

Figure 6 shows an example of TDDB characteristics for 12nm poly-oxide. Thin poly-oxide films sometimes show high random failure rates, as previously report-

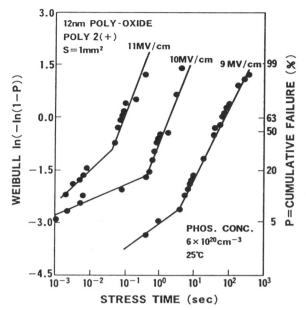

Fig.6 TDDB characteristics for 12nm poly-oxide capacitors with 1mm² area

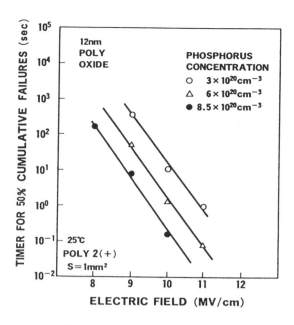

Fig.7 50% MTTF for 12nm poly-oxide capacitors with 1mm² area, as a phosphorus concentration parameter

ed[9][10]. A drastic increase in random or initial failure rate, observed in a low phosphorus concentration case[10], must be due to the insufficient gettering (phosphorus gettering effect) for high contamination level and it is speculated that it is not due to the intrinsic characteristics. When random failure rate is high, due to the defects caused by contamination, intrinsic oxide quality cannot be precisely evaluated. However, in the samples shown in Fig.6, since the random failure rates were relatively low, due to the reduced contamination level, intrinsic characteristics can be observed. The region of abrupt increase in failure rate, which is sometimes called "intrinsic breakdown" can be observed in Fig.6. Intrinsic characteristics were evaluated, using the samples with reduced contamination level.

Times for 50% cumulative failures of poly-oxide(corresponding to intrinsic breakdown region, as shown in Fig.6) as a parameter of phosphorus concentration, are plotted in Fig.7. Lower phosphorus concentration reveals longer time to failure. This result shows that phosphorus incorporation leads to the degradation in poly-oxide quality, evaluated by TDDB measurements. As shown in Fig.1, highest critical field strength can be obtained for $4-6 \times 10^{20} cm^{-3}$ phosphorus concentration. Oxide film quality, however, is not necessarily best in this concentration region. From only the oxide film quality standpoint, evaluated by TDDB measurements, a lower phosphorus concentration is preferable.

Figure 8 shows the TDDB characteristics for 12nm poly-oxide capacitors with 10mm² area, which is 10 times larger than capacitors in Fig.6 and Fig.7. Higher random or initial failure rate can be observed with increasing phosphorus concentration as well as the reduction in "50% mean time to failure". These data show that increased phosphorus concentration not

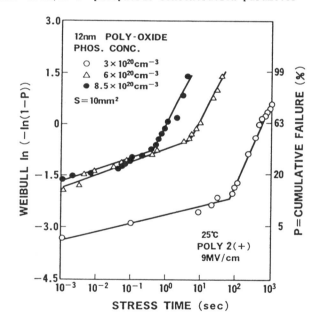

Fig.8 TDDB characteristics for 12nm poly-oxide capacitors with 10mm² area

only leads to the oxide quality degradation, but also to the increase in defect density. Note that, in VLSI non-volatile memory devices, total inter-poly dielectrics area will be as large than 10mm². In 16Mb EPROM, for example, the total inter-poly dielectrics area will be 15.4mm², if the cell reported in[11][12] is adopted.

Judging from the TDDB data, a lower phosphorus concentration would be preferable, especially in the thin oxide region, where leakage current enhancement, due to surface roughness, is fairly small.

267

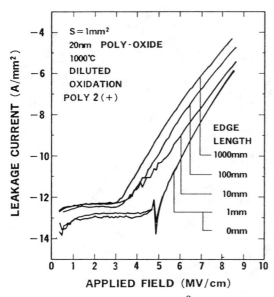

Fig.9 E-I characteristics for 1mm² poly-oxide capacitors with various edge lengths

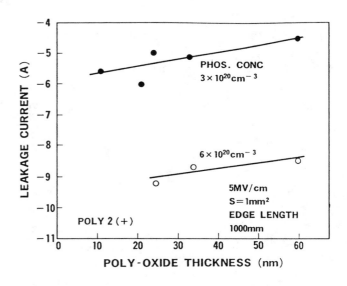

Fig.10 Leakage current in poly-oxide at poly-Si edges: Applied electric field is 5MV/cm

1.4 Leakage Current at Patterned Poly-Si Edges

Results described in 1.1 to 1.3 were obtained in planar capacitors. However, in most cases, actual device structures have patterned edges (floating gate edges) and field enhancement at edges is another big problem. To clearly evaluate the edge leakage current, measurements on capacitors with long patterned edges and various edge lengths are effective.

Figure 9 shows the I-E characteristics for 1mm² poly-oxide capacitors with various edge lengths. In recent non-volatile memory device, the ratio of poly-oxide edge length to the capacitor area is usually around 10^3mm/1mm². In the 0.6μm EPROM cell reported in [11][12], for example, the inter-poly dielectric area is 0.96(1.6x0.6)um² and total edge length is 1.2(0.6x2)um. Thus, the edge length for the 1mm² inter-poly dielectrics area is 1250mm.

As shown in Fig.9, leakage current for a capacitor with 1000mm edge length is 2-3 orders of magnitude larger than for a planar capacitor(without an edge). This indicates leakage currents at edges are 2-3 orders of magnitude larger than total current on a planar part in actual device structure. This edge effect is one of the most serious constraints, when thin poly-oxide is used for inter-poly dielectrics.

Figure 10 shows the leakage current at poly-Si edges, evaluated by capacitors with 1000mm edge length for 3×10^{20}cm^{-3} and 6×10^{20}cm^{-3} phosphorus concentrations. Applied electric field was 5MV/cm. Leakage currents for 3×10^{20}cm^{-3} phosphorus concentration are 3-4 orders of magnitude larger than that for 6×10^{20}cm^{-3} concentration. Since poly-Si edges already exist before oxidation, thinner oxide should not lead to a marked decrease in leakage current, which can be observed in plane capacitors. Edges of poly-Si with low phosphorus concentration cannot be rounded by oxidation at 1000°C [6], leading to oxide thinning and "horn" shape at the edges enhancing the leakage cur-

rent. This high leakage current poly-oxide on patterned poly-Si of low phosphorus concentration can be applicable to erase oxide of triple-poly Flash EEPROM cells. However, it will not be preferable for conventional inter-poly dielectrics of a non-volatile memory cell, which requires low leakage current and high reliability.

1.5 Limitations for Thin Poly Oxide

Increased time-zero defect density is the most serious constraint in thin poly-oxide application[13].

In addition to such extrinsic problems, it has been shown that some intrinsic difficulties exist. There are different problems in both low and high phosphorus concentration regions. In high phosphorus concentration, an increase in oxide defects and oxide quality degradation due to phosphorus incorporation are observed. A more reliable oxide can be formed on plane poly-Si, if the oxide thickness is around the 10nm region with lower phosphorus concentration. Nevertheless, a drastic increase in leakage current occurs when oxide is formed on patterned poly-Si, or when thicker oxide is grown, even on plane poly-Si.

Thus, the reliable poly-oxide formation method, by merely optimizing phosphorus concentration, has confronted various difficulties. To overcome these limitations, many process improvements, such as super clean technology, novel doping or oxidation process to reduce the incorporation of phosphorus into oxide, and new cell structure[22], which can reduce the edge effect, are required.

2. OXIDE/NITRIDE STACKED FILM

2.1 ONO Stacked Films Superiority

In order to solve various difficulties regarding poly-oxide film in a thin film region, ONO(Oxide/Nitride/Oxide) inter-poly dielectrics represent one of the most promising structures. It can realize high critical field strength and low defect density[9][13][14]. Thermally grown Bottom Poly-Oxide / CVD Si_3N_4 / thermally grown Top-Oxide (=B.P.O./ SiN/ T.O.) structure will mainly be investigated.

Figure 11 shows the critical field strength dependence on phosphorus concentration in poly1 for ONO inter-poly dielectric. High critical field strength can be obtained, regardless of phosphorus concentration. Figure 12 shows the E-I characteristics for ONO film on patterned and plane poly-Si. Patterned edge length is as long as 600mm. To evaluate the low level leakage current, capacitor electrodes, surrounded by oxide to eliminate the periphery leakage, were used. I-E characteristics above 10^{-10}A/mm^2 region are almost the same, regardless of capacitor structure. In a low level leakage region, somewhat larger leakage current can be observed in capacitors with patterned edges.

These ONO stacked film characteristics are explained by considering electron trapping in SiN layer as shown in Fig.13. At edges or asperities, large leakage current flows at an initial stage, due to the field enhancement effect. After that, electrons are trapped in the SiN layer and trapped electrons lower the electric field in the bottom oxide layer. Larger leakage current, observed in a low electric field region, corresponds to the enhanced leakage current at

an initial stage. A similar healing effect, due to trapped electrons, is expected for capacitors with degraded bottom-oxide layer.

This trapping effect is also observed in EPROM cell structure, as shown in Fig.14. In this case, CVD bottom-oxide (C.B.O.)was used to enhance the edge effect, because edges cannot be rounded off by oxidation [13]. Figure 14 shows the charge leakage characteristics from floating gate to control gate. Electrons were injected to the floating gate by hot elec-

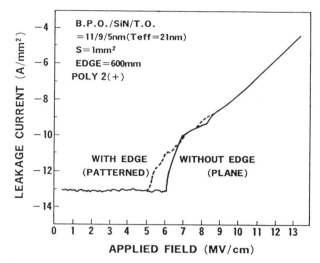

Fig.12 E-I characteristics for ONO film, on patterned and plane poly-Si

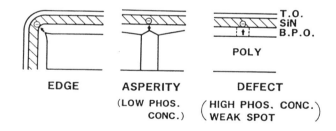

Fig.13 Electron trapping effect in nitride film

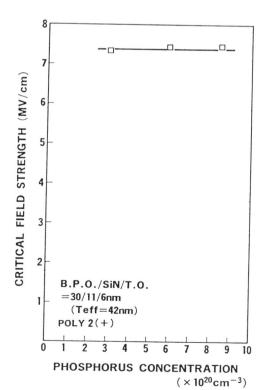

Fig.11 Inter-poly ONO critical field strength dependence on phosphorus concentration in poly1

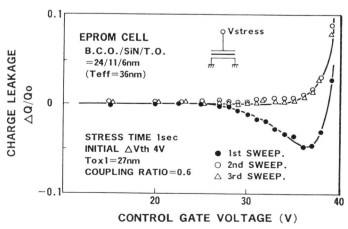

Fig.14 Trapping effect observed in EPROM cell structure:Qo= initial stored charge in floating gate, Δ Q= deviations in floating gate charge by stress bias

tron injection method and stress voltage was applied to the control gate. At the 1st sweep measurement, charge leakage can be observed below the 38V region. With increasing gate voltage, electron injection occurs from substrate to floating gate. At the 2nd sweep measurement, charge leakage phenomena disappears ,due to the electron trapping during the 1st sweep measurement. Cell threshold voltage after UV erase showed little change in this stress test. Therefore, the increase in threshold voltage by trapped electrons is small, leading to a localized distribution model of such trapped electrons. Positive charge accumulation in a floating gate during UV irradiation also may partly contributes to the small threshold voltage shift.

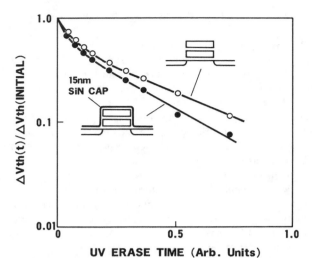

Fig.16 15nm SiN cap influence on EPROM cell erase characteristics

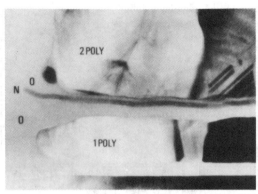

Fig.15 TEM cross sectional view near floating gate edges

2.2 UV Erase Characteristics for EPROM Cells

ONO inter-poly dielectric has many advantages. However, some precautions should be taken when it is used in UV erase EPROM cells. UV erase speed for EPROM cells with ONO inter-poly dielectric usually becomes slower than that with poly-oxide inter-poly dielectric [13]. In this section, this difference will be discussed.

Since SiN film is overhanging from the floating gate edges, as shown in Fig.15, this overhanging region may reduce the UV light intensity irradiated to floating gate edges. To investigate the permeability of UV light in SiN film and its effect on erase speed, erase characteristics for EPROM cells, with and without 15nm SiN cap, were evaluated. 15nm SiN cap, deposited by LPCVD method, does not lead to a reduction in UV erase speed, as shown in Fig.16. Thus, it is concluded that overhanging SiN does not degrade UV erasing speed. Therefore, the difference in photo-current flow is another candidate for the reason. To investigate the photo-current difference, threshold voltage shifts for non-programmed EPROM cells by UV light irradiation under control gate bias applications were evaluated, as shown in Fig.17. The threshold voltage shifts are described as

$$\Delta V_{th} = (1/C_2) \int_0^t (I_{p1} - I_{p2})dt \quad (2)$$

where I_{p1} is photo-current from substrate to floating gate and I_{p2} is photo-current from floating gate to

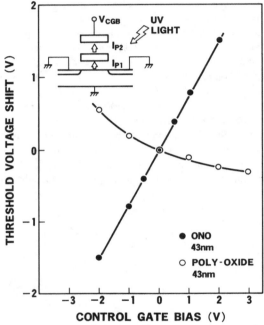

Fig.17 Threshold voltage shift for EPROM cells with control gate bias application under UV irradiation conditions

control gate. Since the coupling ratios for the investigated cells were 0.65-0.69 and since the inter-poly dielectric was thicker than 1st gate oxide thickness, the electric field in the inter-poly dielectric is smaller than that in the cell 1st gate oxide. For cells with poly-oxide, positive gate bias leads to negative threshold voltage shift. This indicates that the photo-current from floating gate to control gate is larger than that from floating gate to substrate, in spite of the lower electric field($I_{p1} < I_{p2}$). Photo-current mainly flows in a thinner gate oxide region, because it is proportional to electric field in SiO_2 [15]. Note that photo-current can flow only near the poly-Si gate periphery and that the total periphery length between poly1 and poly2 is longer than that between substrate and poly1. Moreover, the lower poly-oxide quality and field enhancement at floating gate edges also contribute to the increase in photo-current.

On the contrary, for the ONO cell, positive bias leads to positive threshold voltage shift, which corresponds to negative charge accumulation in a floating gate. This results show photo-current from a floating gate to a control gate is much smaller than that from a substrate to a floating gate($I_{p1} > I_{p2}$).

The degradation in UV erase speed for ONO cells is mainly caused by the decrease in photo-current through the ONO inter-poly dielectric, compared with that through poly-oxide. This phenomena is closely related to electron trapping and carrier transport mechanisms in ONO film under UV light irradiation.

2.3 ONO Scaling vs. Charge Retention

The ONO inter-poly dielectric composition strongly affects the characteristics and many factors should be taken into consideration, in order to scale down the effective thickness.

Experimental results, concerning the dielectric reliability for 20nm inter-poly ONO, have already been reported [16], in which it was shown that thicker SiN resulted in longer MTTF and larger Charge to Break-down(Q_{BD}). Thin(~1.5nm) top-oxide resulted in larger Q_{BD}, but it revealed shorter MTTF.

In addition to these issues, charge retention capability, evaluated by high temperature bake test, should also be taken into consideration, especially in a thinner effective oxide thickness region.

In this section, charge retention capability dependence on ONO composition is described to obtain ONO scaling methodology. The relation between charge retention and E-I characteristics at room temperature is also discussed.

2.3.1 Leakage Current for ONO film and
Top Oxide Thickness Dependence

Before discussing the charge retention characteristics, leakage current characteristics for ONO film will be described. It was known that thicker anode-side oxide results in smaller leakage current in the relatively high electric field region for ONO films formed on Si substrate [17][18][19] and on poly-Si[9]. This was attributed to the top-oxide blocking effects against hole injection. Figure 18 shows the E-I characteristics for ONO film with various top-oxide thicknesses. Thicker anode side oxide resulted in smaller leakage current in high electric field region. Moreover, larger leakage current can be observed also in a low electric field region in thinner top-oxide case. Figure 19 shows the energy band diagram for ONO structure. E-I characteristics for the ONO structure have three parts. In the low electric field region, Poole-Frenkel(P-F) current of holes and electrons in SiN(component 2 and 3) is larger than Fowler-Nordheim current in the B.P.O.(component 1). It was reported that hole conduction in SiN (component 2) is much larger than electron conduction (component 3) [18]

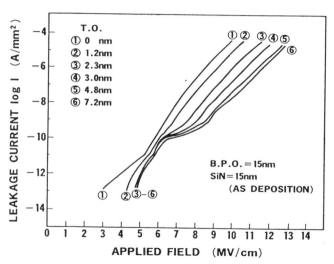

Fig.18 E-I characteristics for inter-poly ONO film with various top-oxide thicknesses

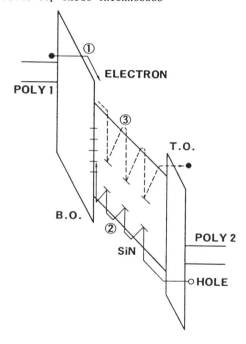

Fig.19 ONO structure energy band diagram

when T.O. is thin and holes are easily injected from an electrode by direct tunneling. Holes injected by component 2 accumulate at the B.P.O./SiN interface and enhance the electron conduction in B.P.O.(component 1). Therefore, in case of thin T.O., enhanced leakage current can flow in a low electric field region. A thicker anode side top-oxide markedly reduces component 2 and leakage current level becomes low. In higher electric field, F-N current in B.P.O. becomes larger than P-F current in SiN and electrons are trapped in SiN/B.P.O. interface. This phenomena becomes pronounced, in case of a thicker anode side oxide, because hole injection, which can partly compensate for the electrons, is reduced to a low level. The first kink in E-I characteristics, observed in around 6MV/cm electric field, shows this electron trapping phenomena. Positive flat band voltage shift by more than around 6MV/cm stress reported in reference[24] is also caused by this electron trapping effect. When the amount of electrons accumulated at B.P.O./SiN interface becomes a certain value, P-F current(components 2 and 3) becomes larger, due to electric field enhancement. Then, F-N current in the B.P.O. limits the leakage current. The 2nd kink in E-I characteristics shows this position. Judging from this mechanisms, it can be well understood that thicker anode-side oxide can reduce the leakage current in both high and low electric field regions.

Next, charge retention capability dependence on top-oxide thickness will be discussed. Figure 20 shows the charge loss dependence on top-oxide(T.O.) thickness in EPROM cells. After programming, the cells were baked at 300°C to measure the decrease in threshold voltage. Degradation in charge retention capability is observed in cells with less than 3nm T.O.. Similar experiments on VLSI memories (1Mb EPROMs) were also carried out. After programming and baking 1Mb EPROMs, Vccmax (corresponding to the amount of residual electrons in floating gate) was measured. Figure 21 shows the Vccmax distributions for 1Mb EPROMs after 300°C 20 hour bake. 1Mb EPROMs with 2.3nm T.O. show smaller Vccmax than that with 3nm T.O.. In addition, deviations for Vccmax are larger for 2.3nm T.O.. These results show that more than around 3nm T.O. is required to realize good charge retention. Although arguments regarding leakage current characteristics at room temperature, described before, cannot be directly applicable to charge retention capability at high temperature bake test, because carrier conduction mechanisms, which dominate charge retention at high temperature, may be different from those for well known mechanisms, charge retention capability dependence on T.O. thickness coincides well with the hole injection model. It can be concluded that hole injection from the control gate not only leads to the increase in leakage current at room temperature E-I measurements, but also to the degradation in data retention capability.

Top-oxide thickness should be preserved more than a certain critical value(~3nm) which can block hole injection.

2.3.2 SiN Thickness Dependence

Figure 22 shows the charge loss for EPROM cells with various SiN thicknesses and thin(~2nm) top-oxide. When the top-oxide layer is thin and hole injection from the control gate can occur, a thicker nitride will lead to enhanced charge loss, if effective oxide thickness is kept constant. The reason is that thicker SiN means thinner bottom poly-oxide in this condition. Even if the same amounts of holes were injected and trapped at B.P.O./SiN interface, the field enhancement in B.P.O. becomes larger in thicker nitride with thinner B.P.O. conditions. Increased leakage current at low electric field caused by similar mechanisms in thicker nitride film can also be observed in E-I measurements at room temperature, as

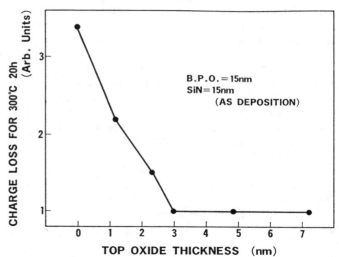

Fig.20 Charge loss dependence on top-oxide thickness in EPROM cells

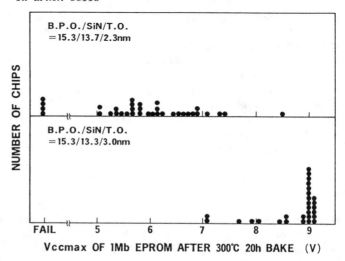

Fig.21 Difference in charge retention characteristics for 1Mb EPROMs with 2.3 and 3nm top-oxide layer

shown in Fig.23. However, the results indicated in Fig.22 cannot be fully explained by this mechanism alone. ONO with 18/8.5/2nm composition also shows larger charge loss than 18/6.3/2nm. In this case, bottom-oxide thickness for the former is the same as the latter. Therefore, SiN thickness must have some additional effects on charge loss phenomena. The total amount of traps and/or charge transport in SiN can be dependent on SiN thickness and such factors also affect the charge retention capability.

Figure 24 shows the charge loss dependence on SiN thickness for thick(~5nm) blocking top-oxide(Sample A) In this case, SiN thickness dependence becomes small. Though initial (<20h) decrease becomes somewhat greater in thicker (>8.4nm) SiN film, the difference is small, compared to thin top-oxide samples. This is due to the decrease in field enhancement by blocking of hole injection. Residual small dependence on SiN thickness still exists. In E-I measurements, a thicker SiN reveals less leakage current, in both low and high electric field regions at room temperature, as shown in Fig.25 and in Reference[21]. Therefore, in

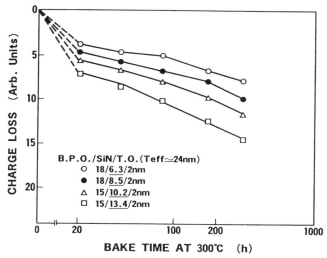

Fig.22 Charge loss for EPROM cells with various SiN thicknesses and thin top-oxide

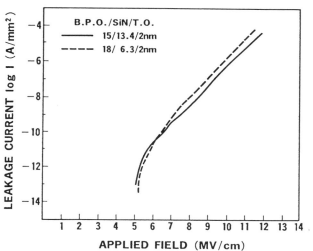

Fig.23 E-I characteristics for inter-poly ONO films with 15/13.4/2nm and 18/6.3/2nm composition

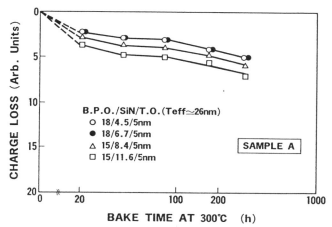

Fig.24 Charge loss for EPROM cells with various SiN thicknesses and thick top-oxide (Sample A)

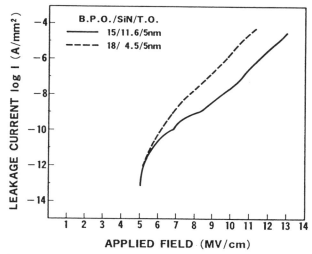

Fig.25 E-I characteristics of inter-poly ONO films with 15/11.6/5nm and 18/4.5/5nm composition

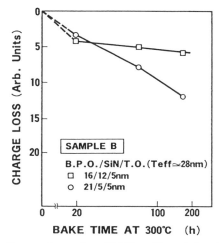

Fig.26 Charge loss for EPROM cells with 16/12/5nm and 21/5/5nm composition (Sample B)

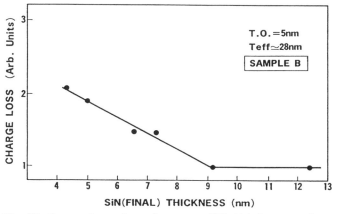

Fig.27 Charge loss dependence on SiN thicknesses for EPROM cells after 168 hour bake at 300°C, in case of sample B

273

this case, E-I characteristics do not coincide with retention characteristics. Therefore, this phenomena also relates to the total amount of traps and/or charge transport in SiN, which can be affected by the SiN thickness.

SiN thickness scaling down to 5nm does not lead to degradation in data retention capability. However, SiN thickness scaling should be carefully carried out, considering the results described below.

Figure 26 shows another charge loss dependence on SiN thickness in case of thick(-5nm) blocking top-oxide (Sample B). Difference in ONO composition ,between Sample A and Sample B, are small. However, in case of Sample B, a thin SiN layer leads to enhanced charge loss, especially in long time bake test. Figure 27 summarizes the charge loss dependence on final SiN thickness after 168 hour bake -at 300°C in Sample B. It is clear that too much SiN thinning leads to the degradation of charge retention capabili-ty. Though the origin of the differences between Sample A and Sample B are not clear at this stage, the difference in bottom-oxide quality is one possible causes. Direct tunneling of electrons in thin SiN can lead to the enhanced charge loss, if barrier height for bottom oxide layer is low.

It is known that SiN scaling also leads to degra-dation in TDDB characteristics [16][23]. Therefore, SiN thickness should be carefully scaled down, consid-ering the factors described above.

2.3.3 Bottom-Oxide Thickness Dependence and Nitride/Oxide(NO) Structures

Figure 28 shows the charge loss dependence on bottom-oxide thickness for the samples with a thick top-oxide layer. Bottom oxide scaling, down to around 10nm, thus, does not lead to the degradation of data retention capability. ONO thickness scaling down to around 20nm, corresponding to devices with 0.6μm design rule (such as 16Mb EPROMs) , will have no serious problems, when appropriate SiN/T.O. composi-tion are adopted.

To scale the inter-poly dielectric thickness down to 10nm or less, NO(Nitride/Oxide: without bottom-oxide structure) has been reported. It was shown that thin nitride, directly deposited on poly1, realizes high critical field strength and low defect density by surface oxidation [9]. The detailed reliability data were also reported and usefulness for DRAM capacitors has been shown[20]. However, for non-volatile memory devices, charge retention capability should be taken into consideration as the 1st priority. Actually, the NO structure shows initial rapid (<20h) charge loss as shown in Fig.28. This will be attributed to trap assisted electron conduction (Component 3 in Fig.21) in SiN at a low electric field region. 4nm top-oxide cannot block direct electron tunneling to the control gate. An increase in leakage current at a low electric field region can also be observed in E-I characteris-tics at room temperature as shown in Fig.29. To im-prove the reliability for this structure, thicker top-oxide will be required to reduce the electron

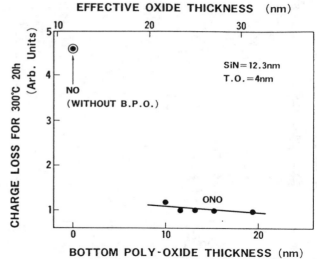

Fig.28 Charge loss dependence for EPROM cells on bottom-oxide thickness: NO(Nitride/Oxide) structure is also shown

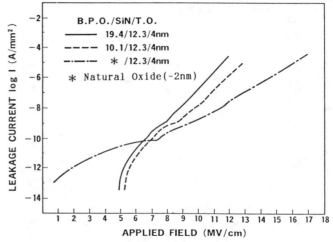

Fig.29 E-I characteristics for inter-poly ONO film as a bottom-oxide thickness parameter

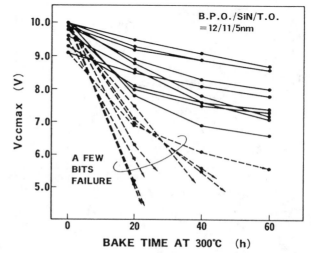

Fig.30 Charge retention characteristics example for 1Mb EPROMs with thin and degraded bottom poly-oxide layer

tunneling and thin(2nm) top-oxide recommended for DRAM capacitors [20] cannot be used for non-volatile memories.

Even though the ONO structure is adopted, a few bits initial rapid failure sometimes occurs in VLSI memories, as shown in Fig.30, if bottom oxide has high defect density and thin thickness. In this case, bottom oxide quality evaluated by control samples(without SiN/T.O.) were rather poor. Since the NO structure cannot block the charge leakage, as shown in Fig.28, such a rapid charge loss will be observed at the cells with extremely weak bottom-oxide area. Therefore, an appropriate control for achieving good bottom-oxide quality must be required, especially in a thin film region, even if ONO structure is adopted.

Intrinsic bottom-oxide scaling limitation in ONO structure must be thicker than 5nm, which can block direct electron tunneling at a low electric field region and preserve high reliability. In case of poly-oxide, however, oxide quality is not so good as oxide grown on single-Si substrate. Therefore, actual limitation will be thicker than 5nm. Good quality thin bottom-oxide formation will be one of the most important factors for ONO scaling.

2.4 ONO Scaling Methodology

ONO scaling methodology, mainly considering charge retention capability, is as follow.

Top-oxide thickness should be preserved, more than a critical value (-3nm) which can effectively block hole injection from the top electrode. Usually, SiN thickness scaling can improve charge retention and thinning down to 5nm may be possible. However, SiN scaling leads to degradation in TDDB characteristics and too much thinning sometimes lead to degradation in charge retention capability. Therefore, SiN scaling should be carefully carried out. Thinning of bottom oxide down to 10nm does not lead to degradation if bottom oxide quality can be well controlled. This thick top-oxide and thin SiN composition methodology is somewhat different from that obtained from dielectric reliability (Breakdown) study [16].

It is necessary to choose the ONO composition carefully, considering both charge retention and dielectric reliability. For dielectric reliability, there exists other method to moderate and reduce the degradation due to scaling, such as elimination of process induced damages by process improvement. It should be noted , however, that data retention capability directly determines the reliability of non-volatile memories and should be the most important issues.

CONCLUSIONS

It has been shown that some intrinsic difficulties exist in thin poly-oxide applications to the device structures. In poly-oxide grown on poly1 with high concentration phosphorus , an increase in oxide defects and degradation of oxide quality due to phosphorus incorporation is observed. For poly-oxide grown on low phosphorus doped poly-Si, relatively reliable oxide can be formed on plane poly-Si. A drastic increase in leakage current, however, is observed, when oxide is formed on patterned poly-Si.

On the other hand, ONO(Oxide/Nitride/Oxide) structure can solve such difficulties. It shows little leakage current dependence on phosphorus concentration. Moreover, the edge effect is small, due to the electron trapping effect. UV erase speed degradation in EPROM cells with ONO structure is caused by the decrease in photo-current flow from a floating gate to a control gate. ONO films composition affects the charge retention capability. More than a certain amount(-3nm) of top-oxide, which can block the hole injection, is required. SiN thickness reduction leads to improved initial rapid charge loss. However, too much thinning sometimes leads to enhanced charge loss in long time bake test. Bottom poly-oxide thinning down to 10nm does not lead to degradation. NO(Nitride-Oxide) double layer structure show large initial rapid charge loss. Even if the ONO structure is adopted, an initial rapid few bits failure is sometimes observed in VLSI memories, when the bottom-oxide layer is thin and its quality is rather poor. These cells must have rather poor quality bottom-oxide, because upper NO structure cannot block the charge loss completely. The ONO composition should be scaled down, considering these key factors concerning charge retention, as well as dielectric reliability.

ACKNOWLEDGEMENT

The authors wish to thank N.Hosokawa, Y.Mikata, K.Ishihara, K.Kanzaki, K.Shinada, T.Usami, M.Shiozaki, T.Yanase, N.Yasuhisa, J.Shiozawa, K.Yamabe, S.Tanaka, S.Tozawa, T.Matsuda, N.Matsukawa, and H.Nozawa for their contributions and helpful discussions. The authors also wish to thank Drs.Y.Nishi, S.Kohyama, O.Ozawa, S.Shinozaki, J.Matsunaga, and M.Wada for their continuous support and encouragement.

REFERENCES

[1]T.Ono, T.Mori, T.Ajioka, and T.Takayashiki, Extended Abstracts of ECS spring meeting, pp.316(1982)
[2]K.Shinada, Y.Nagakubo, K.Yoshikawa, and K.Kanzaki, Extended Abstracts of ECS fall meeting, pp.354(1983)
[3]K.Shinada, S.Mori, and Y.Mikata, J.Electrochem. Soc.,132, pp.2185(1985)
[4]Y.Mikata, S.Mori, K.Shinada, and T.Usami, Proc.1985 IEEE IRPS, pp.32(1985)
[5]T.Ono, T.Mori, T.Ajioka, and T.Takayashiki, IEDM Digest of Technical Papers, pp.380(1985)
[6]K.Yoshikawa, Y.Nagakubo, and K.Kanzaki,Extended Abstracts of the 16th ICSSDM, pp.475(1984)
[7]R.B.Marcus and T.T.Sheng, J.Electrochem.Soc.,129, pp1278(1984)

[8]Y.Sakina, T.Ohno, and S.Matsumoto, Japanese J. Appl. Phys., 22, ppL514(1983)

[9]S.Mori, N.Yasuhisa, T.Yanase, M.Sato, K.Yoshikawa, and H.Nozawa, VLSI Symposium Digest of Technical Papers, pp71(1986)

[10]K.Shinada, N.Matsukawa, S.Morita, Y.Mikata, T.Usami and H.Nozawa, Proc. 1986 IEEE IRPS, pp.247(1986)

[11]S.Mori, Y.Kaneko, N.Arai, Y.Ohshima, H.Araki, K.Narita, E.Sakagami, and K.Yoshikawa, IEEE Non-volatile Semiconductor Memory Workshop, Vail August(1989)

[12]K.Yoshikawa, S.Mori, Y.Kaneko, Y.Ohshima, N.Arai, and E.Sakagami, IEDM Digest of Technical Papers, pp.587(1989)

[13]S.Mori, T.Matsuda, T.Yanase, Y.Mikata, M.Sato, K.Shinada, K.Yoshikawa, and H.Nozawa, VLSI Symposium Digest of Technical Papers, pp.16(1985)

[14]S.Mori, M.Sato, Y.Mikata, T.Yanase, and K.Yoshikawa, VLSI Symposium Digest of Technical Papers, pp.40(1984)

[15]R.D.Katznelson and D.F.Benchokowsky, IEEE Trans. on Electron Devices, vol 27, pp1744(1980)

[16]S.Mori, N.Matsukawa, Y.Kaneko, N.Arai, T.Shinagawa, Y.Suizu, N.Hosokawa, and K.Yoshikawa, IEDM Digest of Technical Papers, pp556(1987)

[17]E.Suzuki, H.Hirahashi, K.Ishii, and Y.Hayashi, IEEE Trans. on Electron Devices, vol 30, pp122(1983)

[18]F.T.Liou and S.O.Chen, IEEE Trans. on Electron Devices, vol 31, pp1736(1984)

[19]M.Aminzadeh, S.Nozaki, and R.V.Gridihar, IEEE Trans. on Electron Devices, vol 35(1988)

[20]Y.Ohji, T.Kusaka, I.Yoshida, A.Hiraiwa, K.Yagi, and K.Mukai, Proc.1987 IEEE IRPS, pp55(1987)

[21]A.Bergemont, S.Deleonibus, G.Guegan, B.Guilliaumot, M.Laurens, and F.Martin, IEDM Digest of Technical Papers, pp591(1989)

[22]S.Mori, Y.Ohshima, E.Sakagami, K.Yoshikawa, and N.Arai, Exteded Abstracts of the 36th Spring Meeting (No.2) of the Japan Society of Applied Physics and Related Societies,pp669(1989)(in Japanese)

[23]A.Nishimura, S.Murata, S.Kuroda, O.Enomoto, H.Kitagawa, and S.Hasegawa, Proc.1989 IEEE IRPS, pp158(1989)

[24]T.Watanabe, A.Menjou, T.Mochizuki, S.Shinozaki, and O.Ozawa, Proc.1985 IEEE IRPS, pp18(1985)

HIGH TEMPERATURE AND EXTENDED ENDURANCE CHARACTERISTICS OF EEROM

Ching S. Jenq, Ting Wong and Bharati Joshi
SEEQ Technology, Inc, San Jose, Ca
and
Chenming Hu
University of California, Berkeley, Ca

ABSTRACT

This paper presents data resulting from an investigation on the endurance characteristics of EEROM cells at elevated temperatures, and on the possibility of extending the endurance of EEROM memory arrays to beyond the current spec of 10K cycles. It will first show that the intrinsic endurance limit of an oxynitride E^2 cell is higher at 125°C than at room temperature due to thermal detrapping of trapped electrons in the tunneling dielectric. The endurance of EEROM memory arrays will be shown to be limited by random defects. Data will be presented to demonstrate that by combining clean processing and proper screening, the endurance spec of EEROM memory arrays can be extended to beyond 100K cycles. It is projected that in the very near future the endurance spec of an EEROM memory array can reach the intrinsic endurance limit of single E^2 cells, which is more than 10^7 cycles.

INTRODUCTION

With the increasing adaptation of electrically erasable and programmable memories (EEROM) in system applications, a very unique characteristic of this class of memory, namely the write/erase cycling endurance, has become one of the most critical reliability parameters. Many studies have been done in the past on this particular subject. However, they are all limited to room temperature testing and less than 10K W/E (write/erase) cycles. In this paper, we extend the investigation of endurance characteristics to that at 125°C, which represents the upper temperature limit of military applications. We will also report the endurance data of a 16K bit EEROM memory after 100K cycles of endurance cycling and discuss the possibility of extending the endurance of EEROM memory to its intrinsic limitation, i.e., beyond 10^7 cycles.

CHARGE TRAPPING AND INTRINSIC ENDURANCE
At 125°C

It has been shown[1] that the intrinsic endurance characteristics of EEROM cells is limited by the build-up of negative charges in the tunneling dielectrics, and that the negative charges are caused by the trapping of injection electrons into the pre-existed electron traps of the dielectric as well as the traps that are generated during the W/E cycling owing to the high electrical stress on the dielectric. This model applies to all types of tunneling dielectrics, particularly SiO_2 and oxynitride. Comparing to SiO_2, oxynitride exhibits much less negative charge trapping[2]. As a consequence, the intrinsic endurance of an oxynitride E^2 cell is extended by more than a factor of 10 to beyond 10^7 cycles. To examine the effect of temperature, it is natural that one investigate first the negative charge trapping at elevated temperatures.

The samples used in the study are oxynitride capacitors with N-doped polysilicon gate. The dielectric thickness is 100A°. The film is formed by first growing a layer of thermal SiO_2 in dry O_2 ambient, followed by a high temperature NH_3 annealing. The area of the capacitors is 2500u². Using a standard technique[1] of constant current stress, in which a constant current is forced through the capacitor while simultaneously the terminal voltage developed across the capacitor is monitored, the amount of negative charge trapping can be determined as a function of total injected charges. The result is plotted in Fig. 1 for stresses performed at both 25°C and 125°C. It clearly demonstrates that at 125°C, the amount of negative charge trapping is in fact less than that at 125°C.

As a consequence of reduced charge trapping at 125°C, the intrinsic endurance of an E^2 cell is expected to be better. This is shown in Fig. 2, where the write and erase thresholds of typical E^2 cells are compared between 25°C and 125°C. Less reduction in cell threshold window, if not

Reprinted from the *IEDM Tech. Dig.*, pp. 585–588, 1983.

by much, is indeed demonstrated at 125°C, implying a slightly improved intrinsic endurance.

To further study the effect of temperature on charge trapping, a particular oxynitride run-split was chosen, which had a higher electron trap concentration than that of a typical production oxynitride film. The cell is first cycled with 10^7 W/E pulses, causing the threshold window to reduce as shown in Fig. 3(a). The reduction is clearly more than that of a normal oxynitride cell, as shown in Fig. 1(a). The cell is then baked at 250°C, and the threshold window is monitored as a function of time. The result is plotted in Fig. 4. It is clear that the 250°C bake has caused some trapped electrons in the oxynitride to detrap, which in turn leads to the opening-up of threshold window. The semi-logrithmic plot cannot be approximated by a single-slope linear fit, indicating that the process of thermal detrapping may involve multiple trap species. The cell is then cycled again to 10^7 W/E cycles, as shown in Fig. 4(b). The cell window begins to reduce rapidly at around 1000 W/E cycles, which is much earlier than that of a fresh sample. This indicates the existence of more electron traps after prolonged W/E cycling, as in accordance with the trap generation theory[1][2], and that either all or some of these generated traps cannot be thermally annealed.

RANDOM DEFECTS AND STRESS FAILURE

Although charge trapping sets the limit of intrinsic endurance, endurance failures in EEROM memory array are more often caused by problems associated with random defects. This phenomenon can also be seen in tunneling capacitors. A group of oxynitride capacitors with a worse-than-average stress failure is chosen for the study. The capacitors have an area of $2500u^2$, and a thickness of 100A°. They were stressed with a constant current source until breakdown. The voltage increment, ΔV, across the capacitor at the time of breakdown is then plotted against the total amount of injected charges, as shown in Fig. 5. Since ΔV is proportional to the amount of trapped charges, it is a direct measure of charge trapping. Fig. 5 clearly shows that although the capacitors demonstrate different stress endurance, the amount of charge trapping in a capacitor that can be stressed to, say, 9 coul/cm of charge injection is essentially the same as that in a capacitor that can take only, say, 3 to 4 coul/cm^2. It implies that the stress failure of these capacitors is not caused by charge trapping, but rather, is due to some defect-related phenomena.

EXTENDED ENDURANCE OF EEROM

The presently available EEROM memory arrays all have an endurance spec of 10^4 W/E cycles, which is limited, obviously, not by the intrinsic endurance characteristics of the cell itself, but by random defects which often cause certain bits in the array to fail before they reach the intrinsic limitation. These defects can be minimized by clean processing and can mostly be screened out by proper screening procedures. A very effective way of screening is to stress the array with W/E cycling and follow with a high temperature bake to catch bits that show early signs of charge leakage. In comparison with SiO_2, we have found that oxynitride exhibits not only less charge trapping, but also less susceptibility to defects. Shown in Fig. 6 is the endurance failure rate of a 16K EEROM memory. At each data point, a high temperature bake is performed to accelerate any potential endurance failure. The failure rate is extremely low and keeps a decreasing trend to beyond 100K cycles.

A more detailed look on endurance is shown in Fig. 7, where the threshold voltage of the worst bit in the memory array of several 16K bit EEROM's is plotted against the number of W/E cycles. Due to the circuit limitation, the test boundary is 6V from the erase state and 0V for the written state. It is clear that even with up to 100K of W/E cycles, every single bit in the array still maintains a threshold window of more than 6V. This demonstrates that the combination of clean processing and proper screening can effectively eliminate parts that contain defects, and push the endurance limit of the good EEROM arrays to well beyond the current 10K limit to more than 100K W/E cycles. We project that in the very near future, the endurance of EEROM's will approach its intrinsic limit, which is more than 10^7 W/E cycles for the case of oxynitride.

As a footnote, a cycling experiment has also been conducted at 125°C, followed by the examination of the worst-bit threshold margin. A similar result is seen as that in Fig. 7. This is consistent with the previous discussions on single-cell endurance at 125°C.

CONCLUSIONS

It has been shown that at elevated temperatures, or 125°C, to be exact, the intrinsic endurance of an E^2 cell is improved over that at room temperature. This is caused by the reduction of negative charge trapping in the tunneling dielectric owing to thermal detrapping.

The endurance characteristics of EEROM memory array is mainly limited by defects rather than charge trapping. However, by combining clean processing and proper screening procedures, the endurance of an existing 16K EEROM is shown to be extended to beyond 100K cycles with extremely low failure rate. Examination of the worst-bit threshold margin indicates that further extension of the endurance characteristics to reach the intrinsic limit of more than 10^7 cycles is possible and will be accomplished in the very near future. Finally, the cycling experiment at 125°C indicates that no difference in endurance data can be expected from room temperature results.

REFERENCES

(1) C.S. Jenq, T.R. Rangarath, C.H. Huang, H.S. Jones and T.L. Chang, IEDM81, 388 (1981).

(2) C.S. Jenq, T.L. Chiu, B. Joshi and J. Hu, IEDM82, 811 (1982).

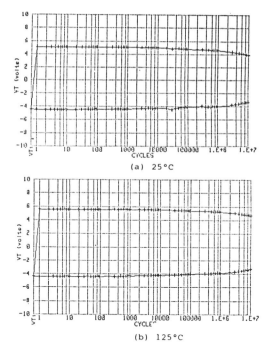

(a) 25°C

(b) 125°C

Fig. 2. Effect of Temperature on the Endurance of Single EEROM Cells. Plotted are W/E Threshold Window vs. Number of W/E Cycles.

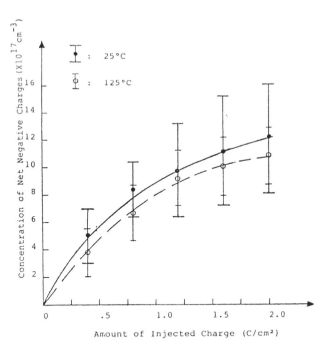

Fig. I. Effect of Temperature on Charge Trapping in Oxynitride

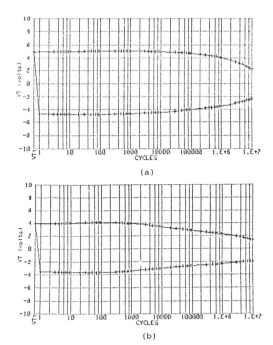

(a)

(b)

Fig. 3. (a) Endurance characteristics of a single cell with higher-than-normal electron trap concentration.
(b) Endurance characteristics of the same cell as in (a) after it was cycled for 10^7 W/E cycles and baked at 250°C for 46 hours.

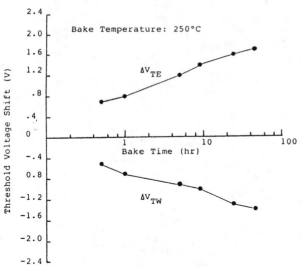

Fig. 4. Threshold-window widening of
the cell of Fig. 3(a) as a
function of bake time at 250°C.
ΔV_{TE}: Increment of cell threshold
at erase state.
ΔV_{TW}: Increment of cell threshold
at written state.

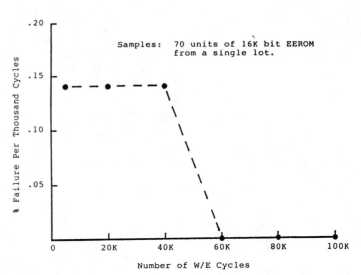

Fig. 6. Endurance failure rate of 16K
bit EEROM's. The failure rate
is accelerated with high temperature bake (250°C/1 hr.).

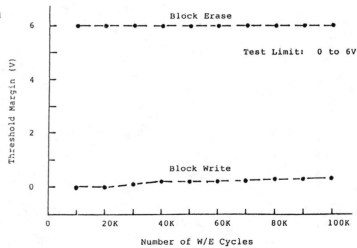

Fig. 7. Worst-Bit Margin of a 16K Bit EEROM

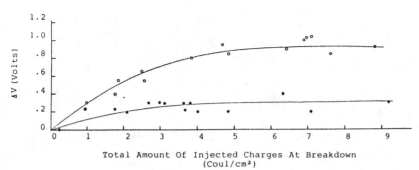

Fig. 5. Increase in terminal voltages at the time
of capacitor breakdown vs the total amount
of injected charges. Solid dots are for
negative, and open dots for positive current
stress.

THIN OXIDE RELIABILITY
(Invited Paper)

Chenming Hu

Department of Electrical Engineering and Computer Sciences
and the Electronics Research Laboratory
University of California, Berkeley, California 94720

ABSTRACT

Dielectric breakdown and oxide and interface charge trapping set the scaling limits for thin oxides. Oxide leakage is far from being the limit. Dielectric breakdown is modeled by hole trapping at "weak" sites with local, above-average current density or large hole trap density. This model predicts a linear relationship between ln t_{BD} and $1/F$ rather than E. It provides a framework for predicting oxide reliability as a function of area and stress condition from limited data. Using this model and the field experience of thin-oxide EEPROM, it is estimated that 0.01% failure per thousand hour is achievable with 9.5 nm oxides at 5V. This is adequate for 1M-bit DRAMs. Charge trapping and interface trap generation sets a slightly less restrictive limit for gate oxides. "Defect" reduction holds promise for improving oxide reliability. New dielectrics will probably be necessary at 4M-bit level unless 10 μm^2 capacitors are available or cell operation is changed. 6.5 μm oxide should be acceptable for 3.3V operation. Again EEPROMs will provide the real-life test for production thin oxide at that thickness.

INTRODUCTION-TWO CATEGORIES OF RELIABILITY CONCERNS

It is now commonplace to use gate oxides as thin as 20 nm; DRAM oxide thickness is below 15 nm; and EEPROM tunneling oxide is less than 10 nm thick. MOSFET current gain continues to increase with decreasing oxide thicknesses even below 5 nm without surprises such as mobility drop-off [1]. 4 Mbit DRAM will require 4.4 nm capacitor oxide or its equivalent unless three-dimensional capacitors are used [2]. EEPROM needs thin tunneling oxides in order to use a low programming voltage. Given such incentives, oxide thickness will surely continue to trend downward.

Thin oxide reliability concerns may be divided into two categories -- dielectric breakdown and MOSFET degradation. Dielectric breakdown is a concern for all thin oxide applications and encompasses such issues as the time-zero breakdown voltage (ramp voltage test), time-dependent dielectric breakdown (TDDB), "defect" versus "intrinsic" breakdown, and "leaky" oxide. MOSFET degradation results from field-stress-induced charge trapping in the oxide or at the interface (interface state generation). To the first order, charge trapping does not represent a reliability problem for the DRAM capacitor oxide or even the EEPROM tunneling oxide.

A DIELECTRIC BREAKDOWN MODEL

Recent research at Berkeley [3] has supported the "impact-ionization" model [4,5] and suggested some modifications. In the modified model, electrons injected form the cathode into the oxide by Fowler-Nordheim tunneling generate holes via impact ionization (or some other mechanism). Holes are trapped near the cathode causing an increase in the cathode field (see Fig. 1) and hence an increase in the electron current density, which leads to increased hole generation rate. This positive feedback eventually causes breakdown. Breakdown, of course, occurs at localized weak areas, where the feedback gain is higher due to reduced oxide thickness or

large hole trap density, etc. Notice that our model (Fig. 1) also considers electron trapping [3,6].

Figure 2 compares the I-V characteristics of a ramp-voltage test predicted by this model and the experimental result. The model predicts the current rise, saturation (due to electron trapping) and breakdown very well. While the weak area occupies only 10^{-6} of the total area [3] and carries 10^{-6} of the total current initially (dotted curve in Fig. 2), the positive feedback in the weak area eventually leads to oxide breakdown. Notice that the ratio of weak area to the total area is obviously quite unimportant for the prediction of the breakdown voltage. Roughly speaking, breakdown occurs when the trapped hole density Q_{ot}^+ reaches a certain critical value, i.e. when

$$Q_{crit}^+ = Q_{ot}^+ \propto \eta \int J(E)\alpha(E)dt$$

$$\propto \eta \int e^{-(B+H)/E} dt \qquad (1)$$

where η is a "weakness factor" representing the local high hole trapping efficiency or local current enhancement; E is the oxide field; $J \propto e^{-B/E}$ is the Fowler-Nordheim electron current density, and $\alpha \propto e^{-H/E}$ is the coefficient of impact ionization. $B \approx 230$ MV/cm and $\alpha \approx 80$ MV/cm [3,7].

ACCELERATED TESTING OF TIME-DEPENDENT DIELECTRIC BREAKDOWN

According to Eq. (1), the time-to-breakdown under constant field stressing is

$$t_{BD} \approx \frac{A}{\eta} e^{(B+H)/E} \qquad (2)$$

Figure 3 shows that measured t_{BD} indeed follows Eq. (2), i.e. ln t_{BD} is a linear function of 1/E. In the ln t_{BD} vs E curve in Fig. 3, the slope, i.e. the "field acceleration factor" [8-12] is obviously a function of E. This is the main reason for the wide range of a acceleration factors reported in the literature as illustrated in Fig. 4. We propose that ln t_{BD} vs 1/E is a better plot for extrapolating the oxide lifetime from accelerated test data. The ln t_{BD} vs E plot leads to underestimation of the oxide lifetime.

Charge-to-breakdown is

$$Q_{BD} \approx J \cdot t_{BD} \approx \frac{K}{\eta} e^{H/E} \qquad (3)$$

For a ramp-field test, the field at breakdown is [7]

$$\frac{1}{E_{BD}} \approx \frac{K + \ln \eta}{B + H} \qquad (4)$$

CHARACTERIZATION OF THE WEAKNESS FACTOR OR OXIDE DEFECTS

The only variable in Eqs. (2), (3), and (4) is the weakness factor η [7]. η is the collective representation of local thickness

Reprinted from the *IEDM Tech. Dig.*, pp. 368–371, 1985.

reduction, barrier height reduction, or interface asperities which cause field enhancement, or local high efficiency of hole trapping, etc. If an oxide sample contains a high-η spot this sample will breakdown early. "Pinholes," early failures, and "intrinsic" breakdown are all reflections of or can be represented by weak factors of different magnitude. Indeed, we can define a defect density, $D(\eta)$, such that $D(\eta)\Delta\eta$ is the density (per cm^2) of weak spots, or defects, having weakness factors between η and $\eta + \Delta\eta$. If $D(\eta)$ is known, one can easily model the distribution of t_{BD} for any oxide area similar to IC yield modeling [13]. Every histogram or cumulative failure rate plot of t_{BD}, Q_{BD}, or E_{BD} is but a reflection of $D(\eta)$.

It can be shown [13] that the log-normal portion of Fig. 5 or the early breakdown corresponds to

$$D(\eta) \propto \eta^{-a} \qquad (5)$$

These failures have been correlated with particulate contaminations [14,15], heavy metal precipitates in the starting silicon material [15], and stacking faults [16] (the latter two observations could be related). Equation (5) is a familiar form for the size distribution of particulates. Perhaps there is also a power-law relationship between the density and the size of metal precipitates in silicon. The "intrinsic breakdown" portion of Fig. 5 is due to either thickness variations or very small particulates. Figure 5 shows that distributions of ln t_{BD} and E_{BD} are strikingly similar as they both reflect the distribution of η according to EQs. (2) and (4). A graph that maps the E_{BD} test (a simple test) results to the t_{BD} (a lengthy test) results may be generated [7] from Fig. 5 or by eliminating η between Eqs. (2) and (4).

MAXIMUM ACCEPTABLE OXIDE FIELD

As the "defect" density $D(\eta)$ is reduced through process and material improvements, higher oxide fields will be acceptable. Nevertheless, it would be very useful for technology scaling to know the "acceptable oxide field," if it exists, of state-of-the-art thin oxides. Accelerated tests have provided values of 2 MV/cm to 5 MV/cm [8-12]. This range is too wide for technology projection. Furthermore, the values have no support from field experience or quantity production.

There is one product that employs ~10 nm oxides and has been mass produced by several manufacturers for a few years -- floating-gate EEPROM. Single-cell ("intrinsic") oxide breakdown occurs after 10^7 program/erase cycles corresponding to $Q_{BD} \approx 10$ coul/cm^2 at E = 12 MV/cm in good agreement with laboratory capacitor test data [7]. After suitable screening, a 64 K-bit EEPROM with ~2×10^5 μm^2 of thin oxide area has a program/erase cycle specification of 10^4 cycles (or 10^{-2} coul/cm^2) for a cumulative failure rate of a few percent with an approximately constant failure rate. If we reduce this cumulative failure by 10 (to 10^{-3} coul/cm^2 at 12 MV/cm) and spread it over a 10 year lifecycle, we can achieve better than 0.01% per 1000 hour. The maximum acceptable oxide field is the solution of the following simultaneous equations (Eq. (3) and Ref. 7, E in MV/cm)

$$Q_{BD} = 10^{-3} e^{H/ E-H/ 12} = 10^{-3} e^{40/ E-40/ 12} \qquad (6)$$

$$Q_{BD} \approx J \cdot t = 10^6 E^2 e^{-230/ E} \cdot 3 \times 10^8 \qquad (7)$$

The solution is E = 5.7 MV/cm and Q_{BD} = 4 × 10^{-2} coul/cm^2. While 2×10^5 μm^2 thin oxide area is sufficient for a medium sized logic circuit. A 4M-bit DRAM may require ~ 4×10^7 μm^2 of oxide [2]. The 10^{-3} factor in Eq. (6) has to be replaced by 5×10^{-6}. The solution is E = 5.3 MV/cm at Q_{BD} = 6 × 10^{-4} coul/cm^2. From accelerated testing, Hokari [12] also concluded that 10 nm thick oxide could have 10 year life at 5 MV/cm.

FIELD-INDUCED MOSFET DEGRADATION

Channel hot-carrier induced MOSFET degradation has been well documented [17]. To the extent that the rate of degradation depends on the oxide and interface quality or technology. This may

be considered an oxide reliability issue. However, channel field reduction via the use of lightly-doped-drain (LDD) and other means is a more practical and effective way to deal with the hot-carrier-induced degardation.

Here we only consider the charge trapping and interface states generation induced by stressing the gate oxide with the drain shorted to the source [6,18]. Figure 6a shows the three identifiable charge components vs the Fowler-Nordheim current fluence (Jt/q) and Fig. 6b shows their influences on surface mobility, threshold voltage, and subthreshold current swing [6]. It appears that the cumulative fluence during the device lifetime must not exceed 10^{17} cm^{-2} for a cumulative charge passage of 1.6×10^{-2} coul/ cm^2 at ~ 10 MV/cm. At ~ 5 MV/cm, ten times higher may be accepted. This is only slightly larger than the Q_{BD} at the maximum acceptable oxide field (Sec. V). These two reliability concerns, then, set similar field limits.

THE PRACTICAL LIMIT OF OXIDE THICKNESS

Figure 7 outlines the practical limits of oxide thickness. Starting from the top, tunneling leakage current limit is taken to be 10^{-6} A/cm -- one tenth of the junction leakage current. This sets a limit of 60 Å for 5V operation. Field-induced MOSFET degradation (Sec. VI) sets a limit at 10^{17} per cm^2 per year (for 10^{18} cm^{-2} in ten years). Dielectric breakdown (Sec. V) sets a limit at 4×10^{14} per cm^2 per year (for $Q_{BD} = 6 \times 10^{-4}$ coul/cm^2 in 10 years). The lowest limit is expectedly set by dielectric breakdown at 9.5 nm for 5V operation (or E = 5.3 MV/cm). The discrepancy between the thickness value (9.5 nm) and Fig. 8 is due to band bending in silicon which consumed part of the applied V_g in Fig. 7.

One other limit in Fig. 7 is set at J = 10^{-15} A/ cm^2 for 10 year data retention in EEPROM. This limit, together the signal voltage that is desired to remain across the thin oxide after 10 year data storage. For example, if 3V signal voltage is desired, 6.5 nm is needed.

Reliability date is scarce for oxides thinner than 8 nm. Q_{BD} is known to become very large (> 10^4 coul/ cm^2) when the oxide is very thin (~ 3 nm) and operated in or near the direct tunneling regime. Charge trapping becomes less important in very thin oxides due to detrapping and lower rates of trap generation [1]. Dielectric breakdown roughly follows the same trend as the thicker oxides (Fig. 8) and will probably set the bottom limit around 6.5 nm for 3.3V operation.

SUMMARY

Dielectric breakdown is a result of hole trapping at local weak area. Each weak area is characterized by a weakness factor, η, which represents the relative rate of hole trapping. η may be large because of local high oxide field or large hole trap density, which in turn may be the results of particulate contamination or thickness variations, etc. The oxide reliability is fully defined by the defect density function, $D(\eta)$. This model suggests that ln t_{BD} is proportional to 1/E, not E. It suggests a way to correlate the simple ramp field test and the time-consuming time-dependent breakdown test. From the field and production experiences of floating-gate EEPROM, the acceptable oxide field for 10 year breakdown lifetime is estimated to be 5.3 MV/cm, or 9.5 nm for 5V operation. A similar limit is set by field-induced MOSFET degradation. 6.5 nm may be acceptable at 3.3V.

Further reduction of particulates in air and in chemicals holds promise for improving thin oxide reliability. Thicker oxides have been shown to benefit dramatically from gettering before oxidation [11].

New dielectrics, in which hole generation and trapping rates are lower, perhaps together with very thin layers of oxides, in which electrons cannot gain sufficient energy to create holes will probably be developed for DRAM capacitors. This is so because capacitor oxides, unlike gate oxides, are not being limited by charge trapping and interface states and because simple oxide, without breakthrough will not meet the need of 4M-bit DRAM unless 3-D capacitors are used. The dielectric breakdown problem can be dramatically eased by biasing the top plate midway between the high and low voltages.

Thinner tunneling oxides (~ 6.5 nm) will be used in EEPROMs for high speed programming or for reduced programming voltage. This will again provide a real-life test for the next generation production thin oxides.

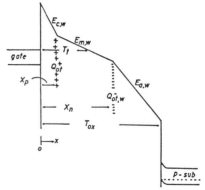

Fig. 1. SiO₂ energy diagram showing trapped holes, Q_{ot}^+. Field and current enhancement due to Q_{ot}^+ eventually leads to breakdown.

ACKNOWLEDGEMENT

My sincerest thanks go to Ih-Chin Chen for providing several figures and much data for this paper. I also borrowed from the published work by Steve Hollanmd and Mong-Song Liang. Dr. Wayne Bailey of Texas Instrument provided the samples for Fig. 5. This research was supported by the Innovative Science and Technology Office of the Strategic Defense Initiative Organization administered through the Office of Naval Research and by Advanced Micro Devices, Rockwell International, and Texas Instruments.

REFERENCES

[1] M.S. Liang, J.Y. Choi, P.K. Ko, C. Hu, Technical Digest of 1984 IEDM, pp. 152-155.

[2] W.P. Noble, W.W. Walker, IEEE Circuits and Devices Magazine, Vol. 1, Jan. 1985, pp. 45-51.

[3] I.C. Chen, S.E. Holland, and C. Hu, IEEE Trans. Electron Devices, Vol. 32, Feb. 1985, pp. 413-322.

[4] T.H. DiStefano and M. Shatzkes, Appl. Phys. Lett., Vol. 25, Dec. 1974, p. 685.

[5] I. Kashat and N. Klein, J. Appl. Phys., Vol. 48, Dec. 1977, p. 5217.

[6] M.S. Liang, et.al., IEEE Trans. Electron Devices, Vol. ED-31, Sept. 1984, pp. 1238-1244.

[7] I.C. Chen, S. Holland, and C. Hu, presented at International Reliability Physics Symposium, March 1985.

[8] D.L. Crook, Proc. Int. Reliability Phys. Symp., 1979, p. 1.

[9] A. Berman, Proc. Int. Reliability Phys. Symp., 1981, p. 204.

[10] D. Bagles, Proc. Int. Reliability Phys. Symp., 1984.

[11] K. Yamabe and K. Taniguchi, IEEE Trans. Electron Devices, Vol. ED-32, Feb. 1985, pp. 423.

[12] Y. Hokari, T. Baba, and N. Kawamura, Proc. Int. Reliability Symp., 1982, p. 46.

[13] To be published.

[14] J.R. Monkowsik and R.T. Zahour, Proc. Int. Reliability Phys. Symp., Apr. 1982, p. 244.

[15] K. Yamake, K. Taniguchi, and Y. Matsushita, Proc. Inter. Rel. Phys. Symp., 1983, pp. 184-190.

[16] P.S.D. Lin, R.B. Marcus, and T.T. Sheng, J. Electrochem. Soc., Vol. 130, Sept. 1983, p. 1878.

[17] C. Hu, et.al., IEEE Trans. Electron Devices, Vol. ED-32, Feb. 1985, pp. 375-385.

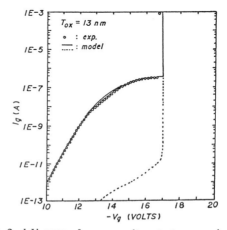

Fig. 2. I-V curve of a ramp-voltage test measured and predicted by the model. The dotted curve is the current carried by the weak area, which is responsible for breakdown.

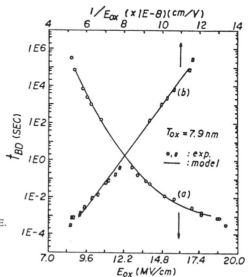

Fig. 3. log (t_{BD}) is a linear function of 1/E, not E.

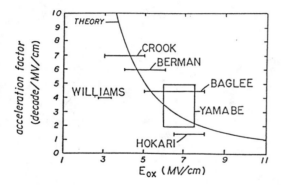

Fig. 4. "Field Acceleration Factor," the slope of the log(t_{BD}) vs E curve is not a constant but a function of E. This explains the divergence among most of the published reports.

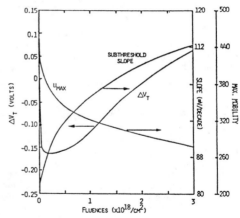

Fig. 6b. Trapped charge and interface traps cause the mobility, capacitance and subthreshold swing to degrade much like hot-carrier-induced degradations.

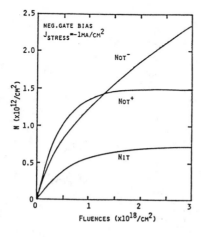

Fig. 5. The distributions of log(t_{BD}) and E_{BD} resemble each other because they both reflect the distribution of η.

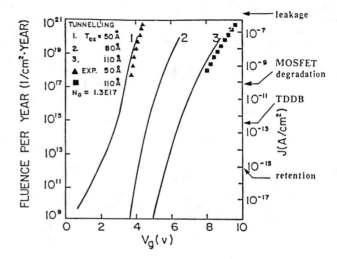

Fig. 7. The oxide thickness is limited by dielectric breakdown to 9.5 nm for 5V and 6.5 nm for 3.3V.

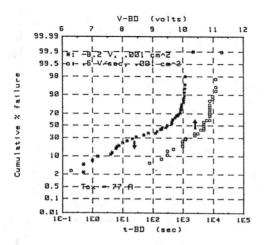

Fig. 6a. Charge trapping and interface state generation due to Fowler-Nordheim Stressing of a 10 nm gate oxide.

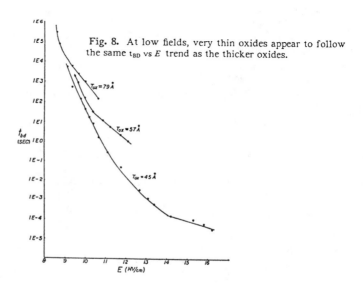

Fig. 8. At low fields, very thin oxides appear to follow the same t_{BD} vs E trend as the thicker oxides.

CONDUCTION IN THERMAL OXIDES GROWN ON POLYSILICON AND ITS INFLUENCE ON FLOATING GATE EEPROM DEGRADATION

G. Groeseneken and H.E. Maes

ESAT-Laboratory, Katholieke Universiteit Leuven
Kardinaal Mercierlaan 94, 3030 Heverlee, Belgium

ABSTRACT

A new model is presented which describes the electrical conduction in thermal oxides grown on polysilicon. The model is based on a well-considered non-uniform distribution of field enhancement factors at the polysilicon-polyoxide interface, combined with the conventional Fowler-Nordheim current injection and a first order kinetic trapping model. It is found that the current-voltage behaviour measured in oxides during consecutive voltage ramps can only be explained quantitatively by this model. From this analysis it is shown that polyoxides have nearly the same trapping properties as oxides grown on single crystalline silicon. Furthermore, the model was used to investigate the degradation of floating gate EEPROM cells, relying on polyoxide conduction. It is shown that, in spite of the good trapping properties of the oxide layer itself, the number of write/erase cycles is mainly limited by the non-uniformity of the field enhancement.

INTRODUCTION

The conductivity of oxides thermally grown on polycrystalline silicon is known to be much higher than the conductivity of oxides grown on single crystalline silicon (1). This feature is successfully applied in some types of floating gate EEPROM's for programming and/or erasing of the non-volatile memory device (2). The increased conduction has been qualitatively explained in recent years by the injection field enhancement caused by the surface roughness of the polysilicon-polyoxide interface (3,4). A model that is able to explain and to predict the experimentally observed injection current behaviour in a quantitative way is however missing. Different attempts have been made but these models were inaccurate because they either considered only one mean enhancement factor for the complete injection area (5) or/and they neglected the effect of electron trapping, which made them useless in the modeling of EEPROM degradation (6).

This paper introduces a new model which satisfactorily explains the injection current behaviour including the effects of charge trapping in the oxide layer. The model is verified by using two types of current measurements, referred to as the ramp I-V, where the current is measured as a function of the linearly ramped gate voltage, and the step I-t, where the current is recorded as a function of time after application of a voltage step.

Since the complete current behaviour, including the effect of electron trapping in the oxide, can be described by the model, it has been used in the study of the degradation behaviour of floating gate EEPROM memory cells, that are relying on this type of conduction.

THE MODEL

The new conduction model starts from the well-known Fowler-Nordheim tunnel injection current

$$J = C \, E_{inj}^2 \, \exp \, (-E_c/E_{inj}) \qquad (1)$$

where E_{inj} is the electrical field at the polysilicon-polyoxide interface, and C and E_c are the Fowler-Nordheim conduction parameters. The injection field is calculated as the average field in the oxide, multiplied by a field enhancement factor μ. The values of these enhancement factors are distributed over the area of the capacitor according to a well-considered distribution. Finally, electron trapping in the oxide is accounted for by using a first order kinetic trapping model, introducing a density of trapping centers N_t and a capture cross section σ :

$$\frac{\partial n_t}{\partial t} = \frac{\sigma J}{q} (N_t - n_t) \qquad (2)$$

The trapped electron density obtained from the solution of this equation is then used again in the calculation of the injection field E_{inj}. The non-uniform current distribution, caused by a non-uniformity of the field enhancement factor, is essential in this model, and is due to the fact that the field enhancement at an interface asperity is obviously a function of the location on the asperity (4). Different distribution schemes have been investigated but it was found that the exponential decreasing distribution,

$$P(\mu) = \frac{1}{\mu_0(1-e^{-\frac{\mu_{max}-1}{\mu_0}})} \, e^{-\frac{\mu-1}{\mu_0}} \qquad (3)$$

Reprinted from the *IEDM Tech. Dig.*, pp. 476–479, 1984.

where μ_o is a characteristic exponent factor and μ_{max} is the maximum enhancement factor, gives by far the best fitting results. The distribution function is shown in fig. 1 for $\mu_{max}=10$ and different values of μ_o. The corresponding variation of the enhancement factor μ as a function of the location on an asperity is shown on fig. 2. Equations (1)-(3) are combined into a calculation sequence, executed by a computer program, that is able to simulate different measurement procedures, such as the ramp I-V, step I-t, EEPROM erasing and degradation.

EXPERIMENTAL RESULTS

As an example, fig. 3 compares the experimental and the calculated current densities for a ramp I-V measurement on an 80 nm thick polyoxide. The results for two consecutive ramps are shown. Through model fitting, the trapping probability $P_t = \sigma N_t t_{ox}$ was found to be 4×10^{-5}, which is comparable with trapping probabilities, measured in oxides grown on single crystalline silicon. The characteristic exponential factor for the enhancement factor distribution is 0.6 and the maximum enhancement factor is 8, which corresponds to values found by others (4). Obviously, the experimental behaviour is excellently simulated by the new model. For the first time the typical difference of the current voltage behaviour during the first ramp and consecutive ramps and the characteristic voltage dependence in the trapping regime could be quantitatively modelled. This is impossible if only 1 enhancement factor is used instead of a distribution of enhancement factors. This is illustrated on fig. 4, where a uniform μ of 4 over a 0.1% area is considered. Obviously the current behaviour is fundamentally different for the uniform case. A steep pure Fowler-Nordheim-like current behaviour is followed by a flat part, caused by the electron trapping. Such a behaviour has never been observed on polyoxides. Fig. 5 shows ramp I-V measurements on samples, fabricated using different oxidation temperatures. It is found that for increasing temperatures the characteristic enhancement factor μ_o decreases, resulting in orders of magnitude lower currents, while the trapping probability increases. The parameters obtained from the ramp I-V fitting have then been used in the simulation of the step I-t measurement. An example of the comparison between experiments and model prediction is shown on fig. 6 for two applied voltages. In all cases, both measurements could be simulated with the same parameters, proving the validity of the model.

EEPROM DEGRADATION

Since the complete current behaviour, including electron trapping in the oxide is described by this model, it can be used in studying the degradation behaviour of floating gate EEPROM memory cells which rely on this type of conduction. Fig. 7 shows the results of both the experimental and the calculated degradation, using parameters, extracted from a ramp I-V measurement on a capacitor on the same chip. Also shown by the dashed line are the results from the calculation, assuming uniform injection. From this figure it can be concluded that the maximum number of cycles that can be allowed is strongly affected by the non-uniform nature of the polyoxide current, in spite of the good trapping properties of the oxide layer itself.

CONCLUSION

The new conduction model that takes into account the non-uniformity of field enhancement factors together with electron trapping, leads to a better understanding of the current behaviour observed in polyoxides. It allows to quantify the oxide and the polysilicon-polyoxide interface quality, therefore enabling improvement by adapting processing conditions. Finally, it is able to predict the endurance of a memory cell, relying on this type of conduction.

ACKNOWLEDGEMENT

The authors are supported by the Belgian National Foundation for Scientific Research (NFWO).

REFERENCES

(1) D.J. DiMaria and D.R. Kerr, Appl. Phys. Lett., 27 (9) 505 (1975).

(2) R. Klein, W.H. Owen, R.T. Simko, W.E. Tchon, Electronics, October 11 (1979).

(3) R.M. Anderson and D.R. Kerr, J. Appl. Phys., 48 (11) 4834 (1977).

(4) H.S. Lee and S.P. Marin, J. Appl. Phys., 51 (7) 3746 (1980).

(5) P.A. Heimann, S.P. Murarka and T.T. Sheng, J. Appl. Phys., 53 (9) 6240 (1982).

(6) R.K. Ellis, H.A.R. Wegener, J.M. Caywood, IEDM Tech. Dig. 1982, p. 749 (1982).

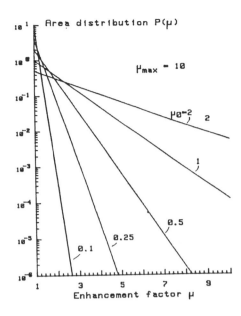

Fig.1. Area distribution of enhancement factors for different values of μ_o.

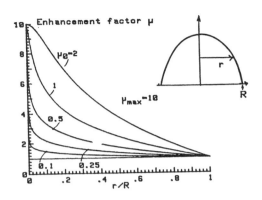

Fig. 2. Enhancement factor variation on the asperity, according to the distribution of fig. 1.

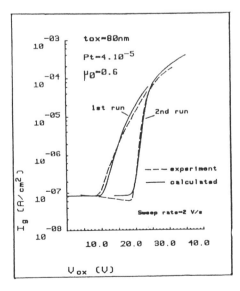

Fig.3. Comparison of the experiments and model calculations of the current for two consecutive voltage ramps.

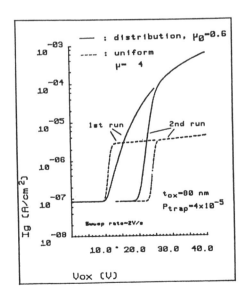

Fig. 4. Comparison of the model calculations and of the results when assuming a mean enhancement factor.

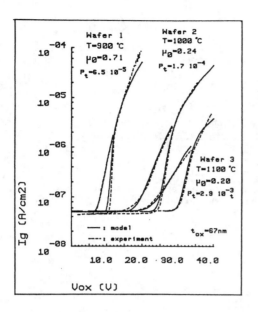

Fig. 5. Comparison of experiments and model
calculations for the ramp I-V for
different oxidation temperatures.

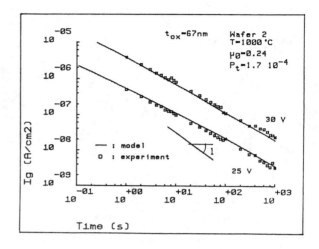

Fig. 6. Comparison of experiments and model predictions for the step I-t behaviour.

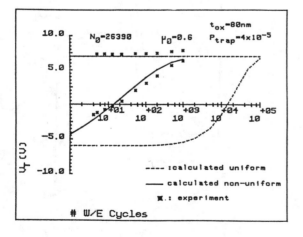

OXIDES GROWN ON TEXTURED SINGLE-CRYSTAL SILICON FOR
LOW PROGRAMMING VOLTAGE NON-VOLATILE MEMORY APPLICATIONS

Y. Fong, A.T. Wu, R. Moazzami, P.K. Ko, and C. Hu

Department of Electrical Engineering and Computer Sciences
University of California, Berkeley
Berkeley, CA

ABSTRACT: Oxides grown on textured single-crystal silicon (TSC oxides) have been fabricated for use in low programming voltage non-volatile memories.   A 230 A TSC oxide exhibited enhanced electron injection in both polarities, reducing the voltage necessary for J_g = +1 mA/cm^2 from 21 V for normal (untextured) 230 Å oxides to 5 V.   This made the 230 Å TSC oxide equivalent to a 55 A normal oxide.   Charge-to-breakdown (Q_{BD}) measurement show a larger intrinsic Q_{BD} and also a much better Q_{BD} histogram (for 1.1 mm^2 capacitors) for the 230 A TSC oxide than for 230 A and 60 A normal oxides.

Presently, floating-gate EEPROMs are fabricated with either very thin tunnel oxides or thicker oxides grown on polycrystalline silicon (Polyoxides).   For very thin tunnel oxides, careful growth of the 100 A oxide is required to avoid early oxide breakdown due to defects.   Further scaling of the oxide thickness for lower programming voltages may be difficult .   Polyoxides, which utilize the electric field enhancement at the polysilicon-oxide interface, can be thicker (600A).   Polyoxides have higher electron trapping rates and memory window closing due to electron trapping limits the memory endurance. Future scaling of the polyoxide thickness for lower programming voltages is not straightforward since the enhanced electron injection effect is reduced for thinner polyoxides. We report here the electrical properties and integrity of oxides grown on textured single-crystal silicon (TSC oxides),   showing that TSC oxides can overcome limitations of both very thin tunnel oxides and thicker polyoxides.

Texturing of the single-crystal surface was carried out in a plasma parallel plate reactor with a gas mixture of CCl$_4$/O$_2$/He.   The silicon surface was etched to a depth of approximately 500 A.   Increasing the O$_2$ content increased the surface roughness. Fig. 1 shows the effects of etching the surface through a 170 A sacrificial oxide with and without an As implant. Also shown are results from etching the bare silicon (without an oxide) and that of a normal oxide. Etching through the 170 A sacrificial oxide increased the surface roughness because of the preferential etching of silicon over oxide (i.e. any non-uniformity when etching the oxide will be magnified when the silicon is etched). This caused the slightly greater enhanced injection. The As implantation of the oxide is believed to improve the uniformity across the wafer and also increase the number of weak oxide areas thus increasing the density of the enhanced injection regions or "bumps". This led to the higher capacitance and the larger Q_{BD}. Fig. 2 shows SEM photographs of the textured surface before oxidation.   Visual examination of the etched areas revealed a shiny surface.

Figs. 3-6 compare the electrical characteristics a 230 A TSC oxide (Fig. 1 case (I)) and those of a 230 A and a 60 A normal oxides. The enhanced electron injection at the textured substrate-oxide interface (positive V_g) reduced the average electric field necessary for J_g = +1 mA/cm^2 from 9.1 MV/cm for the normal oxides to 2.2 MV/cm (Fig. 3). Slightly less enhancement is seen for injection from the n+ poly-oxide interface (negative V_g).   I-V uniformity across the 4-inch TSC oxide wafer was   ± 0.2 V for a given current density.   Both the TSC and the normal 230 A oxides exhibited similar ΔV_g's due to electron trapping (Fig. 4).   It should be noted that the ΔV_g observed for the TSC oxide is approximately ten times smaller than those observed for thicker polyoxides. This may be due to a smaller pre-existing electron trap density for the TSC oxide compared to polyoxides which are grown from heavily-doped polycrystalline silicon. Fig. 5 shows the intrinsic Q_{BD} as a function of the stressing current density for the three oxides. According to the hole trapping oxide breakdown model, the lower bulk electric field for the TSC oxide reduces the hole generation rate which would increase Q_{BD}.   On the other hand, the injection area will be smaller which would decrease Q_{BD}.   The net effect in our

Reprinted from the *IEDM Tech. Dig.*, pp. 889–891, 1987.

289

case is a larger Q_{BD} for the TSC oxide compared to the normal oxides. Fig. 6 shows the QBD histograms for large area, 1.1 mm2, capacitors. While approximately 25% of the 230 A and 60 A normal oxide capacitors failed before 1 C/cm^2 of charge has passed through the oxide, none of the 50 TSC oxide capacitors failed before 1 C/cm^2. This difference can be explained by the smaller effective injection area for the TSC oxide as compared to the normal oxides and the reduced hole generation rate. Certain device applications may require an undoped region underneath the TSC oxide. Fig. 7 shows that enhanced electron injection and a larger Q_{BD} can still be achieved when Si is implanted instead of As.

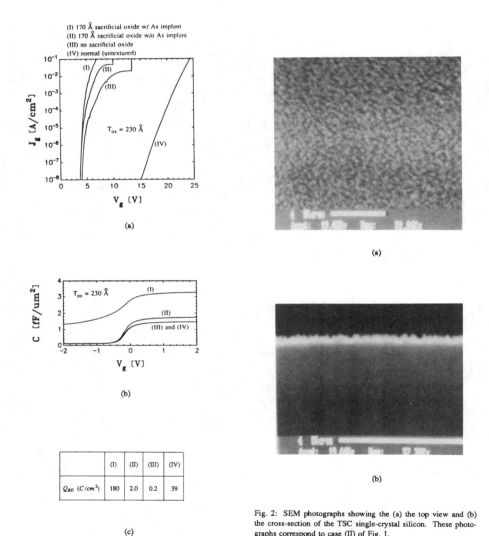

(I) 170 Å sacrificial oxide w/ As implant
(II) 170 Å sacrificial oxide w/o As implant
(III) no sacrificial oxide
(IV) normal (untextured)

(a)

(b)

	(I)	(II)	(III)	(IV)
Q_{BD} (C/cm^2)	180	2.0	0.2	39

(c)

Fig. 1: (a) I-V, (b) C-V, and (c) Q_{BD} characteristics showing the effects of etching the surface through a sacrificial oxide with (I) and without (II) an As implant. Also shown are results from etching the bare silicon (III) and that of a normal oxide (IV). Q_{BD} data were taken on 100 um^2 capacitors using a current density of 100 mA/cm^2. The oxide thickness is 230 Å.

(a)

(b)

Fig. 2: SEM photographs showing the (a) the top view and (b) the cross-section of the TSC single-crystal silicon. These photographs correspond to case (II) of Fig. 1.

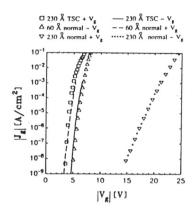

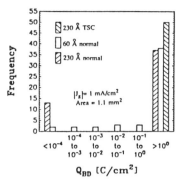

Fig. 6: Q$_{BD}$ histograms for the oxides in Fig. 3.

Fig. 3: Positive V$_g$ and negative V$_g$ characteristics for the 230 Å TSC oxide (case (I) of Fig. 1) and also those of the 230 Å and 60 Å normal oxides. The two 230 Å oxides on n-type substrates were fabricated together except at the texturing step. The 60 Å normal oxide was fabricated on a p-type substrate.

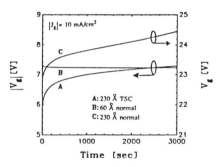

Fig. 4: Charge trapping characteristics due to constant current stressing for the oxides in Fig. 3.

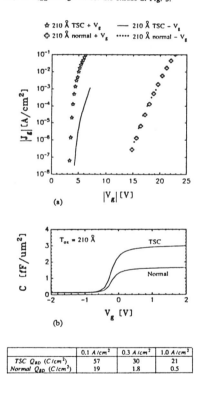

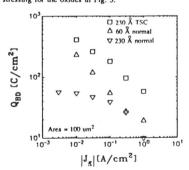

Fig. 5: Intrinsic charge-to-breakdown, Q$_{BD}$, as a function of stressing current density for the oxides in Fig. 3.

	0.1 A/cm²	0.3 A/cm²	1.0 A/cm²
TSC Q$_{BD}$ (C/cm²)	57	30	21
Normal Q$_{BD}$ (C/cm²)	19	1.8	0.5

Fig. 7: (a) I-V, (b) C-V, and (c) Q$_{BD}$ characteristics for 210 Å TSC and normal oxides. Texturing the single-crystal surface was accomplished by etching through a 150 Å Si implanted sacrificial oxide. Q$_{BD}$ data were taken on 100 um² capacitors.

Electrically-Alterable Memory Using A Dual Electron Injector Structure

D. J. DiMARIA, K. M. DeMEYER, AND D. W. DONG, MEMBER IEEE

Abstract—A novel type of electrically-alterable memory which uses the phenomenon of enhanced electron injection into SiO_2 from Si-rich SiO_2 to charge or discharge a floating polycrystalline Si storage layer in a metal-oxide-semiconductor field-effect-transistor is described. This non-volatile memory differs from others using floating polycrystalline Si in the charging or discharging process. This improvement is accomplished by using a chemically-vapor-deposited stack of Si-rich-SiO_2–SiO_2–Si-rich-SiO_2 between the floating polycrystalline Si layer and the control gate electrode. This device is capable of being written or erased in 5 msec at voltages of $\leq$ 16 V and in 2 μsec at voltages $\leq$ 23 V with excellent charge retention.

In this communication, a new non-volatile electrically-alterable read-only-memory (EAROM) is described which uses a floating polycrystalline silicon (poly-Si) storage layer [1] and Si-rich SiO_2 electron injectors [2-4]. This device, as shown schematically in Fig. 1, is similar to commercially available floating-gate avalanche-injection metal-oxide-silicon (FAMOS) devices [1] except for the replacement of the SiO_2 layer between the floating poly-Si layer and control poly-Si electrode by a dual electron injector structure (DEIS) consisting of sequentially chemically-vapor-deposited (CVD) layers of Si-rich SiO_2, SiO_2, and Si-rich SiO_2. The DEIS allows the floating poly-Si layer to be written or erased by putting electrons on or taking them off this storage layer using enhanced electron injection from the top or bottom Si-rich SiO_2 injectors, respectively. The enhanced electron injection phenomenon is thought to be caused by localized electric field enhancement at the Si-rich-SiO_2–SiO_2 interface due to the two phase nature (Si and SiO_2) of this material [2,3]. This localized field distortion gives a very large enhancement ($\gtrsim 10^5$) in the injected current for a given gate voltage which is believed to be controlled by Fowler-Nordheim tunneling [2,3]. In contrast, commercially available FAMOS structures are written by hot electron injection from a Si junction pulsed to avalanche breakdown and usually rather slowly erased by ultra-violet (UV) light which optically discharges the trapped electrons on the floating poly-Si storage layer [1]. As will demonstrated here, the DEIS EAROM can be *both* written and erased in $\leq$ 5 msec at least 10^4 times with very little degradation,

Manuscript received June 24, 1980; revised received July 18, 1980. The authors are with I.B.M. Thomas J. Watson Research Center, Yorktown Heights, New York 10598.

*This research was supported by the Defense Advanced Research Projects Agency, and was monitored by the Deputy for Electronics Technology (RADC) under Contract No. F19628-78-C-0225.

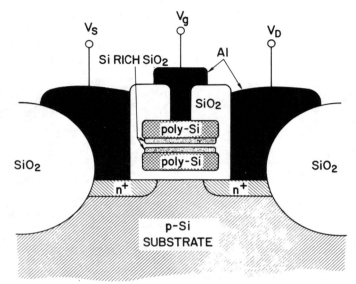

Figure 1. Schematic representation of a non-volatile n-channel field effect transistor memory using a dual electron injector stack between a control gate and floating poly-Si layer. Writing (erasing) is performed by applying a negative (positive) voltage V_g^-(V_g^+), to the control gate which injects electrons from the top (bottom) Si-rich SiO_2 injector to the floating poly-Si storage layer (back to the control gate). Structure is not drawn to scale.

using lower voltage and power than FAMOS type structures but with similar retention characteristics. The DEIS EAROM can also be written and erased at lower voltages than metal-silicon nitride-silicon dioxide-silicon (MNOS) devices which depend on electron and hole tunneling (write and erase operations, respectively) from the Si substrate through a thin tunnel SiO_2 layer into the Si_3N_4 layer which stores the charge via trapping states lying energetically in the bandgap [5]. Furthermore, the DEIS like the FAMOS structures has better charge retention characteristics than MNOS devices.

The EAROM n-channel field effect transistors (FETs) used here were fabricated using a self-aligned, double poly-Si process with a DEIS stack deposited between the poly-Si layers. The FET channel area was 2.9×10^{-6} cm^2, but the actual injecting area was 8.4×10^{-6} cm^2. To increase the capacitive coupling effect so that most of the applied voltage is dropped across the DEIS stack, the thermal gate oxide between the Si substrate and floating poly-Si layer was made thin (100 Å). Although in the devices described here the poly-Si control gate electrode and floating gate storage electrode are equal in area, higher coupling also

Reprinted from *IEEE Electron Device Lett.*, vol. EDL-1, no. 9, pp. 179–181, September 1980.

could have been realized with a control gate which was smaller in area than the floating poly-Si layer. The DEIS stack consisted of 100 Å of Si-rich SiO_2 for the bottom injector, 100 Å of SiO_2 for the intervening oxide layer, and 100 Å of Si-rich SiO_2 for the top injector. The Si-rich SiO_2 and SiO_2 layers were deposited at 700°C using concentration ratios R_o of N_2O to SiH_4 in the gas phase of 3 and 100, respectively [2,3,6]. This Si-rich SiO_2 material with $R_o = 3$ has 46% atomic Si [2,3,6].

Figures 2 and 3 show write/erase cycling data for 5 msec and 2 μsec pulse widths, respectively. In Fig. 2 for 5 msec operation, write voltages were varied from –14 V to –16 V while erase voltages were varied from +11 V to +13 V. In Fig. 3 for 2 μsec operation, write voltages were varied from –20 V to –23 V, while erase voltages were varied from

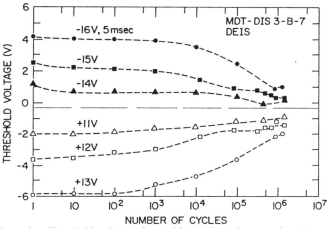

Figure 2. Threshold voltage after writing and erasing as a function of the number of cycles for various write/erase voltage conditions on DEIS FETs from wafer MDT-DIS 3-B, as described in the text of this communication. Solid and open symbols correspond to the threshold voltage after writing and erasing for 5 msec, respectively. The horizontal dashed line indicates the initial threshold voltage of the as-fabricated FETs before cycling.

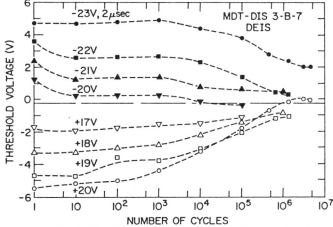

Figure 3. Threshold voltage after writing and erasing as a function of the number of cycles for various write/erase voltage conditions on DEIS FETs from wafer MDT-DIS 3-B. Solid and open symbols correspond to the threshold voltage after writing and erasing for 2 μsec, respectively. The horizontal dashed line indicates the initial threshold voltage of the as-fabricated FETs before cycling.

+17 V to +20 V. The threshold voltage indicates the charge state of the floating poly-Si layer with the horizontal dashed line indicating the initial threshold voltage on an approximately uncharged as-fabricated device. Threshold voltages more positive than this dashed line indicate stored electrons, while those more negative indicate ionized donors when the device is over-erased. The degradation in the cycling characteristics resulting in a threshold-voltage window collapse which becomes important after approximately 10^4 cycles is due to trapped electronic charge build-up in the intervening CVD SiO_2 layer [3,7]. This trapping is believed to be caused by H_2O related impurities in these films [3,7,8] and can be improved with high temperature annealing [3,7].

Figures 2 and 3 also show that the erase operation (electron ejection from floating poly-Si back to the control gate using the bottom Si-rich SiO_2 injector) is more efficient than the write operation (electron injection from the control gate to the floating poly-Si using the top Si-rich SiO_2 injector). This same phenomenon was also seen on large area (.006 cm^2) capacitor structures with DEIS stacks deposited on smooth single crystal Si or rough poly-Si substrates with poly-Si or Al control gate electrodes [4,9]. This asymmetry in the enhanced currents from the Si-rich SiO_2 injectors is believed to be caused by differences in the two Si-rich-SiO_2–SiO_2 interfaces [4]. The bottom injector interface is formed by depositing SiO_2 on top of it, while the top interface is formed by depositing the top injector on top of this SiO_2 layer.

Control structures identical to the DEIS EAROMs discussed here with only the 100 Å CVD SiO_2 layer between the control gate and floating poly-Si were also fabricated. These structures could not be written with any significant number of electrons using the same voltages and times in Figs. 2 and 3. However, they could be erased somewhat due to localized field-enhanced tunnel injection near asperities on the rough top surface of the floating poly-Si storage layer [10,11]. This phenomenon has been reported before and actually used with FAMOS-like devices in some cases for erase operations [12]. However, it is very difficult to reproduce due to subtleties in processing conditions affecting the surface roughness.

Figure 4 shows retention characteristics of the DEIS EAROMs in a grounded control gate condition for temperatures in the range of from 25°C to 300°C and compares them to control structure EAROMs for approximately 3×10^{12} stored electrons/cm^2. Clearly, the DEIS and control structure without the Si-rich SiO_2 layers behave in a very similar fashion. Temperatures of 300°C are needed to observe any significant charge loss in 10^4 sec. This loss has been shown to be due to electronic thermal activation out of an approximately 2.2 eV energetically deep well formed by the electric field lowered energy barrier between the Fermi level of the n-degenerate poly-Si storage layer of the control structure or the bottom of the conduction band of the last layer of Si islands in the

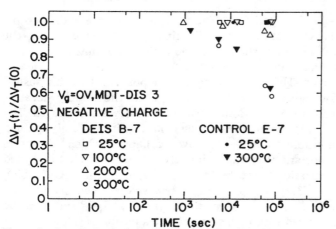

Figure 4. Stored electronic charge loss as a function of time on DEIS and control FETs from the MDT-DIS 3 series as described in the text of this communication for a grounded gate condition $V_g = 0$ V at temperatures of 25°C, 100°C, 200°C, and 300°C. Charge loss is calculated in normalized units of $\Delta V_T(t)/\Delta V_T(0)$ where $\Delta V_T(0)$ is the threshold voltage shift due to the initial stored charge of $\approx 3 \times 10^{12}$ electrons/cm^2 and $\Delta V_T(t)$ is the threshold voltage shift due to the stored charge left after time t under the indicated temperature and voltage stressing conditions.

bottom injector of the DEIS and the conduction band of the CVD SiO$_2$ layer [9]. If large enough positive gate voltages are applied to the DEIS EAROM, another loss component which is weakly temperature dependent will occur during the times considered here [9]. This is due to Fowler-Nordheim tunneling of electrons off the last layer of Si islands in the bottom Si-rich SiO$_2$ injector into the CVD SiO$_2$ layer (the injector starts ejecting electrons back to the control gate). This loss mechanism will also occur at higher positive gate voltages on the control EAROM structure in a localized fashion from near the tips of the asperities on the rough poly-Si surface into the intervening CVD SiO$_2$ layer. From the higher temperature data in Fig. 4, a 5% charge loss in $\geq 10^7$ years by thermal activation is predicted for DEIS EAROM operation at temperatures from 25°C to 80°C. The principle charge loss mechanism over periods of years will be by Fowler-Nordham tunneling. However, this process will be self-limiting since as electrons are lost off the floating gate the internal electric fields which drive this loss component will decrease [9].

Other sets of devices similar to those reported here with thicker SiO$_2$ layers were also fabricated. They operated in a similar fashion to those reported here, but at higher voltages. Varying the Si-rich SiO$_2$ injector thickness from 100 Å to 500 Å or the Si content by a few percent from the 46% atomic Si used here had little effect on write/erase operation making the DEIS processing non-critical. Write or erase voltages could be increased by significantly decreasing the Si content of the Si-rich SiO$_2$ injectors either separately or together. If either the top or bottom injector is replaced by SiO$_2$, the expected behavior of enhanced injection only from the remaining injector is observed [4]. The sum of the current-voltage characteristics of structures with a single top or bottom injector has been shown to be approximately equivalent to the current-voltage characteristic for a DEIS with the same SiO$_2$ thickness [4]. The DEIS stacks have also been shown to have excellent voltage breakdown characteristics, and they are capable of drawing very high currents as would be needed for the 2 μsec operation shown in Fig. 3 with very few low voltage breakdown events occurring [9]. This phenomenon is believed to be due to localized field screening by a reversible space charge build-up on the Si islands near the injecting contact at low applied fields [9,13]. In fact, even 200 nsec write/erase operation for 10^2 to 10^5 cycles depending on the magnitude of the voltage pulses has been demonstrated for these devices before the *gate* insulator between the floating poly-Si layer and the single crystal Si substrate broke down.

Smaller area FETs using capacitive coupling considerations will allow even lower voltages and faster write/erase switching times than those reported here. In the future, $\leq$ 100 nsec write/erase operation at $\approx$ 20 V should be attainable. If oxide trapping can be reduced significantly so that the number of cycles before a pronounced threshold-voltage window collapse is increased to $\geq 10^9$, then a pure non-volatile Random-Access-Memory (NVRAM) structure might finally be obtained.

ACKNOWLEDGEMENTS

The authors would like to acknowledge the critical reading of this manuscript by D.R. Young and M.H. Brodsky; the sample preparation by the Silicon Process Studies Group at the T.J. Watson Research Center; the technical assistance of F.L. Pesavento; and helpful discussions with D.R. Young regarding H$_2$O related trapping sites in SiO$_2$ layers, with P. Cook regarding NVRAM operation, and with C.M. Osburn regarding processing. This Research was supported in part by the Defense Advanced Projects Agency, and was monitored by the Deputy for Electronics Technology (RADC) under Contract No. F19628-78-C-0225.

REFERENCES

[1] D. Frohman-Bentchkowsky, Solid State Electronics *17*, 517 (1974).
[2] D. J. DiMaria and D. W. Dong, J. Appl. Phys. *51*, 2722 (1980).
[3] D. J. DiMaria, R. Ghez, and D.W. Dong, to be published J. Appl. Phys. (No. 9467R).
[4] D. J. DiMaria and D. W. Dong, Appl. Phys. Lett. *37*, 62 (1980)
[5] J. J. Chang, Proc. IEEE *64*, 1039 (1976) and references contained therein.
[6] D. Dong, E. A. Irene, and D. R. Young, Electrochem Soc. *125*, 819 (1978).
[7] D. R. Young, E. A. Irene, D. J. DiMaria, R. F. DeKeersmaecker, and H. Z. Massoud, J. Appl. Phys. *50*, 6366 (1979).
[8] E. H. Nicollian, C. N. Berglund, P. F. Schmidt, and J. M. Andrews, J. Appl. Phys. *42*, 5654 (1971).
[9] D. J. DiMaria, K. M. DeMeyer, C. M. Serrano, and D. W. Dong, unpublished.
[10] D. J. DiMaria and D. R. Kerr, Appl. Phys. Lett. *27*, 505 (1975).
[11] R. M. Anderson and D. R. Kerr, J. Appl. Phys. *48*, 4834 (1977).
[12] S. A. Abbas and C. A. Barile, *13th Annual Proceedings Reliability Physics*, Las Vegas, Nevada, 1975 (IEEE, New York, 1975), Vol. 13, p.1.
[13] D. J. DiMaria, D.R. Young, and D. W. Ormond, Appl. Phys. Lett. *31*, 680 (1977).

A Nitride-Barrier Avalanche-Injection EAROM

SHINPEI HIJIYA, TAKASHI ITO, MEMBER, IEEE, TETSUO NAKAMURA, MEMBER, IEEE,
HAJIME ISHIKAWA, MEMBER, IEEE, AND HIDEKI ARAKAWA

Abstract—A 10 nm graded band-gap insulator obtained by oxidizing the surface of a very thin thermal nitride film has been used as the first insulator of a floating gate avalanche-injection EAROM cell. A low-energy barrier of thermal nitride and a cell optimization considering the capacitive coupling of the floating gate to the drain has enabled low single-polar voltage alterability on a 2 kbit test vehicle. Good write/erase endurance has been also obtained owing to the low injection field applied to the first insulator of the avalanche injection approach.

I. INTRODUCTION

RECENTLY, Fowler-Nordheim tunneling oxide approaches [1], [2] have been pursued to electrically change the floating gate charge. Low-power write/erase is possible for these structures, but the thin oxide of less than 20 nm must be sufficiently reliable under a high injection field of about 7–8 MV/cm. This high injection field is also provided by a high programming voltage of about 17–21 V.

This paper describes a new avalanche-injection approach that enables hot carrier injection under a lower electric field as compared to the tunneling oxide approaches and the former avalanche-injection approach [3]. The conventional avalanche-injection approaches needed bipolar voltage supplies to change the data. This has caused a difficulty in transferring the avalanche-injection EAROM cell to the mass production stage. In this paper, this difficulty has been overcome by a cell optimization that enables single-polar voltage alterability.

II. MEMORY CELL

The memory cell consists of a select transistor and a memory transistor (Fig. 1). The memory transistor is called a nitride-barrier avalanche-injection MIS (NAMIS) [4]. A 10 nm graded energy band-gap insulator is incorporated into an n-channel stacked polysilicon gate FET. This insulator has been obtained by oxidizing the surface of a 6 nm thermal silicon nitride grown by the newly developed plasma-assisted technique [5]. Plasma-assisted thermal nitridation is possible at a reduced temperature of 1050°C compared to 1200°C of thermal nitridation. This lowered nitridation temperature reduced the diffusion length of the impurities from the isolation area and thus, has enabled integration of the nitride barrier cell. This first insulator has reduced the programming voltage to as low as 12 V while maintaining a good charge retention [6].

Manuscript received April 5, 1982; revised June 23, 1982.
S. Hijiya, T. Ito, T. Nakamura, and H. Ishikawa are with the Semiconductor Device Laboratory, Fujitsu Laboratories, Ltd., Kawasaki 211, Japan.
H. Arakawa is with Fujitsu, Ltd., Kawasaki 211, Japan.

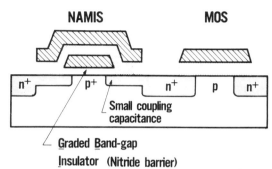

Fig. 1. Cross section of the memory cell. First insulator is 10 nm thick and is obtained by oxidizing the surface of the plasma assisted thermal nitride. The second insulator is a 70 nm thick polysilicon oxide.

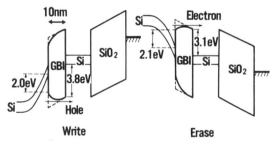

Fig. 2. Energy band diagram for writing and erasing. Writing is done by hot hole injection with the grounded gate. Erasing is done by hot electron injection with a positive gate bias.

Fig. 2 shows the mechanism of the low voltage alterability. A newly developed cell optimization considering the drain breakdown voltage and the capacitive coupling between the floating gate and the drain has enabled single-polar voltage alterability. For writing, hot holes are injected from the silicon substrate into the polysilicon floating gate with the grounded gate. For erasing, hot electrons are injected with a positive gate supply. The graded energy band-gap insulator (GBI) has a narrow band gap of silicon nitride at the silicon substrate interface. Then, the barrier height as seen from the silicon substrate is lower than the silicon dioxide barrier. This reduced barrier height enhances hot carrier injection under a low injection field of 1–2 MV/cm. This low injection field and the extreme thinness of the first insulator have reduced the programming voltage drastically. A good write/erase endurance is also expected from this low injection field. This field is very low compared to the 7–8 MV/cm injection field of Fowler-Nordheim tunneling EEPROM's.

Fig. 3 shows an energy band diagram for electron storage. The main mechanism of the charge loss is assumed to be the

Reprinted from *IEEE J. Solid-State Circuits*, vol. SC-17, no. 5, pp. 852–856, October 1982.

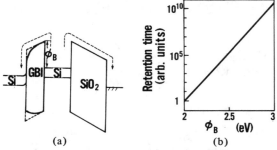

(a)   (b)

Fig. 3. Mechanism of the charge retention. (a) Band diagram of electron storage. (b) Calculated charge retention time as a function of the barrier height at the silicon floating gate interface. Calculation is done assuming the thermionic emission of the stored charge at room temperature.

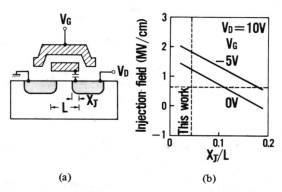

(a)   (b)

Fig. 4. Mechanism of single-polar voltage alterability. (a) Cross section of the memory transistor showing capacitive coupling. (b) Calculated hole injection fields as functions of the ratio x_j/L. Calculation is done assuming a 10 nm thick first insulator and 70 nm second insulator. Hole injection field is calculated at the experimentally determined most probable injection point.

thermionic emission of the injected carriers from the silicon floating gate over the energy barrier at the silicon floating gate interface. This is because we found the activation energy of charge loss to be 1.83 eV for the memory device with the silicon nitride first insulator and that it agreed well with the barrier height between silicon nitride and silicon floating gate [4]. Calculation results of the memory retention time at room temperature as a function of the barrier height at the silicon floating gate interface is also shown in Fig. 3. This calculation has been done by assuming a thermionic emission mechanism. If the barrier height is increased from 2 eV of silicon nitride to 3 eV of silicon dioxide, the memory retention time increases by about ten orders of magnitude. Thus, the high-energy barrier of the first insulator at the silicon floating gate interface provides sufficient memory retention.

Fig. 4 shows the mechanism of the single-polar voltage alterability. A former approach of the avalanche-injection EAROM cell needed negative gate voltages to inject hot holes. This is because the floating gate potential goes up when a breakdown voltage is applied to the drain junction due to the capacitive coupling of the floating gate to the drain. Then, hole injection without a negative gate bias becomes possible by reducing the capacitive coupling between the floating gate and the drain. This can be done by reducing the ratio of the drain junction depth x_j to the floating gate length L. In Fig. 4, the calculation of hole injection fields as functions of the above-mentioned ratio has been done assuming a 10 nm thick first insulator and a 70 nm thick second insulator. The hole injection field has been calculated as follows. First, the floating gate potential has been calculated considering the capacitive coupling between the floating gate and the control gate, the source, the drain, and the substrate. Then, surface potential near the drain was calculated neglecting a field effect of the floating gate, a channel current, and a fringe effect of the drain junction [4]. Finally, hole injection field was calculated dividing the potential difference between the floating gate and the substrate by the thickness of the first insulator at the experimentally found most probable injection point within the drain depletion region. This point was found to be located at around 60 percent length of the drain depletion length. If the ratio of the junction depth to the floating gate is over 0.1, the hole injection field with the grounded gate is less than 0.6 MV/cm. It was shown experimentally by the authors that hole

injection did not occur under a field of less than this critical field. In that case, a negative gate bias was needed [3], [4]. If the ratio is reduced below 0.05, a sufficient hole injection field under zero gate bias is obtained. We have reduced the ratio below 0.05 by applying a shallow junction technique of arsenic ion implantation with an energy of 50 keV. Thus, a single-polar voltage alterability has become possible.

III. CELL CHARACTERISTICS

Above-mentioned features of this proposed cell have been shown experimentally. Fig. 5 shows the write/erase characteristics. For writing and erasing, an avalanche breakdown is induced at the drain junction through a load resistor of 1 kΩ. In this cell, channel implantation is done to reduce the drain breakdown voltage to under 10 V. Writing is done by applying a single 10 V, 10 ms pulse to the drain with the grounded gate. Erasing is done by applying a single 12 V, 10 ms pulse to the drain with a positive gate bias. In this case, the gate is connected to the drain. Thus, the write/erase has become possible with an exceptionally low and single-polar voltage of less than 12 V.

Fig. 6 shows the high- and low-level threshold voltages as a function of the number of programming cycles. Writing is done with a 10 V, 10 ms pulse. Erasing is done with a 12 V, 10 ms pulse. The threshold window, the high level, and the low level remain constant until 10^4 programming cycles. By this point, the threshold window gradually narrows and collapses at around 10^6 cycles. These endurance curves are very similar to those of the tunneling oxide approaches [1]. Thus, an extremely thin graded band-gap insulator of 10 nm is very stable during programming cycles. Furthermore, the curves do not show such instabilities at the initial stage as are observed in tunneling oxide EEPROM cells [1], [7]. The stability of these threshold voltages are supposed to be due to the low injection field of 1-2 MV/cm. For the transconductance g_m, it did not show a degradation during 10^4 to 10^5 programming cycles, while the high and low threshold levels changed drastically. These effects show that the mechanism of the window closing cannot be attributed to the increase of surface states

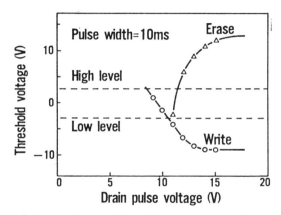

Fig. 5. Write/erase characteristics of the memory cell. Avalanche breakdown is induced for both writing and erasing through a resistor of 1 kΩ. For the writing, the control gate is grounded. For the erasing, the control gate is connected to the drain.

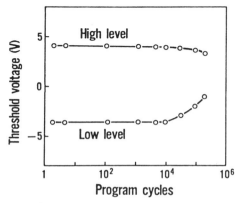

Fig. 6. Changes of the threshold voltage during programming cycles. Writing is done with a 10 V, 10 ms pulse. Erasing is done with a 12 V, 10 ms pulse.

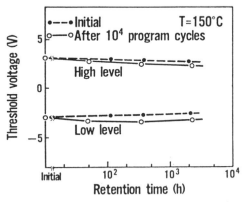

Fig. 7. Program cycling effects on the memory retention at 150°C. Dotted line shows the memory retention before program cycles. Real line shows the memory retention after 10^4 program cycles.

and may be attributed to electron trapping in the first insulator.

Fig. 7 shows the program cycling effects on the charge retention. Samples before and after 10^4 programming cycles have been baked at 150°C for both high and low levels. It is seen that 10^4 programming cycles do not have a significant effect on the charge retention. Charge retention time of more than ten years at room temperature is expected even after 10^4 pro-

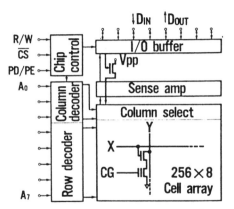

Fig. 8. Block diagram of NAMIS 2 kbit EAROM. $\overline{CS}$, R/W, and Pd/Pe are chip control commands.

gramming cycles by these charge retention characteristics at 150°C.

IV. 2 KBIT EAROM

Advantages of the nitride-barrier avalanche-injection EAROM cell have been demonstrated on a 2 kbit test vehicle. Fig. 8 shows a block diagram of the 2 kbit EAROM. The chip consists of 256 words by 8 bits. The cell consists of two transistors. The select transistor prevents a current leak through nonselected negative threshold cells in the reading mode. In the programming mode, the select transistor prevents drain junction breakdown of nonselected cells. Write/erase is done by applying 10 ms TTL level pulses to three chip controlling pins of $\overline{CS}$, R/W, and Pd/Pe under an exceptionally low power supply of 15 V, while 12 V are applied to the cell due to the voltage drops in the peripheral circuits. In this chip, bytes must be erased before new data are written. Erasing is done by raising bit lines to 15 V while setting the control gate of the memory transistor at 12 V. This causes hot electron injection into floating gates. Drain current of about 1 mA for a cell is needed in this erase operation. Writing is done by raising bit lines to 15 V only when data inputs are at high levels while setting the control gate of the memory transistor at the grounded level. This causes hot hole injection into floating gates. In this case the drain current is at the level of 100 μA. In the reading mode, the "ON" state cell consumes about 30 μA.

Fig. 9 shows a photomicrograph of the completed 2 kbit EAROM chip. The chip size is 2.4 × 2.7 mm² and the minimum gate length used is 4 μm. Fig. 10 shows an enlarged view of the cell array and the memory cell. 4 μm aluminum column lines and 4 μm polysilicon row lines are used. The floating gate is 7 μm long and 10 μm wide. The cell size is 635 μm². Fig. 11 shows a typical output waveform from address changes. It is seen that address access time of less than 200 ns is possible under V_{cc} = 5 V. Table I summarizes the main features of the completed EAROM. Power supply for programming is 15 V. This programming voltage is exceptionally low compared to MNOS approaches (25 V) [8] or tunneling oxide approaches (17–21 V) [1], [2]. Programming cycles of more than 10^4 cycles have been also obtained in this 2 kbit test vehicle. Power dissipation for programming is a bit higher

Fig. 9. Photomicrograph of completed 2 kbit EAROM. Size is 2.4 × 2.7 mm².

Fig. 10. Enlarged view of the cell array and the memory cell. Cell size is 635 μm².

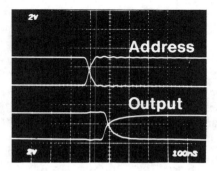

Fig. 11. Typical output waveforms from the address change.

TABLE I
MAIN FEATURES OF NAMIS 2 KBIT EAROM

Configuration		256 × 8
Power supplies:	Read	5V
	Program	5V, 15V
Power dissipation:	Read	200mW
	Program	620mW
Write time/word		10ms
Erase time/word		10ms
Access time		200ns
Retention		10 years
Program endurance		10^4 cycles

polar voltage alterability of the nitride barrier avalanche-injection MIS EAROM cell and the feasibility of plasma assisted thermal nitride process.

V. DISCUSSIONS

In order to clarify the erase mechanism of the NAMIS cell, a memory cell without channel dope was fabricated. This cell without the channel dope needed higher erase voltage of more than 14 V compared to the 10 V of the NAMIS cell. In this case, the erase mechanism was identified as tunneling of electrons from the floating gate to the drain by the exceptionally low drain current needed. Thus, it is concluded that the erase mechanism of the NAMIS cell with a drain breakdown voltage at around 10 V is hot hole injection. If the drain breakdown voltage is set higher than 14 V, the erase mechanism changes to electron tunneling from the floating gate to the drain.

The band structure of the first insulator is difficult to be measured explicitly because of its extreme thinness, but is speculated to have a graded band-gap structure by the results of the Auger electron spectroscopy. The first insulator was etched step by step by argon ions and analyzed by AES. The ratio of nitrogen peak width to oxygen peak width is about 0.1 at the surface and gradually increases to about 10 at the silicon substrate interface. Although the knock-on effect by the argon ion bombardment is not eliminated in these data, it can be said that the surface is almost silicon oxide and the interface is almost silicon nitride.

ACKNOWLEDGMENT

The authors express their appreciation to M. Shinoda for his organization of this project, to K. Nakamura for his cooperation, to T. Fukano, H. Horie, and I. Kato for the fabrication of the device, and to T. Misugi and Y. Fukukawa for their encouragement.

compared to tunneling approaches. But, power dissipation would be decreased by narrowing the width of the avalanche breakdown region and setting the source of the memory transistor at open node.

This 2 kbit test vehicle has demonstrated the low and single-

REFERENCES

[1] W. S. Johnson, G. Perlegos, A. Renninger, G. Kuhn, and T. R. Ranganath, "A 16 Kb electrically erasable non-volatile memory," in *ISSCC Dig. Tech. Papers,* Feb. 1980, pp. 152–153.
[2] E. K. Shelton, "Low-power EEPROM can be reprogrammed fast," *Electronics,* pp. 89–92, July 31, 1980.
[3] M. Kikuchi, S. Ohya, M. Kayama, M. Koike, and Y. Yamamoto, "A 2048 bit n-channel fully decoded electrically writable erasable nonvolatile read only memory," in *1st ESSCIRC IEEE Conf. Pub.,* vol. 130, Sept. 1975, pp. 66–67.

[4] T. Ito, S. Hijiya, T. Nozaki, H. Arakawa, H. Ishikawa, and M. Shinoda, "Low-voltage alterable EAROM cells with nitride-barrier avalanche-injection MIS (NAMIS)," *IEEE Trans. Electron Devices,* vol. ED-26, pp. 906–913, June 1979.

[5] T. Ito, I. Kato, T. Nozaki, T. Nakamura, and H. Ishikawa, "Plasma-enhanced thermal nitridation of silicon," *Appl. Phys. Lett.,* vol. 38, no. 5, pp. 370–372, 1981.

[6] S. Hijiya, T. Ito, T. Nakamura, N. Toyokura, and H. Ishikawa, "Electrically alterable read-only memory cell with graded energy band-gap insulator," in *IEDM Tech. Dig.,* Dec. 1980, pp. 590–593.

[7] B. Euzent, N. Boruta, J. Lee, and C. Jenq, "Reliability aspects of a floating gate EEPROM," *Proc. Reliability Physics,* vol. 19, pp. 11–16, 1981.

[8] T. Hagiwara, R. Kondo, Y. Yatsuda, S. Minami, Y. Itoh, and K. Uchiumi, "A 16 Kb electrically erasable programmable ROM," in *ISSCC Dig. Tech. Papers,* Feb. 1979, pp. 50–51.

EEPROM Cell with HB (One Half Barrier Height) Oxide for VLSI

Hiroshi Nozawa, Naohiro Matsukawa, Shigeru Morita
Jun-ichi Miyamoto and Tetsuya Iizuka
Semiconductor Device Engineering Laboratory, Toshiba

Kawasaki, Japan

EEPROM for VLSI requires the scaling of programming voltage as well as device size. In order to write and erase the cell by lower voltage, the thickness of tunnel oxide should be decreased, while it is strictly limited by malfunction of storage due to direct tunneling mechanism. One way to resolve this contradiction is to lower the barrier height of tunnel oxide, keeping the thickness. Therefore, several kinds of injectors, which is rather thick oxide with moderate barrier height such as oxide grown on poly-Si and Si-rich SiO_2 or silicon nitride, have been proposed and investigated. Since, all of them, however, use CVD method, they have certain problems of controllability and reliability to form a very thin layer.

In this paper, a new simple method of fabricating efficient electron injector will be reported. It is thermally grown on highly doped single Si and shows moderate barrier height, which can realize more integration of high performance EEPROM. This phenomenon was investigated and applied to EEPROM successfully. Furthermore, a prospect of the new injector is discussed.

Thin oxide as electron injector is usually formed between highly doped single Si and floating gate as shown in Fig. 1. The barrier height of thermal oxide grown on highly doped single Si which can be measured from F-N plot, depends on the doping level and the oxidation atmosphere. The barrier height decreases with dopant dose. The degree of the barrier height lowering of oxide grown in a (H_2O+Ar) is markedly larger than that of it in a (O_2+Ar) as shown in Fig. 2. At highly doped region, 5×10^{15} /cm^3, the barrier height of the oxide grown in a (H_2O+Ar) at 900°C reduced to about 1.8eV which is about one half of ordinary value. This barrier height lowering may be caused by off-stoichiometric SiO_2.[1] And it is expected that high performance and high reliability EEPROM can be realized by utilizing this phenomenon.

EEPROM cells with double level poly-Si gate structure were fabricated. The write/erase characteristics of the cell with the HB oxide were also measured.

In spite of thick tunnel oxide, 225A, short time programming and erasing, less than 1ms can be realized by low voltage pulse, 20V. Fig. 3 shows writing or erasing times of EEPROM cells with two kinds of barrier height injector, 2.8 and 1.8eV, as a function of the average applied field. With 1.8eV barrier height injector, write/erase time can be design to be fast by two

orders of magnitude or electric field applied to injector can be reduced to three fourth. This results in a high and reliable performance.

The barrier height lowering makes the write/erase voltage lowered. Therefore, a prospect for the scaling of write/erase voltage are required, considering the retention characteristics limited by the barrier height lowering. Fig. 4 shows an optimized region between a retention time more than 10 years and a write/erase time less than 1ms for four kinds of effective floating gate voltages. In a thin oxide region less than 60A, retention time is degraded to be shorter than 10 years, due to direct tunneling. With ordinary thin oxide of 3.2eV, the thickness can be allowed to be 60 to 110A at the high effective floating voltage, 12V, but no window for the oxide thickness is remained at 6V. On the other hand, even at 6V, the thickness of the HB oxide can be allowed to be 100 to 135A. This means that writing and erasing voltage can be reduced to 8V. Therefore, this technology is very promissive for the VLSI applications where scaling of writing and erasing voltage is inevitable.

In summary, a new simple method for fabricating efficient electron injector for floating gate devices was proposed. Thin oxide formed on highly doped single Si in H_2O+Ar shows lower barrier height than in O_2+Ar. It decreases to 1.8eV when dopant dose is 5×10^{15}/cm^3. By utilizing this phenomenon high performance EEPROM was realized. Furthermore, a prospect for the scaling of write/erase voltage was promissively presented.

Reference

(1) D.J. DiMaria et. al., J. Appl. Phys., 54, p.5801 1983.

Reprinted from the *Dig. 1984 Symp. VLSI Technol.*, pp. 42–43, 1984.

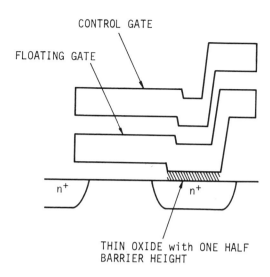

Fig. 1 Schematic cross section of EEPROM cell with HB oxide.

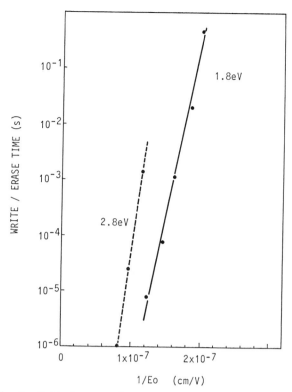

Fig.3 Write/erase time for cells with two kinds of barrier height oxide as a function of the average applied field.

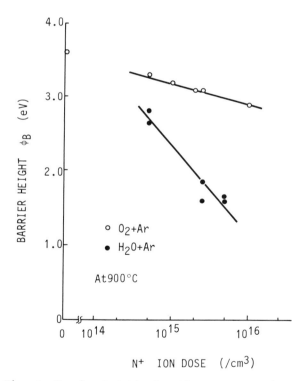

Fig. 2 Barrier height of oxides grown on highly doped single silicon in two kinds of **atmosphere**, O_2+Ar and H_2O+Ar as a function of ion implanted dose.

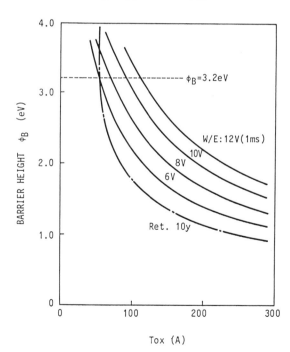

Fig. 4 Optimized regions between a retention time more than 10 years and a write/erase time less than 1ms for four kinds of effective floating gate voltages.

Part 8
EPROM, EEPROM, and Flash Memory Designs

CIRCUIT DESIGN is usually learned through case studies. This part presents a number of case studies of the design of EPROM, OTP EPROM, flash EEPROM, and full-featured EEPROM.

Paper 8.1 illustrates the basic EPROM design. It, together with Paper 3.3, also gives a historical perspective of EPROM designs. Paper 8.2 emphasizes the on-chip test circuits. Retention test circuits allow all word lines to be raised to V_{cc}. Thus, all the memory cells, rather than those in a single row, are stressed. This saves the test time in a temperature-bias data retention test (see Papers 9.1 and 9.3). Another circuit raises all the bit lines or all the word lines to the programming voltage to test for charge leakage from the floating gates to the drain diffusion or the control gates, phenomena known as PROGRAM disturb and dc ERASE. Yet another test circuit monitors the threshold voltages of the individual cells.

Paper 8.3 relates the highest density reported for EPROMs to date at 16 Mb. It has an alterable work organization with 8 or 16 bit words and uses trench isolation and 0.6-μm technology (see [5] in Part 6 introduction). Typical for large memories, many redundant rows and columns are included for yield improvement. The addresses of defective rows and columns are stored in special unerasable EPROMs, possibly shielded from UV by metal so that their contents are not erased by UV irradiation [1].

Paper 8.4 describes another 4-Mb EPROM, which is also intended to be packaged as an OTP (one-time-programmable, see Paper 3.12) EPROM or ROM. OTP ROM has a testability problem. When the chip is assembled (in a plastic package), all the cells are in an unprogrammed state and the chip cannot be tested for speed in any other data patterns. A special circuit addressing this problem is presented. More details of this circuit can be found in [2].

OTP EPROMs serve a high-density, high-volume, low-cost market. A different market favored by smaller-sized vendors is the lower-density, very-high-speed EPROMs. Here, innovative design and aggressive technology development, rather than low-cost, high-yield manufacturing, are the key to success. Paper 8.5 describes a 16-ns 1-Mb EPROM. The high speed is obtained through a combination of aggressive transistor scaling, double-metal technology, and differential sensing using two cells per bit. Reference [3] describes a 23-ns 256K EPROM.

Paper 8.6 together with Paper 5.2 describe the design of a flash EEPROM based on stacked-gate cells. To avoid over-erasing, a microprocessor-controlled adoptive ERASE algorithm is employed. More information, including the uniformity of ERASE speed and improved ERASE/PROGRAM endurance is reported in [4]. Paper 8.7 reports the incorporation of the ERASE-verify controller on-chip. Paper 8.8 reports a 1-Mb flash EEPROM based on the split-gate cell (see Paper 5.3).

The circuit design is simpler because there is no danger of over-ERASE.

Paper 8.9 describes a typical EEPROM design. Paper 8.10 presents the state-of-the-art EEPROM using a 1-μm, triple-poly, double-metal technology with 30-μm^2 FLOTOX cell and 1-Mb density. Further details of this design can be found in [5]. Defects in the thin-tunnel oxide cause early random single-bit failures (see Paper 9.4) and error correction coding (ECC) circuit is employed to achieve acceptable PROGRAM/ERASE endurance. ECC was also described in [6]. Paper 8.11 describes a different approach to error correction. Instead of using the efficient Hamming code for ECC, it uses a novel automatic two-cells-per-bit redundancy. This approach saves the delay time in the ECC circuit and can handle more than one error bit per byte. More details can be found in [7].

Paper 8.12 presents a fast 50-ns 256-kb EEPROM design using a double-metal 1.25μm technology and ECC circuit. Another 35-ns 64-K EEPROM design is described in [8].

Paper 8.13 describes the concept of storing one of four rather than two states in an EEPROM cell in an attempt to increase the stored-data density. The four states are represented by four ranges of the cell-threshold voltage. Extrapolating from this concept, we can let an EEPROM cell store continuously variable analog signals as has been done for neural network applications (see Paper 10.10). Another novel technique for increasing the data-storage density is to use the NAND cell (Paper 4.5) as described in [9]. On the other end of the design spectrum, we have large-cell-size single-polysilicon EEPROMs [10]. MNOS or SONOS EEPROM design examples can be found in Papers 4.7 and 4.8,

Two other design topics are worth noting, but have not yet been addressed in the open literature. One is the design issues (extra decoding and large bit-line capacitance) that must be resolved before the virtual ground EPROM and flash EEPROM (see Papers 3.8, 5.9, and 5.10) can be widely adopted to exploit its small-cell-size advantage. The other is the application of negative voltage to the word lines (see Papers 5.10 and 5.11). If this very new circuit technique is proven and widely used, it can open doors to many new nonvolatile memory designs.

Additional articles on nonvolatile memory design can be found in the *IEEE International Solid-State Circuits Conference* (ISSCC) *Digest of Technical Papers*, published every February, and the *IEEE Journal of Solid-State Circuits*. The latter publishes a special issue on logic and memory in October and a subject index in the December issue.

REFERENCES

[1] A. C. Folmsbee, "PROM cell made with an EPROM Process," in *Tech. Dig. Internat. Electron Devices Meet.*, 1983, pp. 574–576.
[2] N. Ohtsuka *et al.*, "A 4-Mbit CMOS EPROM," *IEEE J. Solid-State Circuits*, vol. SC-22, no. 5, pp. 669–674, Oct. 1987.

[3] D. Hoff *et al.*, "A 23ns 256K EPROM with double-layer metal and address transition detection," in the *Internat. Solid-State Circuits Conf. Dig. Tech. Papers*, 1989, pp. 130–131.

[4] V. N. Kynett, "A 90ns one million erase/program cycle 1-Mbit flash memory," *IEEE J. Solid-State Circuits*, vol. 24, no. 6, pp. 1259–1264, Oct. 1989.

[5] Y. Terada *et al.*, "120-ns 128Kx8-bit/64Kx16-bit CMOS EEP-ROMs," *IEEE J. Solid-State Circuits*, vol. 24, no. 5, pp. 1244–1249, Oct. 1989.

[6] S. Mehrotra, "A 64Kb CMOS EEPROM with on-chip ECC," in the *Internat. Solid-State Circuits Conf. Dig. Tech. Papers*, 1984, pp.

[7] 142–143.

D. Cioaca *et al.*, "A million-cycle CMOS 256K EEPROM," *IEEE J. Solid-State Circuits*, pp. 684–692, Oct. 1987.

[8] R. D. Jolly *et al.*, "A 35ns 64K EEPROM," *IEEE J. Solid-State Circuits*, pp. 971–978, Oct. 1985.

[9] M. Momodomi *et al.*, "An experimental 4 Mbit CMOS EEPROM with a NAND structured cell," *IEEE J. Solid-State Circuits*, pp. 1238–1243, Oct. 1989.

[10] J-I. Miyamoto *et al.*, "An experimental 5-V-only 256Kbit CMOS EEPROM with a high performance single-polysilicon cell," *IEEE J. Solid-State Circuits*, pp. 852–859, Oct. 1986.

512K EPROMs

Darrell Rinerson, Michael Ahrens, Jih Lien, Brimachar Venkatesh,

Tien Lin, Paul Song, Steve Longcor, Lewis Shen, Dave Rogers

Advanced Micro Devices

Sunnyvale, CA

Michael Briner

Advanced Dynamics, Inc.

San Jose, CA

THE DEMAND for high-density and high-performance non-volatile memory has continued to drive EPROM technology advances. Recently, the need for lower-cost programmable nonvolatile memory has been addressed through the use of EPROMs in plastic packages. In this paper a family of Electrically Programmable ROMs (EPROMs) achieving a 512Kb density, utilizing two layers of polysilicon and floating gate technology with floating gate programming via hot electron injection, will be described. These circuits are designed to function either as ultraviolet light erasable EPROMs or one time programmable (OTP) EPROMs in plastic packaging. The family includes a 512K at 150ns, 256K at 150ns, 128K at 120ns, and a 64K at 120ns. Typical room temperature access times for all are below 120ns; Figure 5. The EPROMs all utilize redundant memory elements selected by electrically programmed polysilicon fuses.

N channel technology scaled to 1.7μm is used. Dry etching of metal and polysilicon and contacts serves to define the small geometries. Automatic alignment* is used during photolithography. The designs can be scaled further using a wafer stepper. The cell size is 36μm^2. Technology and process features are summarized in Table 1; circuit characteristics in Table 2.

Row and column redundancy provides increased yields. For row redundancy a complete X NOR decoder is replaced instead of a single row. This replaces eight rows at a time. The redundant elements are themselves replaceable by other redundant memory elements. Polysilicon fuse technology allows fuses to be blown at low voltages (equal to VPP) at all stages in the manufacturing test flow. The fuses and related structures are designed to go into plastic packaging. This includes the use of a guard ring structure around the fuse. Test modes allow parts to be fully tested, including speed binning and program margins of all cells.

Differential sensing is used to sense the smaller threshold shifts seen on this technology. The minimum threshold shift is 2V. The minimum read current is 20μa. Reference cells are placed in the memory matrix, resulting in an improvement in end-of-life sensing capability; Figure 1.

Bit line clamping is used to eliminate pattern sensitive access variations. Bit lines not selected, are actively held at ground by clamping transistors. Word lines are pumped to a voltage above VPP during programming to achieve fast EPROM programming without the use of bipolar assisted programming. The word lines are pumped to approximately 15V. The X decoder and pump circuit are shown in Figure 2.

The EPROMs have been designed with performance over die size considerations. This includes the use of a split architecture to minimize word line delay, high speed X decoders, fast and sensitive sensing, and output buffers optimized to minimize noise on VCC and VSS.

Only hot electron injection caused by operating the EPROM transistor in saturation is used to program the EPROM transistor. The EPROM transistor is not programmed in the punch through mode. This is justified by the fact that the 10-year data retention is not a strong function of the initial threshold voltage, because a higher initial V_T decays at a faster rate. An advantage of this method, which prevents possible reliability problems, is the elimination of the destructive programming phenomena. The EPROM transistor programming characteristic is shown in Figure 3.

EPROMs have become the dominant nonvolatile memory in density and performance and will continue to replace other types of mask programmable nonvolatile memories. A key reason for this achievement is that higher density EPROMs, through the use of redundancy and plastic packaging, will cost less than ROMs on a per bit basis. EPROMs now are being designed with higher performance than ROMs.

The floating gate technology has been proven to be a reliable means of achieving nonvolatile storage. Considerable field experience on this technology has shown reliability comparable or better than other approaches. Data retention far in excess of ten years is seen.

Acknowledgments

The authors wish to express their appreciation to P. O'Hare and A. Morrison for layout, to Fab 7 for wafer processing, and NVM product engineering for testing and characterization.

---

*PE 341 is used for the alignment.

	512K	256K	128K	64K
organization	64K × 8	32K × 8	16K × 8	8K × 8
chip size	59K mils^2	42K mils^2	24K mils^2	18K mils^2
cell size	36.60μ^2	48.75μ^2	41.0μ^2	41.0μ^2
feature size	1.7μ	2.0μ	1.8μ	1.8μ
tacc	150 ns	150 ns	120 ns	120 ns
toe	80 ns	70 ns	60 ns	60 ns
Active Power	350 mW	300 mW	275 mW	225 mW
Standby Power	75 mW	60 mW	60 mW	60 mW
VPP	12.5V	12.5V	21V/12.5V	21V/12.5V
tpp (ave)	4 ms	4 ms	4 ms	4 ms
No. Redundant elements	4 Bytes 32 Rows	24 Rows	24 Rows	24 Rows

TABLE 2—EPROM circuit characteristics.

Reprinted from the *IEEE ISSCC Dig. Tech. Pap.*, pp. 136–137, 327, 1984.

process features
N channel silicon gate
Two layers of polysilicon
Poly 1 floating gate programmed by hot electron injection
PE 341 photolithography with automatic alignment
1.7μ smallest feature size
plasma etched metal, polysilicon and contacts

transistors

leff (minimum)	1.9μ
gate oxide	400 Å
X_j	0.3μ

storage cell

unshrunk dimensions	$7.5\mu \times 6.5\mu = 48.75$
gate oxide	400 Å
interpoly oxide	450 Å
V_T (initial)	1.0 Volts
V_T (programmed, after 1ms)	3.0 Volts
weff	1.0μ
leff	1.3μ
word line material	polysilicon
bit line material	aluminum
ground connection	n +
contacts per cell	1/2

TABLE 1—Summary of process and technology parameters.

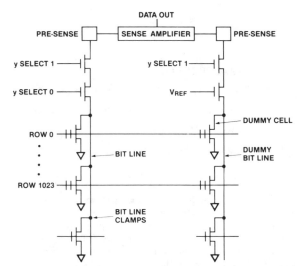

FIGURE 1—Sense amplifier circuit; pre sense, core and dummy cells.

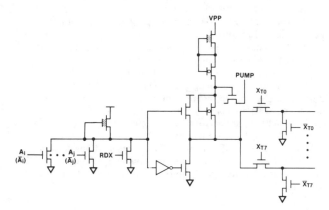

FIGURE 2—X Decoder circuit showing VPP loads and pump circuit.

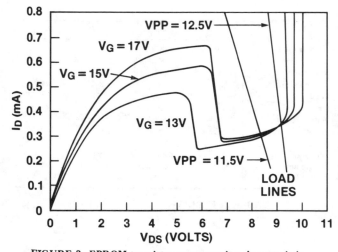

FIGURE 3—EPROM transistor programming characteristic.

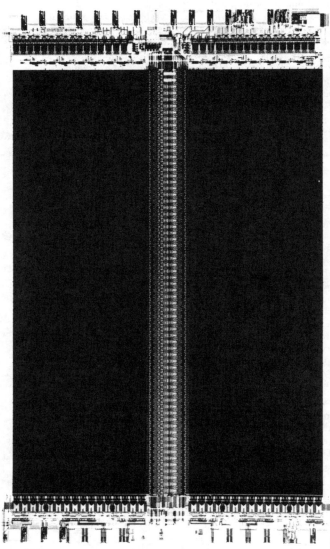

FIGURE 4—Photomicrograph of a 512K EPROM fabricated in a 1.7μm process technology.

306

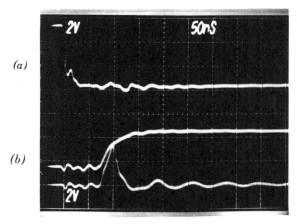

FIGURE 5—Oscilloscope waveform of data output (a)—
chip enable; (b)—data out.

Fast Programmable 256K Read Only Memory with On-Chip Test Circuits

SHIGERU ATSUMI, SUMIO TANAKA, KAZUYOSHI SHINADA, KUNIYOSHI YOSHIKAWA,
KOHJI MAKITA, YOSHIHIDE NAGAKUBO, and KOICHI KANZAKI

Abstract —A 32K×8 bits EPROM, which satisfies all requirements for a high-density EPROM, has been developed. The fast programming time is achieved by introducing a DSA structure into the memory cell. The low power consumption and fast access time are realized by utilizing n-well CMOS peripheral circuits. Various test circuits are implemented to alleviate lengthy screening time. Typical programming time, access time, and power dissipation are 3 μs/byte, 100 ns, and 5 mA, respectively.

I. INTRODUCTION

WITH THE progress of high-performance micro-processors, the demand for high-density and high-performance erasable and programmable read-only memory (EPROM) has been increased rapidly. In realizing a high-density 256K EPROM, it is necessary to overcome several problems.

First, an increase of the total programming time is a severe problem. If the conventional programming time of 50 ms for an individual cell [1] is applied, the total time per chip would be about 30 min. This programming time is unpractically long both for testing and applications. Therefore, it is necessary to reduce the programming time by improving the cell structure. The avalanche-mode injection cell has been suggested to shorten the programming time [2].[1] In our work, a diffusion self-align (DSA) structure [3], [4] is introduced into the cell to solve the problems. The details of the DSA structure will be described in Section III.

Second, an increase of power dissipation which comes from the fundamental problem of the conventional NMOS E/D/I circuit [5] should be avoided especially for high-density memories. To solve this problem, an n-well CMOS structure is used in the peripheral circuits. In addition to the low power consumption, the fast access time is realized by introducing a new CMOS sense amplifier circuit. These techniques will be described in Sections IV and V.

As bit density increases, the screening time becomes longer and becomes a great burden to testing [6]. Typical test routines are related to the gate leakage current of the

memory cells [7]. Most of the test circuits raise word lines or bit lines simultaneously to reduce the screening times.

It is also important to know the exact threshold voltage shift of the memory cell during the test routines. Therefore, the detector circuit is implemented to know the exact voltage shift. The circuits will be described in Section VI.

II. OUTLINE OF THE 256K EPROM

The 256K EPROM uses an n-well CMOS double poly-Si technology, and features a 2-μm design rule, which is realized by combining wafer stepper lithography with reactive ion-etching technology.

The memory cells are fabricated by the self-aligned double poly-Si technology. The first and second gate oxide thicknesses are scaled down to 500 and 600 Å, respectively. To obtain stronger coupling between the first and the second gate for a faster programming time, efforts are made to have the largest area possible in a given cell area.

The voltage rise at the source of the memory cell causes much programming delay due to the source wiring resistance. One aluminum ground line is taken for four cells to reduce the wire resistance. The top view of the memory cell is shown in Fig. 1. The cell size is 8 μm×8 μm, which includes the source aluminum lines.

The memory cell arrays are surrounded by the p^+ (at ground) and n^+ (at V_{CC}) guard rings to prevent the internal latchup, which may be caused by the substrate current from the memory cells during programming [8].

High-voltage transistors are formed in the peripheral circuits applying the lightly doped drain (LDD) structure to both n- and p-channel transistors. The low-concentration diffusion layer of the LDD structure reduces the electric field near the drain region. The breakdown voltages, thus obtained, are larger than 30 V both for p- and n-channel transistors. The breakdown voltage is sufficiently high in the 21-V V_{PP} operation.

The cell array consists of 64×8 column lines and 512 word lines. The chip size is 5.69 mm×6.10 mm, where about 280 000 transistors are integrated. The memory cell area occupies about 45 percent of the whole chip size.

Two spare rows are implemented to improve the yield. The replacement of the malfunctional rows by the spare rows is performed by cutting the poly-Si fuse by laser [9].

Manuscript received July 6, 1984; revised October 1, 1984.

The authors are with the Semiconductor Device Engineering Laboratory, Toshiba Research and Development Center, Kawasaki, 210 Japan.

[1] The idea of an avalanche-mode injection cell was suggested at the 6th IEEE Non-Volatile Semiconductor Memory Workshop during the panel discussion, 1983.

Reprinted from *IEEE J. Solid-State Circuits*, vol. SC-20, no. 1, pp. 422–427, February 1985.

TABLE I
SUMMARY OF 256K PROCESS PARAMETERS

TECHNOLOGY	N-WELL CMOS DOUBLE POLY SILICON
CELL	W = 2.3 μm L = 2.0 μm FIRST GATE 500 Å SECOND GATE 600 Å
PERIPHERAL	L = 2.0 μm(N), 2.5 μm (P) FIRST GATE 500 Å VT = 0.7 V(N), -0.8 V(P) XJ = 0.35 μm(N), 0.55 μm(P) FIELD 0.8 μm
SUBSTRATE	20 Ω-cm

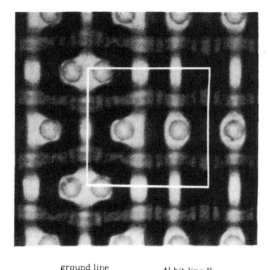

ground line   Al bit line II

Al bit line I

word line I

word line II

Fig. 1. Photograph of the top view of the memory cell. The unit area consists of four memory cells and one aluminum source line.

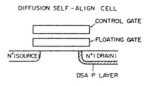

Fig. 2. Cross-sectional view of the DSA cell.

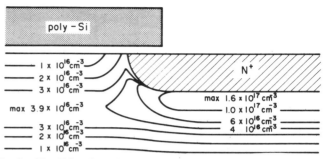

Fig. 3. The DSA channel concentration profile simulated by the two dimensional process simulator TOPMODE.

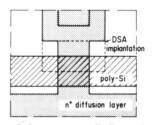

Fig. 4. The schema of the memory cell. Boron implantation area for DSA p-layer is only limited around the cell gate region.

The chip size increase due to redundancy circuits is less than 5 percent.

The main process parameters are summarized in Table I.

III. FAST PROGRAMMING

In order to realize the fast programming time, the DSA structure is introduced into the memory cell. Fig. 2 shows the cross sectional view of the DSA cell. In this cell, hot electrons are injected near the drain region similarly to the conventional cell [10]. The key feature of the DSA cell is that p-layer is localized only in the vicinity of the drain region. The other channel region is lightly doped commonly with the peripheral transistors. The p-layer makes the electric field near the drain region stronger, and increases the gate injection current. Fig. 3 shows the calculated result from the two-dimensional process simulation under typical process conditions (TOPICS) [11]. The p-layer concentration is optimized by the simulator. The peak concentration of the p-layer is $1.6 \times 10^{17} \mathrm{cm}^{-3}$. The channel impurity concentration for other peripheral MOSFET's is about $3.9 \times 10^{16} \mathrm{cm}^{-3}$. The p-layer width is about 0.1 μm.

As the threshold voltage almost depends on lightly doped concentration at the source side, the cell current is as large as a conventional cell in the read operation. As the boron-implantation area for the p-layer is only limited around the cell gate region (Fig. 4), the bit line capacitance increases by only about 10 percent. The delay time caused by the p-layer is negligibly small.

Fig. 5 shows the programming characteristics of the DSA cell compared with the conventional cell. These unit cells' characteristics are measured under the same conditions as the internal programming, that is, $V_G = 16$ V and $V_D = 10$ V. The DSA cell improved the programming time by one order of magnitude compared with the conventional cell.

IV. SENSE AMPLIFIER CIRCUIT

The fast access time was realized by a new CMOS sense amplifier circuit. The sense amplifier circuit consists of the bias circuit and the CMOS differential amplifier (Fig. 6).

The reference circuit when $S =$ "1" is discussed in this section, and the reference circuit when $S =$ "0" will be described in Section VI.

The bias voltage (V_{BIAS}) in the bias circuit is set to about 3 V. The bias circuit limits the bit line voltage below 1.5 V to suppress unintentional writing during the reading operation [12], and restricts the bit line swing less than 0.2 V to achieve the high-speed reading operation. The small signal

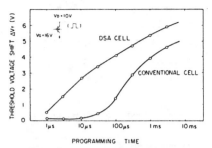

Fig. 5. The programming characteristics of the DSA cell and the conventional cell.

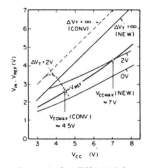

Fig. 7. The input voltage to the differential amplifier as a function of the supply voltage V_{CC}.

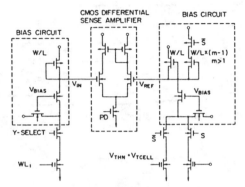

Fig. 6. Sense amplifier circuit.

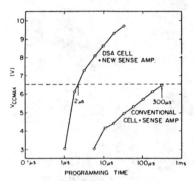

Fig. 8. The programming characteristics; programming time versus maximum supply voltage V_{CCMAX}.

is amplified by the p-channel transistor in the bias circuit. The gate of the p-channel transistor is connected back to the drain terminal. The combination of the new p-channel load and the CMOS differential amplifier assures the stable operational margin both for the programmed and unprogrammed cells.

Fig. 7 shows the input voltages to the differential amplifier (V_{IN}) as a function of V_{CC}. The bottom solid line shows the input voltage for unprogrammed cell, that is, the threshold voltage shift of the programmed cell (ΔV_{TH}) is 0 V. The top of the solid line shows the input voltage of the completely programmed cell, that is, ΔV_{TH} is infinite. As the source of the p-channel load transistor is connected to V_{CC}, and the transistor is free from the voltage loss caused by the body effect, the high level of V_{IN} is $V_{CC} - V_{THP}$, where V_{THP} is the threshold voltage of the p-channel peripheral transistor. The thick solid line shows the reference level. The level is set to be the intermediate of the two levels, unbalancing the dimension of the p-channel load transistor in the reference circuit [5]. Four reference circuits are implemented outside the memory cell array area to give a fast recovery time from the CE signal change to the differential amplifier.

As the gate of the selected cell is biased at V_{CC}, the incompletely programmed cell is "off-state" for lower V_{CC} region. The cell becomes "on-state" for the higher V_{CC} region and pulls down the input level. In the case of incompletely programmed cell, for instance $\Delta V_{TH} = 2.0$ V, a kink appears in the input level. In the case of conventional p-channel active load scheme, the input voltage for the programmed cell goes easily to the low level as soon as the cell goes "on-state." The new p-channel load scheme

can sustain the high level even when the cell becomes "on-state" for the higher V_{CC} region. Thus the programming state of the cell is concerned with the supply voltage V_{CC}. As a result, the detectable minimum ΔV_{TH} is improved as low as 1.5 V, when V_{CCMAX} reaches 6.5 V, in the new scheme, where V_{CCMAX} is the maximum voltage supply with which the "off-state" cell can be detected.

This also helps to get the short programming time together with the DSA cell. Fig. 8 shows the programming characteristics: V_{CCMAX} versus programming time. The upper curve in Fig. 8 corresponds to the combination of the newly developed DSA cell and the new sense amplifier circuit. The lower curve corresponds to the combination of the conventional cell and the conventional sense amplifier circuit. By defining the minimum programming time when V_{CCMAX} reaches 6.5 V, the programming time is improved by two orders of the magnitude compared with the conventional scheme. The typical programming time is drastically reduced to less than 3 μs. The effects of the DSA cell and the new sense amplifier on the programming characteristics are almost comparable.

The delay time of the bit line swing and sense amplifier is relatively larger in the total delay time, that is, access time. Several efforts were made to decrease the bit line delay. First, the channel implantation area is limited only around the gate region with peripheral transistors to decrease the drain junction capacitance. Second, eight sense amplifier circuits for each I/O are implemented to decrease the bit line capacitance. Third, the bit line swing is restricted less than 0.2 V. Simulated waveforms under typical conditions are shown in Fig. 9. The delay of the

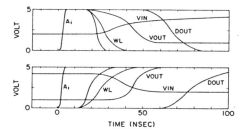

Fig. 9. Simulated waveforms under typical conditions.

TABLE II
DC POWER DISSIPATIONS

MEMORY CELL	0 8 mA
SENSE AMPLIFIER	1 0
REFERENCE CIRCUIT	0 4
ROW DECODER	0 6
COLUMN DECODER	0 5
TOTAL	3 7 mA

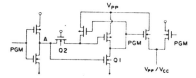

Fig. 10. V_{PP}/V_{CC} switching circuit.

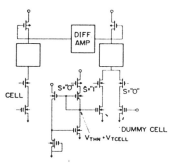

Fig. 11. The threshold voltage shift detector circuit.

new sense amplifier is small also with the bit line delay. The delay time is about 15 ns, which is about 20 percent of the total delay time.

As the whole bit lines are precharged to the ground level during the standby mode ($\overline{CE}$ = "1"), the chip enable access time is determined by the delay time when the bit line goes to the high level. Therefore, the reference voltage is also precharged to the ground level in order to detect rapidly the bit line voltage change by the differential sense amplifier. This realizes the fast chip enable access time.

V. LOW-POWER CMOS PERIPHERAL CIRCUITS

The n-well CMOS peripheral circuits are introduced to realize the low power consumption. Most of the peripheral circuits are made by CMOS circuits. The circuits with a dc current path are only limited in the first stage of the address buffer circuit, the sense amplifier circuit, the reference circuit, the p-channel active load in the row decoder circuit, and the selected memory cell. The total dc currents are minimized to be 4 mA without sacrificing the access time. The simulated main dc power dissipations are summarized in Table II.

The standby power is decreased to the junction leakage current level by cutting off the whole dc current path by the internal $\overline{CE}$ signal. The standby current measured is less than 10 nA. The n-well CMOS technology is compatible to the low-power CMOS micro-processors.

Most of the peripheral circuits consist of the CMOS logic circuit except for the high-voltage generating circuit. The circuit needs the help of the n-channel transfer gate transistor, which reduces the operational margin for supply voltage V_{CC}. The V_{PP}/V_{CC} switching circuit is controlled by a high-voltage isolation circuit, as illustrated in Fig. 10, which draws zero I_{pp} during the reading operation without a complicated voltage booster. In the isolation circuit, output (A) of the inverter is directly connected to a n-channel transistor ($Q1$) to eliminate the voltage drop by the transistor ($Q2$), thus providing a wide operational margin.

VI. ON-CHIP TEST CIRCUITS

The EPROM has three on-chip test circuits to shorten the screening time.

The first one is the threshold voltage shift detector circuit as shown in Fig. 11. The circuit provides the exact threshold voltage shift during the test routine. This circuit is activated by setting the $\overline{OE}$ pin to a higher voltage than V_{CC}. The internal signal S in Fig. 6 is set to "0." As the sense amplifier circuit discussed in Section IV has a high sensitivity for the small threshold voltage shift of the memory cell, the exact threshold voltage shift cannot be estimated by measuring V_{CCMAX}. The circuit is obtained by introducing some modifications to the reference circuit, which has been discussed in Section IV. Two points are different. The first point is that the p-channel transistors in the bias circuits are equally balanced in the transistor size. The second point is that the gate of the dummy cell is biased to constant voltage, threshold voltage of the memory cell (V_{TCELL}) plus threshold voltage of the peripheral n-channel transistor (V_{THN}), which is independent of the V_{CC}. The voltage applied to the dummy cell is generated by the feedback-type constant-voltage circuit.

The operational principle is qualitatively described as follows. As the gate of the selected cell is biased to V_{CC}, and the cell current (I_{CELL}) is expressed by

$$I_{CELL} \propto V_{CC} - V_{TCELL} - \Delta V_{TH}. \tag{1}$$

The dummy cell current (I_{DCELL}) is given by

$$I_{DCELL} \propto V_{THN}. \tag{2}$$

Comparing the currents in the selected cell and dummy cell, V_{CCMAX} is determined by

$$V_{CCMAX} = V_{TCELL} + V_{THN} + \Delta V_{TH} \tag{3}$$

that is

$$V_{CCMAX} \propto \Delta V_{TH}. \tag{4}$$

311

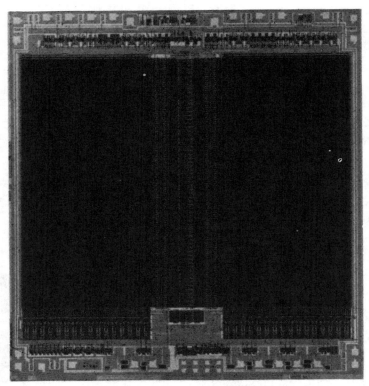

Fig. 12. Chip photograph of 256K CMOS EPROM.

ΔV_{TH} can be estimated exactly by measuring the $V_{CC\,\mathrm{MAX}}$.

The second test circuit is the retention test circuit during reading operation. Bad cells, which have gate oxide leakage current between the first and the second gate poly-Si at high temperature, are rejected by the bias temperature stress test. As only one word line is selected during the usual read operation, the screening time becomes rather long in the case of a high-density EPROM. The retention test circuit raises all word lines to V_{CC} and stresses the control gate of whole memory cells at the same time. This circuit drastically reduces the screening time for the bias temperature test to $1/512$. This circuit is activated easily by setting the A11 pin to a higher voltage than V_{CC}.

The third test circuit is the retention test circuit during programming operation. Since high-voltage stress is applied to either the drains or control gates of the unselected memory cells, the total screening time for this test routine amounts to the total programming time. The circuit raises all word line to the programming voltage, or raises all bit lines to the programming voltage, with all word lines at ground level. The circuit reduces the test time for gate oxide leakage current in unselected cells during programming drastically. This circuit is activated easily by setting the A11 pin (for word line stress) or A10 pin (for bit line stress) to a higher voltage than V_{CC}.

VII. ELECTRICAL CHARACTERISTICS

A chip photograph is shown in Fig. 12. The row decoder is placed at the center of the memory cell array in order to reduce the word line delay time.

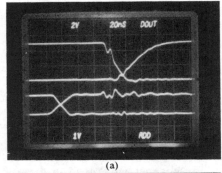

(a)

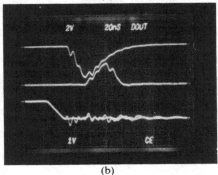

(b)

Fig. 13. Output waveform of 256K CMOS EPROM.

Fig. 13(a) shows the address access time, and Fig. 13(b) shows the chip enable access time. They are measured under typical conditions. A fast access time of less than 100 ns has been achieved.

The schmoo plot of access time is shown in Fig. 14. A wide operational margin has been obtained for supply voltage V_{CC} ranging from 2.5 to 10.0 V.

TABLE III
DEVICE CHARACTERISTICS

ORGANIZATION	32K × 8 (256K)
CHIP SIZE	5.69 mm × 6.1 mm
ACCESS TIME	100ns TYPICAL
OE ACCESS TIME	32ns TYPICAL
OPERATING CURRENT	20mA (at 5MHz)
STANDBY CURRENT	10nA
PROGRAMMING	21±0.5V, 100μS/BYTE
	$V_{BD} > 30V$
REDUNDANCY	2 ROWS POLY SILICON
	LASER FUSE

```
VCC
10.00V  +. . . . . . CPPPPPPPPPPPPPPPPPPPPPPPPPPPPPPPPPPP!
 9.50V  !. . . . . . CPPPPPPPPPPPPPPPPPPPPPPPPPPPPPPPPPPP!
 9.00V  +. . . . . . PPPPPPPPPPPPPPPPPPPPPPPPPPPPPPPPPPPP!
 8.50V  !. . . . . . CPPPPPPPPPPPPPPPPPPPPPPPPPPPPPPPPPPPP!
 8.00V  +. . . . . .CCPPPPPPPPPPPPPPPPPPPPPPPPPPPPPPPPPPPP!
 7.50V  !. . . . . . CCPPPPPPPPPPPPPPPPPPPPPPPPPPPPPPPPPPP!
 7.00V  +. . . . . .CCPPPPPPPPPPPPPPPPPPPPPPPPPPPPPPPPPPPP!
 6.50V  !. . . . . . CCPPPPPPPPPPPPPPPPPPPPPPPPPPPPPPPPPPP!
 6.00V  +. . . . . . .CCPPPPPPPPPPPPPPPPPPPPPPPPPPPPPPPPPPP!
 5.50V  !. . . . . . CCPPPPPPPPPPPPPPPPPPPPPPPPPPPPPPPPPPP!
 5.00V  +. . . . . . . CCPPPPPPPPPPPPPPPPPPPPPPPPPPPPPPPPP!
 4.50V  !. . . . . . . CCPPPPPPPPPPPPPPPPPPPPPPPPPPPPPPPPP!
 4.00V  +. . . . . . . . CCPPPPPPPPPPPPPPPPPPPPPPPPPPPPPPP!
 3.50V  !. . . . . . . . CPPPPPPPPPPPPPPPPPPPPPPP!
 3.00V  +. . . . . . . . . . . CCCPPPPPPPPPPPPPP!
 2.50V  !. .                              CCCC!
 2.00V  +. . . . . . . . . . . . . . . . . . . !
        +---------+---------+---------+---------+---------+
TACC/TCE  0.0NS    50.0NS   100.0NS   150.0NS   200.0NS   250.0NS
```

Fig. 14. The schmoo plot of address (sign *P*) and chip enable (sign *C*) access time.

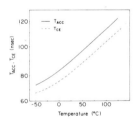

Fig. 15. Access time as a function of temperature.

Fig. 15 shows the access time as a function of temperature. The stable read operation is obtained at temperatures between −50° and 100°C.

These characteristics result from the CMOS peripheral circuit and the sense amplifier circuits.

The chip enable access time is faster than the address access time, because the reference voltage V_{REF} in Fig. 6 is set to the ground level during the standby mode as described in Section IV.

The main device characteristics are summarized in Table III.

VIII. CONCLUSION

A 256K CMOS EPROM, which meets the requirement for a high-density EPROM, has been developed. A fast programming time is achieved by introducing a DSA structure into the memory cell. The low power dissipation and fast access time have been realized by the n-well CMOS peripheral circuits. Various on-chip test circuits are implemented to shorten the screening time.

ACKNOWLEDGMENT

The authors wish to thank Dr. T. Iizuka, Dr. Y. Uchida, Dr. S. Kohyama, and Dr. Y. Nishi for their encouragement and helpful discussions, M. Sato and A. Ohmichi for the two-dimensional process simulation, and M. Momodomi, S. Saito, T. Okuda, T. Kishida, N. Tozawa, and T. Komuro for their valuable contributions and support.

REFERENCES

[1] "128K (16K × 8) UV erasable PROM," in *Intel's Memory Components Handbook*, pp. 4-29–4-38, 1983.
[2] M. Wada, S. Mimura, and H. Iizuka, "Limiting factors for programming EPROM of reduced dimensions," in *IEDM Tech. Dig.*, pp. 38–41, 1980.
[3] Y. Tarui, H. Hayashi, and T. Sekigawa, "Diffusion self-aligned MOST: A new approach for high speed device," in *Proc. 1st Conf. Solid-State Devices* (Tokyo, Japan), 1970; also *J. Japan. Soc. Appl. Phys.*, vol. 39, pp. 105–110.
[4] M. Kikuchi, S. Ohya, and M. Yamaguchi, "A DSA-type non-volatile memory transistor with self-aligned gates," in *Proc. 9th Conf. Solid-State Devices*, (Tokyo, Japan), 1977; also *J. Japan Soc. Appl. Phys.*, vol. 17, pp. 49–54.
[5] G. Perlegos, S. Pathak, A. Renninger, W. Johnson, M. Holler, J. Skupnak, M. Reitsma, and G. Kuhn, "A 64K EPROM using scaled MOS technology," in *Dig. Tech. Papers*, pp. 142–143, 1980.
[6] M. Knecht, M. Manley, D. Perass, J. Thomas, P. Keshtbod, N. Tandan, and G. Simmons, "A high-speed ultra-low power 64K CMOS EPROM with on-chip test function," *IEEE J. Solid-State Circuits*, vol. SC-18, pp. 441–446, 1983.
[7] N. R. Mielke, "New EPROM data loss mechanisms," in *Proc. 21st Ann. Process Reliability Phys. Symp.*, pp. 106–109, 1983.
[8] J. Matsunaga, H. Momose, H. Iizuka, and S. Kohyama, "Characterization of two-step impact ionization and its influence in NMOS and PMOS VLSI'S," in *IEDM Tech. Dig.*, pp. 736–739, 1980.
[9] S. Fujii, K. Natori, T. Furuyama, S. Saito, H. Toda, T. Tanaka, and O. Ozawa, "A low-power sub 100 ns 256K bit dynamic RAM," *IEEE J. Solid-State Circuits*, vol. SC-18, pp. 441–446, 1983.
[10] S. Tanaka and M. Ishikawa, "One-dimensional writing model of n-channel floating gate ionization-injection MOS (FIMOS)," *IEEE Trans. Electron Devices*, vol. ED-28, pp. 1190–1197, 1981.
[11] K. Taniguchi, T. Shibata, and H. Iwai, "Two-dimensional computer simulation models for MOS LSI fabrication process," *IEEE Trans. Electron Devices*, vol. ED-28, pp. 574–580, 1981.
[12] S. Tanaka and S. Watanabe, "A model for the relation between substrate and gate currents in N-channel MOSFET's," *IEEE Trans. Electron Devices*, vol. ED-30, pp. 668–675, 1983.

An 85ns 16Mb CMOS EPROM with Alterable Word Organization

Misao Higuchi, Mikio Koike, Kazuhisa Ninomiya, Takeshi Watanabe, Shoji Koyama, Toshikatsu Jinbo, Takeshi Okazawa

NEC Corporation

Sagamihara, Japan

This 85ns 16Mb CMOS EPROM featuring alterable word organization can be configured as either 1M x 16 bits or as 2M x 8 bits by controlling an input signal. The redundancy circuit consists of an erasable PROM cell and an unerasable PROM cell for the storage of a nonfunctional address. Divided bit lines and tungsten polycide word lines are the keys to 85ns access time. This device meets the requirements for high-density EPROMs to be used with 16b or 32b microprocessors.

The EPROM uses 0.6µm n-well CMOS technology. The 2.0x1.8µm core cell has been scaled using; (1) self-aligned trench isolation refilled with BPSG, (2) oxide-nitride-oxide (ONO) interpoly dielectrics and (3) a bit line contact with a silicide pad and selective CVD tungsten. The resulting 16Mb EPROM has a die area of 7.1 x 17.1mm. Trench isolation technology minimizes the spacing between memory cells and assures durability against the high gate voltage used in programming. Two ONO structures with a thickness equivalent to 20nm of oxide serve as the interpoly dielectrics for the EPROM cell. To reduce the parasitic resistance of the core cell transistor, a 200nm-thick tungsten silicide layer and a selectively-deposited tungsten plug are used for the bit-line contact. Key technology parameters are listed in Table 1.

This EPROM is housed in a standard 42-pin dual-in-line package with transparent lid. The pin assignment is compatible with a standard 16Mb mask programmable ROM. The EPROM can be configured as either 1M x 16 bits or as 2M x 8 bits by tying the WORD/BYTE/VPP pin high or low, respectively, for the word or byte read operation. In the word configuration, pins O0-O15 are active. In the byte configuration, pins O0-O7 are active, pins O8-O14 are high impedance, and pin O15/A-1 becomes the additional bit required to address 2M bytes. Programming is performed with a 12.5V external supply on Vpp. Figure 1 shows program/verify/read timing.

Failure mode analysis indicates there can occur not only defective rows and columns but also clusters of defective cells in the failed devices. Figure 2 shows the block diagram of the chip, illustrating the redundancy system. To enhance manufacturing yield, a spare row cell array, consisting of eight word lines, and two spare column cell arrays, consisting of sixteen bit lines, have been implemented. In this cell array redundancy system, one nonfunctional row cell array or two nonfunctional column cell arrays can be replaced by the spare arrays during testing.

Laser-blown fuses are not suitable for EPROM redundancy, since additional screening steps are required at die sort. A redundancy address circuit, shown in Figure 3, overcomes this problem. Instead of using laser-blown fuses, two kinds of PROM cells are employed for the storage of nonfunctional addresses. One is an erasable PROM cell, HM1, and the other is an unerasable PROM cell, HM2. A main cell array of defective rows or columns can be replaced by the appropriate spare cell array, using the erasable PROM cell. This allows complete testing both before and after assembly. For final testing, the unerasable PROM cell is programmed.

A micrograph of the die is shown in Figure 4. The cell array configuration is optimized for minimum bit line and word line delays. An 85ns access time is realized using divided bit lines and tungsten polycide word lines.

Table 2 shows the 16Mb EPROM characteristics. The waveforms shown in Figure 5 indicate a typical access time of less than 85ns. Typical active and standby currents are 18mA and 1µA, respectively. To reduce programming time, the word lines are pumped to a level above VPP by a charge-pump circuit. Typical programming time is less than 10µs per word, resulting in a total programming time for the chip of less than 10 seconds.

Acknowledgement

The authors thank J. Takashima, H. Yamamoto, A. Nagami, Y. Inoue, I. Sasaki, M. Kikuchi for encouragement in this work.

Technology	0.6µm lithography n-well CMOS	
	1- polysilicon, 1- polycide, 1- silicide	
Cell structure	Gate length	0.9µm
	Gate width	1.4µm
	Gate oxides	20nm
	Xj	0.3µm
Peripheral transistors	Tox	20nm
	Ln	1µm
	Lp	1.3µm
	Xjn	0.3µm
	Xjp	0.4µm
Contact size	0.6 x 0.6µm	

TABLE 1 — **Summary of 16M technology parameters**

Organization	2M x 8bits or 1M x 16bits
Cell size	2.0 x 1.8µm
Chip size	7.1 x 17.1mm
Access time	85ns
Active current	18mA (8.3MHz)
Standby current	1µA (max.)
Programming time	1 0µs/word
Package	42-pin cerdip

TABLE 2 — **Typical 16Mb EPROM characteristics**

Reprinted from the *IEEE ISSCC Dig. Tech. Pap.*, pp. 56–57, 265, 1990.

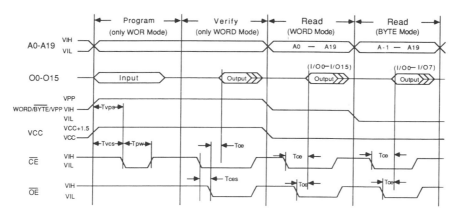

FIGURE 1 — Timing diagram

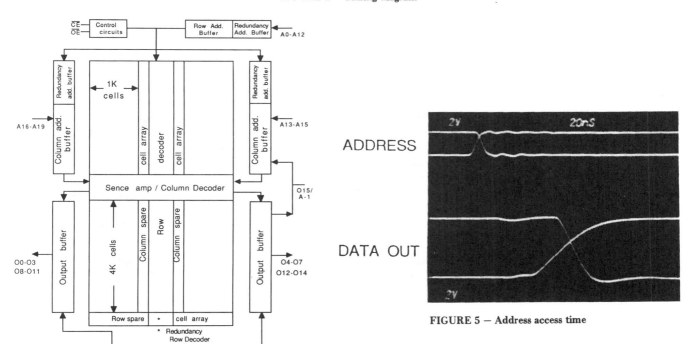

FIGURE 2 — EPROM block diagram

ADDRESS

DATA OUT

FIGURE 5 — Address access time

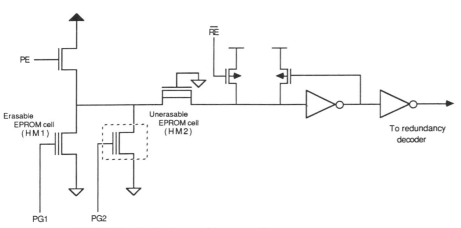

FIGURE 3 — Redundancy address circuit

315

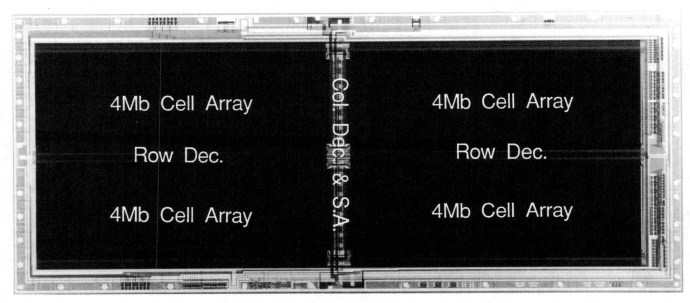

FIGURE 4 — Photograph of 16Mb EPROM chip

AN OTP TEST CIRCUIT ON THE 4Mb CMOS EPROM

Nobuaki Ohtsuka, Sumio Tanaka, Junichi Miyamoto, Shinji Saito*
Shigeru Atsumi, Kenichi Imamiya and Tetsuya Iizuka

Semiconductor Device Engineering Laboratory TOSHIBA Corp.
* Integrated Circuit Division
1-Komukai Toshiba,Saiwai-ku,Kawasaki 210,JAPAN

1. INTRODUCTION

Recently, in the field of the nonvolatile memories, the demand for OTP-ROM (One Time Programmable-ROM) devices has been rapidly increasing. The OTP-ROM is an EPROM enclosed in a plastic package. From the market research, EPROMs are programmed only once in many cases. If an EPROM is enclosed in a more inexpensive plastic package rather than a package with a window for UV (Ultra-Violet) erasure, it could become cheaper and more competitive with a MASK-ROM device in cost. Moreover, it is more attractive for the users to get the ROM programmed as they want, in shorter time.

However, the OTP has a problem of "low testability". When the EPROM chip is put into the plastic package, all of the data are set to be "1" state, and are unable to be changed by the vendor. It is impossible to monitor the access time, just before the shipping. To overcome this problem, a new OTP test circuit is implemented to the 4Mb CMOS EPROM[1] (Figure 1).

2. ACCESS TIME OF 4Mb CMOS EPROM

The memory cell has a double poly-silicon gate structure. It can be programmed by applying the high programming voltage (V_{pp}) on both the control gate and the drain of the cell transistor to inject channel hot-electrons into the floating gate. In the reading mode, the control gate of the unprogrammed cell is biased to the supply voltage (V_{cc}=5V), and the cell becomes "on-state". After the programming, the threshold voltage of the cell, V_{thcell}, is raised and the cell becomes "off-state" even if the control gate is biased to V_{cc}. The "on-state" and "off-state" of the cell correspond to "1" and "0" state of the data output, respectively.

When the output data changes from "0" to "1" ("1" read), the access time depends on the conductance of the selected cell, because this cell current pulls down the high level of the selected bit line to the low level. The cell current is affected by the process fluctuation. This is just the case in high density EPROMs such as 4Mbit, because it is getting more difficult to control the uniformity of the characteristics among all the cells. So the maximum access time is determined by the cell having a minimum current.

When the output data changes from "1" to "0" ("0" read), the access time depends on the threshold voltage shift of the selected cell (ΔV_{thcell}). If an incompletely programmed cell is selected, it takes much time to charge up the selected bit line. However, the current high density EPROMs take the "intelligent programming method". This method makes "off-state" of the "0" cell stable by providing additional programming pulses until the threshold voltage of the cell reaches enough value for the "0" state under the worst condition. Therefore, there should not be much access time difference among the "0" state cell characteristics.

Consequently, it is more important to evaluate the "1" reading access time. For the purpose, it is necessary to make a pseudo-"off-state", since all of the cells in the OTP-ROM are unprogrammed state.

3. OTP TEST CIRCUIT

The OTP test circuit is implemented to the 4Mb CMOS EPROM in order to monitor the precise access time for the OTP application. The test mode is selected by providing the high level ($\gg V_{cc}$) to /CE pin. /OE is utilized for the word line selection as shown in Figure 2. Figure 3 shows the timing chart of the test mode. When the level of /CE becomes higher than ($V_{cc}+2V_{thp}$), where V_{thp} is the threshold voltage of the p-channel peripheral transistor, MOD becomes low and the test mode begins. As shown in Figure 3, the test sequence is divided into two states of A and B according to /OE. In the state of A, the logical low level of /OE makes /OTP low. /OTP disables the

row partial decoders and no word line is selected. In another word, all of the word lines are set to the low level independent of the row address. This makes all of the cells apparently "off-state" and the output data comes out as "0" state, even though all the cells are actually "on-state". In the state of B, the logical high level of /OE makes /OTP high. /OTP enables the row partial decoders and the word lines selected by the row address are pulled up to the high level. Since all of the cells are "on-state", the selected bit line is discharged and the output data is changed to "1". Thus, the output data varies from "0" to "1" and from "1" to "0" according to the /OE change from "0" to "1" and from "1" to "0", respectively. By repeating these states, it is possible to read out the pseudo-checker patterns for all the memory cells selected by address.

In the normal reading mode, the address access time is determined by the total delay time of row address buffer, the row decoder, the word line, the bit line, the sense amplifier and the output buffer. For this OTP test mode, the delay of the /OE buffer circuit corresponds to that of the address buffer circuit. In addition, the dominant factors for the access time are the word line delay and the bit line delay. So the difference between /OE and address buffer circuit delay is negligibly small. Therefore, the access time can be monitored as the delay time from /OE to the data output, and the time is surely determined by the selected "on-state" cell characteristics.

4. EXPERIMENTAL RESULT

Figure 4 shows typical access waveforms in the normal reading mode of the EPROM programmed in the checker data. As indicated in this figure, the access time of 100ns is observed in both cases of "1" read and of "0" read. (The output data is defined as high and low when it transits above 2V and below 0.8V, respectively.) Figure 5 shows typical access waveforms in the OTP test mode of the unprogrammed EPROM. The delay from the change of /OE to that of the output data is shown. Figure 5 (a) and (b) indicate that each delay time of "1" read and "0" read is 100ns, which is equal to the access time in the normal reading mode, respectively.

Figure 6 shows the histograms of the access time in the normal reading mode and of the delay time in the OTP test mode dependent on the selected address. The worst values meet with each other in the both modes. The access times of "1" read fluctuate much widely in comparison with those of "0" read, because the former is determined by the cell current. The histograms of Figure 6 (a) and (b) show the almost same spectrum, which indicates that this OTP test circuit successfully simulates the real address access. So the test circuit is quite useful to monitor the precise access time of the OTP.

5. CONCLUSION

A new OTP test circuit is proposed and is well implemented to the 4Mb CMOS EPROM. This circuit makes it possible to monitor the precise access time of the EPROM chip without programming the test patterns. Therefore, the OTP chips which are out of the specifications will be able to be screened off after the packaging, easily. This circuit will be more important for the higher density EPROM, as getting the uniformity of the cell characteristics becomes more difficult.

6. ACKNOWLEDGEMENT

The authors would like to thank Y.Unno and O.Ozawa for their continuous encouragement and Y.Muroya, T.Sako and Y.Iyama for their contributions.

7. REFERENCE

[1] S.Atsumi et al, "A 120 ns 4Mb CMOS EPROM," to be presented at 1987 ISSCC.

Reprinted from the *Dig. 1987 Symp. VLSI Circuit*, pp. 55–56, 1987.

317

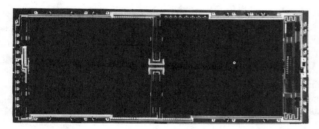

Fig.1 Chip photomicrograph of the 4Mb CMOS EPROM.

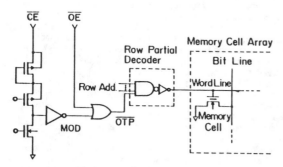

Fig.2 New OTP test circuit.

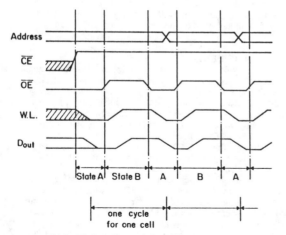

Fig.3 Timing chart of the OTP test mode.

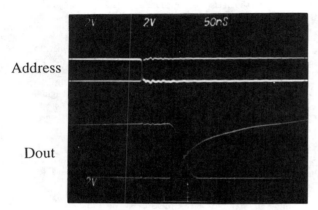

Fig.4 Waveforms in the normal reading mode.

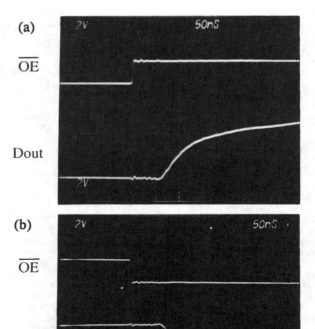

Fig.5 Waveforms in the OTP test mode
(a): "1" read
(b): "0" read

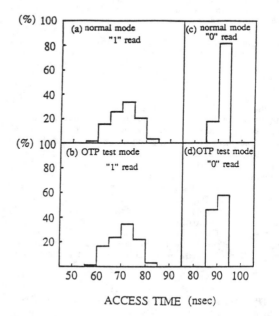

Fig.6 Fluctuation of the access time.
(a): "1" read in the normal mode
(b): "1" read in the OTP test mode
(c): "0" read in the normal mode
(d): "0" read in the OTP test mode

A 16-ns 1-Mb CMOS EPROM

MASAO KURIYAMA, SHIGERU ATSUMI, KEN-ICHI IMAMIYA, YUMIKO IYAMA,
NAOHIRO MATSUKAWA, HITOSHI ARAKI, KAZUHITO NARITA,
KAZUNORI MASUDA, AND SUMIO TANAKA

Abstract —A 16-ns 1-Mb CMOS EPROM has been developed, utilizing high-speed circuit technology and a double-metal process. In order to achieve the fast access time, a differential sensing scheme with address transition detection (ATD) is introduced. Moreover, a double-word-line structure, based on a double-metal process, is introduced to reduce word-line delay. High noise immunity is obtained by a newly developed bit-line bias circuit and a data-latch circuit. Sufficient threshold voltage shift, which is indispensable for fast access time, is guaranteed by a newly developed threshold monitoring program (TMP) scheme. The array is organized as 64K × 16 b, which is suitable to 32-b high-performance microprocessors. The active power is 425 mW. The programming time is 100 μs. The chip size is 4.94 × 15.64 mm².

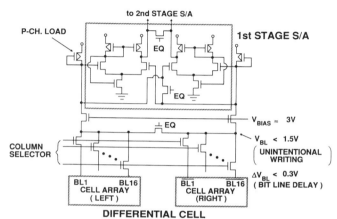

Fig. 1. Sense-amplifier circuit structure.

I. INTRODUCTION

WITH THE progress achieved in 32-b high-speed microprocessors, the demand for high-density and high-speed EPROM has been increasing. Although a high-speed 256-kb EPROM has been reported [1], it is not sufficient in its bit density for 32-b microprocessors. In order to meet these requirements, a 16-ns 1-Mb EPROM [2] has been developed by utilizing high-speed circuit technology, double metal, and 0.8-μm minimum design rule. The 1-Mb EPROM has a 16-b-wide data bus, which is suitable for 32-b high-speed microprocessors.

In order to achieve a fast-access 1-Mb EPROM, it is necessary to overcome several problems. First, a conventional sense amplifier has a disadvantage in regard to sensing speed. In order to achieve high-speed sensing operation, a differential sensing scheme with address transition detection (ATD) is introduced. Second, *RC* delay in the word line is very large in the conventional EPROM. A double-word-line structure, utilizing double metal, is introduced to reduce word-line delay. These details are described in Section II.

Third, high-speed devices require large conductance data-out buffers, which generate a large peak current, and cause a supply voltage instability. Moreover, this

device has a 16-b-wide data bus, and the noise generated in the output buffer is very large. Therefore, high noise immunity is one of the key issues in obtaining high-speed sensing speed. A bit-line bias circuit, with a depletion-load transistor, was developed to increase sense-amplifier noise immunity. The data-out latch circuit is implemented to prevent output data glitch, which induces large V_{CC} bounce. These details are described in Section III.

Fourth, in order to achieve fast access time, it is also important to guarantee sufficient threshold voltage shift for memory transistors. A threshold monitoring program scheme was developed for the 1-Mb EPROM, which is described in Section IV.

Typical device characteristics are outlined in Section V. Conclusions are given in Section VI.

II. HIGH-SPEED CIRCUIT TECHNOLOGY

In order to obtain fast access time, a high-speed sensing scheme, a double-word-line structure, and a high-speed decoder are introduced to reduce word-line and bit-line delay, respectively.

A. High-Speed Sensing

A differential sensing scheme with ATD is introduced to achieve fast access. Fig. 1 shows a sense-amplifier circuit structure. Complemental data are programmed

Manuscript received April 18, 1990; revised June 22, 1990.
M. Kuriyama, S. Atsumi, K. Imamiya, N. Matsukawa, H. Araki, K. Narita, K. Masuda, and S. Tanaka are with Semiconductor Device Engineering Laboratory, Toshiba Corporation, Kawasaki, 210 Japan.
Y. Iyama is with Toshiba Microelectronics Corporation, Kawasaki, 210 Japan.
IEEE Log Number 9038259.

Reprinted from *IEEE J. Solid-State Circuits*, vol. 25, no. 5, pp. 1141–1146, October 1990.

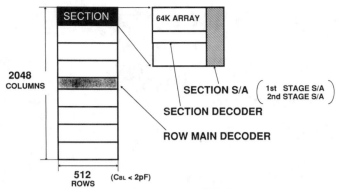

Fig. 2.   1-Mb EPROM array structure.

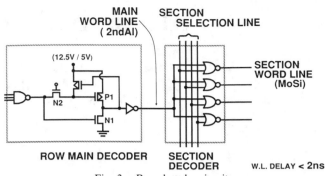

Fig. 3.   Row decoder circuit.

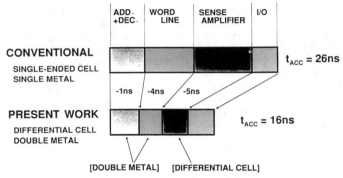

Fig. 4.   1-Mb EPROM simulated access-time components.

into a pair of stacked gate transistors that form one memory cell. Hereafter, we refer to this memory cell scheme as a differential cell [3]. In order to suppress unintentional writing during the reading operation, the bit-line voltage is limited to below 1.5 V by constant bit-line bias voltage, which will be described in detail in Section III. The bit-line swing is restricted to less than 0.3 V, to achieve high-speed operation.

The bit-line swing is amplified by a gate–drain connected p-channel load transistor, and fed to a following differential sense amplifier. The differential sense amplifier consists of three-stage differential sense circuits. Each differential sense circuit consists of paired current-mirror circuits to obtain highly symmetrical outputs. Individual complementary nodes are equalized by the ATD pulse to accelerate the sensing speed.

The first-stage sense amplifiers and the second-stage ones, which correspond to data-out buffers, are placed in each section. These second-stage sense amplifiers output the complemental data to the third-stage sense amplifiers via main sense lines. The main sense lines are fabricated by 2nd Al, and are wired across the chip. In order to minimize the delay from the third-stage sense amplifier to the data-out buffer, the third-stage sense amplifier is placed near the corresponding data-out buffer.

By utilizing the differential sensing scheme with ATD, the sense-amplifier operation speed is 5 ns faster, compared with optimized single-ended sense amplifiers.

B. Word-Line / Bit-Line Delay Reduction

In order to reduce the word-line and bit-line delay, a double-word-line structure [4] is implemented. Fig. 2 shows an array structure for the 1-Mb EPROM. The cell array consists of 512 rows by 2048 columns. The column lines are divided into eight sections. A row main decoder is placed at the center of the array. Section decoders are placed at the center of each section. Main word lines are fabricated by 2nd Al to reduce the main word-line delay. Section word lines are fabricated by MoSi to reduce the section word-line delay. Thus, only 128 cells belong to each section word line. By introducing the double-word-line structure, the word-line delay is reduced to less than

2 ns. As only 512 cells are connected to each bit line, the bit-line capacitance is less than 2 pF, greatly reducing the bit-line delay.

In order to achieve high-speed decoding, a new row decoder circuit was developed. Fig. 3 shows the row decoder circuit. The row main decoder consists of a feedback circuit, and serves to convert the V_{CC} (= 5 V) level signal to the V_{PP} (= 12.5 V) level during programming. A p-channel load transistor gate P_1 is connected via n-channel transfer gate N_2, and n-channel driver gate N_1 is directly connected to the output node for the NAND gate. The row decoder circuit, which is free from voltage drop in the transfer gate, achieves high-speed operation. The section decoder consists of an NOR gate controlled by the main word line and one of the four section selection lines.

C. Access-Time Components

Fig. 4 shows simulated access-time components for the 1-Mb EPROM, with differential cell and double metal, and conventional EPROM, with single-ended cell and single metal. The simulated conditions, for fair comparison, are as follows:

1) the cell currents for both EPROM's are 200 μA;
2) the chip sizes for both EPROM's are nearly equal: the conventional EPROM has eight divided word lines, while the 1-Mb EPROM has 16 divided word lines with double-word-line structure;
3) $V_{CC} = 5$ V, at room temperature, with a 30-pF load capacitance.

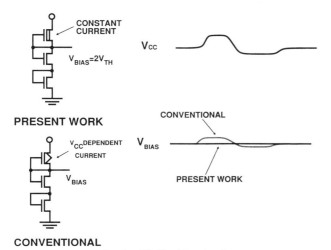

PRESENT WORK

CONVENTIONAL

Fig. 5. Bit-line bias circuit.

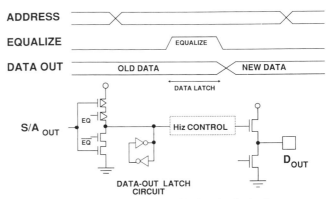

Fig. 6. Data-out buffer with data-latch circuit.

By introducing the double-metal process, 1-ns improvement is achieved at the peripheral circuit, and 4-ns improvement is achieved by introducing the double-word-line structure. Thus, a total 5-ns improvement is achieved by using the double-metal process. A 5-ns improvement is achieved at sense amplifiers by introducing a differential sensing scheme with ATD.

The 16-ns total access time is 60% of that for the conventional 1-Mb EPROM. The contributions from the double-metal process and the differential sensing scheme to fast access time are almost the same.

III. Noise Immunity

High-speed devices require large conductance buffers to achieve fast output. These devices with a 16-b-wide data bus, like the 1-Mb EPROM, generate a large current, and cause supply voltage instability (V_{CC} bounce). Thus, high noise immunity is required particularly for wide data-bus systems. In order to obtain high noise immunity and fast sensing, it is important to keep the sensing level independent of V_{CC} bounce. A new bit-line bias circuit was developed to overcome the V_{CC} bounce problem [5]. In order to decrease noise, the data-out latch circuit is implemented.

A. Bit-Line Bias Circuit

The bit-line voltage is limited below to 1.5 V, to suppress unintentional writing during the reading operation. Fig. 5 shows a bit-line bias circuit, newly developed for the 1-Mb EPROM, and shows the conventional EPROM's for comparison. The conventional circuit utilizes a p-channel load transistor, and draws V_{CC}-dependent current. Thus, the conventional circuit generates V_{CC}-dependent bit-line bias voltage V_{BIAS}. Therefore, the bit-line voltage overshoots when V_{CC} bounce occurs. The bit-line overshoot takes a long recovery time because the bit-line capacitance is very large. Thus, once the bit-line voltage overshoots, the sense amplifier outputs incorrect data. It

is necessary to keep the bit-line voltage constant under the V_{CC} bounce to obtain high noise immunity.

In order to obtain high noise immunity, a new constant voltage bit-line bias circuit was developed. The bias circuit utilizes an n-channel depletion-load transistor, whose gate is connected to the source terminal. The gate–source connected depletion-load transistor draws a constant current, independent of supply voltage. Thus, the bias circuit outputs the $2V_{TH}$ bias voltage (about 3 V) independent of supply voltage. The bit-line bias circuit guarantees high noise immunity for sense amplifiers.

B. Data-Out Buffer

During equalization, incorrect data may be output before the correct data are output, and generate data-out glitch. Fig. 6 shows a data-out buffer with a data-latch circuit. During the equalization, the equalization pulse separates the data-out buffer from the sense amplifiers. The data-latch circuit holds the previous data, utilizing a data-latch circuit to prevent data-out glitch.

In addition, an n-channel enhancement-load transistor is applied to the data-out buffers to narrow the data-out swing for saving power and noise.

IV. Threshold Monitoring Program (TMP) Scheme

Fig. 7 shows simulated access time as a function of threshold voltage (V_{TH}) shift. The minimum threshold shift required for the memory cell to obtain a fast access time is as large as 2 V. If the data are verified with minimum cycle time, the differential sensing scheme guarantees sufficient V_{TH} shift, more than 2 V. However, the commercial programmer verifies the data with a much longer cycle time, such as 1 μs. For 1-μs cycle verification, only more than a 0.1-V V_{TH} shift is needed for verification. Therefore, the differential sensing scheme is unsuitable for program verification with a commercial programmer. In order to overcome this problem, a threshold monitoring program (TMP) scheme was developed.

Fig. 8 shows a TMP circuit. The TMP circuit consists of a single-ended sense amplifier parallel with the normal

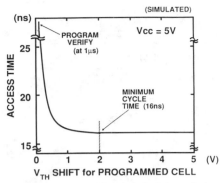

Fig. 7. Access-time characteristic as a function of threshold voltage (V_{TH}) shift.

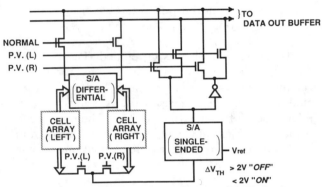

Fig. 8. Threshold monitoring program (TMP) circuit.

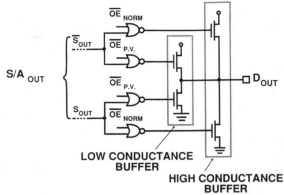

Fig. 9. Data-out buffer for program verify test mode.

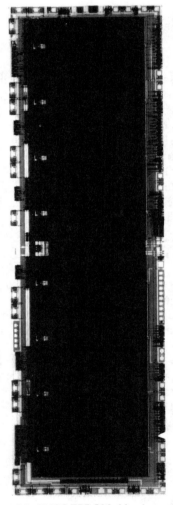

Fig. 10. 1-Mb CMOS EPROM chip photomicrograph.

differential sense amplifier, and transfer gates, which select a right or left cell to verify. The single-ended sense amplifier is the same type of circuit used in our conventional works such as a 256-kb EPROM [6]. During the program mode, the input data are latched, and select the cell transistor to be programmed. During the subsequent program verify mode, the programmed cell is connected to a single-ended sense amplifier via the transfer gate controlled by the latched data. The single-ended sense amplifier is designed to detect a minimum V_{TH} shift, as large as 2 V. When the programmed cell has insufficient V_{TH} shift (< 2 V), the single-ended sense amplifier outputs opposite data with the latched data. If an insufficiently programmed cell is detected, the detected cell is additionally programmed by intelligent programming, until the detected cell is sufficiently programmed.

The single-ended sense amplifier is also used during the blank-check test mode. The test mode is selected by a third-level $\overline{PGM}$ signal ($> V_{CC}$). The $\overline{OE}$ signal is used as an address signal, which selects a right or left memory transistor for the differential cell. During the test mode, the single-ended sense amplifier operates all cell transistors as 2-Mb memory cells. The single-ended sense amplifier is placed near the corresponding data-out buffer, which greatly reduces the layout area. At the program verify or blank-check mode, the data-out buffer conductance is decreased to reduce noise, because the single-ended sense amplifier has less noise immunity than the differential sense amplifier (Fig. 9).

By developing the TMP scheme and utilizing a less conductive data-out buffer, the 1-Mb EPROM can be programmed by a commercial programmer, like conventional EPROM's.

V. DEVICE CHARACTERISTICS

Fig. 10 shows a chip photomicrograph of the 1-Mb EPROM. The address buffers are located on the right-

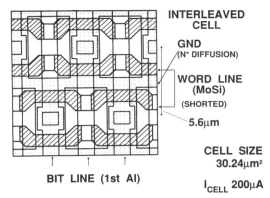

Fig. 11. Memory cell schema.

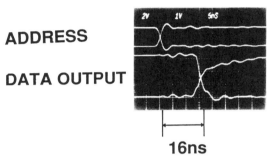

Fig. 12. 1-Mb EPROM output waveform.

TABLE I
DEVICE PARAMETERS

• PROCESS	0.8μm N-WELL CMOS DOUBLE METAL, MoSi
• GATE OXIDE	240A (PERIPHERAL)
	200A (1st GATE)
	300A (INTERPOLY ONO)
• GATE LENGTH	1.0μm (N-CH. LDD)
	1.2μm (P-CH. LDD)
	0.9μm (CELL)
• SELL SIZE	30.24μm²

TABLE II
CHIP PERFORMANCE

• ORGANIZATION	64K x 16b (1Mbit)
• OPERATION	FULLY STATIC
• POWER SUPPLY	V_{CC} = 5V, V_{PP} = 12.5V
• ACCESS TIME	16ns
• POWER CONSUMPTION	425mW (30MHz)
• PROGRAM PULSE	100μs
• REDUNDANCY	4 MAIN WORD LINES
• PACKAGE	40PIN CERDIP

hand side of the chip, and the data-out buffers are located on the left-hand side of the chip. Chip size is 4.94×15.64 mm². The organization is 64K word × 16 b. Four spare main word lines, each of which has four section word lines, are implemented to improve the yield.

Fig. 11 shows a top view of the memory cell. An interleaved cell scheme is introduced to the 1-Mb EPROM. The word-line pitch was doubled to 5.6 μm, which makes the NOR-gate layout in the section decoder very simple. The differential cell size is 30.24 μm². Strong coupling between the floating gate and control gate and a 2.2-μm-wide channel result in a large cell current, 200 μA in the reading operation. The 1-Mb EPROM is housed in a standard 600-mil 40-pin JEDEC standard cerdip package. All inputs and outputs are TTL compatible.

Fig. 12 shows output waveforms for the address access time. A 16-ns high-speed access is measured at $V_{CC} = 5$ V and room temperature, with a 30-pF load capacitance. The active power is 425 mW. The 100-μs programming time was achieved at 12.5-V program voltage.

The 1-Mb EPROM is fabricated by a 0.8-μm n-well CMOS technology. In order to achieve fast access, a double-metal process is introduced. A masked LDD structure is applied to both peripheral n-channel and p-channel transistors to suppress the hot-electron effect. The interpoly dielectrics consist of an ONO structure.

The device parameters are summarized in Table I. The chip performance is summarized in Table II.

VI. CONCLUSION

A 16-ns 1-Mb EPROM has been developed by introducing a differential sensing scheme, a double-metal process, and three-stage differential sensing with ATD to acquire high-speed access. By developing a bit-line bias circuit with an n-channel depletion-load transistor, high noise immunity is achieved. By developing a data-out buffer with a data-latch circuit, data-out noise is greatly reduced. A threshold monitoring program (TMP) scheme guarantees sufficient threshold voltage shift for the memory cell to achieve fast access.

ACKNOWLEDGMENT

The authors thank K. Shinozaki, M. Wada, and Y. Unno for encouragement, and J. Miyamoto, K. Yoshikawa, N. Ohtsuka, N. Arai, Y. Muroya, T. Sako, and M. Higashino for technical contributions and discussions.

REFERENCES

[1] D. Hoff *et al.*, "A 23-ns 256K EPROM with double-layer metal and address transition detection," *IEEE J. Solid-State Circuits*, vol. 24, pp. 1250–1258, Oct. 1989.
[2] S. Atsumi *et al.*, "A 16ns 1Mb CMOS EPROM," in *ISSCC Dig. Tech. Papers*, Feb. 1990, pp. 58–59.
[3] S. Pathak *et al.*, "A 25ns CMOS EPROM using a 4-transistor cell," in *ISSCC Dig. Tech. Papers*, Feb. 1985, pp. 162–163.
[4] T. Sakurai *et al.*, "A low power 46ns 256kbit CMOS static RAM with dynamic double word line," *IEEE J. Solid-State Circuits*, vol. SC-19, pp. 578–585, Oct. 1984.
[5] K. Imamiya *et al.*, "A 68ns 4Mbit CMOS EPROM with high noise immunity design," in *Symp. VLSI Circuit Dig. Tech. Papers*, 1989, pp. 37–38.
[6] S. Tanaka *et al.*, "A programmable 256K CMOS EPROM with on-chip test circuits" in *ISSCC Dig. Tech. Papers*, Feb. 1984, pp. 148–149.

Paper 8.6

A 90ns 100K Erase/Program Cycle Megabit Flash Memory

Virgil Kynett, Jim Anderson, Greg Atwood, Pat Dix, Mick Fandrich, Owen Jungroth, Susan Kao, Jerry A. Kreifels, Stefan Lai, Ho-Chun Liou, Benedict Liu, Richard Lodenquai, Wen-Juei Lu, Roy Pavloff, Daniel Tang, George Tsau, J. C. Tzeng, Branislav Vajdic, Gautam Verma, Simon Wang, Steven Wells, Mark Winston, Lisa Yang

Intel Corporation

Folsom, CA

ADVANCES IN PHOTOLITHOGRAPHY have made possible an electrically-erasable, reprogrammable, 90ns 1 Mb flash memory capable of greater than 100,000 erase/program cycles. This memory implements a command port and an internal reference voltage generator, allowing microprocessor-controlled reprogramming[1].

The 90ns access time results from $95\mu A$ memory cell current, low resistance poly-silicide word lines, advanced scaled periphery transistors, and a di/dt - optimized data-out buffer. Using CMOS inputs, power dissipation is 40mW in the active state and $20\mu W$ in standby. The memory electrically erases in 900ms and programs at the rate of $10\mu s$/byte. The device contains thirty-two columns of redundant elements and utilizes flash memory cells to store the address of repaired columns. The use of flash memory reduces silicon area significantly compared to that required by metal-shielded EPROM cells[2].

The memory was fabricated on a $1\mu m$ double poly N-well CMOS process. Silicide was used on the word lines to achieve the 90ns access time. The CMOS periphery circuits were constructed with $0.9\mu m$ L_{eff}, 250 Å gate oxide LDD transistors. The density of this $1\mu m$ flash technology is demonstrated on the $1.0\mu m$ and $1.5\mu m$ memory cell comparison shown in Figure 1. The $1.0\mu m$ memory cell has a $15.2\mu m^2$ area, which is over twice as small as the $1.5\mu m$ memory cell. A micrograph of the 245 mil^2, 128k x 8 flash memory is shown in Figure 2. The process/device characteristics are summarized in Table 1.

A typical cell erase/program Vt margin is shown as a function of reprogramming cycles in Figure 3. After 100,000 cycles there is still 2.5V program-read margin to ensure data retention. Accelerated retention bake experiments done at 250°C for 168 hours indicate that after 10,000 cycles the memory will exhibit only 0.7V program Vt shift. Program and erase time degrade slightly due to normal charge trap-up in the tunnel oxide (Fig. 4). In addition, endurance reliability has been excellent, with no tunnel oxide breakdown.

To build a manufacturable 1Mb flash memory, it is essential to control the memory array erase Vt. The key is proper selection of the erase Vt maximum and maintenance of a tight Vt distribution. The maximum erased Vt is set to 3.2V by the erase algorithm and the internal erase verify circuits[3]. Good oxide quality gives an erased Vt distribution width that does not change appreciably with cycling. The tight distribution gives an order of magnitude of erase time margin for the fastest erasing cell. (Fig. 5).

Array erase is executed by switching high voltage onto the source junction of all cells and grounding all select lines. The array source switch, shown in Figure 6, switches high voltage onto the source junctions. Transistor M16 is a large device which pulls the source to ground during read and program modes. During erase mode, the high-voltage latch formed by M5-M8 enables transistor M15, which then pulls the array source up to 12V. To obtain fast array erase times, this device must supply the grounded-gate breakdown current which occurs on the sources of the memory array. The upper boundary on M15 current-sourcing capability is set by the maximum allowable substrate current. If VPP is raised to 12V before VCC is above approximately 1.8V, the low VCC detect circuit formed by M1-M4 drives the node LOWVCC to 9V. Transistors M9-M11 then force the erase circuit into a non-erase state with M15 off and M16 on. When VCC rises above 1.8V, the chip will be reset into a read state.

[1] Kynett, V., et. al., "An In-System Reprogrammable 256K CMOS Flash Memory", ISSCC DIGEST of TECHNICAL PAPERS, p.132-133,; Feb., 1988

[2] Canepa, G., et. al., "A 90ns 4Mb CMOS EPROM", ISSCC DIGEST of TECHNICAL PAPERS, p.120-121; Feb., 1988.

[3] Kynett, V., et. al., "AN In-System Reprogrammable 32K x 8 CMOS Flash Memory", IEEE J. Solid-State Circuits, vol. 23, p.1157-1163; Oct., 1988.

Technology	Cell	Periphery	Device
1.0-um Lithography	Area = 3.8um x 4um	Tox = 250 Å	Die Size: 36743 mils²
1-Poly, 1-Silicide	Gate Oxide >100 Å	Leff N+P = 0.9um	Organized: 128K x 8
N-Well CMOS	Read Current = 95uA	Xjn = 0.3um	Access Time: 90nS
Epi on P+	Terase = 900mS	Xjp = 0.6um	Active Power: 8mA
	Tprog = 10uS/byte		Standby Power: 4uA
			Package: 32-pin Cerdip

TABLE 1 — Device parameters

Reprinted from the *IEEE ISSCC Dig. Tech. Pap.*, pp. 140–141, 317, 1989.

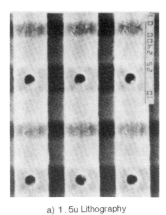

a) 1.5u Lithography

(5,000 × magnification)

FIGURE 1 — Array micrograph

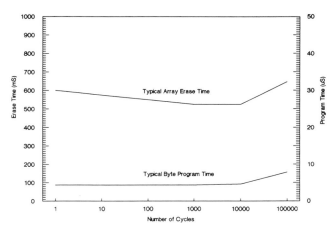

FIGURE 4 — Erase/program time versus cycling

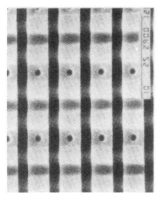

b) 1.0u Lithography

(5,000 × magnification)

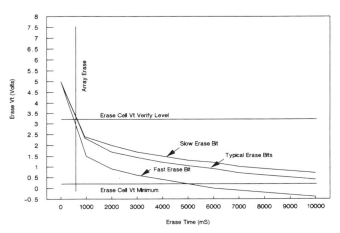

FIGURE 5 — Array erase V_T versus erase time

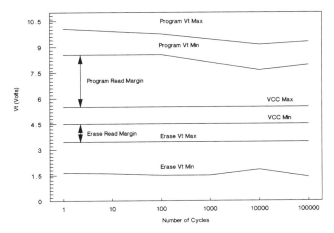

FIGURE 3 — Array V_T versus cycles

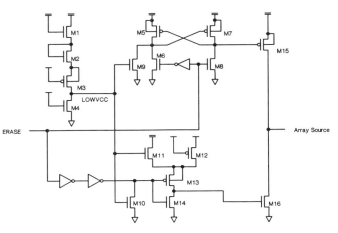

FIGURE 6 — Array source switch

325

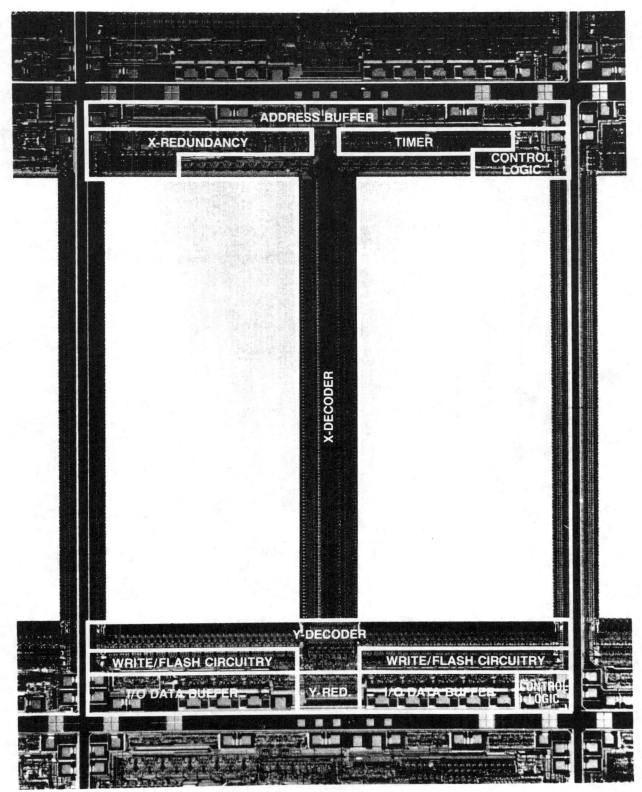

FIGURE 2 — 1Mbit die micrograph

An 80-ns 1-Mb Flash Memory with On-Chip Erase/Erase-Verify Controller

KOICHI SEKI, MEMBER, IEEE, HITOSHI KUME, MEMBER, IEEE, YUZURU OHJI, MEMBER, IEEE, TAKASHI KOBAYASHI, ATSUSHI HIRAIWA, TAKASHI NISHIDA, TAKESHI WADA, KAZUHIRO KOMORI, KAZUTO IZAWA, TOSHIAKI NISHIMOTO, YASUROH KUBOTA, AND KAZUYOSHI SHOHJI

Abstract —An internal erase and erase-verify control system has been implemented in an electrically erasable, reprogrammable, 80-ns 1-Mb flash memory, which is suitable for in-system reprogram applications. The memory utilizes a one-transistor type cell with a cell area of 10.4 μm^2. The die area is 32.3 mm^2. An erase mode is initiated by a pulse of 50-ns duration. An erase and erase-verify sequence is automatically conducted in a chip without any further external control. The internal status can be checked through a status polling mode. The 80-ns access time results from advanced sense amplifiers as well as low-resistance polysilicide word lines and scaled periphery transistors. To realize high-sensitivity and high-speed sense circuits, a pMOS transistor, whose gate is connected to its drain, is used as a load transistor.

I. INTRODUCTION

FLASH memories feature both high density, like EPROM's, and electrical erasure capability [1]–[5]. Hence, they essentially suit any application that requires high density and reprogrammability without removing them from a system. However, previously reported flash memories would have some problems if they were used for these applications. One problem was an increase in the system load due to its complicated erase procedure. To conduct chip erase, a microprocessor outside of the chip had to control the memories according to a certain erase and erase-verify sequence so that the maximum threshold voltage in the memory would be low enough to be read out as a logic ONE. It makes a system bus busy during the electrical erase. Another problem was the slow access time. Even though the maximum threshold voltage in a memory is tightly controlled, it is higher than that found in a conventional EPROM, meaning a smaller cell current. It usually results in a slow access time.

This paper describes a 1-Mb flash memory suitable for in-system reprogram applications. For the purpose of

Manuscript received April 18, 1990; revised June 1, 1990.
K. Seki, H. Kume, Y. Ohji, T. Kobayashi, A. Hiraiwa, and T. Nishida are with the Central Research Laboratory, Hitachi Ltd., Kokubunji, Tokyo 185, Japan.
T. Wada, K. Komori, K. Izawa, and T. Nishimoto are with the Semiconductor Design and Development Center, Hitachi Ltd., Kodaira, Tokyo 187, Japan.
Y. Kubota and K. Shohji are with the Hitachi VLSI Engineering Corporation, Kodaira, Tokyo 187, Japan.
IEEE Log Number 9037782.

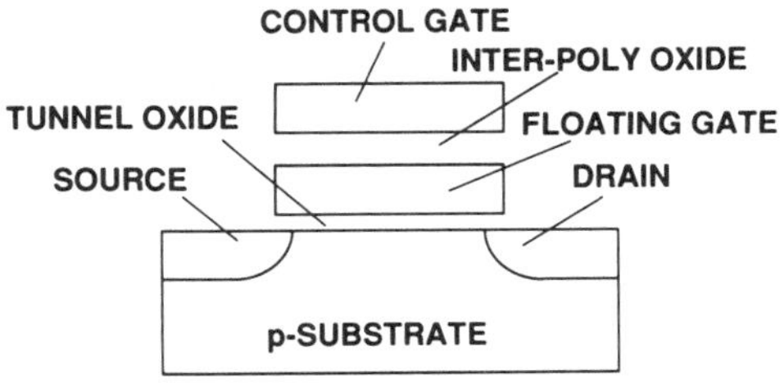

Fig. 1. Schematic cross-sectional view of a memory cell.

reducing the system load, an erase and erase-verify control system has been implemented in a chip. Advanced sense amplifiers have been developed, which provide a high-speed access overcoming small cell currents.

II. MEMORY CELL

A schematic cross-sectional view of a memory cell is shown in Fig. 1. A one-transistor type cell is adopted, which has a stacked gate structure with a tunnel oxide of 10 nm. The memory cell uses hot-carrier injection for the programming mechanism like in conventional EPROM's. It can be erased through the source by Fowler–Nordheim tunneling. The process parameters are summarized in Table I. The memory is fabricated by a 0.8-μm, one-poly, one-polysilicide, single-metal CMOS process based on a conventional EPROM process. Polysilicide is used on the word lines to achieve a high-speed access time. The cell area is 10.36 μm^2 and it can be directly applicable to a 4-Mb flash memory. The tunnel oxide thickness is 10 nm and the interpoly dielectric layer is a 30-nm-thick SiO_2 fabricated by thermal oxidation of polysilicon.

III. CIRCUIT DESIGN

A. On-Chip Controller

A time chart in an electrical erase mode is shown in Fig. 2. A simple initialization procedure of an electrical erase mode was chosen rather than a command-port architecture [2], [3] to realize a compatibility with a byte-

Reprinted from *IEEE J. Solid-State Circuits*, vol. 25, no. 5, pp. 1147–1152, October 1990.

TABLE I
PROCESS PARAMETERS

MIN. FEATURE SIZE	0.8μm
TECHNOLOGY	1-POLY 1-POLY-SILICIDE SINGLE METAL
CELL SIZE	10.36 μm²
TUNNEL OXIDE	10nm
INTERPOLY OXIDE	30nm

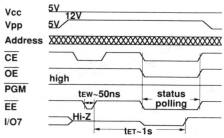

Fig. 2. External timing in an electrical erase mode.

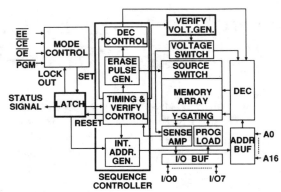

Fig. 3. Block diagram of 1-Mb flash memory.

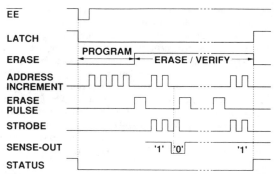

Fig. 4. Internal sequence in an electrical erase mode.

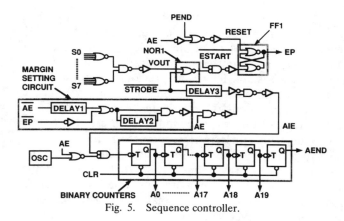

Fig. 5. Sequence controller.

wide 1-Mb EPROM. The erase mode is initiated by an $\overline{EE}$ pulse with a duration of around 50 ns applied to pin 30, when $\overline{OE}$ and $\overline{PGM}$ are high and $\overline{CE}$ is low.

An erase and erase-verify sequence is automatically conducted in the chip without any further external control. The internal status can be checked through a status polling mode at I/O port 7, where $\overline{CE}$, $\overline{OE}$, and $\overline{EE}$ are low, and $\overline{PGM}$ is high. This check reveals that the status signal is low during an electrical erase.

This simple erase procedure reduces the load of the microprocessor, especially in a system that contains more than one flash memory. After the $\overline{EE}$ signal is latched, no external control signal affects the electrical erase operation. Thus, electrical erase of one device A and programming of the other device B can be done at the same time. Even after the end of electrical erase of device A, programming of device B cannot destroy the data in device A, because each flash memory is usually connected to a different $\overline{CE}$ signal line.

A schematic block diagram of the memory is shown in Fig. 3. The on-chip erase and erase-verify control system features a control signal latch, a sequence controller, and a verify voltage generator. The control signal latch locks out any control signals and address signals except status polling instructions, and the sequence controller carries out an erase and erase-verify operation until the end of the erase mode. The verify voltage generator supplies low voltage to decoders and sense amplifiers in the verify operation to guarantee an adequate read operational margin.

The internal sequence is shown in Fig. 4. After the EE signal is latched, all bits in the memory are programmed. Without this stage, memory cells having low threshold voltages would deplete. Address increment signals generated by an internal oscillator are supplied to binary counters and converted to internal address signals as shown in Fig. 5, where AIE and AE are low. Then they are supplied to address buffers.

Next, the chip is switched to an erase and erase-verify stage. The signal AE becomes high and $ESTART$ goes to a low level. The $ESTART$ sets a flip-flop $FF1$ and electrical erase signal EP goes high. Chip erase is executed by applying a high voltage onto the source of all cells and grounding all word lines according to this signal EP. After a 10-ms electrical erase, verification starts by resetting the flip-flop $FF1$ through $PEND$, which is high at the end of electrical erase pulse. A NOR gate NOR1 in the sequence controller reads each byte selected by the internal address signal generator at the strobes shown in Fig. 4. The verification continues until a high-threshold-voltage byte is found, that is, until at least one of the

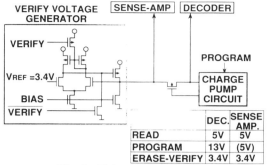

Fig. 6. Voltage switch circuit.

	DEC.	SENSE AMP.
READ	5V	5V
PROGRAM	13V	(5V)
ERASE-VERIFY	3.4V	3.4V

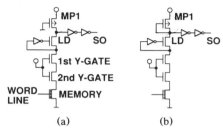

Fig. 7. Sense-amplifier circuit. (a) Conventional circuit. (b) Proposed circuit.

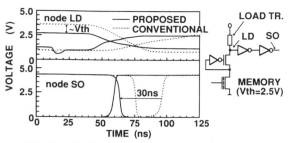

Fig. 8. Simulated waveforms of sense amplifiers.

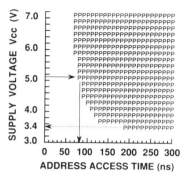

Fig. 9. Typical schmoo plot with checkerboard pattern.

sense-outs $SO-S7$ becomes high. If high-threshold-voltage bytes remain, address increment and verification stops by holding *AIE* in a low level, and electrical erase restarts. This erase and erase-verify sequence is repeated until all bits in the memory are judged to have a low threshold voltage. Finally, *AEND* becomes high and *AE* goes to a low level. This sets a high status signal and the entire erase operation is terminated.

A voltage switch circuit is shown in Fig. 6, which controls the supply voltages to decoders and sense amplifiers. As described earlier, to get adequate operational margins in a read mode, an erase-verify should be conducted under low-power-supply conditions, for example, 3.4 V. It guarantees a read operation at a V_{cc} of 3.4 V. On the other hand, decoders and sense amplifiers need a 5-V power supply in usual read operations, and 13 V should be supplied to decoders in a program mode. This circuit coordinates these complicated power supply conditions. A MOSFET switch is combined with a buffer amplifier, which is the final stage of the generator, and a charge-pump circuit. A verify voltage generator supplies 3.4 or 5 V to both word decoders and sense amplifiers according to the signal named VERIFY. To get a high programming speed, 13 V is generated by the charge-pump circuit from a V_{pp} supply of 12 V.

B. Sense Amplifier

A single-end-type sense amplifier is used in the memory, which is a kind of inverter as shown in Fig. 7. A memory cell is used as a driver and a pMOS transistor is used as a load, both in a conventional sense amplifier and in the proposed one. In a conventional sense amplifier, when the cell current is small, a pMOS transistor with a

very long channel length is required to get a large equivalent resistance. Otherwise, the read operational margin would decrease. Usually this large channel length causes a large stray capacitance at node LD, and it leads to a slow access. In the proposed sense amplifier, the gate of the pMOS transistor $MP1$ is connected to its drain, to realize high-sensitivity and high-speed sense circuits. Compared with a conventional sense amplifier, the shorter channel length of $MP1$ gives the same sensitivity, leading to a much smaller stray capacitance. A small signal voltage swing reduced by the threshold voltage of $MP1$ is also effective in getting a high-speed access of 80 ns.

Circuit simulation results are shown in Fig. 8 for both the conventional and the proposed sense amplifiers. Fig. 8 shows the waveforms at node LD and node SO. A signal voltage reduction and an access time reduction of 30 ns at $V_{cc} = 4.25$ V can be seen, where each circuit is optimized to have the same read operational margin for memory cells with a threshold voltage of 2.5 V. It indicates that the proposed sense amplifier realizes a high-speed access even for a small cell current of around 10 nA.

A typical schmoo plot of the address access time of the 1-Mb flash memory is shown in Fig. 9. Here, a high-speed access of 80 ns at a V_{cc} of 5 V is achieved. The plot also indicates that the memory can operate at a V_{cc} of 3.4 V, which demonstrates that the new automatic erase and erase-verify sequence operates properly.

IV. PERFORMANCE

A microphotograph of the flash memory is shown in Fig. 10. The increase in the die area due to the on-chip

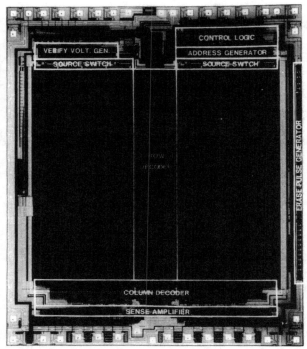

Fig. 10. Die micrograph.

TABLE II
PERFORMANCE OF 1-Mb FLASH MEMORY

DIE SIZE	5.2 x 6.22 mm^2
ORGANIZATION	128k x 8
Vcc/Vpp	5/12V
ACCESS TIME	80ns
ACTIVE CURRENT	10mA
STANDBY CURRENT	150µA
ERASE TIME	1s
PROGRAM TIME	50µs/byte

controller is about 5%. The performance of the memory is summarized in Table II. This 1-Mb flash memory is compatible with a byte-wide 1-Mb EPROM except in an electrical erase operation. The die area is about 32.3 mm^2. The memory can be erased in 1 s and it can be programmed at a rate of 50 µs/byte.

A typical erase time and a typical program time are shown as a function of reprogramming cycles in Fig. 11. Even after 1000 cycles, no appreciable change in erase time and program time could be observed. The read operational margin ($V_{cc\text{min}}$) and the access time also show no change.

In order to achieve good endurance results, it is effective to reduce the peak electric field applied to a tunnel oxide in an erase operation. This reduction is achieved by a MP2 transistor with reduced channel width in a source driver circuit as shown in Fig. 12. Transistor MP2 limits the gate-induced junction breakdown current, which occurs on the sources of the memory array, and forces a slow rise time in the erase pulse.

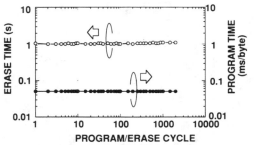

Fig. 11. Endurance characteristics.

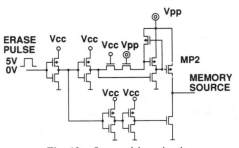

Fig. 12. Source driver circuit.

V. CONCLUSIONS

A 1-Mb flash memory was developed. It is suitable for in-system reprogramming. This is because it features an on-chip erase and erase-verify controller. An 80-ns access time was achieved by an advanced sense amplifier with a diode-like load as well as scaled periphery transistors and polysilicide word lines. The technology is based on a 0.8-µm CMOS process utilizing a one-transistor cell. The cell area is 10.36 µm^2 and the die area is 32.3 mm^2.

ACKNOWLEDGMENT

The authors thank S. Asai, T. Masuhara, H. Sunami, K. Shimohigashi, Y. Kawamoto, T. Tsukada, K. Mukai, S. Tachi, Y. Kamigaki, S. Itoh, S. Kiyota, M. Ogirima, M. Tsunematsu, T. Hagiwara, T. Yoshimi, S. Meguro, Y. Hara, M. Aoki, and N. Miyake for their encouragement and fruitful discussions. They are also grateful to T. Mutoh, K. Furusawa, A. Matsuo, T. Tanaka, N. Ogawa, and S. Saeki for chip design, to N. Miyamoto for testing chips, and to M. Ushiyama and the fabrication staff in the laboratory and in Musashi Works for chip fabrication.

REFERENCES

[1] G. Samachisa et al., "A 128K flash EEPROM using double-polysilicon technology," IEEE J. Solid-State Circuits, vol. SC-22, pp. 676–683, Oct. 1987.
[2] V. Kynett et al., "An in-system reprogrammable 32K×8 CMOS flash memory," IEEE J. Solid-State Circuits, vol. 23, pp. 1157–1163, Oct. 1988.
[3] V. Kynett et al., "A 90-ns one-million erase/program cycle 1-Mbit flash memory," IEEE J. Solid-State Circuits, vol. 24, pp. 1259–1264, Oct. 1989.
[4] S. D'Arrigo et al., "A 5V-only 256k bit CMOS flash EEPROM," in ISSCC Dig. Tech. Papers, Feb. 1989, pp. 132–133.
[5] R.-A. Cernea et al., 'A 1 Mb flash EEPROM," in ISSCC Dig. Tech. Papers, Feb. 1989, pp. 138–139.

A 1Mb FLASH EEPROM

Raul-Adrian Cernea, Gheorghe Samachisa, Chien-Sheng Su, Hui-Fang Tsai, Yu-Sheng Kao,
Cheng-Yuan Michael Wang, Yueh-Shing Chen, Alan Renninger, Ting Wong / James Brennan, Jr., Jeff Haines
SEEQ Technology Inc. / National Semiconductor
San Jose, CA / West Jordan, UT

A 1Mbit FLASH EEPROM with a 5.6 x 4.4µm cell is fabricated with a double-polysilicon single-metal N-well CMOS process (Fig. 1). A double-diffused drain structure is used to reduce hot-electron degradation of N-channel peripheral devices. A summary of the process is presented in Table 1. The memory is organized into 1024 rows and 128 columns for each output. Erase and programming operations are internally controlled by a timer that is stabilized against temperature and voltage supply variations. Addresses and data are latched during program and erase operations. Internal pumps generate the high voltage for the erase operation. Six redundant rows and two redundant columns are provided to enhance yield. Flash EEPROM cells similar to the array cells are used as the programmable elements in the redundancy circuits.

During the read operation, the sense current of the array cell, with drain kept at a constant voltage and gate at VCC, is compared to a mirrored reference current (Fig. 2). An inverter, using a depletion transistor as the pull-up device for VCC insensitivity, senses the bit line voltage while feeding it back to the gate of a native pass transistor that regulates the bit line voltage and separates the bit line capacitance from the sensing node. An identical circuit is used to regulate the drain voltage of the UV-erased flash EEPROM reference cell. The same circuit configuration is used to clamp the sensing node at a voltage higher than that of the bit line while keeping the native transistor saturated for faster bit line precharge. With a poly-II-only word line, the access time is typically 120 ns (Fig. 3). For latching the addresses, a master-slave latch is set at the falling edge of the control signal (either WE or CE), while data is latched at the rising edge of the control signal. The internal timer controls the duration of the erase/programming operations with no need for external signals. Timing of these operations is optimized by the internal circuitry in order to minimize the voltage stress experienced by the memory cell.

The oscillator has two symmetrical halves with two capacitances alternatively charged to a voltage Vref by a current Vref/R, R being the resistance of a poly-II resistor (Fig. 4).The period is 2RC, independent of Vref and thus of VCC, and has a low temperature coefficient. Measured period has ±2% variation over VCC range and ±10% variation over temperature range.

The 10MHz oscillator drives 29 shift registers organized in three loops of shift register generators, to provide all the waveforms needed for programming (ms range) and flash (seconds range) operations. Also the timer provides a fail-safe feature which prevents unintentional erasing of the memory. The erase operation brings the whole chip or a column to the FF state. Internal pumps, powered from Vpp, supply the drain current of the cells to be erased. In order to supply DC current, depletion devices are used as the drivers of a cross-coupled system of diode-connect MOS transistors (Fig. 5). During the erase operation the drain voltage rises with time as the floating gate becomes less negatively charged through Fowler-Nordheim tunnelling. The gate of the cell remains grounded during this period. Programming operation is similar to EPROM and is also controlled by the timer. During power-up, a special circuit protects the memory against false write or erase. For testing and process monitoring, charge gain stress test, DC erase, and program disturb stress modes are implemented. In addition, the clock frequency can be read from an I/O pin. A micrograph of the chip is shown in Figure 6.

Acknowledgement

The authors thank D. Anderson and B. Dockter for layout, D. Laughlin and B. Khoury for testing and characterization, M. Villott for support and P. Salsbury for guidance.

1.5µm Lithography	
Double Polysilicon	
N-Well CMOS	
Cell Size	14.6µm²
Cell Gate Oxide	200 Å
Interpoly Dielectric	375 N
Periphery Gate Oxide	340 Å
N+ Junction Depth	.4µm
P+ Junction Depth	.5µm
N-Well Junction Depth	3.75µm
N-Channel Min Left	1.2µm
P-Channel Min Left	1.4µm

TABLE 1 — Process parameters

Reprinted from the *IEEE ISSCC Dig. Tech. Pap.*, pp. 138–139, 316, 1989.

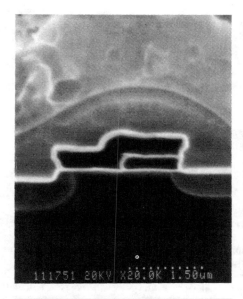

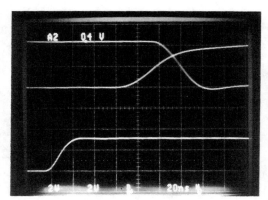

FIGURE 3 — Access time

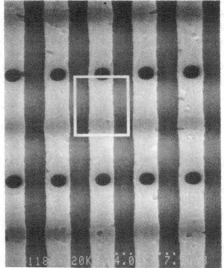

FIGURE 1 — (a) Flash EEPROM cell cross section (b) Flash EEPROM array

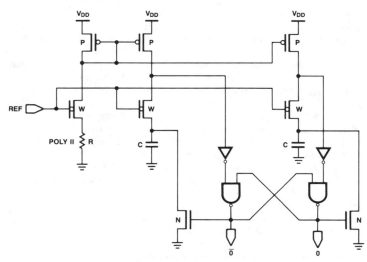

FIGURE 4 — Oscillator

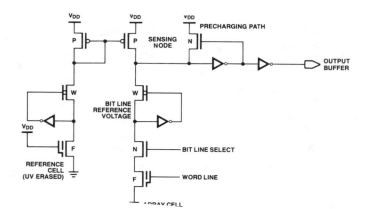

FIGURE 2 — Sense amplifier

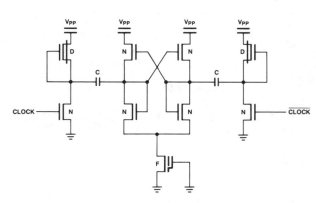

FIGURE 5 — Write/flash pump

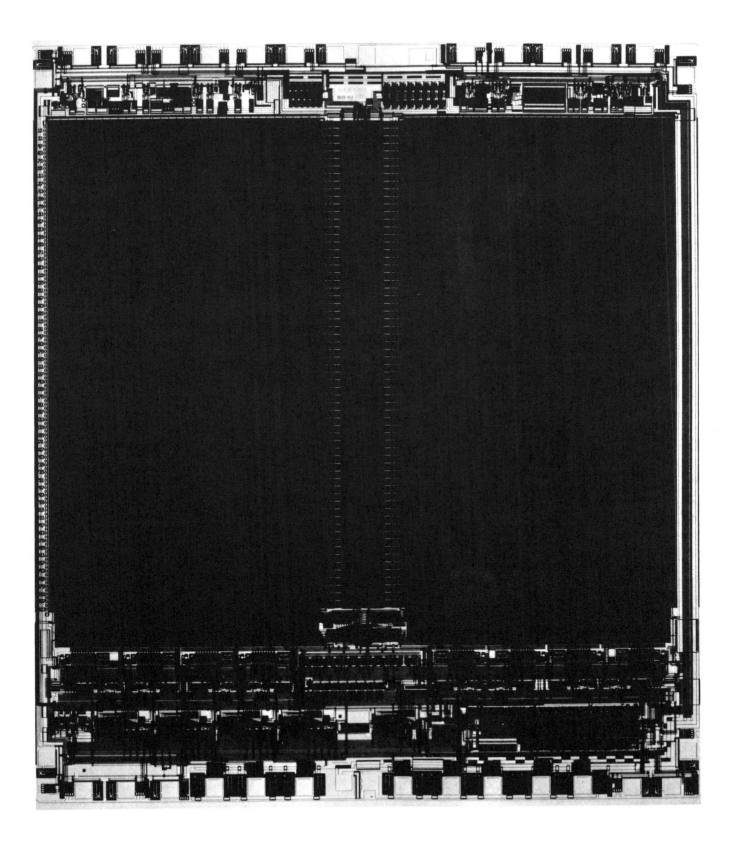

FIGURE 6 — Chip micrograph

A Temperature- and Process-Tolerant 64K EEPROM

COLIN S. BILL, PAUL I. SUCIU, MEMBER, IEEE, MICHAEL S. BRINER, MEMBER, IEEE, AND
DARRELL D. RINERSON, MEMBER, IEEE

Abstract —A 64K EEPROM is described with emphasis on the circuit techniques employed to achieve extended temperature operation. The core architecture is considered and a suitable byte layout which eliminates possible punchthrough in the memory cell is shown. A feedback-controlled substrate bias generator is described which delivers -1.0 V ± 0.05 V and reduces significantly field transistor leakages. In addition, a ± 1-percent stable voltage reference is shown to accurately control the programming voltage for the memory array to 20 V ± 1 V over the full military temperature range ($-55°$ – $+125°$C) and ± 10-percent power-supply variation. A process-insensitive write timing pulse, trimmed by E2 fuses and a description of the PAGE-MODE WRITE circuitry with reference to the bit-line (BL) latches, concludes the paper.

I. INTRODUCTION

THE 5-V-only 64K EEPROM with page-mode [1] writing capability is the latest advancement in the quest for the ideal alterable nonvolatile memory. The 64K EEPROM with these features has the high density required for most microprocessor applications, and the ease of use of the static RAM. The PAGE-MODE WRITE operation will allow up to 32 bytes of data to be written in one 10-ms WRITE cycle, significantly reducing the amount of time to write each byte. However, the achievement of this 64K EEPROM puts stringent requirements on the technology and the circuit design that must be met, in order to obtain a high-speed highly manufacturable reliable memory that will work over the full military temperature range (-55– $+125°$C).

This paper describes the circuit techniques used in extending the operating temperature range of a 64K EEPROM particularly as it relates to the WRITE cycle. The 5-V-only part is based on NMOS technology and its nonvolatility is attributed to a floating gate memory cell employing the Fowler–Nordheim tunneling principle [2]. Several temperature-related effects are described as well as the circuit techniques used to reduce their influence on the operation of the part. The high-voltage operation of 5-V-only EEPROM's is limited by the high-voltage decoder pumps [3]. The pumps are used during the WRITE cycle to charge selected word lines and bit lines (BL's). Due to their limited current sourcing ability, the design approach taken must ensure minimal leakage from the pumped nodes. Use

of individual bit grounds (BG's) ensures that punchthrough in core devices is avoided. Increased field transistor leakage at high temperatures has been dealt with through the application of back bias via a stable back-bias generator.

A closely regulated programming voltage is required for achieving good sensing margin and improved reliability. A temperature-insensitive voltage reference accurate to ± 1 percent over the full military operating range is used in generating a stable V_{pp}. Individual bit-line pumps have proven effective in sourcing increased diode leakage currents at high temperatures. By combining the bit-line pump with a latch, a simple page-mode implementation is achieved. We now look at the details of the circuit techniques.

II. BYTE ORGANIZATION

The programming voltage applied to the memory cell during a WRITE cycle is generated by a centrally regulated pump and distributed to word lines and bit lines through high-voltage decoder pumps. One individual pump under the worst-case conditions of temperature and supply voltage cannot source more than a few nanoamperes. This limitation leads to a choice of cell design such that the bit line offers minimum dc loading to the pump. The byte architecture is illustrated in Fig. 1. There are eight cells of two transistors each (eg., $T2$ and $T3$) for each byte. $T1$ is a decoding transistor for the program gate (PG) voltage. Each cell has its own bit line and bit ground. The reason for this organization can be illustrated by considering a voltage condition that will appear during the WRITE cycle that is used to discharge (program) the cell. That is 20 V on bit line 0 $BL0$ and 0 V on $BL7$. The bit ground line $BG0$ which is floating, may pull up to around 10 V during this mode. If a common byte ground had been used, equivalent to $BG0$ and $BG7$ connected together, then this 10 V at the source of $T5$ would be enough, under certain conditions, to punch through the device and hence create a leakage path to ground via $T4$ and $BL7$. In turn, the pump on $BL0$ would see an excessive load and therefore fail to provide the required 10 V. The effect is mostly observed at high temperatures. Separate bit ground lines avoid this condition without any penalty in die area and allows programming at temperatures in excess of 125°C.

Manuscript received April 1, 1985; revised June 10, 1985.
The authors are with Advanced Micro Devices, 901 Thompson Place, P.O. Box 3453, Sunnyvale, CA 94088.

Reprinted from *IEEE J. Solid-State Circuits*, vol. SC-20, no. 5, pp. 979–985, October 1985.

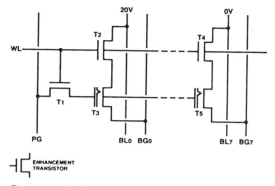

Fig. 1. Byte organization. BL and BG are bit line and bit ground, respectively. T1 decodes the control gate voltage PG.

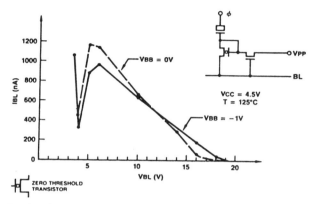

Fig. 2. Load line of the bit-line pump. Back bias reduces field transistor leakage leaving more current available to junction leakage hence extending temperature range.

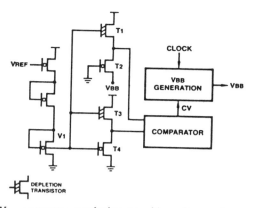

Fig. 3. V_{BB} generator employing on chip voltage reference V_{ref} to control $V1$. V_{BB} regulates at $-V1$.

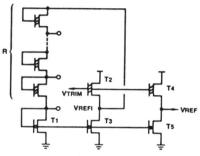

Fig. 4. The voltage reference used to control V_{pp}. V_{trim} adjusts the output to 3 V.

III. SUBSTRATE-BIAS GENERATOR

One possible contributor to the total leakage current seen by the bit-line pumps is leakage due to field transistors between the bit lines and adjacent grounded BG lines. This leakage is particularly noticeable at high temperature and the use of a substrate-bias voltage is justified. Fig. 2 shows the load line for the bit-line pump with 0 V and −1.0 V back bias applied. The measurement was made with the pump connected to the bit line and hence with junction and field leakages in effect. Comparing the two load lines shown, it can be clearly seen that in the high-voltage area of interest the pump with back bias can source extra current to junction leakage by virtue of negligible field leakages. The temperature range was therefore extended as more junction current could be delivered. Subthreshold field transistor leakages were reduced by approximately two orders of magnitude using back bias. As a result, lower field implant doses were used which produce lower threshold voltages for the narrow width pump transistors and thus better low V_{cc} operation at extreme temperatures.

The implementation of the substrate-bias generator is based on a feedback loop that involves a temperature-insensitive voltage reference V_{ref}, as illustrated in Fig. 3. V_{ref} in turn is used to create voltage $V1$, via a

temperature-stable level shifter. Transistors $T1$–$T4$ form two output stages which are of similar geometry. $T4$ is biased with $V_{gs} = V1$. The output from each of the two stages is equal when the V_{gs} of $T2$ is also equal to $V1$. Since the gate of $T2$ is connected to ground, the source must be at $-V1$, for equal outputs. The comparator senses the difference between these outputs and generates a logical control signal CV used for gating the V_{bb} generator pump. The pump is operating so long as the source of T_2 is greater than $-V1$. In this way, accurate regulation is achieved. The steady-state value of V_{bb} is -1 V ± 0.05 V. An additional benefit of the substrate bias voltage is approximately a 10-percent improvement in access time of the memory to 140 ns.

IV. VOLTAGE REFERENCE

The internally generated programming voltage V_{pp} must be accurately controlled in order to achieve good endurance failure rates at acceptable test yields. In the present design a temperature and supply-insensitive voltage reference is used to control V_{pp}. The circuit shown in Fig. 4 is capable of a ± 1-percent accuracy in V_{REF} across the full military temperature range and 10-percent supply variation.

Transistors $T4$ and $T5$ make up a buffer stage to eliminate loading on the internally generated reference V_{REFI}. The value of V_{TRIM} has a direct influence on the final reference voltage. V_{TRIM} is connected via an adjustable tap to the

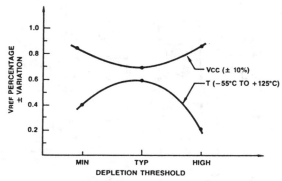

Fig. 5.   Stability plot for the voltage reference.

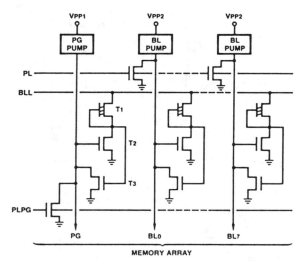

Fig. 6.   Circuit of bit-line latches and associated pumps.

ladder of depletion devices that constitute the resistor R so that the required reference voltage of 3.0 V is obtained. The tap is selected by a set of $E2$ fuses and a simple decoder from the address inputs of the memory. Devices $T1$, $T3$, and R form a current mirror. V_{REFI} is nominally at 3 V which forces the depletion transistors in R to be biased in their linear regions. The change of depletion threshold due to temperature variation causes a minimal change in current through $T1$. As temperature increases, the mobilities of the transistors in R decrease faster than the mobility of the intrinsic device $T1$. This creates a net drop in the voltage at the drain of $T1$ and also in V_{TRIM}. The mistracking of mobility in $T1$ and R causes a reduction of current in $T3$ additional to the reduction that would normally occur in $T1$ and $T3$ as temperature increases. $T2$ is in saturation and the reduction of V_{TRIM} as temperature increases lowers the gate drive to $T2$ and compensates for the reduction of current in $T3$. Consequently the conductance ratio of $T2$ and $T3$ is constant and therefore V_{REFI} is held constant. In addition, $T2$ and $T3$ form a V_{cc} insensitive arrangement due to $T2$ being in saturation. Channel-length modulation and drain-induced barrier lowering are minimized by using a long-channel transistor.

Fig. 5 describes the performance of the voltage reference as a function of the possible depletion thresholds at various process corners. The top curve shows that at 25°C and a power-supply variation of ± 10 percent, the stability of V_{REF} is typically ± 0.7 percent. Similarly, the lower curve shows that for nominal 5-V V_{cc}, V_{REF} stability over the full temperature range is ± 0.6-percent worst case.

It should be noticed that the two curves diverge at the extreme ends of the process corners. This results in a V_{REF} stability of approximately ± 1 percent, independent of process variation.

This temperature-insensitive V_{REF} is used to control the programming voltage V_{pp}. A six-stage pump driven from a high-speed clock generates the V_{pp} [4]. A capacitively divided sample of V_{pp} is compared with the voltage reference [3]. A digital control signal is created which gates the high-speed clock driving the V_{pp} pump. In this way the magnitude of V_{pp} is accurately controlled to ± 1 V over the full military temperature range and ± 10-percent V_{cc} variation.

V.   PAGE-MODE WRITE

Having minimized field transistor leakage from the bit lines, individual bit-line pumps have been most effective in supporting increased diode leakage currents at high temperature, leading to a simple page-mode implementation.

The PAGE-MODE WRITE operation is an important feature of the EEPROM since it allows high-speed writing. The chip is divided into 256 pages of 32 bytes, each page being written in approximately 10 ms. Each byte has associated with it a set of latches, one connected to each bit line. Also for each byte there is a PG line and latch. The PAGE-MODE WRITE cycle is divided into two parts: the loading of 1–32 bytes of data and the actual storing of this data in the memory cell. Each byte of information is transferred to the bit-line latches via a common data bus and a column select gate. For the duration of this load period $V_{pp_1} = V_{pp_2} = 5$ V (Fig. 6).

The bytes that are to change are tagged with a logic "1" on PG. The PG latch is composed of devices $T1$, $T2$, and $T3$. The PG operates by first taking BLL high and sensing the state of PG with the gate of $T2$ (Fig. 6). If PG is still at its preset value of 0 V, the drain of $T2$ charges to 5 V and $T3$ continues to hold PG = 0 V. On the other hand if PG has been pulled up to the pumping threshold of the PG pump, device $T2$ is on, $T3$ will offer no loading to the PG line and the pump will maintain a logic "1" state. The minimum requirement of the pump is to provide junction and field leakage currents for the remainder of the WRITE cycle. The BL latch works similarly. Flexibility exists in being able to charge the same byte again during the page load and in choosing the page address at the end of the load. Fig. 7 shows some of the important page-mode clocks. At the start of the loading cycle, the clocks PL and $PLPG$ preset all PG and BL's to 0 V in preparation for selective latching. All of the bytes that will not change retain this 0-V level throughout the WRITE cycle. This feature protects the bytes from unnecessary changes and increases the effective endurance of the memory. The clocks

336

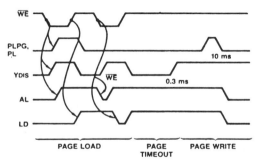

Fig. 7. Principal page-mode clocks.

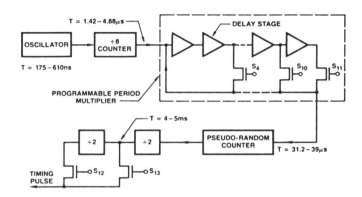

Fig. 8. Block diagram of the programmable divider. The oscillator period is divided and compressed to supply a 4–5-ms WRITE cycle timing pulse.

AL and *LD* latch the address and data lines, respectively, on the falling and rising edges of the $\overline{WE}$ input.

Y_{dis} deselects all bit lines from the data bus except those in the byte that are currently accepting new information. Once the byte data to be stored is loaded, the load cycle is terminated by exceeding a fixed 300-μs waiting period after which time the latched information is written to the memory array. This is achieved by means of two separate subcycles, page charge and page discharge. During page charge, which is of 5-ms duration, the internally generated programming voltage forces V_{pp_1} to 20 V and this in turn allows all PG lines at logic "1" to be pumped to 20 V. This charges (erases) those bytes in the page that have been addressed. It should be noted that bits holding 5 V on the bit line will perform only a partial erase. This is acceptable as these bits will subsequently be discharged (programmed) during the next 5 ms of the WRITE cycle. Once the charge cycle is complete, the *PLPG* clock makes a transition to 5 V, to remove high voltages from the internal nodes of the memory array prior to grounding V_{pp_1} and the word lines. This sequence is important to avoid trapped charge on the control gate and drain of the memory cell which would ultimately corrupt the stored data. The second 5-ms period of the WRITE cycle is used for the page discharge. V_{pp_2} is pumped to 20 V with PG lines at 0 V. Those bit lines initially at logic "1" will follow V_{pp_2} to 20 V and the related memory cell will become discharged. Bit lines originally latched to 0 V will continue to sink the pump current through $T3$ (Fig. 6) and protect the cell from programming. The final 10 μs of the WRITE cycle removes V_{pp} voltages from the array and establishes the READ conditions.

VI. PROGRAMMABLE WRITE TIMING CIRCUITS

To achieve less than a 10-percent variation in the length of the timing pulse used to control the charge and discharge PAGE WRITE cycle V_{cc}, temperature and process variations had to be minimized. A five-state ring oscillator with reduced temperature variation and V_{cc} insensitivity was employed. A control voltage which depends on the V_t of a depletion device with temperature, was used to adjust the oscillation period. Each of the five states has a deple-

tion capacitor which must charge and discharge in order to propagate the signal through the ring circuit. The control voltage regulates this capacitor current and, hence, the period of the oscillator is modified to render it less temperature sensitive. Initially, the oscillator period (175–610 ns) is divided by a three-stage binary counter using static logic. Process variations have been minimized by use of a programmable period divider. Fig. 8 shows how this has been designed. The programmable period divider is an eleven-stage ring counter employing a two-stage clock to propagate the signal from stage to stage. The oscillating loop can be tapped off from any one of eight adjacent stages by taking one of $S4$ to $S11$ to logic one. Selection of the appropriate tapping will vary the output period from 31.2 to 39 μs which is a considerably compressed range relative to the initial spread of the master oscillator. The tapping is implemented using electrically erasable fuses similar to those cells in the memory array, in conjunction with a test program which measures the unadjusted oscillator period. A pseudorandom counter, chosen for its low component count further divides the signal by 64 and finally, two more EEPROM fuses select the required adjusted period. This last stage, when selected, effectively increases the die yield as slower silicon can still be programmed if a 20-ms WRITE cycle time is used.

VII. FUSES

EEPROM fuses have proven to be a powerful tool in the present design for achieving operation at military temperatures. These fuses trim the V_{pp} programming voltage, the PAGE WRITE time period, and select redundant elements in the memory array. Fig. 9 shows the fuse circuit implementation. The EEPROM element is in two sections $T1$ and $T2$. Transistor $T2$ contains the tunnel oxide and $T1$ is the stacked gate device with a common floating gate to $T2$. In order to charge the fuse, REG is taken to 20 V while *An* is held high thereby grounding the drain of the tunnel device via $T3$. For discharging the fuse, REG is held at 0 V

337

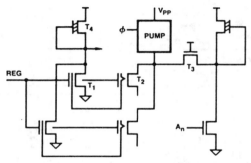

Fig. 9. Fuse element employs EEPROM cells. Used in redundancy circuits to select rows and columns. Also used to trim V_{ref} and WRITE cycle timing pulse.

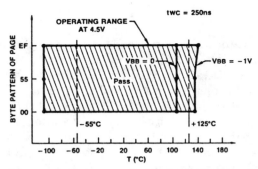

Fig. 10. Schmoo plot for page mode showing wide temperature operation and the effect of V_{BB}.

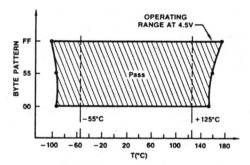

Fig. 11. Temperature range for the byte mode.

TABLE I
64K EEPROM CHARACTERISTICS

CELL SIZE	188 μm^2
CHIP SIZE	44 Kmil^2
tACC (TYP)	140 ns
ICC (ACTIVE)	50 mA
MINIMUM FEATURE	1.8 μm
METAL PITCH	6.75 μm
Δ VPP (-55°C $+125^\circ$C)	± 1V
Δ VREF (-55°C $+125^\circ$C)	$\pm 1\%$

and *An* is put to logic "0." The resulting voltage at the drain of $T2$ allows the pump to take this node all the way to 20 V and electrons tunnel from the floating gate.

During READ cycles, the state of the fuse is detected using $T4$. The fuse, in conjunction with this depletion pull up, acts as an inverter stage. The drain of $T1$ is pulled to V_{cc} for a charged fuse and to V_{0L} for a discharged fuse. In addition, the length of time that V_{pp} is applied to the fuse during testing is externally controlled and generally longer than the period used for the memory cells. This ensures reliable operation for continuous reading of the fuse throughout the life of the chip. Increased reliability of the fuses is obtained by connecting two in parallel. In the unlikely event that one cell should become of intrinsic V_t, then the other fuse element would adequately retain the functionality of the circuit.

VIII. MEMORY PERFORMANCE

Figs. 10 and 11 demonstrate the exceptional performance of this 64K EEPROM under the worst-case condition of $V_{cc} = 4.5$ V. Fig. 10 applies to the PAGE-MODE operation. The WRITE cycle time t_{wc} is the minimum time allowed between the presentation of one byte of data to the chip and the next byte that is to be written on the same page. Worst case this cycle time may be as short as 250 ns. For the PAGE-MODE cycle, performance is independent of the byte pattern stored. At the lower temperatures, oper-

ation down to -100°C was achieved, far in excess of that required by the military. At the higher temperatures, the Schmoo plots show the effectiveness of the back bias in reducing field transistor leakages. Lower leakage implies a more effective bit line pump for a given temperature. Hence the range over which the pumps will operate is extended until junction leakage finally dominates. An extra 30°C of range has been obtained due to the back bias. Fig. 11 shows the operation where only 1 byte is to be written for each 10-ms WRITE cycle. Further improvement is gained at high temperature.

IX. CONCLUSION

A 64K page-mode EEPROM with extended temperature operation in excess of military specification has been presented. Table I summarizes some of the important characteristics of the chip. The major effects due to temperature variations have been described and the techniques to solve these limitations have been demonstrated.

Fig. 12 shows a photomicrograph of the die. The V_{pp} pump can be seen top left, the bit-line latches across the top of the array, the voltage reference far top left and the programmable timing pulse and write circuitry top right. Fig. 13 shows that a typical access time of 140 ns was obtained.

ACKNOWLEDGMENT

We wish to express our thanks to S. Cagnina, B. Cox and N. Radjy for technology development, D. Berlan for testing, D. Rogers for device models, and L. Cleveland for experimental measurements.

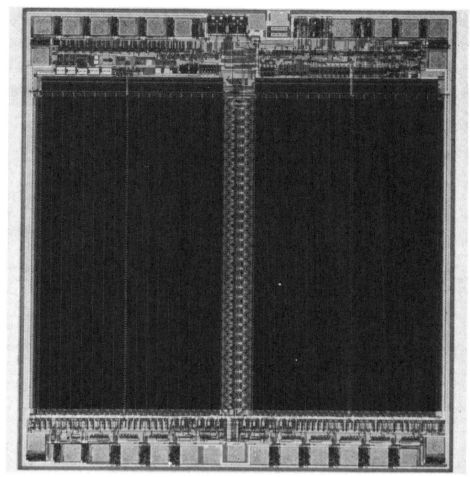

Fig. 12.   Photomicrograph of the die.

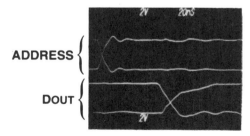

Fig. 13.   Typical access time 140 ns.

References

[1] A. Lancaster, B. Johnstone, J. Chritz, G. Talbot, and D. Wooten, "A 5V only EEPROM with internal program/erase control," in *ISSCC Dig. Tech. Pap.*, Feb. 1983, pp. 164–165.

[2] P. I. Suciu *et al.*, "Cell model for EEPROM floating gate memories," in *IEDM Tech. Dig.*, Dec. 1982, pp. 737–739.

[3] V. K. Dham *et al.* "A 5V only EEPROM using 1.5 lithography," in *ISSCC Dig. Tech. Pap.*, Feb. 1983, pp. 166–167.

[4] D. H. Oto *et al.* "High voltage regulation and process considerations for high density 5V EEPROM'S," *J. Solid-State Circuits*, vol. SC-18, pp. 532–538, Oct. 1983.

Paper 8.10

120ns 128k x 8b / 64k x 16b CMOS EEPROMs

Yasushi Terada, Kazuo Kobayashi, Takeshi Nakayama, Masanori Hayashikoshi, Yoshikazu Miyawaki,

Natsuo Ajika, Hideaki Arima, Takayuki Matsukawa, Tsutomu Yoshihara

LSI R & D Laboratory, Mitsubishi Electric Corporation

Itami, Japan

A 1Mb CMOS EEPROM using a $1.0\mu m$ triple polysilicon, double-metal process is described. The design is aimed at achieving manufacturable 120ns 1Mb EEPROM with a small chip. Therefore, a memory cell with high current drive, improved differential sensing technique, and error correcting code (ECC) was developed. The cell size is $3.8\mu m$ x $8\mu m$ and the chip is 7.73mm x 11.83mm. The device is configured as either 128k x 8 or 64k x 16 by a through-hole mask option.

The memory array is laid out as 64k x 16, and during programming, five parity bits generated using a modified Hamming code are stored alongside each data word. In order to convert the 16b word organization into a byte organization, input data latches and output data switching circuits controlled by LB (lowest address input) are provided. The 128k x 8 part is housed in a 32pin DIP and 44pin PLCC package, and the 64k x 16 part is in a 40pin DIP and 44pin PLCC package. In the byte-wide configuation, two bytes of data switched by LB must be input serially at the same address. The first byte is latched in the input buffer, and after the second byte is input, five parity bits are generated.

120ns read access time has been achieved by use of a memory cell with high current drive, double metallization, and a differential sensing scheme which uses an output of the current sense amplifier connected to an unselected memory array as a reference level. The cross section view of the memory cell is shown in Figure 1. First-level polysilicon is the word-select transistor gate and a control gate. Second-level polysilicon is a floating gate. Third-level polysilicon is a control gate. As the floating gate is sandwiched by two layers of control gate, 0.8 capacitance coupling ratio is achieved, so that the cell programmed by a 16V, 2ms pulse can drive a $25\mu A$ cell current.

The sense amplifier and the clock timing diagram are shown in Figure 2. The sense amplifier consists of a current sensing circuit, a differential amplifier, and a latch. The memory array is divided into two planes (left and right), and each memory plane has current sensing circuit. When the memory cell in the left plane is selected in the read operation, X_9 goes low to turn on the load transistor T1 and X_9 goes high to turn off T2. A selected Y-gate (Y_i) turns on and corresponding Y-gate of the unselected plane also turns on. A selected word line is activated, and all word lines in the unselected plane remain low. Clock RST goes low and bit lines are charged up by the load transistors connected to node A and B. The output of both current sensing circuits (nodes A and B) go low, then the level of node B goes high. If the selected memory cell is programmed in the unconductive "1" state, the level of node A goes high but is higher than that of node B, because the number of the load transistors is doubled. If the memory cell is programmed in the conductive "0" state, the level of node A remains low because the current flows constantly. After predetermined period, S_0 goes low and the differential amplifier is activated to amplify the level difference between node A and B. Sensing is several tens of nano seconds faster than that of a conventional scheme.

In the page mode, one to 128 words (X 16) or one to 256 bytes (X 8) is programmed in approximately 4ms. The column latch circuit is shown in Figure 3. If high is latched, transistors T3 and T4 recover the bit line level which has been charged through the memory transistor in the erase cycle, preventing destruction of the latched data when DL_p goes high. When RC and DR go high and the sensing circuit is activated, latched data can be read out. If high is latched, the current flows through Y-gate, T4 and T5, and "0" is read out in the left plane. If low is latched, current does not flow and "1" is readout. The column latch acts as a static register.

Two groups of four redundant rows are provided on each memory plane for yield improvement. An address switch circuit for redundancy which determines the output as X_i or X_i is shown in Figure 4. It consists of two EEPROM cells with a separate floating-gate transistor, and a latch. A micrograph of the chip is shown in Figure 5. The access waveform is shown in Figure 6. Typical process parameters are listed in Table 1.

Technology	$1\mu m$ lithography
	2-Poly, 1-Polycide, 2-Al
	N-well CMOS
Cell	First Gate = 350 Å
	Tunnel Oxide = 90 Å
	Interpoly Dielectric = 300 Å
Peripheral	T_{ox} = 200 Å
	L_{eff} = $0.8\mu m$ (N-channel)
	$1.2\mu m$ (P-channel)
	X_{jn} = $0.25\mu m$
	X_{jp} = $0.35\mu m$

TABLE 1 – Process parameters

Reprinted from the *IEEE ISSCC Dig. Tech. Pap.*, pp. 136–137, 315, 1989.

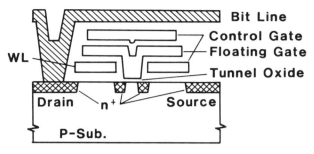

FIGURE 1 — Cross section of memory cell

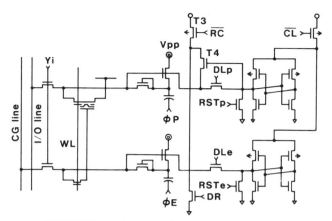

FIGURE 3 — Schematic of column latch circuitry

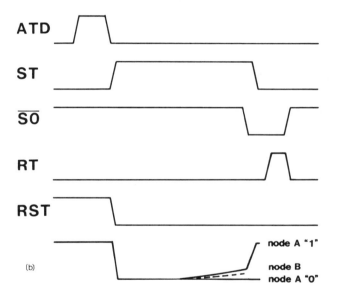

(b)

FIGURE 2 — Sense amplifier (a) circuit (b) clock timing

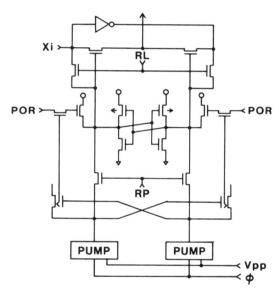

FIGURE 4 — Schematic of address switch

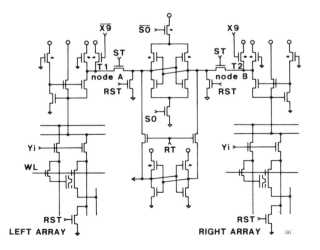

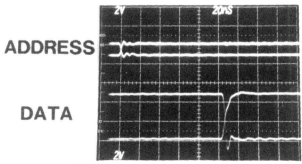

FIGURE 6 — Typical access time

341

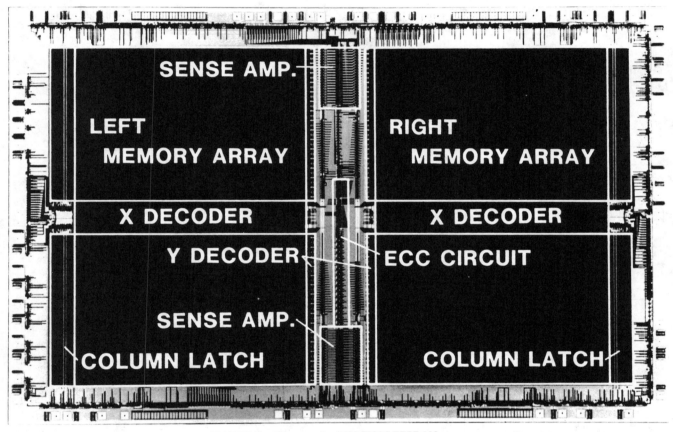

FIGURE 5 — Micrograph of 1M CMOS EEPROM

A Million-Cycle CMOS 256K EEPROM

DUMITRU CIOACA, TIEN LIN, MEMBER, IEEE, AGNES CHAN, LING CHEN, MEMBER, IEEE, AND
ANDREI MIHNEA, MEMBER, IEEE

Abstract —A single 5-V supply 256K EEPROM was designed, manufactured, and tested. A newly developed double-poly N-well CMOS process with 1.25-μm minimum feature size was successfully used to manufacture this part. Using this technology, a 54-μm^2 EEPROM cell has been realized. A novel autoredundant Q-cell concept used in the memory core combined with the very high-endurance oxynitride dielectric provides the breakthrough needed to increase the endurance of the 256K EEPROM up to one-million WRITE cycles. Descriptions of the internal timer, all relevant programming signals, the byte/page switch, the bit and byte latches, the sense amplifier, and the CMOS EE fuses give insight into the complexity of the peripheral circuits. The measured device performance and the chip architecture description will also be presented in this paper.

I. INTRODUCTION

ENDURANCE is the most critical reliability parameter for EEPROM products. For many applications, a higher than 10^4 WRITE-cycle endurance is required. However, some parts may still fail within the 10^4 cycles. The failure mechanism is usually explained by the breakdown in tunneling dielectric. Therefore, it is essential to improve this endurance problem for high-density EEPROM's not only to keep the failure rate below 1 percent at 10^4 WRITE cycles, but also to open new fields of applications which require two to three orders of magnitude higher endurance.

There are three dominant EEPROM devices to date. The textured polysilicon device has an intrinsic problem of low endurance caused by very high electron trapping in the tunneling polyoxide [1]. The MNOS device, however, has limited endurance because of data retention [1], [2]. On the contrary, the floating-gate device with thin tunneling dielectric has proved to be cost effective for making high-density high-endurance EEPROM's with excellent data retention [3], [4].

The development of a new technology with improved tunneling dielectrics and reduced defect density has increased endurance for floating-gate EEPROM's. In addition, new circuit techniques can be used to eliminate the effects of a single bit failure to the functionality of the part. This paper describes the technology and the design used to extend the endurance of a 256K EEPROM from 10^4 to 10^6 WRITE cycles.

The 5-V-only part is based on a newly developed double-poly N-well CMOS process [5] which allows a cell programming voltage as low as 17 V with a programming time of 0.1 ms. The intrinsic cell endurance has been demonstrated to be greater than 10^8 WRITE cycles.

Using a design approach [6] in which a bit of information stored in two different EEPROM cells (autoredundant storage unit) can be read out correctly even if one of the thin oxides breaks down, a two order of magnitude increase in endurance has been obtained. Furthermore, the write time for the part has been decreased to 80 μs/byte by extending the page size to 64 bytes and reducing the programming time per page to 5 ms. An extended byte load window (200 ns to 300 μs) has been obtained by using a flexible page load architecture and a fully static bit latch. An internal byte/page-mode recognition circuit assures that the part can fit into the socket of existing byte or page-mode EEPROM's without additional microprocessor software requirements. The main portion of the paper will concentrate on key circuit descriptions, memory architecture, and the measured performance.

II. TECHNOLOGY FEATURES

A. Floating-Gate CMOS Technology

The 256K EEPROM is fabricated with a double-polysilicon gate N-well CMOS process [5]. A minimum feature size of 1.25 μm is realized by employing stepper lithography and dry etching. The process makes a high-quality oxynitride tunneling dielectric [5], [7], [8] which results in a single cell endurance higher than 10^8 cycles as shown in Fig. 1. The use of borophosphosilicate glass which provides flow and reflow topologies at a temperature below 900°C further improves the integrity of tunneling dielectric. The technology utilizes a graded-drain device structure with 400-Å gate oxide for the charge pumping circuit to generate a voltage of 19 V from a single 5-V supply. Table I summarizes the key process features.

B. Memory Cell

The technology scaling and layout design improvement permit a 4.5×12.0-μm^2 memory cell for the 256K EEPROM. Fig. 2 shows the layout and cross section of the two-transistor EEPROM cell. With an interpoly oxide of approximately 520 Å, a floating-gate oxide of approxi-

Manuscript received April 13, 1987; revised June 16, 1987.
D. Cioaca, A. Chan, L. Chen, and A. Mihnea are with SEEQ Technology, Inc., San Jose, CA 95131.
T. Lin was with SEEQ Technology, Inc., San Jose, CA 95131. He is now with General Instruments, Chandler, AZ.
IEEE Log Number 8716434.

Reprinted from *IEEE J. Solid-State Circuits*, vol. SC-22, no. 5, pp. 684–692, October 1987.

PWerase = .1 ms   PWwrite = .1 ms

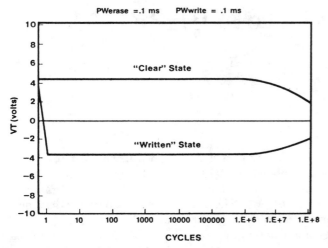

Fig. 1.   Endurance characteristics of EEPROM cell. The erased cell has 4-V threshold, and the written cell has −4-V threshold. After 10^6 programming cycles the cell thresholds decrease to +2 and −2 V, respectively.

TABLE I
KEY PROCESS FEATURES

CMOS N-Well Silicon Gate	
Two Layers of Polysilicon	
Floating Gate Programmed by Fowler-Nordheim Tunneling	
Single Layer of Metal	
Stepper Photolithography, Dry Etching	
1.25 μm Minimum Feature Size	
Low Temperature Reflow Glass (BPSG)	
Transistors	
N-Channel Minimum L_{eff}	1.6 μm
P-Channel Minimum L_{eff}	1.5 μm
N+ Junction Depth	0.4 μm
P+ Junction Depth	0.5 μm
Gate Oxide	~ 400 Å
EEPROM Cell	
Dimensions	4.5 μm x 12 μm = 54 μm²
Gate Oxide	~ 500 Å
Interpoly Oxide	~ 500 Å
Tunneling Dielectric	~ 80 Å
W_{eff}	0.8 μm
L_{eff}	1.6 μm

mately 500 Å, and tunneling dielectric of approximately 80 Å, the cell coupling ratio is improved over previous EEPROM's. Thus, the programmed threshold window is maintained even with a reduced programming voltage of about 18–19 V compared to higher than 21 V for the previous generation EEPROM [3], [4]. The EEPROM cell transistor has been designed in a 4.5-μm pitch and processed to obtain a cell current higher than 15 μA under normal process variations. This makes the access time less than 250 ns at 125°C.

III. Q-CELL APPROACH, BYTE ORGANIZATION, AND BYTE PROGRAMMING

The autoredundant Q-cell approach and the byte architecture are illustrated in Fig. 3. The Q cell, which constitutes the building block of the memory core, consists of a pair of identical two-transistor cells programmed simultaneously with the same data through two adjacent bit lines BL_1 and BL_2.

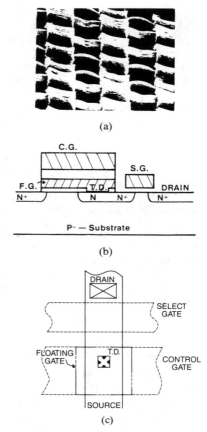

Fig. 2.   SEM photograph and cross section of a two-transistor EEPROM cell. (a) The metal bit line runs over the source–drain transistor diffusion, interfacing it by a shared contact. The polysilicon word line and sensing line run perpendicular to the bit line. The polysilicon floating gate can also be seen under the sensing line. (b) Cell cross section. (c) Cell layout. Cell size is 54 μm².

The Q cell is read out through two separate sense amplifiers which in turn are combined in a NOR gate. The effect of this arrangement is that the correct information will be read out as long as at least one of the Q-cell halves is not defective. The probability of two adjacent EE cells wearing out at the same time is extremely low. In fact, the array can tolerate all single-cell failures under the condition that every Q cell has no more than one of its branches failing. In the Q-cell approach, redundancy is included at the bit level. Measurements of parts with an error-correction Hamming code [4] and of the Q cell show an approximately one order of magnitude difference in endurance in favor of the Q cell.

The only penalty for using the Q cell is an increase in die size. A different byte layout configuration has been applied to alleviate that problem. The nonredundant two-transistor EE cell published earlier [9] has two metal lines per bit: one for the bit line and one for V_{ss}. By using diffusion for V_{ss} in the Q-cell approach, two metal lines, BL_1 and BL_2, per bit can be maintained. An array V_{ss} diffusion is shared by four neighboring bytes, two in the X direction and two in the Y direction, and is strapped in the middle by an array V_{ss} metal line separating two adjacent byte columns. A metal select line is provided for each byte column. A Q-cell byte needs 17.5 metal lines compared to

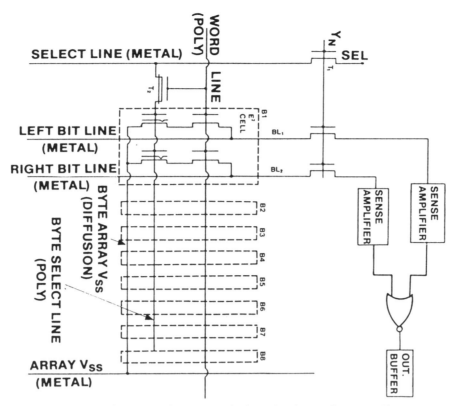

Fig. 3. Schematic of the byte organization using the Q-cell concept. The byte has 17.5 metal lines and a common array V_{ss} diffusion.

17 used in the nonredundant byte with a separate V_{ss} metal line for each bit [9].

For a byte to be programmed, a high voltage (HV) should be applied to both the page/word line and the selected column decoder latch (CDL) output Y_N. During byte erase, the central select line SEL is pumped to HV. The byte column select transistor T_1 and the single byte select transistor T_2 allow HV on the byte select line. The array V_{ss} line is grounded and the bit lines are unbiased. A negative Fowler–Nordheim tunneling current charges the floating gates to a negative potential which raises the threshold of the erased EE devices to approximately 4 V.

During byte write, SEL and the byte select line are grounded while array V_{ss} is floating. The column/bit latches (shown on Fig. 8) with ZERO data stored in them begin the HV pumping on the corresponding bit lines. A positive tunneling current will charge the floating gates to a positive potential. This lowers the written EE-device threshold to approximately -4 V. All the latches with ONE data stored in them will not pass HV to their corresponding bit lines so the EE devices will maintain their "erased" status.

IV. The Timer and the Page Programming Cycle

Parallel byte programming or page-mode operation has been previously reported [9], [10]. This is a very important feature especially in high-density EE memories since it reduces the write time per byte dramatically. The standard for the 64K EE devices with page-mode operation is a 32-byte page and a 10-ms page write time, resulting in a 320-μs effective byte write time. By increasing the page size to 64 bytes and decreasing the writing time per page to 5 ms, a 80-μs byte write time has been obtained.

The page programming cycle is divided into four distinctive portions: data and address loading (LOAD), page erase (CLEAR), page write (WRITE), and HV write recovery (RECOVERY). The main signals used to control the programming cycle are shown in Fig. 4.

The page load is started by the rising edge of $\overline{OE}$ and the last falling edge of either $\overline{CE}$ or $\overline{WE}$. $\overline{OE}$ will remain high throughout the loading cycles. The X-decoder addresses are latched such that X-address inputs become "don't care" during the whole programming cycle. At the same time, the page load signal $\overline{LD}$ is activated to allow access to bit latches from data input latches.

On every falling edge of $\overline{WE}$ and $\overline{CE}$, Y addresses are latched by $\overline{ALY}$ while data are latched by $\overline{DL}$ on the first occurring rising edge of $\overline{CE}$ or $\overline{WE}$. The transfer of data from data input buffer latch to bit latch takes place when $\overline{WE}$ and $\overline{CE}$ are high. At the same time, the column decoder is enabled with $\overline{YC}$ such that the accessed Y-decoder output can be latched into one of the 64 byte latches.

The page load can be terminated in two different ways:

1) by executing a read, i.e., $\overline{CE} =$ low, $\overline{OE} =$ low, and $\overline{WE} =$ high, not sooner than 200 ns after the last data are loaded; and

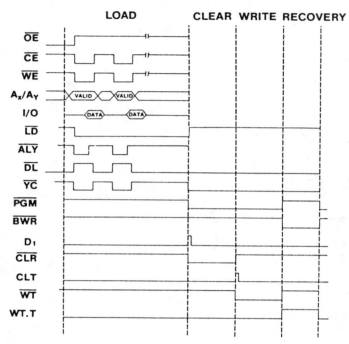

Fig. 4. Principal page-mode programming signals. The page loading signals are controlled by $\overline{OE}$, $\overline{CE}$, and $\overline{WE}$. The signals needed during clear, write, and recovery are controlled by the timer.

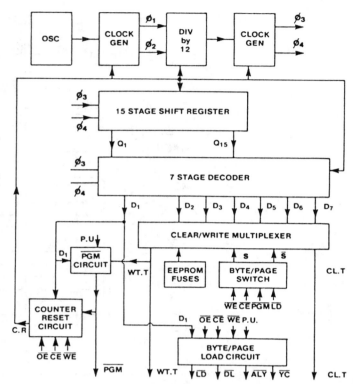

Fig. 5. The timer block diagram.

2) by using the internal timer which resets $\overline{LD}$ 300 µs after the last data are loaded and no other byte loading occurs.

By using these two load termination features, the byte loading speed can be varied from 250 ns to 300 µs.

The page clear is started when the single-shot signal D_1 resets $\overline{LD}$ and sets the programming $\overline{PGM}$ and clear $\overline{CLR}$ signals. The 2.5-ms clear cycle is defined by the timer through the single-shot clear termination signal CLT. This signal resets $\overline{CLR}$ and sets the page write signal $\overline{WT}$. After another 2.5 ms, the page write is completed by the single-shot write termination signal WTT. The write termination signal not only secures the reset of $\overline{PGM}$ and $\overline{WT}$, but also guarantees the main signal for the final step of page programming, i.e., write recovery. The HV write recovery signal $\overline{BWR}$ discharges to 0 V all nodes pumped to HV during the previous WRITE so that no write disturb may occur during the next READ cycle.

All the programming signals presented in Fig. 4 are generated by the internal timer as shown in Fig. 5. The output of the oscillator goes into a clock generator which in turn drives a divide-by-12 shift register. ϕ_3 and ϕ_4 are nonoverlapping clocks for a 15-stage shift register and a seven-stage decoder. The first decoder output D_1 is used for page load termination and clear start as described previously. From the other six decoder outputs, only two pass the clear/write multiplexer to generate the single-shot pulses CLT and WTT. Using the byte/page switch and EE fuses to control the multiplexer configuration, the timer becomes very flexible and the part can be adjusted during wafer test to one of the four possible byte/page write cycle

times: 1 ms/5 ms, 1 ms/10 ms, 2 ms/5 ms, and 2 ms/10 ms.

The counter reset signal CR enables the counter when the page load starts and disables it after the page programming cycle is completed. A power up/down signal PU is generated by a bandgap reference voltage circuit which is designed so that the timer can be activated only for a supply voltage over 4 V.

V. KEY CIRCUITRY

A. Byte/Page Switch

In order to obtain full compatibility between the 256K memory and the existing byte-mode parts (1- or 2-ms WRITE cycle), the use of a byte/page switch and CMOS EE fuses is necessary.

The schematic of the byte/page switch is shown in Fig. 6. The output signal S is normally low and sets the multiplexer in the byte write time range. The switch is activated during page load only.

At the first $\overline{CE}$ or $\overline{WE}$ falling edge, S remains low. At the second $\overline{CE}$ or $\overline{WE}$ falling edge, S becomes high and the multiplexer is set in the page write time range. For any subsequent $\overline{CE}$ or $\overline{WE}$ falling edge during page load, S maintains its high level. After the page load cycle, the $\overline{PGM}$ signal freezes the status of the S so that no accidental switching caused by noise or other disturbances may occur.

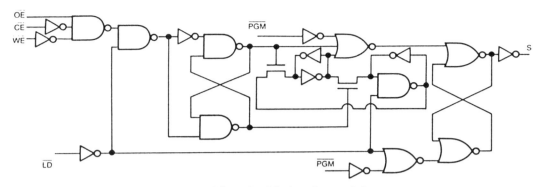

Fig. 6. Schematic of the byte/page switch.

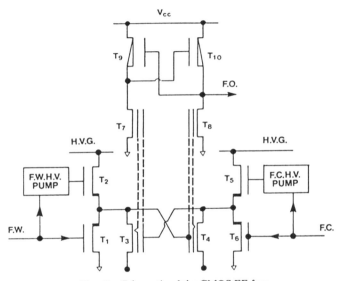

Fig. 7. Schematic of the CMOS EE fuse.

B. CMOS EE Fuses

In the 256K memory, EE fuses are used in the timer, word-line redundancy logic, and for on-chip in-house test features.

Two major problems are solved by implementing the EE fuses shown in Fig. 7:

a) elimination of any fuse disturb by separating the EE fuses from the fuse output FO circuitry; and

b) zero standby current on the fuses by using a modified flip-flop configuration for FO.

The programmable part of the fuse is realized by two cross-coupled EE transistors T_3 and T_4, four access transistors T_1, T_2, T_5, and T_6, and two HV pumps. The pull-down devices of the flip-flop T_7 and T_8 share the same floating gates with EE transistors T_3 and T_4, respectively.

The fuse programming is executed at the wafer test level. It can be started by a fuse clear which enables the fuse-clear HV pump (FCHV) such that T_3 will be erased while T_4 will be written. Accordingly, T_7 will be OFF, T_8 will be ON, and FO will be low. There is only one FCHV whereas the fuse clear operation is common for all the fuses.

To activate a selected fuse, a fuse write should follow after fuse clear for that particular fuse. Through a fuse decoder, the fuse-write HV pump (FWHV) becomes active such that T_4 will be erased and T_3 will be written. FO then changes from low to high.

After the fuse programming cycle is completed, all the HV pumps are disabled and the access nodes of the EE transistors are grounded.

C. Column Bit Latch and Column Decoder Latch

One of the 512 column bit latches CL used in the 64-byte page is shown in Fig. 8. The CL is composed of two inverters connected in series (T_2, T_3 and T_5, T_6, T_9), a high-impedance feedback depletion transistor T_4, a data-load access transistor T_{15}, two data output transistors T_{11} and T_{12}, two HV access transistors T_{13} and T_{14}, one CL reset transistor T_1, and the CL HV pump (T_7, T_8, T_{10}).

The reset signal R_2 is high during all nonprogramming modes of the part to maintain a low on latch output LO. During page load, R_2 and OiP are taken low, LD is taken high, and the eight CL's of a selected byte will store $\overline{DATA}$ from their respective BL_2 lines, taken from data input buffer latches. In order to avoid any CL clear disturb, the CL's are completely isolated from the bit lines during page clear. The following page write cycle keeps LD low but activates the clock and pumps OiP to HV. For stored $\overline{DATA}$ of ZERO, LO is low and the latch HV pump is cut off from the bit line access devices T_{11} and T_{12} such that the corresponding Q cell retains its "erased" status. For stored $\overline{DATA}$ of ONE, LO is high allowing the latch pump to raise its voltage level to HV. A direct connection between the bit lines and the high-voltage generator permits the Q cell to be written.

The complexity of CL which is laid out in the 9-μm pitch is justified by its features listed below:

a) has a wide variation in the byte load rate (250 ns to 300 μs) due to the fully static nature of the latch; and

b) has no bit-line-related disturbance because the data path for latch loading is separated from the Q-cell writing.

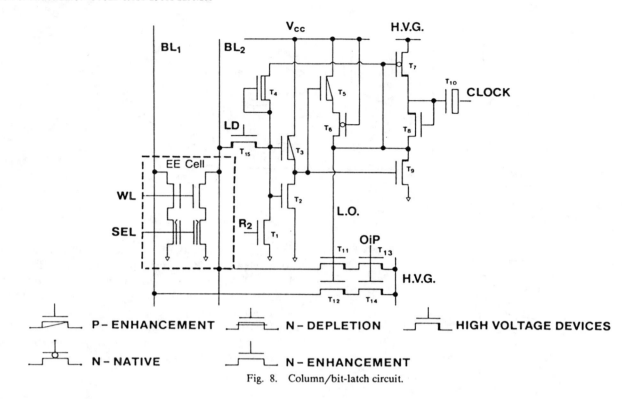

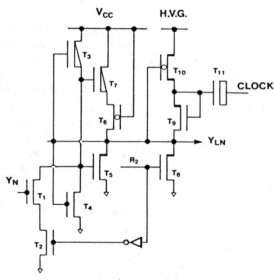

P – ENHANCEMENT   N – DEPLETION   HIGH VOLTAGE DEVICES

N – NATIVE   N – ENHANCEMENT

Fig. 8. Column/bit-latch circuit.

Fig. 9. Column decoder latch.

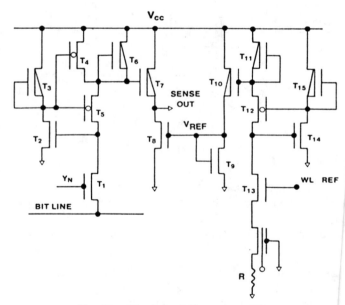

Fig. 10. Schematic of the sense amplifier.

The *CL* does not draw standby current and the p-channel device T_5 is protected against HV punchthrough by the n-channel native device T_6.

The column decoder latch *CDL* shown in Fig. 9 works similarly to *CL* except for one difference. The *CL* can be set and reset by its input signal BL_2. The *D*-flip-flop nature of the latch gives the user the possibility to correct the stored level by reloading the byte during page load. The *CDL* works like an *SR* flip-flop which is reset by R_2 and set by the *Y*-decoder output Y_N. The number of *CDL*'s set during page load gives the actual page size which can vary from 2 to 64 bytes. The remaining reset

CDL's make sure that the corresponding byte columns cannot be affected by the ongoing programming cycle.

D. The Sense Amplifier

Fig. 10 shows a new sense amplifier which is designed to improve the sensing speed while maintaining the bit-line voltage swing used in the 64K memories. The sense amplifier consists of two sensitive current detectors: one for the bit line and the other for an EE reference cell. Bit-line capacitance is precharged to a 2-V level through the native

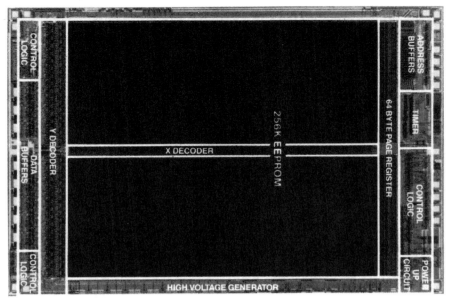

Fig. 11.   Die photograph of 256K EEPROM. The die size is 247×353 mil^2.

n-channel devices T_4 and T_5. Thereafter, the feedback inverter T_2 and T_3 cuts off the precharge device T_4 and the only current that flows into the bit line is provided by the p-channel sensing device T_6. If the selected EE cell is written or conductive, the bit-line voltage increases only slightly over 2 V, because the EE-cell current and the T_6 current are approximately equal. The sense-amplifier output, SENSE OUT, stays high. For an erased or nonconductive EE cell, T_6 continues to charge up the bit line until T_5 cuts off (~ 2.3 V) by the feedback inverter T_2 and T_3. Consequently, the sense-amplifier output goes low. Current sensing of the native EE cell uses an almost identical structure. The sensed current is converted into a reference voltage V_{REF} which is then applied to the gate of T_8. By using a reference sensing scheme, the speed of the sense amplifier is improved and has a lower sensitivity to process and V_{cc} variations.

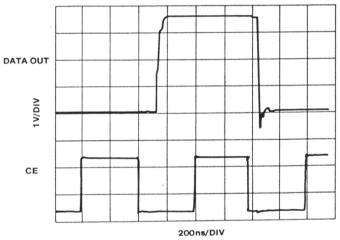

Fig. 12.   Typical access time.

VI.   LAYOUT

A photomicrograph of the memory is shown in Fig. 11. The core is organized as an array of 512 rows (pages) of 512 bits. The X decoder is placed in the middle of the array. The Y decoder is located in the bottom next to the array. Next to the Y decoder are the data input/output buffers including the sense amplifier and special testing logic. The high-voltage generator circuitry is located on the right side of the die. Every odd and even word line is connected to a HV pump on its left and right side, respectively.

The colum bit latches are located on the top of each bit line. The timer, control circuitry, write protect circuitry, and most of the address buffers are located on the top. The output pull-downs have a separate V_{ss} pad from the circuit V_{ss} to minimize ground-noise effects. Double guard rings are used to protect most latch-up sensitive areas.

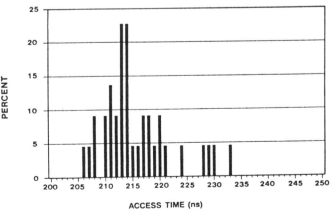

Fig. 13.   Read access-time distribution after programming and reading at $+125°C$.

349

TABLE II
MAIN CIRCUIT PARAMETERS

Supply Voltage	5V±10%
Active Current	30 mA
Standby Current	2 mA (TTL)
	100 μA (CMOS)
Access Time	150 ns (typical)
	<250 ns (+125°C)
Write Time	1 ms (byte)
	5 ms (page)
Byte Load Time	<200 ns
Load Time-out	300 μs
	200 ns (read termination)
Chip Write/Clear	10 ms
V_{CC} Write Protect Level	4V ±0.1V
Programming Cycles	1 M (Special Screen)
	>10K (Standard Screen)
Operating Temperature	−55°C to+125°C
Pin Out	28 Pins, 8 Bit Outputs
Organization	32K x 8
Die Size	247 x 353 Square Mils

VII. DEVICE CHARACTERISTICS

The measured access time at room temperature is below 150 ns as shown in Fig. 12. The measured operating current under typical conditions at room temperature, 5-V supply, and minimum cycle operation is 30 mA. The worse-case standby current is below 100 μA, 40 μA of which is dissipated by a power-up bandgap reference voltage for write protection.

The measured write protect voltage provided by the bandgap is 4±0.1 V. The read access-time distribution after programming and reading the part at +125°C is shown in Fig. 13. The part had no reliability problem up to one-million cycles of programming.

VIII. SUMMARY

A 256K byte/page EEPROM with a very high-endurance EE device and a new autoredundant cell concept have been presented. The main circuit parameters are summarized in Table II.

The device has been fabricated with a double-poly N-well CMOS technology. The combination of a very high-endurance EE oxynitride tunneling dielectric device and the Q-cell design concept has allowed successful fabrication of parts with a one-million WRITE-cycle endurance. New circuits have been used to provide full compatibility between the 256K memory and the existing micro-processors and EEPROM's. Some important features of this design are low standby current, functionality over the full military temperature range, and a temperature- and process-insensitive write protect voltage level.

ACKNOWLEDGMENT

The authors would like to express their thanks to C. S. Jenq, S. W. Owen, A. L. Renninger, E. Mitchell, and J. Fattaruso for their technology and design contributions; G. Smarandoiu and D. Palaima for characterization of the circuit; C. Moriyama for the chip planning and layout; and Dr. P. Salsbury for his constant support throughout this project.

REFERENCES

[1] S. K. Lai, V. K. Dham, and D. Guterman, "Comparison and trends in today's dominant E2 technologies," in *IEDM Tech. Dig.*, Dec. 1986, pp. 580–583.
[2] W. D. Brown, "MNOS technology—Will it survive?," *Solid-State Technol.*, p. 77, July 1979.
[3] A. Gupta, T. Chiu, M. Chang, A. Renninger, and G. Perlegos, "A 5V-only 16K EEPROM utilizing oxynitride dielectric and EPROM redundancy," in *ISSCC Dig. Tech. Papers*, Feb. 1982, pp. 184–185.
[4] S. Mehrotra, T. C. Wu, T. L. Chiu, and G. Perlegos, "A 64Kb CMOS EEPROM with on-chip ECC," in *ISSCC Dig. Tech. Papers*, Feb. 1984, pp. 142–143.
[5] L. Chen, S. W. Owen, C. S. Jenq, and A. L. Renninger, "A 256K high performance CMOS EEPROM technology," in *IEDM Tech. Dig.*, Dec. 1985, pp. 620–623.
[6] D. Cioaca, T. Lin, A. Chan, L. Chen, and A. Mihnea, "A million-cycle CMOS 256K EEPROM," in *ISSCC Dig. Tech. Papers*, Feb. 1987, pp. 78–79.
[7] C. S. Jenq, T. L. Chiu, B. Joshi, and J. Hu, "Properties of thin oxynitride films used as floating-gate tunneling dielectrics," in *IEDM Tech. Dig.*, Dec. 1982, pp. 811–812.
[8] C. S. Jenq, T. Wong, B. Joshi, and C. Hu, "High temperature and extended endurance characteristics of EEPROM," in *IEDM Tech. Dig.*, Dec. 1983, pp. 585–588.
[9] C. S. Bill, P. I. Suciu, M. S. Briner, and D. D. Rinerson, "A temperature- and process-tolerant 64K EEPROM," *IEEE J. Solid-State Circuits*, vol. SC-20, no. 5, pp. 979–985, Oct. 1985.
[10] R. D. Jolly *et al.*, "A 35-ns 64K EEPROM," *IEEE J. Solid-State Circuits*, vol. SC-20, no. 5, pp. 971–978, Oct. 1985.

A 50-ns CMOS 256K EEPROM

TAH-KANG J. TING, MEMBER, IEEE, THOMAS CHANG, MEMBER, IEEE, TIEN LIN, CHING S. JENQ, MEMBER, IEEE, AND KENNETH L. C. NAIFF

Abstract — A 32K × 8 EEPROM, which operates with a single 5-V power supply and achieves 100K cycle endurance, 50-ns typical READ access time, and 1-ms page programming time, equivalent to 16 μs per byte was designed. A double-poly, double-metal, n-well CMOS process with 1.25-μm minimum feature size was developed to manufacture the device. The required and optional extended JEDEC standards for software data protection and chip clear are implemented along with parity check, toggle bit, page-load timer, and data-protection status bit. A modified Hamming code, which uses four parity bits per byte, was implemented to detect and correct single-bit errors.

I. INTRODUCTION

SINCE the introduction of the first 16K floating-gate EEPROM in 1981 [1], these higher density EEPROM devices have been gradually gaining marketplace acceptance. EEPROM is used mainly for its nonvolatility and the capability of in-system alterability. Because higher density EEPROM memories are now more readily available, applications of EEPROM have been expanded into various areas such as smart cards, automobiles, communication, and military equipment. Recently, the demand for high-density and very high-speed EEPROM's (sub 100 ns) has been increasing rapidly because of the improved instruction cycle times being achieved by high-performance microprocessors. In this paper, a high-performance 256K EEPROM which achieves 50-ns typical READ access time and 1-ms page programming time, equivalent to 16 μs per byte, will be described. By using a modified Hamming code [2] for single-bit error detection and correction (SEDC), the part is also designed to meet an endurance specification of 10^5 cycles with a minimum of ten-year data retention over the full military temperature range. This enhances the reliability of the device significantly, making it ideally suitable for military applications.

II. TECHNOLOGY

The device is fabricated with a double-poly floating-gate, n-well CMOS technology. A double-layer metal process was developed which reduces the chip size and enhances the speed. Tapered metal-1 and via etching were applied to improve the metal-2 step coverage. The minimum feature

Manuscript received March 8, 1988; revised May 12, 1988.
The authors are with Microchip Technology, Inc., Chandler, AZ 85224.
IEEE Log Number 8822444.

TABLE I
TECHNOLOGY PARAMETERS

access time Tacc	35 ns
Tce	50 ns
active current	60 mA
standby current	100 uA
page programming time	1 msec
endurance	> 100K
process	N-well CMOS, double poly, double metal
chip size	253 x 350 mil²
cell size	66 um²
interpoly dielectric	300 Å
gate dielectric	350 Å
tunnel dielectric	< 100 A
minimum channel length	2.5 um
junction depth XJN	0.3 um
XJP	0.45 um
minimum feature size	1.25 um

size of 1.25 μm made possible the design of a 66-μm² EEPROM cell with a wide cell-threshold window for fast program/erase and also a high cell current for fast sensing. The technology features are summarized in Table I.

III. ARCHITECTURE

The functional block diagram of the 256K EEPROM is shown in Fig. 1. The memory array is arranged as 512 × 64 bytes. Each byte contains eight data bits and four parity bits for SEDC. A single-ended X decoder is utilized with a metal-2 strapped poly-2 word line. During WRITE, the parity generator generates four parity bits according to a modified Hamming code. These four parity bits, along with the eight data bits, are loaded into the column latches before they are written into the memory array. During READ, the 12-bit data are sensed out through the sense

Reprinted from *IEEE J. Solid-State Circuits*, vol. 23, no. 5, pp. 1164–1170, October 1988.

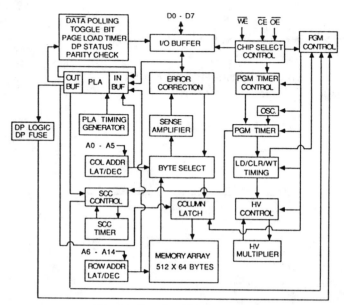

Fig. 1. Functional block diagram.

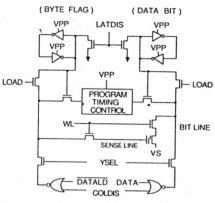

Fig. 2. Column latches.

amplifier. The error correction unit corrects any single-bit errors and provides eight data bits to the output buffers.

The programming control logic generates control signals to latch the address and data, to initiate the programming timing generator, and to control the on-chip high-voltage multiplier. A two-phase clock generated by an *RC* oscillator clocks a nine-stage timer to provide the proper timings to define the loading and the programming sequences. A 20-ns noise filter is designed to prevent inadvertent WRITE by noise glitches on the $\overline{WE}$ and $\overline{CE}$ pins. The PLA state machine recognizes the software instructions and generates the control signals to set or reset the data-protection fuse, to set or reset the parity-check mode, and to execute the software chip clear functions. The programming status bit circuitry provides the data-polling bit on I/O 7, the toggle bit on I/O 6, the page-load timer status on I/O 5, and the data-protection status on I/O 3.

IV. PROGRAMMING LOGIC

A. Page-Mode Programming

A page is defined as a physical row in the array, which contains 64 bytes. The page-mode cycle includes a loading period and a programming period. During the loading period, the user can load up to 64 bytes of data into the column latches, and these data are written into the memory array within one programming cycle. During the programming cycle, an automatic clear-before-WRITE mechanism is performed.

The page address is determined by the row address of the last byte loaded. If the same address is loaded more than once, only the last data are written. The unselected bytes will not experience high voltage during the programming period, preserving the endurance of those bytes that

have no data change. The programming status bits can be read throughout the page-mode cycle.

B. Column Latches

The schematic of the column latches is shown in Fig. 2. Each byte contains one byte-flag latch and 12 data-bit latches. In the loading period, LOAD is high and data are loaded into the data-bit latch. The byte-flag latch of the selected byte is also set. During the programming period, the latched data bit controls the high-voltage path to the bit line. Similarly, the byte flag controls the high-voltage path to the sense line. The byte flags of unselected bytes are not set, and as a consequence, the unselected bytes will not experience high voltage.

At the beginning of the loading period, the column discharge signal COLDIS is high. All bit lines are discharged to avoid false loading of the unselected bytes. After programming, all column latches are cleared through the LATDIS gated discharging devices.

C. Byte-Mode Programming

For compatibility with conventional byte-mode-only EEPROM, the byte-mode programming is also included in this design. By programming an EEPROM fuse, the page-mode functions can be disabled. The byte WRITE operation is triggered by the falling edge of the WRITE control signal, which is the logical OR of $\overline{CE}$ and $\overline{WE}$. If the WRITE control signal is kept low for a period longer than 4 μs, the programming cycle will be automatically started by an internal timer. The edge-triggering design prevents multiple WRITE's in case of a prolonged WRITE control signal.

V. SOFTWARE ALGORITHMS

The first three or six bytes loaded in the loading period can be identified as instruction codes. A code is defined as a specific address-data pair, and an instruction is defined as a specific sequence of a set of codes. Once a legal code sequence is recognized, the device will perform the designated functions according to the instruction. In this design, we have included the software data protection, the

A14-A0	D7-D0	A14-A0	D7-D0	A14-A0	D7-D0
5555	AA	5555	AA	5555	AA
2AAA	55	2AAA	55	2AAA	55
5555	A0	5555	80	5555	80
ADDR	DATA	5555	AA	5555	AA
		2AAA	55	2AAA	55
		5555	20	5555	10
		ADDR	DATA		
(a)		(b)		(c)	

Fig. 3. Three software instructions. (a) Set data protection. (b) Reset data protection. (c) Software chip clear.

software chip clear, and the parity-check mode in the instruction set.

A. Software Data Protection

To set the data-protection mode, a three-code instruction, which is illustrated in Fig. 3(a), has to be issued during the loading period. Once the data-protection mode is set, no further programming can be accomplished unless the same three-code instruction is issued at the beginning of each loading period. A six-code instruction (Fig. 3(b)) is used to reset the data-protection mode which is controlled by an EEPROM fuse. The circuit is designed to prevent repetitive fuse programming and thus the maximum endurance of the fuse is maintained.

B. Software Chip Clear

The conventional way of issuing the chip-clear command is through the use of an extra 12-V power supply. The software chip-clear design allows the user to clear the whole memory array to state ONE with a 5-V-only power supply. The software chip-clear instruction is shown in Fig. 3(c).

C. Parity-Check Mode

The parity-check mode can be set by issuing a three-code instruction. Once it is set, I/O 4 is dedicated to signaling whether there is an error bit in the addressed byte. In this mode, a new set of parity bits is generated and compared with the original set of parity bits stored in the array. Any single-bit errors will result in a mismatch, and the result of the comparison is reflected on I/O 4.

D. PLA State Machine

A six-state state machine was designed to implement all the software algorithms. Fig. 4 is the state diagram of the state machine. *FSTWR* is a signal indicating the first WRITE cycle. The sequence of code $C1$, $C2$, $C3$ sets the data-protection mode, while the sequence of code $C1$, $C2$, $C4$, $C5$, $C2$, $C6$ resets the data-protection mode. Any non-code byte sets the machine back to the default state 00. The instructions for the software chip clear and the parity-check mode are also indicated in the state diagram.

The state machine is implemented with a PLA approach [3] as shown in Fig. 5 because of its simplicity, flexibility, and compactness. The input signals to the PLA include the address and data, and the outputs of the PLA are execu-

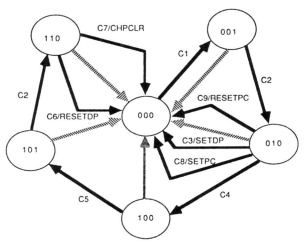

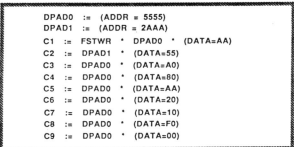

DPAD0	:= (ADDR = 5555)
DPAD1	:= (ADDR = 2AAA)
C1	:= FSTWR · DPAD0 · (DATA=AA)
C2	:= DPAD1 · (DATA=55)
C3	:= DPAD0 · (DATA=A0)
C4	:= DPAD0 · (DATA=80)
C5	:= DPAD0 · (DATA=AA)
C6	:= DPAD0 · (DATA=20)
C7	:= DPAD0 · (DATA=10)
C8	:= DPAD0 · (DATA=F0)
C9	:= DPAD0 · (DATA=00)

Fig. 4. State diagram for software algorithms.

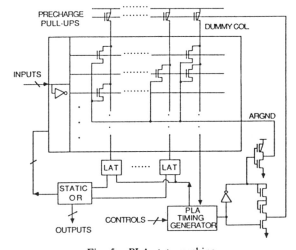

Fig. 5. PLA state machine.

tion commands which carry out the software functions. During precharge, all the columns and the array ground of the PLA array are charged high. During PLA cycling, a dummy column is used to generate a time reference, which triggers the latch control signal. The dummy column is discharged every time the PLA cycles. The loading of the dummy column is designed by physical layout to reflect the worst case. The discharging time of the dummy column varies with temperature, supply voltage, and process parameters, but it is always the optimum time reference for latching the valid data. The pull-up devices are biased

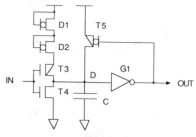

Fig. 6. Temperature-insensitive delay circuit.

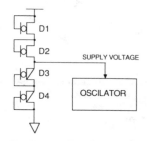

Fig. 7. Supply voltage for the oscillator.

to conduct minimally by applying a level of two-diode drop from V_{CC} to the gates, so that the column voltage can be restored even if the column is falsely discharged due to any late arrival of the input signals.

VI. TIMING GENERATION

A. Temperature-Insensitive Delay Circuit

A temperature-insensitive delay circuit as shown in Fig. 6 is designed to provide stable time constants across the full military temperature range. $D1$ and $D2$ are zero-threshold n-channel devices with threshold voltage of around 0.1 V at 0°C. The threshold reduction of $D1$ and $D2$ at high temperature compensates for the mobility degradation of $T3$ [4], [5], thus providing a relatively temperature-insensitive charging current. The time constant of the delay circuit depends on the size of $T3$ and the capacitance loading on node D. $G1$ is used to isolate node D so that the time constant of the delay circuit is independent of the next stage. $T5$ is a very weak native p-channel device with a threshold voltage of around 1.8 V. It is used as a feedback device to charge node D to full V_{CC} level to prevent the leakage current.

B. Oscillator

The frequency of an MOS RC oscillator is typically sensitive to the variation of temperature, supply voltage, and process parameters. The temperature sensitivity is compensated through $D1$ and $D2$ in Fig. 7, which is the same technique described in the previous section. Two native p-channel devices $D3$ and $D4$ are used to regulate the supply voltage for the oscillator at high V_{CC}. Fig. 8 shows the page-load time, which is directly proportional to

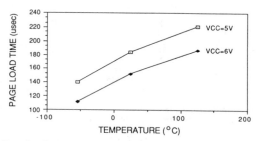

Fig. 8. Page-load time versus temperature measured at $V_{CC} = 5$ V and $V_{CC} = 6$ V.

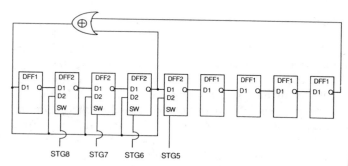

Fig. 9. Multivalued counter.

TABLE II
NUMBER OF STAGES VERSUS
COUNTS OF THE MULTI-
VALUED COUNTER

No. of Stages	Counts
5	21
6	63
7	93
8	217
9	511

the oscillator period, across full military temperature range at different supply voltages. The slopes of the curves in Fig. 8 can be flattened by inserting one extra zero-threshold n-channel diode between $D1$ and $D2$. The loading capacitor in the oscillator is trimmable for frequency adjustment.

C. Multivalued Counter

There are five important time constants for the loading and the programming periods. The ratio of these time constants is $1:3:5:10:25$. A multivalued counter as shown in Fig. 9 is designed to generate all five time constants. It is basically a shift-register sequence generator. $DFF2$ is a two-input D flip-flop multiplexed by the control input SW. If $SW = 0$, $D1$ is chosen as the input of the D flip-flop. If $SW = 1$, $D2$ is chosen as the input. With the two-input D flip-flop design, the number of stages can be altered by the control signals $STG5-STG8$. The counts for various stages are listed in Table II.

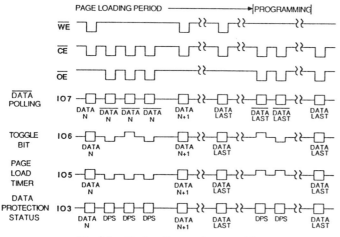

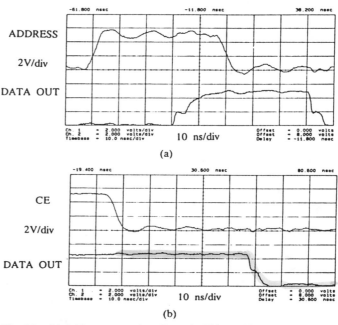

Fig. 10. Timing diagram for status bits.

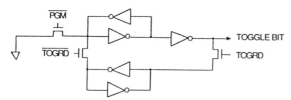

Fig. 11. Toggle-bit circuit.

Fig. 13. (a) Address access time T_{ACC}. (b) Chip-enable access time T_{CE}.

Each READ cycle toggles the latch once. During the loading and programming periods, $\overline{PGM}$ is low, and $TOGRD$ is high when $\overline{OE}$ and $\overline{CE}$ are low and $\overline{WE}$ is high. $TOGRD$ and $\overline{TOGRD}$ are designed to be nonoverlapped to avoid race problems. By reading the same address twice and comparing bit 6 of those two results, the user can detect whether the programming cycle is completed. In this way, the user does not have to remember the last loaded byte, and the data toggling ceases at the same time the programming cycle is completed regardless of the status of the memory array.

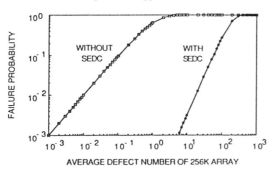

Fig. 12. Endurance improvement with SEDC.

VII. PROGRAMMING STATUS BITS

Four programming status bits are designed to enhance the communication of the device with the system. Data polling and toggle bit are used to detect the completion of the programming cycle. The page-load timer status bit indicates the expiration of the loading period. The data-protection status bit indicates whether the device is in the data protection mode. Fig. 10 is the timing diagram for these status bits.

Although the data-polling feature serves the purpose of providing the programming status, it has some disadvantages. First, the user has to memorize bit 7 of the last loaded data for comparison. Second, it relies on the success of the programming. For example, if bit 7 of the last byte was not written correctly into the memory, then the data-polling bit will not flag the completion of the internal programming cycle. With toggle bit, these two concerns are eliminated.

The toggle-bit circuit is shown in Fig. 11. The toggle-bit latch is initialized to be zero before the loading period.

VIII. SEDC

In order to improve the endurance of the device, an SEDC scheme is incorporated into this design. Fig. 12 illustrates a mathematic model of the endurance improvement with SEDC technique based on a random defect generation model in tunnel dielectric. For example, to achieve a 1-percent failure probability, one is allowed to have 0.01 defects in the 256K array without the error correction. But with the error-correction design, one is allowed to have 15 defects in the array, which represents an improvement of three orders of magnitude.

A Hamming code was selected according to the principle of optimizing the speed and minimizing the hardware implementation. Each parity bit is generated as an EXCLUSIVE-OR of five input data. Each check bit is an EXCLUSIVE-OR of a parity output and five data sense outputs. The parity-bit generator and the check-bit generator share the same EXCLUSIVE-OR circuits, and a multiplexer is used to swap the proper inputs to the EXCLUSIVE-OR gates according to the READ/WRITE status [6]. The SEDC circuitry increases the access time by 7 ns under typical conditions and occupies 23 percent of the chip area.

Fig. 14.   Photomicrograph of the CMOS 256K EEPROM.

IX.   Conclusion

A 50-ns high-speed full-feature CMOS 256K EEPROM has been designed and fabricated with an n-well technology. The combination of the speed, density, and reliability has been achieved through the use of a high cell-current EE cell, the implementation of a double-layer metallization, and the use of the SEDC scheme. A typical address access time T_{ACC} of 35 ns is realized as shown in Fig. 13(a). A chip-enable access time T_{CE} of 50 ns is achieved at 5 V and 25°C as shown in Fig. 13(b). The required and optional extended JEDEC standards for software data protection and chip clear are implemented along with parity check, toggle bit, page-load timer, and data-protection status bit. Fig. 14 is a photomicrograph of the chip.

References

[1]   W. Johnson, G. Perlegos, A. Renninger, G. Kuhn, and T. Ranganath, "A 16Kb electrically eraseable non-volatile memory," in *ISSCC Dig. Tech. Papers*, Feb. 1980, p. 152.

[2]   R. W. Hamming, "Error detecting and error correcting codes," *Bell Syst. Tech. J.*, vol. 26, pp. 147–160, Apr. 1950.

[3]   C. Mead and L. Conway, *Introduction to VLSI System.* Reading, MA: Addison-Wesley, 1980.

[4]   O. Leistiko, Jr., A. S. Grove, and C. T. Sah, "Electron and hole mobilities in inversion layers on thermally oxidized silicon surfaces," *IEEE Trans. Electron Devices*, vol. ED-12, no. 5, pp. 248–254, 1965.

[5]   L. Vadasz and A. S. Grove, "Temperature dependence of MOS transistor characteristics below saturation," *IEEE Trans. Electron Devices*, vol. ED-13, no. 12, pp. 863–867, 1966.

[6]   S. Mehrotra, T. C. Wu, T. L. Chiu, and G. Perlegos, "A 64Kb CMOS EEPROM with on-chip ECC," in *ISSCC Dig. Tech. Papers*, Feb. 1984, pp. 142–143.

A Four-State EEPROM Using Floating-Gate Memory Cells

CHRISTOPH BLEIKER, STUDENT MEMBER, IEEE, AND HANS MELCHIOR, SENIOR MEMBER, IEEE

Abstract—An electrically erasable programmable read-only memory (EEPROM) is used in a novel way as a four-state memory by charging the floating gate to determined values. We present a description of the memory cell and the complete programming and readout circuit. Retention characteristics are investigated and found to confirm a thermionic emission model. Retention time is estimated to more than 22 years at 125°C. Secondary effects like charge trapping in the oxide are successfully suppressed by a controlled writing procedure. Using such a four-state EEPROM instead of a binary cell, a reduction in chip area of 40 percent can be expected for a 1-kbit memory.

I. INTRODUCTION

THE FAST GROWTH of memory applications has lead to an increasing demand for electrically erasable programmable read-only memories (EEPROM's). Enlargement of their storage capabilities is actively pursued by scaling the devices and enlarging the chips. In the first case charge retention is getting worse due to the enhanced hot-carrier injection, while for larger chip surfaces the productivity decreases. An additional possibility for enhancing capacity is to store more than one bit per memory cell.

In this paper we introduce a novel EEPROM with four distinct logic states using a floating-gate memory cell. Besides a 50-percent reduction in cell area, this memory has all of the advantages of an alterable ROM. Cells with complete access circuitry are described and results of their storage capabilities presented.

II. CIRCUIT DESCRIPTION

The layout and the cross sections of the injector drain and the channel regions of the proposed four-level EEPROM cell are shown schematically in Fig. 1. The cell consists of a gate G_{EN} for selecting the reading transistor, the source and drain of this transistor, a control gate G_2 for erasing, and an injector drain D_I for writing. A summary of the terminal configurations for the different operation modes is given in Table I.

Manuscript received July 14, 1986; revised October 20, 1986. This work was supported in part by a grant from project NFP-13 of the Swiss National Foundation of Science.

The authors are with the Swiss Federal Institute of Technology Zürich, ETH Hönggerberg, CH-8093 Zürich, Switzerland.

IEEE Log Number 8714393.

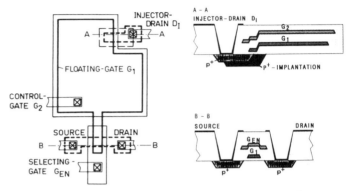

Fig. 1. Layout and cross sections of the EEPROM cell.

TABLE I
TERMINAL CONFIGURATIONS FOR THE OPERATION MODES

Mode	Logic-State	V_{G2}	V_{DI}	V_{EN}	Source	A_0	A_1	CLK
Read	x	0	0	V_{SS}	0	x	x	off
Erase	0	V_{ER}	0	x	x	x	x	off
Write	1	0	V_p	V_{SS}	0	1	0	on
Write	2	0	V_p	V_{SS}	0	0	1	on
Write	3	0	V_p	V_{SS}	0	1	1	on

Reading of the memory is achieved by applying the negative supply voltage V_{SS} to the gate G_{EN} and 0 V at the source of the cell transistor. By sensing the drain current, the logic state of the cell can be determined. Writing and erasing are accomplished by applying a high negative voltage (V_p, V_{ER}) to the injector drain D_I or the control gate G_2. This causes a Fowler–Nordheim tunneling current [1] to flow through the thin injection oxide and leads to an increase or decrease of the charge stored on the floating gate. In the writing mode the cell transistor is additionally used to monitor the actual state of the memory and to control its programming.

During WRITE and READ periods, the transfer characteristic of the transistor is approximated by

$$I_{DS} = \frac{\beta}{2}(V_{G1} - V_T)^2. \tag{1}$$

The floating-gate voltage V_{G1} is determined as

$$V_{G1} = \frac{C_{12}}{C_T}V_{G2} + \frac{C_{1D}}{C_T}V_{DI} + \frac{Q_{G1}}{C_T} \tag{2}$$

Reprinted from *IEEE J. Solid-State Circuits*, vol. SC-22, no. 3, pp. 460–463, June 1987.

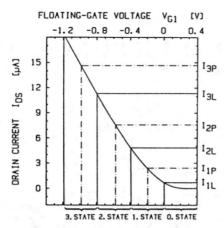

Fig. 2. Measured transfer characteristics of the reading transistor with chosen state distribution.

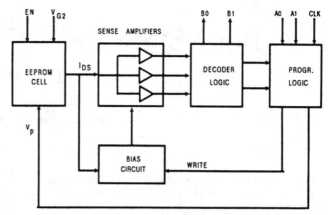

Fig. 3. Block diagram of the four-state memory.

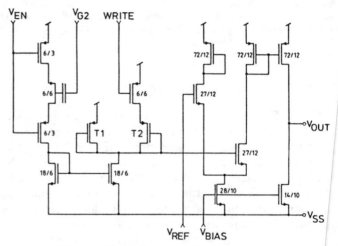

Fig. 4. Circuit diagram of the sense amplifier.

TABLE II
LOAD-TRANSISTOR DIMENSIONS

State	Transistor	W	L
1	T1	$6\,\mu m$	$42\,\mu m$
	T2	$6\,\mu m$	$24\,\mu m$
2	T1	$6\,\mu m$	$9\,\mu m$
	T2	$6\,\mu m$	$14\,\mu m$
3	T1	$9\,\mu m$	$6\,\mu m$
	T2	$6\,\mu m$	$12\,\mu m$

where C_{12} and C_{1D} are the capacitances of the floating gate with the control gate and the injector drain, respectively, and C_T is the sum of all capacitors contributing to the floating gate. The current I_{DS} can therefore be adjusted by varying the charge Q_{G1} on the floating gate, as follows from (1) and (2).

The distribution of the four levels within the available current range is illustrated in Fig. 2. Each state is characterized by its lower and upper current limits I_{nL} and I_{nH} and by a nominal current level I_{nP} which is reached after programming of the cell. With the assumption of equal charge losses for all levels, the four states are distributed equidistantly with respect to the floating-gate voltage and the nominal values I_{nP} are placed in the middle of the corresponding level. This assumption is justified as long as no universal retention model is available, which includes initial losses [2], detrapping of oxide charges, as well as long time retention behavior.

A block diagram of the complete memory circuit is shown in Fig. 3. For conversion of the drain current into 2-bit output information (B_0, B_1) three sense amplifiers and a decoder logic are used. During writing the nominal current levels I_{nP} are defined by a supplementary bias circuit and the comparison of the actual B_0, B_1 with the desired state A_0, A_1 is performed by the programming logic. In a memory array these access circuits are needed only once for a large number of EEPROM cells which are arranged in a matrix form.

The diagram of the conversion circuit and transistor dimensions are given in more detail in Fig. 4 and Table II, respectively. The detecting levels of the sense amplifiers are defined by different loads consisting of a permanently connected p-channel transistor and a mode-controlled transistor pair, which alters the detection level to the nominal value I_{nP} during writing of the cell. The sense amplifiers are built as conventional one-stage differential amplifiers and are designed for minimal power consumption with a dc differential gain A_{v0} of 39 dB. To avoid reading errors the maximum frequency of the subsequent latch is limited to less than 100 kHz. For faster applica-

tions one has to increase the cell transistor current I_{DS} as well as the differential gain A_{v0} of the amplifiers.

The decoder logic consists of AND and OR gates in two logic stages while the programming logic is composed of XOR gates and an $R-S$ flip-flop, which is set and altered corresponding to the states during programming.

The timing diagram of the programming procedure for writing the second state is given in Fig. 5 as an example. Applying the programming voltage V_p to the injector drain causes the current I_{DS} to rise. When the desired state is reached ($I_{DS} = I_{2P}$, $B_0 = A_0$, and $B_1 = A_1$) V_p is removed on the next negative transition of CLK. Due to the capaci-

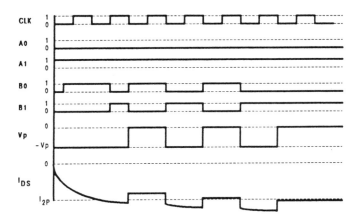

Fig. 5. Timing diagram of the programming sequence for writing the second state.

tive coupling of the injector drain to the floating gate, the current I_{DS} decreases after removing V_p causing an incorrect output ($B_0 = 1$, $B_1 = 0$). V_p will therefore be reapplied with the clock rate until the corresponding current level is also reached for $V_p = 0$ V.

III. RETENTION BEHAVIOR

The retention behavior at elevated temperatures is described by the relation for the stored charge $Q_{G1}(t)$ given by Nozawa et al. [3], [4] and Nishi and Iizuka [5]:

$$Q_{G1}(t) = Q_{G1}(t = 0) \exp\left(- \nu t e^{(-\phi_B/kT)}\right) \quad (3)$$

where ν is the dielectric relaxation frequency of electrons in the polysilicon and ϕ_B is the barrier height at the polysilicon–SiO$_2$ interface. For correct operation the minimum necessary charge $Q_{G1}(\min)$ for state n is

$$Q_{G1}(\min) = C_T \left(\sqrt{\frac{2}{\beta} I_{nL}} + V_T \right). \quad (4)$$

Equation (4) is obtained from (1) and (2) with $V_{DI} = V_{G2} = 0$. Substituting $Q_{G1}(t)$ for $Q_{G1}(\min)$ in (3) leads to an expression for the maximum retention time τ_R:

$$\tau_R = \ln \left(\frac{\sqrt{\frac{2}{\beta} I_{nP}} + V_T}{\sqrt{\frac{2}{\beta} I_{nL}} + V_T} \right) \Big/ \left(\nu e^{(-\phi_B/kT)} \right). \quad (5)$$

The values of

$$a = \left(\sqrt{\frac{2}{\beta} I_{nP}} + V_T \right) \Big/ \left(\sqrt{\frac{2}{\beta} I_{nL}} + V_T \right)$$

vary slightly for the three states and are 1.46, 1.19, and 1.10 for the first, second, and third level, respectively. The third state is considered as worst case if the barrier height and the relaxation frequency are assumed to be constant.

The values for ν and ϕ_B given by [3]–[5] range from 800 to 10^{12} s^{-1} and 1 to 1.7 eV, respectively. Due to this wide spread of parameter values reliable prediction of the retention behavior must be based on individual measurements of ν and ϕ_B.

IV. RESULTS

To demonstrate the principle of operation, single EEPROM cells with current outputs for tests and complete access circuits were integrated. We used a 4-μm minimum size, double-poly CMOS technology for low voltage. Measured data of the test circuit with $\Phi = 100$ kHz and $CLK = 10$ kHz are summarized in Table III and a chip photograph is shown in Fig. 6.

Programming of the cell was performed for each state with various programming voltages V_p and clock rates CLK as summarized in Table IV. It is evident that both the programming precision, defined as $(I_{DS} - I_{nP})/(I_{nH} - I_{nP})$, and the writing duration are influenced by V_p and CLK. Note that a programming precision of less than 100 percent means a correct operation even if the nominal current levels I_{nP} are exceeded. Due to remarkable endurance problems caused by enhanced injection-oxide stressing [6], the clock rates are limited to values less than 50 kHz.

Due to the controlled writing approach the typical threshold-voltage lowering with increasing WRITE–ERASE cycles was not observed. Instead, the programming time varied to compensate for trapped oxide charges so that the desired state was correctly reached. For applications without timing restrictions endurance will not be limited by threshold walk-off but by oxide breakdown.

The retention behavior of the memory was tested at several samples which were programmed to the upper three states. The devices were stored in an oven at temperatures of 150 and 200°C and thermal treatment was interrupted only for measuring the current at room temperature.

Using the above-mentioned thermionic emission model, ϕ_B is calculated with knowledge of the time t_x needed to reduce the floating-gate charge by a fixed amount of the initial charge at different temperatures T_x according to

$$\phi_B = \frac{\ln(t_1/t_2)}{(1/kT_1 - 1/kT_2)}. \quad (6)$$

The barrier height was determined for all levels to 1.03 eV while ν was chosen for best fit of the measured retention characteristics. The value of ν is about 1420 s^{-1} for all states. From the measured and calculated behavior in Fig. 7 it is obvious that the minimal retention time τ_R for the third state is about 72 days at 200°C. By using (5) and the extracted values for Φ_B and ν the retention time τ_R is calculated to 22 years at 125°C.

To estimate the gain in chip area for a 1-kbit memory the surfaces needed for the cell structure and the access circuits are compared. From Fig. 6 it is clear that a cell

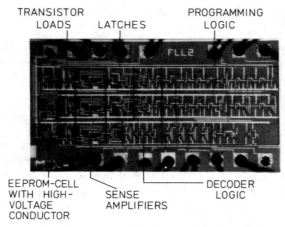

Fig. 6. Photograph of the test die (1×2 mm^2).

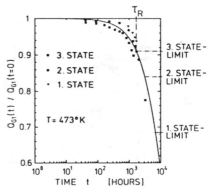

Fig. 7. Measured and calculated (solid line) retention characteristics at 200°C.

TABLE III
TYPICAL MEMORY PERFORMANCE

Parameter	Symbol	Typ. Value
Supply Voltage	V_{SS}	-3 V
Supply Current	I_S	< 1 mA
Write Voltage	V_P	-20 V
Erase Voltage	V_{ER}	-20 V
Access Time[1]	t_{AC}	15 μsec
Write Time	t_{WR}	< 30 msec
Erase Time	t_{ER}	100 msec

[1] With an output load of 20 pF

TABLE IV
PROGRAMMING PRECISION AND TIME

V_P	CLK	Min. Precision	Progr. Time
-18 V	100 Hz	50.0 %	600 msec
-18 V	1 kHz	3.5 %	600 msec
-18 V	10 kHz	0.3 %	675 msec
-20 V	1 kHz	42.0 %	25 msec
-20 V	10 kHz	5.0 %	28 msec

needs about one-thirtieth the area of the access circuits. A reduction of at least 40 percent could therefore be achieved for a 1-kbit memory using the four-state technique instead of binary cells.

V. CONCLUSIONS

A four-state memory using an EEPROM cell is proposed and its working principle demonstrated. Our results show that data retention is sufficient for device operation at temperatures below 125°C. Writing the cell by means of a feedback loop eliminates the influences of trapped charges and variations in the programming voltage. To reduce programming errors this writing principle would also be advantageous in ordinary binary EEPROM memories.

ACKNOWLEDGMENT

The authors are indebted to the staff of 'Centre Suisse d'Electronique et de Microtechnique SA' for fabrication of the test devices.

REFERENCES

[1] M. Lenzlinger and E. H. Snow, "Fowler–Nordheim tunneling into thermally grown SiO$_2$," *J. Appl. Phys.*, vol. 40, no. 1, pp. 278–283, 1969.
[2] D. Frohman-Bentchkowsky, "FAMOS—A new semiconductor charge storage device," *Solid-State Electron.*, vol. SSE-17, pp. 517–529, 1974.
[3] H. Nozawa and S. Kokyama, "A thermionic electron emission model for charge retention in SAMOS structures," *Japan. J. Appl. Phys.*, vol. 21, pp. L111–L112, 1982.
[4] H. Nozawa, Y. Niitsu, N. Matsukawa, J. Matsunga, and S. Kohyama, "Characteristics and reliability of the SAMOS cell," *IEEE Trans. Electron Devices*, vol. ED-31, pp. 1413–1419, 1984.
[5] Y. Nishi and H. Iizuka, "Nonvolatile memories," in *Applied Solid State Science*, D. Kahng, Ed. New York: Academic, Suppl. 2A, 1981, pp. 121–251.
[6] G. Yaron, S. J. Prasad, M. S. Ebel, and B. M. K. Leong, "A 16K E2PROM employing new array architecture and designed-in reliability features," *IEEE J. Solid-State Circuits*, vol. SC-17, pp. 833–840, 1982.

Part 9
Nonvolatile Memory Reliability

RELIABILITY assurance is a costly, time-consuming, difficult, and important task in IC development and production. This is particularly true with nonvolatile memories. Nonvolatile memories are subject to the usual IC failure mechanisms such as package and bonding failures, electrostatic discharge, electromigration, oxide breakdown, etc. Additionally, they must meet two other reliability requirements: retain data for 10 years and to function normally (within specification) after repeated PROGRAM and ERASE operations. These two requirements are known as data retention and endurance.

In floating-gate memories, stored electrons can leak away from the floating gate through the interpoly dielectric or through the gate oxide. The symptom is a decrease in the memory transistor threshold voltage. The same "charge loss" symptom can also be caused by the migration of mobile positive ions to the floating gate [1a], detrapping of electrons from the oxide traps, or generation of positive interface charge due to temperature-bias stress [1b]. As a rule, it is difficult, if not impossible, to distinguish these mechanisms. The opposite effect, charge gain, can occur when the floating gate slowly gains electrons with the control gate held at V_{cc}. The symptom is an increase in the threshold voltage. This symptom can also be caused by detrapping of holes from oxide traps [2]. The test of long-term (10 years) data retention is usually accelerated by temperature to a period of days. Temperature-bias stress can generate (exacerbate) certain defects, which can cause data retention failures [3].

Endurance is a more important issue for EEPROMs and flash EEPROMs than for EPROMs for obvious reasons. Repeated ERASE and PROGRAM subjects the oxide in the memory transistor to electrical stresses that can cause failures. For example, a major endurance failure made of FLOTOX EEPROM is tunnel-oxide breakdown (Paper 9.4). There are more subtle endurance failure modes. For example, electron trapping in the interpoly oxide slows down the speed of PROGRAM/ERASE in textured-polyoxide EEPROM (see Paper 7.7). This is its major endurance failure mechanism [4]. Similarly, electron trapping in the oxide can slow down the hot-electron programming speed of flash EEPROMs after endurance stress.

An even more subtle, i.e., hard to detect, endurance failure mode is a loss of the data retention ability after endurance stress. Apparently, oxide can become more conductive after electrical stress. Similarly, endurance stress can result in charge loss or gain during programming. Programming disturb occurs when the high voltage applied to the control gate or drain diffusion of an unselected cell, i.e., one that is not being programmed, causes the cell threshold voltage to increase or decrease. Endurance stress can aggravate or bring on PROGRAM disturb.

Paper 9.1 is a survey of the EPROM failure modes, a case study of how to screen out the defective parts, and accelerated tests that project the long-term failure rates. Paper 9.2 is a classic study that identifies several mechanisms for data loss and their activation energies. Paper 9.3 updated the data retention study, highlighting the interpoly oxide as the charge loss path, and the roles of mobile ions and electron detrapping from oxide traps.

Paper 9.4 surveys the FLOTOX EEPROM failure mechanisms. The principal reliability concern is the tunnel-oxide breakdown caused by PROGRAM/ERASE cycling. Failures occur at a small number of random bits. This failure mode has continued to be the major barrier to improving EEPROM reliability. In addition to reducing the thin-oxide defect density, on-chip error coding and correction has proven to be essential for achieving acceptable reliability in high-density EEPROMs (Papers 8.10–8.12).

All the charge loss mechanisms observed in EPROMs (Papers 9.2 and 9.3) also apply to EEPROMs. In addition, PROGRAM/ERASE cycling severely worsens the data retention ability of EEPROM. Paper 9.5 shows that thin oxides become more conductive at low fields after tunneling stress (PROGRAM/ERASE). This problem is more severe for thinner oxides. This phenomenon has been observed in many studies [5], but is not yet understood. One can expect this problem to be further exacerbated at defects.

Paper 9.6 is a study of the reliability of a flash EEPROM. Expectedly, PROGRAM/ERASE cycling slows down the PROGRAM and ERASE speed and brings on thin-oxide leakage (charge loss and PROGRAM disturb). Thin-oxide disturb appears to be caused by hole injection during ERASE. Channel-hot-electron injection during programming is more benign. Paper 9.7 confirms and expands on the role of hole injection. The overall picture is consistent with the dominant role played by holes and the minimal role played by hot electrons in oxide wearout [6], [7].

Papers 9.8 and 9.9 are experimental studies of the effects of radiation on FLOTOX and MNOS EEPROMs, with emphasis on the modeling of memory transistor threshold voltage change due to radiation. Radiation effects on data retention of ferroelectric memory cells have also been studied recently [8]. MNOS EEPROMs have better radiation hardness and comparable-to-better endurance than FLOTOX EEPROMs. MNOS (SONOS) memories, however, have only marginal intrinsic data retention capability due to the presence of the 20-Å oxide (see Paper 4.9). Some MNOS memories (Paper 6.3) claim only one year data retention time rather than the customary ten years.

Ferroelectric memories are too new to have their reliabilities thoroughly studied. One reliability problem is their limited cycling endurance (see Paper 6.6). Actually, a ferroelectric memory's endurance of $\sim 10^{12}$ switching cycles far exceeds those of FLOTOX and MNOS memories ($\sim 10^5$

cycles). However, the dense ferroelectric memories most widely studied today use one switching cycle for every READ cycle, and 10^{12} switching cycles can be used up in 10^5 s if a memory cell is continuously read at 10^7 Hz. Paper 6.8 shows a design solution to this problem.

Finally, there is a recent study of dielectric antifuse reliability [9]. At the same conference, EPROM charge loss through ONO interpoly dielectric [10] and through PROGRAM disturb [11] were also addressed.

REFERENCES

[1a] G. Crisenza et al., "Charge loss in EPROM due to ion generation and transport in interlevel dielectric," *Tech. Dig. Internat. Electron Devices Meet.*, 1990, pp. 107–110.

[1b] A. K. Sinha and T. E. Smith, "Kinetics of the slow-trapping instability at the Si/SiO_2 interface," *J. Electrochem. Soc.*, vol. 125, pp. 743–746, May 1978.

[2] Y. Fukuda and H. Kodama, "Retention characteristics of hole-injection-type EEPROM," *IEEE Trans. Electron Devices*, vol. ED-27, no. 11, pp. 2080–2085, Nov. 1980.

[3] R. E. Shiner, N. R. Mielke, and R. Haq, "Characterization and screening of SiO_2 defects in EEPROM structures," in *Proc. Internat. Reliability Phys. Symp.*, 1983, pp. 248–256.

[4] N. Mielke, "Reliability comparison of FLOTOX and textured-poly-silicon E^2PROMs," in *Proc. Internat. Reliability Phys. Symp.*, 1987, pp. 85–92.

[5] D. A. Baglee and M. C. Smayling, "The effects of write erase cycling on data loss in EEPROMs," in *Tech. Dig. Internat. Electron Devices Meet.*, 1985, pp. 624–627.

[6] I. C. Chen, S. Holland, and C. Hu, "Oxide breakdown dependence on thickness and hole current—*Enhanced reliability of ultra thin oxides*" in *Tech. Dig. Internat. Electron Devices Meet.*, 1986, pp. 660–663.

[7] I. C. Chen, J. Y. Choi, T. Y. Chan, and C. Hu, "The effect of channel hot carrier stressing on gate oxide integrity MOSFET," *IEEE Trans. Electron Devices*, vol. 35, pp. 2253–2258, Dec. 1988.

[8] J. F. Scott, C. A. Araujo, H. B. Meadows, L. D. McMillan, and A. Shawabken, "Radiation effects on ferroelectric thin-film memories: Retention failure mechanisms," *J. Appl. Phys.*, vol. 66 (3), pp. 1444–1453, Aug. 1989.

[9] S. Chiang et al., "Oxide–nitride–oxide antifuse reliability," in *Proc. Internat. Reliability Phys. Symp.*, 1990, pp. 186–192.

[10] K. Wu et al., "A Model for EPROM intrinsic charge loss through oxide–nitride–oxide (ONO) interpoly dielectric," in *Proc. Internat. Reliability Phys. Symp.*, 1990, pp. 145–149.

[11] T. Miller, S. Illyes, and D. Baglee, "Charge loss associated with program disturb stresses in EPROMs, in *Proc. Internat. Reliability Phys. Symp.*, 1990, pp. 154–158.

Tests and screens weed out failures, project rates of reliability

by Stuart Rosenberg, *Intel Corp., Phoenix, Ariz.*

□ To determine the failure rate of a group of erasable programmable read-only memories—or any integrated circuit, for that matter—various short cuts must be employed or the testing time would become intolerable. Some E-PROM failure modes only occur after the device has been working properly for years (proper operation of an E-PROM is described in part 1 of this article). Obviously, production testing cannot afford this kind of time, so the aging process is accelerated with high temperatures and extreme supply voltages. This form of testing, called screening, will both pinpoint bad chips and help determine the overall failure rate that can be expected for a batch of devices.

The purpose of reliability testing is to quantify the expected failure rate of a device at various points in its life. Fundamental principles of reliability engineering predict that the failure rate for a group of devices will follow the bathtub-shaped curve depicted in Fig. 1. This curve is divided into three regions: infant mortality, random failures, and wear-out failures. All classes of failure mechanism can be assigned to one or more of these regions.

Infant mortality, as the name implies, represents the earliest failures in a device's life and is usually associated with one or more manufacturing defects. After a time, usually in the high tens to low hundreds of hours, the failure rate approaches a constant low value where it

remains for a period of hundreds of thousands to millions of hours (for integrated circuits), depending upon temperature, applied voltages, and other operational and environmental factors.

This random-failure region of the curve represents the useful life of the device. During this period there is a slight decline in the failure rate as potential random failures are weeded from the general population. Wear-out failures are characterized by a rapidly rising failure rate with time as the devices wear out both physically and electrically.

Characterizing a given device type in the shortest possible time requires tests that simulate accelerated aging. To choose the right acceleration factor, it is first necessary to understand what makes E-PROMs fail in each region of Fig. 1.

Table 1 lists the common failure mechanisms for n-channel MOS E-PROMs. The table also shows the region of the bathtub curve most affected by each mechanism, as well as the thermal activation energy (E_a) of the mechanism. The thermal activation energy indicates the effect that increased temperature has on the frequency of the failure; the higher the activation energy, the greater the effect. For example, a temperature rise from 70°C to 125°C increases the failure rate resulting from oxide-hopping conduction ($E_a = 0.6$ electronvolt) by a factor of 16.5. This same temperature rise causes oxide

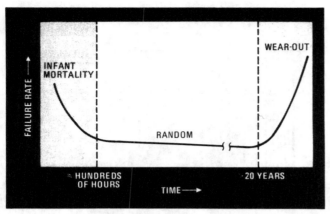

1. Failure tub. The reliability of an integrated circuit follows a bathtub-shaped curve. Infant failures happen right after the chip is made. Wear-out failures do not start until after 20 years, a time span representing the useful life of the device.

rupture failures ($E_a = 0.3$ ev) to increase by only a factor of 6.

A detailed explanation of each mechanism is beyond the scope of this article, but charge loss, oxide-hopping conduction, and hot-electron injection are responsible for the majority of failures. A buildup of electrons trapped in the oxide layer mentioned in part 1 commonly causes devices to wear out.

Charge loss from the floating gate is due to thermal emission. It affects most E-PROM cells to some degree over their 20-year life, and typically amounts to less than 10% of the charge stored on a cell.

Failure modes

Oxide-hopping conduction between the floating gate and the silicon substrate is typically less than 10^{-19} ampere, or about one electron per second. The electrons flow onto or off the floating gate depending on bias conditions, so they may cause bit errors on either stored 0s or 1s. Oxide-hopping conduction is related to manufacturing defects and does not occur in most devices. Thus, this failure mechanism affects the random and infant portions of the bathtub curve most strongly.

Undesirable hot-electron injection occurs when an MOS transistor is in saturation. Accelerated electrons in

the pinch-off region may be scattered or attracted because the gate field is perpendicular to the silicon-oxide interface.

As covered in part 1 of this article, cell programming of an E-PROM is accomplished through hot-electron injection. During a programming cycle, as electrons travel to the floating gate, a small percentage of these carriers may become trapped in the thin gate oxide. Since ultraviolet radiation is relatively ineffective at removing these trapped electrons during erasure, repeated programming and erase cycles may result in a build-up of charge. These trapped electrons may, in turn, cause significant degradation in the operating margins of the device and, ultimately, device wear-out.

Measuring mortality

To measure the infant-mortality failure rate, a 48-hour dynamic burn-in at 125°C is used. Depending on the failure mechanism, the test correlates with 240 to 2,000 hours of operation at 55°C. To perform such a test, E-PROM samples are gathered on a weekly basis, programmed with a checkerboard pattern, and burned in. Results of infant mortality tests done on the Intel 2716 E-PROM for 1979 are shown in Table 2. The data reveals an average infant-mortality failure rate of 0.2% for the year, with failures heavily dominated by hopping conduction (67 of a total of 73 failures).

To best characterize the random portion of the bathtub curve, burned-in E-PROMs that no longer exhibit infant mortality are used. Long-term failures are measured with 1,000-hour 125°C life tests; results for the 2716 are shown in Table 3, along with the failure analysis. There were 23 failures in 5.2×10^6 device hours for a failure rate of 0.4% per 1,000 hours at 125°C.

With more than one failure mode, and with different thermal activation energies, the effect of operation at 125°C varies for different devices. It should also be pointed out that since failures occur at the die level, any extrapolations must be made from junction, and not ambient, temperatures. Thus a 125°C to 55°C ambient derating corresponds to a derating of junction temperatures from 130°C to 65°C for a 2716.

Although there are many ways to compute a 55°C failure rate, only one is realistic: by simply calculating

TABLE 1: E-PROM FAILURE MECHANISMS			
Mode	Lifetime region affected (in Fig. 1)	Thermal activation energy (eV)	Primary detection method
Slow trapping	wear-out	1.0	high-temperature bias
Surface charge	wear-out	0.5 – 1.0	high-temperature bias
Contamination	infant/wear-out	1.0 – 1.4	high-temperature bias
Polarization	wear-out	1.0	high-temperature bias
Electromigration	wear-out	1.0	high-temperature operating life
Microcracks	random	–	temperature cycling
Contacts	wear-out/infant	–	high-temperature operating life
Silicon defects	infant/random	0.3	high-temperature operating life
Oxide breakdown/leakage	infant/random	0.3	high-temperature operating life
Hot-electron injection	wear-out	–	low-temperature operating life
Fabrication defects	infant	–	high-temperature burn-in
Charge loss	infant/random/wear-out	1.4	high-temperature storage
Oxide-hopping conduction	infant/random	0.6	high-temperature storage/burn-in

TABLE 2: INFANT MORTALITY EVALUATION FOR THE 2716	
Month (1979)	Burn-in results (number failed/number stressed)
January	3/1956
February	2/964
March	6/4085
April	4/3813
May	9/3602
June	7/3822
July	9/2995
August	7/3055
September	3/1893
October	8/5025
November	2/1726
December	13/3321
Total	73/36,257 = 0.2% failure rate

Failure analysis:

    33 charge-lose failures
    34 charge-gain failures
    3 decoder failures due to oxide breakdown
    2 ac failures from slow trapping or contamination
    1 dc parametric failure from contamination

TABLE 3: 2716 DYNAMIC LIFE TEST DATA AND RANDOM-FAILURE RATE EVALUATION			
Month started	Results at 125°C		
	168 hours	500 hours	1,000 hours
Before 5/79	5/3983	7/3874	3/3969
5/79	0/128	1/128	1/127
6/79	0/128	2/128	0/126
6/79	0/286	0/286	0/286
6/79	0/29	0/29	0/29
6/79	0/299	0/299	0/299
7/79	0/192	0/192	0/192
8/79	0/64	0/64	0/64
8/79	0/99	0/99	0/99
8/79	0/102	0/102	0/102
8/79	0/102	0/102	0/102
8/79	0/100	0/100	0/100
8/79	0/100	0/100	0/100
8/79	0/128	0/128	0/128
9/79	0/64	1/64	0/63
10/79	0/75	0/75	0/75
10/79	0/31	0/31	0/31
Cumulative	5/5894 (A)	12/5065 (B)	6/5055 (C)

FAILURE ANALYSIS

(A) 5 single-bit hopping conduction (0.6 eV)

(B) 11 single-bit hopping conduction (0.6 eV)
    1 double-bit charge retention (0.6 eV)

(C) 5 single-bit hopping conduction (0.6 eV)
    1 single-bit fabrication defect (0.3 eV)

FAILURE RATE CALCULATION

Failure-mode activation energy (eV)	Actual device-hours at 125°C	Equivalent device-hours at 55°C	Number of failures	Failure rate at 60% confidence level (% per 1,000 hours)
0.3	5.2×10^6	2.7×10^7	1	0.007
0.6	5.2×10^6	2.2×10^8	22	0.011
Total failure rate: 0.018% per 1,000 hours				

the rate due to each mechanism and then adding them up. In another method, one that yields overly optimistic results, a single thermal activation energy is chosen to represent all failures in the population. A common choice is 0.7 ev since this value is used in military testing procedures. Based upon the number of device-hours in Table 3 (5.2×10^6) and this activation energy, the acceleration factor from 130° to 65°C corresponds to 48:1. This acceleration factor was read off an Arrhenius plot (Fig. 2).

For this scheme the equivalent number of device hours at 55°C works out to 2.5×10^8. At a 60% confidence level with the tabulated number of failures (23), the 55°C failure rate becomes 0.01% per 1,000 hours. The pitfall of this method is that the acceleration factor is determined independently of the failure types and their corresponding activation energies. Unless all the failures are 0.7 ev, which is not generally the case, the extrapolation has little meaning.

Accurate results are given at the bottom of Table 3, where a 55°C failure rate of 0.018% for 1,000 hours is calculated. The first method's failure rate, 0.01%, is two times too optimistic.

Testing for wear-out

There are two failure mechanisms by which E-PROMs wear out that significantly affect reliability. These are charge loss and stress from program-erase cycling.

Since charge loss has a high thermal activation energy (1.4 ev), a test involving storage at a very high temperature (250°C) can determine where on the bathtub curve devices begin to wear out. So units with a high percentage of programmed bits (typically more than 90%) are placed in storage at 250°C for up to 1,000 hours. Intermediate data is taken to determine the shape of the failure-rate curve.

Figure 3 illustrates the cumulative percentage of fail-

ures versus time for the 2716 after a storage test at 250°C. This graph is based on data from more than 1,000 units, taken over a period of more than six months. This curve shows no sign of an increase in failure rate, indicating that the failures are defect-related and symptomatic of the infant and random failure regions. No indication of wear-out resulting from intrinsic charge loss is seen at 1,000 hours at 250°C. This corresponds to 1,950 years at 125°C or 1.3 million years at 70°C.

To evaluate the effect of program-erase cycling on device wear-out, supply voltage maximum and minimum measurements (V_{CCmax} and V_{CCmin}, respectively) are made after subjecting an E-PROM to multiple programming and erasing cycles. V_{CCmax} is the greatest supply voltage that will support proper operation, and V_{CCmin} is the lowest value. Each cycle comprises programming of the E-PROM with more than 90% 0s; measuring V_{CCmax}; erasure via UV light with an intensity of 10 watt-seconds/square centimeter; programming to a pattern with more than 90% 1s; measuring V_{CCmin}; and erasure.

The results of 225 program-erase cycles on 48 2716s showed only one failure, which occurred after 56 cycles.

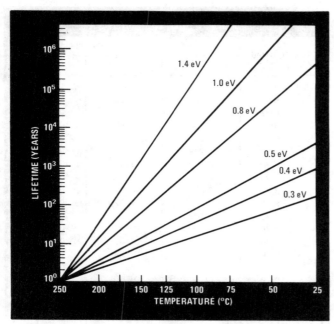

2. After Arrhenius. The Arrhenius plot shows the extent that an increase in temperature will accelerate a failure mechanism. Using the thermal activation energy for the failure mode of interest — see Table 1 — a device's life is deduced from a temperature differential.

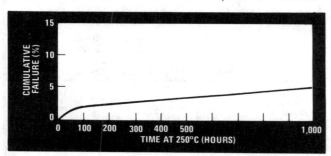

3. In sum. The cumulative percentage of failures is charted against time after storage tests done at 70°, 100°, and 250°C. The data was gathered from more than 1,000 units over a period of more than six months. Charge loss is not seen for an extended period of time.

The cause of the failure was determined to be partial oxide breakdown due to high field stressing during programming. Figures 4a and 4b show the 10%, 50%, and 90% points for program and erase margins (the cell's threshold voltage after programming and erasing) versus the number of program and erase cycles for the remainder of the sample. No appreciable shift can be seen in either the program or the erase margin and, for the 2716, degradation of operating margins due to hot electron injection did not occur.

Achieving acceptable reliability

To produce reliable E-PROMs, it is necessary to know the types of failures that may afflict the device and then devise tests to weed out those parts with latent defects. These tests are called failure-mode screens because they are effective only on those E-PROMs with latent defects due to a particular failure mechanism or mode. Figure 1 shows that infant mortality and wear-out failures each have an order of magnitude greater effect on reliability

than do random failures. For this reason, failure-mode screens are designed to isolate mechanisms that strike in these two regions of the bathtub curve.

Screens are also region-specific, so two different screens are needed to reduce failures during both the infant mortality and wear-out periods. Although the infant-mortality screen does not lower the random-failure rate, it does reduce the cumulative failure rate, thereby improving overall reliability.

Infant-mortality screens reduce a population's early-life failure rate by prematurely aging each part just beyond the first change in slope of the bathtub curve. If the manufacturer can eliminate most parts with latent defects before they leave the factory, the balance of each shipment should be error-free until the parts begin to wear out. Wear-out screens attempt to extend the random-failure portion of the curve further to the right, extending useful device life. Infant-mortality screens have a negligible impact on the wear-out failure rate because of the relative time scales; premature aging of a part — even by two months — means little after 20 years.

When faced with a raw population of E-PROMs whose reliability is to be improved by screening, the first step is thorough reliability life testing, followed by a detailed analysis of the failures. Once the dominant failure mechanisms have been identified and a failure rate computed, the number of screens and their types must be settled on.

Avoiding screen overkill

Screens cost money, though, because of the time and equipment needed to implement them. Overkill is a measure of the number of parts that fail a screen but that would never have failed in the field. A good screen has little overkill yet still lowers the failure rate. Ideally, screens should be part of a normal test program and should take less than a second to perform. A screen may be put into production to combat a new failure mode with little regard to overkill or complexity. Once the failure rate is under control, the screen can be modified to optimize its cost with respect to its effectiveness in improving reliability.

Two infant-mortality screens — one for defect-related charge loss and another for charge gain (both are manifestations of oxide-hopping conduction) — were developed for the 2716. The combined objective of those screens was to reduce the total early-life failure rate to less than 0.2% of the population. To measure the effectiveness of the screens, it was decided to follow each with a dynamic burn-in at 125°C for 48 hours — a typical infant-mortality period.

Charge-loss screen

The charge-loss screen was devised only after an analysis of indicators of latent manufacturing defects, as these are most responsible for charge-loss failures. Though indicative of the number of electrons on the floating gate, ease of programming and erasure and programming margin were evaluated — but without success, in this case.

The next step was to examine the effect on charge loss of bias voltage and temperature. Earlier work with E-PROMs showed charge loss to be more than two orders of magnitude greater at 150°C than at 55°C, so a high-

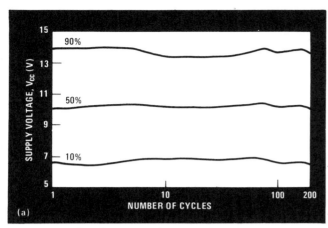

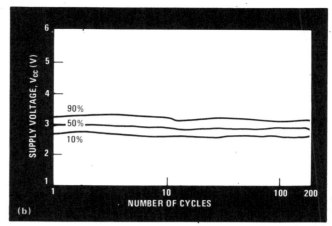

4. Good margins. To evaluate the effect of program-erase cycling on wear-out, a V$_{CCmax}$ test is done after multiple programming cycles (a), and a V$_{CCmin}$ test is done after numerous erasures. The near-horizontal lines indicate no degradation in program or erase margins.

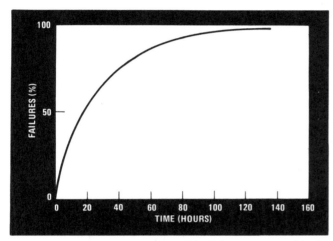

5. Charge-loss screen. A lot of 10,000 2716s was screened for 72 hours at 150°C, then burned in for 48 hours to check for charge-loss failures. The optimum duration for such a screen corresponds to the curve's leveling out; this happens after 72 hours.

temperature bake was selected as the basic screen. To determine whether bias voltage affected the charge loss, programmed cells with and without bias were compared, but found to be similar. Therefore, it was decided to make the screen an unbiased high-temperature bake, for reasons of simplicity.

The final step was to determine how high in temperature and how long in duration the screen should be. Since it was intended for production runs of 2716s in tin-plated ceramic packages, temperatures were limited to 150°C to prevent severe lead oxidation. To determine the optimum bake time, the screen was applied to known charge-loss rejects with pass/fail tests every 20 hours. The results (Fig. 5) indicate that about 72 hours would be sufficient to weed out the majority of charge-loss rejects.

To confirm this time estimate, a 10,000-piece lot of 2716s was first screened for 72 hours at 150°C and then dynamically burned in for 48 hours. Approximately 0.1% of the parts that passed the charge-loss screen failed the burn-in. This percentage of charge-loss failures compared favorably with an overall infant-mortality failure rate of 0.27%.

Unlike charge loss, a well-known failure mechanism in older designs, charge gain seemed unique to advanced E-PROMs. Earlier work at Intel hinted at a relationship between supply voltage and charge gain, so a biased, dynamic burn-in for 48 hours at 125°C became the first screen attempted.

The temperature was later raised to 150°C when it was decided to run the screen on 2716s in their power-down mode. During power-down, all select gates are driven to V$_{CC}$ and are stressed more effectively. By running the screen in power-down, the burn-in temperature could be safely raised to 150°C.

The supply voltage was the final parameter to be determined. Since the failure rate increases linearly with the stress voltage for charge gain, a V$_{CC}$ level greater than 5 volts was desirable for the screens. But a conflict arose because the power-down mode at an elevated V$_{CC}$ supply is also the programming mode. Fortunately, computer simulations of the 2716 revealed that 7.5 v could be used without going into the programing mode. Because of the increased voltage, temperature (150°C), and duty cycle, the screening time was reduced to six hours. The final result: a charge-gain screen done at 150°C for six hours at 7.5 v in the power-down mode.

With screens devised for both charge gain and charge loss, data was collected and measured against the 0.2% infant-mortality goal. Samples pulled weekly from an inventory awaiting shipment were subjected to a dynamic 48-hour burn-in at 125°C. Results for 1979 showed 72 failures out of 35,783 units stressed, or an infant mortality rate of 0.2%.

Wear-out can have a dramatic impact on reliability if it occurs in an operating piece of equipment. To minimize wear-out resulting from intrinsic charge loss, another type of screen was called for. As opposed to infant-mortality screening—where a small freak population must be eliminated—wear-out screening should insure that at least 99% of all parts will not fail during a specified lifetime.

It was known that temperature aggravates charge loss and that no external bias is necessary to induce charge loss in programmed cells. A good method for identifying charge-loss wear-out was found to be a 168-hour bake at 250°C. Using known acceleration factors from Arrhenius plots, this correlates with more than 220,000 years at 70°C. The acceptable percentage of failures for this test

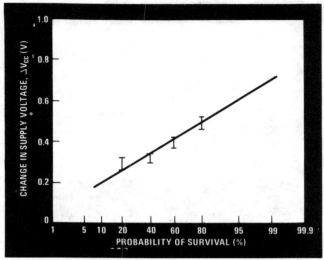

6. Wear-out. Wear-out screening should guarantee at least 99% of all parts will not fail during a specified lifetime. Both elevated temperature and maximum V$_{CC}$ were used to screen for charge-loss wear-out. For a 1% failure rate, V$_{CC}$ had to be increased 0.7 V.

TABLE 4: RESULTS OF DATA-RETENTION MONITOR			
Month	Number of devices	Data-retention failures	% fail
1/78	293	14	4.7%
2/78	200	0	0%
3/78	300	4	1.3%
4/78	100	3	3.0%
5/78	300	1	0.3%
7/78	165	1	0.6%
8/78	260	3	1.1%
9/78	323	11	3.4%
10/78	176	4	2.2%
11/78	323	11	3.4%
12/78	535	9	1.6%
This test was run for 168 hours at 250°C			

is 5%, which corresponds with 2×10^{-4}% failures due to charge loss in 10 years. If this rate is not exceeded, then wear-out has not yet begun.

Monitoring margins

Through the logging of cell programming margins (based on V$_{CCmax}$) at the beginning and end of the 168-hour bake at 250°C, an average degradation was determined. This was fed into the standard manufacturing test sequence—where cell programmability is checked—to insure that all parts have sufficient margin to weather a normal lifetime.

To determine a value for V$_{CCmax}$, experiments were conducted to discover the change in V$_{CCmax}$ for 99% of the 2716s tested. Although the target for failures was 5%, a 1% ceiling was considered more appropriate to account

for normal statistical variations in the small 50-piece sample.

The changes in V$_{CCmax}$ for the 168-hour 250°C bake are plotted in Fig. 6 against the probability of seeing a given change in V$_{CC}$. From this plot, a ΔV$_{CC}$ of 0.7 v corresponds to the 99% pass criterion. Thus, to insure that all 2716s have sufficient margin to withstand normal life, the standard manufacturing testing sequence includes a test with ΔV$_{CC}$ set to $+0.7$ v.

By incorporating the screen in the normal product flow there is a minimum of disruption and no increase in testing time (the screen takes less than 1 millisecond to perform). The final test of this wear-out screen is its effectiveness. Results through the first 11 months of 1979 pinpointed 100 failures in 3,800 devices stressed. This works out to a failure rate of 2.5%, well below the target of 5% (see Table 4). □

DATA RETENTION IN EPROMS

R. E. Shiner, J. M. Caywood, and B. L. Euzent
INTEL CORPORATION
Santa Clara, California 95051
(408) 987-8080

INTRODUCTION

Electrically programmable read only memories (EPROMs) which are eraseable by ultraviolet irradiation long have been used in the development of microprocessor based systems and have more recently found wide applications in systems shipped into the field where the ability to correct errors or easily provide field upgrade of the system software has proven appealing to systems manufacturers. In these latter applications it is essential to the integrity of the system that the EPROMs retain their data over tens of years under operating conditions.

In this paper we shall first review the mechanisms by which patterns stored in EPROMs can be disrupted, and then discuss the technique we used to study degradation mechanisms. Experimental data will be presented which will lead to a discussion of physical models for data loss. Finally, screens will be reviewed in light of the previous discussion. A schematic cross-section of the memory cell to be discussed here is shown in Fig. 1. The effective threshold of the stacked gate MOSFET depends on the charge on the lower gate which is electrically isolated by virtue of being completely surrounded by SiO_2. This gate is referred to as the storage gate; the top gate is referred to as the access gate.

FLOATING GATE EPROM CELL

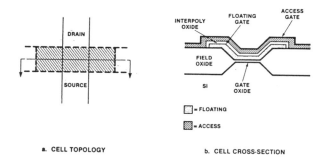

Figure 1: Plane, a, and cross-sction, b, views of an EPROM memory cell showing the floating storage gate wholly surrounded by SiO_2.

A potential diagram of an erased cell (which has very little net charge on the floating gate) with the access gate at VSS, the substrate potential, is shown in Fig. 2a. The electric fields across the oxides are due to the work function difference between the n-type select gate and the p-type substrate. If the access gate is raised to some positive voltage, the diagram shown in Fig. 2b results. For the access gate voltage levels used in normal "read" operation, the field at the sili-

con substrate/oxide interface is high enough to invert the surface and allow current to flow.

POTENTIAL DIAGRAMS ERASED CELL

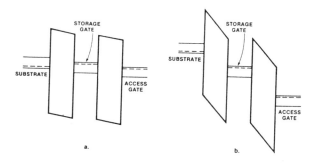

Figure 2: Electron potential band diagram of an EPROM memory cell in the erased state for the cases of the access gate at substrate potential, a), and of the access gate at potential typical of the "read" condition, b). The electric field noticable in the a) is the result of the difference in fermi level in the p-type substrate and the n-type access gate.

A programmed cell is one in which hot electrons have been injected and trapped on the floating gate. When the access gate is at VSS, the potential diagram is as shown in Fig. 3a. If the access gate voltage is raised on the programmed cell, the potential diagram shown in Fig. 3b results. Because of the charge on the floating gate, a much higher voltage must be applied to invert the surface. The voltage applied to the access gate under normal "read" conditions is too small to cause this inversion.

Traditionally, data retention studies have focused on charge loss off a programmed gate (the situations illustrated in Fig. 3a and 3b). In these cases the field, which is caused by the electrons trapped on the floating gate, is directed to tend to cause electrons to flow from the floating gate to either the substrate or the access gate. Either flow removes the electrons from the floating gate. In the unprogrammed case illustrated in Fig. 2b, the case is different. In this case the fields are directed to tend to cause electrons to move from the substrate to the floating gate and from the floating gate the the access gate. That is, there may be a net gain or loss of electrons on the floating gate depending upon which current dominates. If there is a net gain of electrons on the floating gate, the cell threshold becomes higher. If there is a net loss, the threshold becomes lower. The sign of the threshold shift allows determination of whether charge passes through the oxide between the floating gate and substrate or through the

Reprinted from *Proc. IRPS*, pp. 238–243, 1980.

interpoly oxide.

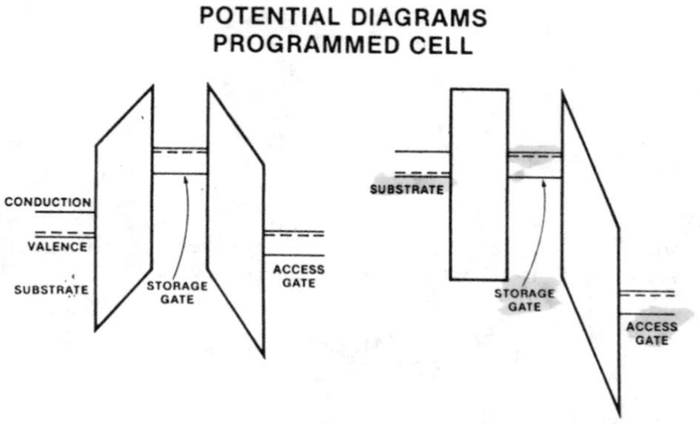

POTENTIAL DIAGRAMS
PROGRAMMED CELL

Figure 3: Electron potential band diagram of EPROM
memory cell in the programmed state for
the cases of the access gate at substrate
potential, a), and of the access gate at
a positive voltage, b).

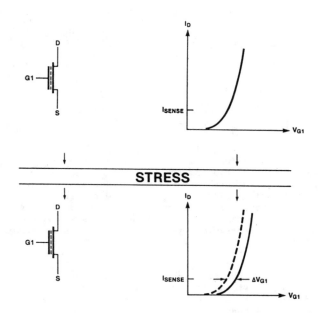

Figure 4: Schematic illustration of the experimental
procedure showing how increasing the access gate voltage until the cell sinks the
sense amplifier trip current may be used
to measure a shift in cell threshold.

Experimental Technique:

As was discussed in the previous section, change in the
charge on the floating gate manifests itself as a parallel shift in the transfer response of this double gate
transistor. Since the transfer response of this transistor is known to be otherwise stable, monitoring the
change in transfer response is a direct measure of the
change in floating gate charge. One good way to accomplish this in an EPROM memory array is to modulate the
access gate voltage in order to keep the drain current
of the transistor constant. Using linear superposition,
it can be shown that the relation between change in access gate voltage and change in floating gate charge is
given by:

$$\Delta V_{G1} = \Delta Q_G / C_1$$

where ΔV_{G1} is the change in access gate voltage, ΔQ_{G1}
is the change in floating gate charge, and C_1 is the
capacitance between access gate and floating gate.

We were fortunate to have available for this study a
part (the INTEL 2716) in which the sense amplifier trip
current is approximately independent of VCC over the
range of 3.5 to 9 volts. If VPP is held equal to VCC,
the voltage on these pins appears on the access gate
over this range. Thus, VPP and VCC can be swept to
find the access gate voltage at which the memory transistor conducts enought current to trip the sense amplifier as is illustrated in Fig. 4. Changes in this trip
level are a measure of changes in charge on the floating gate. The range of experimentally accessible access voltages can be somewhat extended on the low side.
If VCC is set between 4 to 5 volts and VPP is set between zero volts and VCC, the voltage on the access
gate is approximately the average of the voltages on
VPP and VCC; the sense amplifier trip current is unin-
fluenced by VPP.

One further convenient feature of the 2716 for the purposes of this study is that it is possible to take all
gates high at once so that all bits may be stressed simultaneously with the access gates either high or low.

Experimental Evidence:

Fig. 5 shows the results of a 6 hour, 125°C stress of
erased parts performed with the access gate taken to
7.5 volts. These units were chosen from production
charge loss screen rejects because we wish to study the
defect mechanisms. The results show that 78 bits gained
enough electrons to shift the cell threshold more than
0.5 volts positive; one bit lost enough electrons to
shift the cell threshold more than 0.5 volts negative.
Referring to the introductory discussion shows that this
means that for the bits with large net changes in storage gate charge, conduction through the gate oxide pre-
dominated. Since other studies of production screen reject charge loss failures have shown that 85% are 1 or 2
bit failures and the other 15% are 3 to 10 bit failures,
this result strongly argues that a substantial majority
of the charge loss rejects detected by the production
screen lose electrons through the oxide between the substrate and the floating gate. Other experiments too
numerous to describe here were performed in which the
identity of the defect bit was tracked. The results of
these experiments showed a very high correlation between
bits which lost electrons at an abnormally high rate
from the storage gate when stored at elevated temperatures in the programmed state and those bits whose storage gates gained electrons at an abnormally high rate
when subjected to elevated temperature with the access
gate high while in an erased state. Because of their
overwhelming predominance, the study of oxide defects
reported here is focussed on these defects in the oxide
between the substrate and the storage gate.

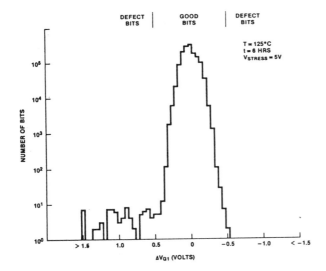

Figure 5: Histogram of the number of bits vs. the shift in threshold voltage following a stress of erased memories sampled from production charge loss screen rejects. Note that the vertical scale is logrithmatic.

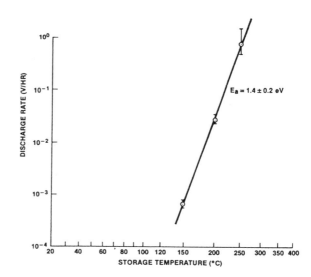

Figure 6: Plot of initial discharge rate vs. storage temperature for the worst case bit on typical programmed parts.

To gain perspective on what "abnormally high rate" means, let's first focus on the behavior of typical bits. Fig. 5 shows that 99.99% of the bits from reject parts exhibited a threshold voltage of 0.35 volts or less after the stress. Fig. 6 shows data on the shift exhibited by the worst bit on the ninetieth percentile (e.g., 90% of the parts shifted less) of a sample of 300 parts which passed the production screen after a programmed bake. There are several things to note about this data. One is the very high activation energy measured for this shift, 1.4eV. Another is the small magnitude of the loss rate which amounts to only about 7×10^{-5}V/hr. at 125°C. Even this rate overstates the case because this rate is calculated from the time the threshold of the worst bit takes to drop an initial 0.4V. The loss rate, however, is not constant but decreases with voltage shift. Had the time for the threshold to drop 0.7 volts been chosen for the loss calculation, the activation energy would have been the same, but the magnitude lower still.

Compare the loss rate from a typical bit (or more accurately the worst case bit on typical EPROM) shown in Fig. 6 to that of a defect bit shown in Fig. 7. The comparison shows that the loss rate for the defect bit has a much lower activation energy, 0.6eV, and a much greater magnitude (≈0.3V/hr. at 125°C) than that of the typical bit. An important implication of this high rate is that the defect bits are screenable in times consistent with a volume manufacturing flow.

It was noted above that defect related negative threshold shift on a programmed cell (hereafter denoted as "charge loss") has a strong tendency to occur on the same bits which exhibit defect related positive threshold shift when stressed with the access gate at positive bias. (This effect will be called "charge gain"). The simplest explanation is that both effects are manifestations of the same defect. Fig. 8 shows data yielding an activation energy of about 0.6eV for charge gain. Thus it is seen that these two phenomena not only occur on the same bit but exhibit the same activation energy.

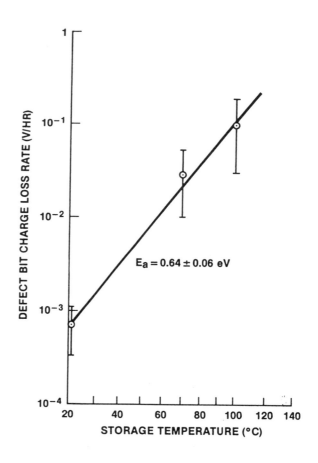

Figure 7: Plot of discharge rate vs. storage temperature for erased defect bits in the programmed state.

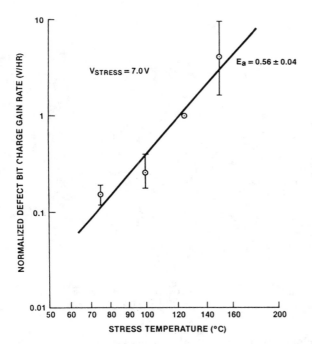

Figure 8: Plot of charge gain rate vs. stress temperature for erased defect bits stressed with the access gate positive. Note that the rates have been normalized at 125°C.

In order to more thoroughly study the charge gain phenomenon, an experiment was set up so that a tester under computer control measured the access gate voltage, V_{g1}, necessary for the cell to sink the sense amplifier trip current at one minute intervals while the device was under stress. Some of one set of data so gathered are displayed in Fig. 9. It is clear that the current through the defect (which is related to the time derivative of V_{g1} by the inverse of the gate capacitance) is not constant with time. To find if this resulted from the field dependence of the current or some other effect, the computer controlling the experiment was reprogrammed to adjust the stress voltage after each measurement so the difference between the stress voltage and V_{g1} (and hence the field across the gate oxide) remained constant. Under these experimental conditions V_{g1} increase linearly with time (i.e., the current through the defect was constant). If it is assumed that the current through the defect depends linearly on the field across the gate oxide, the temporal dependence of V_{g1} should be described by the equation:

$$V_{g1} = V_{g1}(0) + \emptyset gc(1-\exp(-t/RC_1)) \qquad 1)$$

where $V_{g1}(0)$ is the initial measured value of V_{g1}, $\emptyset gc$ is the initial potential difference between the floating gate and channel, R is the effective resistance of the defect, and C_1 was defined previously to be the capacity between the storage gate and access gate. The solid line in Fig. 9 is the curve defined by equation 1 with $\emptyset gc$ taken as 3.9 volts and RC taken as 10 hours. As can be seen, the fit is excellent over a range of effective field of more than a factor of two.

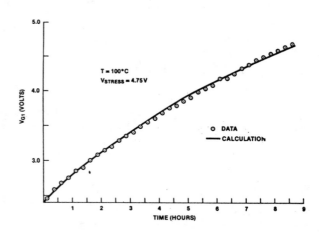

Figure 9: Temporal variation of the threshold of an erased defect bit when stressed with the access gate at 4.75 volts.

Of the various known insulator conduction mechanisms the only one with a positive temperature coefficient and a linear field dependence is hopping conduction between spatially isolated impurity or defect states.[1] The data suggests this as the probable conduction mechanism.

An interesting aspect of the phenomenology of these defects is shown in Fig. 10. The experiment consisted of alternately stressing parts at 125°C with the access gates at 5 volts for 16 hours and erasing the parts with UV light. The measured values of V_{g1} on the defect bits on two different parts at the end of each half cycle are plotted in this figure versus the number of cycles. Note that the magnitude of the threshold shift and thus oxide conduction decreases rather dramatically after a number of cycles, but that a 30 minute bake at 400°C with the part in the programmed state leads to rejuvenation of the "dormant" conduction mechanism. Subsequent cycles lead to reduction of the magnitude of the shift again.

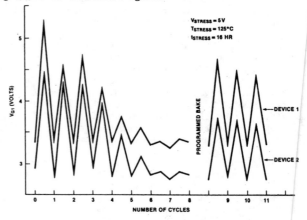

Figure 10: Shift of threshold of defect bits on two devices in response to sequential stresses and UV erasures. Note that the magnitude of the stressed shift is greatly reduced after several cycles. The effect is reinitialized after a 400°C bake in the programmed state.

The behavior illustrated is a general one for the defect bits. They differ in that some will exhibit "dormant" conduction after 2 to 3 cycles while others require 6 or 8 cycles before the conduction mechanism becomes dormant.

A possible explanation for this behavior is illustrated in Fig. 11. It is envisioned that some electrons which enter the SiO₂ may become trapped on deep states physically located near the substrate. Fig. 11 is a potential band diagram for the idealized case of charge trapped as a sheet at a single location near the substrate for the case of no applied voltage. If the access gate is taken to a positive voltage, the diagram shown in Fig. 11b results. Here the local field resulting from the trapped charge cancels the field resulting from the applied voltage and prevents further conduction. If the cell is programmed, the fields reverse direction as illustrated in Fig. 11c. During a high temperature bake of programmed cells these field conditions will tend to drive the trapped charge back to the substrate and hence allow further subsequent conduction along the defect.

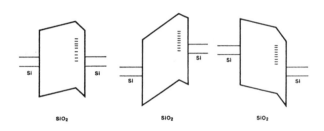

Figure 11: Schematic potential band diagrams of an oxide containing trapped charge for the three possible cases of bias. Note that charge trapped near one interface will have high enough local field to inhibit conduction in one direction, 11b, and not in the other direction, 11c.

It should be pointed out that the defect bits program and erase normally when the conduction mechanism is "dormant". If the above explanation is basically correct, the defect through which conduction takes place must be small with respect to the horizontal dimensions of the active gate area. Otherwise, the trapped charge would alter the programming or erase characteristics depending on the exact defect location. Programming is known to be very sensitive to trapped charge near the pinch-off region and trapped charge which was distributed over a large portion of the source region would shift the effective erased state threshold just as it would for a conventional MOS transistor. We estimate defect horizontal dimensions on the order of a micron or less.

One practical aspect of the behavior shown in Fig. 10 is that the effectiveness of screens is dependent upon the history of the device; for an inappropriate sequence may render the defect dormant only to have it reappear later.

Electron conduction through defects in oxides is not the only mechanism which can cause premature data loss in EPROMs. Fig. 12 shows data on failure rates of two device types from two manufacturers. The failure rates have activation energies (1.2 - 1.3eV) which are the same within experimental error. Moreover, the failure patterns have the same topology. These failures always begin on bits on the edge of the array and may spread inwards affecting more and more bits. This is in clear distinction to the oxide defect mechanism which typically appears as a single bit failure located randomly in the array. We interpret this high activation energy mechanism as resulting from ionic impurities which penetrate under the layers of protective glasses at the scribe line where these layers terminate. The impurities subsequently diffuse along interfaces to the storage gates where they compensate the electrons on the storage gate.

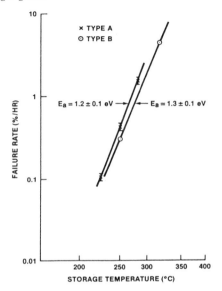

Figure 12: Failure rate resulting from ionic contaminants compensating the storage gate charge vs. temperature for two different types of EPROMs from two manufacturers.

These several charge loss mechanisms, one which has an activation energy of 0.6eV and two which have activation energies greater than 1eV, may explain the rather surprising results of Alexander.[2] It seems possible that the 1eV activation energy charge loss he observed at high temperatures was a result of one of the high activation energy mechanisms reported here since these mechanisms become more important at high temperatures. The 0.5eV activation energy he reported under lower temperature operating lifetests is in reasonable agreement with the 0.6eV reported here for defect related charge loss.

Reliability of Screened Parts:

The motivation for the detailed study of failure mechanisms for a device manufacturer is to be able to ship reliable products to the customer by eliminating failure modes when possible and screening defective parts when not. Fig. 13 shows data on over seven million actual device hours of operation of the INTEL 2716 sampled from production units over a period of one year. The data shows that although defective cell oxide failures such as discussed in this paper dominate the failure rate, the failure rate from this cause is less than 0.02%/1000 hours extrapolated to 55°C (60%UCL) for this material sampled from that which has gone through the standard commercial manufacturing screens. The total failure rate of this sample (including failures of the peripheral circuitry from oxide wearout) is .025%/1000 hours extrapolated to 55°C (60%UCL). This data clearly shows that with proper controls EPROMs can be manufactered with excellent reliability.

SUMMARY

Three mechanisms for loss of data from EPROM cells have been discussed. As can be seen from Table I each mechanism has a unique activation energy. One of the mechanisms, hopping conduction through the oxide between substrate and storage gate, can manifest itself as loss of either "∅'s" or "1's" depending on bias conditions. Data is shown to demonstrate that with the use of this knowledge devices and manufacturing flows can be designed to yield EPROMs with excellent reliability.

FAILURE RATE PREDICTIONS

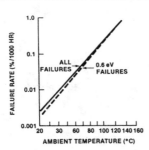

ACTUAL DEVICE HOURS 150°C	125°C	ACTIVATION ENERGY	EQUIVALENT HOURS 55°C	70°C	LIFETEST FAILURES	FAILURE RATE PER 1000 HOURS (60% UCL) 55°C	70°C
1.15E+06	5.90E+06	0.3	4.39E+07	2.83E+07	2	0.007%	0.011%
1.15E+06	5.90E+06	0.6	2.86E+08	1.18E+08	47	0.018%	0.042%
			COMBINED FAILURE RATE:			0.025%	0.054%

Figure 13: Predicted failure rate vs. temperature for INTEL 2716's sampled from the commercial product over a period of a year. Note that over seven million device hours is included in this data base.

TABLE I

MECHANISM	MANIFESTATION	ACTIVATION ENERGY
Intrinsic wearout	Charge loss, entire array	1.4eV
Oxide defect	Charge loss, random bit or Charge gain, random bit	0.6eV
Contamination compensation	Charge loss, edge bits	1.2eV

Acknowledgements:

The authors would like to thank Dave Willmott for stimulating discussions and Leonard Kaufer for his valuable assistance throughout the work described herein.

References:

1. S. M. Sze, "Physics for Semi-Conductor Devices", Wiley-Interscience, 1969, New York, p496.

2. R. M. Alexander, "Accelerated Testing in FAMOS Devices – 8K EPROM", Proceeds of the 16th Annual Reliability Physics Symposium, p229 (1978).

NEW EPROM DATA-LOSS MECHANISMS

NEAL R. MIELKE
INTEL CORPORATION
3065 BOWERS AVENUE
SANTA CLARA, CA. 95051

ABSTRACT

Data-loss mechanisms in present-generation EPROMs have been studied. Defect-related data loss is primarily due to interpoly-oxide defects. This is a change from the previous generation and introduces a new EPROM failure mode--column data loss. Contamination-compensation is found to be due as much to field-driven motion as to diffusion, and one result is that contaminated regions can exhibit charge gain as well as charge loss. Intrinsic charge loss is attributed to detrapping of electrons from the oxide layers rather than to loss of stored charge, suggesting that with proper screening of defects EPROM data retention is effectively unlimited.

INTRODUCTION

Widespread use of electrically-programmable read-only memories (EPROMs) in production systems requires data retention for ten years or more. Three data-loss mechanisms have been previously identified[1]: 1) conduction of electrons to and from the floating gate through an oxide defect; 2) compensation of stored charge by ionic contamination; and 3) an "intrinsic" mechanism which causes even non-defective cells to lose some charge over time.

This paper first reviews the EPROM cell and the methods used to study its data retention. It then presents experimental data on a new oxide defect in present-generation EPROMs and models the resulting failure mode. Further data are then presented on the contamination-compensation and intrinsic mechanisms, resulting in improved models for these effects.

FLOATING GATE EPROM CELL

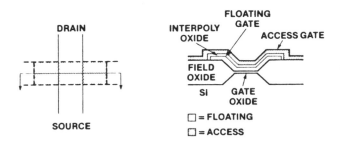

a. CELL TOPOLOGY   **b. CELL CROSS-SECTION**

Figure 1: Top view (a) and cross-section (b) of an EPROM cell. The floating gate is surrounded on all sides by thermal SiO_2.

An EPROM cell (Fig. 1) is an MOS transistor with a layer of polysilicon called the floating gate buried within the oxide layers between the access gate and the channel. A hot-electron programming mechanism is used to inject electrons to the floating gate, where they become trapped by the potential barrier of 3.1eV at the polysilicon-oxide interface. Exposure to ultraviolet light of energy greater than 3.1eV discharges, or erases, the cell by photo-emitting electrons over the potential barrier.

Programming raises a cell's threshold voltage (Fig. 2) because the negative stored charge tends to screen the channel from positive voltage on the access gate. In normal memory operation, the access-gate voltage (V_{ref} in Fig. 2) is only high enough to turn on an erased cell. The on-chip sense amplifier, connected to the drain, reads a cell as erased if the drain current is above the amplifier's trip current (I_{trip} in Fig. 2) and reads it as programmed otherwise.

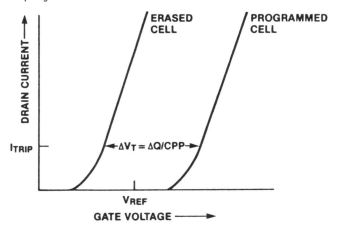

Figure 2: Drain current as a function of access-gate voltage.

Temperature extrapolations of the intrinsic mechanism mentioned above predict that a typical non-defective cell will retain data for over 1000 years at 125°C, losing about one electron per day, and one million years at 70°C, losing less than one electron per year[2]. These impressive storage times are due to the large potential barrier trapping the stored electrons. An oxide defect may greatly reduce this barrier and thereby greatly reduce the storage time. In general, any mechanism which changes a cell's threshold voltage can cause data loss. For example, data loss may occur if mobile oxide charge (either ionic or electronic) moves into or out of a cell, since the threshold voltage is sensitive to any charge between the access gate and the channel. By convention, a decrease in the threshold is called

Reprinted from *Proc. IRPS*, pp. 106–113, 1983.

charge loss whether due to loss of stored electrons or to movement of oxide charges, and an increase in the threshold voltage is called charge gain.

The electric fields within a defective cell will drive electrons either to or from the floating gate, depending upon the applied bias and the amount of stored charge. For example, the floating gate of an unbiased, programmed cell has a negative potential because of the stored charge, so stored electrons are attracted to both the access gate and the substrate. A defect in any of the surrounding oxides will thus cause charge loss. An erased cell has negligible floating-gate voltage and so should not gain or lose charge in a simple bake. However, positive gate bias will attract electrons from the substrate to the floating gate and from the floating gate to the access gate, causing charge gain through a gate-oxide defect and charge loss through an interpoly-oxide defect. Previously only the charge gain effect, and thus only gate-oxide defects, have been reported.

EXPERIMENTAL METHOD

INTEL 2764 and 27128 EPROMs which failed reliability screens for data loss were used to characterize the defect mechanisms. Non-defective memories and individual cells from test patterns made on the same fabrication process were used to characterize the intrinsic mechanism.

Since EPROM data loss is caused by threshold instability, characterizing data-loss mechanisms involves measuring changes in threshold. When the instability is caused by a change in the stored charge Q, the threshold shift can be related to the actual loss or gain of charge by the simple proportionality $\Delta V_t = \Delta Q / C_{pp}$, where C_{pp} is the capacitance between the floating gate and the access gate.

In many commercial devices, such as those used in this study, the access-gate voltage (V_{ref} in Fig. 2) is connected to the power supply voltage (V_{cc}), whereas the drain voltage and current trip level are relatively independent of V_{cc}. If V_{cc} is raised, eventually even the drain current of a programmed cell will exceed I_{trip}. From Fig. 2 it can be seen that the voltage at which this occurs, called the margin voltage, is just the threshold voltage plus a constant offset. This allows the threshold voltage of a cell in a memory array to be measured externally.

OXIDE DEFECTS

Fig. 3 is a bit-map display of a defective, programmed device after a retention bake and later after a bake with positive access-gate bias. If the defect causing the charge loss were similar to the gate-oxide defect found in the previous generation of EPROM, the bias would have caused the cell to gain charge--i.e., recover[1]. Instead, the entire column containing the defective bit failed, as if all bits on the column had lost charge. Experiments on a large number of charge-loss failures showed that about 75% developed column failures under such a bias.

A characteristic of the column failures is that, except for the bit which fails the retention bake,

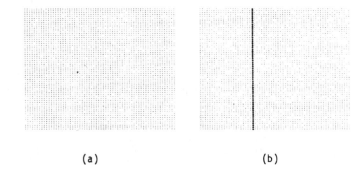

(a)   (b)

Figure 3: Raster or bit-map display of a portion of a defective 27128 after a 140°C retention bake (a) and after a 140°C stress with positive bias applied to the access gate (b). Each dot represents one cell. A failing cell is darkened.

the bits on the column cannot be programmed. Attempting to program the original failing bit, however, causes the bit to program correctly and the entire column to recover. Thereafter, the column programs and erase normally.

Experiments in which a computer continually monitored the margin of a defective cell in bake as the access-gate bias was changed found that the charge loss was accelerated by positive bias (Fig. 4). Because such a bias tends to attract electrons from the floating gate to the access gate, this acceleration implies that the charge loss is due to an interpoly-oxide defect.

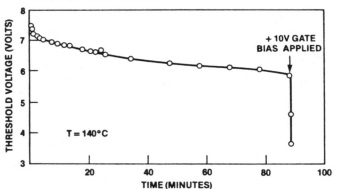

Figure 4: Decay of the cell threshold with time at 140°C.

Charge loss due to an interpoly oxide defect can explain the observed column failure. As shown in the Appendix, for an access-gate voltage above about 2V, the accelerated charge loss would be expected to stop only after the cell's threshold fell below zero. With a negative threshold, the cell would become a resistive short from the column to ground (Fig. 5), causing the column to appear erased. Programming the cell would restore its threshold to a normal, positive level and thereby cause the column to recover.

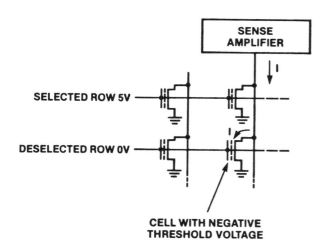

Figure 5: Schematic diagram of four cells in an EPROM memory array. A cell with a negative threshold draws drain current I even when its gate is grounded, causing a selected cell on the same column to be read as erased.

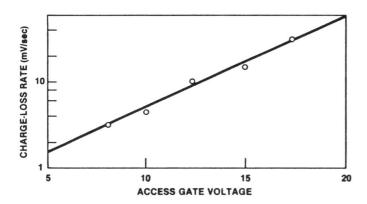

Figure 6: Rate of charge loss at 150°C in a defective cell as a function of access-gate bias.

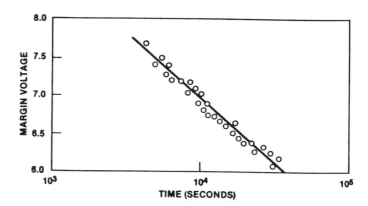

Figure 7: Decay of the threshold voltage of a defective cell with time at 140°C.

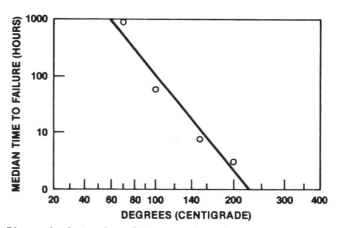

Figure 8: Arrhenius plot of median-time-to-failure of programmed devices versus inverse bake temperature. Each data point was measured on a separate group of 50 defective 27128's known to contain interpoly-oxide defects. The line is a least-squares fit whose slope yields an activation energy of 0.6eV.

It is thus concluded that charge loss in the present-generation devices is primarily due to interpoly-oxide defects. A number of experiments were run to characterize this defect.

Fig. 6 shows that the rate of charge loss in a cell with an interpoly-oxide defect increases exponentially with access-gate bias. The rate of charge loss is proportional to the current through the defect, and the voltage across the interpoly oxide increases linearly (via capacitive coupling) with applied bias, so this result implies that the defect's I-V dependence is exponential. By comparison, the gate-oxide defect previously studied had a linear I-V dependence[1].

Under constant access-gate bias, the voltage across the interpoly oxide will decrease with time as the floating gate loses charge. The dependence of the charge loss on time can then be predicted from an assumed I-V dependence for the defect. In the Appendix it is shown that an exponential I-V dependence should cause a cell's margin voltage to decline in proportion to the logarithm of time, and this is confirmed in Fig. 7. Often a measurement of the time-dependence of charge loss is used to determine the defect I-V dependence instead of vice-versa.

Fig. 8 shows the temperature dependence of charge loss caused by the interpoly-oxide defect. The activation energy, about 0.6eV, is the same as that for the earlier defect[1].

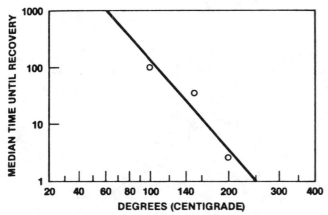

Figure 9: Arrhenius plot of median-time-to-recovery versus inverse bake temperature. Each data point was measured on a separate group of 50 27128's containing cells with negative thresholds. The line is a least-squares fit whose slope yields an activation energy of 0.55eV.

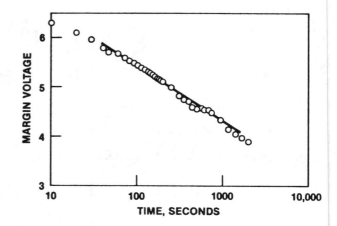

Figure 10: Decay of the margin voltage with time in bake at 150°C for a cell with a negative threshold. The margin voltage was measured with the access gate grounded. Decreasing margin voltage indicates actual cell threshold becoming less negative.

Polysilicon-oxide current with an exponential I-V dependence has been reported in the past and found to be caused by asperities on the polysilicon surface.[3] Conduction due to floating-gate asperities would be rectifying because current would be enhanced only for injection from the floating gate to the access gate.[4] The present defect was found to be non-rectifying: units with failed columns recover if baked with the bias removed, indicating electron flow from the access gate back to the floating gate. Fig. 9 shows results from a multiple-temperature experiment for this recovery effect, again finding an activation energy of about 0.6eV. The I-V characteristic is not as easily found for current in the reverse direction because the threshold voltage, which is negative, cannot be measured with the usual methods. An alternate method was used which relied on the fact that the sense-amplifier trip current in the INTEL 27128 increases gradually with increasing supply voltage, so that with the access gate of the defective cell grounded the cell can be made to appear programmed (i.e., will fail to trip the sense amplifier) if the supply voltage is raised high enough. Computer circuit simulations showed that again the supply voltage at which the cell changes logic state should give a nearly linear measure of the threshold voltage, with a higher supply voltage corresponding to a more-negative threshold voltage. Fig. 10 shows that the recovery of the cell proceeds in proportion to the logarithm of time.

From these results it is concluded that the defect is a bulk defect with an exponential I-V dependence and an activation energy of 0.6eV for current in either direction. As with the previously-studied defect, the defect conductivity decreases with successive retention bakes, typically by 30% per program/bake cycle. This is taken as evidence of electron trapping along the conduction path. Because of the bulk nature of the defect, it is assumed that this trapping occurs in the bulk of the oxide, and it is suggested that the current transport mechanism involves field-assisted thermal emmission from trapping sites along this path (Poole-Frenkel conduction), which possesses both thermal acceleration and an exponential I-V dependence.

CONTAMINATION CHARGE LOSS

Charge loss from contamination has been reported previously[1] and occurs when positive ions enter the memory array and neutralize the negative charge stored on the EPROM floating gates. The ionic motion is usually viewed as simple diffusion, but analysis of a new failure mechanism--charge gain from positive ionic contamination--indicates that electric field effects may actually dominate.

Fig. 11a is a bit-map display of a programmed device with contamination entering the upper-right corner of the array, causing charge loss. Ultraviolet erase brought the cell thresholds down to normal erased levels, but a subsequent bake caused a threshold increase--charge gain (Fig. 11b).

Several observations from Fig. 11 clarify this behavior. The cells in the non-failing diagonal in Fig. 11a were unprogrammed and thus might not be expected to fail a retention bake. Having thresholds of only about 2V at the start of the bake, however, these cells were actually very sensitive to contamination: a threshold drop of more than 2V would have caused column failures. Since most of the programmed cells on either side of the diagonal lost several volts of threshold, it is apparent that the contamination became concentrated only on the floating gates of programmed cells. The obvious explanation is that the negative charge stored on the floating gates attracted the contamination. Diffusion may bring the contamination to the array, but significant threshold loss occurs only when the ions are driven to the floating gates by the electric field from the stored negative charge. This electric field binds the ions to the floating gates despite a concentration gradient which tends to cause them to diffuse out of the cells.

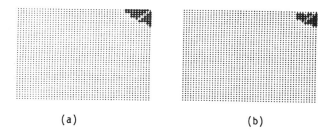

(a)   (b)

Figure 11: Bit-map display of (a) a programmed
           27128 after it failed a 250°C
           retention bake and (b) the same device
           after UV erase and another 250°C bake.
           Failing cells have lost charge in (a)
           and gained charge in (b).

This concentration gradient can explain the
observed charge gain. The fact that the cells erased
to the normal erased threshold shows that after erase
the cells were left with an excess of electrons which
balanced the attracted ionic charge, leaving the
floating gates neutral. With the floating gates
neutral, the contamination was no longer strongly
bound by an electric field, and the concentration
gradient then caused ions to diffuse out of
the cells. This would cause apparent charge gain
because the excess electrons left by the UV erase
would no longer be balanced by the ionic charge.

Being a field-driven effect, contamination
motion is affected by applied gate bias. In most
cases it is found that positive bias causes charge
gain. This is expected, because the bias increases
the floating gate potential just as UV erase does.
In some cases, however, such a bias has caused
enhanced charge loss and a column failure. A
positive-bias stress on an array with a large
contaminated region such as in Fig. 11 will
occasionally, for example, cause widespread charge
gain plus one or two failed columns. This is
attributed to contamination being driven by the bias
from the floating gate down to the SiO_2-
substrate interface above the channel, where the
charge has an enhanced affect on the threshold.

INTRINSIC CHARGE LOSS

The intrinsic charge-loss mechanism has been
reported previously[1] but has not been well
understood. It affects all cells but causes only a
fraction of the stored charge to be lost. The charge
loss slows with time and eventually stops, producing
about 0.5V or less of threshold drop in a few days of
250°C bake but negligible charge loss thereafter.

Several experiments investigated this cessation
of the charge-loss rate. It was found that a cell
baked until its charge loss stopped would not resume
losing charge even if programmed back up to its pre-
bake threshold voltage; the bake actually
deactivated the charge-loss mechanism. If instead
such a cell were erased with ultaviolet light and
then reprogrammed to its pre-bake threshold voltage,
the charge loss was found to resume at about the
former rate. An erase/program cycle thus reactivated
the mechanism. To investigate this effect further,

three groups of 2764's were given different
variations of an erase/program cycle before a bake
(Fig. 12). The first group, simply erased and then
programmed, lost an average of 0.23V in the bake.
The second group, erased but then baked before being
programmed, lost only 0.09V, indicating that even
baking erased units largely deactivates the
mechanism. The third group, erased and baked like
the second group but then erased again before being
programmed, lost 0.20V--about the same as the first
group. A UV erase alone is thus found to reactivate
the intrinsic charge loss mechanism.

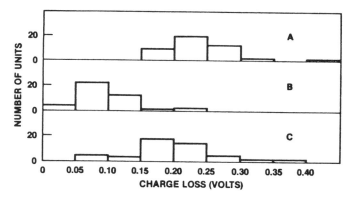

Figure 12: Distribution of the intrinsic charge loss
            in three groups of 2764's. All bakes
            were 48 hrs., 250°C. Charge loss was
            measured on the worst-programmed cell in
            each 2764.

Three possible mechanisms for intrinsic charge
loss were considered: 1) motion of contaminants
within the oxides; 2) conduction of electrons
through the oxides; and 3) detrapping of electrons
trapped within the oxides. Since ultraviolet light
can affect electrons through photoemission from the
floating gate or from oxide traps but would not be
expected to affect ionic contamination, the first
possibility seems unlikely. Transistors without a
floating gate (or with an ohmic contact made between
the access gate and the floating gate) were also
found to have stable thresholds at high temperature
even under bias, indicating very low contamination
levels.

Charge loss from oxide conduction could become
deactivated during bake if electrons became trapped
along the conduction path. UV exposure could
reactivate the mechanism by photo-depopulating these
traps. Since electrons trapped in the oxides over
the channel or near the floating gate will increase
the threshold voltage just like stored charge,
detrapping in bake could also cause apparent charge
loss. The charge-loss would stop when the traps were
emptied, but UV exposure could reactivate the
mechanism by photoemitting electrons into the oxides,
filling the traps.

The spectral dependence of the reactivation
mechanism was investigated to distinguish between the
two mechanisms. The intrinsic charge loss in a group
of 2764's was measured by fully erasing the

devices, programming them, and baking them for three hours at 250°C. The mechanism was then deactivated with a three-day 250°C bake. The devices were then given varying amounts of ultraviolet exposure, reprogrammed, and given another three-hour bake. The ratio of the charge loss in the second three-hour bake to that in the first was used as a measure of the reactivation caused by the UV exposure. Fig. 13 shows this reactivaction ratio as a function of erase dose for three of the seven wavelengths used (the other four are omitted for clarity). (The scatter in the ratio data are caused by scatter of about 25mV in the margin measurements.) For a given wavelength the amount of reactivation increases from zero at low dose to about 50% at the largest doses used. Longer wavelengths required larger doses to produce a given amount of reactivation.

To quantify the wavelength dependence, the curves were fit with straight lines of the form

$$R = C\ln(AD),$$

where R is the reactivation ratio, C is a constant independent of wavelength, A is a function of wavelength only, and D is the dose. (This equation was chosen simply because it fit the data over the limited range of doses used; no physical significance is attached.) The variable A is a measure of the efficiency of a given wavelength in reactivating the charge-loss mechanism because the dose required to produce a given amount of reactivation is inversely proportional to A. An efficiency of this type would be expected to have a power-law dependence on photon energy[5]. Fig. 14 shows the cube root of the

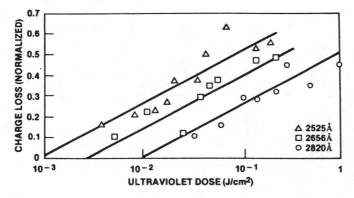

Figure 13: Normalized charge loss (or reactivation ratio) as a function of erase dose for three wavelengths. Each data point represents data from 16 adjacent cells on one 2764. All cells were programmed to 7.0V following the erase and preceeding the bake. Lines are least-squares fits to the data as described in the text.

efficiency as a function of photon energy. The data extrapolate to two thresholds, one at about 4.1eV and one at about 3eV. Within experimental error, the spectral dependence of the reactivation mechanism is the same as the spectral dependence of photoemission of electrons from n-type Si to SiO2, which has a threshold energy of 4.2eV for photoemission from the valence band and a low-energy tail with a threshold energy of 3.1eV for photoemission from the conduction

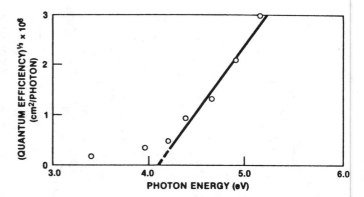

Figure 14: Quantum efficiency for reactivation of the intrinsic charge-loss mechanism as a function of photon energy. The line is a fit to the higher-energy data points.

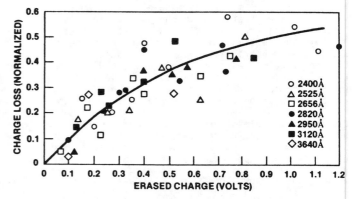

Figure 15: Reactivation ratio as a function of the amount of charge UV erased instead of the erase dose. Data points are the same as those in Fig. 13.

band. This result suggests that the reactivation is caused by photoemission of electrons into the oxides. Since the total amount of charge passed through the oxides during erase is simply proportional to the resulting decrease in threshold, the reactivation ratio should then be a pure function of the threshold decrease during erase, independent of wavelength. Fig. 15 shows this to be the case. These results suggest that intrinsic charge loss is due to the detrapping of electrons trapped in the oxides during UV erase.

CONCLUSIONS

Column charge loss caused by a defective cell with a negative threshold voltage is a new type of failure mode which can occur in actual use, since in the read operation the access gate of a selected cell is held at positive voltage. Since most cells are at any one moment deselected, simple charge loss on a single bit is nevertheless the most likely failure mode in lifetest and actual use.

Contaminated cells, exhibiting either charge
gain or charge loss under bias, can easily be
mistaken for cells with oxide defects, and an understanding of the difference in the behavior is helpful
in evaluating and improving EPROM reliability.
Charge gain from contamination is also a failure
mechanism that can occur in real use. Although
charge loss from contamination must occur before
charge gain from contamination may, the mechanism is
of some importance because many EPROMs are more
sensitive to charge gain than to charge loss. A
level of contamination which causes only a volt of
threshold drop in a programmed cell will usually be
insufficient to cause data loss, but if the
contaminated cell is erased and subsequently gains a
volt of threshold, data loss is likely.

With the probable association of intrinsic
charge loss with detrapping rather than oxide
conduction, it is likely that true loss of stored
electrons has never been observed in a non-defective
cell. Storage times of millions of years based upon
extrapolations of the intrinsic charge loss mechanism
may actually underestimate the intrinsic reliability
of the cell. By understanding and screening the
defect mechanisms, therefore, EPROM data-retention
reliability can be made comparable or superior to
that of devices employing non-floating-gate
mechanisms, such as mask-programmable ROMs and
fusible-link PROMs. Fig. 16 shows the data-retention
performance of the INTEL 2764 as measured on over
5000 devices in 250°C retention bake. The middle
axis shows the equivalent time scale at 55°C
predicted from the activation energy of 0.6eV
appropriate for the oxide-defect mechanism, which
caused most of the observed failures. As shown,
about 1% of the devices are predicted to fail within
15 years, resulting in an average failure rate of
0.008%/1000 hrs. (80 FIT). The lower axis shows the
equivalent time scale at 55°C predicted from the
activation energy of 1.4eV for intrinsic charge
loss[1]. As shown, failure of non-defective cells has
not occured even after an equivalent ten million
years.

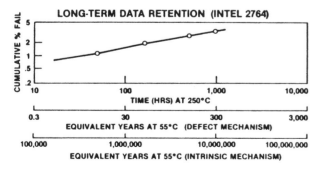

Figure 16: Long-term data-retention performance of
the INTEL 2764. Cumulative percent
failing a 250°C retention bake is shown
as a function of time.

APPENDIX--DYNAMICS OF CHARGE LOSS AND CHARGE GAIN

Figure A-1 is a schematic electrical model for
an EPROM transistor based on two coupling capacitors
and an ideal, single-gate transistor. The basic
equation relating the floating gate potential to
applied bias and stored charge is

$$V_{fg} = RV_{tg} + Q/(C_{pp} + C_s) \qquad (1)$$

where $R=C_{pp}/(C_{pp} + C_s)$ is known as the
coupling ratio of the cell, and the other variables
are defined in Fig. A-1.

The channel will invert when $V_{fg}=V_{to}'$.
The measured cell threshold voltage is just the
access-gate voltage necessary to attain this
floating-gate potential. From equation (1),

$$V_{to}' = RV_t + Q/(C_{pp} + C_s) \qquad (2)$$

so that

$$V_t = V_{to}'/R - Q/C_{pp}$$
$$= V_{to} - Q/C_{pp} \qquad (3)$$

where V_{to} is the threshold voltage when $Q=0$.

Q can be eliminated by combining (1) and (3),
which yields

$$V_t = V_{to} + V_{tg} - V_{fg}/R \qquad (4)$$

A conductive defect in one of the insulating
oxides between the floating gate and another
electrode (either the access gate or the substrate)
will cause current to flow until the voltage across
the defect falls to zero (*). Equilibrium will thus
be established when $V_{fg}=0$ for a gate-oxide
defect or $V_{fg}=V_{tg}$ for an interpoly-oxide
defect. From (4), the equilibrium thresholds under
bias will be

$$V_t = V_{to} + V_{tg}$$

for a gate-oxide defect and

$$V_t = V_{to} - V_{tg}(1/R-1)$$

for an interpoly-oxide defect.

For a reasonable case in which $R=.5$,
$V_{to}=2V$, and $V_{tg}=5V$, the final thresholds
will be 7V for a gate-oxide defect and -3V for an
interpoly-oxide defect.

----

*More accurately, equilibrium will be reached when
the chemical potentials of the two electrodes become
equal. This derivation is exact provided that
V_{fg} is considered to be the chemical potential
of the floating gate, including both electrical and
chemical contributions, and provided that Q is
considered the excess floating-gate charge above the
thermal-equilibrium level.

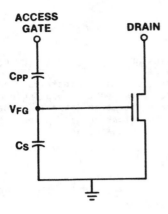

ACCESS GATE

DRAIN

C_{PP}

V_{FG}

C_S

Figure A-1: Schematic diagram of a simple electrical model for an EPROM cell.

V_{tg} = applied access-gate voltage
V_{fg} = floating gate potential
C_{pp} = capacitance between floating gate and access gate
C_s = capacitance between floating gate and substrate
V_{to}'= threshold voltage of ideal transistor

The rate of charge-loss can be derived in terms of the defect I-V dependence and position. For an interpoly-oxide defect with an exponential I-V dependence, the current I flowing to the floating gate is

$$I = I_o exp(C(V_{tg}-V_{fg}))$$

$$= dQ/dt$$

$$= -C_{pp}dV_t/dt,$$

where I_o and C are constants determining the I-V dependence, t is the time, and (3) has been used in the last step. Substituting (4) to remove V_{fg} and integrating,

$$V_t = -(1/CR)ln(exp(-CRV_{ti}) +$$

$$(CRI_ot/C_{pp})exp(C(V_{tg}-RV_{tg}-RV_{to})))$$

where V_{ti} is the threshold voltage at t=0. For large t, the second term in the logarithmic expression will dominate the first, yielding

$$V_t = -(1/CR)ln(CRI_o/C_{pp}) -$$

$$(1/R)(V_{tg}-RV_{tg}-RV_{to}) - (1/CR)ln(t).$$

The threshold voltage should thus decline in proportion to the logarithm of time.

ACKNOWLEDGEMENTS

The author would like to thank Bruce Euzent and Murray Woods for useful discussions and Nick Righos for performing many of the experiments described in this paper.

REFERENCES

1. R. Shiner, J. Caywood, B. Euzent, "Data Retention in EPROMs", 18th Annual Proc., Reliability Physics Symposium, p. 238 (1980).

2. S. Rosenberg, "Test and Screens Weed Out Failures, Project Rates of Reliability", Electronics, p. 136 (8/14/80).

3. R.M. Anderson and D.R. Kerr, "Evidence for Surface Asperity Mechanism of Conductivity in Oxide Grown on Polycrystalline Silicon", J. Appl. Physics, Vol. 48, No. 11, p. 4834 (11/77).

4. H.R. Huff, R.D. Halvorson, T.1 Chui, and D. Guterman, "Experimental Observations on Conduction Through Polysilicon Oxide", J. Electrochem. Soc., Vol. 127, No. 11, p. 2482 (11/80).

5. E.O. Kane, "Theory of Photoelectric Emission from Semiconductors", Phys. Rev., Vol. 127, No. 1, p. 131 (7/62).

RELIABILITY ASPECTS OF A

FLOATING GATE E^2 PROM

Bruce Euzent, Nick Boruta, Jimmy Lee and Ching Jenq
INTEL CORPORATION
Santa Clara, California 95051
(408) 987-8080

INTRODUCTION

Electrically eraseable programmable read only memories (E^{2}PROMS) that can be electrically erased and written one byte at a time are new components to be used in computer systems. The E^2 PROM is particularly attractive in applications requiring field update of program store memory or nonvolatile data capture. It is only recently that E^2 PROMs which operate via Fowler-Nordheim tunneling to a floating poly-silicon gate have become available. The E^2 PROM has the data retention requirements of earlier generations of PROMs, but also must maintain its field programmable characteristics over its device life.

In this paper we shall first review the basic operation of the Intel 2816 E^2 PROM cell. Intrinsic failure mechanisms which limit the applications of E^2 PROMs will be examined, and then defect mechanisms will be discussed. Finally lifetest data will be presented to predict operating failure rates.

Device Operation:

The Intel 2816 uses the FLOTOX structure, which has been discussed in detail in the literature[1]. Basically, it utilizes an oxide of less than 200Å thick between the floating polysilicon gate and the N+ region as shown in Figure 1.

FLOTOX DEVICE STRUCTURE

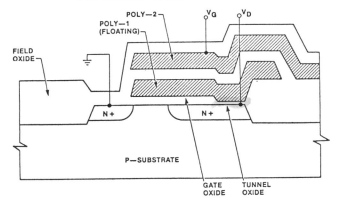

Figure 1: Flotox Device Structure Cross-section.

Both erase and writing are accomplished by tunneling the electrons through the thin oxide using the Fowler-Nordheim mechanism[2]. The I-V characteristic of Fowler-Nordheim tunneling is shown in Figure 2, where the current is approximately exponentially dependent on the electric field within the oxide.

FOWLER-NORDHEIM TUNNELING I-V CHARACTERISTICS

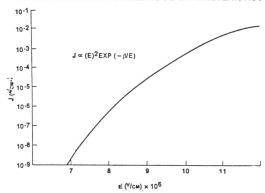

$$J \propto (E)^2 EXP(-\beta/E)$$

Figure 2: Fowler-Nordheim Tunneling I-V Characteristics.

During the erase operation, approximately 20V is applied to the top gate of each cell in the byte while the drain is kept at V_{SS} potential. The electrical field in the thin oxide region is directed from the floating gate to the N+ region such that electrons are tunneling through the oxide and stored on the floating gate shifting the cell threshold in the positive direction. This causes the cell to shut off current flow through it and a logical "1" is output, as seen in Figure 3a.

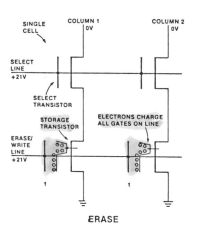

Figure 3a: Schematic of Memory Cell Operation During Erase.

Reprinted from *Proc. IRPS*, pp. 11–16, 1981.

On the other hand, when the cell is written, the top gate is pulled down to V_{SS} potential and the high voltage is applied to the drain (with the source end floating) for cells to be written. Electrons are depleted from the floating gate as seen in Figure 3b, and the cell is left with a negative threshold. Since the interpoly oxide is much thicker than the "tunnel oxide" and also the electric field across the interpoly oxide is much smaller, the erase and write operations are predominantly controlled by the thin oxide region.

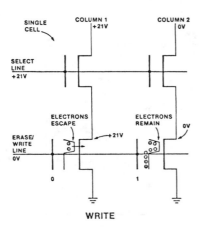

Figure 3b: Schematic of Memory Cell Operation During Write.

Read Retention:

The floating gate structure is known for its excellent charge retention. The reliability of this structure in the case of the EPROM device has been reported before[3]. The only remaining concern of the data retentivity of the 2816 is possible charge gain or loss through the tunnel oxide due to Fowler-Nordheim tunneling. The maximum electric field is built up across the tunnel oxide for a written cell, one that has a net positive charge on the floating gate. In this state the positive top gate voltage creates an electric field which adds to the field created by the positive charge on the floating gate, and there exists the probability that electrons may tunnel to the floating gate and shift the cell threshold. The band diagram of this condition is shown in Figure 4. However, the amount of current which may pass through the thin oxide during read or deselect is kept low by biasing the top gate of the memory cell to an internally generated voltage less than Vcc. The effect on the threshold shift of the cell can only be observed after long term stress. Under this condition, the accelerated voltage test can be very useful.

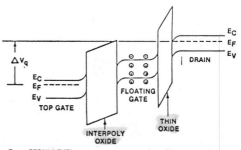

BAND DIAGRAM DURING READ OF WRITTEN CELL

E_F • FERMI LEVEL
ΔV • VOLTAGE DIFFERENCE BETWEEN TOP GATE AND DRAIN IN WORST CASE READ CONDITION

Figure 4.

If we assume Fowler-Nordhiem tunneling is the predominant mechanism governing the movement of electrons, the threshold shift of the cell will be dependant solely on the voltage between the top gate and the N+ region. This has been proven to be true in both simulations and experiments, where we found that there is a one-to-one relationship between the V_T and the stress voltage. In other words, we can stress the device by applying a higher voltage to the top gate such that the change of the threshold voltage can be measured. The data then will be used to predict the same characteristics at the much lower normal read voltage. In Figure 5, the aforementioned simulation and experimental data are shown. The cell was biased at a voltage 4V higher than the normal read condition and the threshold voltage of the cell was monitored over a period of a week. A simulation was also generated to compare with the observed threshold shift and to demonstrate the technique we use to predict whether the data retention of the cell is accurate. As can be seen in the Figure 4, even under the accelerated voltage test the cell V_T still will not cross above the sense level after more than 10 years. Similar data has also been taken by writing the cell to a more negative initial threshold. In this case, the shift of the threshold can be observed at a stress of normal read voltage. Clearly, a 1V/1V relationship holds and an extrapolation can be made that the correct data will be retained for more then 10 years of continuous read.

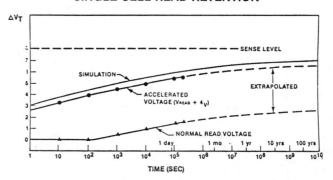

SINGLE CELL READ RETENTION

Figure 5: Single Cell Threshold Voltage Shift vs. Log Time During Read of a Written Cell

Intrinsic Charge Trapping:

An ideal feature of a tunneling dielectric is that it should never remember the number of electrons that passed through it or the voltage that was previously applied across the film. Unfortunately, for thermally grown SiO_2 there always exists a certain number of electron and hole traps [4-9]. When these traps are occupied the net charging state of the tunnel oxide will be changed and thus cause the tunneling current across the film to vary if the applied voltage has remained the same.

Figure 6 plots the threshold voltage of a 2816 cell in erase (charged) and write (discharged) states as a function of erase/write cycles. The solid line is for a single cell, while the dashed line is for a typical 2816 array. It is seen that the threshold window, defined as the difference between the erase and write threshold, is increased in the first few E/W cycles and then saturates and remains almost constant until 10^4 cycles. From that point, the window begins to narrow gradually until around 10^6 cycles where the window is collapsed.

TYPICAL CELL ENDURANCE

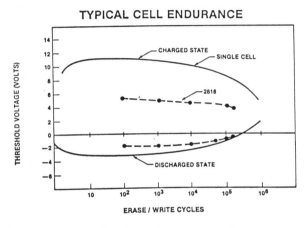

Figure 6: Typical Cell and Device Window vs. log cycles.

Our study shows that the behavior of the widening and narrowing of the threshold window can be explained by charge trapping in tunnel oxide. The window widening effect is found to be caused by the following mechanism:

Assume a cell is to be erased following a write cycle. During the preceeding write cycle, the floating gate is biased negatively relative to the substrate. A layer of positive charge will be formed, either through the tunneling of holes from Si into SiO_2 or electrons in the reverse direction. These positive charges are in general at 20-30Å away from the SiO_2/Si interface, as in Figure 7a. At the beginning of the erase step, the positive charges will cause an increase in electric field at the injection interface, i.e., SiO_2/Si interface, as shown in Figure 7b. This will in turn increase the tunneling current to the floating gate, where the amount of stored electrons is thus increased, causing the erase threshold to increase. During the erase cycle, however, the polarity of bias voltage across the tunnel oxide will cause the positive charge at SiO_2/Si interface to be neutralized through the reverse tunneling mechanism that forms these charges. At the same time a new layer of positive charges is formed near the anode[11, 12], i.e., poly/SiO_2 interface, as shown in Figure 7c. These charges will then cause the write threshold to

increase through the same mechanism as that discussed for the erase threshold. In addition to positive charge trapping, our study also shows that there is a uniform distribution of electron traps throughout the oxide[11,12]. When the cell is erased or written, electrons are injected through the oxide and some of them will be captured by these traps, causing the build-up of negative charges in the oxide, as shown in Figure 8. The negative charges will reduce the electric field at the injection interface, thus decreasing the tunneling current and causing the threshold window to be narrowed. It has been found that the electron traps are not only pre-existing in the oxide but also generated during the E/W cycles[9-12] because of the high field stress and the accompanying high current flow. The non-saturated build-up of negative charges, because of the continuous generation of electrons traps will finally cause the threshold window to collapse.

Figure 7:   THRESHOLD WINDOW WIDENING

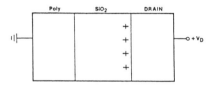

a) Positive charge induced at the SiO_2 - Si interface at the end of the write operation.

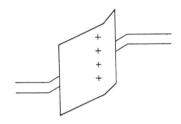

b) Band diagram of subsequent erase showing lowering of the tunneling barrier by the trapped positive charge.

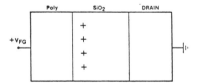

c) Positive charge near polysilicon - SiO_2 interface at the end of the erase operation.

THRESHOLD WINDOW NARROWING— NEGATIVE CHARGE TRAPPING

• BEGINNING OF ERASE

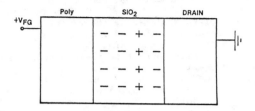

Figure 8: Negative Charges Trapped Uniformly Across Tunnel Oxide.

Defect Charge Loss:

EPROMs have been shown to have excellent data retention[3]. In this section we will discuss data retention studies that have been performed on the Intel 2816 E^2 PROM. Since in E^2 PROMs the number of Erase/Write cycles during the device lifetime is 3 to 4 orders of magnitude greater than in the EPROM, we will also need to address the effects of cycling on data retention.

As in the case of EPROMs the charge loss from the floating gate can be described as either intrinsic or defect related. We will discuss the defect related charge loss since the intrinsic charge loss on a typical device is identical to the EPROM and has been described before[3].

Devices exhibiting defect related charge loss were erased to a logical "1" (electrons on floating gate) and stored at 250°C, 200°C and 150°C. The erase margins on the devices were monitored over various time intervals and the charge loss rate in volts per hour was determined. The results are shown in Figure 9. This data is normalized to 1 volt at 150°C. A best fit to the data shows an activation evergy of .6 eV. This compares favorably to the defect related charge loss observed in EPROMs.

DEFECT BIT CHARGE LOSS

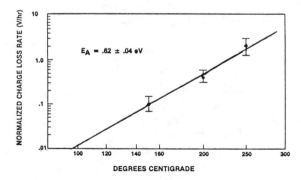

Figure 9: Plot of Defective Bit Charge Loss vs. Storage Temperature.

Erase/write cycling effects on data retention were then studied by comparing 250°C retention before cycling to that after 10,000 cycles. Figure 10 shows a plot of the cumulative %data retention failure during 500 hours 250°C retention bake. Data from the Intel 2716 EPROM is included as a comparison. From this data it is clear that cycling to 10,000 cycles has minimal if any effect on data retention and that the retention failure rate closely resembles that of the Intel 2716 EPROM.

Since the defect charge loss failure mechanism is temperature activated it is simple to construct screens on a production basis for these types of failures similar to those used on EPROMs.

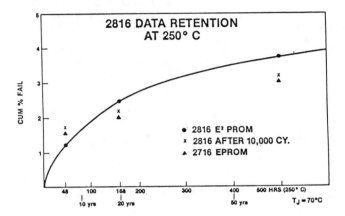

Figure 10: Intel 2816 Data Retention at 250°C, Percent Fail vs. Time. Data are shown for the Intel 2816 before and after 10,000 Erase Write Cycles and Compared to Data from the Industry Standard Intel 2716.

Accelerated Test Results:

An E^2 PROM has an additional reliability requirement over standard PROMs. Besides the integrity of data retention an E^2 PROM must withstand up to 10,000 erase and write programming pulses per byte. Besides the previously discussed window closing phenomenon there are reliability considerations due to high voltage operation. Dielectric breakdown[13] is a common MOS failure mechanism, which has been shown to be highly voltage accelerated. The reliability of the Intel 2816 during erase/write cycles was measured by performing the full number of erase/write cycles on each byte. Erase/write cycling was done at 70°C and 25°C with no difference in observed failure rate between these temperatures.

The results of erase/write cycling are shown in Figure 11A. The devices under test are completely tested after 2,000, 5,000 and 10,000 total cycles on each byte. The devices are programmed to several data patterns and tested to data sheet specifications. In addition, the devices are tested for high temperature data retention. As can be seen from Figure 11A, the failure rate per 1000 cycles decreases as a function of the number of cycles, which is typical for defect mechanisms such as dielectric breakdown[13].

Figure 11: **ERASE / WRITE CYCLING RESULTS**

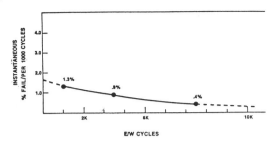

a) Instantaneous Percent Fail vs. Number of E/W Cycles

FAILURE DISTRIBUTION

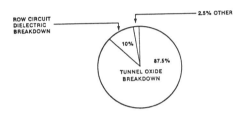

b) Failure Mechanism Distribution.

Two major types of failures were found: Tunnel oxide breakdown and oxide breakdown in the row select circuitry. These failures were minimized by using standard screening techniques for oxide breakdown. Figure 11b shows the failure mode distribution found during erase/write cycling of 549 devices.

Tunnel oxide breakdown failures are cells which fail to erase or show very conductive oxides. These retention failures can be made to both gain and lose charge and exhibit no temperature acceleration. Tunnel oxide failures lose enough charge to cause data loss within hours. No failures have been found with longer retention times as is illustrated in the life test results of Table II.

Table I shows expected failure rates in %/1000 hours at a 60% upper confidence level based on expected device life and the average number of cycles per byte. In a typical system it is expected that some bytes will be written more often than others, so these failure rates are only a guideline.

ERASE/WRITE CYCLING FAILURE RATE

Device Life	No. of Cycles		
	2000	5000	10,000
5 years	.065%	.11%	.17%
10 years	.032%	.054%	.087%
20 years	.016%	.032%	.043%

Table I: Erase/Write Cycling Failure Rate
(per 1000 cycles at a 60% UCL)

As can be seen in Table II, acceptable failure rates are achieved for the design goal of 10,000 erase/ write cycles per byte. To achieve 10,000 cycles per byte in ten (10) years, each byte must be altered approximately three times per day.

As a final verification of device reliability a standard high temperature lifetest at 125°C was performed on devices programmed with a checkerboard data pattern. The lifetest was performed on devices with no additional cycles and devices with 10,000 cycles on each byte. As can be seen from the data in Table II standard MOS failure mechanisms were observed. This data is significant in that it shows no additional defect mechanisms related to data retention or erase/ write cycling of the Intel 2816 E^2 PROM.

TABLE II

125°C LIFETEST RESULTS

Cycles	48 Hrs	168 Hrs	500 Hrs	1000 Hrs	2000 Hrs
0	0/1422	1/1244 [a]	1/443 [b]	0/429	0/270
10,000	0/336	0/336	0/336	0/150	-
Total	0/1758	1/1758	1/779	0/579	0/270

Failure Analysis:

a) = Non-repeatable charge gain, contamination, lev.
b) = Input leakage, contamination, lev.

Failure rate predictions are made in Table III at a 60% upper confidence level for both 55°C and 70°C operation. The .013%/1000 hrs. failure rate at 55°C shows good reliability comparable to other semiconductor memories.

TABLE III

FAILURE RATE PREDICTIONS AT A 60% U.C.L.

125°C Device Hrs.	Activation Energy	Equivalent Hours		Lifetest Failures	Failure Rate % per 1000 Hrs	
		55°	70°		55°C	70°C
1.1x10⁶	0.3 eV	6.8x10⁶	4.5x10⁶	0	.010	.020
1.1x10⁶	0.6 eV	4.4x10⁷	1.8x10⁷	0	.002	.005
1.1x10⁶	1.0 eV	5.3x10⁸	1.2x10⁸	2	.001	.003
				COMBINED	.013	.028

SUMMARY

This paper has discussed a number of E^2PROM failure mechanisms for both erase/write cycling and data retention. It has been shown that Fowler-Nordheim tunneling used for programming does not affect data retention. Erase/write cycling has been shown to degrade device margins by only a small amount and is easily guardbanded. Erase/write cycling does contribute to a significant portion of the observed failure rate due to oxide breakdown under high field operation. Defect related charge loss has been shown to be similar to that observed in EPROMs. Finally, it has been shown that E^2PROMs can perform reliably in applications requiring up to 10,000 erase/write cycles per byte.

Acknowledgements:

The authors would like to thank B. L. Barfield for his technical assistance throughout the course of this work and Geoff Gongwer for many stimulating discussions.

References:

1. W. S. Johnson, et al "16-K EE-PROM Relies on Tunneling for Byte-Eraseable Program Storage", Electronics, February 28, 1980, p113-117.

2. R. Williams, Phys. Rev. Vol. 140, p569, 1965.

3. R. E. Shiner, J. M. Caywood, B. L. Euzent, "Data Retention in EPROMs", 1980 Proceedings of the 18th Annual Reliability Physics Symposium, p238-243.

4. E. H. Nicollian, C. N. Berglund, P. F. Schmidt, I. M. Andrews, J. Appl. Phys. Vol. 42, p5654, 1971.

5. M. H. Woods and R. Williams, J. Appl. Phys., p47, 1082, 1976.

6. W. C. Johnson, IEEE Trans. Nucl. Sci., pNS-22, 2144, 1975.

7. D, J. DiMaria, Proceeding of the International Topical Conference on the Physics of SiO_2 and its Interfaces, p160, 3/78.

8. E. Harari, Appl. Phys. Letter, p30, 601, 1977.

9. C. S. Jenq, "High Field Generation of Interface States and Electron Traps in MOS Capacitors", Ph.D. dissertation, Princton Univ., 12/77.

10. C. S. Jenq, W. C. Johnson, "High Field Generation of Electron Traps in MOS Capacitors", presented in Semiconductor Interface Specialist Conference, 12/77.

11. C. S. Jenq, T. R. Rangarath, C. H. Huang, "Charge Trapping in Floating Gate Tunnel Oxide" presented in 1980 Non-Volatile Semiconductor Memory workshop to be published.

12. D. R. Young, "Electron Trapping in SiO_2", presented in 1980 Non-Volatile Semiconductor Memory workshop.

13. D. Crook, "Method of Determining Reliability Screen for Time Dependent Dielectric Breakdown", 1979 17th Annual Reliability Physics Symposium Proceedings, p1-5.

STRESS INDUCED LEAKAGE CURRENT LIMITING TO SCALE DOWN
EEPROM TUNNEL OXIDE THICKNESS

K.Naruke, S.Taguchi,and M.Wada

Semiconductor Device Engineering Laboratory,Toshiba Corporation
1,Komukai-Toshiba-cho,Saiwaiku,Kawasaki,210,Japan.

ABSTRACT

The effects of thinning FLOTOX EEPROM tunnel oxide on its reliability are investigated by using capacitors and cell structures with oxide thickness ranging from 47 to 100A. The low electric field oxide leakage current is induced by charge injection stressing and it increases with decreasing the oxide thickness. Its conduction mechanism is found to be different from that caused by the positive charge accumulation because of their opposite thickness dependence. Corresponding increase of charge loss in Write/ Erase cycled EEPROM cell is observed with decreasing the oxide thickness at the room temperature retention test. When oxide thickness is decreased, the maximum number of W/E cycling to tunnel oxide breakdown decreases corresponding to charge to breakdown of negatively biased gate. While, the Vth window narrowing is hardened with decreasing the oxide thickness. For scaling down the EEPROM tunnel oxide, the most serious limiting factor among them is oxide leakage current induced by W/E cycling stress resulting in the data retention degradation.

1.INTRODUCTION

Scaling down the FLOTOX EEPROM tunnel oxide gives advantages of such as the reduction of internal programming voltage(Vpp) and shrinkability of memory cell or peripheral circuitry related to high voltage operation. While, thinning the tunnel oxide results in reliability degradation in terms of data retention as well as increased defect density in a manufacture environment.

The reliability of thin oxide has been extensively investigated with concern in the oxide breakdown, charge generation and trapping under high electric field stressing. It has been already reported that the leakage current at low electric field increases after the charge injection in thin oxide of 50A thickness [1] and also EEPROM cell shows charge loss due to tunnel oxide leakage current at low electric field caused by Write/Erase stress [2].

The purpose of this paper is to clarify the most serious limiting factor for scaling down the EEPROM tunnel oxide at when they are stressed with numbers of W/E cycling. It must be carefully taken into account for realizing the advanced higher density EEPROMs.

2.DEVICE FABRICATION

Polysilicon capacitors and EEPROM cells used in our investigation are fabricated on a n-type silicon and p-type silicon substrate, respectively. And they have a n- region beneath the thin tunnel oxide. The area of the capacitor is 2.5×10^{-3} cm^2. The cell has a FLOTOX structure with 1.4×1.4 um^2 tunnel window.

The EEPROM cells are fabricated by means of self aligned stacked gate process. After isolation and n- implantation for the bottom electrode of the tunneling area, the gate oxide (450A) was grown. The oxide was then patterned and etched and a tunnel oxide ranging from 47 to 91A was grown. Then the first polysilicon was deposited. After the poly silicon was patterned and etched, interpoly oxide was grown followed by the second polysilicon deposition. These stacked poly layers were then patterned and etched for self-aligned stacked gates. The n+ source / drain was implanted followed by deposition of oxide and contact opening. After Al/Si metalization and definition, the wafers were sintered in forming gas at 450 C for 15 minutes.

3.EXPERIMENTAL TECHNIQUES

A HP 4145A parameter analyzer and 4140B picoammeter were used to perform charge injection stress and measure I-V characteristics of the capacitor oxide. Charge injection into the oxide was performed by constant current tunneling injection. In data retention test, cell's threshold voltage was defined by the control gate voltage at which the drain current of 1uA was measured with drain voltage of 0.1V in order to suppress the disturbance caused by the measurement itself. W/E cycle stressing was performed by applying 0.2 msec programming pulse alternately with interval of 0.2 msec to the control gate in charging operation and applying to both the drain and the substrate in discharging operation. In endurance test, programming pulse was applied to the control gate and drain alternately with the same pulse width and interval as mentioned above. Tunnel oxide breakdown was detected by monitoring the cell current of discharged state. When tunnel oxide was broken, the cell current disappears suddenly.

4.RESULTS AND DISCUSSIONS

4.1 STRESSING IN CAPACITOR OXIDE

Fig.1 shows the oxide current density versus electric field before and after stress of electron injection from the substrate under positive gate polarity, where measurements are performed on the

Reprinted from the *IEDM Tech. Dig.*, pp. 424–427, 1988.

capacitors having 51-96A thickness oxide. It can be seen that the oxide leakage current at low electric field induced by the charge injection stress increases with decreasing the oxide thickness.

The origin of the low electric field oxide leakage current is not well understood at this time,however, it does seem to be well fit by a Frenkel-Poole type conduction, as shown in Fig.2. Fig.3 shows the stress induced leakage current at 6MV/cm as a function of the injection charge passed through the capacitor oxide.The oxide leakage current increases monotonically with increasing the amount of injection charge.

Charge to oxide breakdown is another important property of tunnel oxide. $Qbd(+)$ and $Qbd(-)$, which are charge to oxide breakdown measured under positive and negative gate polarity, respectively, are plotted in Fig.4 as a function of oxide thickness. An abrupt increase in $Qbd(+)$ is observed in the oxide with the thickness thinner than 70A.

According to positive feedback mechanism in oxide breakdown[3], oxide breakdown is to occur when the amount of trapped hole in the oxide reaches to a certain critical amount of Qot. The increase in $Qbd(+)$ with decreasing oxide thickness means the reduction of hole trapping rate,probably due to the reduction of hole generation rate, rather than the change of trapping efficiency.

In order to clarify a relation between the hole trapping and the cause of leakage current,the ratio of total charge Qinj injected during the stress test under positive gate polarity to $Qbd(+)$ are plotted as a function of oxide thickness in Fig.5. Considering that the ratio of Qinj to $Qbd(+)$ is equivalent to the ratio of the amount of trapped hole to Qot, it can be seen that the stress induced leakage current increases with decreasing the oxide thickness while the trapped hole density decreases. This different oxide thickness dependence means that the cause of stress induced leakage current is not the hole trapping. One of possible mechanisms is the state-assisted conduction, such as Frenkel-Poole type hopping or local tunneling through a potential barrier modified by trapped state, as described in ref.[1,2].

On the other hand, it can be seen that $Qbd(-)$ decreases with decreasing oxide thickness. An available model is not found to explain this difference.

4.2 STRESSING IN EEPROM CELL

EEPROM cells show the consistent results with above ones in their retention and endurance test. They present three kinds of degradation. That is (i) degradation of data retentivity due to the low electric field leakage current, (ii) Vth window narrowing due to electron trapping and (iii) the reduction in maximum number of W/E cycling due to tunnel oxide breakdown.

Fig.6 shows the threshold voltage of EEPROM cells as a function of retention time at the room temperature. As expected,the EEPROM cells subjected 1×10^4 W/E cycles show large charge loss compared to unstressed (only 5- W/E-cycled) cells and this tendency becomes remarkable in thinner oxide cell, where the W/E cycle stressing was carried out with the same V_{th}-window of 12 volts in order to pass the same amount of charge through the tunnel oxide.

Before the retention test, EEPROM cells were programmed to the low V_{th} state and started with

the same electric field across the tunnel oxide. In order to obtain large Vth window, memory cells without select transistor were used in this retention experiments and a discharging operation was performed by applying programming voltage both to the drain and the substrate to prevent drain breakdown. This oxide thickness and W/E cycle dependence on data retention can be well explained as a result of tunnel oxide leakage current in stressed cells varying along corresponding J-E curves shown in Fig.1.

As the W/E programming is repeated, Vth window becomes narrow as shown in Fig.7, and the tunnel oxide goes to breakdown at last. Vth window narrowing is due to electron trapping in the tunnel oxide. Dependence of Vth window narrowing on the tunnel oxide thickness is shown in Fig.8. As can be seen in Fig.8, thinning the tunnel oxide makes the cell hardened in Vth window narrowing, resulting from reduction of the amount of trapped electron. This is one of the favorable results for thinning down the tunnel oxide.

Dependence of Nmax on the tunnel oxide thickness is shown in Fig.9, where Nmax is a number of W/E cycle to failure of programming due to tunnel oxide breakdown. It can be seen that Nmax decreases with decreasing the tunnel oxide thickness. This thickness dependence is consistent with the dependence of $Qbd(-)$ shown in Fig.4 and it means that Nmax is affected by the discharging operation. Even a cell with 47A thickness of tunnel oxide, however, withstands to 1×10^6 W/E cycling.

4.3 ANNEALING EFFECT

Since the high temperature baking accelerates the thermal emission of charges stored in the floating gate, the convetional life testing are performed at high temperature about 250 C. On the other hand, the high temperature baking has an effect on the annealing of the oxide damage caused by charge injection stress, resulting in the reduction of stress induced oxide leakage current. Stress induced oxide leakage current at 6MV/cm after annealing at 200, 250 and 300 C are shown in Fig.10 as a function of annealing time. The stress induced oxide leakage current reduces rapidly in higher annealing temperature. In retention test on our EEPROM cells with tunnel oxide thickness of 70A, larger Vth shift was obtained in the cell baked at 200C as shown in Fig.11, because the reduction of the oxide leakage current occurs slowly at the temperature below 200C and rapidly at higher than 250C as shown in Fig.10.

5. CONCLUSION

We have made clear the effects of thinning EEPROM tunnel oxide on charge loss due to tunnel oxide leakage current, maximum number of W/E cycling to breakdown, and Vth window narrowing due to electron trapping. we conclude that the stress induced leakage is the dominant degradation mode in thin oxide and the mechanism is different from the positive feedback mechanism due to hole trapping explained in dielectric breakdown behaviour[3]. Charge loss in retention tests of stressed EEPROM cell can be explained by this stress induced current of tunnel oxide and annealing effect. Since this degradation is enhanced in thinner oxide,it is the most serious limiting factor for scaling down EEPROM tunnel oxide.

ACKNOWLEDGMENT

The authors would like to thank Mr.K.Maeguchi for his valuable discussions and Mr.D.Tohyama, Mr.S.Yamada and Mr.H.Taneda for their support in device fabrication.

REFERENCES

[1] T.N.Nguyen, P.Olivo and B.Ricco, Proc. of 1987 IRPS, p.66.

[2] D.A.Baglee and M.C.Smayling, Tech. Dig. of 1985 IEDM, p.624.

[3] S.Holland, I.C.Chan, T.P.Ma and C.Hu, IEEE Elec. Dev. Lett.,EDL-5(8), p.302, Aug. 1984.

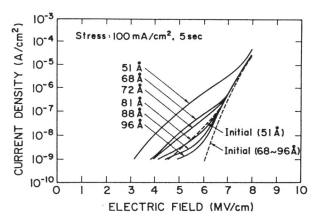

Fig.1 J-E characteristics measured by capacitors having 51-96A oxide thickness before and after charge injection stress.

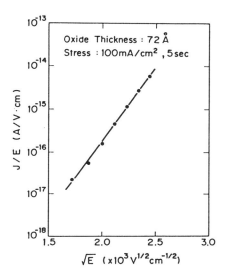

Fig.2 Frenkel-Poole plot of low field leakage current in 45A oxide.

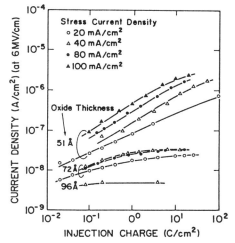

Fig.3 Stress induced current at 6MV/cm as a function of injection charge passed through the capacitor oxide (51,72,96A).

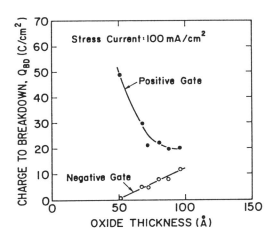

Fig.4 Oxide thickness dependence of charge to breakdown(QBD) under the same stress current (100mA/cm²).

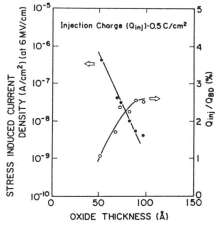

Fig.5 Stress induced current at 6MV/cm and injection charge to QBD ratio (Qinj/QBD) corresponding to trapped hole density as a function of oxide thickness.

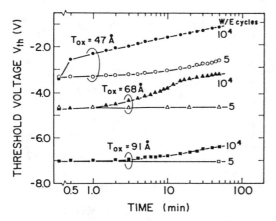

Fig.6 Threshold voltage of EEPROM cells as a function of retention time at room temperature. EEPROM cells having 47, 68, and 91A oxide are subjected to 5 to 10^4 write/ erase cycles.

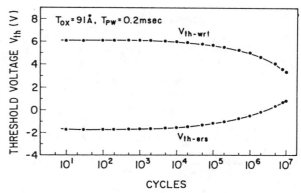

Fig.7 Endurance characteristic of a single EEPROM cell with 91A tunnel oxide.

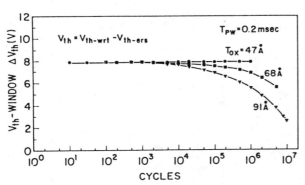

Fig.8 Vth window of single EEPROM cells as a function of write/erase cycles, where cells have 47,68,and 91A tunnel oxide.

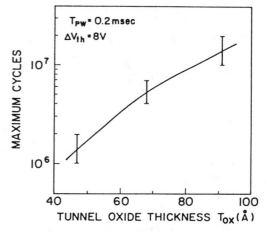

Fig.9 Maximum programming cycles to tunnel oxide breakdown as a function of tunnel oxide thickness.

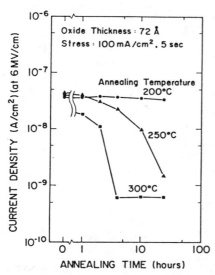

Fig.10 Capacitor current at 6MV/cm as a function of annealing time. Annealing temperature are 200, 250,and 300 C,respectively.

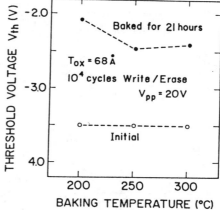

Fig.11 Threshold voltage of initial and baked EEPROM cells as a function of baking temperature. EEPROM cells with 68A tunnel oxide are subjected to 10^4 write/erase cycles and baked at each temperature.

RELIABILITY PERFORMANCE OF ETOX BASED FLASH MEMORIES

Gautam Verma & Neal Mielke
Intel Corporation
2250 Mission College Blvd.
Santa Clara, CA 95052

ABSTRACT

Flash memories are a recent addition to the class of non-volatile memories. This paper discusses the reliability performance of a 64K Flash memory based on a single-transistor, floating-gate memory cell. The reliability performance of these memories, before program/erase cycling, matches that of UV EPROMs. Cycling generally does not introduce defect-related failures common to some EEPROMs. However, it may aggravate two intrinsic instabilities found in the UV EPROM (intrinsic charge loss and the DC Program disturb mechanism). Our experiments show that these are related effects caused by injection of holes, during the erase step of the cycle. High source to substrate electric fields, during erase, generate these holes. Channel hot electron injection, for programming, pays no significant role in the observed degradation. These cycling effects can be addressed through incorporation of additional margin into the Flash cell. Through such cell optimization, the reliability of these memories is made equivalent to that of conventional UV EPROMs, even after hundreds of program/erase cycles.

INTRODUCTION

Flash memories have recently been developed by several IC manufacturers. They are similar to conventional UV EPROMs but can be both programmed and erased electrically, thus eliminating the need for UV light sources and window packages. This feature offers advantages over UV EPROMs in packaging costs and enhanced functionality [1].

Several approaches have been considered for the Flash memory cell such as a 3-poly approach [2] and a step gate approach [3]. The present work describes the operation and reliability of Flash memories based on a single EPROM type floating gate transistor cell [4] without a select transistor. These 64K arrays are byte electrically programmable and block electrically erasable. The 1-transistor nature of this technology provides the compactness and scalability of traditional EPROMs with the electrical erasability of EEPROMs.

In this paper we shall first review the basic operation of the Intel 27F64 Flash memory. Reliability results gathered from cycling, lifetest and retention bake will be presented to predict operating failure rates for 64K memories. The degradation mechanisms seen in programming, erase, data retention and disturb behavior of the memories will be discussed and explained with supporting data from single cell performance.

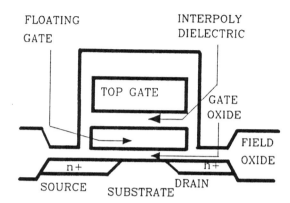

FIG. 1. Schematic cross-section of Flash memory cell.

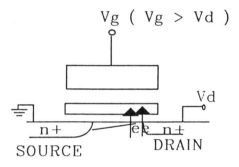

FIG. 2. Schematic description of Flash memory programming by CHE injection.

DEVICE STRUCTURE AND OPERATION

The Intel Flash memory cell is similar to the conventional double polysilicon, EPROM structure, as shown in Fig. 1, but uses a thinner tunnel gate dielectric. It is manufactured using ETOX [4] technology. Important features of the cell are the thin first gate dielectric (about 100Å), abrupt drain and graded source junctions, and a scaled interpoly dielectric.

Programming of the cell is done in a similar fashion to the traditional EPROMs, i.e. by channel hot electron injection (CHE), as shown in Fig. 2. The shallow drain junction and an optimum channel profile is used to enhance CHE injection.

Electrical erasure is accomplished by Fowler-Nordheim (F-N) tunneling of electrons from the floating gate to the source diffusion, as shown in Fig. 3. A graded source junction permits the application of high voltages (typically 12.5V) to it, which, coupled with the reduced gate oxide thickness, facilitates the erasure.

Reprinted from *Proc. IRPS*, pp. 158–166, 1988.

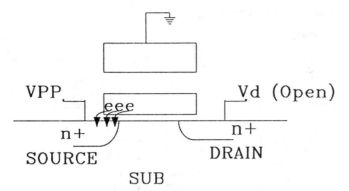

FIG. 3. Schematic description of Flash EPROM electrical erase by F-N tunneling of electrons from floating gate to source.

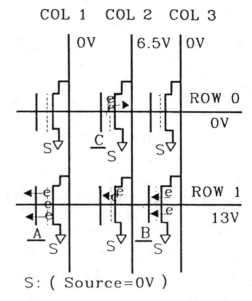

S: (Source=0V)

FIG. 4. Schematic description of disturb mechanisms during programming in Flash memory array.

Type A cell experiences DC Erase disturb.
Type B cell experiences DC Program disturb.
Type C cell experiences Program disturb.

CELL DISTURBS

Except during erase, Flash memory cells experience the same stresses during operation as those in UV EPROMs. These stresses, which arise principally during programming of the array, may cause different kinds of disturbs. An important design consideration is the proper selection of read and programming voltages to minimize these disturbs. As will be shown later, program/erase cycling of the array may also affect these disturbs. In this section we discuss the nature of the disturb stresses and also define the terms assigned to them.

The three principal memory cell disturbs that can occur during programming of an array are called DC Erase, DC Program and Program Disturb. They impact memory cells sharing a common wordline (Row) or a Column, with the cell being programmed. The effect of these disturbs, on a portion of the memory array, is shown in Fig. 4.

DC Erase occurs on programmed cells (type A in Fig. 4), which are on the same wordline as the cell being programmed. Those type A cells have electrons on their floating gates. During the programming operation the common wordline is brought to a high voltage (13V maximum). The resultant electric fields across the interpoly dielectric may be large enough to cause conduction, such as through tunneling, across it and loss of charge from the floating gate. This effect translates into a reduction of the threshold (margin) voltage of the cell and in severe cases causes loss of data. This data loss is not due to oxide breakdown. DC Erase data failure occurs as follows: A cell (cell A in Fig. 4) programs successfully. As each remaining bit on the same Row is programmed, cell A loses a bit more charge.

DC Program occurs on cells in the unprogrammed or Erased state (type B in Fig. 4). These cells have few electrons on their floating gates and thus low threshold (margin) voltages. Raising the voltages on the wordlines of these cells creates high electric fields across the tunnel gate dielectric and may cause tunneling of electrons to the floating gate from the substrate. In this case the threshold voltages of the cells will increase.

Finally, a programmed cell (type C), sharing a Column with the cell being programmed, will experience high electric fields between floating gate and drain. This may cause electrons to tunnel from the floating gate to the drain, and lead to

reduced cell threshold voltages. This effect is termed Program Disturb. This stress occurs at lower voltages (6.5V) compared to those during DC Program and DC Erase (13V).

In this paper we distinguish between Cell Margin and Array Margin voltages. The former refers to the threshold voltage of a single cell in the memory array. Array Margin is the Cell Margin of the limiting cell in the array – the worst programmed or erased bit. Performance and reliability of memories often hinges on the worst bit. Cell Margin voltages are used to illustrate behavior of typical bits.

OTHER FAILURE MECHANISMS

Apart from the disturbs, other failure mechanisms in Flash memories are expected to be those seen in similar non-volatile memories, such as EPROMs and EEPROMs. These include charge loss due to defective bits, destructive oxide breakdown during program/erase cycling, and trapup degradation during cycling [5].

As with any floating-gate memory, data loss can occur if one of the dielectrics surrounding the floating gate is defective, allowing electrons to leak off from the floating gate. Program/erase cycling subjects the cell's dielectrics to high electric fields (>10MV/cm for the gate oxide), so dielectric breakdown during cycling is a concern. Cycling also passes significant electronic charge through the gate oxide. Trapping of this negative charge could potentially inhibit further tunneling and CHE injection, causing degradation of erase and program margins with cycling. This mechanism is referred to as trapup.

ACCELERATED TEST RESULTS

Since for Flash memories the number of Program/Erase cycles may be orders of magnitude greater than in UV EPROMs, reliability evaluations will need to address the effects of cycling just as in EEPROM devices. Flash memories must withstand a certain number of cycles for oxide trapup and dielectric breakdown failures.

Extensive cycling was performed on our 64K memories, under worst-case conditions unlikely to be encountered in normal operation. Table I summarizes the cycling results. Memories with 100 cycles were tested to full specs for program and erase times and showed no problems. They were also tested for worst-case disturbs and again met the required quality criteria. Memories with 10,000 cycles were tested for functionality and data retention. No failures were observed in either the evaluation shown in Table I or in other evaluations. This contrasts with many EEPROMs which suffer 1% to 5% failure rates in 10,000 cycles because of oxide breakdown.

TABLE I

64K Flash EPROM Cycling Results

Cycles	No. of Failures
100	0/1396
10,000	0/200

We ascribe this improvement to several factors. First, because the Flash erase involves tunneling only through the gate-source overlap, the area of oxide involved in the tunneling is very small. The Flash cell can therefore tolerate a higher oxide

defect density than an EEPROM cell with a mask-defined tunneling area can. Second, the Flash cell is erased using a longer, lower-voltage erase pulse, resulting in lower stress on the oxide. Finally, the quality of the oxide has been improved through explicit process improvements and through implicit advantages of the Flash cell (such as the lightly-doped silicon on which the oxide is grown).

However, changes in Program and Erase times, corresponding to window widening and narrowing effects due to charge trapping as in EEPROMs did arise. Complete verification of device reliability for 100 cycles is presented here.

TABLE II

64K Flash EPROM 250°C Retention Bake Results

Cycles	48 Hrs.	168 Hrs.	500 Hrs.
1	0/125	0/125	2*/125
100	0/390	2*/390	0/388
Total	0/515	2/515	2/513

*Single-bit charge loss.

The results of data retention bakes are shown in Table II. The data integrity of Flash memories is comparable to that of UV EPROMs, both before and after 100 cycles.

A standard high temperature lifetest at 125°C was performed on devices programmed with a checkerboard pattern. Some of the units were cycled 100 times; others were not. Table III shows lifetest results. As can be seen from this data, the usual low-level failure mechanisms are observed, with or without cycling. Failure rate predictions are made in Table IV at a 60% upper confidence level for both 55°C and 70°C operation. The predicted failure rate of 54 FITs at 55°C and 60% confidence is comparable to that of UV EPROMs and other common IC's.

CYCLING BEHAVIOR

The cycling endurance of our ETOX based Flash memory is limited on one side by the CHE induced degradation and on the other by the trapping effects during F-N tunneling. Even beyond 100 cycles these degradations in performance are small. Fig. 5 shows the reduction in the Array Program Margins after 100 cycles. Program Margins were measured after a worst-case programming pulse of 12.5V for 100μ sec. Each data point represents the threshold voltage of the worse-programmed bit of one array (the Array Margin). There is a small, 0.3V reduction after 100 cycles, but we see that each device still has approximately 3V of extra margin above the required 5.5V. At 12.5V the Program Margin comfortably exceeds 5.5V beyond 1000 cycles.

TABLE III

64K Flash EPROM 125°C Lifetest Results

Vcc	Cycles	48 Hrs.	168 Hrs.	500 Hrs.	1000 Hrs.	2000 Hrs.
5.25V	1	0/3807	1*/3794	1*/576	0/575	0/575
	100	0/416	0/416	1/416	0/415	0/415
	Total	0/4223	1/4210	2/992	0/990	0/990
7.25V	1	0/264	0/264	0/264	0/264	
	100	0/168	0/168	0/168	0/168	
	Total	0/432	0/432	0/432	0/432	

*Single Bit Charge Loss

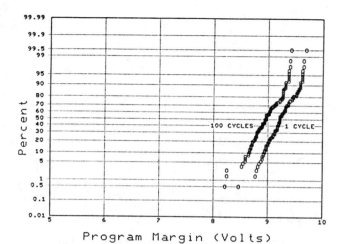

Program Margin (Volts)

FIG 5.   Program margins of Flash memory arrays
after a 100μ sec, 12.5V program step. Each
point represents the worst programmed bit
of one device.

The Erase times for Flash Memory devices are shown
in Fig. 6, before and after cycling. During the
first hundred cycles these times actually decrease
(improve). This behavior corresponds to window
widening in EEPROMs and is believed to be due to
hole injection in the oxide. In our case, holes
injected above the source will enhance the
tunneling of electrons from the floating gate and
cause the observed decrease in Erasetimes. This
decrease is followed by a steady increase, as
shown in Fig. 7, again seen in EEPROMs and
considered to be due to the effects of electron
trapping. This steady increase is somewhat higher
than is found in FLOTOX EEPROM cells but
dramatically lower than is found in triple-poly
EEPROM cells.

The DC Erase and Program Disturb characteristics of
the Flash memory devices are excellent with no
measureable change until several thousand cycles.
Reasonable stresses were unable to cause any shifts
in Margins even after 10000 cycles. However,
cycling impacts the DC Program behavior. The
allowable disturb, as measured by the Array Margin

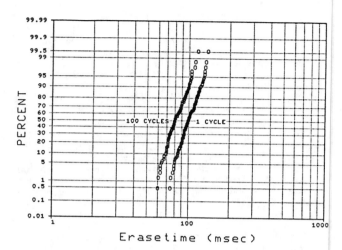

Erasetime (msec)

FIG 6.   Electrical erase times of Flash memory
arrays, before and after 100 cycles, at
12.5V.

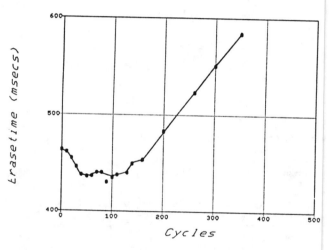

Cycles

FIG. 7.   Erase time vs cycling behavior of a Flash
memory. Erase time was measured at the
worst-case Vpp of 12.5V.

TABLE IV

64K Flash EPROM Failure Rate Predictions at 60% UCL

Activation Energy (eV)	125°C Device Hrs.	Equivalent Hours 55°C	70°C	Lifetest Failures	Failure Rate % per KHr 55°C	70°C
0.3	2.25×10^6	1.33×10^7	8.4×10^6	0	–	–
0.3+422*	4.32×10^5	1.08×10^9	6.8×10^8	0	0.00008	0.00013
0.6	2.69×10^6	9.2×10^7	3.6×10^7	3	0.0045	0.0110
1.0	2.69×10^6	9.6×10^8	2.0×10^7	0	0.0009	0.0046

Total Combined Failure Rate =   0.0054   0.0157
                             =   54 FITs   157 FITs

*For the 0.6eV and 1.0eV categories, which correspond to charge loss and
contamination, respectively, the hours from 7.25V lifetest and 5.25V
lifetest have simply been combined. For the 0.3eV category (oxide
breakdown), a voltage-acceleration factor of 422 was first applied to
the 7.25V lifetest hours before they were added to the 5.25V lifetest
hours.

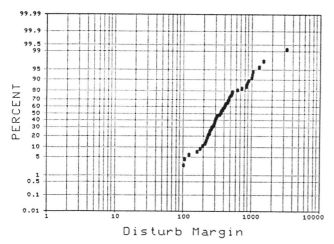

FIG. 8. DC Program disturb margin factor after 100 cycles.

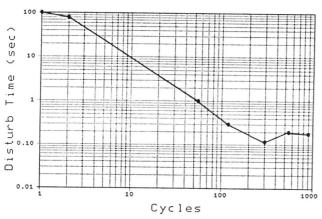

FIG. 9. DC Program disturb time behavior as a function of cycling.

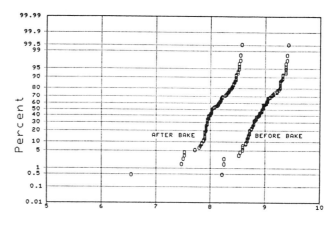

FIG. 10. Array margins, for 100 cycled units before and after 250°C/168-hour retention bake. Each point represents worst programmed bit of one device.

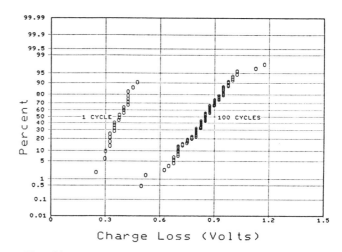

FIG. 11. Charge loss comparison between cycled and uncycled arrays. Each point represents the worst-bit margin shift in one array.

shift, depends on design and speed related issues. In our case a Margin shift of 0.5V for the erased state is considered to be the onset of parametric degradation. The measurement of the DC Program disturb time is done by first erasing the array and then applying a high voltage (13.0V) to all the wordlines. The time for the Array Margin shift of 0.5V is measured. This represents the time for the worst bit in the array.

Typically, before cycling, the disturb times are hundreds of seconds corresponding to 5 to 6 orders of magnitude greater than required. In Fig. 8 this 5 to 6 order of magnitude margin is decreased to between 2 to 3 orders of magnitude, after 100 cycles. Although this is a significant reduction, it is still 100 to 1000X more than necessary and ensures that the memories have substantial guardband for disturbs. Fig. 9 shows the disturb time as a function of cycling. It levels after a few hundred cycles. For this reason, even cycling out to 10,000 cycles does not result in failure to specifications.

Both the improvement in erase time and the degradation in DC Program margin involve enhancement of the normal tunneling characteristic of the gate oxide. Comparing Figs. 7 and 9, it is clear that both effects saturate after about 100 cycles. These observations suggest that the

effects may have the same fundamental cause and that both may involve hole trapping, even though the DC Program effect is far larger.

CHARGE LOSS

UV EPROMs are known to have excellent data retention properties even beyond hundreds of hours of retention bake at 250°C. Typical margin shifts for EPROMs are 0.3V after 250°C/168-hour bakes. For Flash memories, with 1-2 cycles, the charge loss is comparable to that of UV EPROMs. However, after 100 cycles, enhanced margin shifts of up to 1V are seen. The results of 250°C/168-hour bake are shown in Fig. 10. Each point represents the lowest margin bit in an array. Although the charge loss, shown in Fig. 11, exceeds 1 volt, the Array Margins after bake are still substantially higher than 5.5V. The high initial program margins of our Flash memory cells guarantee data retention properties equivalent to UV EPROMs, as demonstrated in Table II.

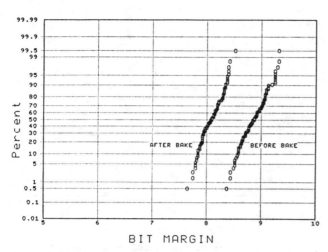

FIG. 12. Charge loss distribution for all 64K bits from one Flash array.

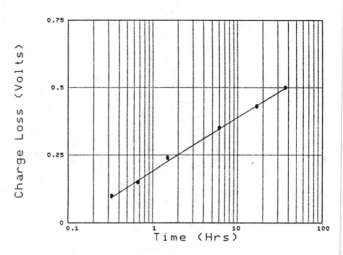

FIG. 14. Logarithmic dependence of charge loss of typical bits from cycled arrays at 220°C.

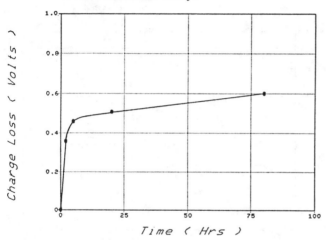

FIG. 13. Temporal behavior of charge loss seen for cycled arrays at 250°C. Each point represents the mean worst bit margin shift in the arrays.

This enhanced charge loss is not due to defective bits. In fact, all cycled parts lose about the same amount of charge and this charge loss is normally distributed without a tail (Fig. 11). We find that in a single array, typically all the bits lose equivalent quantities of charge. Thus in Fig. 12, the program margins of bits from a single array are shown. The uniform shift across all the bits suggests an intrinsic phenomenon affecting the entire array.

One possible source of the enhanced charge loss is contamination. For EPROMs this cause of failure can be investigated using a series of Program/Erase bakes [6]. In our case, no charge gain was observed as the outcome of this experiment, implying that contamination is not the cause of the charge loss.

When the devices with 100 cycles, which showed enhanced charge loss, were reprogrammed after the first bake and then subjected to another 250°C/168-hour bake, the charge loss was reduced

and comparable to uncycled devices. This suggests that the charge loss is not due to any irreversible, permanent damage to the array due to cycling, but the mechanism responsible for it is removed by high temperature bakes.

It is also observed that after retention bakes the cycled devices recover their original, uncycled DC Program characteristics and erase times too. These experiments strongly suggest the source of the enhanced charge loss, after cycling, is intimately related to the phenomenon causing reduction in erase time and degradation in DC Program disturb behavior - holes in the oxides. High temperature bakes may cause thermal detrapping of these holes and their migration to the floating gates, thus neutralizing some of the negative floating gate charge.

In Fig. 13 we show the temporal behavior of the 100-cycle Flash; the charge loss occurs within an hour of 250°C bake. Thereafter, the charge loss rate is similar to that of UV EPROMs. We believe that the crossover behavior seen in Fig. 13 is the outcome of two different mechanisms. The bulk of the charge loss, within a very short period, is due to the cycling induced mechanism; thereafter the usual EPROM mechanism operates [6]. An activation energy of the cycling induced mechanism has been determined by measuring the charge loss at lower temperatures. Figure 14 shows that this charge loss behavior is logarithmic in time. The activation energy plot, in Fig. 15, yields a value of 1.12 ±0.25eV. At this activation energy, the 20 hours required for appreciable charge loss at 180°C corresponds to over 100 years at 55°C.

SINGLE CELL CYCLING EVALUATIONS

Hot-carrier generation within the silicon substrate is a likely source of trapped charge in the overlying gate oxide. Both the program and erase steps of the cycle involve some carrier generation - the program step because it is by nature a hot-carrier effect and the erase step because the source is biased close to the junction breakdown limit. To separate the effects during program from those during erase, single Flash memory cells were

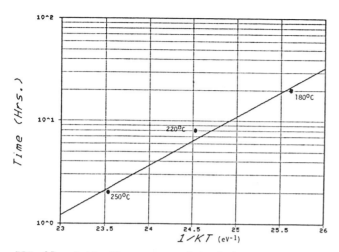

FIG. 15. Activation energy plot of charge loss after cycling. Each point represents the mean charge loss of typical bits in arrays.

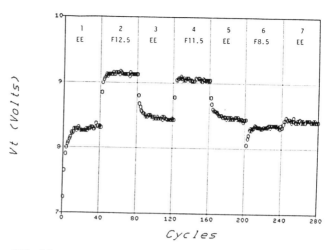

FIG. 16. Program threshold voltages (Vts) of a single cell as function of cycling.

EE:	EEPROM program and erase.
F12.5:	EEPROM program/Flash erase at 12.5V.
F11.5:	EEPROM program/Flash erase at 11.5V.
F8.5:	EEPROM program/Flash erase at 8.5V.

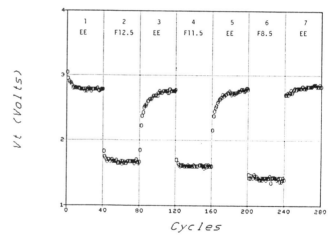

FIG. 17. Erase threshold voltages (Vts) as function of cycling.

used for the studies discussed in this section. The use of single cells is advantageous as it provides a greater flexibility of experiments with a larger range of voltages that can be directly applied to the cell nodes. In memory arrays, the peripheral circuitry imposes limits on the maximum voltages that can be applied to the array.

The scheme utilized to separate the program and erase steps in the Flash cycle takes advantage of the bi-directional F-N tunneling nature of the first gate oxide. The cell can be programmed simply by applying a high positive voltage to the top gate. The cell can be erased by simply applying a negative voltage. This type of tunneling can replace either the CHE program step or the Flash erase (high voltage on the source) step. Thus we can distinguish between the effects due to CHE injection from those of Flash erase. In fact, planar F-N tunneling constitutes the conventional Erase/Write mechanism for FLOTOX based EEPROMs. We will refer to the programming of the cell by F-N tunneling across the channel by EEPROM program. Similarly, tunneling in the reverse direction to erase will be termed EEPROM erase. A complete cycle of this type is called an EEPROM cycle.

One of the advantages of using EEPROM program and erase steps is that their behavior provides an indication of trapped charge in the tunnel oxide. Thus, enhanced tunneling effects seen in the EEPROM cycle are suggestive of trapped positive charge and inhibited tunneling behavior points to electron trapping. EEPROM tunneling characteristics provide an in-situ measurement technique in our case. We also verified that the Flash memory cells did not exhibit any charge trapup or endurance problem with EEPROM cycles, up to at least 2000 cycles. This EEPROM program and erase technique on our Flash cells is a clean way for looking for trapped charge.

One experiment compared the effects of Flash and EEPROM erase. A single cell was cycled a few hundred times, and its programmed and erased Vt's were measured after every half cycle (Figs. 16 and 17). The programming condition was kept the same

for every cycle (EEPROM programming throughout), but the erase condition was changed every 40 cycles. Because the programming condition was unchanged, variations in programmed Vt were due to variations in the trapped charge in the oxide. In particular, any enhancement of the EEPROM programming was directly analogous to the DC Program degradation observed in the 64K memories.

Referring to Fig. 16, the first 40-cycle section is labelled EE because EEPROM erase was used. The programmed Vt shows a moderate rise due to the normal buildup of positive charge expected from planar tunneling.

In the second section, labelled F12.5, the EEPROM erase was replaced with a 12.5V Flash erase (source at 12.5V, top-gate grounded). The programmed Vt jumped 1V during the first few Flash erase cycles, implying that the first few Flash erases caused holes to become trapped in the gate oxide. The Vt reached a steady-state value after a few cycles when the rate of hole trapping from the Flash erase equaled the rate at which the trapped holes recombined with the tunneling electrons. The third section, again labelled EE, reverted to EEPROM cycling, and the programmed Vt gradually returned to the same value as in the first EE section. This behavior tends to confirm the hole-trapping model. During the second EE section, no more holes were injected and those remaining from the F12.5 cycling gradually recombined with the tunneling electrons.

The fourth section, labelled F11.5, used an 11.5V Flash erase. The lower voltage would normally result in a lower tunneling field and therefore less overall erasure, so a bias of -1.5V was added to the top gate to assist in the tunneling. This bias was calculated to maintain the same tunneling field, and indeed (Fig. 17) the resulting erased Vt was about the same as in the previous 12.5V Flash erase. The main result of the change in erase condition was therefore to reduce the voltage drop from source to substrate, not the tunneling field itself. As shown in Fig. 16, the programmed Vt again jumped by about a volt, although slightly less than before. Again reversion to EEPROM erase (section 5) gradually reversed the effect.

The sixth section, labelled F8.5, used an 8.5V Flash erase assisted by a -6V top-gate bias. This bias combination drastically reduced the voltage drop in the source depletion region, but the -6V gate bias maintained about the same tunneling field. As shown in Fig. 16, the jump in the programmed Vt's disappeared altogether.

The results of Fig. 16 imply, therefore, that the Flash erase step injects holes into the gate oxide, resulting in tunneling enhancement analogous to the observed DC Program degradation. The hole trapping is not a direct result of the erase tunneling itself, but rather hinges on the voltage drop from the source diffusion to the substrate - i.e., on the electric field in the silicon depletion region. The onset of the effect between 8.5V and 11.5V coincides with the onset of the gate aided junction breakdown in this region. This implies that hole trapping results from hot-hole generation/multiplication in the source-substrate depletion region.

The results of Fig. 17 provide further support to the above conclusions. In this figure, the erased cell Vt's are plotted during the cycling sequence discussed above. In Fig. 17, the Vt's vary not only because of trapping effects (as in Fig. 16) but also because changing the erase bias conditions directly changes erase Vt's. An abrupt Vt jump in the first cycle of a 40-cycle section simply indicates the effect of the new erase bias condition on the erase Vt. A gradual Vt shift within a section indicates the trapping and detrapping occurring within that section.

Thus, the abrupt Vt drop of 1V from the first EE section to the F12.5 section indicates that the F12.5 erase was simply 1V more effective than the EE erase. After 40 F12.5 cycles, however, the first EE Vt was almost 1V lower than before. This

tends to confirm that the F12.5 erases injected holes which caused enhanced tunneling in the gate oxide. As in Fig. 16, further EE cycling (section 3) gradually restored the Vt to the same value as before because the trapped holes gradually recombined with the tunneling electrons.

The F11.5 section caused the same behavior, except somewhat reduced. The F8.5 section, however, eliminated this behavior altogether. After the F8.5 cycling, the first EE Vt jumped immediately back to its steady-state value, confirming the result of Fig. 16 that no hole trapping occurred.

These results tend to confirm our previous conclusion that the Flash erase step is responsible for injecting holes into the gate oxide. We also see that these holes enhance tunneling in both directions, causing degraded DC Program margin in the product, but also enhanced EEPROM erase observed in single test-pattern cells. Such bi-directional enhanced tunneling is typical of hole-trapping effects in FLOTOX EEPROMs.

The behavior of the erased Vt's (Fig. 17) within the Flash-erase sections presents an apparent contradiction. In the first few F12.5 cycles, the programmed Vt's (Fig. 16) jumped quickly by about a volt, indicating a large injection of holes into the oxide. We saw further evidence of these holes in the first EE erase Vt following the F12.5 cycling (Fig. 17). Yet the erase Vt's themselves did not react more than 0.2V during the F12.5 cycling. A similar contradiction exists in the product data. We have concluded that the DC Program degradation and the decrease in the erase time are due to the same effect, yet the DC Program effect is far larger (compare Figs. 7 and 9).

Our explanation for this contradiction is as follows. We believe that the holes are largely generated in the source diffusion as a result of the high vertical tunneling field, which penetrates the silicon in the source diffusion. Once generated, the holes are swept out of the source region through the 12.5V drop in the depletion region under the channel. This 12.5V drop generates the energy necessary for the holes to become injected into the gate oxide. As a result, most of the holes are injected into the gate oxide over the channel, not over the source. Since the erase occurs over the source, the erase is not as strongly affected as the EEPROM program/erase behavior, which involves planar tunneling over the channel.

We investigated the effects of CHE injection by replacing the Flash erase step with EEPROM erase, and performing a sequence of experiments similar to above. No significant charge trapping effects in the tunnel oxide could be inferred due to CHE injection. It is concluded that the breakdown associated with the source junction during Flash erase is solely responsible for hole injection in the tunnel oxide.

In a separate experiment several hundred single Flash cells from a single wafer were split into four groups corresponding to EE, F12.5, F11.5, and F8.5 cycling conditions. 100 cycles were performed on each group. The cycled cells were subjected to a 250°C/72-hour bake along with uncycled cells to measure charge loss. The average charge loss in each group is shown in Table V. The maximum charge loss was seen for the group cycled according to F12.5 conditions followed by F11.5 and F8.5 in magnitude. The charge loss for F8.5 was comparable to that of uncycled and cells having EEPROM cycles (EE). This experiment demonstrated that maximum charge loss occurs for the Flash erase step with the highest source voltage during erase – the same condition causing maximum hole trapping in the tunnel oxide as seen in the experiments of Figs. 16 and 17.

TABLE V

Flash EPROM Cell Charge Loss after 100 Cycles

Cycling Condition	Average Charge Loss
EE	0.1
F12.5	0.51
F11.5	0.33
F8.5	0.24
Uncycled	0.12

From this we conclude that the flash erase step is responsible for the enhanced charge loss after cycling, in addition to the previously-discussed enhancement of erase time and the degradation in DC Program margin. We believe that trapped holes can become thermally detrapped during bake, drifting to the floating gate and compensating some of the negative charge there. This results in a V_t drop which appears due to charge loss, even though no stored electrons have actually leaked off the floating gate. The detrapping model also explains why the charge loss saturates with time (Fig. 13). The charge loss must saturate after the holes are fully detrapped. The model also explains why cycled units do not show enhanced charge loss in a second bake: the holes were all baked out in the first bake. Finally, the model explains why the enhancement of erase time, DC Program rate and charge loss all begin to level off after about 100 cycles. This occurs because hole trapping itself levels off as the limited number of hole traps becomes filled. It is this intrinsic limit to these mechanisms that allows functionality out to 10,000 cycles (Table I).

CONCLUSION

We have demonstrated that our ETOX based Flash memory technology has reliability performance, even after 100 cycles, comparable to conventional UV EPROMs. For extensive cycling (10,000 cycles and beyond) no failures due to dielectric breakdown are observed. In this case performance is limited by the trapup behavior of the gate oxide.

Cycling does introduce new degradation mechanisms such as decrease in DC Program disturb margin and enhanced charge loss. Our Flash memory arrays are optimized to provide several orders of magnitude guardband for DC Program disturb and sufficient margin to ensure data retention equivalent to UV EPROMs.

The presence of holes in the gate oxide is considered the most likely source of these degradation mechanisms. We have shown that during erase, the high source to substrate voltages are responsible for injecting these holes. Using planar tunneling across the channel, to program and erase the Flash cell, we can also show that the CHE program step does not create the holes responsible for DC Program disturb and charge loss.

ACKNOWLEDGEMENTS

The authors would like to thank Greg Atwood, Stephan Lai, and Simon Tam for useful discussions.

REFERENCES

[1] N. Kynet et al, "An In-System Programmable 256K CMOS Flash Memory", to be presented in the IEEE ISSCC, 1988.

[2] F. Masuoka et al., "A 256K-bit Flash EEPROM Using Triple-Polysilicon Technology, "IEEE J. Solid-State Circuits, vol. SC-22, Aug. 1987.

[3] G. Samachisa et al., "A 128K Flash EEPROM Using Double-Polysilicon Technology," IEEE J. Solid-State Circuits, vol. SC-22, pp 676-683, October, 1987.

[4] S. Tam et al., "A High Density CMOS 1-T Electrically Erasable Non-Volatile (Flash) Memory Technology," to be presented in 1988 Symposium on VLSI Technology.

[5] B. Euzent, C. Jeng, J. Lee, and N. Boruta, "Reliability Aspects of a Floating Gate EEPROM," 19th Proc. IEEE Reliability Physics Symposium, p. 11 (1981).

[6] N. Mielke, "New EPROM Data-Loss Mechanisms," 21st Proc. IEEE Reliability Physics Symposium, p. 106 (1983).

Degradations Due to Hole Trapping in Flash Memory Cells

SAMEER HADDAD, CHI CHANG, BALAJI SWAMINATHAN, AND JIH LIEN

Abstract—Degradation in the hot-electron programmability of the flash memory cell is observed after erasing from the drain. Trapped holes in the oxide near the drain junction are found to be responsible for this degradation. Hole trapping in the oxide also causes another problem known as "gate disturb," which is the undesired increase in the threshold voltage of an erased cell during programming of the other cells on the same word line. Threshold-voltage shifts due to gate disturb are used to monitor the amount of trapped holes in the oxide after cell erasure. It is determined that the trapped holes are mainly externally injected from the junction depletion region rather than directly generated in the oxide by the Fowler–Nordheim (F–N) tunneling process.

FLASH memory [1]–[3] has recently emerged as an important nonvolatile memory which combines the advantages of EPROM density with EEPROM electrical erasability. Programming of the cell is achieved by hot-electron injection at the drain side, and erasure is usually accomplished by electron tunneling from the floating gate to either the drain [2] or the source [1], [3]. However, due to the presence of high voltage at the gated-diode junction during erasure, holes are inevitably generated by band-to-band tunneling [4] and a small amount of them are injected into the oxide after being accelerated in the depletion region. Hot-hole injection during erasure has been reported to cause variations in the erased threshold voltages of the cells in the memory array [1], and trapped holes in the oxide were shown to degrade the charge-retention characteristics of the memory cells [5]. However, no work has been reported on the effect of hole trapping on the programmability of the flash cell when erasing is done at the drain. In this work this effect is studied and the degradation in programmability is characterized. Since hole trapping in oxide is known to alter the tunneling characteristics of the oxide [6], [7], we have devised a method to compare hole trapping produced by Fowler–Nordheim (F–N) tunneling with that produced by hot-hole injection. Results clearly demonstrate that oxide hole trapping in flash structures is indeed attributable to the externally injected hot holes.

The flash cell used in this work has a structure very similar to that of a conventional stacked-gate EPROM cell. The channel length is about 1 μm long and the S/D arsenic diffusion is about 0.25 μm deep. The gate oxide used is less than 120 Å thick and the erasure mechanism is dominated by F–N tunneling [7]. In Fig. 1(a) three dc programming curves are presented for a fresh cell, for the cell electrically erased

Manuscript received October 21, 1988; revised December 19, 1988.
The authors are with Advanced Micro Devices, Inc., Sunnyvale, CA 94088.
IEEE Log Number 8926657.

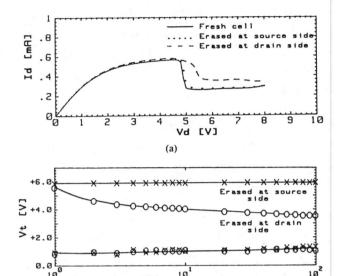

Fig. 1. (a) DC programming curves for (V_g = 12 V) a fresh cell (solid), electrically erased from the source side (dotted), and electrically erased from the drain side (dashed). (b) Programming/erase threshold voltage of the flash memory cell versus number of cycles, for drain-side and source-side erasure.

from the source, and for another cell electrically erased from the drain. It shows significant degradation in the programmability of the cell that has been erased from the drain side. Fig. 1(b) shows the programmed and erased threshold voltages as a function of the number of program/erase (P/E) cycles for a cell erased from the source and another erased from the drain. Fig. 1(b) clearly shows the programming threshold voltage is reduced after erasure from the drain, and as the cell is cycled the programming window continues to close. No degradation in the programmability is observed after erasure from the source. We believe that the degradation in programmability is caused by hole trapping in the oxide.

To demonstrate hole trapping in the oxide as a result of high-voltage erasure, poly gate transistors with similar gate oxide thickness and junction profile to the flash cell were used to monitor the hot-electron-generated substrate current and the gated-diode leakage current before and after the high-voltage stress. The stress was performed by applying a constant voltage of 11.5 V to the drain junction for 10 s while the gate and substrate were grounded with the source left floating. Fig. 2(a) shows the substrate current as a function of the gate voltage for V_D = 4 V, before and after the stress. The substrate current becomes lower after the stress due to a

Reprinted from *IEEE Electron Device Lett.*, vol. 10, no. 3, pp. 117–119, March 1989.

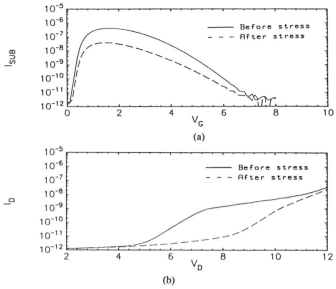

Fig. 2. (a) Substrate current versus the gate voltage at $V_D = 4$ V with the source grounded. (b) Drain leakage current versus drain voltage at $V_G = 0$ V with the source floating, measured before (solid) and after (dashed) high-voltage stress ($V_D = 11.5$ V for 10 s).

reduction in the channel field, indicating hole trapping in the oxide near the drain junction [8]. Fig. 2(b) shows the band-to-band tunneling current as a function of the drain voltage before and after stress. The drain leakage current versus V_D curve after the stress is shifted to a much higher drain voltage, also suggesting the fact that the surface field at the junction corner has been reduced due to hole trapping [4]. Hole trapping in the oxide near the drain has the effect of reducing the maximum channel electric field during programming, thereby decreasing channel hot-electron generation. This explains the degradation in programmability after drain-side erase.

By erasing from the source, programmability degradation is eliminated and, furthermore, the drain and source junctions can be independently optimized. The drain junction can be made shallow and abrupt to enhance the hot-electron effect for programming, and the source junction can be graded (for example, using a double-diffused junction) to reduce the junction field during erasing. A flash cell using this concept, which was first proposed by Kume et al. [1], is used in the following study to determine the origin of the trapped holes in the oxide during the erase cycle.

It is known that hole trapping inside the oxide reduces the barrier for electron tunneling [6]. This barrier lowering effect will lead to the so-called "gate disturb" problem for a memory array. Gate disturb refers to the undesired increase in the threshold voltage of the unselected "erased" cell during programming of the other cells on the same word line. During programming, a fraction of the word-line voltage will be coupled to the floating gate, and a high field (about 6–7 MV/cm) will appear across the thin gate oxide. As a result, electrons can tunnel to the floating gate through the thin oxide causing the threshold voltage to increase The gate disturb at a given field is proportional to the F–N tunneling current which is enhanced by the hole trapping in the oxide. Therefore gate

disturb is used in this work as a monitor of the amount of trapped holes in the oxide due to erasure.

We believe that holes were introduced into the oxide through hot-hole injection during flash erasure. However, another possible mechanism is hole generation by impact ionization in the oxide during F–N tunneling itself [9], similar to that experienced in EEPROM erasure. The gate disturb test was used to compare positive charge trapping in the oxide using flash erasure with that using EEPROM-type erasure. For EEPROM-type erasure a negative voltage pulse (-16 V) is applied to the control gate, while the source junction is kept at a low positive voltage (2 V). The source voltage is low enough not to generate hot holes, while electron tunneling still occurs predominantly at the gate–source overlap region. On the other hand, the flash erasure is exercised by applying a high positive voltage pulse (11 V) to the source with the gate grounded and the drain floating. Fig. 3 shows the threshold voltage of the flash cell versus the erase time using the two different erase conditions mentioned above. For both erasures, the erasing speed is controlled by F–N tunneling. The voltages were chosen such that the oxide field during the EEPROM-type erasure is slightly larger than that for the flash erasure. This is done to ensure that the F–N tunneling-induced hole generation in the oxide for the EEPROM-type erasure is no less than that in the flash erasure.

Fig. 4 compares the gate disturb after EEPROM and flash erasures. The cell was first alternately programmed and erased to V_t's of 6 and 1 V, respectively, for 20 cycles in order to saturate the hole trapping in the oxide. Then the threshold voltage was measured as a function of gate disturb time. During the gate disturb, the gate of the erased cell was biased at 12 V while the other terminals were at ground. As shown in the figure, no V_t shift is observed for the cell erased under EEPROM condition. This suggests that the holes that are

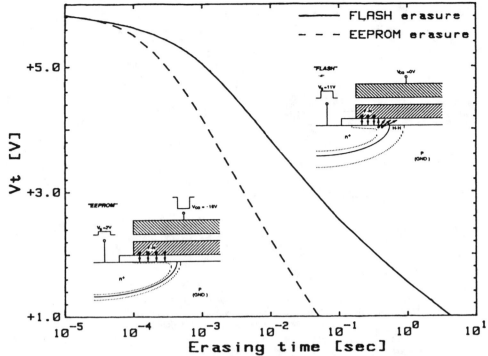

Fig. 3. Threshold voltage versus erasing time during flash erasure (solid) and EEPROM-type erasure (dashed). The faster erasure time of the EEPROM-type erasure is due to the higher applied field across the oxide. The insets are schematic representations of the two erase conditions.

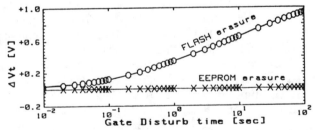

Fig. 4. Threshold-voltage shifts ($\Delta V_t = V_t - V_t\{$before disturb$\}$) during gate disturb after the cells having been cycled 20 times, using flash ($\bigcirc$) and EEPROM (X) erasure. The cells were erased to a V_t of 1 V before gate disturb measurement.

generated and trapped in the oxide by the F–N tunneling electrons are insignificant in contributing to gate disturb. However, the gate disturb after the flash erasure is significant. These data strongly support a model of external hot-hole injection and hole trapping in the oxide during the flash erasure.

In summary, we have demonstrated that the hot-electron programming efficiency of the flash cell is degraded after erasure from the drain. Degradation in programmability has been shown to be caused by trapped holes in the gate oxide at the drain junction. By comparing the flash erasure to EEPROM-type erasure, it has been determined that these trapped holes are externally injected from the junction

depletion region. Furthermore, the trapped holes in the gate oxide will lead to gate disturb. Therefore, in a properly designed flash structure, it is essential that hot-hole injection is minimized.

REFERENCES

[1] H. Kume *et al.*, "A flash-erase EEPROM cell with an asymmetric source and drain structure," in *IEDM Tech. Dig.*, 1987, pp. 560–563.
[2] G. Samachisa *et al.*, "A 128K flash EEPROM using double-polysilicon technology," *IEEE J. Solid-State Circuits*, vol. SC-22, pp. 676–683, Oct. 1987.
[3] S. Mukherjee, T. Chang, R. Pang, M. Knecht, and D. Hu, "A single transistor EEPROM cell and its implementation in a 512K CMOS EEPROM," in *IEDM Tech. Dig.*, 1985, pp. 616–619.
[4] C. Chang and J. Lien, "Corner-field induced drain leakage in thin oxide MOSFET's," in *IEDM Tech. Dig.*, 1987, pp. 714–717.
[5] G. Verma and N. Mielke, "Reliability performance of ETOX based flash memories," in *26th Proc. IEEE Reliability Phys. Symp.*, Apr. 1988, pp. 158–166.
[6] I. C. Chen, S. Holland, and C. Hu, "Electrical breakdown of thin gate and tunneling oxides," *IEEE Trans. Electron Devices*, vol. ED-32, no. 2, pp. 413–422, 1985.
[7] C. Chang, S. Haddad, B. Swaminathan, and J. Lien, "Drain avalanche and hole-trapping induced gate leakage in thin-oxide MOS devices," *IEEE Electron Device Lett.*, vol. 9, no. 11, pp. 588–590, 1988.
[8] Y. Nissan-Cohen, G. Franz, and R. Kwasnick, "Measurement and analysis of hot-carrier-stress effect on NMOSFET's using substrate current characterization," *IEEE Electron Device Lett.*, vol. EDL-8, pp. 451–453, 1987.
[9] I. C. Chen, S. Holland, and C. Hu, "Hole trapping and breakdown in thin SiO$_2$," *IEEE Electron Device Lett.*, vol. EDL-7, no. 3, pp. 164–166, 1986.

RADIATION RESPONSE OF FLOATING GATE
EEPROM MEMORY CELLS*

E. S. Snyder, P. J. McWhorter, T. A. Dellin, and J. D. Sweetman[†]

Sandia National Laboratories

Albuquerque, NM 87185

Abstract

The effect of radiation on a floating gate EEPROM nonvolatile memory cell is determined experimentally and modeled analytically for the first time. The new model predicts the threshold voltage change resulting from radiation. A screen based on the initial "1" state (excess electron) threshold voltage is shown to be necessary to assure data retention during irradiation. Techniques to increase radiation hardness are also described. The hardness of floating gate cells is shown to be limited to less than 100 krad(Si) for a fixed reference sense amplifier. The use of a differential sense amplifier may increase this limit. Therefore, floating gate memories should be useful for those applications requiring low total-doses.

I. INTRODUCTION

Traditionally, radiation hardened electronic applications requiring Electrically Erasable Programmable Read Only Memories (EEPROMs) have used integrated circuits (ICs) composed of Silicon Nitride Oxide Silicon (SNOS) memory transistors. Significant understanding of the radiation characteristics of SNOS memory transistors has been achieved [1,2]. Radiation hardness in excess of 1 Mrad(Si) has been demonstrated and accurate models have been developed. However, only a few vendors are able to supply these parts.

The most popular commercial EEPROM ICs consist of floating gate (FG) memory transistors. FG memory arrays as large as 1 megabit are available [3,4]. Because of its popularity and the abundant number of FG manufacturers, there has been considerable interest in using FG EEPROMs in applications with low total-dose radiation levels. However, little has been done to characterize the radiation response of FG EEPROMs.

Most published FG radiation studies have dealt with another FG technology, namely the Electrically Programmable Read Only Memories (EPROM). An EPROM differs from an EEPROM in that it is erased by exposure to an ultraviolet lamp. The EEPROM is programmed *and* erased electrically. However, the effective device cross-section exposed to radiation is similar for both memory transistors.

For EPROMs, Frohman-Bentchkowsky suggested hole injection into the FG as a possible mechanism for x-ray erasure during irradiation [5]. In addition, numerous radiation measurements for a particular EPROM IC have been performed [6,7,8,9]. Although these studies answered questions about the radiation hardness of a particular EPROM IC, the observed failures could have resulted from peripheral circuitry, the memory cell, or a combination of both. The radiation response of the memory transistor was not measured or modeled. An understanding of the radiation behavior of EPROM memory cells is important in order to assess the radiation limits of the technology.

The authors are unaware of any published study on the radiation response of FG EEPROM memory cells. Therefore, we have undertaken the first study of the radiation response of individual FG EEPROM memory cells. Because EPROM transistors have similar device cross-sections, this study may also be applied to the radiation response of EPROM transistors. This paper will be useful in understanding the issues involved in hardening FG memories (both EPROM and EEPROMs) as well as in designing harder memory cells.

We first describe the memory window behavior during irradiation. It will be shown that the logic "1" state (excess electrons) limits the radiation performance. This performance is then analytically modeled and used to examine design trade-offs in hardening FG memories. A practical screen to assure radiation hardness will then be described. Finally, upper limits for radiation hardness of FG memories are proposed.

II. OBSERVATIONS

The memory cell examined consists of an n-channel FG transistor in series with an n-channel access transistor. Arrays of these cells are used in Seeq's 256K n-well CMOS EEPROM [10,11]. The modeling cross-section of the memory transistor is shown in Figure 1. It consists of a polysilicon control gate deposited over a 40 nm SiO_2 region. This region insulates the control gate from the FG. A 47.5 nm SiO_2 region is sandwiched between the FG and the p-type silicon substrate. An 8 nm oxy-nitride tunneling region, which is used to program and erase the transistor, is not shown in this figure. Since its volume is significantly smaller than the SiO_2 regions, it will have a second-order effect on the radiation response [12].

The cells were bonded out to a 28-pin ceramic dual-in-line package to facilitate irradiation. They were then

*This work was performed at Sandia National Laboratories and supported by the U.S. Department of Energy under contract number DE-AC04-76DP00789.

[†]Seeq Technology, Inc., San Jose, CA 95131

Reprinted from *IEEE Trans. Nucl. Sci.*, vol. 36, no. 6, pp. 2131–2139, December 1989.

405

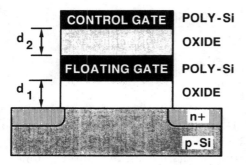

Figure 1: Cross-section of the FG EEPROM memory transistor used for modeling.

written into a "1" state or erased into the "0" state using the conditions present on the 256K EEPROM IC. The "1" state represents excess electrons stored on the the FG. The "0" state represents either the lack of electrons or excess holes stored on the FG. The cells were then subjected to radiation from a cobalt-60 source with a dose rate of 142 rad(Si)-sec^{-1}. During the irradiations, the parts were placed in conductive foam in order to simulate typical unbiased use conditions.

The threshold voltage of the cell was measured at various dose levels up to 100 krad(Si). The results are shown in

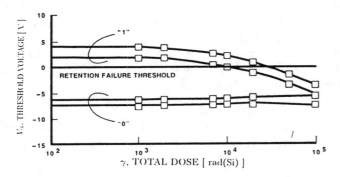

Figure 2: Experimental threshold voltage data as a function of dose for various pre-radiation thresholds.

Figure 2. Note that the "1" state threshold voltage decays quickly with dose in comparison to the "0" state threshold voltage. Relatively little variation in the "0" state was measured. In the Seeq 256K EEPROM design, a fixed reference sense amplifier is used. A cell threshold voltage which is greater than 0 V is read as a "1," while a cell threshold voltage less than -2 V is read as a "0." The data shows that the "1" state always crosses its failure threshold voltage (0 V) before the "0" state is even close to approaching its failure threshold voltage (-2 V). Retention failure of the "1" state is seen to occur in 10-30 krad(Si) dose range. Therefore, in a radiation environment, the "1" state decay will be the major cause of retention failures.

The radiation dose necessary for a retention failure is also a function of the initial (pre-irradiation) "1" state:

the larger the initial "1" threshold voltage, the larger the dose necessary for a retention failure. Since longer cell write-times will result in a larger initial "1" state, a larger dose for retention failure may be achieved at the expense of longer cell write-times. This indicates a performance trade-off between cell write-time and dose for retention failure.

In addition, it may be possible to increase the radiation hardness of the memory transistor by using a differential sense amplifier. In differential sensing, the difference between a "1" state threshold voltage and "0" state threshold voltage is used to sense a particular logic state. A retention failure will occur when the "1" and "0" threshold curves approach each other. In Figure 2, the logic threshold curves collapse around 100 krad(Si). Thus, a differential sensing scheme may increase the FG hardness to 100 krad(Si). However, differential sensing requires twice as many memory transistors as fixed reference sensing. This indicates a trade-off between memory density and radiation hardness.

Finally, the program/erase cycling and data retention characteristics (with time) after irradiation were not investigated. These effects need to be characterized in order to use FG EEPROMs effectively in a radiation environment.

III. QUALITATIVE DESCRIPTION OF MODEL

In the "1" state, an excess amount of electron charge is stored on the floating gate as shown in Figure 3. This en-

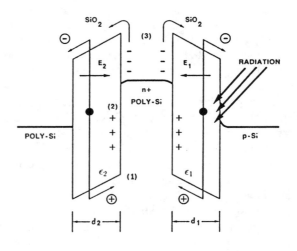

Figure 3: Energy band diagram of the FG when programmed into the excess electron or logic "1" state.

ergy band diagram also illustrates the mechanisms which could cause a threshold voltage decrease (net electron charge loss) during radiation. The bold numbers in parentheses in Figure 3 correspond to the following mechanisms: 1. Holes injected into the FG, 2. Holes trapped in the oxides, and 3. Electron emission over the poly-silicon/oxide barriers. These are discussed next.

A. *Hole Injection and Trapping*

Radiation imparts energy to the oxide regions, and electron-hole pairs are generated. The number of electron-hole pairs generated depends on the material and the volume available. A fraction of the electron-hole pairs generated will recombine. This fraction depends to a great extent on the electric field, E, across the radiated oxide [13]. The greater the electric field, the greater the fraction that escape recombination. The remaining electrons are significantly more mobile in SiO_2 than the remaining holes [14]. The electrons quickly drift toward the poly-silicon control gate and the silicon substrate under the influence of the oxide electric field. The remaining holes are either trapped in the oxide or drift under the influence of E toward the FG. The holes not trapped in the oxide are injected into the FG, reduce the net amount of electron charge stored on the FG, and decrease the threshold voltage.

Most oxide vacancies occur near the oxide/substrate and oxide/FG interfaces [15]. Because of the direction of the electric field in the "1" state, the majority of hole charge which is trapped during irradiation will occur at the oxide/FG interfaces. The positive charge of these trapped holes will tend to mask the negative electronic charge on the floating gate. This will also reduce the threshold voltage of the FG transistor.

Thus, the effect of the trapped and injected holes on the threshold voltage shift under irradiation is similar: electronic charge on the FG is reduced by hole charge. Both effects will also decrease as the thickness (and hence the volume available for charge generation assuming a constant area) of the oxide is decreased. Because the parts are not built with hardened oxides, it is assumed that oxide trapping and transport processes will dominate interface-trap generation. Therefore, the model does not include interface-traps. This assumption should be checked by measuring the subthreshold voltage characteristics of the memory transistor before and after radiation [16].

Oxide-trapped charge in MOSFETs is known to anneal over time [17]. If annealing of the oxide-trapped charge occurs in FGs, the hole charge should tunnel into the FG over time. This will not change the threshold voltage of the memory transistor. However, electron charge may be injected into the FG to compensate for this hole charge and to refresh the logic state of the memory transistor. The annealing process and the ability to refresh FG transistors needs to be demonstrated.

Hole injection will not decrease in hardened oxides. The charge which is no longer trapped in hardened oxides will be injected into the FG. Thus, the threshold decay with radiation should not improve with hardened oxides.

B. *Electron Emission*

Electron emission over the FG/oxide barrier is the third mechanism present during irradiation. This emission is responsible for erasure of a FG EPROM part under ultraviolet light. An EEPROM will also loose charge if exposed to ultraviolet light.

During irradiation, photons with an energy exceeding 4.3 eV will cause electrons to be emitted over the potential barrier [5]. Once the electron is in the oxide, it is quickly swept to the substrate or control gate by the electric field. The loss of this electron will decrease the threshold voltage.

The relative importance of electron emission will be discussed later. It should be noted that this mechanism does not decrease as the FG poly-silicon thickness or oxide thickness is reduced. In section VI, this mechanism will be shown to ultimately limit the radiation hardness of the memory cell.

As electronic charge is continuously removed during irradiation, the electric fields across the oxides decrease. The reduced oxide electric fields result in less holes available for injection and trapping (recall the fraction of holes available depends on E). Eventually, all charge generation processes due to irradiation are balanced. Since there will be no further redistribution of charge, there will be no change in the threshold voltage. The threshold voltage at which this occurs is called the radiation saturation voltage, V_{rs}. It is not understood, in detail, what physical parameters of the FG transistor control the position of V_{rs}. However, for the purpose of the model to be developed, we understand that this is the point where all charge transport and trapping processes due to radiation are balanced.

C. *"0" State Response*

The previous discussion focused on the excess electron, or "1," state. For the "0" state, we observe a slight shift toward a more positive threshold voltage as the radiation dose is increased. A band diagram of the "0" state during irradiation is shown in Figure 4. The oxide electric fields point in the opposite direction from the "1" state.

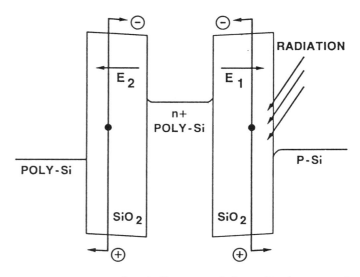

Figure 4: Energy band diagram of the FG when erased into logic "0" state.

This causes electrons generated during irradiation to be injected into the FG, and the threshold voltage to increase (assuming negligible hole emission). Since $|E|$ is smaller than in the "1" state (less charge on FG), the observed shift in threshold voltage is smaller. When the transport processes balance, the threshold voltage saturates.

We believe this saturation condition will occur when the oxide electric fields are close to 0. The "1" and "0" state energy band diagrams in Figures 3 and 4 illustrate this point. Since the electric fields in the "1" and "0" states point in opposite directions, there will be a threshold voltage where the oxide electric fields are close to 0. This threshold voltage is V_{rs}. When $E \approx 0$, the transport and trapping processes will balance. Thus, there will be no further redistribution of charge or change in the threshold voltage.

This is a qualitative description of the FG threshold shift during irradiation. A quantitative model will now be described.

IV. QUANTITATIVE DESCRIPTION OF MODEL

The threshold voltage of a FG memory transistor is directly related to the electronic charge stored on the floating gate [18]. The threshold voltage may be written as

$$V_{th} = V_{si} + \frac{\sigma_{fg} d_2}{\epsilon_2}, \tag{1}$$

where V_{si} is the threshold of the transistor due to processing and is a function of many variables including d_1 and d_2. d_1 is the oxide thickness between the FG and silicon substrate, d_2 is the oxide thickness between the control gate and the FG, while ϵ_2 is the permittivity for that region. σ_{fg} is the net electronic charge per unit area stored on the FG. Since altering the amount of charge on the floating gate will shift the threshold voltage, we must determine how the FG charge changes during irradiation. The radiation response of the FG charge is modeled by the following charge conservation equation:

$$\begin{aligned}
\frac{\partial \sigma_{fg}(\gamma)}{\partial \gamma} = & -qG_h \alpha \{d_1 f(E_1) + d_2 f(E_2)\} \\
& -qG_h (1-\alpha)\{d_1 f(E_1) + d_2 f(E_2)\} \\
& -e_c \sigma_{fg}.
\end{aligned} \tag{2}$$

where γ is the total radiation dose, q is the electron charge and G_h is the number of electron-hole pairs generated per cm^3 per rad(SiO$_2$). d_1 and d_2 are the oxide thicknesses noted in Figure 3. $f(E)$ is the collection efficiency. It is the ratio of the density of electron-hole pairs remaining after recombination to the density generated in the oxide. E_1 and E_2 are the electric fields across the oxide regions 1 and 2 in Figure 3. α is the fraction of holes which are injected into the floating gate and $(1-\alpha)$ is the fraction which are trapped in the oxide. e_c is the emission constant for electrons emitted over the FG-oxide barriers.

Equation 2 states that the net loss in electronic charge on the floating gate per radiation dose results from three separate processes. The first process, represented by the first term on the right side of the (2), is the hole injection rate (i.e. the holes per area injected into the floating gate per radiation dose). The second process, shown by the second term, is the hole trapping rate. The final term is the net emission rate for electrons emitted over the FG-oxide barrier.

In order to solve (2) for σ_{fg}, some assumptions must be made. For oxide electric fields, $|E|$, less than 0.5 MV-cm^{-1}, it has been shown [13] that

$$f(E) \approx kE, \tag{3}$$

where k is the slope of the $f(E)$ versus E curve. Since the oxide electric fields are related to σ_{fg} by Gauss's law,

$$E_1 = \frac{\sigma_{fg} - \sigma_{rs}}{\epsilon_1 + \epsilon_2 d_1/d_2}, \tag{4}$$

and

$$E_2 = \frac{\sigma_{fg} - \sigma_{rs}}{\epsilon_1 d_2/d_1 + \epsilon_2},$$

where σ_{rs} is the radiation saturation charge on the FG. σ_{rs} represents the charge on the floating gate when all radiation processes are balanced. As discussed in section III, we assume that this radiation saturation condition will occur when $E \approx 0$. Hence, equation 4 assumes that when $E \approx 0$, $\sigma_{fg} = \sigma_{rs}$. ϵ_1 and ϵ_2 are the permittivity of oxide regions 1 and 2. Substituting (3) and (4) into equation 2, and solving for σ_{fg} yields,

$$\sigma_{fg}(\gamma) = \frac{B}{A} + (\sigma_i - \frac{B}{A})exp(-A\gamma), \tag{5}$$

where

$$\begin{aligned}
A = & \ qG_h \alpha h(d_1, d_2) + \\
& qG_h(1-\alpha)h(d_1, d_2) + \\
& e_c,
\end{aligned}$$

$$\begin{aligned}
B = & \ qG_h \alpha h(d_1, d_2)\sigma_{rs} + \\
& qG_h(1-\alpha)h(d_1, d_2)\sigma_{rs},
\end{aligned}$$

$$h(d_1, d_2) = \frac{d_1 k_1}{\epsilon_1 + \epsilon_2 d_1/d_2} + \frac{d_2 k_2}{\epsilon_1 d_2/d_1 + \epsilon_2},$$

and

$$\sigma_i = \sigma_{fg}(\gamma = 0).$$

The first term on the right hand side of the A equation results from the hole injection. The second term results from hole trapping and the final term is due to electron emission. Substituting (5) in (1) results in an analytical solution for the threshold voltage in terms of radiation dose,

$$V_{th}(\gamma) = V_{rs} + [V_{th}(0) - V_{rs}]exp(-A\gamma), \tag{6}$$

where

$$V_{th}(0) = V_{si} + \frac{\sigma_i d_2}{\epsilon_2},$$

$$V_{rs} = V_{si} + \frac{B d_2}{A \epsilon_2}.$$

$V_{th}(0)$ is the pre-irradiation threshold voltage. It is determined by the process (V_{si}) and the amount of charge initially electrically injected (σ_i) into the FG. V_{rs} is the radiation saturation threshold voltage. Again, this is the voltage where all the charge transport and trapping are balanced.

For larger electric fields, an exponential fit to the collection efficiency data is more accurate [19]. Equation 2 can then be solved assuming

$$f(E) \approx 1 - exp(-E/b), \qquad (7)$$

where b is a fitting parameter. This results in a transcendental equation for the threshold voltage as a function of γ. When both linear and exponential fit were compared, little difference was noted. The small difference is primarily due to the small internal electric fields ($|E| < 1$ MV-cm^{-1}) that appear across the oxides when the FG is in the logic "1" or "0" state. Since the linear fit results in a simple analytical form, it is the preferred approximation.

Using (6), and the V_{th} versus γ data from a single memory transistor, A and V_{rs} may be determined. For the EEPROM cells used in this study, $A = 1/46500$ rad(SiO$_2$)$^{-1}$ and $V_{rs} = -5.5$ V. V_{rs} and A may vary depending on the process used to manufacture the FG.

All other $V_{th}(\gamma)$ curves are then determined by using the same A and V_{rs} parameters derived from the measurement of a single FG transistor. Because these parameters are determined only once, the model allows one to determine the FG cell hardness level by only measuring (and controlling) its pre-irradiation threshold voltage. Therefore, the model is predictive. Figure 5 is a comparison between the model and data. Each curve in Figure 5 represents the model fit (using the same A and V_{rs} for all curves) to the data from a memory cell. The $V_{th}(\gamma) > 0$ region is the most important portion of the curves. It represent the region where the memory cells still read out their assigned "1" logic state. A good agreement between the data and model is noted in this region. In addition, the model predicts the data for doses up to 100 krad(Si).

The deviations around 100 krad(Si) are due to several factors. First, the parts tested represent extremes in process variations. All parts tested were written and erased with the same time and voltages parameters. However, there is a large variation in the resulting distribution of "1" threshold voltages. Typical parts do not show this much variation in threshold voltage. The initial threshold voltage differences are due to geometric variations (e.g. d_1 and d_2) resulting from processing. Since A and B in equation 5 are directly related to oxide thicknesses, some deviation from the model is to be expected with parts that have

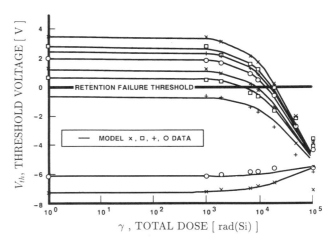

Figure 5: Comparison of model with data.

a large variation in oxide thickness. Second, since these parts are not built with hardened oxides, higher doses will result in some interface-trap generation. For the threshold voltages measured, negatively charged interface states will result in a positive shift in the threshold voltage [20]. The model does not include interface-traps.

V. RADIATION SCREEN

The threshold voltage model will now be used to develop a practical radiation screen for the Seeq 256K EEPROM IC. The relationship between the pre-irradiation "1" threshold voltage and radiation hardness will first be established.

The dose for retention failure, γ_f, is the dose where the $V_{th}(\gamma = \gamma_f) = 0$ V (for a fixed reference sense amplifier). By setting (6) equal to 0 V, and solving for $V_{th}(0)$, a theoretical relationship between the pre-radiation "1" state and the dose for retention failure may be found:

$$V_{th}(0) = V_{rs}\{1 - exp(A\gamma_f)\}. \qquad (8)$$

The correlation between the model and data is shown in Figure 6. This figure also shows a trade-off between $V_{th}(0)$ and γ_f. A larger "1" (from a longer write-time) will allow a larger dose for retention failure. This figure also indicates that in order to achieve a certain hardness level, one must insure that the initial "1" state is large enough (i.e. implement an effective screen).

Even if the FG part is written longer to achieve a higher radiation hardness, normal process variations will result in a distribution of "1" threshold voltages across the part. Therefore, the statistical distributions resulting from process variations must be included [21]. The fraction of parts from the inspection lot that yield a desired dose for retention failure, γ_{fd}, is

$$Y(\gamma_{fd}) = P(V_{th}(0) > 0)P(\gamma_f > \gamma_{fd}|V_{th}(0) > 0), \qquad (9)$$

where $P(V_{th} > 0)$ is the probability that $V_{th}(0)$ is greater

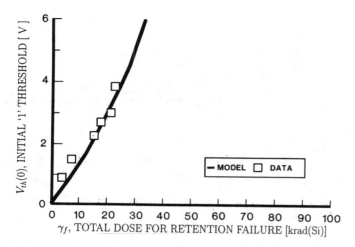

Figure 6: Pre-radiation threshold voltage as a function of dose for retention failure.

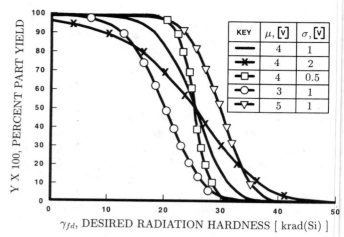

Figure 7: Percentage of parts yielding a desired radiation hardness for various process targets (μ) and process variations (σ) in pre-irradiation "1" threshold voltage, $V_{th}(0)$.

than 0 V and $P(\gamma_f > \gamma_{fd}|V_{th}(0) > 0)$ is the probability that γ_f exceeds γ_{fd} given that $V_{th}(0) > 0$.

The initial "1" state distribution for the 256K EEPROM parts may be modeled by a normal probability density function,

$$f(V_{th}(0)) = \frac{1}{\sigma\sqrt{2\pi}}exp\left\{\frac{-1}{2}\left[\frac{V_{th}(0) - \mu}{\sigma}\right]^2\right\}, \quad (10)$$

where μ is the mean and σ is the standard deviation of the distribution. The probability density function for γ_f is then

$$g(\gamma_f) = \frac{f(V_{th}(0))}{P(V_{th}(0) > 0)}\frac{dV_{th}(0)}{d\gamma_f}, \quad (11)$$

where

$$P(V_{th}(0) > 0) = \int_0^\infty f(V_{th}(0))dV_{th}(0),$$

and the derivative is evaluated using equation 8. Since

$$P(\gamma_f > \gamma_{fd}|V_{th}(0) > 0) = \int_{\gamma_{fd}}^\infty g(\gamma_f)d\gamma_f, \quad (12)$$

the fraction of parts yielding γ_{fd}, is

$$Y(\gamma_{fd}) = \int_{l(\gamma_{fd})}^\infty \frac{1}{\sigma\sqrt{2\pi}}exp\left\{\frac{-1}{2}\left[\frac{z - \mu}{\sigma}\right]^2\right\}dz, \quad (13)$$

where $Y(\gamma_{fd})$ is the part yield, z is a variable of integration, and $l(\gamma_{fd}) = V_{rs}\{1 - exp(A\gamma_{fd})\}$. By performing this integration for a range of desired hardness levels, a plot of part yield versus γ_{fd} may be generated. The effect of varying the target (μ) as well as the process control (σ) of the pre-irradiation "1" threshold voltages may then be fully examined.

Since an analytic solution of the integral of (13) is not possible, a numerical integration was performed. A normal distribution table may also be used. Figure 7 shows the part yield as a function of γ_{fd}. The various curves that are shown represent different process μ's and σ's. Note that with the current process ($\mu = 4$ V,$\sigma = 1$ V), more than 85 % of the parts will function up to 20 krad(Si). Failure doses in the 20-30 krad(Si) region have been observed during 256K EEPROM IC radiation tests.

Thus, based on the distribution of pre-irradiation "1" state threshold voltages (once A and V_{rs} are determined), one can predict the percentage of parts that will pass a particular radiation hardness goal. Higher part yields may be achieved by increasing the mean "1" threshold voltage and tightening controls on the "1" variation.

VI. IMPROVING RADIATION HARDNESS

In order to increase the radiation hardness of FG memory cells, several techniques may be used. A longer write-time will produce a larger initial "1" state threshold voltage (more charge stored of floating gate). We may also reduce the oxide thicknesses, increase the radiation saturation voltage, refresh the FG transistor or use a differential sensing scheme. These are discussed next.

A. Oxide Scaling

The use of thinner oxides can increase the radiation hardness. Thinner oxides reduce the volume available for charge generation during irradiation. In order to examine the quantitative effect of thinning the oxide regions, the following physical parameters are used: $G_h = 8.1 \times 10^{12}$ electron-hole pairs-cm^{-3}-rad(SiO$_2$)$^{-1}$ [22], $k = k_1 = k_2 = 1 \times 10^{-6}$ cm-V^{-1} [13], $d_1 = 47.5$ nm, $d_2 = 40.0$ nm, $q = 1.6 \times 10^{-19}$ Coulombs, $\epsilon_1 = \epsilon_2 = 3.9 \times 8.854 \times 10^{-14}$ Farad-cm^{-1}, $V_{si} = -4$ V. $A = 1/46500$ rad(SiO$_2$)$^{-1}$ and $V_{rs} = -5.5$ V, which are from the fit to the data for these parts (see section IV). Using the A equation in (5), we find that the electron emission constant, e_c,

410

is 5.2×10^{-6} rad$(SiO_2)^{-1}$. This e_c may be process dependent. Using the V_{rs} equation in (6), we determine B. Using the B equation in (5), we find σ_{rs}. We may then reduce the oxide thicknesses, d_1 and d_2, and recalculate A and B. We will then be able to determine V_{rs} and $V_{th}(\gamma)$ using (6).

If d_1 and d_2 were reduced by the same ratio, there would be no increase in radiation hardness. This is due to the trade-off between charge generation volume during irradiation, and the amount of charge initially stored in the FG, σ_i. Reducing the total oxide thickness will reduce the amount of charge generated during irradiation. However, reducing d_2 will reduce $V_{th}(0)$ (for a constant σ_i) as shown in (6). This will offset the gain achieved by reducing the oxide thicknesses. This assumes that the same electric field and write times are used with reduced oxide thicknesses (which will produce the same σ_i). To achieve a gain in the radiation hardness, we must reduce d_1 while keeping d_2 constant. This non-symmetric scaling will change the writing and erasing characteristics of the memory transistor.

Once A and B have been calculated for various oxide thicknesses, a plot of initial threshold voltage versus dose for retention failure may be generated using equation 8. Figure 8 shows the expected improvement in hardness (for

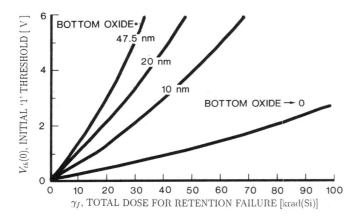

Figure 8: Initial threshold as a function of dose for retention failure. Additional hardness is obtained by thinning the d_1 oxide thickness while maintaining $d_2 = 40$ nm. The last curve is a theoretical maximum where d_1 approaches zero.

fixed reference sensing) achieved by reducing the d_1 oxide thickness while maintaining d_2 at 40 nm. When the present d_1 of 47.5 nm is reduced to 20 nm, we see that the expected dose for retention failure increases from 25 to 36 krad(Si). These hardness levels are for an average $V_{th}(0)=4$ V. Since d_2 has not changed, a constant initial threshold voltage corresponds to a constant σ_i. If d_1 were then reduced to the theoretical minimum value of 0 nm, the maximum hardness limit of the FG cell could be determined. Figure 8 shows this limit to be approximately 100 krad(Si).

By examining the components of A in (5), the radiation mechanisms dominating the response may also be determined. For the present d_1 oxide thickness, hole trapping and injection dominate the radiation response. The response of $d_1 = 20$ nm and 10 nm shows about equal contribution from both holes and emitted electrons. When d_1 is very thin, the radiation response is theoretically dominated by electron emission.

B. Radiation Saturation Voltage

A threshold voltage implant may be performed in order to shift the pre-irradiation "1" threshold positive. This should increase the initial "1" state. It should also increase the radiation saturation voltage, V_{rs} (see (6)). An arsenic implant was performed in the parts studied in order to lower the "0" state threshold below -4 V. We believe this accounts, in part, for the -5.5 V radiation saturation voltage. Using (8), we find that the dose for retention failure will increase to 40 krad(Si) if the V_{rs} is increased to -3 V. It may be possible to achieve this shift in V_{rs} by increasing V_{si} from -4 V to -1.5 V. However, this change will increase the access time of the EEPROM IC.

C. Refreshing

If the oxide-trapping at the poly-Si/oxide interfaces could be reduced, it may be possible to refresh the FG transistor and extend its hardness level. This refresh is completely analogous to the refresh of a dynamic memory. The lost electron charge on the FG would be refreshed by re-writing the part. Based on the dose-rate environment and the known dose to failure, a refresh may be performed at constant time intervals.

The ability to refresh will depend upon hardening the oxide interfaces between the FG and the oxides. Standard MOSFET hardening oxide techniques concentrate on the oxide to silicon substrate interface [23]. It may be difficult to harden the top oxide to FG and FG to bottom oxide interfaces of the FG transistor. For example, the high temperature (1000 °C) at which top oxide is grown as well as the high temperature annealing of the n$^+$ diffusions is known to increase in oxide-trapped charge [24]. A significant re-design of the process may be necessary to reduce the oxide-trapped charge.

Annealing of the oxide-trapped charge may occur in FGs. The annealed oxide-trapped charge should tunnel into the FG over time. It would then be possible to refresh the part. The extent of the annealing process and the ability to refresh FG transistors needs to be demonstrated.

Therefore, as seen in Figure 8, electron emission should limit the retention to less than 100 krad(Si) for a fixed reference sense amplifier. This 100 krad(Si) theoretical upper bound on the radiation hardness is based on thinning the oxides, and writing the largest possible $V_{th}(0)$ into the FG. A threshold implant may also be used to increase the initial threshold voltage.

D. Differential Sensing

It may be possible to extend the 100 krad(Si) radiation hardness limit by using a differential sense amplifier. Using equation 6, a relationship between the pre-radiation threshold voltage difference, $\Delta V_{th}(0)$ and the dose for a retention failure, γ_f may be found. Namely,

$$\Delta V_{th}(0) = m_{sa} exp(A\gamma_f). \tag{14}$$

$\Delta V_{th}(0)$ is the difference between the pre-radiation logic "1" and "0" state threshold voltages. m_{sa} is the differential sense amplifier voltage margin. It represents the minimum voltage difference the sense amplifier can detect. By scaling the oxides to the theoretical limits noted before, and using $\Delta V_{th}(0) = 8$ V and $m_{sa} = 0.5$ V, equation 14 shows a radiation hardness limit of less than 500 krad(Si). This should be considered a theoretical limit, and not a realistically achievable hardness limit. For differential sensing, a more realistic radiation hardness limit may be less than 200 krad(Si).

Even though the practical FG radiation hardness limit is less than the the 1 Mrad(Si) data retention demonstrated by SNOS memory transistors [1], there are a large number of applications that do not require a 1 Mrad(Si) EEPROM. Thus, using the techniques outlined in this paper, it should be possible to use FG EEPROMs in low total-dose environments.

VII. SUMMARY

We have presented the characterization of a FG memory cell in a radiation environment. We have identified the physical mechanisms responsible for its radiation response, developed an accurate model, illustrated the necessary radiation screens, and proposed upper radiation limits for the technology. This study should prove useful to FG manufacturers (both EPROM and EEPROM) interested in hardening their FG parts as well as those considering using FG EEPROMs in their systems.

It has also been shown that the FG EEPROM may be used in low total-dose environments. Since the FG cell is the most popular EEPROM memory technology, a large portion of the radiation hardened EEPROM demand could be met by suitably modified FG EEPROMs.

ACKNOWLEDGEMENTS

We wish to thank S.L. Miller, D.M. Fleetwood, P.V. Dressendorfer, C.L. Axness and W.M. Miller of Sandia National Laboratories for enlightening and useful technical discussions. R.A. Pastorek and B. Lyngen, also of Sandia National Laboratories, are recognized for their excellent testing support during this project. W.F. Filter, F.W. Sexton and J.R. Schwank of Sandia National Laboratories are also acknowledged for their critical review of the manuscript.

REFERENCES

[1] P. J. McWhorter, S. L. Miller, and T. A. Dellin, "Radiation response of SNOS nonvolatile transistors," *IEEE Trans. Nucl. Sci.*, vol. NS-33, no. 6, pp. 1414–1419, 1986.

[2] P. J. McWhorter, S. L. Miller, T. A. Dellin, and C. A. Axness, "Retention characteristics of SNOS nonvolatile devices in a radiation environment," *IEEE Trans. Nucl. Sci.*, vol. NS-34, no. 6, pp. 1652–1657, 1987.

[3] V. Kynett, J. Anderson, G. Atwood, P. Dix, M. Fandrich, O. Jungroth, S. Koa, J. A. Kreifels, S. Lai, H. Liou, B. Liu, R. Lodenquai, W. Lu, R. Pavloff, D. Tang, G. Tsau, J. C. Tzeng, B. Vajdic, G. Verma, S. Wang, S. Well, M. Winston, and L. Yang, "A 90ns 100K erase/program cycle megabit flash memory," in *IEEE ISSCC*, pp. 140–141, 1989.

[4] R. Cernea, G. Samachia, C. Su, H. Tsia, Y. Kao, C. M. Wan, Y. Chan, A. Rennisnger, T. Wong, J. Brennan, and J. Haines, "A 1Mb flash EEPROM," in *IEEE ISSCC*, pp. 138–139, 1989.

[5] D. Frohman-Bentchkowsky, "FAMOS-a new semiconductor charge storage device," *Solid-State Electron.*, vol. 17, pp. 517–529, 1974.

[6] D. K. Myers, "UVPROM erasure in flash x-ray and Co60 total dose environments," *IEEE Trans. Nucl. Sci.*, vol. NS-28, no. 6, pp. 4038–4040, 1981.

[7] G. D. Rensner, D. A. Eckhardt, and M. Page, "Nuclear radiation response of Intel 64K bit and 128K bit HMOS UVPROMS," *IEEE Trans. Nucl. Sci.*, vol. NS-32, no. 6, pp. 4056–4060, 1985.

[8] H. Yue, R. Jennings, and R. Gray, "Radiation response of 64K-bit and 128K-bit ultraviolet erasable programmable read only memories (UVPROMs)," *IEEE Trans. Nucl. Sci.*, vol. NS-30, no. 6, pp. 4282–4284, 1983.

[9] D. F. Sampson, "Time and total dose response of nonvolatile UVPROMS," *IEEE Trans. Nucl. Sci.*, vol. NS-35, no. 6, pp. 1542–1546, 1988.

[10] L. Chen, S. W. Owen, C. S. Jenq, and A. R. Renninger, "A 256K high performance CMOS EEPROM technology," in *IEDM Tech. Dig.*, pp. 620–623, 1985.

[11] D. Cioaca, T. Lin, A. Chan, and A. Mihnea, "A million-cycle CMOS 256K EEPROM," in *IEDM Tech. Dig.*, pp. 78–79, 1987.

[12] T. P. Ma and P. V. Dressendorfer, *Ionizing radiation effects in MOS devices and circuits*, pp. 87–192. New York: John Wiley and Sons, 1989.

[13] J. M. McGarrity, "Considerations for hardening MOS devices and circuits for low radiation doses," *IEEE Trans. Nucl. Sci.*, vol. NS-27, no. 6, pp. 1739–1744, 1980.

[14] R. C. Hughes, "Time-resolved transport in a-SiO2," *Phys. Rev. B*, vol. 15, no. 4, pp. 2012–2020, 1977.

[15] R. J. Powell and G. F. Derbenwich, "Vacuum ultraviolet radiation effects in SiO2," *IEEE Trans. Nucl. Sci.*, vol. NS-18, no. 6, pp. 99–105, 1971.

[16] P. J. McWhorter and P. S. Winokur, "Simple technique for separating the effects of interface traps and trapped-oxide charge in metal-oxide-semiconductor transistors," *Appl. Phys. Letts.*, vol. 48, no. 2, pp. 133–135, 1986.

[17] J. R. Schwank, P. S. Winokur, P. J. McWhorter, F. W. Sexton, P. V. Dressendorfer, and D. C. Turpin, "Physical mechanisms contributing to device rebound," *IEEE Trans. Nucl. Sci.*, vol. NS-31, no. 6, pp. 1434–1438, 1984.

[18] D. Kwang, *Applied Solid State Science, Supplement 2, Silicon Integrated Circuits*, pp. 121–246. New York: Academic Press, 2nd ed., 1981.

[19] C. M. Dozier, D. M. Fleetwood, D. B. Brown, and P. S. Winokur, "An evaluation of low-energy x-ray and Cobalt-60 irradiations of MOS transistors," *IEEE Trans. Nucl. Sci.*, vol. NS-34, no. 6, pp. 1535–1539, 1987.

[20] P. M. Lenahan and P. V. Dressendorfer, "Hole traps and trivalent silicon centers in metals/oxide/silicon devices," *J. Appl. Phys.*, vol. 55, no. 10, pp. 3495–3499, 1984.

[21] A. Namenson, "Lot uniformity and small sample sizes in hardness assurance," *IEEE Trans. Nucl. Sci.*, vol. NS-35, no. 6, pp. 1506–1511, 1988.

[22] J. M. Benedetto and H. E. Boesch, "The relationship between ^{60}Co and 10-keV x-ray damage in MOS devices," *IEEE Trans. Nucl. Sci.*, vol. NS-33, no. 6, pp. 1318–1323, 1986.

[23] J.R. Schwank, Sandia National Laboratories, private communication, 1989.

[24] J. R. Schwank and D. M. Fleetwood, "Effect of post-oxidation anneal tempature on radiation-induced charge trapping in metal-oxide-semiconductor devices," *Appl. Phys. Letts.*, vol. 53, no. 9, pp. 770–772, 1988.

Paper 9.9

RETENTION CHARACTERISTICS OF SNOS NONVOLATILE DEVICES IN

A RADIATION ENVIRONMENT[*]

P. J. McWhorter, S. L. Miller, T. A. Dellin, C. A. Axness
Sandia National Laboratories
P. O. Box 5800
Albuquerque, New Mexico 87185

ABSTRACT

A quantitative model is developed that can accurately predict the threshold voltage shift, and hence data loss, in SNOS nonvolatile memory transistors over a wide range of dose rates. The model accounts for both the time dependent and radiation induced mechanisms leading to data loss. Experimental measurements are made to verify the validity and accuracy of the model under a variety of irradiation conditions.

I. Introduction

Radiation hardened Electrically Erasable Programmable Read Only Memories (EEPROMs) are finding increased usage in military and space systems. EEPROMs can be used to store critical alterable data, circumvent high dose rate environments that would upset volatile RAMs, and develop adaptable systems.

The increased popularity of radiation hardened nonvolatile memories puts additional importance on developing techniques to overcome the difficult testing and characterization of such devices. CMOS devices are nominally stable over time. Therefore, single measurements can generally be used to characterize CMOS parts. However, SNOS devices are not stable, the trapped charge needed to produce the nonvolatile threshold voltage shift slowly leaks out, so characterization of SNOS parts requires a series of measurements over time. The possibility of the nonvolatile part being exposed to irradiation further complicates the characterization. Many SNOS nonvolatile memories are specified to retain data for ten years or more in a radiation environment where the part might receive a total dose of 500 krad or more. Since these memories go into a wide variety of systems, the radiation could come in a burst, or over the course of many years. In the case of a burst of radiation, that burst could occur soon after the memory was written, or years later. In a low dose rate environment, the part could receive a constant dose rate irradiation over the life of the system, or in an SDI environment, the part might receive radiation at a very low dose rate in space for many years followed by a burst of radiation. It becomes apparent that it is not feasible to test the part in all possible scenarios, and it is not clear which scenario would be the worst case. Thus, an accurate quantitative model is needed to predict data loss in SNOS EEPROM devices in a variety of radiation scenarios.

This paper will first review the operation of SNOS EEPROM devices and examine qualitatively what happens to the device in a radiation environment. A quantitative model will then be derived which will accurately predict data loss in a wide variety of radiation conditions. The paper will describe six simple measurements which can be made to determine the four model parameters needed to predict the memory retention characteristics of the SNOS memory in almost any radiation scenario. This model's predictions will then be compared to data taken on SNOS test transistors in a moderate, low, and very low dose rate irradiation. It will be shown that the retention characteristics in all three cases were accurately predicted by the model, and that once the four model parameters are determined, the radiation response can be accurately predicted for almost any radiation scenario of interest.

II. Qualitative Description of SNOS EEPROM Operation

This section will briefly review the structure and operation of present generation SNOS memory devices and qualitatively describe the effect of radiation on stored data.

The structure of present generation SNOS transistors is similar to the structure of MOS transistors. The gate dielectric of the SNOS transistor is composed of a 200-500 angstrom LPCVD nitride deposited on a thermally grown 15-25 angstrom "tunnel" oxide. Present generation SNOS transistors are typically n-channel devices. Unlike an MOS transistor which has a fixed threshold voltage, the threshold voltage of the SNOS transistor is adjustable. It is possible to inject electrons from the silicon substrate through the tunnel oxide and into the nitride by applying a 15-25 volt pulse to the gate for some fraction of a second. These electrons become trapped in the nitride, and shift the threshold voltage positively. Similarly, it is possible to inject holes into the nitride by applying a negative 15-25 volt pulse to the gate for some fraction of a second. These holes will become trapped in the nitride and will shift the threshold voltage negatively. In typical circuit operation, an SNOS transistor with a positive threshold voltage (excess electrons) corresponds to the logic "1" state, and a transistor with a negative threshold voltage (excess holes) corresponds to the logic "0" state. Data is stored by programming the threshold voltages of the SNOS transistors, and data is read by sensing the threshold voltages of the SNOS transistors. A complete review of the standard operation of SNOS devices can be found in reference 1.

Over the course of time after a transistor is written, the injected charge slowly tunnels out of the nitride, and the threshold voltage decays back toward the virgin threshold voltage; that is, the threshold voltage of the charge free state. At some time the threshold voltage will decay to a point such that the sense amps on the circuit can not distinguish between the two logic states and the data is lost. For most circuit configurations, data is lost when the threshold voltage decays to 0 volts. This point in time is referred to as end of life. At any time it is possible to reprogram the transistors into the same or a different state. Temperature and the number of write/erase cycles are also important in studying the memory retention characteristics of SNOS devices, but in this paper we assume the parts are operated at room temperature and are uncycled.

In a radiation environment there are three fundamental mechanisms which will cause a threshold voltage shift, and hence data loss in an SNOS device. Figure 1 represents the three mechanisms leading to a threshold voltage shift in a radiation environment for

---
*This work performed at Sandia National Laboratories was supported by the U. S. Department of Energy under contract number DE-ACO4-76DP00789.

Reprinted from *IEEE Trans. Nucl. Sci.*, vol. NS-34, no. 6, pp. 1652–1657, December 1987.

a transistor programmed into the logic "1" state (excess electrons). First, there is the normal time dependent tunneling of charge out of the nitride. Second, radiation can cause stored charge to be emitted from traps in the nitride. Third, radiation will cause radiation-induced electron-hole pair generation in the nitride. The electrons are swept by the internal electric field toward the gate electrode, and the holes are swept toward the silicon dioxide/ silicon nitride interface, where some will be trapped. The model we presented last year only accounted for the second and third mechanisms, and not the time-dependent decay of the threshold voltage. For this reason, the old model would only predict the threshold voltage shift at relatively large dose rates. Furthermore, it was not able to predict the time dependent decay pre- and post-irradiation, nor the threshold voltage shift in a low dose rate irradiation. By accounting for all three mechanisms, the model is accurate at most all dose rates of interest. It has been shown that interface traps build up very slowly in SNOS structures, and the density of interface traps is negligible for total doses less than 10^7 rads. For this reason, the model does not need to account for interface traps in predicting the radiation-induced threshold voltage shift for doses of practical interest [2].

When the transistor is in the logic "1" state (excess electrons) the two radiation mechanisms (loss of injected electrons, build up of radiation induced holes) will add to give a large negative threshold voltage shift. When the transistor is in the logic "0" state (excess holes) the two radiation mechanisms (for this case, loss of injected holes, build up of radiation induced holes) tend to cancel and lead to a small threshold voltage shift. This is consistent with many experiments which show that radiation causes a much larger shift in the threshold voltage of transistors in the "1" state than in the "0" state [2].

Since there is an asymmetry in the effect of radiation on the logic "1" and logic "0" states, transistors in the "1" state will always lose their data before transistors in the "0" state in a radiation environment. It can be seen that, in a radiation environment, end of life will be determined by when the threshold voltages of the transistors programmed into the "1" state decay to 0 volts. Therefore, in quantitatively modeling the threshold voltage decay of SNOS transistors, we need to only consider the "1" state for present generation transistors in typical design configurations.

In the next section, a quantitative model is derived which predicts the threshold voltage decay of the logic "1" state as a function of radiation scenario. It accurately predicts the pre-irradiation decay of the threshold voltage, the shift due to the irradiation, and the post-irradiation threshold voltage decay. It also predicts the threshold voltage decay in the case of very low dose rates, when both time-dependent tunneling and radiation are important.

III. Derivation of Quantitative Model

In modeling the threshold voltage decay, and hence data loss, in SNOS devices in a radiation environment, the three mechanisms indicated in Figure 1 must be considered. To quantitatively model the retention characteristics, we must derive differential equations for each of the above mechanisms. The equations must then be solved in such a way that a useful predictive model is obtained.

A. Normal Time Decay

Tunneling of charge out of the nitride can be

modeled by assuming a one electron W. K. B. approximation [3]. It is assumed that the injected charge in the nitride does not significantly affect the electric field, and hence the tunneling barrier. It is assumed that all of the traps are at the same energy level in the nitride, and that the concentration of traps is constant across the nitride. With these assumptions, the tunneling equation can be written as:

$$n(x,t) = n(x,0)\exp\{-\alpha * \exp(-\beta_1 * t_{ox}) \qquad (1)$$

$$* \exp(-\beta_2(x - t_{ox}))*t\}$$

where:

$n(x,t)$ is the injected electron density as a function of time and position in the nitride,

α is the attempt to escape frequency,

β_1 is the tunneling barrier through the oxide,

β_2 is the tunneling barrier through the nitride,

and

$n(x,0)$ is the initial charge distribution in the nitride.

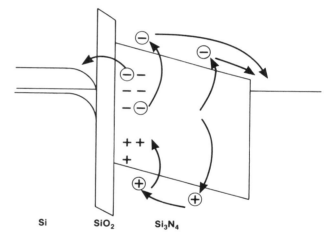

Figure 1. Mechanisms leading to a threshold voltage shift of an SNOS transistor in a radiation environment.

The derivation from this point depends on the functional form of the initial injected charge distribution selected. The literature indicates that the charge distribution can be a square or an exponential distribution [1]. For the logic "1" state on present generation Sandia SNOS transistors, the data fits best by assuming an exponential distribution. The derivation will be presented for the exponential distribution. For other technologies, it is possible that a square charge distribution would better fit the data. For the case of a square charge distribution, the following derivation would yield a slightly different result for the time decay equation.

For an exponential distribution, the initial charge distribution can be described by the equation:

$$n(x,0) = C_0 \exp(-\frac{(x - tox)}{\lambda}), \qquad (2)$$

where C_0 is the charge distribution at the silicon

dioxide/silicon nitride interface, t_{ox} is the tunnel oxide thickness, and λ is the decay constant of the exponential charge distribution.

Substituting (2) into equation (1) yields:

$$n(x,t) = C_0 \exp(-\frac{(x - tox)}{\lambda}) * \exp\{-\alpha * \exp(-\beta_1 * t_{ox}) \quad (3)$$
$$* \exp(-\beta_2(x - t_{ox})) * t\}$$

The transition rate of charge out of the nitride can now be calculated by differentiating the above equation with respect to time.

$$T(x,t) = \frac{\partial n(x,t)}{\partial t} = C_0 \exp(-\frac{(x - tox)}{\lambda}) \quad (4)$$
$$* \exp\{-\alpha * \exp(-\beta_1 * t_{ox})$$
$$* \exp(-\beta_2(x - t_{ox})) * t\}$$
$$* \{-\alpha * \exp(-\beta_1 t_{ox})$$
$$* \exp(-\beta_2(x - t_{ox}))\}$$

The transition rate equation can now be differentiated with respect to x to find the position in the nitride as a function of time at which the maximum tunneling occurs. Since this is a sharply peaked function, it is appropriate to assume that all of the charge at $x < x_m$ is gone, and all of the charge at $x > x_m$ is still there. The position of maximum tunneling is found by differentiating the transition equation, setting to zero, and solving for x.

$$x_m = 1/\beta_2 * Ln[\frac{\alpha \; \exp(-\beta_1 t_{ox})\exp(\beta_2 t_{ox}) * t}{1/(\lambda\beta_2) \qquad + \quad 1}] \quad (5)$$

This is the location of the tunneling front as it sweeps through the nitride. This makes it possible to calculate the total charge in the nitride as a function of time by integrating the initial charge distribution from x_m to ∞ (notice x_m is a function of time, so the integral will yield an equation which is a function of time). The integration is done to infinity to simplify the calculation, and is a reasonable assumption since, for most nitride thicknesses, the charge is located close to the silicon dioxide/silicon nitride interface. Now to find the total charge as a function of time,

$$Q(t) = \int_{x_m}^{\infty} n(x,0)dx \; , \quad (6)$$

$$Q(t) = C_0\lambda \exp[\frac{-x_m + t_{ox}}{\lambda}] \; . \quad (7)$$

The total charge leaving the nitride as a function of time can be obtained by differentiating the above equation with respect to time.

$$\partial Q(t)/\partial t = C_0\lambda \exp[\frac{-x_m + t_{ox}}{\lambda}] * (-1/\lambda) \; * (\partial x_m/\partial t), \quad (8)$$

which can be reduced to

$$\partial Q(t)/\partial t = Q(t) * (-1/(\beta_2\lambda)) * t^{(-1)}. \quad (9)$$

The differential equation for the transfer of charge out of the nitride due to tunneling has now been reduced to a simple differential equation with one unknown parameter ($1/(\beta_2\lambda)$). In performing this simplification, information has been lost about the position of the charge in the nitride. However, since the charge is distributed close to the interface, this assumption is justified, especially for thick nitrides (>200 angstroms).

B. Effect of Radiation on Charge Distribution

Reference 2 provides differential equations describing the effect of radiation on the charge distribution in the nitride. These are simple rate equations which say that the probability of charge capture is proportional to the number of empty traps, and the probability of emission is proportional to the number of filled traps. There are equations for both holes and electrons. The equations are:

$$\frac{\partial n(x,Dose)}{\partial DOSE} = c_n[N_{nt} - n(x,DOSE)] - e_n n(x,DOSE), \quad (10)$$

$$\frac{\partial p(x,Dose)}{\partial DOSE} = c_p[N_{pt} - p(x,DOSE)] - e_p p(x,DOSE) \; , \quad (11)$$

where:

N_{nt} - Number of electron traps/cm^3 in the nitride

$n(x,DOSE)$ - Number of occupied electron traps/cm^3

N_{pt} - Number of hole traps/cm^3 in the nitride

$p(x,DOSE)$ - Number of occupied hole traps/cm^3

e_n - Emission constant for holes trapped in nitride during irradiation

e_p - Emission constant for holes trapped in nitride during irradiation

c_n - Capture constant for electrons in nitride during irradiation

c_p - Capture constant for holes in nitride during irradiation

It is assumed that the sum of the capture and emission constants is the same for holes and electrons, that is

$$(c_n + e_n) = (c_p + e_p) = e_c \; . \quad (12)$$

It is also assumed that this constant is independent of position in the nitride and independent of trap occupancy. With these assumptions, equations (10) and (11) can be integrated with respect to x and combined to form an equation for the change in the net charge with respect to dose:

$$\frac{\partial Q(t)}{\partial DOSE} = d[c_p N_{pt} - c_n N_{nt}] - Q(t)e_c \; , \quad (13)$$

where d is the thickness of the nitride. Since the tunneling differential equation is in terms of time and not dose, the chain rule can be applied to the above equation to put it in terms of time.

$$\frac{\partial Q(t)}{\partial DOSE} = \frac{\partial Q(t)}{\partial t} * \frac{\partial t}{\partial DOSE} \tag{14}$$

Since $\frac{\partial t}{\partial DOSE}$ is the inverse of the dose rate, $\dot{\gamma}(t)$, we may write

$$\frac{\partial Q(t,\dot{\gamma}(t))}{\partial t} = d\dot{\gamma}(t)[c_p N_{pt} - c_n N_{nt}] - Q(t)\dot{\gamma}(t)e_c. \tag{15}$$

C. Combined Effects of Time and Radiation

It is now possible to write the complete differential equation describing the loss of charge in the nitride due to radiation and normal tunneling. The net rate of charge decay is given by the sum of the contributions from each component.

$$\frac{\partial Q(t,\dot{\gamma}(t))}{\partial t} = -Q(t)[\dot{\gamma}(t)e_c + 1/(t\beta_2\lambda)] + d\dot{\gamma}(t)[c_p N_{pt} - c_n N_{nt}] \tag{16}$$

This differential equation can not be solved in closed form, but it can be solved in such a way that only one numerical integration is required. Also, if it is assumed that the charge is located near the silicon dioxide/silicon nitride interface, the charge, $Q(t)$, can easily be converted to threshold voltage, $V(t)$. In doing this conversion, we must include terms to account for the charge leading to a shift in the virgin threshold voltage V_v. Solving the differential equation, and converting the charge to a shift in the threshold voltage from the virgin state, yields the equation:

$$V_{th}(t,\dot{\gamma}(t)) = (V_0 - V_v) * [t/t_0]^{[-1/(\beta_2\lambda)]}\exp(-e_c\gamma(t))$$

$$- t^{[-1/(\beta_2\lambda)]}\exp(-\gamma(t)e_c)*(e_c A)$$

$$* \int_{t_0}^{t} \dot{\gamma}(t)*t^{[+1/(\beta_2\lambda)]}\exp(\gamma(t)e_c)dt + V_v. \tag{17}$$

This is the final solution which describes the decay of the threshold voltage in a radiation environment as a function of time and dose rate.

$\dot{\gamma}(t)$ is the dose rate as a function of time

$\gamma(t)$ is the total dose as a function of time

V_v is the virgin threshold voltage, that is, the threshold voltage before the part has been written, erased or irradiated

$(1/(\beta_2\lambda))$ is the term which describes the time dependent tunneling of charge out of the nitride

$A = \frac{qd^2}{2\epsilon_{ni}} * \frac{(c_p N_{pt} - c_n N_{nt})}{e_c}$, and is determined experimentally

e_c is the radiation emission constant in the nitride

V_0 is the boundary condition of the problem and represents the initial threshold voltage of the part some short time t_0 after the part is written.

4. Using the Model

This section explains how to use equation 17 to model the data retention characteristics of SNOS nonvolatile devices in a radiation environment. It is shown that a total of only six threshold voltage measurements are needed to determine the parameters needed to use equation 17 to accurately predict the retention of the part in a wide variety of radiation scenarios. As an example, Sandia National Laboratories' SA2999-2 16K radiation-hardened EEPROM will be examined.

In order to use equation 17, one must first determine $(1/\beta_2\lambda)$, V_v, e_c, and A for a transistor which is representative of the memory transistors in the actual EEPROM. The SA2999-2 memory transistors have a 15 angstrom tunnel oxide, 250 angstroms of nitride, and when written with the standard write pulse (250 µsec, 16 Volt), have an initial "1" state threshold voltage of 2.3 volts 5 seconds after the transistor is written ($V_0 = 2.3$, $t_0 = 5$ sec). Different write conditions will yield different initial threshold voltages, but this can easily be measured. V_v represents the threshold voltage of the transistor in the charge free state. This can easily be determined by measuring the threshold voltage of the transistor before it has been written or erased. For the SA2999-2, we find that $V_v = -.3$ volts. The term $(1/\beta_2\lambda)$ can be found by making two threshold voltage measurements if equation 17 is simplified to the case for which there is no irradiation, that is $\dot{\gamma}(t)=0$. Equation 17 then becomes

$$(V(t) - V_v) = (V_0 - V_v)*(t/t_0)^{(-1/(\beta_2\lambda))}, \tag{18}$$

which can be rewritten as

$$(1/\beta_2\lambda) = \frac{- Ln[\frac{V(t)-V_v}{V_0 - V_v}]}{Ln[t/t_0]} \tag{19}$$

In order to determine $(1/\beta_2\lambda)$, a threshold voltage measurement V_0 is made at some short time t_0 after the transistor is programmed. Another threshold voltage measurement $V(t)$ is then taken sometime later (t seconds after the transistor is programmed). The times at which V_0 and $V(t)$ are measured are not important, and typical times might be at 5 and 30 seconds. All times represent the time which has elapsed since the part was written. Once these measurements are made, equation 19 may be used to calculate $(1/\beta_2\lambda)$. For the transistor we are examining, it is found that $(1/\beta_2\lambda) = .055$.

417

The radiation parameters e_c and A are determined by irradiating a transistor in its virgin state and measuring its threshold voltage at several irradiation levels. A simple equation exists which predicts the radiation induced threshold voltage shift of an SNOS transistor in the virgin state (Equation 16 of reference 2).

$$V_{th}(\gamma) = A*[exp(-e_c*\gamma) - 1] + V_v \qquad (20)$$

It is found that if the threshold voltage measurement of a virgin SNOS transistor is made pre-irradiation, at 250 krad, and at 1 Mrad, the values can be used to accurately solve for e_c and A in the above equation. Performing these measurements and calculations, it is found that for an SA2999-2 memory transistor A = 1.05 volts and $e_c = 1 * 10^{-6}$ /rad.

Now that these parameters have been determined, equation 17 can be used to model any radiation scenario of interest. The equation can easily be evaluated numerically on a simple personal computer or programmable calculator, since it involves only one numerical integration. The radiation scenario is represented in the equation by the dose rate term ($\dot\gamma(t)$). Since the dose rate term is included as a function of time, almost any radiation scenario can be modelled by allowing the dose rate to change. As an example of the use of the model, let us examine the effect of a constant irradiation of .09 rad/sec on the retention characteristic of the device ($\dot\gamma(t)$ = .09 rad/sec for all t). The solid line in Figure 2 represents the calculated threshold voltage decay of the above described transistor if exposed to a constant low dose rate irradiation immediately after writing the part. The initial decay of the threshold voltage is dominated by the normal time dependent tunneling of charge out of the nitride. Further out in time, where the decay begins to increase, the decay is dominated by the radiation. As explained earlier, the stored data is lost at the point where the threshold voltage crosses zero volts. The model predicts that the part will lose its data at about $6 * 10^6$ seconds if exposed to a constant dose rate irradiation of .09 rad/sec for the indicated initial "1" state threshold voltage. In order to check the accuracy of the model, the part was then written with the standard write pulse, and irradiated at .09 rad/sec, with threshold voltage measurements made at varying times. In Figure 2, the solid line represents the predicted threshold voltage, and the dots represent the measured threshold voltages. The model accurately predicted the threshold voltage decay for this irradiation. Also notice that the model accurately predicted the time to end of life ($\approx 6 * 10^6$ seconds, total accumulated dose $\approx$ 540 krad)) for this irradiation.

The model can also be used to predict the decay of the part when exposed to a constant dose rate irradiation of 33 rad/sec. In Figure 3, the solid line represents the model prediction and the dots represent actual data. The model again accurately predicts the decay. It is important to remember that the measurements were made only to verify the model. The predictions were made based on the original six threshold voltage measurements.

The model is not limited to predicting the decay for a constant dose rate. It is also possible to predict the decay for the case of the part receiving irradiation over only part of its lifetime. Figure 4

represents the threshold voltage decay of a transistor which is programmed into the logic "1" state, allowed to sit with no irradiation for 7000 seconds ($\dot\gamma(t)$= 0 for t<7000)), and is then exposed to a 250 krad irradiation at a dose rate of 330 rad/sec ($\dot\gamma(t)$ = 330 for 7000< t < 7760). After the irradiation, the decay is followed with no irradiation ($\dot\gamma(t)$ = 0 for t>7760). Notice that the model accurately predicts the pre-irradiation decay, the shift due to the irradiation, and the post irradiation decay. Again, the prediction was based solely on the original six measurements, and data from the actual test were not used in the predictions.

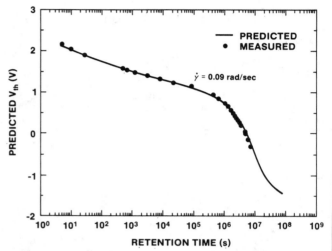

Figure 2. Comparison of predicted and measured threshold voltage decay of an SNOS transistor exposed to a constant dose rate irradiation of .09 rad/sec.

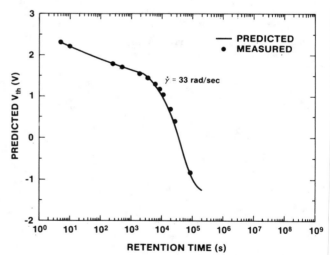

Figure 3. Comparison of predicted and measured threshold voltage decay of an SNOS transistor exposed to a constant dose rate irradiation of 33 rad/sec.

Several important points should be noted about the above examples. First, the model is predictive. All of the above decay curves were predicted based on a total of 6 measurements. Second, the model is accurate. It can be seen that, when the experiments were actually performed, the model accurately predicted the actual decay curve. Third, the model is versatile. it works correctly when time and radiation are important, when only radiation is important, and when only time decay is important.

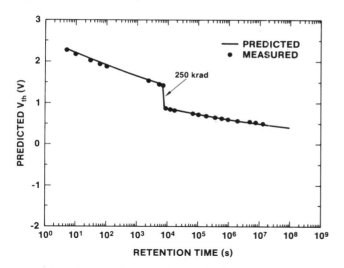

Figure 4. Comparison of predicted and measured threshold voltage decay for an SNOS transistor exposed to a 330 rad/sec irradiation to a total dose of 250 krad.

We have performed tests similar to those above on test transistors with nitride thicknesses varying from 170 to 350 angstroms. Tests were also performed on samples with oxynitride instead of nitride as the memory layer. In all cases, the model accurately predicted the threshold voltage shifts. It is found that the radiation decay terms (A, e_c) and the time decay term $(1/\beta_2\lambda)$ vary depending on the thickness of these dielectric layers, but once these parameters are determined for a given dielectric stack, there is very little variation from wafer to wafer and device lot to device lot.

5. Predicting End of Life

The model can also be used to predict end of life by finding the time at which the threshold voltage decays to zero for a given radiation scenario. It is possible, therefore, to create curves such as those in Figure 5 by plotting the time to end of life vs. dose rate. The different curves in Figure 5 represent the calculation done for different initial "1" state threshold voltages. It can be seen that the harder a part is written, the longer it will retain data for any given dose rate. The calculations used in generating Figure 5 use the parameters for the SA2999-2. It is assumed that the constant dose rate irradiation starts shortly after the part is written. It can easily be seen that it would be very difficult to generate an experimental curve such as this. Plots similar to Figure 5 could be very useful to system designers. This plot could be useful in determining the maximum dose rate the part could receive, and still have 10 year retention, for a given initial "1" state threshold voltage. It could also be used in examining the tradeoffs between important system parameters. Longer write times increase the initial "1" state threshold voltage, but also slow down the operation speed of the

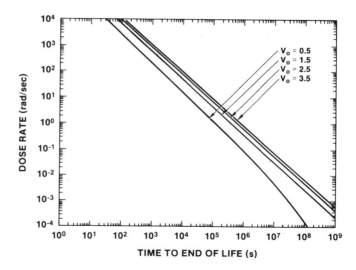

Figure 5. Predicted time to end of life for the SA2999-2 vs. dose rate, with initial "1" state threshold voltage as a parameter.

system. A larger initial threshold voltage will yield a longer time to end of life. If a system had the ability to refresh the nonvolatile memory, plots like Figure 5 would show how often the part should be refreshed in a given space mission.

IV. Conclusions

A model has been presented which accurately predicts the threshold voltage shift of an SNOS transistor in a variety of irradiation conditions. It has been shown that this model is predictive, accurate and works for a variety of stack geometries. It has also been shown that this model greatly reduces the number of measurements needed to determine whether a given part will be able to retain data through a given radiation scenario. It has been demonstrated that the model works correctly for dose rates ranging from .09 to 330 rad/sec.

Acknowledgements

The authors would like to express their appreciation to Gary Zimmerman for organizing, scheduling, and performing all of the tests and measurements presented in this paper. This work would not have been possible without his dedicated efforts and careful attention to detail. We would also like to thank Peter Winokur for help with the dosimetry of the low dose rate irradiations, and Jose Rodriguez for helpful technical discussions.

REFERENCES

1. Dawon Kahng, Applied Solid State Science, Supplement 2, Silicon Integrated Circuits, Part A, (Academic Press, 1981) p 121-246

2. P. J. McWhorter, S. L. Miller, T. A. Dellin, IEEE Trans. Nucl. Sci.,NS-33, 1414, 1986

3. F. B. McLean, U. S. Government Report # HDL-TR-1765, October 1976.

Part 10
Logic, ASIC, WSI, Neuronetwork, and Other Applications

AS AFFORDABLE electrically erasable memories become available, they will be used not only for alterable program code storage but also for the storage of data or large operating systems that are now stored on magnetic disks. Psion Inc., Watertown, CT, for example, makes a laptop computer that substitutes the usual disk drive with small, reliable, low-power-consumption nonvolatile memory based on flash EEPROM [1]. Several flash EEPROM chips are packaged in each plastic "solid-state disk (memory card)" and several cards can be inserted into or removed from the computer at will. The economics of disk replacement is discussed in Fig. 8 of Paper 5.1. Reference [1] projects that, by the year 2000, a 256-megabyte flash EEPROM memory using 0.25-μm technology on a die of 1.8 cm on a side will be available for $1 per megabyte. The potential for replacing magnetic storage is exciting.

"Smart card" represents another new market for non-volatile memories with remarkable growth potential. These cards are of similar size and shape as ordinary credit cards but contain nonvolatile memory chips. Records of transactions, account balances and other pertinent information can be stored in the card and made available at the point of sales. Similar cards are being evaluated for storing personal medical records. Obviously these cards are potentially useful as a convenient medium for storing a wide range of personal and general data. In this respect, the smart card is closely related to the solid-state disks described earlier.

In the introduction to Part 6, it was mentioned that ferro-electric nonvolatile memories (Papers 6.5–7) offer RAM-like WRITE speed. This suggests the possibility of their replacing DRAMs so that the large main memory becomes nonvolatile. This vision is encouraged by the notion that ferroelectric memories, as well as EPROMs, are more scalable than DRAMs, whose memory cell must provide a large storage capacitance due to the soft error problem.

The preceding discussions address the outstanding *memory* applications, made feasible by low-cost electrically erasable nonvolatile memories. Logic circuits is the next new world for nonvolatile memories to conquer, and the papers in this section concentrate on nonmemory applications.

Paper 10.1 gives a historical review and simple explanation of the earlier field programmable logic devices (FPLD or PLD). The basic principle of PLDs is illustrated by Fig. 2 of Paper 10.1. Logic-circuit modules (AND/OR gates in this case) are selectively interconnected and connected to the inputs and outputs to produce the desired logic function. The connections are made (programmed) by the user. Fusible links (fuses) were the first programmable elements used and their need for large programming currents dictated that these circuits be made with bipolar technologies (see Part 2). In the

1980s, floating-gate memory elements (both EPROMs and EEPROMs), and CMOS technology became the preferred choice for PLD. Paper 10.2 is a recent example of high-speed PLDs.

To build a high-gate-count programmable logic circuit, it may be advantageous to use programmable elements to interconnect larger logic-circuit modules (blocks) instead of the single-level AND/OR gate architecture. This greatly improves the gate utilization efficiency. Paper 10.3 is an elementary illustration of this general architecture utilizing EEPROM devices to form the programmable switching matrix. Notice the importance of high EEPROM conductance in the ON-state. Paper 10.4 describes a more refined example and a commercial product. Hundreds of logic modules are interconnected by over one hundred thousand programmable elements. In newer versions, over half-a-million switching elements are used. Because so many programmable elements are used, ONO-based antifuses were chosen as the elements for their small size and low resistance (see Paper 2.8). More detailed discussions of this design can be found in [2]. Because of the similarity to gate arrays, with routing channels and logic modules, this type of PLD is often called programmable gate array.

Paper 10.5 reviews several high-gate-count PLD architectures. In one implementation of programmable gate arrays, the "programmable elements" are SRAM cells that are set according to the routing configuration stored in ROM or magnetic disk [3]. It is well accepted by users and competes against nonvolatile memory-based PLD's. The more traditional AND/OR gate-based PLD can also be modified to achieve high gate counts. Techniques reviewed in Paper 10.5 include using AND/OR gate arrays as modules that are then interconnected, adding feedback, etc.

A well-established application of fuses, EPROMs, or EEPROMs is to select redundant rows and columns to replace defective ones in order to improve the yield of memory ICs. Paper 10.6 is an early description of the use of polysilicon fuse in SRAM redundancy circuits. For redundancy circuits in EPROMs and EEPROMs, either polysilicon fuses or EPROM/EEPROM devices may be used as the programmable elements (see Papers 8.1, 8.3, etc.). Providing redundancy for mask-programmed ROMs is more difficult. Redundant rows or columns of PROMs (using fuses) or EPROMs must be provided to the ROM [4].

Since programmable elements have been successfully used to select redundant rows and columns in memory ICs and to interconnect logic-circuit modules in programmable gate arrays or PLDs, it would be natural to use these elements to select and interconnect modules, each of which is the size of a normal IC. The result is wafer-scale integration (WSI),

421

i.e., a method of making very large, perhaps wafer-sized, ICs. WSI is usually thought of as a way of increasing the fabrication yield of large-sized ICs and can be accomplished by using electrically programmable elements or other means such as cutting metal lines with lasers [5], [6]. In addition, it may be a way of field-customizing a large system, similar to using a PLD, as well as repairing a system in the field (by bypassing the failed module), if electrically programmable (or reprogrammable) elements are used for the interconnections. These benefits will no doubt be exploited in the future.

Paper 10.7 gives an overview of the many approaches that have been studied for accomplishing WSI. One specific, though very brief, description of a WSI approach using vertical amorphous silicon antifuses is given in Paper 10.8. There are several good general references on WSI but without emphasis on electrically programmable elements [7], [8].

Paper 10.9 is a review of the hardware requirements and experiences of neural network computers. A neural network requires a large number of interconnection S (synapses) among many signal lines. Each interconnection needs to multiply the input signal with a programmable gain to produce an output signal. Paper 10.10 describes a chip containing 10 240 synapses based on floating-gate EEPROM devices. The chip performs 10 billion multiplications per second by virtue of the large number of analog multipliers working in parallel.

Paper 10.11 describes an exciting and important emerging application of EPROMs and flash EEPROMs—the memory cards. They can store system and application softwares as well as data in place of magnetic disks and drives. The advantages in power consumption (battery life), speed, reliability, and size are very attractive for portable equipments.

Besides the new logic and memory applications mentioned so far, one should be aware of the role of EPROMs and EEPROMs in microcontrollers, standard cell ASICs, and analog circuits. Single-chip microcontrollers containing OTP EPROMs or EEPROMs instead of mask-programmable ROMs for storage of program codes can be cheaper or produced with shorter turnaround time.

The speed and cell-size improvements developed for the nonvolatile memory products will soon show up in the microcontroller memory arrays as well. The same can be said about nonvolatile memories in the ASIC cell libraries. In analog circuits, EPROMs and EEPROMs are used to store calibration codes and serve as the bases of programmable switched capacitor filters [9]. The application of nonvolatile memory elements in analog circuits is at an early stage, but the possibilities are limited only by the imagination.

REFERENCES

[1] R.D. Pashley and S. K. Lai, ''Flash memories: The best of two worlds,'' *IEEE Spectrum*, pp. 30–33, Dec. 1989.
[2] A. El Gamel *et al.*, '' *An architecture for electrically configurable gate arrays*,'' *IEEE J. Solid-State Circuits*, vol. 24, no. 2, pp. 394–398, Apr. 1989.
[3] R. Freeman, ''User-programmable gate arrays,'' *IEEE Spectrum*, pp. 32–35, Dec. 1988.
[4] Y. Naruke *et al.*, ''A 16Mb mask ROM with programmable redundancy,'' in *IEEE Internat. Solid-State Circuits Conf. Dig. Tech. Papers*, Feb. 1989, pp. 128–129.
[5] M. A. Fischetti, ''Why Trilogy dropped WSI,'' *IEEE Spectrum*, p. 37, Oct. 1983.
[6] N. MacDonald *et al.*, ''200Mb Wafer Memory,'' in *IEEE Internat. Solid-State Circuits Conf. Dig. Tech. Papers*, 1989, pp. 240–241.
[7] S. K. Tewksbury and L. A. Hornak, ''Wafer level system integration: A review,'' *IEEE Circuits Devices Mag.*, Sept. 1989, pp. 22–30.
[8] R. M. Lea, ed., ''Wafer Scale Integration, II.'' New York: North-Holland, 1988.
[9] B. C. Cole, ''How the US is leading the way in strategic nonvolatile technology,'' *Electronics*, pp. 80–83, Mar. 1989.

FIELD-PROGRAMMABLE LOGIC: A NEW MARKET FORCE

FASTER AND DENSER DEVICES PUSH INTO SEMICUSTOM MARKET

by Bernard Conrad Cole

Field-programmable logic devices are showing strong signs of becoming a major force in application-specific integrated circuits. Up until just recently, they were not regarded as a threat by the vendors of gate arrays and standard cells, even though they were smaller and simpler to use than gate arrays, had a faster production turnaround time, and could be programmed by the user. The problem was that FPLDs were neither as dense nor as fast as the competition. They ran no larger than 100 to 300 gates, compared to 1,000 to 6,000 for gate arrays, and at 50 to 75 ns weren't all that fast compared with the tens-of-nanoseconds speeds of gate arrays.

Now gains in density and speed are putting FPLDs on a par with gate arrays in performance. And thanks to computer-aided design tools, they have remained easy to use, with a turnaround time of 1 to 6 weeks where gate arrays require 6 to 18 months.

By 1984, sales of field-programmable logic had grown from a minuscule share of the $5.5 billion ASIC market to $230 million. By 1990, they will more than quadruple, to $1.02 billion of a $13.7 billion market, according to Dataquest Inc., San Jose, Calif. Other companies in the market are even more optimistic. Robert Hartmann, vice president of engineering at Altera Corp, Santa Clara, Calif., predicts that field-programmable logic will account for $2.12 billion in sales in 1990. He also expects that $300 million of that will come out of the gate-array market, leaving gate arrays with a $2.4 billion share (Fig. 1).

Another sure sign that field-programmable logic is maturing as a semicustom alternative is the rapid increase in the number of companies coming out with products. From a market with essentially two players—Monolithic Memories Inc. and Signetics Corp., which were the first to develop programmable-logic chips—it has grown to include such major semiconductor manufacturers as Advanced Micro Devices, Fairchild Semiconductor, GE/Intersil, Harris Semiconductor, Intel, and National Semiconductor, as well as such startups as Altera, Lattice Semiconductor, VLSI Technology, and Xilinx. Other indicators that the technology is coming into its own are new process alternatives, the proliferation of new logic architectures and programming techniques, and the development of CAD tools as field-programmable logic becomes denser and more complex.

One of the more obvious changes in the programmable-logic market has been a shift from bipolar to CMOS and from fusible-link to floating-gate-based ultraviolet- and electrically erasable logic arrays

(EPLDs and EEPLDs). Although about 90% of the field-programmable logic devices sold are of the bipolar fusible-link variety, CMOS EPLDs and EEPLDs are growing more popular. Even traditional bipolar suppliers such as Monolithic Memories and AMD are planning to introduce CMOS versions sometime this year.

CMOS EPLDs are favored now because of their higher density, lower power, and lower manufacturing cost per function, says Altera's Hartmann. With bipolar technology, which is used to manufacture fusible-link PLDs, only a limited number of functions can be designed onto a chip because the high speed requires high power, resulting in high operating temperatures. Because CMOS provides lower power dissipation, designers can pack more functions onto a smaller chip.

Like bipolar FPLDs, CMOS EPLDs are user-programmable. But the CMOS technology allows higher levels of integration—up to 2,000 gates in the standard 20-pin package. Moreover, UV-erasable technology enables PLDs to be reprogrammed in the event of a design mistake or a change in the design approach. "Erasability puts a much greater degree of control in the designer's hands," Hartmann says.

The first company to use electrically erasable CMOS technology in a family of field-programmable logic devices is Lattice Semiconductor Corp., Beaverton, Ore., which is providing pin-for-pin replacements for bipolar circuits with field-programmable array logic—devices with programmable AND arrays and fixed OR arrays. The advantage of EEPLDs is that they can be reprogrammed repeatedly in the same circuit during system prototyping and can be reprogrammed for use in different circuits, says Dean Suhr, Lattice's marketing manager for programmable logic products. "This feature

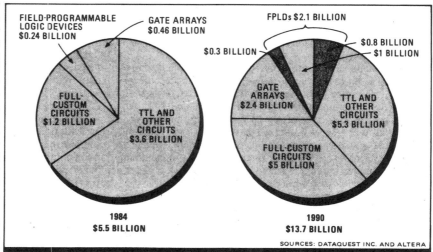

1. MOVING UP. Consumption of FPLDs could total $2.1 billion by 1990. About half of those sales would be won away from gate arrays and from TTL and other standard devices.

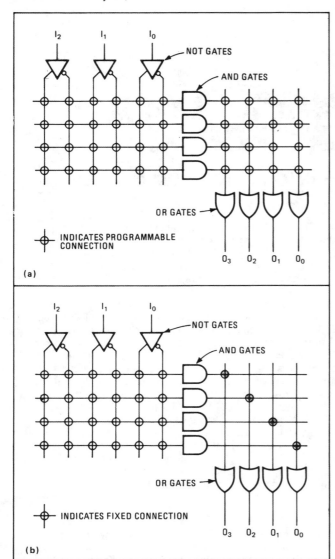

(a)

- I₂ I₁ I₀ → NOT GATES
- → AND GATES
- OR GATES →
- ⊕ INDICATES PROGRAMMABLE CONNECTION
- O₃ O₂ O₁ O₀

(b)

- I₂ I₁ I₀ → NOT GATES
- → AND GATES
- OR GATES →
- ⊕ INDICATES FIXED CONNECTION
- O₃ O₂ O₁ O₀

2. TWO METHODS. Unlike a programmable logic array (a), in which both the AND and the OR arrays are programmed, in a programmable-array-logic device (b) the OR devices are fixed.

Straddling the fence between the two approaches is National Semiconductor Corp. In addition to its high-speed emitter-coupled-logic FPLDs, the Santa Clara company is developing a family of FPLDs using a combination of bipolar and CMOS technologies. The devices use standard bipolar junction-isolated fusible-link technology in the internal array and CMOS on the periphery, giving the devices the speed of bipolar and the low power and noise immunity of CMOS.

THE ORIGINAL ARCHITECTURES

Until recently, the market for field-programmable logic devices has been dominated by two architectural types: field-programmable logic arrays and fusible-link programmable array logic. First to be introduced, in the early 1970s by Signetics, was the FPLA. Monolithic Memories followed in 1975 with its PAL series. It quickly dominated the market, mainly because its architecture is less sophisticated and easier to use but also because the Santa Clara company gave extensive support to the family and to programming tools it developed. It now claims about 80% of the FPLD market.

Similar to programmable read-only memories, Signetics' FPLAs are multiple input/output structures with field-programmable AND and OR arrays (Fig. 2a). Unlike PROMs, though, FPLAs do not internally decode the binary input signals down to the minimum-term level.

A PAL is basically an FPLA where the interconnections in the OR assembly are fixed and only the AND array is programmable (Fig. 2b), making the chip simpler to program. As the market has evolved, more-complex PAL offerings have emerged, incorporating feedback buffers along with the basic array. That addition allows creation of more than one level of logic by linking on-chip latches, counters, shift registers, and even oscillators. Special fuse functions, such as polarity control, output enables, register/nonregister selection, and buried registers, have also been added.

Architecturally, however, it has been the FPLA portion of the market that has evolved the most, with such variations as field-programmable gate arrays (FPGAs) and field-programmable logic sequencers (FPLSs). Programmable gate arrays are similar to PALs in that they have only field-programmable AND arrays and lack the OR capability needed to generate sum-of-product output functions. Field-programmable sequencers, on the other hand, are basically FPLAs that, in addition to their product-summation combinatorial capability, contain internal storage elements, usually type D or JK circuits, whose clock steering inputs are configurable by the on-chip programmable AND and OR arrays.

PALs are fabricated by Monolithic Memories and second-sourced by AMD, Altera, Harris, Intel, Lattice, National Semiconductor, TI, and VLSI Technology. Only Signetics and TI support FPLAs and their more complex extensions.

Traditionally, users weigh simplicity and programming, flexibility, speed, and logic density when choosing between PALs and FPLAs. PALs overtook the older FPLAs because their fixed OR arrays make them seem easier to use, says Kathryn Douglas, strategic marketing engineer for application-specific products at Signetics.

Fusible-link bipolar PALs are also faster. The original bipolar FPLAs and their extensions had speeds of 60 to 70 ns. By comparison, the simpler PALs were twice as fast at 30 to 40 ns and improvements have pushed propagation delays down to 20 ns. Also, though the FPLA and its variations are extremely flexible switching networks that can mix and match a variety of logic terms to any output, more silicon is needed to make both AND and OR gates programmable. "And more silicon means an inherently larger die size, which translates into higher cost," says Stephen M. Donovan, PAL division marketing manager at Monolithic Memories.

On the other hand, says Signetics' Douglas, the advantage of an FPLA structure, in which both the AND and OR arrays

makes it possible for users to cut the number of standard FPLDs kept in inventory." In addition, because they're reprogrammed easily, EEPLDs can be tested thoroughly for programmability and ac performance before shipment, which is not possible with bipolar or UV-erasable PLDs.

Improvements also continue in bipolar fusible-link arrays. For example, Signetics has a two-level-metal bipolar process with 2½-μm emitter structures, which it is using to boost the speed of its programmable logic devices by some 20%. And the Sunnyvale, Calif., company is developing an improved process that will feature emitters smaller than 2 μm. In building the fuse structures, Signetics uses oxide encroachment to form a very small fuse element, minimizing the programming current and cell area. For example, less than 50 mA is needed to produce the 0.2- to 0.4-μm-diameter shorting spike.

In its programmable logic family, Advanced Micro Devices Inc., Sunnyvale, uses IMOX-S, a high-speed oxide-isolated bipolar process with 2-μm geometries [*Electronics*, June 28, 1984, p. 131]. And Texas Instruments Inc., Dallas, is applying the newest version of its high-speed bipolar process, Impact X, to its family of programmable logic devices [*Electronics*, Dec. 23, 1985, p. 45].

are programmable, is that it allows the custom implementation of sum-of-product logic equations. Because all logic interconnections between the input and output pads are programmable, the need for active logic-level definition—a requirement associated with first-generation PALs—is eliminated, making it possible to have direct, mixed logic functions in one programmable logic device. Moreover, FPLAs are closing the gap with speeds in the 20- to 25-ns range (roughly comparable to the simpler PALs) and with the introduction of CMOS versions, which have potentially higher densities.

Monolithic Memories' Donovan argues that such flexibility may be overkill in most traditional FPLD applications—the replacement of small- and medium-scale-integration standard logic in the 100- to 500-gate range. But Douglas responds by pointing to two trends: the density of SSI and MSI devices is increasing toward and beyond 1,500 gates, and users are becoming more sophisticated. As a result, PLDs are being used to replace standard circuits and as an alternative to other custom and semicustom implementations of large-scale integration.

"The argument could be made that PALs are a programmable alternative whose time has passed," Douglas says. "Users were not ready for the higher sophistication that FPLAs and their extensions allow—and Monolithic Memories was there with a simpler architecture, the PAL. But engineers and systems designers who learned the ins and outs of programmable logic with PALs are now ready for something more complex." In addition, the more-complex devices are now much easier to use, thanks to a wide range of new design tools.

The first efforts at developing more-complex FPLDs have been relatively conservative. The initial architectural variations in PALs can be categorized broadly as incorporating more of the same kind of functions on the same chip to provide all-in-one PLAs. Examples are Monolithic Memories' MegaPALs and similar variations from AMD, Altera, and Lattice Semiconductor.

The newest FPLDs are incorporating mixed logic functions

The bipolar 40- to 84-pin MegaPALs offer the equivalent of 1,500 to 5,000 gates and 16-MHz operation—about four to eight times the complexity of earlier fusible-link FPLDs—but dissipate only 1 W. These chips incorporate such advanced features as product sharing to eliminate redundant terms, buried registers for parallel data capture, and programmable clocks for internal asynchronous operations, says Donovan.

Also from Monolithic Memories comes the field-programmable logic element (FPLE), which uses a PROM-like architecture to create an FPLD that is, in a sense, the mirror image of a PAL. It consists of a fixed AND array whose outputs feed into a programmable OR array. In contrast to a PAL, which typically has many input signals and few product terms, a field-programmable logic element has few inputs and many product terms. In addition, it has a large number of product terms per output signal with full product-term sharing, whereas PALs have a restricted number of product terms per output and no product-term sharing. Thus, says Donovan, the two complement each other both structurally and functionally.

AMD's contribution is its 24-pin AmPAL 22V10 (Fig. 3), the first in a family of second-generation all-in-one PALs. Fabricated using AMD's IMOX-S bipolar process, the chip features propagation delays of 15 ns and a density of about 800 gates. Containing up to 22 input pads and 10 output pads, it can define and program each output individually. Each output is user-programmable for either registered or combinatorial operation. That allows the designer to minimize the number of logic devices he uses for registers, making them available for other functions, says Mitch Richman, marketing manager for programmable logic products.

Another innovation is the use of variable product-term distribution, which allocates from 8 to 16 logic terms to each output pad. "This allows far more complex functions to be implemented than in previous approaches," he says. The device also can preload the output registers to any desired state

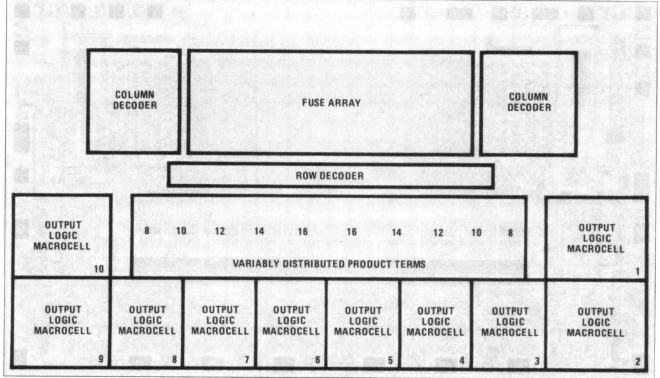

3. SINGLE CIRCUIT. The 22V10 from Advanced Micro Devices replaces any of 10 to 20 standard field-programmable array-logic circuits. Containing up to 22 input and 10 output pads, it can define and program each output individually.

during testing, so its logic can be verified fully.

From Altera comes a range of UV-erasable EPLDs, including the 20-pin 125-mW EP300, the 24-pin 15-MHz EP600, and the 40-pin 20-MHz EP900 and EP1210. These chips have densities ranging from 300 to 1,200 gates, standby power dissipation of only 15 mW, and active power dissipation of 125 to 400 mW. The EP1210, for example, has 28 on-board registers and 236 product terms and takes advantage of term sharing to reduce the need for multiple sum-of-product definitions. Other enhancements include on-board latches to allow input synchronization through the use of a programmable multiclock structure.

The internal 1,200-gate array in this device is divided into two sections, which communicate with each other over a number of internal buses that distribute both the primary input signals and the output signals of each cell. Control circuitry programs any clocking signals and distributes them to all internal latches and flip-flops through two internal signal paths. One path carries a clocking signal to on-chip dedicated input/output latches and to input latches associated with the I/O lines. The other drives the clock inputs to D-type flip-flops within macrocell output blocks, allowing the input latches and flip-flops to be programmed to receive their clock signals from one external source or from independent but related sources.

VLSI Technology Inc., San Jose, offers a 20-pin UV-erasable CMOS programmable logic family that bridges the gap between EPLAs and erasable PALs by taking advantage of what the company calls programmable array combination circuits. Each circuit cell contains a number of product terms, including ORs and exclusive ORs, that can be programmed to allow a shifter, a counter, or any other combinatorial function to be implemented on the same chip. When the XOR function is bypassed, a VLSI Technology EPLD can emulate a variety of industry-standard PALs. But when it is programmed, the chip can be used to design a number of counter and sequencer functions. When the OR feature is implemented, the device can perform shift and combinatorial functions.

A GENERIC LOGIC FAMILY

Using electrically erasable techniques, Lattice has developed what it calls a generic array logic family of programmable devices. The first member of the family is the 20-pin GAL 16V8, which can directly replace any of 21 architectures in the 20-pin, bipolar, fusible-link PAL series from Monolithic Memories and other vendors. Moreover, says Lattice's Suhr, the high-performance CMOS chip runs at bipolar speeds, with propagation delays of 25 ns or less.

Signetics takes the programmable-logic concept one step further with programmable macrologic, which offers the promise of programmable logic devices with densities between 5,000 and 10,000 gates. It takes advantage of the fact that two-level AND-OR gates used in present FPLDs and single-

---

COSTING OUT LOGIC DEVICES CAN BRING SURPRISES

Cost tradeoffs must take their place next to engineering and design considerations when a user is choosing among logic devices—field-programmable logic devices and logic cell arrays based on read-only memory, gate arrays, standard cells, and standard logic. The cost analyses that measure those tradeoffs often yield surprising results, says Mike Roth, vice president of technical sales and marketing at Hamilton Avnet Electronics Inc., Culver City, Calif.

For example, though the unit cost in volume (1,000 per month or more) is lowest for standard cells and gate arrays, many costs are hidden. The most important are those due to nonrecurring engineering and to changes in design.

Semicustom gate arrays and standard cells present a problem, says Roth, in terms of nonrecurring engineering and the time required to translate the design, create tooling, make the prototype run, and produce the product. Changes in these circuits often require new nonrecurring expenses.

Although they provide, on average, half the functional density of gate arrays and standard-cell solutions, FPLDs are a comfortable middle ground because they're easily reprogrammed, Roth argues. Often a complete change can be handled with a new FPLD net list or Boolean equation description, which is usually no more than a one-day job. Indeed, many companies use FPLDs to further customize board designs based on gate arrays or standard cells without redesign or costly nonrecurring expenses in memory expansion, input/output modification, and other areas.

Roth says the logic-cell array based on static random-access memory is the most flexible solution, because it can be reconfigured at any time by reloading its RAM. "This process requires about 1.5-K of data and 10 ms. Thus, one circuit can perform various logic functions without any component part changes."

The cost-tradeoff analyses in the chart illustrate these and other hidden costs. They assume that all nonrecurring engineering is amortized over three months and all capital equipment over six months, and they include costs of printed-circuit boards, power supplies, components, and manufacture and test.

Even with these conservative assumptions, the analyses show that for product quantities of fewer than 15 per month, standard logic might be the best solution. Quantities of 15 to 1,000 units per month are handled most economically by FPLDs, with semicustom approaches paying off at 1,000 per month and up. Logic-cell arrays have a higher parts cost than FPLDs, placing their system cost just slightly higher than that of FPLDs. □

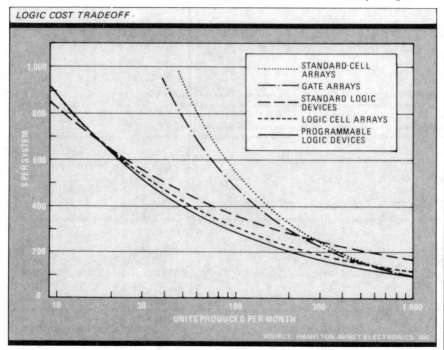

LOGIC COST TRADEOFF

Legend:
- STANDARD-CELL ARRAYS
- GATE ARRAYS
- STANDARD LOGIC DEVICES
- LOGIC CELL ARRAYS
- PROGRAMMABLE LOGIC DEVICES

$ PER SYSTEM

UNITS PRODUCED PER MONTH

SOURCE: HAMILTON AVNET ELECTRONICS, INC.

level NAND-NAND gates are fundamentally equivalent. Therefore, the NAND-NAND gates can be used to express combinatorial logic functions in sum-of-products form (Fig. 4).

And because programmable NAND-NAND logic chains can be formed by coupling identical NAND gates with programmable inputs, NAND array strings can be implemented easily to form a single global array with feedback. More-complex functions can be implemented by programming multilevel logic loops through the array and by introducing into the feedback path higher-level macros such as flip-flops, XOR gates, buffers, counters, shift registers, multiplexers, decoders, arithmetic logic units, and memory blocks (Fig. 5).

The main design advantage of programmable macrologic is that, unlike multilevel AND-OR implementations, it relies on a single array level to interconnect all macros. This reduces the design task to the building of a PROM-like structure, which is more forgiving than the double array in FPLA-type devices and more flexible than PALs, says Napoleone Cavlan, product-architecture manager at Signetics. In addition, he says, the ability to forge the NAND core into multilevel logic paths at will increases the usage efficiency of the on-chip logic resources. Signetics plans to introduce, within the next few months, the first two devices in a programmable-macrologic family, the PLHS501 and the PLHS502, both packaged in 52-pin plastic leadless chip carriers.

The PLHS501 is a combinatorial logic device with only primitive macros. But this simple structure is deceptive, says Cavlan, for it can implement virtually all logic functions provided by existing combinatorial FPLAs and PALs. It also provides true exclusive-OR output functions, in addition to output polarity inversion, as well as multilevel gate constructs and cross-coupled latches on the chip. Built using Signetics' proprietary ZA-2 oxide-isolation process, using vertical avalanched-induced-migration diodes, it has a NAND matrix about the size of a 16-K PROM and features output delays of 17 ns for single passes through the array and 25 ns for double passes.

More complex is the PLHS502, a sequential device including higher-level macros in the form of clock shift registers and D-type flip-flops, split into banks of eight to facilitate control and data-path manipulation. Built with an advanced high-speed oxide-isolation process, the PLHS502 has a NAND matrix about the size of a 21-K PROM and features output delays of 12 to 16 ns. For sequential operation, maximum setup time is 10 to 14 ns and clock-to-output time is 18 ns.

EDGING TOWARD 10,000 GATES

Using a conservative interconnection factor of only 20%, the PLHS501 has a density roughly equivalent to 3,000 two-input NAND gates, according to Cavlan. For the PLHS502, the figure is 3,600. Densities between 5,000 and 10,000 gates are possible if the chip is fabricated using high-performance high-density CMOS, says Signetics' Douglas.

One of the most radical departures in FPLD design is the dynamically reconfigurable CMOS logic cell array from Xilinx Inc., a San Jose startup. The array consists of a large number of configurable static-RAM-based logic blocks that can implement any function of four variables, each integrated with a flip-flop. These logic blocks are interconnected with configurable I/O blocks.

The first family member is the XC2064 (Fig. 6), which is the equivalent of an array with 1,500 gates. It draws its flexibility from a matrix of 64 dynamically reconfigurable logic cells and 58 I/O blocks. At the core of the device is an SRAM matrix that has been divided into an 8-by-8-cell array. Surrounding the matrix are the 58 bidirectional I/O blocks, each of which contains an input register, adjustable input-voltage threshold, and three-state output circuitry. Each block has four logic input paths, a clock input, and two output paths. The four

inputs drive the blocks' RAM-based combinatorial logic, from a simple gate to a three-out-of-four majority-voter circuit, directly implementing a four-variable Karnaugh map. If fewer than four variables are needed, a block can be configured to generate two three-variable output functions. Because each block can both accept and generate positive-true as well as negative-true logic, the need for internal inverters or complements for each input signal is eliminated. Each block also includes a storage element that can serve as a D flip-flop or as a gated transparent latch. Also, the two outputs of each block can be programmed independently.

Contributing to the logic-cell array's reconfigurability are a variety of user-programmable interconnection elements. These include metal lines that run horizontally and vertically between the logic and I/O blocks, crosspoint-switch interchanges that join segments of metal lines, and programmable interconnection points that link the lines with logic and I/O blocks.

Improvements in processing and fabrication of fusible links and erasable cells have slashed programming failure rates from between 10% and 15% to as little as 3% to 5%. Nevertheless, experienced PROM and EPROM users are often puzzled by the fact that not all FPLDs function correctly after successful completion of a programming operation and fuse verification check. That's because the logic devices do not display the one-to-one relationship between address states and programming elements found in PROMs and EPROMs.

The other elements in a programmable logic device, including latches, counters, buffers, shift registers, and oscillators, often go untested. Thus postprogramming failure rates, rang-

Another tack is FPLDs using logic blocks based on static RAM

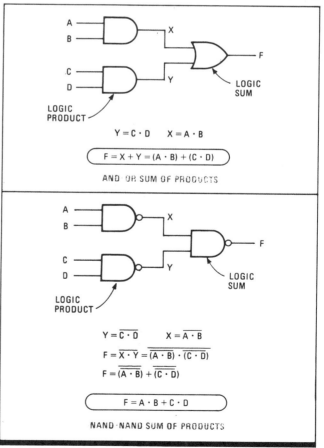

$$Y = C \cdot D \qquad X = A \cdot B$$

$$\boxed{F = X + Y = (A \cdot B) + (C \cdot D)}$$

AND-OR SUM OF PRODUCTS

$$Y = \overline{C \cdot D} \qquad X = \overline{A \cdot B}$$

$$F = \overline{X \cdot Y} = \overline{\overline{(A \cdot B)} \cdot \overline{(C \cdot D)}}$$

$$F = \overline{(A \cdot B)} + \overline{(C \cdot D)}$$

$$\boxed{F = A \cdot B + C \cdot D}$$

NAND-NAND SUM OF PRODUCTS

4. EQUIVALENCE. Signetics' programmable macrologic takes advantage of the equivalence between standard two-level AND-OR structures and single-level NAND-NAND arrays.

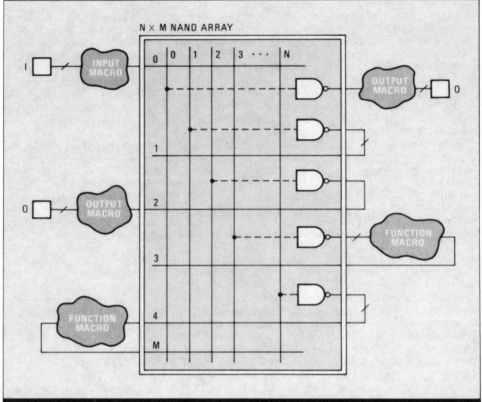

5. SINGLE LEVEL. One plus of NAND-NAND-based programmable macro logic is that complex functions can be implemented by programming multilevel logic loops and adding higher-level macros.

developing a breadboard.

But now, says Douglas, "average FPLD densities are in the 300 to 900 range and some more-advanced designs [are] in the 1,500- to 5,000-gate range, making manual methods completely out of the question. Then there is the problem of working the variety of different architectures." Either the increased density or the variety of architectures alone "requires the support of good CAD tools. But with designers facing both problems, sophisticated CAD tools are an absolute necessity."

The most mature and well-known software programming aid for FPLD users is Monolithic Memories' Palasm (PAL Assembler). Palasm translates Boolean logic equations into a PAL fuse pattern that then can be downloaded to a PAL or PROM programmer to produce the required circuit. It also simulates the logical behavior of the part to verify the design and checks for adequate test coverage. The most recent version, Palasm 2.0, can be used to design most 20-, 24-, 40-, and 84-pin PALs.

A much more sophisticated FPLD design aid is Amaze (Automated Map and Zap Equation Entry) from Signetics, for support of the company's family of integrated fuse logic devices, including FPLAs, FPLSs, and FPGAs. It consists of five modules—the Boolean logic and state-transfer program, the integrated-fuse-logic function simulator, the device-programmer interface, the program-table editor, and the converter for changing PAL to integrated-fuse logic. The modules allow a designer to create the fuse patterns necessary to program the PLDs a number of different ways: as Boolean equations, state-machine equations, truth tables, PAL fuse patterns, integrated-fuse-logic fuse patterns, and schematic entry.

Two high-level languages have been developed as generic design tools to support all FPLD types: PROMs, PALs, FPLAs, FPLSs, FPLEs, EPLDs, and EEPLDs. These are ABEL (Advanced Boolean Expression Language) from Data I/O Corp., Redmond, Wash., and CUPL (Compiler Universal Programming Language) from Assisted Technology Inc., San Jose.

With ABEL, the designer supplies a description of the circuit in the form of Boolean equations or state-machine diagrams. The program takes these descriptions and synthesizes a fuse map for the appropriate FPLD type and then verifies the design by simulating the operation of the actual chip. It incorporates a set-notation feature that groups signals together and operates them as a unit. Various macros and commands are supplied to instruct the compiler to create blocks of text. Also contained in the program is a heuristic-reduction algorithm that minimizes complex logic designs to no more than a few lines of program text.

With CUPL, the designer is relieved of much of the need to supply Boolean equations or state-machine diagrams through the use of a macro, or expression-substitution feature. This capability allows the designer to create a variable name that does not appear on the input or output pins and to write an expression defining it. The variable is then used in any successive equations. When the text for the logic source is compiled

ing from 1% to 4%, are a bugaboo most users believe they have to live with. That may be acceptable for the designer of a small system with relatively low volumes, says AMD's Richman—but large companies using thousands or tens of thousands of such circuits on boards with 100 or more programmable logic devices cannot accept such disastrous yields. "Post-programming yield is the most important aspect to large-volume users, because a failure after programming is more than just a failure of a single component—it is the failure of a complete board, a complete system."

The standard approach to this problem, other than improving the processing, is to use sophisticated test programs. "The problem with such approaches is that, first, they are ineffective and, second, they are something that the vendor tries to shift to the user," Richman says. A better alternative "is to take care of such testing in the factory."

ON-CHIP TESTING

AMD has developed on-chip test circuitry that ensures a better than 99.5% programming yield—compared with the usual 95% to 97%—and a 99.9998% (200 ppm) postprogramming yield, compared with the usual 96% to 99%. "In total, no more than about 5% additional die area is required for this test circuitry," Richman says. "And while this results in a slightly increased die cost, the extra expense is more than offset by the savings due to reduced failure rate."

Acting as a catalyst in the development of ever-more-complex field-programmable logic chips is a wealth of design software and CAD tools, most of which have been introduced within the past 12 months. "There is no way the programmable logic market could have evolved toward higher densities and greater complexities without the development of sophisticated CAD tools," says Douglas of Signetics. When PLDs were in the 100- to 500-gate range, an engineer could generate the appropriate equations by hand, much the way he did when

428

6. DYNAMICALLY REPROGRAMMABLE. A new field-programmable logic device from Xilinx, the XC2064, combines logic blocks based on static RAM with programmable interconnections. The result is dynamic reprogrammability.

for a fuse map of a particular FPLD, the compiler substitutes the defined expression for the variable name wherever it appears. Another CUPL feature allows entire groups of bits to be given a single symbolic name, further simplifying the design process.

Developed to support only Altera's family of EPLDs, the company's A+Plus (for Altera Programmable Logic User System) software system is perhaps the most sophisticated in terms of the number of ways an engineer can enter circuit information, including Boolean equations, state-machine diagrams, schematic diagrams, and net lists, similar to the techniques used in semicustom CAD tools. Key to the input flexibility of the A+Plus system is Altera's design library, which contains a set of schematic primitives divided into categories of input, logic, and I/O primitives.

NEW PARTICIPANTS

The move by more companies to participate in the growing market for programmable logic chips is continuing. Within recent months, two major semiconductor companies—the solid-state division of Sprague Electric Co., of Willow Grove, Pa., and Intel Corp. of Santa Clara—have made the decision to enter the market. And a third, Fairchild Semiconductor Corp.'s High Speed Memory and Logic division, Puyallup, Wash., will formally enter the market in February. Even RCA Corp. is considering a move into the market, mainly in support of its military customers.

Intel's initial entry into the FPLD market is with the 5C060 and 5C121 EPLDs, with 600 and 1,200 gates respectively, fab-

ricated using the Santa Clara company's CHMOS EPROM technology. The 1,200-gate device, for example, is based on 28 macrocells, each of which contains a PAL structure and an I/O architecture control block that can be programmed to create a variety of output logic configurations. Propagation-delay time through the device is 50 ns at 15 MHz. Active power dissipation is 250 mW and standby power is 75 mW.

Another newcomer is Sprague Solid State, whose entries are pin-for-pin CMOS EPLD replacements of industry-standard 20- and 24-pin PALs. In the company's initial circuits, clock-to-output propagation delays are 25 ns for registered parts and 45 ns for nonregistered parts, says Clem Nahmias, director of commercial products. They dissipate 275 mW active and 75 mW standby.

Finally, Fairchild Semiconductor will formally enter the market next month with its FAST PLA family. Fabricated using its Isoplanar-Z vertical-fuse technology, the initial devices will be pin-compatible with the 20-pin series of PALs and will feature propagation delays through the array as low as 15 ns.

Fairchild has several reasons for entering the programmable-logic market, says logic marketing manager Joe Nichols. "First, programmable logic allows us to expand the market for Fairchild Advanced Schottky TTL devices to those whose volumes or logic implementations could not be supported by either standard logic or gate arrays. But just as important is the desire to remain an active participant in the ASIC market. Without field-programmable logic, we would have been locked out of one of the fastest-growing portions of that market."□

Paper 10.2

A 9ns, Low Standby Power CMOS PLD with a Single-Poly EPROM Cell

Scott Frake, Mark Knecht, Philip Cacharelis, Michael Hart, Martin Manley, Richard Zeman, Richard Ramus

National Semiconductor Corp.

Santa Clara, CA

THIS PAPER DESCRIBES a 9ns CMOS PLD with a standby current of $10\mu A$. The circuit implemented is a 24-pin PLD with 10 I/Os and 12 dedicated inputs. Each I/O has eight summed-product terms and an output enable control product term feeding into a programmable macrocell. Most standard 24 pin PLDs can be emulated by selectively programming the macrocell architecture bits. Bit line precharging circuitry is used to reduce the speed degradation caused by designing for low standby current. "Ground bounce" is alleviated by controlling the output buffer speed. The circuit has been fabricated in a $1\mu m$ single-polysilicon CMOS EPROM technology that has been optimized for speed rather than for packing density. A micrograph of the 105 mil x 109 mil die is shown in Figure 1.

Input-transition-detection circuitry limits standby I_{CC} to $10\mu A$ (Figure 2). The circuitry generates two signals: ACTIVE, which determines when the sense amplifier and array are powered up and down, and TRANSFER, which determines when data at the sense amplifier output is latched. The array and sense amplifier are shown in Figure 3. When powered down, VREF precharges the bit line to a "1" level (2V), thereby improving speed on wake-up. Previous zero-standby PLDs have let the bit line discharge to ground (which is lower than the "0" bit line level) when powered-down. This causes a slow transition on wake-up if the bit line must be charged to a "1" level. VREF is set to about $3/5V_{CC}$ by a strong PMOS voltage divider when the sense amp is powered up, and is held there by the weak voltage divider. When an input transition is detected, the bit line current-limiting signal, VBIAS, powers up rapidly with the aid of a fast pull-up pulse. Oscilloscope photographs show the 9ns propagation delay and the 6ns clock-to-output delay (Figure 4).

"Ground bounce" is the voltage that appears across the inductance of the package ground lead when outputs are switched. It can cause low outputs to bounce high, cause dynamic V_{IH} problems, and even trigger oscillation. Ground bounce is minimized if the switching current has a constant rate of change. In this design, the RC delay of the gates of the output devices is used to keep the di/dt of the switching current reasonably constant (Figure 5). The devices which turn off the output transistors are connected in parallel at various points along the output gate resistor, reducing totem-pole current.

The part is intended to be assembled in various package types, each with a different power lead self-inductance and hence each posing different constraints on the output buffer di/dt. Metal options are used to vary the series gate resistance of the output buffer by connecting the gate legs either in parallel, in series,

or some combination, in accordance with the package to be used. Figure 6 shows a circuit simulation of a high-inductance package with a more resistive output buffer gate and a low-inductance package with a less resistive output buffer gate. In each case, nine outputs are switching from high to low and one output is staying low.

The technology used for this circuit has been developed as a modular addition to a standard 5V $1\mu m$ double-metal CMOS Logic process[2]. As high density is not required, a single poly-silicon EPROM cell is used in order to reduce process complexity The simple topography of the cell allows bit lines and word lines to be directly connected in two layers of metal to minimize RC delays. The cell is designed to provide $500\mu A$ of read current, allowing fast sensing without the need for on-chip back-bias. By eliminating the back-bias charge pump, the low standby power was achieved. The process flow requires only two masking steps in addition to the base line process. A buried N+ layer is implanted prior to polysilicon deposition to form a diffused control gate, and an early N+ source/drain implant is used to bypass the LDD spacer and ensure efficient cell programming. Device and technology characteristics are summarized in Figure 6.

Acknowledgments

The authors thank T. Wong, S. Sengir, J. McGourty, and K. Simpson for layout and mask-making, D. Probst for product engineering, and the CMOS Logic Development group for the base-line process and for fabrication.

---

[1] Wong, S.C. et al, "Novel Circuit Techniques for Zero-Power 25ns CMOS EPLDs", *IEEE J. Solid-State Circuits*, p. 766-774; Oct., 1986.

[2] Cacharelis, P.J., et al, "A Modular $1\mu m$ CMOS Single Polysilicon EPROM PLD Technology", *IEDM Technical Digest*, Dec., 1988

Reprinted from the *IEEE ISSCC Dig. Tech. Pap.*, pp. 230–231, 346, 1989.

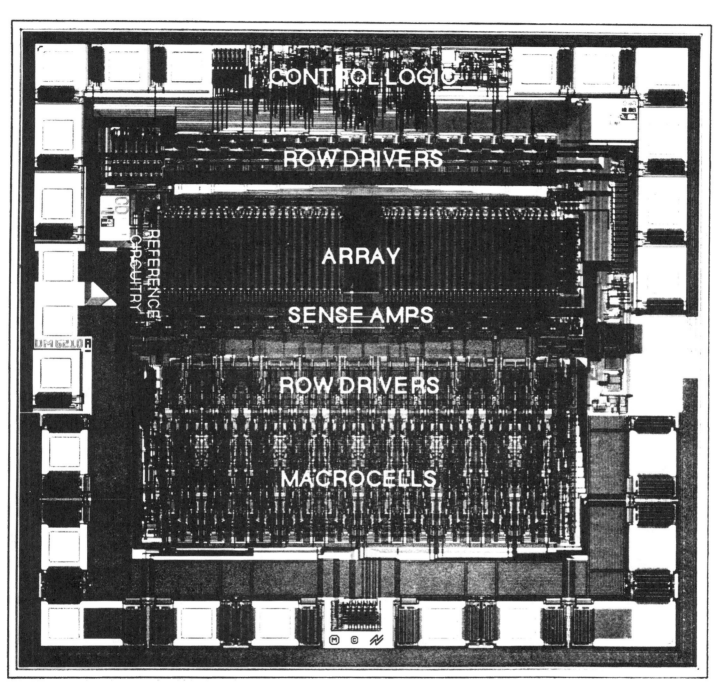

FIGURE 1—Die photograph.

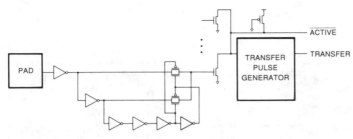

FIGURE 2—Input transition detection circuit.

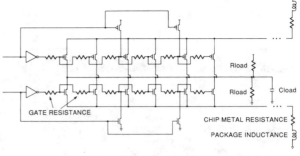

FIGURE 5—Output buffer circuit.

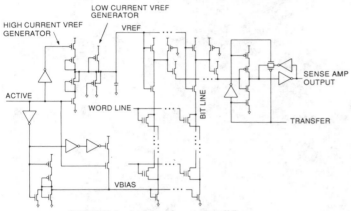

FIGURE 3—Array and sense amplifier.

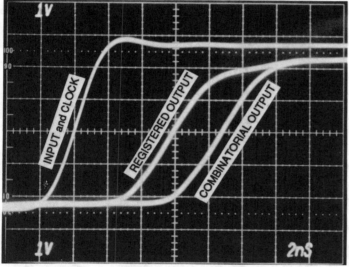

FIGURE 4—Propagation delay and clock-to-output delay.

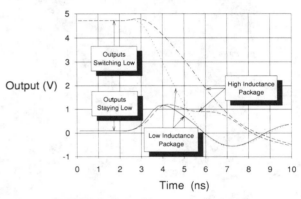

FIGURE 6—Ground bounce simulation.

TABLE 1—Device and technology characteristics.

Device Information		Process Parameters	
Die Size	105mil x 109mil	P-type Material 25-36 ohm-cm	
Input to Output Delay	9.0ns	Twin-well 1um process	
Clock to Output Delay	6.0ns	Double metal, single poly	
Set-up Time	4.5ns	Tungsten metalization	
Active Icc (50Mhz)	100mA	N-channel Leff	0.80um
Standby Icc	10uA	P-channel Leff	0.85um
Package	24-pin, 300mil DIP	Gate oxide	200Ang.
	28-pin LCC		

Memory Cell Parameters		Design Rules	
Cell size	94.5um^2	Composite width/space	1.0um/1.7um
W/L	2.6um/0.9um	Poly width/space	1.0um/1.0um
Coupling ratio	0.78	Metal 1 width/space	1.3um/1.2um
Gate oxide	200Ang.	Metal 2 width/space	1.7um/1.4um
Coupling oxide	250Ang.	Contact size	1.0um x 1.0um
Read current	500uA	Via size	1.0um x 1.0um

432

A One-Day Chip: An Innovative IC Construction Approach Using Electrically Reconfigurable Logic VLSI with On-Chip Programmable Interconnections

YASUO IKAWA, MEMBER, IEEE, KIYOSHI URUI, MASASHI WADA, TOMOJI TAKADA,
MASAHIKO KAWAMURA, MISAO MIYATA, NOBORU AMANO,
AND TADASHI SHIBATA, MEMBER, IEEE

Abstract —A new custom IC design methodology and the associated logic VLSI chip, which offer an ultimately fast turnaround-time logic IC construction method, are proposed.

Using the new VLSI chip, digital system and logic designers can construct their own real IC chip with thousands of logic gates, as easily as if they drew logic diagrams to be implemented in the form of a printed-circuit board, which would utilize standard logic IC families. This construction can even be carried out in a second, because logic structures can be reconfigured electrically, due to on-chip programmable interconnection capability. This chip contains various kinds of logic functional blocks, such as inverters, NOR's, NAND's, flip-flops, shift registers, counters, adders, multiplexers, ALU's, and so on. Up to 200 SSI/MSI standard logic blocks can be provided. The E^2PROM-type MOSFET switch matrix is adjacent to the functional blocks, in order to connect any output to specific inputs of the functional blocks. It also offers a ready-to-test aid, obtained by monitoring the signal waveform developed inside the chip.

These features have the advantage over the present custom IC design methods, such as gate array, standard cell, silicon compiler, or programmable logic array (PLA) approaches, in the sense that the designer can easily redesign the logic to obtain a digital system in an IC even within one day.

I. INTRODUCTION

GREAT PROGRESS in semiconductor devices has been made since the invention of the transistor in 1947. Highlights, which made major breakthroughs toward higher integration of electronic components, include integrated circuits and microprocessors. The advanced IC fabrication technology now enables hundreds of thousands of logic gates to be integrated in a chip. This technology has been successfully applied to memory IC's of megabits per chip level. However, the logic IC's do not fully enjoy this technological potential. There is a diversely wide range of logic systems which are desired to be implemented in the form of IC's. However, only mass-produced circuits, such as general purpose microprocessors, can be cost effective in the category of custom logic IC's. This is because the development time ranges from a month to a year, which

makes frequent redesign of a logic expensive and impractical.

Gate array, standard cell, and silicon compilation are methodologies applied to ease this constraint [1]. However, they still require physical and chemical processing time which is too long for system and logic designers to effectively redesign their ideas. Faster turnaround time is still strongly desired. On the contrary, programmable logic array (PLA) type circuits are available with field programming capability [2], [3]. The logic can be created in a relatively short period of time. This style is restrictive, because programming is basically carried out in terms of Boolean algebra, which cannot be applied to sequential logical circuits. Recently, there have been improved PLA versions [3], which have feedback loops, but they are not advanced enough to let designers feel they are friendly, because most of system ideas are not created in the designer's brain in the form of Boolean algebra. As a result, a large number of small volume logics still remain in the form of a printed-circuit board, instead of being implemented in custom IC's.

It is therefore the purpose of this paper to present a VLSI chip that provides system and logic designers with an innovative IC construction method.

II. CONCEPT OF THE NEW DESIGN METHOD

Using the proposed VLSI, a designer can construct an actual IC chip with more than several thousand logic gates, as if they drew logic diagrams to be implemented in the form of a printed-circuit board, which would utilize standard logic IC families. This construction is carried out in even a few seconds, because logic structure can be reconfigured by changing the interconnections electrically. In addition, it offers frequent reconstruction capability.

Fig. 1 shows a conceptual drawing of this VLSI. Fifty to 200 standard logics of SSI/MSI level integration act as functional blocks and are placed in a chip that is ap-

Manuscript received September 4, 1985; revised December 30, 1985.
The authors are with Toshiba Research and Development Center, 1 Komukai-Toshiba-Cho, Saiwai-ku, Kawasaki 210, Japan.
IEEE Log Number 8607664.

Reprinted from *IEEE J. Solid-State Circuits*, vol. SC-21, no. 2, pp. 223–227, April 1986.

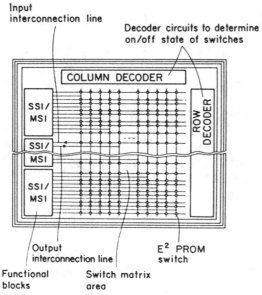

Fig. 1. Conceptual drawing of the proposed VLSI.

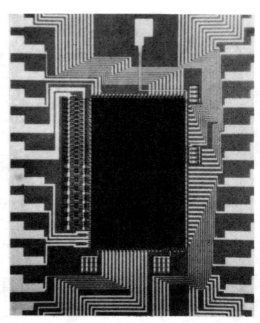

Fig. 2. Photomicrograph of the fabricated test chip. The switch matrix has 34-row × 26-column switches and occupies an 850×520-μm area.

proximately 10×10 mm in size. Inputs and outputs from functional blocks are introduced into the switch matrix area to be connected to any of the desired I/O terminals by selecting the switch that should be turned on. Each switch is realized by E^2PROM-type floating gate MOSFET. The ON/OFF state is kept unchanged, once the state is written. ON switch selection might correspond to the interconnection layout in the conventional custom IC design work, or to the wire lapping work in IC board construction. It is therefore very important to make propagation delay times comparable to those in the printed-circuit board, which is in the range of 1 ns to 20–30 ns. To do this, an output buffer circuit is introduced at each output of the functional block.

The designer can easily change the wiring by designating the switches to be turned on and off, which is accomplished in a drastically short period of time (around a second) and at low cost, compared with the conventional circuit board or custom IC fabrication approach. In addition, this new method offers a logic testing aid. By extending one of the matrix lines to outside the chip and designating a specific switch along the line, the designer can monitor the logic state or even the waveform developed at any node inside the circuit. This is very similar to the probing and the checking of the waveform on the oscilloscope, which is usually carried out in the circuit board design. In this sense, the present VLSI chip is completely different from PLA, which basically carries out programming for the logics that can be expressed in terms of Boolean algebra.

III. TEST CHIP

Fig. 2 shows a photomicrograph of the fabricated test chip. It has 14 inverters, eight two-input NAND gates as functional blocks, and a 34-row × 26-column switch matrix.

It also has four I/O terminals for signals in and out of an IC. Any output can be connected to any desired input through the switch matrix.

An individual switch is realized by dual-control cell-type E^2PROM floating-gate MOSFET ($W_g/L_g = 5$ μm/1.5 μm) [4], and is placed at each crossing point for the output line and the input line. Three types of switch cells are used, as seen in Fig. 3 which summarizes the test chip configuration. Each switch cell has a 25×20 μm size. Individual switch cell types connect or disconnect an output line and an input line that cross each other in the switch cell. Every cell has one input line running horizontally. In the type I switch cell, there is only one output line, which runs vertically. In the type II, horizontally and vertically running output lines form T-shapes to physically connect each other. In the type III, there are two kinds of output lines, one of which runs horizontally, that is, electrically independent from other vertically running output lines. The reason why these three kinds of switch cells are required is implied in Fig. 1. Fig. 4 shows a schematic representation of a switch-cell cross section, designed specially for the new VLSI chip. It has a WRITE/ERASE electrode, which performs ON/OFF writing by using tunnel oxide, causing no interference with a signal that passes through the switch. Plus/minus 20-V voltage was applied to the column and row select stacked gates to write the OFF/ON state for the switch, which was accomplished within 1 ms.

For process simplicity, triple-layer polysilicon lines and single-layer Al lines were used. Decoder circuits for the E^2PROM switch were intentionally omitted in the first version of the chip, to evaluate the principal operation of the new VLSI.

The ON-state switch allowed 1-mA current flow, as shown in Fig. 5. Signal waveform, which was transmitted through an ON switch, was also measured, when 220-pF capacitive

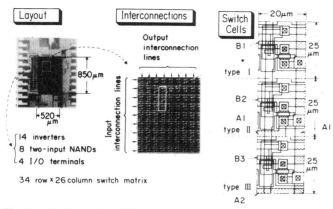

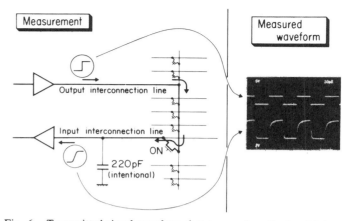

Fig. 3. Configuration of the test chip. The chip has 14 inverters, eight two-input NAND gates as functional blocks, four I/O terminals, and a 34-row×26-column switch matrix. An output interconnection line runs from each functional block into the switch matrix area, forming a *T*-shape to run vertically. An input interconnection line runs horizontally, forming crossing points with output interconnection lines. Also shown are the three types of switch cells. *A*1, *A*2: Output interconnection lines. *B*1, *B*2, *B*3: Input interconnection lines.

Fig. 6. Transmitted signal waveform that appeared on the input interconnection line with 220-pF capacitive load.

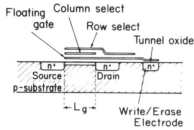

Fig. 4. Schematic representation of a cross-sectional view of an E²PROM-type switch.

IV. FUTURE DESIGN

An advanced version of this VLSI can be fabricated, using triple-layer polysilicon and double-layer Al, with a 2-μm rule CMOS process. It has on-chip decoder circuits with a high-voltage generator from a single 5-V power-supply voltage for WRITE/ERASE operation on E²PROM switches. The schematic drawing of the chip design is like the one shown in Fig. 1. It has 60 high-speed CMOS standard logic SSI's/MSI's as functional blocks, which are equivalent to 3K-gate logics, and a 446-row ×233-column switch matrix to enable any combination of input-to-output connection for functional blocks. This chip also offers a logic testing aid. The waveforms at any 16 nodes inside the circuit can be monitored simultaneously. The user can change the monitoring node by designating the ON/OFF switches which let the desired node voltage go out of the chip. Chip size is approximately 10×10 mm. The switch matrix area is 5×7 mm and the functional blocks occupy a 2×7 mm area.

Circuit simulation was carried out to evaluate the speed performance. Fig. 7 shows the model to simulate the propagation delay of the signal, which transmits from one of the outputs to one of the inputs through the switch matrix area. Here, the following factors were assumed: 1) the output buffer had a gate width of 50 μm formed by a 2-μm CMOS standard process; 2) the ON-state switch cell enabled around a 1-mA current flow; 3) the junction capacitance of an E²PROM source and drain was 5 fF each; and 4) the parasitic capacitance of the output and input interconnection lines was approximately 100 fF/mm, based on the 2-μm-wide wiring. Fig. 8 shows the simulated waveforms that appeared at the output and the input node in the switch matrix. The figure shows the signal transmission upgoing at the switch node (node *A* in Fig. 7). Downgoing signal was also simulated. The average propagation delay in the switch matrix area was found to be 13 ns for the longest transmission path when there were four fan-outs. This speed can be found to be comparable with, or faster than, the rise time or fall time for the CMOS standard logic IC's with the typical 10–100-pF capacitance at an output pin. This means that the users will be able to

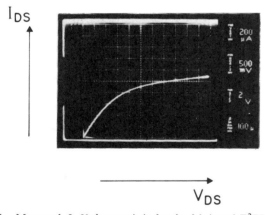

Fig. 5. Measured *I–V* characteristic for the fabricated E²PROM-type MOSFET switch under ON state. $W_g/L_g = 5\ \mu\text{m}/1.5\ \mu\text{m}$.

load existed on the input interconnection line. The result is shown in Fig. 6. The transmission delay is found to be around 2 μs, which means that the signal delay in the switch matrix is about 10-ns/pF parasitic capacitance along the input interconnection line. Signal rise/fall time on the output interconnection line is determined by the current drivability of the output buffer in the functional block and the parasitic capacitance along the output interconnection line. Therefore it is much quicker than the signal transient developed on the input interconnection line.

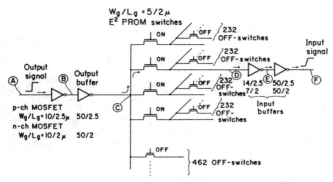

Fig. 7. Model to simulate propagation delay in the switch matrix.

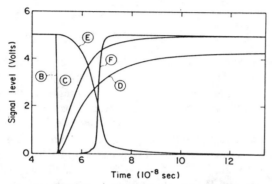

Fig. 8. Simulated signal waveforms at each node when the signal transmits from output to input through switch matrix area. Nodes are represented as B through F, which are identical to the signs in Fig. 7.

construct a several thousand gate logic system, as if they designed a circuit board using conventional CMOS standard logics.

Further designs of this VLSI include partitioning of the functional block and switch matrix combination to permit more logics available in a chip. With the future 1-μm CMOS process, more than 200 standard logics (equivalent to 10K gates) as functional blocks could be installed in a chip.

V. CONCLUSION

The proposed new VLSI chip described above provides system and logic designers with a new tool, which makes their system or circuit idea ready to be implemented in the form of an IC and enables prompt debugging and testing of the circuit. The final design is the finishing off for the customized IC fabrication itself, that is, 2- or 3K gate logics (or even more than 10K gates in the future 1-μm design rule era) can be wired in a second to obtain a fully customized IC. The final IC can be completed in less than a day, depending on the ideas involved. An uncustomized "master" IC can be mass-produced and will be reasonably priced. Therefore the personalization can be made, to obtain even a single chip, which means even a single system can be integrated in an IC at reasonable and affordable cost. This innovative VLSI is featured by and can be called "hardware programmable logic IC without process," as opposed to gate arrays, standard cell, and silicon compilers, which require physical and chemical processing, or microprocessor IC's as "software programmable logics."

ACKNOWLEDGMENT

The authors would like to thank H. Iizuka for his encouragement. They are also grateful to M. Minami and M. Azuma for their contribution in organizing the project for creating the concept of this new VLSI. Thanks also go to S. Inoue and R. Kirisawa for their technical contributions.

REFERENCES

[1] ——, "In pursuit of the one-month chip," *IEEE Spectrum*, p. 28, Sept. 1984.
[2] W.N. Carr and J.P. Mize, *MOS/LSI Design and Application* (Texas Instruments Electronics Series). New York: McGraw-Hill, 1972.
[3] S. Muroga, *VLSI System Design*. New York: Wiley, 1982.
[4] K. Hieda, M. Wada, T. Shibata, S. Inoue, M. Momodomi, and H. Iizuka, "Optimum design of dual-control gate cell for high-density EEPROMS," in *Proc. IEEE Int. Electron Devices Meeting*, 1983, p. 593.

A CMOS Electrically Configurable Gate Array

Khaled El-Ayat, Abbas El Gamal, Richard Guo, John Chang, Esmat Hamdy, John McCollum, Amr Mohsen

ACTEL Corp.

Sunnyvale, CA

PRESENT PLD PROGRAMMING technologies and architectures have not allowed efficient integration of a wide variety of applications exceeding a few hundred gates[1][2]. Mask programmable gate arrays, on the other hand, offer the architectural flexibility and efficiency to integrate thousands of gates, but at the expense of long development time and high engineering development cost.

The architecture of the CMOS electrically-configurable gate array to be described, combines flexibility of mask programmable gate arrays and convenience of user-programmable PLDs; Figure 1. The inplementation is facilitated by a configurable interconnect technology based on a one-time, two-terminal programmable, low-impedance circuit element[3]. The electrical characteristics of this element are more suitable for one chip integration than preciously published anti-fuses[4]; Table 1. The device has been fabricated using $2\mu m$ N-well CMOS technology with two-layer metallization. Four transistor types were used to optimize logic-speed path and programming path operating voltages.

The architecture of the device[5] is similar to that of gate arrays; Figure 1. It consists of configurable logic modules organized in rows and columns and separated by wiring channels. Unlike gate arrays, however, the channels contain segmented *horizontal* metal tracks. The inputs of the logic modules are connected to dedicated *vertical* metal wire segments. Other vertical wire segments not dedicated to any module input or output are also provided for vertical interconnection. Anti-fuse elements are located at the intersection of the horizontal and vertical wire segments, and between adjacent horizontal and vertical wire segments. To program an element, 18V is applied across its terminals, while all other elements are subjected to no more than half that voltage. This is accomplished by a procedure that utilizes the wiring segments, pass transistors between adjacent segments with shared control lines, and serial addressing circuitry at the periphery of the array. A programmed anti-fuse element at the intersection of, or between, two wire segments provides a low resistance bi-directional connection between the two segments.

Choice of the lengths of the horizontal and vertical wire segments, as well as the number of tracks in each channel, provides

routing flexibility comparable to that of gate arrays. The similarity of this architecture to that of gate arrays can be best understood by drawing a parallel between the programmable anti-fuse elements and the vias introduced during the fabrication of gate arrays. The small size of the via allows the gate arrays to contain an extremely large number of potential via sites, of which a very small fraction is needed to implement an application. Similarly, the size of the anit-fuse elements permits packing them as close as the metal pitch of the CMOS technology. Thus, a large number of these elements can be included in the device. Again, only a very small fraction of these anti-fuse elements need to be programmed to implement any application. This allows gate array-like extension of the device architecture by adding more logic modules and incrementally increasing the number of wiring tracks in each channel.

The configurable logic module has 8 inputs and one output. This module was chosen for its efficiency in implementing both combinatorial and sequential circuits and for its optimum utilization of routing resources. This module implements all two- and three-variable functions and some four-variable functions. It may also be connected to form latches and flip flops. No predetermined hardwired latches or flop flops are implemented or needed in this gate array since latches and flip-flops may be implemented anywhere in the array to suit the requirements of the application. The I/O architecture is also quite flexible. Any I/O module may be configured as input, output, or bi-directional I/O by programming the appropriate anti-fuse elements.

An important aspect of the device is that its design is testable. Since the programmable element is an anti-fuse, the array circuits are normally open with no circuit connections established to external I/O buffers. Testability circuits are, therefore, implemented to allow full testing of any module in the array, I/O buffers vertical and horizontal tracks, as well as all programming circuits in the device before configuration. The overhead of these testability circuits is minimized by sharing the periphery circuits and the pass transistors needed for programming. Appropriate test patterns are applied to the testability circuits before configuration to ensure quality devices and programming yield.

The key characteristics of the chip are listed in Table 2; Figure 1. The device is supported by an automated placement and routing software capable of mapping applications utilizing up to 95% of the array modules. The frequency counter circuit uses 283 logic modules, out of the available 295, and 37 I/O modules; Figure 2. The speed of the circuit under normal operating conditions is 25MHz. If implemented with a mask programmable gate array, this example would require over 1,000 gates. The waveform of a counter output is shown in Figure 3. Other examples of applications that have been mapped in the array include a model with a carry-look-ahead circuit and an 8 x 8 parallel multiplier.

[1] Wong,S., So,H., Hung,C., Ou,J., "CMOS Erasable Programmable Logic with Zero Standby Power", *ISSCC DIGEST OF TECHNICAL PAPERS*, p.242-243, Feb., 1986.

[2] Hsieh,H., Duog,K., Ja,R., Kanazawa,R., Ngo,L., Tinkey, L., Carter,W., Freeman,R., "A Second Generation User-Programmable Gate Array", *Proceedings of the CICC*, p.515-521; May 1987.

[3] Patent pending.

[4] Stopper,H., "A Wafer with Electrically Programmable Interconnections", *ISSCC DIGEST OF TECHNICAL PAPERS*, p.268-269; Feb., 1985.

[5] Patent pending.

Reprinted from the *IEEE ISSCC Dig. Tech. Pap.*, pp. 76–77, 309, 1988.

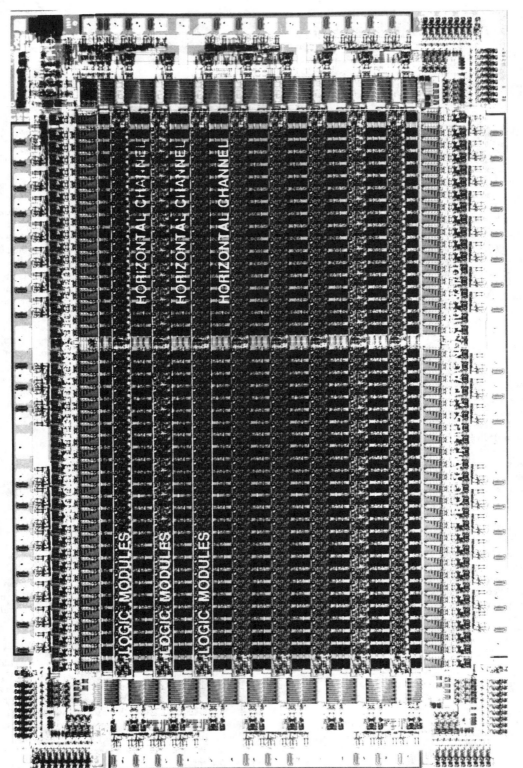

FIGURE 1 – Microphotograph of the chip.

Acknowledgments

The authors would like to acknowledge the special contributions by R.Mack and F.Chu of Data General, Sunnyvale Division and other contributions by K.Bushey, J.Chen, S. Eltoukhy, J.Greene, B.Osann, J.Reyneri, E.Rogoyski, F.Sohail, and E.Takyu of Actel Corp.

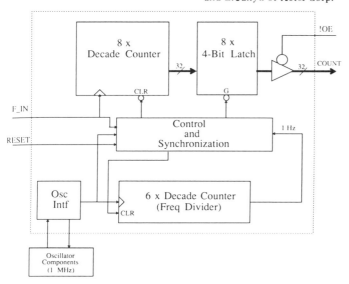

FIGURE 2 — Frequency counter.

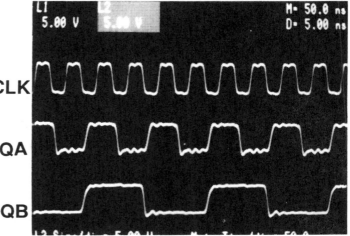

FIGURE 3 — Counter output waveforms.

TABLE 1 — Technology Overview

Process: NWELL, 2 micron,
Double layer metal CMOS

TransistorType	Gate Oxide	Leff	Voltage
N Low Volt	250 A	1.1 u	5 V
P Low Volt	250 A	1.2 u	5 V
N High Volt	400 A	1.5u	20 V
P High Volt	400 A1	.8 u	20 V

Anti-fuse Characteristics:

Programming Voltage	18 V
Programming Time	<10 ms
Programming current	<10 mamps
On Resistance	<1K ohms
Off Resistance	>100M ohms

(right)
TABLE 2 — Chip characteristics.

chip size	240x360 mil^2
package	84 LCC
standby current	<5 mA
number of modules	295
no. of programming elements	112,000
number of transistors	60,000
clock network	delay = 6 ns*
	max skew < 3 ns*
module performance	5 ns
latches	
setup	6 ns*
hold	1.5 ns*
clock to out	5ns*
max no. of user defined pins	55
configurable I/O buffers	TTL
input: delay	6 ns*
output: delay	12 ns*
drive	4 mA
	bi-directional
diagnostic features	microprobes

*All delays are measured at 5 V, 25°C temp, and a typical net with fanout of 3. Output delay and drive is measured at 50 pF loading.

439

PROGRAMMABLE LOGIC

PLD architectures require scrutiny

When you look at high-gate-count programmable devices, whether PLDs or field-programmable gate arrays, you'll see a variety of different architectures. Trying to find the proper architecture for your application can be confusing.

One way to cut through some of the confusion is to look at these devices from the perspective of how many flip-flops you can use. Or, if the device has too many flip-flops, how many you will waste. The number of flip-flops is easy to determine both in your design as well as in the programmable device itself. Furthermore, you usually can't get the job done if you have too few flip-flops. Of course, the number of flip-flops you need depends on which type of flip-flop the device has.

You'll see by looking at **Table 1** that considerable differences exist in the number of flip-flops available. The **table** lists the highest gate-count devices that are currently available (or will be in the near future) from the listed vendors. Many vendors also have a number of devices with fewer equivalent gates, and with correspondingly fewer flip-flops. You must consider many factors when examining the number of flip-flops on these devices. You need to know how they fit into the overall architecture of the devices before determining their usefulness for your application.

Dedicated flip-flops

With its 9000 equivalent gates, the Xilinx XC3090 currently dwarfs all other devices. Not surprisingly, it has the highest number of possible flip-

Doug Conner,
Regional Editor

Field-programmable gate arrays like the Xilinx XC3090 give you thousands of gates. But, to get high gate utilization, you still need to know how well the internal architecture fits your application.

Programmable logic

flops. Note also that this device has the highest number of dedicated flip-flops—that is, gates configured only as flip-flops. If your design calls for few flip-flops, you could easily be wasting 2000 or 3000 equivalent gates. However, if your designs are register intensive, you'll have plenty of equivalent gates available.

The logic-cell-array architecture of the XC3090 comprises a perimeter of 144 programmable I/O blocks (each block contains 2 flip-flops), 320 configurable logic blocks, plus an interconnect structure. **Fig 1** shows a configurable logic block's basic structure. The combinatorial function block uses a 32 × 1-bit look-up table to perform any 5-variable Boolean logic function, any two 4-variable functions, and even some 6- and 7-variable functions. The balance of a configurable logic block includes two flip-flops and a program-memory-controlled multiplexer section, which routes sig-

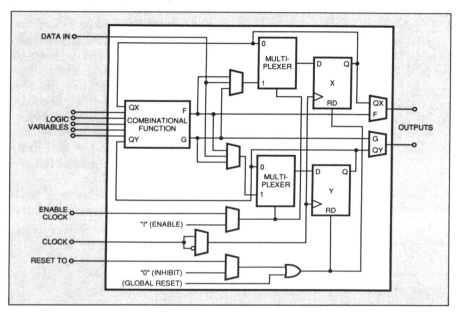

Fig 1—Three hundred twenty of these configurable logic blocks, plus 144 programmable I/O blocks, make up the Xilinx XC3090 LCA. A programmable interconnect structure ties the blocks together. The 64,160 data bits loaded into on-chip static RAM define the configuration.

TABLE 1—REPRESENTATIVE HIGH-GATE-COUNT PROGRAMMABLE LOGIC DEVICES

MANUFAC-TURER	DEVICE	DEVICE TYPE	PROGRAM-MING METHOD	NUMBER OF LOGIC BLOCKS ON MACRO-CELLS	DEDI-CATED FLIP-FLOPS	MAXIMUM POSSIBLE FLIP-FLOPS	MAXI-MUM FLIP-FLOP TOGGLE RATE (MHz)	SINGLE-LEVEL PROPA-GATION DELAY INPUT TO OUTPUT (ASEC)	STANDBY POWER (mA)	OPER-ATING POWER (MHz)	INPUT ONLY PINS	OUTPUT ONLY PINS	I/O PINS	PRICE	ALTERNATE SOURCE
ACTEL	ACT1020	CMOS	ANTIPOSE	546	0	273	70	21	10	26	0	0	69	$79.19 (100s)	TEXAS INSTR.
ALTERA	EMP5128	CMOS	EPLD	128	128	170	50	30	150	155	8	0	52	$96.00 (100s)*	CYPRESS
ICT	PA7040	CMOS	ELEC-TRICALLY ERASABLE	24	60		50	23	120	121	14	0	24	$27.80 (100) AVAILABLE FIRST QUARTER 1990	GOULD AMI
INTEL	5AC324	CHMOS	EPLD	24	34	34	50	30	0.15	20	12	0	24	$21.50 (10,000)	
SIGNETICS	PLHS502	BIPOLAR	FUSE	8 + 8 + 64	16	32	50	22 + 8	250	250	24	16	8	$14.00 (1000)	
XILINX	XC3090	CMOS	STATIC RAM	320	928	928	100	20	2.5	26	0	0	144	$311.00 NOW (1000) $102.00 SECOND QUARTER 1990	

NOTE: *=CERAMIC PACKAGE WITH WINDOW

Programmable logic

nals within the configurable logic block.

If you contrast the logic-cell-array architecture with Actel's ACT1020, you'll note a considerable difference. **Fig 2** shows the logic-module building block for the ACT1020. The 8-input, 1-output logic module can implement a variety of functions, including all 2-variable Boolean functions, and some 3-and 4-variable Boolean functions. The module can also implement a 4:1 multiplexer. You can construct latches from one module; flip-flops require two.

Because you build every function from these logic modules (546 of them on the ACT1020), you never waste a large number of logic blocks on functions you may not need, such as too many flip-flops. Such flexibility lets Actel claim 85 to 95% of the useable gates on almost any design.

One aspect you need to keep in mind when thinking about the ACT1020's architecture is the trade-off of logic modules between flip-flops and other logic functions. If you design a circuit using all 273 flip-flops available on the ACT1020, you'll have no logic modules left for combinatorial functions.

The device architectures of both the Xilinx logic-cell array and the

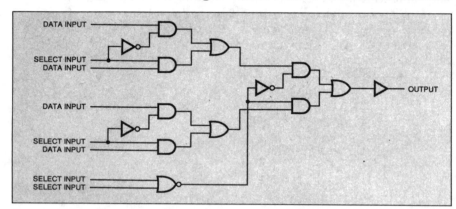

Fig 2—The 8-input, 1-output logic module is the basic building block for Actel's ACT1 family of parts. A variety of logic functions, including latches and a 4:1 multiplexer capability, can be constructed from each of the 546 modules available on an ACT1020. An extensive library of macros relieves you of ever having to design with the logic module itself.

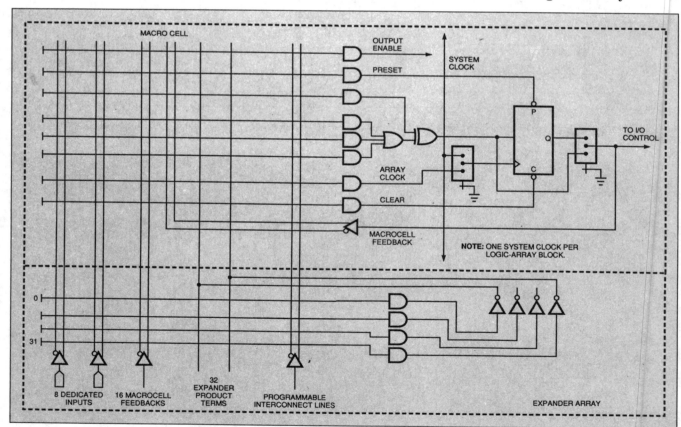

Fig 3—Each of the eight logic-array blocks in Altera's EPM5128 contains 16 macrocells plus a 32-product-term expander array, which lets you use more than three product terms for those macrocells where you require them.

Programmable logic

Actel ACT1 family are quite different from the programmable-AND, fixed-OR architectures common in PLDs. Altera's multiple-array-matrix family uses a variation of the basic PLD architecture. Rather than just trying to make a huge PLD, which often wastes many gates, it took a hierarchical approach, grouping 16 macrocells in each of eight logic-array blocks on its EPM5128.

Altera has done something more significant than just grouping eight PLDs with an interconnect structure on a chip. The three product terms feeding the OR gate in **Fig 3** will handle the majority of designs and never waste more than two product terms per macrocell. Three product terms, however, won't handle *all* designs. If Altera's designers had added more product-term inputs to each macrocell, the gates

would simply be wasted in the majority of designs.

Instead, Altera added what it calls an "expander array" of uncommitted NAND gates that you can use in cases where you need more product terms. The uncommitted NAND gates are also available as "glue logic" or any other logic function you need, including additional registers.

Signetics took another approach to getting lots of logic on a programmable device. It uses what it calls programmable macrologic in its PLHS502 **Fig 4**. The device has much in common with the expander array in Altera's multiple-array-matrix architecture. The chip's large NAND-gate array feeds back on itself, and 16 of the NAND gates drive flip-flops. After your signals have run around the NAND gates' feedback loop enough times to per-

form the desired logic functions, a group of AND gates collects the outputs.

The PLHS502 will not waste product terms because each logic gate is used individually. The large number of inputs to each NAND gate results in high gate utilization in designs where each product term requires many inputs, such as in an address-decode application.

With only 16 dedicated registers and the ability to construct about 16 more with the uncommitted NAND gates, the chip does not suit register-intensive applications. Although gate-utilization percentages will be somewhat application dependent, the device can perform any Boolean-logic function and do so with low propagation delays—8 nsec for each loop through the NAND array. The full matrix of interconnects prevents you from run-

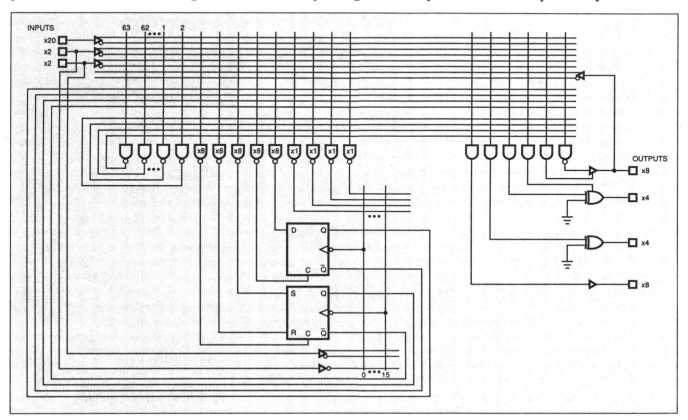

Fig 4—A large NAND-gate structure that feeds back on itself is the conceptually simple, yet flexible, structure of the PLHS502 from Signetics.

Programmable logic

ning out of routing resources, a guarantee that other device manufacturers can't make.

No waiting for product terms

Intel, with its 5AC324, took yet another approach to getting high utilization of product terms. **Fig 5** shows the macrocell building block for this device. Although the device nominally has eight product terms summed for each of the 24 macrocells (not including clock and control product terms), the product terms are switchable in banks of four so that a macrocell can use anywhere from 0 to 16 product terms by robbing banks of four product terms from its neighboring macrocells. When you need 16 terms you get them with no added delay. This feature contrasts with Altera's multiple-array-matrix architecture,

which adds a delay in going through the expander array for sums requiring more than three product terms. Delay times for these devices are listed in the **table**.

To get high gate utilization when designing with the 5AC324, your design should use product terms that require wide inputs. Also, you need to average close to eight product terms per macrocell over the entire device or you'll be wasting product terms. You're limited to one flip-flop per macrocell, plus 10 registered input cells.

One way to get the optimal number of products for each sum in a sum-of-products architecture is to have both a programmable-AND array and a programmable-OR array. The PA7040 PEEL (programmable electrically erasable logic) array from International CMOS Tech-

nology has this programmable-logic-array architecture.

You select the product terms from the programmable-AND array as needed for the four sum terms available at each logic-control cell. These cells, which aren't elements of a traditional programmable-logic architecture, each contain a register and multiplexers, and they control the signal flow within the cell. The PA7040 has a total of 120 product terms available for the 24 logic-control cells—an average of five product terms per logic-control cell.

This count is probably a generous number with this architecture because you need to generate a specific product term only once, and then you can use it as an input to several logic-control cells. Furthermore, you need never waste product terms until you reach the I/O

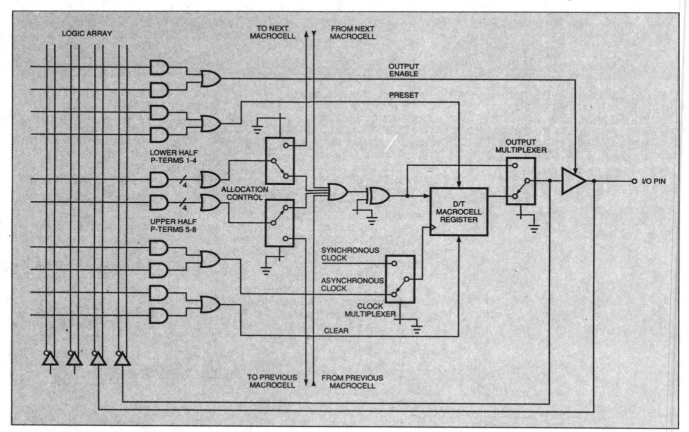

Fig 5—*The ability to switch product terms in banks of four between macrocells means you can use as many as 16 product terms for one macrocell and still incur only a single-level propagation delay. Twenty four of these macrocells go into a 5AC324 from Intel.*

Programmable logic

limit of the device. The PA7040 has a flip-flop in each of its 24 logic-control cells plus 36 registers available in input and I/O cells.

Many applications for programmable logic must be fast. Unfortunately, specific operating-speed numbers are difficult to determine with most devices due to their flexibility. Flip-flop toggle rates, for example, are difficult to work with because even if you derate them about 60% for a typical application, that value might have to be revised down drastically if signals are fed back and have to propagate through multiple logic levels.

Even single-level propagation delays lose meaning because a single level (one logic module) on Actel's ACT1020 is hardly comparable in function to a single level in an XC3090 or a 5AC324. Interconnect delays on the XC3090 can vary widely, depending on the routing. For these reasons, you should use the speed-related values in the table only as rough indicators.

Operating power is another specification that you can determine only with difficulty for programmable devices. The power consumption of most devices will depend on the design programmed into the device and the rate at which logic elements switch states, both internally and at the outputs. Some manufacturers specify parts with only some type of counter circuit programmed into the part. Other manufacturers give detailed methods of how to compute power consumption in your application.

The operating power consumption listed in the table assumes no loads on the outputs. Loading, both resistive and capacitive, can have a significant impact on operating power consumption.

Up to this point we've been looking at products you can get your hands on right now (or by the first quarter of 1990 for the PA7040). To see how programmable-device densities will be going up, it's worthwhile to look at a few of the products that will be available within a year.

Xilinx will introduce its 4000 Series logic-cell array with as many as 20,000 equivalent gates, and as many as 24k bits of on-chip RAM, which will be a separate RAM array available for general-purpose data storage. Actel will soon add a 6000-gate product to its line.

Plessey will introduce its ERA 60100 electrically reconfigurable array. This RAM-based design contains 10,000 cells. Each cell can be a 2-input NAND gate or a D latch. The company credits the array as having 40,000 equivalent gates (it considers each cell to equal four gates for the D latch). The device with development systems is scheduled to be out in the first quarter of 1990. **EDN**

Reference

1. Small, Charles, User-programmable gate arrays, *EDN*, April 27, 1989, pg 146.

Paper 10.6

Redundancy Techniques for Fast Static RAMs

Kim Kokkonen, P. Owen Sharp, Roland Albers, J. Patrick Dishaw, Frank Louie and Ron J. Smith

Intel Corp.

Santa Clara, CA

OVER THE PAST FEW YEARS, there has been a groundswell of support for the use of redundancy in memory components. Redundancy may be the new *innovation* factor which allows bit density to continue growing at the traditional rate of 2X/year.

Previous papers have described redundancy techniques for dynamic RAMs[1-2] and other memory components[3] where speed is not the primary goal. This paper will describe techniques utilized in a 40ns 16KX1 static RAM.

Device failure modes are a function of the chip layout, inherent technological factors and random run-to-run process defect distributions. For this 16K static RAM[4], area ratios and layout density are such that peripheral circuits such as input and output buffers fail rarely and when they do, are often unrepairable. Thus attention was immediately focused on the failure modes of the memory array and its associated row and column decoders.

There are several alternatives for repairing array-associated defects. These methods are best described by stating the group size of the spare repair elements, as shown in Table 1. Spare rows and columns are chosen as the best compromise between modularity and flexibility. Further analysis of the 16K static RAM technology[5] indicates that spare rows provide the biggest payoff, since the polysilicon (word line and single bit) design rules are more aggressive than the metal and contact (bit line) design rules.

This decision made the circuit design more difficult since the row decoders are in the critical access path whereas the column decoders have much looser speed requirements. As a result, new techniques were developed to minimize the speed impact of redundancy.

Goals for the redundancy circuits are: minimize speed/power impact, minimize added die area, allow convenient programming of fuses at wafer probe, and maximize circuit reliability.

The address of a faulty element is programmed into the spare element by electrically blowing polysilicon fuses during wafer probe. The basic circuit block diagram for a spare row is shown in Figure 1. When the spare row is to be used, a fuse is blown within the spare row enable block and the gate of pulldown T_1 is brought to ground. Then the programming elements come into play. Under control of a fuse, either address true or address complement is transmitted through each programming element. Thus by blowing the proper fuses, the address of a faulty row in the array is programmed into the spare row.

Figure 2 gives the basic configuration of a programming element[6]. V_{pp} is a special high-voltage supply used only during programming. It is brought on-chip by an extra pad probed at wafer sort. Later this pad is grounded by an on-chip transistor. Thus no inadvertent programming can occur at the package level. $\bar{P}$ is a logic-level signal that determines which spare row is being programmed.

This circuit offers several advantages in accordance with the overall goals:

1) Minimal access time slowdown is incurred, since $\bar{X}_{pi}$ has low capacitive loading and is only one transfer gate delay behind the normal addresses.
2) Minimal power increase occurs since V_{pp} is grounded during reading. Device D1 and inverter I1 draw minimal power since they have no transient requirements.
3) Minimal area increase occurs since existing signal lines are used to full advantage. The high fusing current is drawn through the existing wide V_{cc} buss. The high voltage V_{pp} line is narrow since it dissipates only logic power.
4) Programming is convenient since the faulty row address can be applied directly to the corresponding address pads in order to correctly program the spare row.
5) Fuse reliability is maximized since no high speed signals (with high slewing currents) are ever passed through the fuse during reading.

Once the spare row is enabled, the other task of the circuit is to deselect the faulty element. Figure 3 illustrates the technique. Whenever any spare select line rises, it causes the *normal element disable* line (NED) to rise as well. NED is connected to one extra input of every normal decoder. Thus when a spare element is selected, it automatically deselects not only the faulty element it replaced, but also every other normal element of the array.

The area and performance impact of this redundant circuit is minimal, as summarized in Table 2. If the technology warranted, the same circuitry could be used for column redundancy with no impact on access time. The die yield gained from redundancy significantly outweighs the small penalties in performance and area.

Acknowledgments

The authors appreciate redundancy circuit concepts contributed by A. Folmsbee and J. Halbert. We also thank C. Fu, L. Anne, S. S. Liu and D. Bruner for process development and support.

[1] Mano, T., et al, "A 256K RAM Fabricated with Molybdenum-Polysilicon Technology," *ISSCC DIGEST OF TECHNICAL PAPERS*, p. 234-235; Feb., 1980.

[2] Cenker, R. P., et al, "A Fault-Tolerant 64K Dynamic RAM," *ISSCC DIGEST OF TECHNICAL PAPERS*, p. 150-151; Feb., 1979.

[3] McKenny, V. G., "A 5V 64K EPROM Utilizing Redundant Circuitry," *ISSCC DIGEST OF TECHNICAL PAPERS*, p. 146-147; Feb., 1980.

[4] Pashley, R. D., et al, "A 16Kx1b Static RAM," *ISSCC DIGEST OF TECHNICAL PAPERS*, p. 106-107; Feb., 1979.

[5] Liu, S. S., et al, "A High-Performance MOS Technology For 16K Static RAM," *IEDM Digest of Technical Papers*, p. 352-354; Dec., 1979.

[6] Folmsbee, A. F., Kokkonen, K. and Spaw, W., Intel patent pending.

Reprinted from the *IEEE ISSCC Dig. Tech. Pap.*, pp. 80–81, 1981.

1) Individual bits.
2) Small clusters of bits (e.g., 8x8).
3) Large blocks of bits (e.g., 16x128).
4) Row of bits plus row decoder.
5) Column of bits plus column decoder.

TABLE 1—Repair alternatives.

Parameter	Before Redundancy	After Redundancy	Conditions
Die area	$40,000 \text{mil}^2$	$42,582 \text{mil}^2$	--
Access time	40ns	43ns	$5V, 25^\circ C$
Active power	500mW	520mW	$5V, 0^\circ C$
Standby power	75mW	77mW	$5V, 70^\circ C$

TABLE 2—Impact of redundancy.

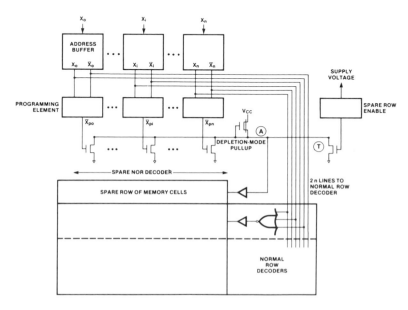

FIGURE 1—Block diagram for a spare row.

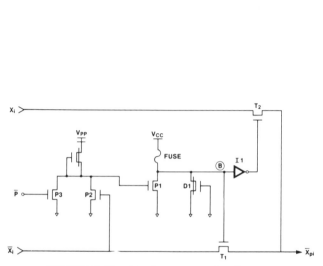

FIGURE 2—Circuitry for programming element.

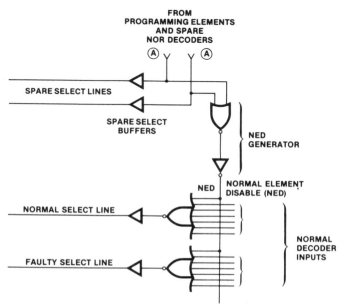

FIGURE 3—Deselecting a faulty element.

DON'T WRITE OFF WAFER-SCALE WORK: IT'S STILL GOING STRONG

Despite costly failures, many see it as a way to meet circuit-density demands

by Bernard C. Cole

Wafer-scale integration refuses to die. A few stalwarts are still hot on the trail—and they are beginning to report some successes. This comes as welcome news to many in the semiconductor industry who believe that WSI is necessary to get the yearly increase of system-level circuit densities back on a healthy growth path.

For a while it looked as though WSI was an impossible dream, one that had eaten up millions of dollars and frustrated leading semiconductor companies and researchers. What has saved WSI is a turn away from the ambitious goal of integrating onto a single wafer all the different ICs needed for a system. Now companies are working along two more cautious routes: wafers that integrate repeated structures, such as memory cells, connected by multiple levels of interconnection, and hybrid-like silicon-on-silicon assemblies in which the wafer constitutes a substrate of interconnections onto which ICs are bonded.

Among the companies taking the first approach are Inova Microelectronics and British companies such as Plessey and Sinclair Research. The hybrid camp includes Mosaic Systems and GE. Also, TRW, GTE, and Honeywell are pushing slowly toward WSI by building ever-larger chips; in Honeywell's case, hybrid-circuit techniques are being used as a part of the interim solution. GM/Hughes Aircraft Co., meanwhile, is working on an ambitious project that not only involves building monolithic WSI, but stacking a number of wafers together as well.

One attraction of WSI is that it reduces the number of pin connections that can fail in a system. But the main reason so many keep plugging along is that semiconductor density improvements are slowing down, just as systems-level users in the military/aerospace industry and others are calling for a leap forward, says Ramesh Varshney, chief technical officer at Inova Microelectronics Corp., Campbell, Calif.

"During the 1960s and early 1970s, the number of components per chip doubled each year as the result of both design and process innovations," Varshney says. But by the mid-1970s, when most of the innovations had been made, the annual increase in density dropped from 100% to under 60% (figure). Around 1990, the rate should plunge to about 25% a year when second- and third-order effects in semiconductor physics, such as hot-carrier injection, become major practical issues. "The skyrocketing costs of semiconductor capital equipment required by each new generation may force a practical roll-off [from the 60% annual increase] even earlier," Varshney says. He thinks WSI is the only way to keep increasing system-level density.

A fundamental problem with many past attempts at WSI, Varshney says, was their focus on mixing device types on a single wafer substrate. "This use of WSI has never been economically viable," he says. "No one universal process has been found that is optimal for every device type." Also, busing can be complex, as is testing; and yields can be very low. For example, he says, the yield of a monolithic WSI device with 20 types of circuits is about 1%, given individual circuit yields of 80%. This can be improved with redundant circuitry, but only at the cost of de-

WAFER-SCALE INTEGRATION WILL SATISFY DENSITY DEMAND

creased density and increased complexity.

The silicon-on-silicon hybrid approach solves the yield problem for wafer-sized subsystems with a mix of IC types; individual chips can be tested prior to mounting on the substrate. A leading proponent of the hybrid approach is Mosaic Systems Inc., Troy, Mich. [*Electronics*, Nov. 27, 1986, p. 39], which is selling its electrically programmable Unipro substrates in two sizes—either a 4-in. wafer (photograph) or a 1-by-1-in. segment. But Robert R. Johnson, chairman and chief technical officer, says that without exception, customers are more interested in the 1-by-1-in. segments than they are in the 4-in. wafers, because of "engineering reasons that start with the packaging." One, two, or three of the 1-by-1-in. segments can be put into existing commercial and military-qualified packages, whereas the wafer-size Unipro substrates cannot.

Also going the hybrid route is General Electric Corp., Schenectady, N. Y., working in conjunction with the Center for Integrated Electronics at Rensselaer Polytechnic Institute in nearby Troy. GE's director of semiconductor packaging, Constantine E. Neugebauer, says the advantage of building a silicon substrate is that "it's an easy substrate to put through photolithography." It's not much different from a printed-circuit board, he says, "but you can have a grid on a 2-mil pitch as opposed to the 20-mil pitch on a pc board. You have 10 times the density."

The more traditional monolithic wafer-scale approach still has a raft of proponents, such as Inova. Its Inroute methodology is a test-before-connect scheme, using deletive hard-wired connections and a common second-metal mask. Two key benefits, says Varshney, are individual die testing and standard, low-cost processing. Inroute does not depend on error-checking or majority-voting schemes to boost yield, but it can be used to build such circuits if necessary.

Another member of the monolithic camp is the Massachusetts Institute of Technology, where until recently researchers were using a laser to form additive links after wafer processing is done. This technology requires complex new techniques, so the goal at the MIT Lincoln Laboratory has been to develop a more practical link technology that uses standard CMOS processes. The lab is now demonstrating a WSI dynamic time-warping circuit for speech memory.

The British are also pursuing monolithic WSI. Among the aims of the UK's Alvey fifth-generation computer project is the study of fault-tolerant WSI—in which yield is enhanced by switching in redundant circuit elements to replace faulty ones—in an attempt to gain an edge in what the project's principals consider to be the technology of the 1990s. Managing the project is the Plessey Co., working in conjunction with General Electric Co. plc's Hirst Research Center, International Computers Ltd., and several British universities. Test cells incorporating such regular circuit

structures as random-access memory and multipliers will be combined in demonstration circuits and at least one full 4-in. WSI part by 1990.

Commercial WSI parts could emerge within the next year from Anamartic Ltd., Cambridge, UK, a company set up earlier this year by Sinclair Research Ltd. The first product, a 160-megabyte RAM using 1.25-μm n-MOS, is due in early 1988.

In the U. S., TRW Inc.'s Electronic Systems Group in Redondo Beach, Calif., is building what it calls "superchips"—parts larger than standard ICs by a factor of 3 to 10, using WSI methodologies [*Electronics*, July 10, 1986, p. 49]. GTE Laboratories, in Waltham, Mass., is also taking an evolutionary approach. Rather than leaping directly into WSI, it is moving slowly to larger ICs.

Straddling the boundary between monolithic and hybrid approaches is Honeywell's Corporate Solid State Laboratory in Plymouth, Minn. Honeywell is fabricating very large CMOS chips, typically 0.7 to 1.0 in. on a side and containing several functional cells. These chips can then be put down in a hybrid-type package.

SILICON ON SILICON. Customers mount chips on Mosaic Systems' wafer substrates after programming interconnections.

The most impressive system-level effort to date in monolithic WSI is the 3-D Computer Project of the Exploratory Studies Department at Hughes Research Laboratories, Malibu, Calif. The Hughes team is building an image-processing cellular array of stacked CMOS wafers that has one processor for each pixel. The team believes that by stacking wafers and fabricating feedthroughs and interconnections, it can create massively parallel communications channels on, between, and passing through wafers. Funded under a Defense Department contract to build a feasibility demonstration machine, the machine currently being developed will be a 32-by-32-processor array in a five-wafer stack. □

Reporting for this story was contributed by Wesley R. Iversen, Steve Rogerson, Craig D. Rose, and Larry Waller

Paper 10.8

A Wafer with Electrically Programmable Interconnections

Herbert Stopper

Mosaic Systems, Inc.

Troy, MI

THIS PAPER WILL REPORT on the development of proto-types of a 100mm wafer with electrically programmable inter-connections that have operated with test configurations such as wafer-wide ring oscillators.

The interconnection system has been deposited on a bare silicon wafer, thus producing a passive interconnection substrate, which can replace other commonly used substrates for hybrid assemblies of pretested chips. Its advantage is that the specific interconnection pattern needed for a given application can be electrically field-programmed. This eliminates the need for a custom mask set per application, minimizes the design turn-around time, and allows circumventing of local defects on the wafer by programming alternate routes around them. An addi-tional advantage is the thermal matching of silicon-on-silcon which sets the stage for low-temperature operation. Future prospects are that a similar interconnection system can be ap-plied to wafers containing active circuits, thus leading to mono-lithic wafer-scale integrated circuits.

The design is based on a four-layer metalization process. The two lower layers facilitate power distribution, the two upper layers implement an array of uncommitted lines which can be linked to each other via *antifuses*; i.e., resistive elements which are fabricated in the off-state ($>200M\Omega$), but which can be switched into the on-state ($<10\Omega$) by an electrical pulse. The antifuses, consisting of an amorphous silicon alloy, are sand-wiched into insulation holes between the third and fourth metal layers. Bonding pads for chip hook-up, I/O lines, and test points are part of the top metal layer. Figure 1 shows a photomicrograph of a typical wafer section with antifuses created in round insula-tor holes which are placed into the intersections of metal runs (minimum line width 10μ). Figure 2 illustrates the vertical structure of the wafer at an antifuse location. Eleven depositions and eight masking steps are needed. The ground plane (bottom metal) is not patterned at all. Barrier metals (black in Figure 2) are patterned together with the metal layer to which they are attached. Figure 3 is a top view SEM picture of a switched anti-fuse after the removal of all layers above the amorphous silicon.

In a typical application, several thousand out of a total of 1.5 million antifuses must be switched from their off-state to their on-state. Targeting of a selected antifuse for switching is accomplished by exploiting its electrical characteristics (Figure 4) in combination with a method of segmenting the initially un-committed lines (Figure 5). Since the anitfuses provide a distinct threshold voltage (U_{TH}) which must be exceeded to initiate the switching process, a half-voltage versus full-voltage matrix selec-tion method can be used to address a specific antifuse. The con-trol voltages can be applied via the existing bonding pads. How-ever, as more and more antifuses are switched, less and less lines remain open to independent voltage control, because the matrix does not and must not include diodes or other decoupling ele-ments in series with the low resistance of already switched anti-fuses. This problem is overcome by constructing nets (heavy lines in Figure 5) from trunk lines (represented by horizontal lines) and feeder lines (represented by vertical lines) in such a way that only one antifuse per feeder line is ever switched. The trunk line can be chosen freely from a large number of candidates which facilitates local defect avoidance and also eliminates the classical routing problem associated with the running of lines in predetermined channels.

The electrical characteristics of the signal lines created on the wafer can be closely approximated by those of RC trans-mission lines (*Thomson cables*). Their most salient attribute is that the delay varies with the square of the line length. Long lines in high-speed systems may therefore have to be cut into segments with intermediate amplifiers. Figure 6 shows the practical design range of wafer transmission lines. Another potential problem is the dc line resistance ($1 \ldots 6\Omega$/mm at $25°C$, less at power temperatures) which can reduce the noise margin of circuits with high dc input currents such as TTL. Increasing line width could alleviate this problem, but not without also increasing the load on the line driver to poten-tially unacceptable levels. On the positive side, RC transmission lines as encountered on a wafer have excellent noise character-istics.

The power distribution system offers adequate dc resistances (150mV maximum ground deviation for a 50A wafer load) and very low dynamic source impedances at the chip tie-in points ($<100m\Omega$). Thus, supply current spikes can be absorbed.

In view of the specific advantages of power spike absorption and of low-temperature operating capability, as well as the specific disadvantage of dc current limitations, the proposed interconnection system for wafers seems to be particularly suitable for high-speed CMOS circuits.

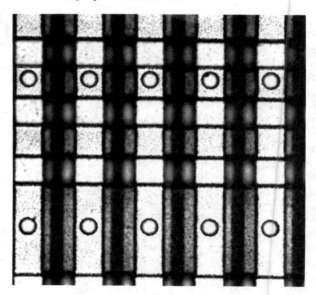

FIGURE 1—Photomicrograph of wafer section.

Reprinted from the *IEEE ISSCC Dig. Tech. Pap.*, pp. 268-269, 1985.

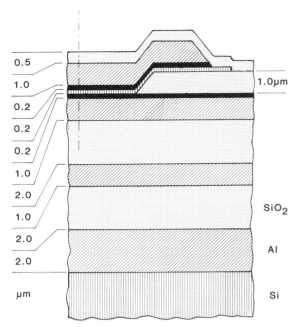

FIGURE 2—Vertical structure of wafer at antifuse location.

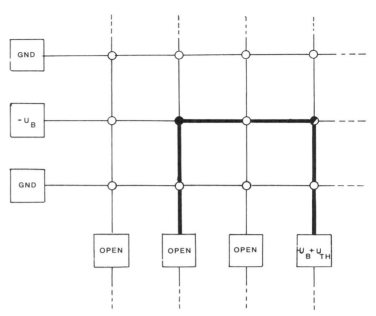

FIGURE 5—Constructing nets by switching of antifuses.

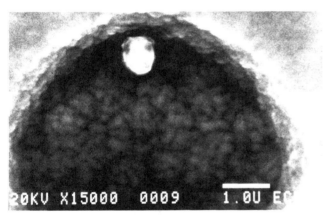

FIGURE 3—SEM picture of switched antifuse. Conductive filament visible after removal of top metal.

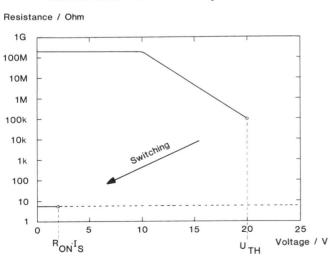

FIGURE 4—Antifuse resistance as a function of voltage.

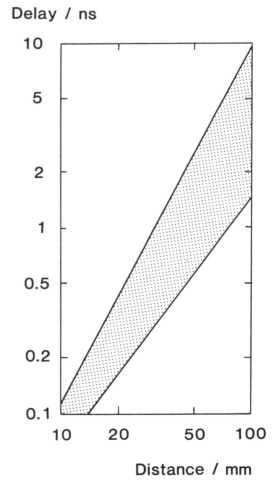

FIGURE 6—Design range of intra-wafer transmission lines.

451

ADVANCES IN NEURAL NETWORK HARDWARE

Hans P. Graf and Lawrence D. Jackel

AT&T Bell Laboratories, Holmdel, NJ 07733, USA

ABSTRACT

Electronic neural networks are receiving widespread attention as new architectures for computing. Massively parallel operation and learning capabilities are two of the most interesting features of these networks. To exploit the full potential of neural networks special purpose hardware must be built. Various ways of building these highly interconnected circuits are being explored. A characteristic of most of the designs is the use of analog computation or a mixture of analog and digital electronics. Neural network chips are now beginning to be applied to practical problems such as machine vision.

INTRODUCTION

A rapidly growing number of researchers are working on hardware implementations of neural network models. Three years ago, about five groups in the US were building electronic neural networks and a similar number were implementing optical networks. This year, at several conferences devoted to neural networks, some fifty groups presented circuits or proposed designs, most of them from the US but also several from Europe and a few from Japan.

The latest wave of interest in connectionist neural network models has been fueled by new theoretical results and by advances in computer technology that make it possible to simulate networks of much higher complexity than was possible before. Moreover, microelectronic technology has reached a stage where large neural networks can be integrated on a single chip. Neural network circuits were built in the sixties demonstrating collective computation and learning. However, these networks were built with discrete components and even a few neurons resulted in very bulky circuits. Such circuits were not practical for applications.

The functioning of biological neural networks is still far from fully understood and the models we consider here are crude simplifications of the nervous system. Nevertheless, these models capture some basic features of neurons. Fig.1 shows a simplified neural model, consisting of the processing node (cell body) interconnected to other neurons with connections of strengths T_{ij} (synapses). The operation performed by an individual neuron can be expressed as:

$$Vout_i = f\left(\sum_{j=0}^{j=N} Vout_j \, T_{ij}\right) \qquad (1)$$

$Vout_i$:   output voltage of neuron i.
T_{ij}:   connection strength between neuron i and neuron j. (conductance of the resistors)
f :   transfer function of the amplifier (neuron).

In this model the activity level of a neuron is expressed as a voltage. Input signals coming from other neurons are summed up and a nonlinear function, typically a sigmoid or a threshold function, is applied to this sum. The particular kind of operation performed by the whole network is determined by the interconnection weights T_{ij}. The large computational power of such a network results from the parallel operation of a large number of these model neurons.

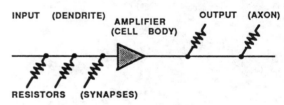

Fig.1: A model neuron with the processing node (amplifier) and a few connections to other neurons. The resistors provide the connections between the model neurons.

A major difference between a model neuron and a digital gate is the high fan-in and fan-out. A biological neuron is typically connected to several thousand other neurons. Such a high interconnectivity is extremely difficult to achieve in an electronic network since one is limited to the two-dimensional surface of a chip. No electronic networks interconnecting more than a few hundred neurons have been reported so far. With optics, interconnections can be made in three dimensions and optical networks have the potential to scale to much larger numbers. Several attempts are being made to build optical neural networks. An overview of this work can be found in Ref. (1), we limit the discussion here to electronic hardware.

Reprinted from the *IEDM Tech. Dig.*, pp. 766–769, 1988.

WHAT ARE NEURAL NETWORKS GOOD FOR?

Several recent review articles, special issues of journals, and books describe the characteristics of neural networks and potential applications (1)-(5). Neural networks are of particular interest for cognitive tasks or control problems. Most of the problems neural networks have been applied to lie in one of the following areas:

- Machine vision
- Speech recognition
- Robotics; Control
- Expert systems

It is in these areas conventional computers perform very poorly compared with our brains.

In cognitive tasks such as vision huge amounts of data of low information content have to be processed. For example, when one is looking for an object in an image, several hundred thousand image pixels have to be processed. The object's position and its orientation is information that can be encoded in just a few bits. Reducing the data in the image down to the relevant part is a problem for which standard computers are not well suited. The CPU has to plow through all the pixel data. It performs operations with a very high precision on pixels that are mostly meaningless. The highly interconnected neural networks, on the other hand, provide an architecture that is very effective in extracting correlations among image pixels.

A variety of well over 30 different types of neural networks performing various functions have been described in the literature. Some of these functions are:

- Self Organization / Category formation
- Associative memory
- Classification
- Feature extraction

Most of these functions are very time consuming to execute on a computer and neural networks have the potential to solve them more efficiently.

One of the key features of neural networks is their learning capability. Learning is done by adaptively changing the interconnection strengths between the neurons. In this way, for example, a classifier can be built, not by programming the network, but by presenting it with a number of training examples and allowing the network to build up the discriminant function automatically. The learning capability of multilayered networks is one of the most active areas of neural network research right now.

All the problems neural networks solve can also be solved with alternative methods, and many algorithms have been developed for the tasks mentioned above. Encouraging results have been obtained with neural network models, but

so far, no convincing evidence has been presented that they provide the most efficient solution for a class of problems. Some studies comparing neural networks with classical algorithms have been done (6)(7) but more research is needed on this problem. The effectiveness of a neural network algorithm strongly depends on the hardware that executes it. In simulations on a standard computer one has to step time-sequentially through each interconnection, a process that is painfully slow when the number of interconnections is large. Only with special-purpose hardware one can hope to exploit the parallelism inherent in neural network models.

HARDWARE IMPLEMENTATIONS

Recent hardware developments include digital emulators to speed up simulations and custom LSI circuits, digital as well as analog. Besides building whole circuits, efforts are also being made to develop novel devices, such as programmable resistors, that eventually can be added to LSI circuits.

A measure that is often used to compare the computational power of various networks is the number of interconnections evaluated per second. In a simulation this is the number of products evaluated and summed per second (see equation (1)). To get an equivalent number for a hardware network the number of interconnections is divided by the time it takes the network to settle to a valid solution. This number can give only a rough estimate of the computational power, and for a particular application other criteria may be of more importance, such as the absolute number of interconnections or the time needed to change a weight value in a learning process. Simulations on workstations run at speeds below 1 million interconnections per second, on a supercomputer in the order of 50 million interconnections per second have been achieved. A study on the simulation speed obtained with various computers can be found in Ref (5).

EMULATORS

Emulators based on standard micro-processors or array-processors are the most mature implementations and some of them are now commercially available. For add-on boards to personal computers or workstations a computational power of around 10 million interconnections per second have been advertised.

Special purpose digital VLSI circuits, eg. systolic arrays, were proposed to emulate neural networks (8). The speed-up gained with such a circuit depends strongly on the size of the network and on the level of interconnectivity.

ANALOG MICROELECTRONIC IMPLEMENTATIONS

To obtain the full benefit of neural network models, they have to be built in hardware. Simulations are very useful to gain an understanding of their behavior, but for applications a simulation, even with an accelerator, is often far too slow. Moreover, if the neural network does not map naturally onto the hardware it is unlikely that it provides the most efficient solution. Emulating a particular hardware architecture just adds boundary conditions to a problem.

Equation (1) shows that computing sums of products is a key operation performed by the network and a hardware implementation has to concentrate on doing this efficiently. Very often only modest precision is required which makes it possible to use analog computation. In an analog network a single resistor can perform a multiplication, and summing of currents is provided "for free" on a wire. Therefore, an analog circuit that computes sums of products can be built much more compactly than a digital circuit. Most of the microelectronic implementations use some form of analog computation.

THE SYNAPTIC INTERCONNECTION

The most important element in a network is certainly the synaptic interconnection. There are large numbers of these interconnections in the network and typically the number of neurons that can be integrated on a chip is limited by the area required for the interconnections. In Fig. 1 the interconnections are drawn as simple resistors. Depending on the function the network is designed for the interconnections may have to be programmable and of variable strength.

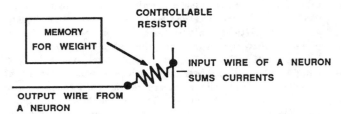

Fig.2: A connection element (synapse) connecting an output wire of a neuron with an input wire of an other neuron. The conductance of the resistor is controlled by the weight. The current flowing through the resistor is its conductance times the voltage drop across it. This is exploited to compute the product terms in equation (1). On an input wire all the partial currents are summed.

Fig. 2 shows a generic interconnection with its two key elements: the storage cell for the weight value and the connecting element controlled by the weight. Various ways of implementing these two elements have been described.

Connecting element:

- Fixed-value resistors have been made of αSi, Ge:Cu, Ge:Al, or Cermets (9,10). The advantage of fixed-value resistors is their small size.

- MOS transistors are the most often used elements for interconnections. They can work as controllable resistors or as controllable current sources.

Storage cell:

- Digital memory cells, static or dynamic, have been used. For interconnections with binary weights the multiplication between the neuron signal and the weight value reduces to a simple logic function (AND, XOR) that can be built in a small area (11). For weights with analog depth several memory cells and a multiplying DA converter are needed (12).

- Analog memory cells, capacitors storing a charge package proportional to the weight value, have attracted a lot of attention since they offer variable weight values and small size (13,14). To reduce leakage, cooling of the device has been proposed. An analog multiplier to multiply the neuron signal and the weight value is required in addition to the storage device.

Devices that combine the storage and connecting element:

- Floating gate MOS transistors can be used as a nonvolatile, analog storage cells. The channel conductance is modulated by the stored charge which can be exploited to do the multiplication with the neuron signal (15).

- An MNOS transistor can be used in a similar way as the floating gate transistor. In this device the charge is stored at a nitride-oxide interface (16).

- Materials are investigated that change their resistivity when an electrical programming pulse is applied. After the programming pulse is removed the resistor value should not change any more while the device is used for the computation. Interconnections that can be written once have been built using αSi:H (10). More desirable is a material that can be programmed repeatedly. WO_3 has shown such behavior in a series of tests (18). The programming speed is slow, in the order of seconds, but this may be improved. A key issue for such a material is that it can be added to integrated circuits.

EXAMPLES OF NEURAL NETWORK CHIPS

A circuit containing 54 neurons interconnected with a network of 2916 programmable, ternary interconnections has been built. This circuit is used for machine vision tasks where it performs operations such as line thinning and feature extraction (11). A newer version of this circuit achieves a performance of 44 billion interconnections per second (19). This chip computes 500 million dot products of two 96 bit vectors per second.

An interconnection matrix using 1024 multiplying DA converters has been built (12). The weights are stored as binary numbers with a resolution of 4 bits plus sign. This circuit has been tested working as an associative memory.

Storing the weight value as a charge package on a capacitor is a concept that is used by several groups. A matrix with 1200 interconnections plus circuitry to update the values in parallel has been built (13).

The circuits mentioned above have programmable

interconnections but the weight values have to be computed externally and are then loaded onto the chip. To do on-chip learning in one design circuitry has been added to the interconnections to update the weights automatically based on local information. A network with 6 neurons and 15 interconnections of this type has been built (20).

Another learning chip implements an algorithm developed by Kohonen (21). It contains 16 nodes and 112 synaptic interconnections (22).

These designs are all fabricated in standard CMOS technology and they use current summing to compute sums of products. An alternative approach is to sum charge packages instead of currents. Ideally suited for this type of computation is CCD technology. One design combining MNOS devices with CCD technology has been presented. The size of this network is 26 neurons and 169 synapses (16). It has been tested working as associative memory.

Other design approaches focus on implementing specific functions of the visual system and try to imitate the biological neurons as closely as possible. These circuits combine photo sensors with subthreshold CMOS technology (23)(24).

DISCUSSION

At present, the hardware implementations of neural networks are explorations of how to build such highly interconnected structures. There is no consensus yet what the best approach is. From device development over subthreshold analog CMOS circuits to digital, pipelined circuits every imaginable approach is tried out.

Closest to practical use are circuits for pattern matching and pattern classification. For these problems the combination of analog computation with digital signal processing may result in a considerable advantage compared with all-digital circuits. Other problems, such as learning and self organization, still need development, both in theory and in hardware, before being useful for applications.

REFERENCES

1. Applied Optics, Vol.26/23, 1987, special issue on neural networks.

2. COMPUTER, Vol.21/3, March 1988, special issue on neural networks.

3. R.P. Lippmann, "An Introduction to Computing with Neural Nets", IEEE ASSP Magazine, Vol.4, 1987, pp.4-22.

4. D.E. Rumelhart, J.L. McClelland, "Parallel Distributed Processing", MIT Press, 1986.

5. DARPA Neural Network Study, Final Report, MIT Lincoln Laboratory, Lexington MA (1988).

6. W.Y. Huang, R.P. Lippmann, "Comparison between Neural Net and Conventional Classifiers", Proc. IEEE First Int. Conf. Neural Networks, San Diego, 1987, Vol. IV, pp.485-493, IEEE Cat. No:87TH0191-7.

7. P. Gallinari, S. Thiria, F. Fogelman, "Multilayer Perceptrons and Data Analysis", to appear in Proc. IEEE Annual Int. Conf. Neural Networks 1988.

8. S.Y. Kung and J.N. Huang, "Systolic designs for State Space Models: Kalman Filtering and Neural Network" in "Concurrent Computation", S.K. Tewksbury et al. (ed.), Plenum 1988, pp.619-644.

9. A.P. Thakoor, A. Moopen, J.L. Lamb, and S.K. Kahanna, "Electronic Hardware Implementations of Neural Networks", in Ref.(1), pp.5085-5092.

10. L.D. Jackel, R.E. Howard, H.P. Graf, B. Straughn, and J.S. Denker, "Artificial Neural Networks for Computing", J.Vac.Sci.Technol. Vol.B61, 1986, p.61.

11. H.P. Graf, L.D. Jackel, and W.E. Hubbard, "VLSI Implementation of a Neural Network Model", in Ref.(2), pp.41-49.

12. J. Raffel, J. Mann, R. Berger, A. Soares, and S. Gilbert, "A Generic Architecture for Wafer-Scale Neuromorphic Systems" Proc. IEEE First Int. Conf. Neural Networks, San Diego, 1987, Vol. IV, pp.485-493, IEEE Cat. No:87TH0191-7.

13. D.B. Schwartz and R.E. Howard, "A Programmable Analog Neural Network Chip", Proc. IEEE 1988 Custom Integrated Circuits Conf., IEEE Cat.No.:88CH2584-1, pp.10.2.1-10.2.4.

14. Y. Tsividis and S. Satyanarayana, "Analog Circuits for Variable-Synapse Electronic Neural Networks", Electronics Letters, vol.23, 1987, pp.1312-1313.

15. S. Tam, M. Holler, and G. Canepa, "Neural Network Synaptic Connections Using Floating Gate Non-volatile Elements", Conf. Neural Networks for Computing, Snowbird, UT, 1988.

16. J.P. Sage, K. Thompson, and R.S. Withers, "An Artificial Neural Network Integrated Circuit Based on MNOS/CCD Principles", Proc. Conf. Neural Networks for Computing, Snowbird, Utah, 1986, J.S. Denker ed., American Institute of Physics Conf. Proc. 151, pp 381 - 385.

17. A.P. Thakoor, J.L. Lamb, A. Moopen, and J. Lambe, "Binary Synaptic Connections Based on Memory Switching in a-Si:H", Proc. Conf. Neural Networks for Computing, Snowbird, Utah, 1986, J.S. Denker ed., American Institute of Physics Conf. Proc. 151, pp 426-431.

18. "JPL Thin-film Solid-state Memistor", in ref.(6), Part VI, p.45.

19. H.P. Graf and L.D. Jackel, "VLSI Implementations of Neural Network Models", in "Concurrent Computing", S.K. Tewksbury et al.(ed.), Plenum 1988, pp.33-46.

20. J. Alspector and R. Allen, "A Neuromorphic VLSI Learning System", in Advanced Research in VLSI, Proc. Stanford Conf. 1987, P.Losleben ed., MIT Press, pp. 351 - 367.

21. T. Kohonen, "Self-Organization and Associative Memory", Springer Verlag, Berlin (1984).

22. J. Mann, R. Lippmann, R. Berger, and J. Raffel, "A Self-Organizing Neural Net Chip", Proc. IEEE 1988 Custom Integrated Circuits Conf., IEEE Cat.No.:88CH2584-1, pp.10.3.1-10.3.5.

23. M. Sivilotti, M. Mahowald, and C. Mead, "Real Time Visual Computations Using Analog CMOS Processing Arrays", in Advanced Research in VLSI, Proc. Stanford Conf. 1987, P.Losleben ed., MIT Press, pp. 295-311.

24. J. Hutchinson, C. Koch, J. Luo, and C. Mead, "Computing Motion Using Analog and Binary Resistive Networks", in Ref.(2), pp.52-63.

An Electrically Trainable Artificial Neural Network (ETANN) with 10240 "Floating Gate" Synapses

Mark Holler, Simon Tam, Hernan Castro, Ronald Benson*
Intel Corporation, Technology Development
Novel Device Group
2250 Mission College Blvd. SC9-34
Santa Clara, Ca. 95052-8125
Ph. 916-351-2704

ABSTRACT

Use of "floating gate" non-volatile memory technology for analog storage of connection strengths or "weights" has previously been proposed and demonstrated. This paper reports the analog storage and multiply characteristics of a new floating gate synapse and further discusses the architecture of a neural network which uses this synapse cell. In the architecture described 8192 synapses are used to fully interconnect 64 neurons and to connect the 64 neurons to each of 64 inputs. Each synapse in the network multiplies a signed analog voltage by a stored weight and generates a differential current proportional to the product. Differential currents are summed on a pair of bit-lines, transferred through a sigmoid function and appear at the neuron output as an analog voltage. Input and output levels are compatible for ease in cascade connecting these devices into multi-layer networks. Processing is done in parallel with an anticipated delay from input to output of approximately 1us. Weights are changed individually similar to the technique used to write data into EEPROM's. The pulse width and height of a weight change pulse must be calculated externally. Synapse cell size is 2009 sq. microns using a 1u CMOS EEPROM technology.

INTRODUCTION

Implementation of modifiable artificial neural connections or synapses using "Floating gate" non-volatile memory technology [1], has been proposed by Alspector, et al [2]. Alspector proposed the use of an analog charge on a floating gate to replace digital flip-flops used to store a connection strength or weight. The purpose of substitution being to reduce the size of the synapse. Since this time several specific floating gate synapse circuits have been revealed [3,4,5]. Electrical results have been reported for one of these cells [3]. This paper describes a new floating gate synapse cell which operates differentially to avoid the problems associated with power supply and temperature changes which occur between the time a network is trained and the time it processes information. Differential operation affords several other benefits such as full four quadrant multiply function and improved linearity of the multiply.

The cell described places a variety of constraints on the architecture of the network in which it is used. The architecture of an Electrically Trainable Analog Neural Network (ETANN) which uses the synapse described will be discussed to elaborate on some of the

issues encountered in using a fully differential, analog, non-volatile synapse. General issues pertaining to VLSI implementation of neural networks are also discussed. Some key aspects of the architecture are: emphasis on speed via parallelism, both feed forward and feedback connections on chip, analog voltage input and output, a large pin count package, and the option to operate in a fast static mode or in a clocked mode useful with multiplexed external buses.

Learning calculations have been left off chip to allow flexibility in applying the network and to avoid the complexity and cost penalties associated with implementing learning on chip. Writing weights into the ETANN will be referred to as training rather than learning as it implies passive involvement of the ETANN. Several additions have been made to the architecture to speed up training and minimize the connection overhead required by external learning and control of training. Addresses are provided which allow the external processor to select individual weights for modification in the same way that a byte of data is addressed in an EEPROM.

SYNAPSE CELL

The synapse cell circuit, shown in Figure 1, is an NMOS version of a Gilbert-Multiplier [6]. A pair of EEPROM cells are incorporated in which a differential voltage representing the weight may be stored or adjusted.

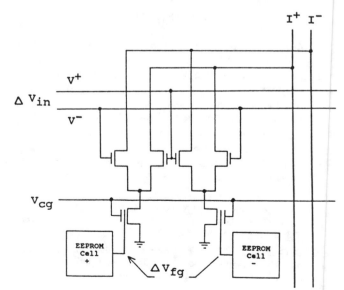

Figure 1. Differential "floating gate" synapse schematic diagram.

Reprinted from *Proc. IEEE Internat. Joint Conf. Neural Networks*, vol. 2, pp. 191–196, January 1989.

Electrons are added to or removed from the floating gates in the EEPROM cells by Fowler-Nordheim tunneling of electrons between the floating gates and the diffusions. A desired differential floating gate voltage can be attained by monitoring the conductances of the respective EEPROM MOSFETs. In particular, the respective floating gate voltages may be expressed as:

$$V_{fg} = \frac{C_{pp}}{C_{tot}} * V_{cg} + \frac{Q_{fg}}{C_{tot}}$$

where C_{pp} is the capacitance between the floating gate and the top gate (control gate) and C_{tot} is the total floating gate capacitance. V_{cg} is a static control gate voltage used for biasing and Q_{fg} is the charge stored on the floating gate. Assuming that all the transistors in the MOS multiplier stayed in saturation, we have the differential output current as:

$$\Delta I_{out} = I^+ - I^-$$
$$\Delta I_{out} = \Delta V_{in} * \Delta V_{fg}$$
$$\Delta V_{fg} = \frac{\Delta Q_{fg}}{C_{tot}}$$

where ΔV_{in} is the differential input voltage and ΔQ_{fg} is the differential charge stored between the two EEPROMs' floating gates.

A photo-micrograph of the synapse circuit is shown in Figure 2. Figure 3 shows the output characteristics of the synapse with symmetrical differential weights. The differential input voltage plotted along the x-axis is defined to be:

$$\Delta V_{in} = V^+ - V^-$$

In this particular illustration V^+ was varied from 1V to 5V while V^- was fixed at 3V. The differential weight was varied symmetrically between approximately -.8V and +.8V. Since the average of V^+ and V^- increased as V^+ was varied from 1V to 5V, we observed that the output current ΔI_{out} is higher in the positive ΔV_{in} regime (right half plane) than the negative ΔV_{in} regime.

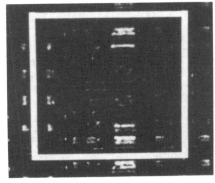

Figure 2. Floating gate synapse cell. Cell size 41.6u x 48.3u.

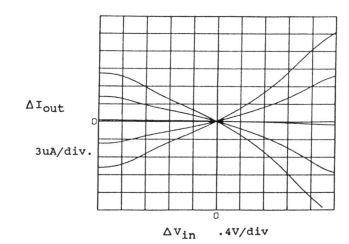

ΔI_{out}

3uA/div.

ΔV_{in} .4V/div

Figure 3. Characteristics of the synapse multiplier for five different values of weight. EEPROM cells written symmetrically.

Figure 4 shows the output characteristics of EEPROM based synapse when the conductance of one of the EEPROM devices was varied through the Fowler-Nordheim tunneling process with the "reference" EEPROM device remaining unchanged. The "weight" EEPROM's threshold was varied from approximately 1.95V below to +1.65V above the "neutral" threshold of the reference EEPROM. These characteristics present how the differential current representing the product changes when the charge on only one floating gate is adjusted.

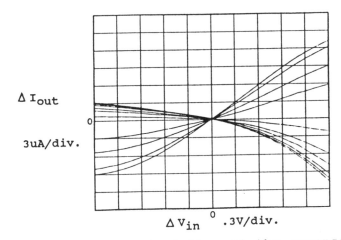

ΔI_{out}

3uA/div.

ΔV_{in} .3V/div.

Figure 4. Characteristics of the synapse multiplier for varying values of the weight. One EEPROM cell written.

In previous work [3] it was demonstrated that the voltage on a floating gate could be adjusted with .4% resolution (8 bits) using channel hot-electron programming. The physical limit on the smallest increment which can be made is the voltage shift due to adding a single electron. For the cell discussed in this paper the smallest increment will not be limited by the discreteness of the charge of a single electron but, rather by the ability of the neuron circuits to detect a change. 250 million electrons have to be stored on one of the floating gates to cause a 2V shift in the threshold of the transistor. If single electron increments could be sensed this cell would be capable of storing 30 bits of information.

No data is presented here which shows that single electrons can be added or removed. This is due to measurement limitations not a physical limitation of Fowler-Nordheim tunneling. Fowler-Nordheim tunneling is exponentially dependent upon the voltage applied making it possible to slow the rate of tunneling down indefinitely. Some finite probability of tunneling remains even under normal operating biases. Scaling of floating gate synapse cells will not likely be limited by the discreteness of the electron charge for some time to come.

To show adequate weight change resolution for this cell the threshold of one of the EEPROM devices in a synapse has been plotted as a function of the number of 20us pulses applied. 180 pulses were applied to shift the threshold by 4 V. See Figure 5. The average threshold change per pulse was 22 mV or .6% which corresponds to more than 7 bit weight setting resolution. Higher weight setting resolution is possible.

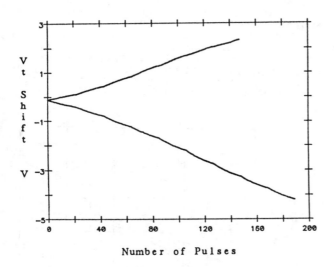

Figure 5. EEPROM threshold vs. the number of 20us pulses applied. Weight change pulse voltage increased by .5 V every 21 pulses.

WEIGHT RETENTION

How well the value of a weight is retained is an important characteristic of any synapse because it limits the amount of information which can be stored in the synapse. For example if a weight changes in time by 10% of full range then no more than 10 different states of the weight can be distinguished from one another. The number of distinct states the weight can have is directly related to its information capacity.

To characterize how much undesirable change in the weights will occur over the life of a device several synapses were baked at 250C to accelerate the charge relaxation phenomenon that is known to occur in floating gate memory devices. Figure 6 shows the percentage change in the weight as a function of

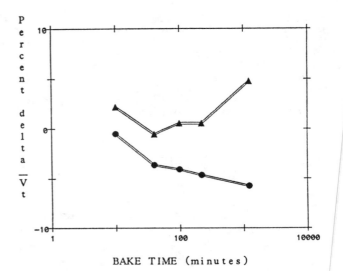

BAKE TIME (minutes)

Figure 6. Percent change in EEPROM threshold vs. bake time at 250C. Upper curve - erased cell, Lower curve - programmed cell.

time in the 250C bake. Since no activation energy has yet been determined for the synapse cell it cannot be said with certainty that any point on this graph is a precise equivalent to the desired lifetime of the device. However, using a 1.1eV activation energy derived from a similar floating gate technology [7] a time on the order of 3200 minutes at 250C is equivalent to a 15 year lifetime for a floating gate device at 125C. Extrapolating out to this time in Figure 5 it is indicated that the weight will change approximately 6-7% which would allow long term storage of one of 14-17 distinct states. Sixteen distinct states corresponds to 4 bits of resolution.

In applications where the network is retrained frequently the high weight setting resolution of the cell can be utilized. In applications where the network is trained only once and used for a long period of time 4-bit resolution appears to be the limit. However, it may be possible to accelerate the relaxation process and retrain the network or pre-compensate for the relaxation phenomenon and bake the network to improve resolution.

NETWORK ARCHITECTURE

Learning vs. Speed

Two of the desirable characteristics of neural networks are their ability to learn and their potential for high speed processing when truly parallel architectures are implemented. The architecture which will be discussed is optimized for processing speed. Learning capability is provided but, only in a rudimentary sense.

For maximum processing speed as much parallelism as possible was attempted, multiplexing was avoided. The limiting factor in the amount of parallelism which could be achieved was the pin count of practical integrated circuit packages. A large pin count pin grid array package was selected for this reason.

Analog input and output were selected to

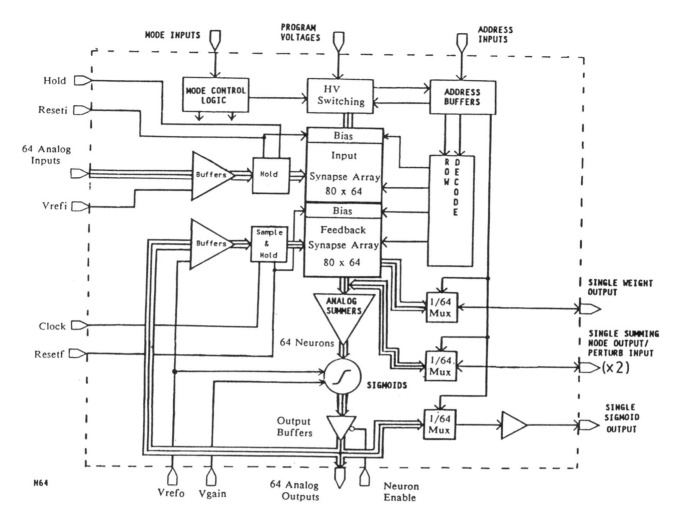

Figure 7. ETANN Block diagram

maximize information throughput on the limited number of pins.

An external intelligent supervisor must
calculate the weight changes and must calculate the voltages to be applied to each
synapse to modify the weight. Weights are
addressed and are changed one at a time.
The learning rate will likely not be any
faster than an average simulation. However,
one benefit of this approach is that the
network can be trained equally well by a
training controller using Hebbian learning,
back-propagation, unsupervised learning,
Madaline or nearly any other learning algorithm. It was necessary to add circuitry to
be able to perturb the neuron inputs as is
necessary in Madaline learning.

Architecture with Feedback

A block diagram of the architecture of the
ETANN is shown in Figure 7. The chip has 64
inputs, and 64 neurons fully interconnected
by 4096 synapses. Neuron outputs are available at 64 output pins.

A 64 signal feedback path from the outputs to
a separate synapse array of 4096 synapses was
provided. It allows implemention of Hopfield
networks [8] and networks capable of process-

ing and producing sequences of patterns [9].
The die size did not increase signicantly
with the addition of the feedback synapse
array since the die size is limited primarily
by the perimeter required for the large
number of bonding pads. See Figure 9.

Feedback is gated by a clock controlling the
sample and hold buffers in much the same way
that feedback is gated by a clock in synchronous digital circuits. "Free-running" Oscil-
lations are prevented regardless of the
values given to the weights in the feedback
synapse array. A repeating sequence of
patterns can still be generated at the neuron
outputs but the rate of repetition is controlled by the clock.

The sample and hold buffer is also useful for
storing data input via the output pins. A
signal is provided which can disable the
neuron output buffers, allowing data to be
input to the chip via the output pins. In
this mode of operation input pattern vectors
with 128 components may be processed.

The ETANN has a single layer of neurons for
maximum flexibility in design of multi-layer
networks at board level. However, multiplexing the use of the neurons is allowed which
makes two layer operation of a single ETANN
possible. Two layer operation is discussed
below.

459

Extra rows of synapses are provided with fixed positive input to allow setting a bias for each neuron. A block of 16 rows of biasing synapses are enabled when the input connections are enabled and a separate block of 16 rows is enabled when the feedback connections are enabled. A total of 2048 synapses are dedicated to setting biases.

Two Layer Operation

Two layer operation is accomplished by first disabling the feedback synapse array and applying 64 input signals to the ETANN.

After sufficient time is allowed for the outputs to settle the outputs are clocked into the sample and hold buffer in the feedback path. Next the input synapse array is disabled which allows the stored previous state of the outputs to be processed without interference. The feedback synapse array is used as a second layer of connections. The neuron amplifiers which are a significant portion of the die area are used twice in two layer processing.

Differential circuitry was used throughout the analog signal path for power supply and temperature immunity as well as speed of operation.

Scaled CMOS technology is used for its packing density, performance and it's ability to power down to very low power levels.

INPUT/OUTPUT

Analog input and output was chosen over digital to maximize the information carrying capacity of the interconnect. Single ended inputs rather than differential inputs were also chosen to conserve pins. Each input is converted to a differential signal in the first stage of the input buffer which is a differential amplifier. The other input to the differential amplifier is a reference voltage supplied by the user. This reference voltage can have any value from 0 to 1.7V. Voltages above the reference are positive quantities while voltages below the reference are negative quantities for purposes of the multiply which occurs in the synapse. If the reference voltage is set to zero the inputs can only take on positive values. And the synapse is used as a 2-quadrant multiplier rather than a 4-quadrant multiplier. If the reference voltage is set to 1.5V the inputs become TTL compatible.

The use of a differential synapse to reduce the sensitivity to voltage and temperature variations yielded a synapse with full 4-quadrant multiply capability. Both the inputs and the stored weights can be positive or negative and the synapse will produce the correct signs for the products in all cases. The inputs may take on inhibitory characteristics and if connected to an inhibitory connection (a synapse storing a negative weight) will cause excitation of the subsequent neuron. Although this type of inhibitory input/inhibitory connection is generally thought not to exist in biological systems there is an indication in simulation results that it can speed up learning.

The neuron amplifiers sum the differential currents produced by the synapses and produce a differential voltage which is fed through an electronic emulation of a sigmoid function. The sigmoid function has variable gain controlled by the voltage applied to one external pin. Simulations of the sigmoidal transfer characteristics with various levels of gain are shown in Figure 8. The output inflection point is controlled by a reference voltage and can be matched with the input zero point by connecting the input and output references to the same voltage.

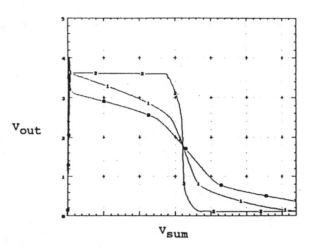

Figure 8. Simulated output characteristics as a function of the total sum of products V_{sum}. Characteristics for three different gain settings shown.

CHANGING WEIGHTS

Modifying weights is done much like programming an EEPROM except that the goal is to end up with a relatively precise amount of charge on the two floating gates in the cell rather than just more than some fixed value as in EEPROMs. To accomplish this an iterative process will likely have to be used. First the present state of the EEPROM cell floating gate is measured by using the multiplexer shown in the lower right hand corner of Figure 7. An address is applied to the 14 address lines to select one of the 10240 synapses. The external processor directing the training calculates the desired weight change based on the network's performance to the training pattern set and then calculates the appropriate pulse height based on the present state of the weight and the desired weight change. The weight can be measured again immediately and if further adjustment is required, another pulse of appropriate height can be applied. Each pulse will be in the range of 10us to 1ms in length and 12-20V in height. Because EEPROM cells are used the weights may be changed in either direction, thus, overshooting a desired value is not a problem.

An output multiplexer was provided to aid in reducing the number of connections the training processor will need to access information at the outputs. The neuron outputs can be read individually at a single output by applying an address to the 6 low order address pins and measuring the output voltage at the pin labeled single sigmoid output in Figure 7.

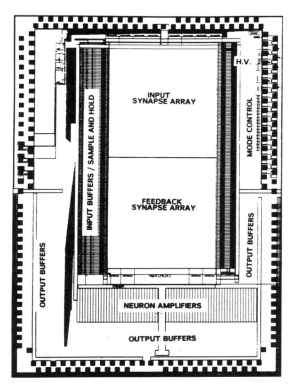

Figure 9. Chip plan of the ETANN discussed.

CONCLUSIONS

Analog weight storage and retention as well as 4-quadrant multiplication in a floating gate synapse cell have been demonstrated. An ETANN which uses 10240 of these cells has been designed and is anticipated to be capable of performing on the order of 10^{10} low precision multiplications per second relevant for pattern recognition tasks. This is several orders of magnitude more processing performance than Von Neumann computer based neural network simulations. Although learning speed had to be compromised significantly to accomplish this performance, this choice was made because it moves computing into a new realm of performance. Had the architecture been optimized for learning speed it is unlikely that the network would learn any faster than fast Von Neumann based computer simulations due to the relative slowness of the Fowler-Nordheim tunneling process and the difficulty of applying many different high voltages to the synapses in parallel. For this reason it seems apparent that floating gate silicon implementations of neural networks provide the most significant new capability by being optimized for speed.

ACKNOWLEDGEMENTS

The authors would like to thank Bruce McCormick and George Canepa for introducing us to neural networks and Dan Seligson for balancing our perspective by championing digital and difference calculating synapse approaches. Special thanks also to FAB 1 and the Flash Memory Group for fabricating the first synapses so quickly. This effort has been assisted by continued technical discussions with the Naval Weapons Center, China Lake in accordance with their need and request for VLSI ANN development or devices as specified in BAA# N60530-88-R-0427. *This material is based partially upon work supported under a National Science Foundation graduate fellowship. Ron Benson is a graduate fellow at the California Institute of Technology.

REFERENCES

[1] Frohman-Bentchkowsky, D., "Memory Behavior in a Floating-Gate Avalanche-Injection MOS (FAMOS) Structure", Applied Physics Letters, Volume 18, Number 8, April 1971.

[2] Alspector, J., et al, "A Neuromorphic VLSI Learning System", Proc. of the 1987 Stanford Conf., Advanced Research in VLSI, pp 313-349, 1987

[3] Tam, S., Holler, M.A., Canepa, G., "Neural Network Synaptic Connections Using Floating Gate Non-Volatile Elements", Neural Networks for Computing, AIP Conference Proceedings, Snowbird, Ut., 1988.

[4] Shoemaker, P., Lagnado, I., Shimabukuro, R., "Artificial Neural Network Implementation with Floating Gate MOS Devices", Hardware Implementation of Neuron Nets and Synapses, A Workshop sponsored by NSF and ONR, January 14,15, 1988. San Diego, Ca.

[5] Faggin, F., Lynch, G., Sukonick, J., "Brain Emulation Circuit with Reduced Confusion", U.S. Patent #4,773,024, Issued September 20, 1988.

[6] Soo, D., Meyer, R., "A Four-Quadrant NMOS Analog Multiplier", IEEE JSSC, Vol. SC-17, No. 6, Dec. 1982

[7] Verma, G., Mielke, N., "Reliability Performance of ETOX Based Flash Memories", Procceeding of the 1988 International Reliability Physics Symposium

[8] Hopfield J.J. & Tank D.W., "Computing with Neural Circuits: A Model", Science vol 233, P625, Aug. 86

[9] Kohonen, T. , Self-organization and Associative Memory, Springer-Verlag, 2nd edition, 1988, New York First edition 1984.

Memories in My Pocket

*Data storage has evolved from paper to magnetic media
to optical media to silicon "credit cards"*

John Reimer

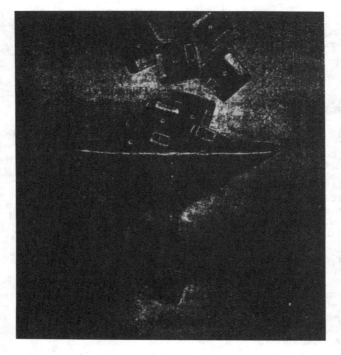

When your computer is finally small enough to fit in your pocket, the mass-storage memory device won't be a floppy or hard disk drive. It will be something far smaller, lighter, and less power-hungry. That "disk drive" won't be magnetic at all; most likely, it will be a solid-state memory card. With about the same dimensions as a credit card or a business card—just a little thicker—each memory card will be able to store several megabytes of data.

Actually, memory cards are here now. They have already found their way into laptop computers. And standardization is the key that has made the use of memory cards possible: the ability to interchange cards from different vendors among different computers. (For information on the standards process, see the text box "Toward a Standard".)

The Standard Choice
Two standards groups, the Japanese Electronic Industry Development Association (JEIDA) and the Personal Computer Memory Card International Association (PCMCIA), have settled on a 68-pin standard for memory cards. This number of pins directly accommodates both 8- and 16-bit bus widths and, with multiple reads and writes per word, can provide for wider buses.

With high-speed semiconductor memory, the extra time needed for multiple writes pales in comparison with the overall speed improvement of memory cards over magnetic media. In addition, 68 pins provide room for additional functions and I/O capabilities. The 68-pin memory card was also the first to be implemented with execute-in-place (XIP) capability (executing on the card itself), adding credence to the choice.

Physical Issues
Once the 68-pin package was chosen as the PCMCIA standard, one important physical issue remaining unresolved was the question of hot insertions and withdrawals. The card, system, and data integrity must be protected in case someone should attempt to insert or remove a card while the system is powered up.

The pins on the plug that mates to the memory card are of three different lengths. The two 3.5-millimeter pins on the outermost edges are the shortest and are referred to as card-detect pins; the 4.25-mm pins are signal/data I/O pins; and the longest pins, measuring 5 mm, are for V_{cc} and ground. Ground is at the outermost edges of the connector, next to the card detect, and V_{cc} is in the center of the connector.

The ground and V_{cc} pins are the longest to ensure that, during insertion, power and ground are supplied before data can flow on or off the card. The early ground

Toward a Standard

In the mid-1980s, the applications for memory cards were mostly in consumer products, especially in video games, such as the Sega that contained a single ROM chip on its memory card. This 32-pin memory card provided an easy and relatively indestructible way to handle the ROM chip while avoiding possible damage due to an electrostatic discharge. Then, Fujitsu developed a 38-pin memory card with an 8K-byte EPROM that was suitable for use in office machines, such as font cards for laser printers and fax machine telephone-number storage.

The next step was a 68-pin card, also from Fujitsu, containing a high-density printed circuit board capable of accommodating newer IC packages. These packages include the thin, small-outline package and the chip on-board in which the unpackaged IC dies are bonded directly to the board and then encapsulated. (COB is the favored mounting technique for calculators.)

Starting in 1985 in Japan, a group called JEIDA (for Japanese Electronic Industry Development Association) formed a working group to standardize memory cards for personal computers. JEIDA had no specific operating-system orientation in mind, not even DOS. It had, however, selected 68 pins as its standard and, by 1989, were in the process of defining pin assignments.

At about the same time, Poqet Computer and Fujitsu Microelectronics, a major Poqet investor, chose this card-based technology as the most attractive disk drive alternative to use in manufacturing a full DOS-based computer that would fit in a coat pocket. Such a silicon diskless drive would be rugged, reliable, and noise-free and would reduce

power requirements so that you could use small flashlight cells.

However, although the technology to produce such a computer was available, the lack of a memory-card standard would seriously inhibit its marketability. Imagine the confusion in a world where each diskless drive used different media and sector format as well.

Fujitsu and Poqet decided to start a standards effort for memory cards. First, they looked at existing standards groups to see if any were poised to set a standard for the card. The ideal group would have participation from companies in the mechanical, electrical, and software portions of the specification.

JEIDA had made considerable progress in the mechanical aspects but did not have adequate representation in the electrical and software aspects. Besides, it wasn't open to U.S. membership and was too far along to be open to alternate pin counts.

In 1989, the Personal Computer Memory Card International Association (PCMCIA) was formed, with members including electrical and semiconductor companies (Advanced Micro Devices, Mitsubishi, NEC, Amphenol, Chips & Technologies, Fujitsu Microelectronics, ITT Cannon, Intel, Micron Technology, OKI Electronics, Texas Instruments, AT&T, and National Semiconductor); software companies (Peter Norton Computing, Lotus, Microsoft, Traveling Software, and WordPerfect); and computer companies (IBM, Dell, Compaq, Databook, Epson, Grid Systems, Hewlett-Packard, MIPS, NEC, Poqet, and Sharp).

PCMCIA decided to approach the memory-card arena anew, to achieve international participation so that the

final standard would be adopted internationally. However, Fujitsu and several others were already committed to JEIDA's 68-pin effort. NEC had introduced its UltraLite computer using its proprietary 60-pin card. Mitsubishi was promoting two cards, a 50- and a 60-pin card (different from NEC's 60-pin version). Atari's Personal Portfolio had its own card. In short, the market was beginning to fracture.

PCMCIA faced two tasks: arriving at a card standard that was flexible enough for future expansion and trying to halt the fracturing process with that standard. It was vital that other standards groups be involved, including JEIDA (now a member of PCMCIA). PCMCIA would also seek JEDEC and International Standards Organization (Geneva) approval for the cards' physical characteristics and software protocols.

By December 1989, three proposals were under consideration (proposals submitted to PCMCIA had ranged from 40 pins for a serial-based card to 128 pins): the 60-pin card from NEC, the 50-/60-pin card from Mitsubishi, and the 68-pin proposal from Fujitsu. The mechanical card choice, for both size and number of pins, was Fujitsu's. On the Monday following the Friday of the PCMCIA-standard press release, Fujitsu, NEC, and Matsushita all introduced products using the 68-pin card.

JEIDA's 4.0 and PCMCIA's 1.0 specifications for the 68-pin memory card have been released independently of each other but are 100 percent compatible. And both organizations are committed to ensuring that future versions remain compatible. I cannot stress too strongly that the PCMCIA standard is a major milestone in portable computing.

---

also provides protection against electrostatic discharge. Likewise, during card removal, power and ground are maintained until the last possible moment. Placing the ground pins at the card edges also ensures that if the card is plugged in askew (i.e., leaning toward one side or the other), ground will always be made first.

The short card-detect pins, which are also placed at the card's edges, permit reads and writes once all the other pin connections are made. On withdrawal, the card-detect pins break, alerting the system that it is about to lose access to the

memory card and should take protective measures.

The memory card is designed to operate in harsh environments. The connectors meet the various environmental specifications, as well as the insertion/withdrawal force limits set by U.S. Military Standard 202F. You can expect to obtain 10,000 insertions and removals in an office environment, and 5000 in a harsh industrial environment rife with noxious fumes.

The PCMCIA cards come in two different thicknesses: The type 1 card is 3.3 mm thick, and the type 2 card is 3.3 mm

thick in the guide and contact area, while the rest of the card is 5 mm thick. The 3.3-mm thickness is sufficient for one-sided mounting of tape-automated bonding and chip-on-board (COB) mounted memory chips or for double-sided mounting of thin small-outline package (TSOP) devices. The 5-mm card provides extra thickness where needed. For example, such a card allows for the thickness required by the glass ultraviolet (UV) erase window used in an EPROM.

Two other physical issues also needed to be resolved: the location of the write-protect switch and the battery location for battery-backed static RAM (SRAM). PCMCIA members (see the text box) agreed that if you place the back of the card away from the connector, the write-protect switch should be on the right, and it should be in protect mode if it's pushed toward the edge of the card. The members also decided that the battery compartment should be opposite the write-protect switch on the left side of the card and facing up. This way, if the compartment is opened, the button-size battery won't drop out.

In addition, the card will have magnetic and x-ray interference specifications that will let you carry them through an airport metal detector or x-ray without

compromising their data integrity. And for those interested in protecting data in case of nuclear attack, a gamma-ray specification will be included in rad units.

Electrical Issues

I/O capability is a major PCMCIA concern. The interface is robust enough to accept enhanced functionality for peripherals (e.g., modems, fax cards, and LANs). If the specification is implemented properly, you can have a computer with, for example, two PCMCIA-compatible slots and interchangeably plug in a memory card, a modem, or even expanded main memory.

Of course, with a business-card-size peripheral, one problem is where to put

the connectors. The connection could be to a virtual connector on the card, through an expansion slot bus on the computer, or even via a fiber-optic cable connected to the card (see the table). Some pins are reserved for future use and should be left inactive to avoid compatibility problems later on.

Software Issues

Memory cards have three principal software-related issues:

1. selecting the file format to be used;
2. providing header information so that the system can identify the card (enabling the same card to be

PCMCIA MEMORY-CARD PIN ASSIGNMENTS

The 68-pin memory card that was chosen as the PCMCIA standard has a 16-bit-wide data path, as shown in signals D0–D15, and a 26-bit-wide address bus, A0–A25, for a maximum addressing range of 64 MB.

Pin	Signal	I/O	Function	Pin	Signal	I/O	Function
1	GND		Ground	35	GND		Ground
2	D3	I/O	Data bit 3	36	CD1	O	Card detect
3	D4	I/O	Data bit 4	37	D11	I/O	Data bit 11
4	D5	I/O	Data bit 5	38	D12	I/O	Data bit 12
5	D6	I/O	Data bit 6	39	D13	I/O	Data bit 13
6	D7	I/O	Data bit 7	40	D14	I/O	Data bit 14
7	CE1	I	Card enable	41	D15	I/O	Data bit 15
8	A10	I	Address bit 10	42	CE2	I	Card enable
9	OE	I	Output enable	43	RFSH	I	Refresh
10	A11	I	Address bit 11	44	RFU		Reserved
11	A9	I	Address bit 9	45	RFU		Reserved
12	A8	I	Address bit 8	46	A17	I	Address bit 17
13	A13	I	Address bit 13	47	A18	I	Address bit 18
14	A14	I	Address bit 14	48	A19	I	Address bit 19
15	WE PGM	I	Write enable (program)	49	A20	I	Address bit 20
16	RDY BSY	O	Ready/busy (EEPROM)	50	A21	I	Address bit 21
17	V_{cc}			51	V_{cc}		
18	$V_{pp}1$			52	$V_{pp}2$		
19	A16	I	Address bit 16	53	A22	I	Address bit 22
20	A15	I	Address bit 15	54	A23	I	Address bit 23
21	A12	I	Address bit 12	55	A24	I	Address bit 24
22	A7	I	Address bit 7	56	A25	I	Address bit 25
23	A6	I	Address bit 6	57	RFU		Reserved
24	A5	I	Address bit 5	58	RFU		Reserved
25	A4	I	Address bit 4	59	RFU		Reserved
26	A3	I	Address bit 3	60	RFU		Reserved
27	A2	I	Address bit 2	61	REG	I	Register select
28	A1	I	Address bit 1	62	BVD2	O	Battery voltage detect 2
29	A0	I	Address bit 0	63	BVD1	O	Battery voltage detect 1
30	D0	I/O	Data bit 0	64	D8	I/O	Data bit 8
31	D1	I/O	Data bit 1	65	D9	I/O	Data bit 9
32	D2	I/O	Data bit 2	66	D10	I/O	Data bit 10
33	WP	O	Write protect	67	CD2	O	Card detect
34	GND		Ground	68	GND		Ground

used in different operating-system environments); and

3. executing programs directly on the cards (XIP).

Like conventional magnetic-media drives, the data stored on a memory card must adhere to some file format. Instead of having the mechanical attributes of spinning media constrain the file format, the read/write/erase characteristics of semiconductor memory are the controlling factors. According to Mike Dreyfoos, chief engineer of Microsoft's MS-DOS division, the file format need not constrain the card to operate only within a particular version of an operating system.

PCMCIA recognizes that a large number of developers understand and have support software for the traditional floppy disk–type file-allocation-table system. PCMCIA adopted the basic MS-DOS FAT system on ROM and RAM cards. Since this approach imposes a block-oriented structure on a byte-oriented medium, it doesn't make the best use of the card's available space. But it is straightforward to implement, and the familiarity of this kind of storage speeds the development of early PC card products.

Flash memory, which is a promising semiconductor-memory technology (see "Store Data in a Flash," November 1990 BYTE), presents a thorny file management problem. Although it's byte-oriented for read/write, it is, at best, sector-oriented for erase. The FAT system must be modified.

To address flash memory, PCMCIA is adopting a special file system for it; it is essentially Microsoft's Flash File System, an extension of MS-DOS for use in a flash environment. Currently, FFS does not recover all memory used by erased files. To recover this memory, you must first copy all files from the card, erase the card, and then copy the files back. Future revisions will address this garbage collection problem.

The memory card's software header identifies its electrical capabilities without having to invent new DOS data structures or impose existing ones on other operating systems. The header distinguishes, for instance, between ROM and RAM, and it provides non-operating-system-specific information, such as error correction for card data and battery-installation date. This "meta-format" for header information describes both the card's logical and physical characteristics.

Architecturally, the card can be formatted into two memory spaces: the

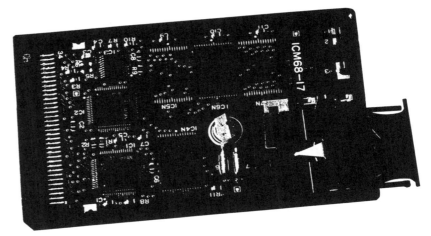

PCMCIA-compatible SRAM cards are now being used in a variety of applications, including pocket-size personal computers. SRAM is a volatile memory; note the button cell used for memory retention.

common memory and the attribute memory. The common memory is conventional storage and is always present, while the attribute memory that contains the header information is optional. A dedicated signal, REG, selects the attribute memory. This allows a system to determine a card's type, even for an unformatted card. The two spaces need not share the same IC memory type. For instance, an SRAM card may use SRAM for common memory and an on-board electrically erasable programmable read-only memory (EEPROM) for nonvolatile attribute memory.

To ensure a future growth path, the memory card's meta-format supports several different file formats, both DOS-compatible and other file systems (e.g., Xenix). It also supports applications, such as data storage for VCRs or musical instruments, which might not use a traditional file system to record their data. Any computer system can query the card and determine its overall size, type, and other basic information.

The ability to read non-DOS cards on DOS-based systems will be significant. The ability to detect that a card is formatted (even if the computer it's plugged into can't read it) is particularly valuable. It lets system designers protect you against some mistakes. For instance, the system could prompt you during the format routine that the card is already formatted as a data-storage card for a VCR.

XIP is still under investigation. Its purpose is to execute the program directly (and quickly) on the card without first loading it into main memory. The program must execute equally well on both portable and desktop machines. The

problem is that the card's memory space exceeds what the microprocessor can address in real mode.

PCMCIA is addressing the XIP problem by providing EMS-like functionality to map portions of the card into the computer's address space. A program loader, tailored for the application, pages the program in and out of RAM. PCMCIA's memory map requires that three windows of 64K bytes each be available in the card's address space for mapping and that one of those windows be divisible into 16K-byte pages.

Memory Types

Memory cards are really a packaging technique, and as such, they let you use any kind of semiconductor memory. Types of memory include ROM (and PROM), EPROM, RAM, EEPROM, and flash (see the photo).

• *ROM:* Programmed once and only mask-programmed during the chip-manufacturing process by etching the programming lines into the IC. When you buy a video game cartridge or a font card for a laser printer, ROMs are used.

PROMs are somewhat similar. Once they are programmed, they are read-only; however, they are supplied unprogrammed and are one-time-programmable (OTP), using a PROM programmer, so you can make your own program cards.

Mask ROMs are dense and yield the lowest cost per byte. Currently available mask ROM cards start at 512K bytes and get as dense as 16 MB. However, with future-density silicon chips, these cards are capable of holding up to 64 MB of

S*RAM*

cards are the first memory cards to be used for both program and data storage.

memory. The first major application of memory cards for pocket-size PCs will employ ROMs.

• *EPROM:* Similar to ROMs and OTPs except that exposing the surface of the IC die to a powerful UV light source will erase them. Then EPROMs can be reprogrammed.

They cannot, therefore, be reprogrammed on the fly. On a memory card, EPROMs present a unique problem: The card must contain a UV window so that it can be erased. Thus, a slightly thicker card must be used.

• *RAM:* You can write to and read from RAMs on the fly; thus, they typically are used for main system memory. They come in two main varieties: SRAMs and DRAMs. Both types are volatile (i.e., they lose data if they lose power). In addition, DRAM requires a frequent data refresh, since data is stored in minute capacitors that lose charge with time. For main-memory expansion, DRAM cards will replace the single in-line mount packages in vogue in desktop computers.

SRAMs are fast, with read/write times in the tens of nanoseconds or less. DRAMs are becoming extremely dense with 4-megabit chips about to ship and 16-Mb chips on the drawing board. However, they are not quite as fast as SRAMs; they have memory-access times below 100 ns. If you use either of them for removable mass storage, you will need some form of battery backup on the memory card, usually in the form of a button cell.

Battery-backed SRAM cards are the first memory cards to be used for both program and data storage. Although they are relatively expensive on a cost-per-byte basis, a single 2-MB SRAM card can typically contain, for instance, a word processing program, a spreadsheet program, and a database program, and still have room for data.

The reasons SRAMs are costly are

that the data-storage cell is larger than it is on DRAM cells, production yields are lower, and SRAMs have not been produced in the same quantities as DRAMs. Still, using an SRAM card eliminates the expense of having a floppy or hard disk drive and associated controllers.

While an SRAM card can cost hundreds of dollars, you'll only need one or two if you're a typical user. You'll be able to download the programs and data from your desktop PC onto an SRAM card for your laptop and take it on the road with you.

• *EEPROM:* The ability to electrically erase an EPROM on the fly makes the EEPROM a seemingly ideal replacement for magnetic disk drives. An EEPROM is nonvolatile memory (no battery backup needed), and you can erase it byte by byte and reprogram it. There are, however, several shortcomings.

While almost all ICs operate on a 5-volt power source, EEPROMs need a 12-V power supply to erase. Some chips, such as those from Texas Instruments, use an on-chip charge pump to produce the needed erase potential, but this greatly adds to the price of the chip.

EEPROMs have not yet achieved the density of DRAMs since their cells are larger and more complex. And there may be a problem with the longevity of the cells if they perform more than 10,000 read/write cycles.

The biggest obstacle, however, is cost. EEPROMs are about eight to 12 times more expensive than DRAMs on a cost-per-byte basis. They are often used in military applications where cost is less of an issue.

• *Flash:* Flash memory is a new nonvolatile memory technology that replaces EEPROMs in many diskless applications. Flash read/access times are on a par with DRAM's and represent a 100-fold improvement over magnetic media; write times are more on a par with those of disk drives. Although presently flash memory costs three times as much as volatile memory, it can theoretically achieve the same density as DRAM (or greater) at a comparable cost.

Flash memory's use in electronic still photography will also drive down its cost. For instance, with a charge-coupled device (CCD) of 540,000 pixels and a compression ratio of 5 to 1, a 2-MB flash card can store up to 20 pictures.

As CCD technology develops, so will the storage technology. With higher-resolution CCD, images made on a printer will resemble photographic-quality

pictures. However, even if flash cards are more expensive than ROM cards, you can update a program at minimal cost by reprogramming the flash memory, but you have to throw the ROM card away.

Flash memory does have one often-discussed (and misunderstood) limitation compared to EEPROM: You can't erase it on a byte-by-byte basis. It must be erased completely or, in some versions, on a sector-by-sector basis. One way you can deal with the sector-erase problem is with hardware that treats any block device as if it were a tape or disk drive. Another way is with software where the file structure anticipates a block device. Since magnetic drives are formatted sector by sector, applying sector erase to flash memory seems reasonable.

According to Kurt Robinson, an Intel flash-memory guru, designers think that they have to erase at the sector level, but that's really not true. "You can write in sector-size chunks; you can read back in sector-size chunks. All you have to do is make sure that you have blocks available that are already erased that you can write to. Even if time is required to swap data into and out of sectors, the flash is orders of magnitude faster than a disk drive to start with, so the user actually sees a significant increase in performance." With the availability of 1- and 2-Mb devices in TSOP packages, both Intel and Fujitsu now offer flash memory cards in 1- and 4-MB densities.

Flash-memory cards will greatly extend battery life in portables. The most clever power management schemes combine screen shutdown, CPU idle mode, and shutting off the hard disk drive when no reads or writes have occurred for a particular period of time. But it takes a lot of power to spin the drives back up.

The MC400 laptop computer from Psion already uses flash-memory modules to replace disk drives. It has four module slots, and each module contains four Intel 128K-byte flash ICs for a total of 2 MB of memory. Psion also makes an accessory that lets you plug the MC400's modules into any MS-DOS computer.

Standardizing flash-memory specifications is a particularly challenging task. PCMCIA has come to the conclusion that there are several technology variants. More specifically, a flash card informs a system of its particular erase/voltage level through the meta format.

Future Trends

Data storage has moved through an evolutionary cycle from paper to magnetic media to optical to silicon. Beyond this, you can expect to see an increase in modularity as all kinds of peripheral functions become easy to implement in a standard card format.

The card socket will look much the same as an expansion bus, so you can plug cards into any vacant socket regardless of card or computer manufacturer. Do you want to expand main memory? How about adding a modem, a video board, a coprocessor, a fax card, or a scanner? Just plug in the right card. ■

ACKNOWLEDGMENT
I wish to thank Michael Bloom, president of Technology Communications Group (West Linn, OR), for his help in preparing this article.

John Reimer is chairman of the Personal Computer Memory Card International Association (San Jose, CA) and marketing manager for the memory card department at Fujitsu Microelectronics. You can reach him on BIX c/o "editors."

Author Index

470

471

Subject Index

Editor's Biography

Chenming Hu (S'71–M'76–SM'83–F'90) received the B.S. degree from National Taiwan University and the M.S. and Ph.D. degrees in electrical engineering from the University of California, Berkeley, in 1970 and 1973, respectively.

From 1973 to 1976, he was an Assistant Professor at the Massachusetts Institute of Technology. In 1976, he joined the University of California, Berkeley, as Professor of Electrical Engineering and Computer Sciences. While on industrial leave from the University in 1980–1981, he was Manager of nonvolatile memory development at National Semiconductor. Since 1973, he has served as a consultant to the electronics industry. He has also been an advisor to many government and educational institutions. He has conducted research on electrooptics, solar cells, and power electronics. His present research areas include VLSI devices, hot-electron effects, thin dielectrics, device reliability, nonvolatile semiconductor memories, power semiconductor devices, and GaAs devices. He has authored or coauthored two books and over 250 research papers. He has been awarded several patents on semiconductor devices and technology.

Dr. Hu is an Honorary Professor of Beijing University, China. He is Director of the Joint Services Electronics Program at Berkeley. He was an Associate Editor of IEEE Transactions on Electron Devices from 1986 to 1988, and Vice Chairman of the IEEE Electron Devices Society, Santa Clara Valley Chapter, 1980–1982. He has delivered twenty keynote addresses and invited papers at scientific conferences, and has received four best paper awards and a grand prize in the 1991 *Design News* Excellence in Design competition. He has been listed in *American Men and Women of Science*, *California Men & Women of Science and Technology*, and *Who's Who in Technology*.